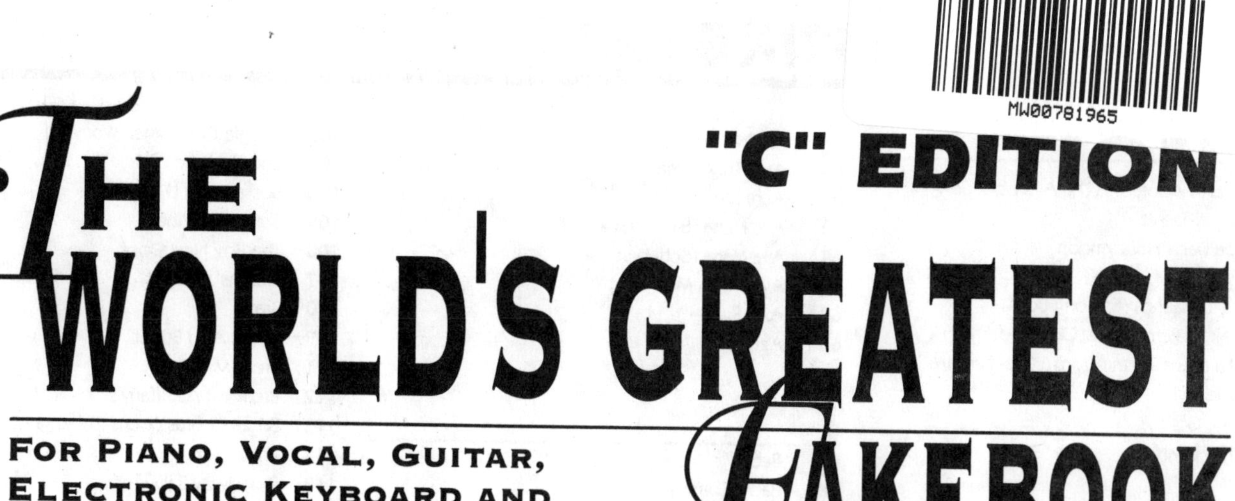

"C" EDITION
THE WORLD'S GREATEST FAKEBOOK
FOR PIANO, VOCAL, GUITAR, ELECTRONIC KEYBOARD AND ALL "C" INSTRUMENTS

Project Manager: Tony Esposito
Senior Editor: Tom Roed
Editors: Bill Galliford, David C. Olsen, David Pugh
Layout: Gayle Giese
Engraving: George Rizov

ALPHABETICAL LISTING

ALPHABETICAL LISTING

ALPHABETICAL LISTING

H

I

ALPHABETICAL LISTING

J

K

L

M

ALPHABETICAL LISTING

ALPHABETICAL LISTING

T

ALPHABETICAL LISTING

CLASSIFIED LISTING

BIG BAND ERA

CHRISTMAS AND INSPIRATIONAL

CLASSICAL THEMES

COUNTRY MUSIC

CLASSIFIED LISTING

CLASSIFIED LISTING

POLKAS

SING-A-LONGS, SPECIAL OCCASIONS & NOVELTY TUNES

CLASSIFIED LISTING

STANDARDS

CLASSIFIED LISTING

WALTZES

CLASSIFIED LISTING

50'S HITS

60'S HITS

70'S HITS

CLASSIFIED LISTING

80'S & 90'S HITS

AFTER THE GOLD RUSH

Words and Music by
NEIL YOUNG

Moderately
D G D G D A G A Bm C G C D A C G D A C G
Well, I dreamed I saw the knights in ar - mor com - ing, say - in' some - thing a - bout a queen. There were peas - ants sing - in' and drum - mers drum - min' and the arch - er split the tree. There was a fan - fare blow - in' to the sun that was float - ing on the breeze. Look at Moth - er Na - ture on the run in the nine - teen sev - en - ties. Look at Moth - er Na - ture on the run in the nine - teen sev - en - ties. 2. I was
ly - in' in a burned out base - ment with the full moon in my eyes. I was hop - in for re - place - ment when the sun burst through the sky. There was a band play - in' in my head and I felt like get - ting high. I was think - in' a - bout what a friend had said, I was hop - in' it was a lie. Think - in' a - bout what a friend had said, I was hop - in' it was a lie. 3. Well, I
dreamed I saw the sil - ver space - ships fly - in' in the yel - low haze of the sun, there were chil - dren cry - in' and col - ors fly - in' all a - round the cho - sen ones. All in a dream, all in a dream the load - ing had be - gun. Fly - ing Moth - er Na - ture's sil - ver seed to a new home in the sun. Fly - ing Moth - er Na - ture's sil - ver seed to a new home.
1.2. G 3. G
AFTER MIDNIGHT
Words and Music by
JOHN J. CALE
© 1966 WARNER-TAMERLANE PUBLISHING CORP.
All Rights Reserved
Fast
C E♭ F C E♭ F C F G C E♭ F C
Af - ter Mid - night we gon - na let it all hang down. Af - ter Mid night we gon - na shake it up and shout. We gon - na stim - u - late some ac - tion we gon - na get some sat - is - fac - tion
Af - ter Mid - night we gon - na shake your tam - bou - rine, Af - ter Mid night it's all gon - na be peaches and cream We gon - na cause talk and sus - pi - cion we gon - na give an ex - hi - bi - tion
we gon - na find out what it is all a - bout Af - ter Mid - night we gon - na let it all hang down.

From the Original Motion Picture Soundtrack "THE THREE MUSKETEERS"

ALL FOR LOVE

Written by BRYAN ADAMS,
ROBERT JOHN "MUTT" LANGE
and MICHAEL KAMEN

Slowly

D Dsus *Verse:* D Dsus D

Bryan: 1. When it's love you give, then love you'll live.
Sting: I'll be a man of good faith. I'll make a stand, I won't blink.

D/F♯ G D/A A

I'll be the rock you can build on, be there when you're old, to have and to hold. *Rod:* 2. When there's love in - side,

Verse: D Dsus D D/F♯

Bryan: I swear I'll al - ways be strong. then there's a rea - son why. I'll prove to you we be - long. *Both:* I'll be the world that pro -
Rod: then it's love you take. I will de - fend I will fight. *All:* I'll be there when you
Sting: (3.) I'll be the fire in your night.

G D/A A Asus A D Em7 D/F♯ N.C. D/F♯

tects you from the wind and the rain, from the hurt and the pain.
need me when hon - or's at stake, this vow I will make:
All: Let's make it / that it's all for one, all for love.

𝄋 *Chorus:* G Em7 D/A A D/F♯ G Bm A D/F♯ G

Let the one you hold be the one you want, the one you need. 'Cause when it's all for one, it's one for all. When there's

Em7 D/F♯ *To Coda* ⊕ G D/A G D/F♯ Em7 A 1. D Dsus

some-one that you know, then just let your feel-ings show and make it all for one, all for love. *Bryan:* 3. When it's love you make,
all,

2. D *Bridge:* Bm G Em7 D/F♯ G A Bm

Don't lay our love to rest, 'cause we could stand up to the test. We've got ev - 'ry - thing and

D/F♯ G Asus A Bm D/F♯ G A G

more than we had planned, more than the riv - ers that run the land, we've got it all in our hands. *(Instrumental solo . . .*

Em7 1. Dsus D Dsus D 2. Asus A N.C. *D.S. 𝄋 al Coda* ⊕ *Coda* G D/A

. . . end solo) Now, it's all for one, all for love. let your feel-ings show. When there's

G/B D/F♯ G D/A Em N.C. Gm7 Gm(♯7) Gm/A D(2)

some-one that you want, when there's some-one that you need, let's make it all, all for one, and all for love.

A-TISKET A-TASKET

Words and Music by
ELLA FITZERGERALD and
VAN ALEXANDER

Brightly
Bb+ Eb Gdim
A - tis - ket a - tas - ket, a green and yel - low bas - ket; I
dropped it, I dropped it, yes on the way I dropped it. A
Fm7 Bb7 Fm7 Bb7 Fm7 Bb7 1. Eb Bb7 2. Eb Eb7
bought a bas - ket for my mom - mie. On the way I dropped it. I - ket. She was
lit - tle girl - ie picked it up and took it to the mar-
Ab Abm Eb Eb+
truck - in' on down the av - e - nue with - out a sin - gle thing to do. She was
Ab Abm Eb F7 Bb7 Eb
peck, peck, peck-in' all a - round, when she spied it on the ground. A - tis - ket a - tas - ket, she
Gdim Fm7 Bb7 Fm7 Bb7 Fm7 Bb7 Eb
took my yel - low bas - ket. And if she does - n't bring it back, I think that I shall die.
THE ABA DABA HONEYMOON
Words and Music by
ARTHUR FIELDS and
WALTER DONOVAN
Copyright © 1914 (Renewed 1942) EMI FEIST CATALOG INC.
All Rights Reserved
Moderately
C
"Ab - a, dab - a, da - ba, da - ba, dab - a, dab - a, dab," said the chim - pie to the monk.
G7
"Bab - a, dab - a, dab - a, dab - a, dab - a, dab - a, dab, said the mon - key to the chimp.
C
All night long they'd chat - ter a - way, all day long they're hap - py and gay,

D7 G7 Dm7 G7 C

swing - ing and sing - ing in their hun - key, ton - key way. "Ab - a, dab - a, dab - a, dab - a,

dab - a, dab - a, dab," means "Monk, I love but you." "Bab - a, dab - a, dab," in
mon - key talk means "Chimp I love you too." Then the big ba - boon, one night in June, he
mar-ried them, and ver - y soon they went up - on their ab - a, dab - a hon - ey - moon.
ABILENE
Copyright © 1963 (Renewed 1991) ACUFF-ROSE MUSIC, INC.
All Rights Reserved
LESTER BROWN, JOHN D. LOUDERMILK
& BOB GIBSON
Moderately
Ab - i - lene, Ab - i - lene, pret-ti-est town I've ev - er seen. Wom-en there will
treat you mean in Ab - i - lene, my Ab - i - lene. I sit a - lone most ev-'ry night, watch those trains
pull out of sight. Don't I wish they were car-ry-ing me back to Ab - i - lene, my Ab - i - lene.
Ab - i - lene, Ab - i - lene, pret-ti-est town I've ev - er seen. Wom-en there don't
treat you mean in Ab - i - lene, my Ab - i - lene. Crowd-ed cit - y,
there ain't noth-ing free, noth - ing in this town for me. Wish to the Lord that
I could be in Ab - i - lene, sweet Ab - i - lene. lene, sweet Ab - i - lene.

ADIOS MUCHACHOS

(So Long Boys)

English Words by HOWARD JOHNSON
Spanish Words by CESAR F. VEDANI
Music by JULIO SANDERS

Tango
C E7 F G7
So long to all my bos - om friends and boon com - pan - ions. Though I must leave you, don't let it

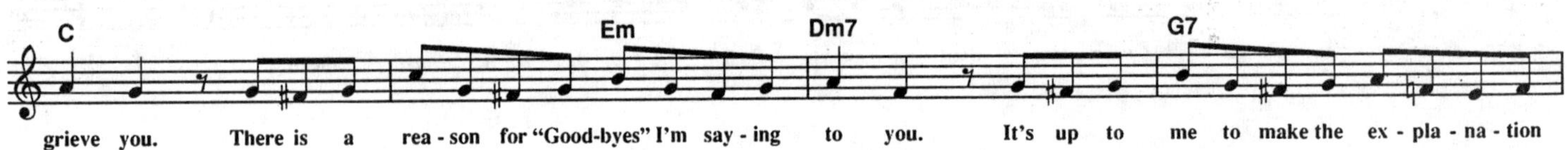
C Em Dm7 G7
grieve you. There is a rea - son for "Good-byes" I'm say - ing to you. It's up to me to make the ex - pla - na - tion

C E7 F G7
due you. Per - haps you've no - ticed that my mind is in the dis - tance, that my mo - rale's gone, I've no re -

C C7 F Fm C D7 G7
sis - tance. Some-one has changed my plan of life, my whole ex - is - tence. You've guessed the an - swer fel - lows, it's a

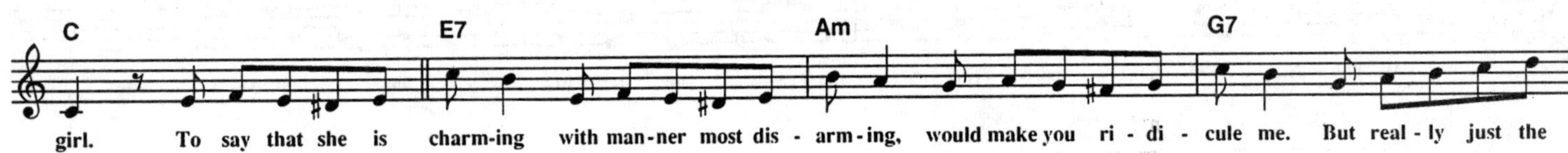
C E7 Am G7
girl. To say that she is charm-ing with man-ner most dis - arm - ing, would make you ri - di - cule me. But real - ly just the

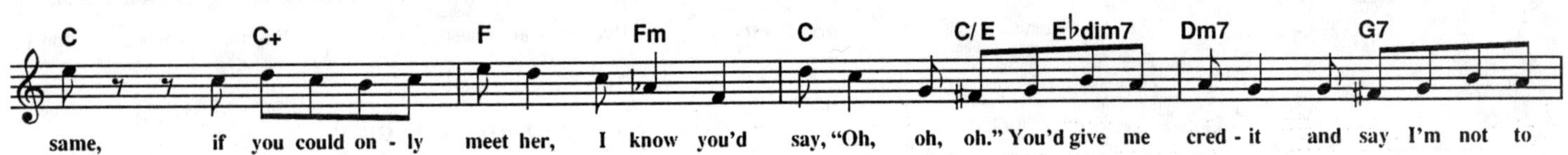
C C+ F Fm C C/E E♭dim7 Dm7 G7
same, if you could on - ly meet her, I know you'd say, "Oh, oh, oh." You'd give me cred - it and say I'm not to

C E7 Am G7
blame. She's more than just at - trac - tive, but al - so re - tro - ac - tive. When she re - turns my kiss - es, a meth - od she em -

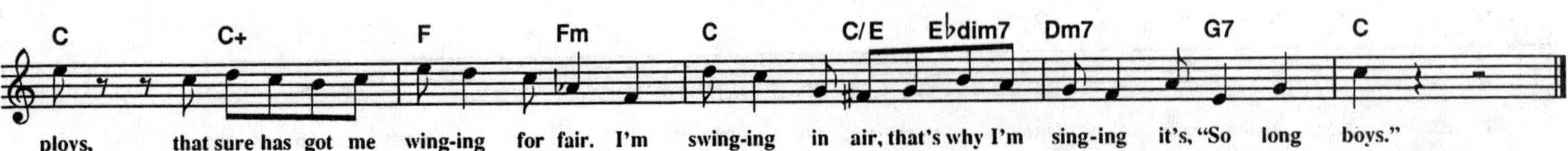
C C+ F Fm C C/E E♭dim7 Dm7 G7 C
ploys, that sure has got me wing-ing for fair. I'm swing-ing in air, that's why I'm sing-ing it's, "So long boys."

AH! SWEET MYSTERY OF LIFE
(The Dream Melody)

Words by
RIDA JOHNSON YOUNG
Music by
VICTOR HERBERT

Flowing
B♭
Cm7
F7
B♭
Ah! Sweet mys - ter - y of life, at last I've found thee. Ah! I know at last the se - cret of it all. All the

B♭m
F/C
C
C7
F7
long - ing, seek - ing, striv - ing, wait - ing, yearn - ing, the burn-ing hopes, the joy and i - dle tears that fall! For 'tis

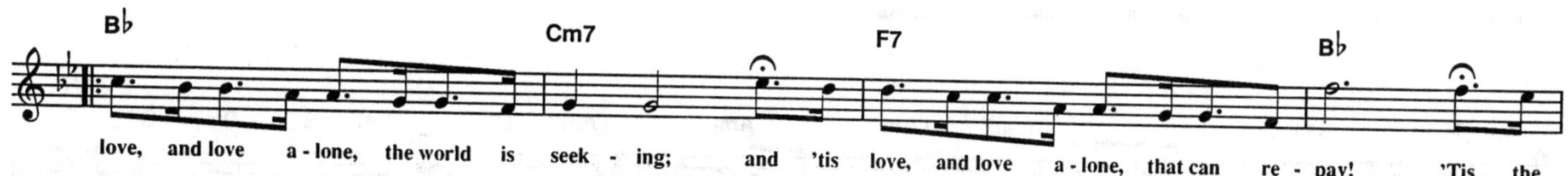
B♭
Cm7
F7
B♭
love, and love a - lone, the world is seek - ing; and 'tis love, and love a - lone, that can re - pay! 'Tis the

G7
Cm
E♭m
B♭/F
Cm7/F
F7
B♭
B♭
1.
2.
an - swer, 'tis the end and all of liv - ing, for it is love a - lone that rules for aye! For 'tis aye!

From the 20th Century-Fox Motion Picture "AN AFFAIR TO REMEMBER"

AN AFFAIR TO REMEMBER
(Our Love Affair)

Words by
HAROLD ADAMSON and LEO McCAREY
Music by
HARRY WARREN

Moderately
F
Fdim7
C
Cm
Gm
C7
F
Our love af - fair is a won - drous thing that we'll re - joice in re - mem - ber - ing. Our

Dm7
G
Em7
Am7
Dm7
G7
Gm7
C9
C+
F
love was born with our first em - brace and a page was torn out of time and space. Our love af -

Fdim7
C
Cm
Gm
C7
Am7(♭5)
D7(♭9)
Gm
B♭dim7
fair, may it al - ways be a flame to burn through e - ter - ni - ty. So, take my hand with a

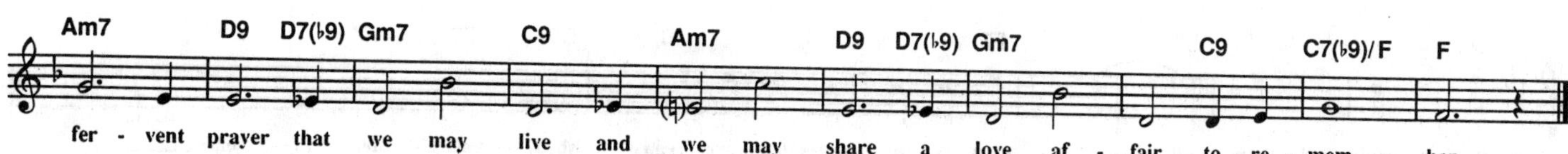
Am7
D9
D7(♭9)
Gm7
C9
Am7
D9
D7(♭9)
Gm7
C9
C7(♭9)/F
F
fer - vent prayer that we may live and we may share a love af - fair to re - mem - ber.

AFTER THE LOVIN'

Words and Music by
ALAN BERNSTEIN and
RITCHIE ADAMS

Moderately

C Cmaj7 C6 C Dm Dm(♯7) Dm7 G7
So I sing you to sleep_ af - ter the lov - in', _ with a song I just wrote_ yes - ter - day, and I
hard to ex - plain_ ev-'ry-thing that I'm feel - in'; _ face to face, I just seem to go dry. But I
sing you to sleep_ af - ter the lov - in'. ___ I brush back the hair ___ from your eyes, and the

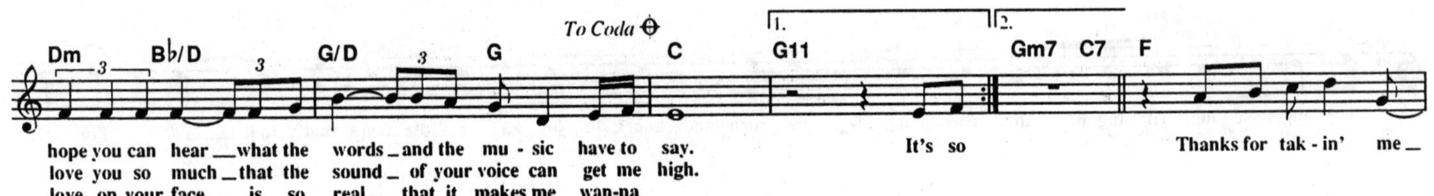
To Coda
Dm B♭/D G/D G C G11 Gm7 C7 F
1. 2.
hope you can hear ___ what the words _ and the mu - sic have to say. It's so Thanks for tak - in' me_
love you so much _ that the sound _ of your voice can get me high.
love on your face ___ is so real ___ that it makes me wan-na

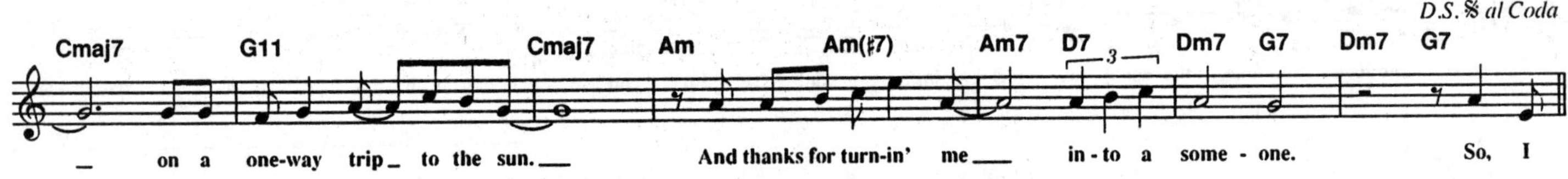
D.S. al Coda
Cmaj7 G11 Cmaj7 Am Am(♯7) Am7 D7 Dm7 G7 Dm7 G7
_ on a one-way trip _ to the sun. ___ And thanks for turn-in' me ___ in - to a some - one. So, I

Coda
A7 F E7 Am Am(♯7) Am7
cry. And I know ___ that my song is - n't say - ing an - y - thing new;

D7 Dm7 Em7 Dm7/F Dm9/G C
oh, ___ but af - ter the lov - in', I'm ___ still in love with you. ___

AFTER THE BALL

Words and Music by
CHARLES K. HARRIS

Moderately

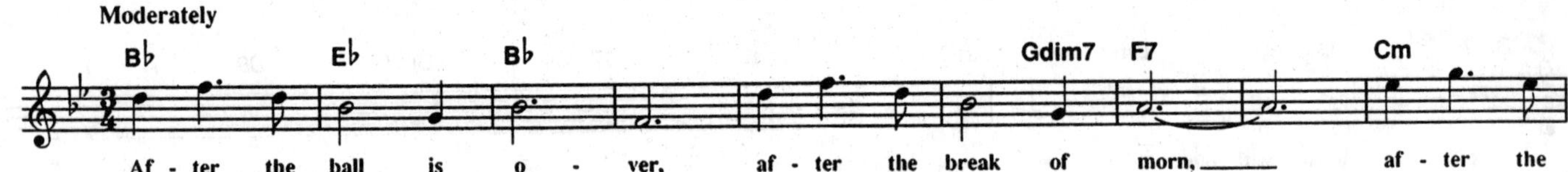
B♭ E♭ B♭ Gdim7 F7 Cm
Af - ter the ball is o - ver, af - ter the break of morn, ___ af - ter the

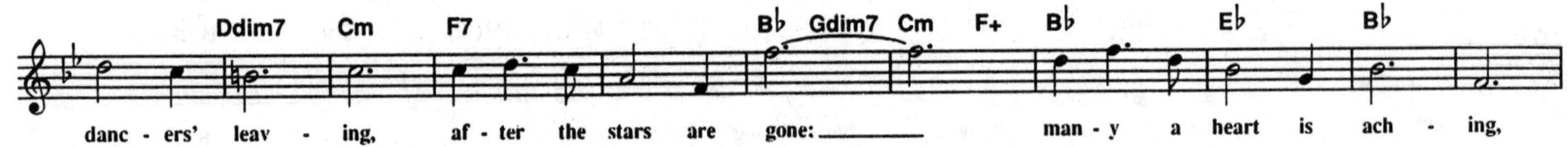
Ddim7 Cm F7 B♭ Gdim7 Cm F+ B♭ E♭ B♭
danc - ers' leav - ing, af - ter the stars are gone: ___ man - y a heart is ach - ing,

G7 C7 F7 B♭ G7 C7 F7 B♭
if you could read them all; ___ man - y the hopes that have van - ished, af - ter the ball. ___

From the Tri-Star Pictures Film "CHANCES ARE"

AFTER ALL

(Love Theme from "Chances Are")

Words and Music by
DEAN PITCHFORD and
TOM SNOW

Slowly, with a beat
Verse 1:
He:
1. Well, here we are a-gain; I guess it must be fate. We've tried it on our
own, but deep in-side we've known we'd be back to set things straight.
She:
I still re-mem-ber when
your kiss was so brand new. Ev-ery mem-o-ry re-peats, ev-ery step I take re-treats.
Both:
Ev-ery jour-ney al-ways brings me back
to you.
Chorus:
Af-ter all the stops and starts, we keep com-in' back to these two hearts, two
an-gels who've been res-cued from the fall. Af-ter all that we've been through,
She:
it all comes down to me and you.
Both:
I
guess it's meant to be,
He:
for-ev-er you and me, af-ter all.
To Coda
To Next Strain
Fine
She:
2. When love is tru-ly
Verse 2:
He:
right, (This time it's tru-ly right.)
She:
it lives from year to year.
Both:
It chang-es as it
goes,
She:
oh, and on the way it grows,
Both:
but it nev-er dis-ap-pears. Af-ter
D.S. al Coda
Coda
Bridge:
Al-ways just be-yond my touch, You know I need-ed you so much. Af-ter all, what else is liv-in' for? Af-ter
D.S. al Fine

Columbia Pictures Presents Rachel Ward, Jeff Bridges and James Woods
in a Taylor Hackford Film "AGAINST ALL ODDS"

AGAINST ALL ODDS
(Take a Look at Me Now)

Words and Music by
PHIL COLLINS

Slow rock
Bb7sus Bbm7 Cm7 Db(2) Ebm7
1. How can I just let you walk a - way, just let you leave with - out a trace? When I
Gb(2) Ab/Gb Fm7 Bbm7 Ebm7 Ebm7/Bb
stand here tak - ing ev - 'ry breath with you; ooh, you're the on - ly one who real - ly knew me at all.
1. Absus Ab 2.3. Absus Ab Chorus: Db/Ab
So take a look at me now, well, there's just an
Eb7/Ab Bbm7 Gb
emp - ty space. And there's noth - ing left here to re - mind me, just the mem -
Ebm7 Absus Db/Ab
- 'ry of your face. Well, take a look at me now, well, there's just an
Eb7/Ab Bbm7 Gb
emp - ty space. And you com - in' back to me is a - gainst the odds, and that's what / it's the chance
Ebm7 1. Absus Ab D.C. 2. Absus Ab Ab7sus/Eb Absus Ab
I've got to face. / I've got to take.
Ab7sus/Eb Ab(9) Ab7sus/Eb Ab3/Db Bb7sus/C Gb(9) Ab
Take a look at me now.

Verse 2:
How can you just walk away from me,
When all I can do is watch you leave?
'Cause we shared the laughter and the pain,
And even shared the tears.
You're the only one who really knew me at all.
(To Chorus:)

Verse 3:
I wish I could just make you turn around,
Turn around and see me cry.
There's so much I need to say to you,
So many reasons why,
You're the only one who really knew me at all.
(To Chorus:)

From the Broadway Musical "AIN'T MISBEHAVIN'"

AIN'T MISBEHAVIN'

Words by ANDY RAZAF
Music by THOMAS "FATS" WALLER and HARRY BROOKS

AIN'T NO SUNSHINE

Words and Music by BILL WITHERS

Moderately
Eb Gm7 Fm7 Bb7 Eb G7(#5/b9) Ab Db7 Eb Gb7
No one to talk with; all by my-self. No one to walk with, but I'm hap-py on the shelf.
I know for cer-tain the one I love. I'm thru with flirt - in' it's just you I'm think - in' of.
Ain't mis-be-hav-in',
Fm7 Bb7 G7 C7 F7 Bb7 Eb Ab7 Eb G7 Cm Cm(#5) Cm6
I'm sav-in' my love for you. you. Like Jack Horn-er in the cor-ner, don't go no-where.
C7 Bbmaj7 G7 Cm7 F7 Bb7 C7(#5) F7(b5) Bb7 Eb Gm7 Fm7 Bb7
What do I care? Your kiss - es are worth wait - in' for, be - lieve me. I don't stay out late, don't care to go.
Eb G7(#5/b9) Ab Db7 Eb Gb7 Fm7 Bb7 Eb
I'm home a - bout eight, just me and my ra - di - o. Ain't mis - be - hav - in' I'm sav - in' my love for you.
Slow rock-blues feel
Tacet
Am7 Em7 /G Am7 Em7 /G Am7
1. Ain't no sun-shine when she's gone. It's not warm when she's a - way. Ain't no sun-shine when she's gone,
gone. Won-der if she's gone to stay. 2.3. Ain't no sun-shine when she's gone,
gone, on - ly dark - ness ev-'ry day.
Em7 Dm7 To Coda Am7 Em7 /G Am7 D.S.
and she's al - ways gone too long
and this house just ain't no home
an - y - time she goes a - way. 2. Won-der this time where she's
Am7 Em7 Am7 Tacet
way. And I know, I know, I know, I know, I know, I know, I know, I know, I know, I
know, I know, I know, I know, I know, I know, I know, I know, I know, I know, I know, I know, I know, I know, I know, I know, I
know, hey, I ought to leave the young thing a - lone, but ain't no sun - shine when she's gone.
Am7 Em7 /G
Am7 D.S. al Coda
3. Ain't no sun - shine when she's
Coda
Am7 Em7 /G Am7 Em7 /G Em7 /G Am9
way. An-y-time she goes a - way. way.

ALL I HAVE TO DO IS DREAM

Words and Music by
BOUDLEAUX BRYANT

Moderately

E♭ Cm A♭ B♭ E♭ Cm A♭ B♭
Dream, dream, dream, dream. Dream, dream, dream, dream. When

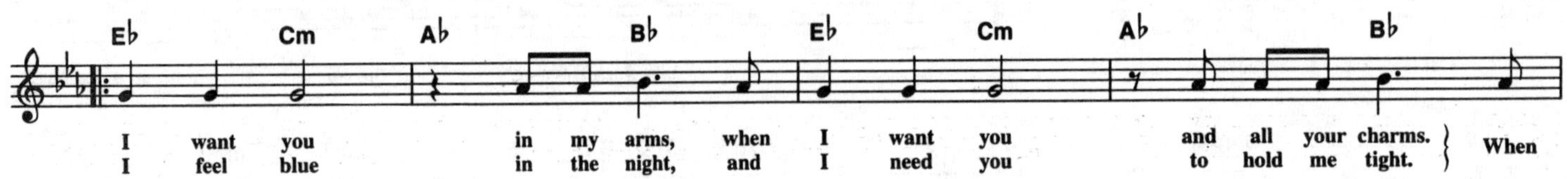
E♭ Cm A♭ B♭ E♭ Cm A♭ B♭
I want you in my arms, when I want you and all your charms.
I feel blue in the night, and I need you to hold me tight.
When

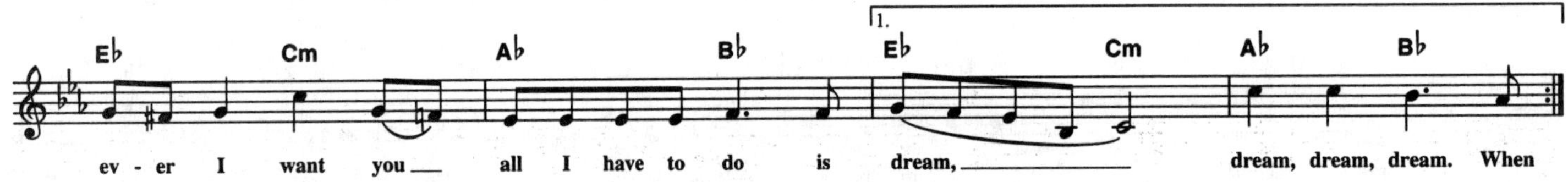
E♭ Cm A♭ B♭ 1. E♭ Cm A♭ B♭
ev - er I want you all I have to do is dream, dream, dream, dream. When

2. E♭ A♭ E♭ E♭7 A♭ Gm Fm B♭
Dream. I can make you mine, taste your lips of wine, an - y - time, night or

E♭ E♭7 A♭ Gm F7 Fm7/B♭ B♭
day. On - ly trou - ble is, Gee whiz, I'm dream-ing my life a - way! I

E♭ Cm A♭ B♭ E♭ Cm A♭ B♭
need you so that I could die, I love you so and that is why when -

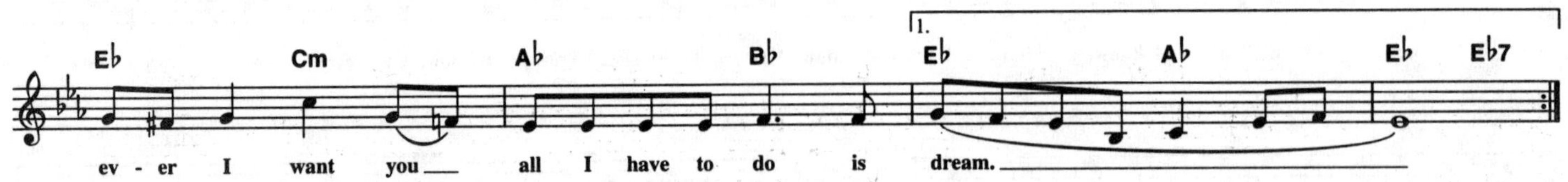
E♭ Cm A♭ B♭ 1. E♭ A♭ E♭ E♭7
ev - er I want you all I have to do is dream.

2. E♭ Cm A♭ B♭ E♭ Cm A♭ B♭ E♭
Dream, dream, dream, dream. Dream, dream, dream, dream, dream.

From the Musical Production "GODSPELL"

ALL GOOD GIFTS

Words and Music by
STEPHEN SCHWARTZ

Moderately
D Am C G D
We plow the fields_ and scat - ter the good seed on_ the land. But it is fed_ and
thank thee then,_ oh Fa - ther, for all things bright_ and good, the seed time and_ the
E7 Gm D Am C
wa - tered by God's al - might - y hand._ He sends the snow_ in win - ter, the warmth to swell_ the
har - vest, our life, our health, our food._ No gifts have we_ to of - fer for all thy love_ im -
G F♯m G G♯m Em A D
grain, the bree-zes and_ the sun - shine and soft re - fresh - ing rain.
parts. But that which Thou_ de - sir - est our hum-ble, thank - ful hearts.
All good
Gmaj7 Cmaj7 Fmaj7 D Gmaj7 Cmaj7 Fmaj7
gifts a - round us are sent from heav - en a - bove.
Bm F♯m Gmaj7 F♯m D D7 C
1. A11
So thank the Lord, oh thank_ the Lord, for all his love. We
2. A11 D Gmaj7 Cmaj7 Fmaj7 D
I real-ly want to thank you, Lord. I want to thank you Lord._
Gmaj7 Cmaj7 Fmaj7 D Gmaj7 Cmaj7 Fmaj7
Thank you for all_ of your love. Oh, thank you, Lord._ I want to thank you, Lord, thank you,
D Am C G D E Gm D
Lord.

AIN'T THAT A SHAME

Words and Music by
ANTOINE DOMINO and
DAVE BARTHOLOMEW

Moderate rock shuffle
G G6 G G6 C7 G
You made me cry when you said __ good - bye.
broke my heart when you said __ we'll part.
Ain't that a shame? __ My tears fell like rain. ____
C7 D7 G G6 G G6
Ain't that a shame? __ You're the one to blame. ____ Oh, well, good - bye, al - though I'll cry. Ain't that a
C7 G C7 1. G Am7 D7 2. G G6
shame? __ My tears fell like rain. ____ Ain't that a shame? __ You're the one to blame. ____ You blame.

"A" - YOU'RE ADORABLE
(The Alphabet Song)

Words and Music by
BUDDY KAYE, FRED WISE, SIDNEY LIPPMAN

Moderately

C A7 D7 Am7 D7 Dm7
"A" you're a - dor - a - ble, "B" you're so beau - ti - ful, "C" you're a cu - tie full o' charms, "D" you're a dar - ling, and

Em A7 Dm7 G7 C Dm9 G7 C A7
"E" you're ex - cit - ing, and "F" you're a feath - er in my arms. "G" you look good to me, "H" you're so hea - ven - ly,

D7 Am7 D7 Dm7 Em A7 Dm7 G7 C C7
"I" you're the one I i - dol - ize, "J" we're like Jack and Jill, "K" you're so kiss - a - ble, "L" is the love - light in your eyes.

F G9 C Am Dm7 G7 G9(♯5) C C7 F G9 C Cm G D7
"M", "N", "O", "P" I could go on __ all day. "Q", "R", "S", "T", al - pha - bet - ic - 'ly speak - ing

G7 C A7 D7 Am7 D7
you're o - kay! __ "U" made my life com - plete, "V" means you're ver - y sweet, dou - ble "U" "X" "Y" "Z" ______ It's

Dm7 D♯dim7 C A7(♯5) Dm7 G7(♭9) 1. C C♯dim7 Dm7 G7 2. C
fun to wan - der thru the al - pha - bet with you to tell you what you mean to me! ____ __

ALABAMY BOUND

TRADITIONAL

Brightly
G6/9
A7
I'm Al - a - bam - y bound; there'll be no "Heeb - ie Jeeb - ies" hang - in' 'round. Just gave the
D7
Em
A7
D7 Ddim D7
mean - est tick - et man on earth all I'm worth to put my toot - sies in an up - per berth.
N.C.
C9
A7
Just hear that choo choo sound. I know that soon we're goin' to cov - er ground
G G9 E7
A7
D7
G
and then I'll hol - ler so the world will know "Here I go." I'm Al - a - bam - y bound.

From the Broadway Musical Production "IRENE"

ALICE BLUE GOWN

Lyric by JOSEPH McCARTHY
Music by HARRY TIERNEY

Moderate waltz

C A A9 A7 D7

In my sweet lit - tle Al - ice blue gown, when I first wan - dered down in to

G7 G7(♯5) C A7 D7

town, I was both proud and shy, As I felt ev - 'ry eye. But in ev - 'ry shop

Dm7/G G7 C A A9 A7

win - dow I'd primp, pass - ing by. Then in man - ner of fash - ion I'd frown, and the

Dm A7/E Dm/F G7 E7 Dm Dm/A A♭dim7 C/G Gm

world seem'd to smile all a - round, till it wilt - ed I wore it, I'll al - ways a -

A7 Dm A7/E Dm/F G7 Fm6/A♭ G7 1. C C6 C♯dim7 G7 2. C

dore it, my sweet lit - tle Al - ice blue gown. In my gown.

ALEXANDER'S RAGTIME BAND

Words and Music by
IRVING BERLIN

Moderate swing

F F/E F/D F/C C7/E C7 F F+
Come on and hear, come on and hear Al - ex - an - der's rag - time band. Come on and

B♭ B♭/A B♭/G B♭/F B♭ F
hear, come on and hear. It's the best band in the land. They can play a bu-gle call like you nev-er heard be-fore.

C/E E♭dim7 G7/D G7 C7
So nat - u - ral that you want to go to war. That's just the best - est band what am,

F F/E F/D F/C C7/E C7 F F+ B♭ B♭/A
hon-ey lamb. Come on a - long, come on a - long. Let me take you by the hand, up to the man, up to the

B♭/G B♭/F B♭ F7 B♭
man who's the lead - er of the band. And if you care to hear the Swa - nee Riv - er played in

G♯dim7 F C7/G C7 1. F 2. F
rag - time, come on and hear, come on and hear Al - ex - an - der's rag - time band. Come on and band.

From the Metro-Goldwyn-Mayer Motion Picture "SADIE McKEE"

ALL I DO IS DREAM OF YOU

Words by ARTHUR FREED
Music by NACIO HERB BROWN

Moderately

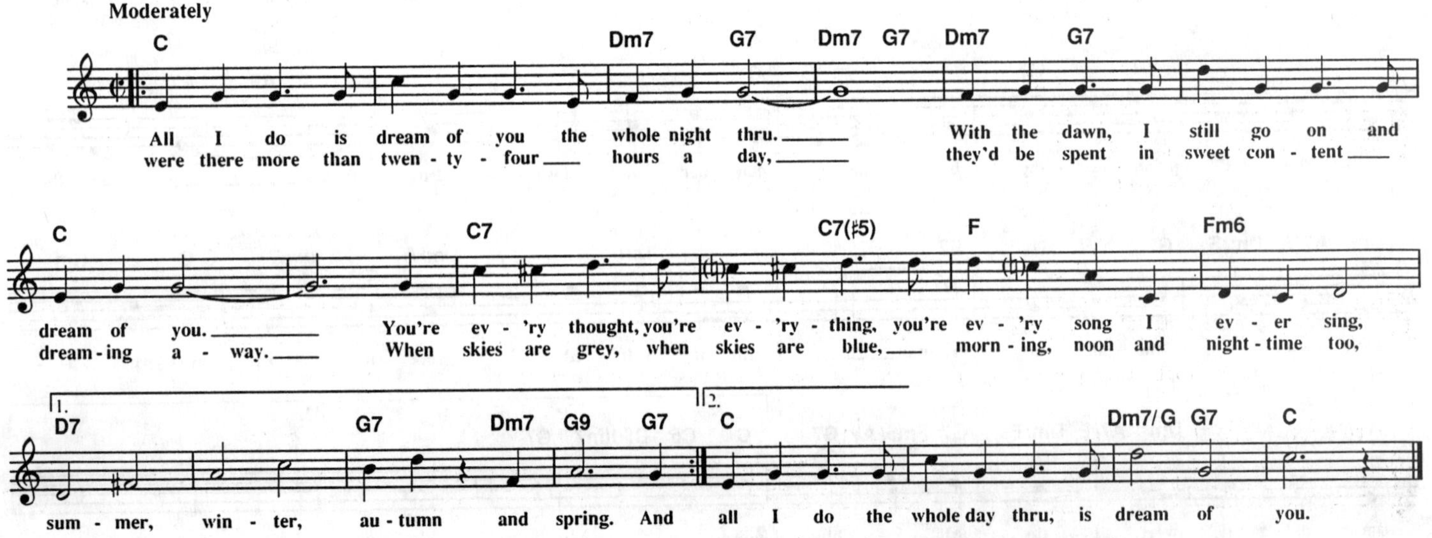
C Dm7 G7 Dm7 G7 Dm7 G7
All I do is dream of you the whole night thru. With the dawn, I still go on and
were there more than twen - ty - four hours a day, they'd be spent in sweet con - tent
C C7 C7(♯5) F Fm6
dream of you. You're ev - 'ry thought, you're ev - 'ry - thing, you're ev - 'ry song I ev - er sing,
dream-ing a - way. When skies are grey, when skies are blue, morn - ing, noon and night - time too,
1. D7 G7 Dm7 G9 G7 2. C Dm7/G G7 C
sum - mer, win - ter, au - tumn and spring. And all I do the whole day thru, is dream of you.

From the Paramount Picture "ALFIE"
ALFIE
Copyright © 1966 by FAMOUS MUSIC CORPORATION
All Rights Reserved
Lyric by HAL DAVID
Music by BURT BACHARACH
Slowly
What's it all a - bout, Al - fie? Is it just for the mo-ment we live? What's it all a - bout when you sort it out, Al - fie? Are we meant to take more than we give, or are we meant to be kind? And if
on - ly fools are kind, Al - fie, then I guess it is wise to be cruel. And if life be - longs on - ly to the strong, Al - fie, what will you lend on an old gold-en rule? As
sure as I be - lieve there's a heav-en a - bove, Al - fie. I know there's some-thing much more. Some-thing e - ven non be - liev - ers can be-lieve in. I be-lieve in love, Al - fie. With-out true love we just ex - ist, Al - fie. Un - til you find the love you've missed you're noth-ing, Al - fie. When you walk let your heart lead the way and you'll find love an - y day, Al - fie.
ALL IN LOVE IS FAIR
Copyright © 1973 by JOBETE MUSIC CO., INC. and BLACK BULL MUSIC, INC.
All Rights Reserved
Words and Music by
STEVIE WONDER
Slow ballad
All is fair in love. Love's a cra - zy game. Two peo - ple vow to stay in love as one they say. But all is changed with time. The fu-ture none can see. The road you leave be - hind, a - head lies mys-ter - y. But all is fair in love.
chance, it's eith - er good or bad. I tossed my coin to say in love with me you'd stay. But all in war is so cold. You eith-er win or lose. When all is put a - way, the los - ing side I'll play. But all is fair in love.
I had to go a - way.
I should have nev-er left your side.
A writ-er takes his pen to write the words a - gain that all in love is fair. All of fate's a
A writ-er takes his pen to write the words a - gain that all in love is fair.

ALL AT ONCE

Words by JEFFREY OSBORNE
and MICHAEL MASSER
Music by MICHAEL MASSER

Slowly and expressively

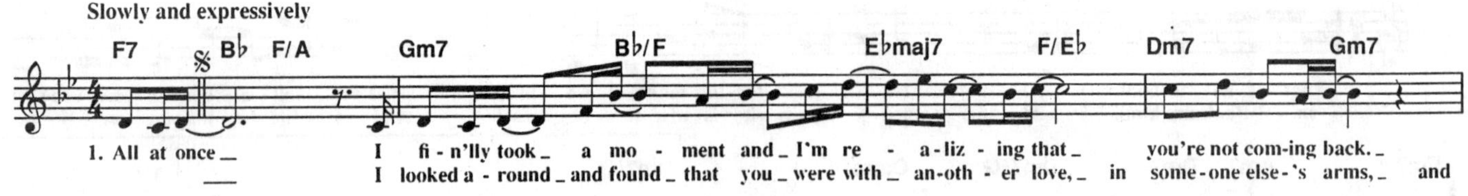
F7 B♭ F/A Gm7 B♭/F E♭maj7 F/E♭ Dm7 Gm7
1. All at once I fi - n'lly took a mo - ment and I'm re - a - liz - ing that you're not com-ing back.
I looked a - round and found that you were with an-oth - er love, in some-one else-'s arms, and

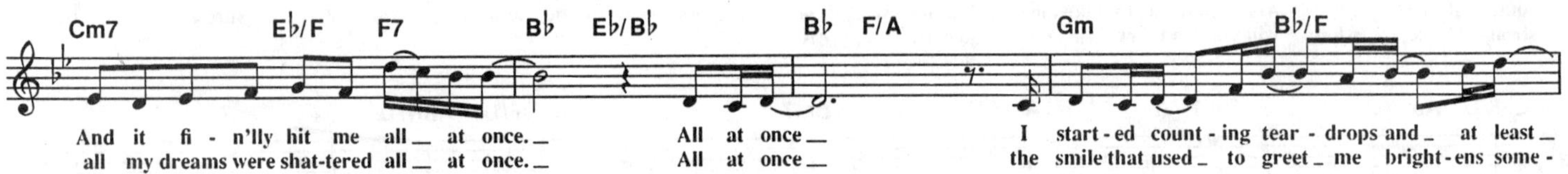
Cm7 E♭/F F7 B♭ E♭/B♭ B♭ F/A Gm B♭/F
And it fi - n'lly hit me all at once. All at once I start-ed count - ing tear - drops and at least
all my dreams were shat-tered all at once. All at once the smile that used to greet me bright-ens some -

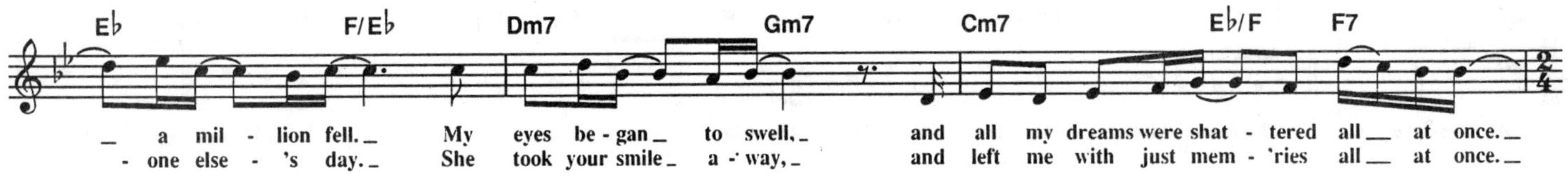
E♭ F/E♭ Dm7 Gm7 Cm7 E♭/F F7
a mil - lion fell. My eyes be - gan to swell, and all my dreams were shat - tered all at once.
- one else - 's day. She took your smile a - way, and left me with just mem - 'ries all at once.

B♭ E♭ B♭/D D7(♭9) D/F♯ Gm F E♭ B♭/D Gm7
Ev-er since I met you, you're the on - ly love I've known. and I can't for-get you, though I must

Chorus:
Cm7 Cm/F G♭/A♭ A♭7 D♭ Fm7/B♭ B♭/D E♭m7 A♭ A♭/G♭
face it all a - lone. All at once I'm drift-ing on a lone - ly sea, wish-ing you'd come back

Fm7 B♭m7 G♭maj9 G♭/A♭ D♭ Fm7/B♭ B♭/D
to me. And that's all that mat - ters now. All at once I'm drift - ing on a lone-

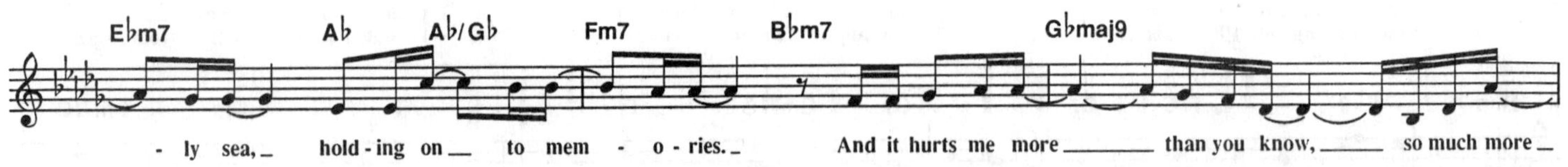
E♭m7 A♭ A♭/G♭ Fm7 B♭m7 G♭maj9
- ly sea, hold - ing on to mem - o - ries. And it hurts me more than you know, so much more

1.
D.S. 𝄋
2.3.
Repeat and fade
G♭/A♭ D♭ Cm7 E♭(9)/F F7 G♭/A♭ A♭7
than it shows all at once. 2. All at once. than it shows. All at once

ALL I EVER NEED IS YOU

Words and Music by
JIMMY HOLIDAY and
EDDIE REEVES

Moderately

G B7 Em G7
1. Some-times when I'm down and all __ a - lone, just like a child _ with-out __ a home. The
2. Some men fol - low rain-bows, I __ am told. Some men search for __ sil-ver some for gold.

C G Em A7 D7 G
love you give _ me keeps me hang-in' on, __ oh hon - ey. All I ev-er need _ is you. You're my first love, you're my
I have found _ my treas-ure in your soul, __ hon - ey. All I ev-er need _ is you. With-out love I'd nev - er find the

B7 Em G7 C G Em
last. You're my fu-ture, you're my past. And lov - ing you is all I ask, hon - ey.
way through ups and downs of ev-'ry sin - gle day. I won't sleep at night un-til you say, "My hon - ey,

A7 Am7/D D7 G *Fine* C D C Bm
All I ev - er need _ is you. Win-ters come and they go, and we watch _ the melt - ing snow. ______
all I ev - er need _ is you".

C G Bm/F♯ Em G/D C C/B Am7 Am7/D *D.C. al Fine* D7
Sure as sum-mer fol - lows spring, all the things _ you do give me a rea-son to build my world a - round you.

ALL THROUGH THE NIGHT

WELSH SONG

Moderately

F B♭ G7 C B♭ C7 F B♭
Sleep, my child, and peace at - tend thee all through the night. Guard - ian an - gels

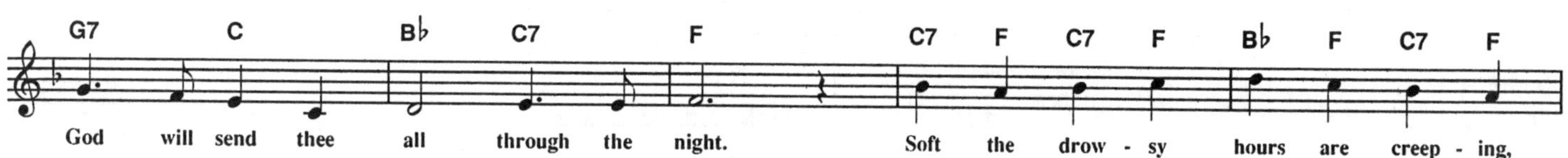
G7 C B♭ C7 F C7 F C7 F B♭ F C7 F
God will send thee all through the night. Soft the drow - sy hours are creep - ing,

C7 F Gm7 G7 F C7 F B♭ G7 C B♭ C7 F
hill and vale in slum - ber steep - ing, I, my lov - ing vi - gil keep - ing, all through the night.

ALL MY EX'S LIVE IN TEXAS

Words and Music by
SANGER D. SHAFER &
LYNDIA J. SHAFER

Moderate country
Chorus:
A E7
All my ex - 's live in Tex - as, and Tex - as is a place
Bm7 E7(♭9) A E7
I'd dear - ly love to be. But all my ex - 's live in Tex - as,
To Coda
A D/F♯ G♯
and that's why I hang my hat in Ten - nes - see. 1. Ro -
Verse:
A Bm7
san - na's down in Tex - ar - ka - na, want - ed me to push a broom. And
E7 A
sweet I - lene's in Ab - i - lene, she for - got I hung the moon. And
Bm7
Al - li - son in Gal - ves - ton some - how lost her san - i - ty. And
1. D.C. 2. D.C. al Coda
B7 E7
Dim - ples who now lives in Tem - ple's got the law look - in' for me. light.
Coda
A/C♯ D E♭7 E7 D7 E♭7 E7
Some folks think I hide, it's been ru - mored that I
D7 E♭7 E7 A
died, but I'm a - live and well in Ten - nes - see.

Verse 2:
I remember that old Brazos River where I learned to swim,
But it brings to mind another time where I wore my welcome thin.
By transcendental meditation, I go there each night.
But I always come back to myself long before daylight.
(To Chorus:)

From the Broadway Musical Production "BRIGADOON"

ALMOST LIKE BEING IN LOVE

Lyrics by ALAN JAY LERNER
Music by FREDERICK LOEWE

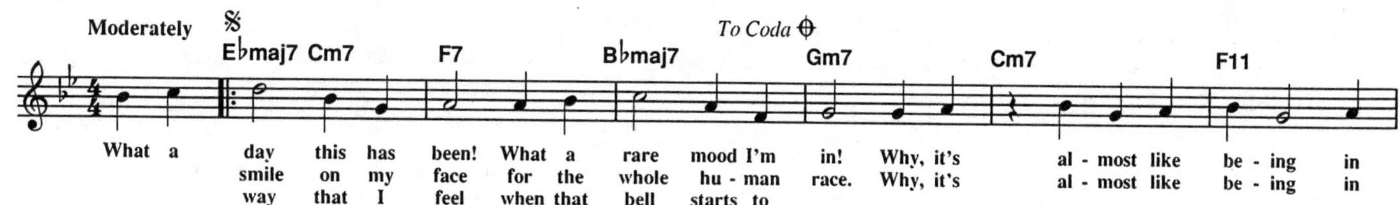
Moderately
To Coda
Ebmaj7 Cm7 F7 Bbmaj7 Gm7 Cm7 F11
What a day this has been! What a rare mood I'm in! Why, it's al - most like be - ing in
smile on my face for the whole hu - man race. Why, it's al - most like be - ing in
way that I feel when that bell starts to

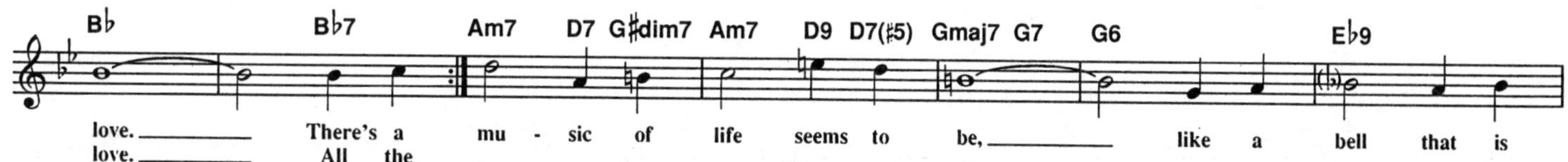
Bb Bb7 Am7 D7 G#dim7 Am7 D9 D7(#5) Gmaj7 G7 G6 Eb9
love. There's a mu - sic of life seems to be, like a bell that is
love. All the

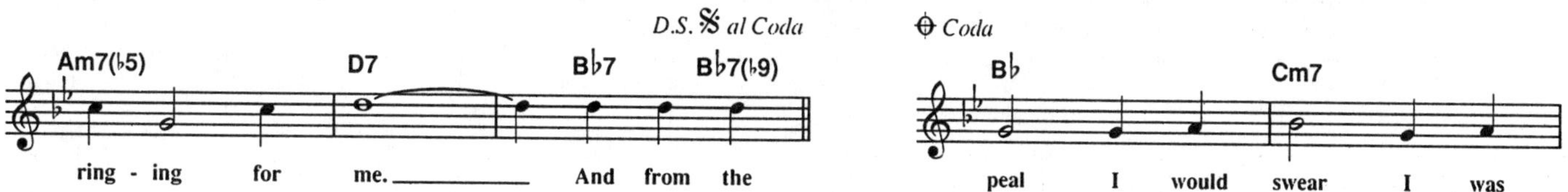
D.S. al Coda
Coda
Am7(b5) D7 Bb7 Bb7(b9) Bb Cm7
ring - ing for me. And from the peal I would swear I was

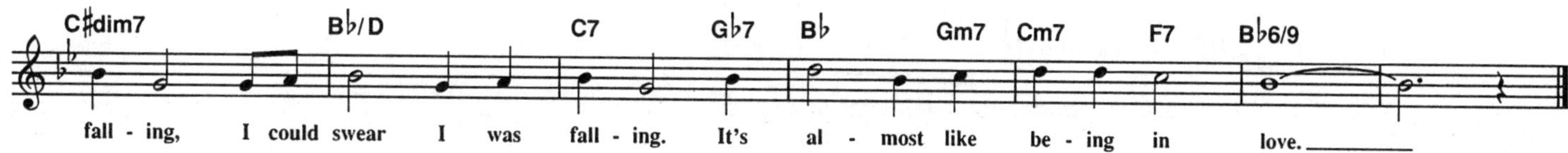
C#dim7 Bb/D C7 Gb7 Bb Gm7 Cm7 F7 Bb6/9
fall - ing, I could swear I was fall - ing. It's al - most like be - ing in love.

ALOHA OE

(Farewell To Thee)

Words and Music by
QUEEN LILIUOKALANI

Moderately
Ab Db Ab Eb
Proud - ly swept the rain cloud by the cliff as on it glid - ed through the

Ab Db Ab Db Eb7 Ab
trees, still fol - low - ing with grief the li ko, the a hi - hi le hua of the vale. Fare -

Db Ab Eb7
well to thee, fare - well to thee, thou charm - ing one who dwells a - mong the

Ab Db Ab Eb7 Ab
bow - ers. One fond em - brace be - fore I now de - part un - til we meet a - gain.

Paramount Pictures Presents a Daniel Melnick Production a Herbert Ross Film "FOOTLOOSE"

ALMOST PARADISE . . .

Love Theme from "FOOTLOOSE"

Words by DEAN PITCHFORD
Music by ERIC CARMEN

Slowly
Verse:
G D/F♯ Em G/D C D/C Bm7 G/B G/A A7 C/D D7
I thought that dreams be-longed to oth-er men, 'cause each time I got close they'd fall a-part a-gain.
It seems like per-fect love's so hard to find. I'd al-most giv-en up; you must have read my mind.

G D/F♯ Em G/D C D/C G(9)/B G/B C D/C G(9)/B G/B
I feared my heart would beat in se-cre-cy; I faced the night a-lone; oh how could I have known that
And all these dreams I saved for a rain-y day, they're fi-n'lly com-in' true. I'll share them all with you, 'cause

C D/C G/B B7/D♯ Em Em/D C C/D
Chorus:
Gsus G D/G G D/E Em D/E Em
all my life I on-ly need-ed you?
now we hold the fu-ture in our hands.
Oh, al-most par-a-dise; we're knock-ing on heav-en's door; al-most

Gsus G D/G G D/E Em C Am7 C/D D7
par-a-dise; how could we ask for more? I swear that I can see for-ev-er in your eyes

C/G G
1.
D/E Em D/C C/D
2. To Next Strain
Gsus G
3.
D/E Em D/C C/D C/G G
Fine
par-a-dise. Par-a-dise.

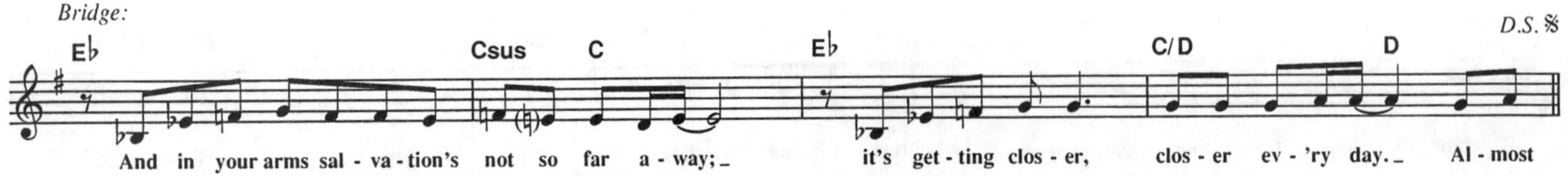
Bridge:
E♭ Csus C E♭ C/D D
D.S. 𝄋
And in your arms sal-va-tion's not so far a-way; it's get-ting clos-er, clos-er ev-'ry day. Al-most

ALONE AND BLUE

Words by ANDY RAZAF
Music by THOMAS WALLER and HARRY BROOKS

Moderate swing
Am Dm Am D7 C C♯dim7
Noth-in' seems right, no ap - pe - tite, can't sleep at night, no hope in sight. What did I do

G7 G9 G+ C E7 Am Dm Am
to be a - lone and blue? Since you've been gone life has no dawn. I need you so.

D7 C C♯dim7 G7 A♭7 G7 C F7 C G7(♯5) C A♭7
Why did you go? What did I do to be a - lone and blue? Since your

C Cdim7 C E♭7 A♭7 Am D F7
good - bye, life's all out of key. Blue birds fly by, they won't sing for

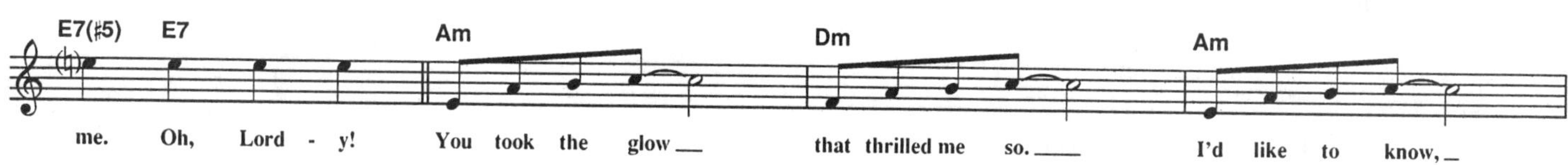
E7(♯5) E7 Am Dm Am
me. Oh, Lord - y! You took the glow that thrilled me so. I'd like to know,

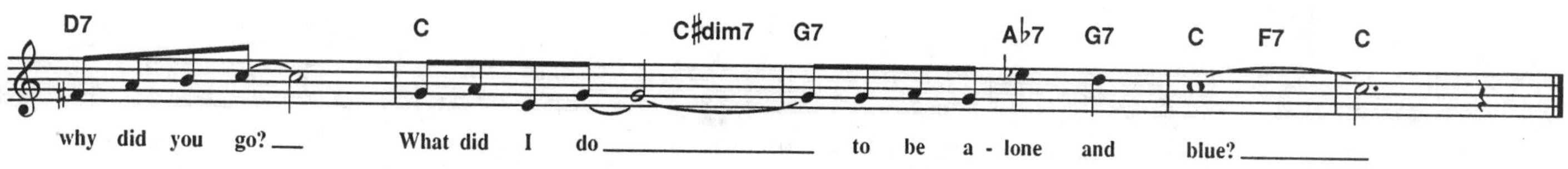
D7 C C♯dim7 G7 A♭7 G7 C F7 C
why did you go? What did I do to be a - lone and blue?

ALONG COMES MARY

Words and Music by
TANDYN ALMER

Moderate rock

Am D7 Am7 D7 Am D7 Am7 D7

Ev - 'ry time I think that I'm the on - ly one who's lone - ly, some-one calls on me. ___ And
sire ___ is the fire ___ in the eyes of chicks whose sick-ness is the games they play ___ And when the

Am D7 Am7 D7 Am7 D7 Am7 D7

ev - 'ry now and then I spend my time at rhyme and verse and curse the faults in me. ___ But then A -
mas-quer-ade is played and neigh-bor folks make jokes at who is most to blame to - day. ___ And then A -

E A E7 A E A E7 A

long comes Mar - y, ___ and does she wan - na give me kicks and be my stead - y chick and give me pick of
long comes Mar - y, ___ and does she wan - na set them free and make them see re - al - i - ties in which she

E A D7 G B E B E

mem - o - ries? ___ Or may - be rath - er gath - er tales from all the fails and trib - u - la - tions no one
got her name? ___ And will they strug-gle much when told that such a ten - der touch of hers will make them

B E A Dm Em F7

ev - er sees? ___ When we met, I was sure out to lunch. ___ Now my emp - ty
not the same? ___

Repeat and fade

Dm7 Am7 | 1. Am D Am7 D | 2. Am D Am7 D Am D

cup tastes as sweet as the punch. ___ 2. When vague de - ___ Sweet as the punch. ___

ALOUETTE
(The Lark)

FRENCH FOLK SONG

Brightly

F C7 F Gm7 C7 F
A - lou - et - te, gen - tille a - lou - et - te, a - lou - et - te, je te plu - me - rai.
C7 F C7
Je te plu - me - rai la tête, je te plu - me - rai la tête. Et la tête, et la tête, et la tête, et la tête.
a tempo
F C7 F Gm7 C7 F
O! A - lou - et - te, gen - tille a - lou - et - te, a - lou - et - te, je te plu - me - rai.

ALWAYS

Written by JONATHAN LEWIS,
DAVID LEWIS and WAYNE LEWIS

Moderately slow

G D/G Dm/G C Am7 Am7/D G(9)
1. Girl you are to me all that a wom-an should be, and I ded - i - cate my life to you al - ways. A
2. Come with me my sweet; lets go make a fam - i - ly. And they will bring us joy for al - ways. Oh,

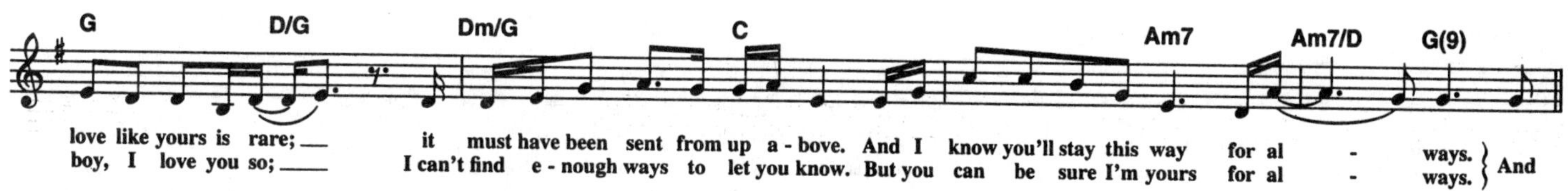
G D/G Dm/G C Am7 Am7/D G(9)
love like yours is rare; it must have been sent from up a - bove. And I know you'll stay this way for al - ways.
boy, I love you so; I can't find e - nough ways to let you know. But you can be sure I'm yours for al - ways.
And

Cmaj7 Bm7 Cmaj7 Bm7 Am7 Bm7 Cm7 A♭maj9 Am7/D D C/E D/F♯
we both know that our love will grow. And for - ev - er it will be you and me.

Chorus:

G D/G Dm/G C Am7 Am7/D G(9)
Ooh, you're like the sun, chas-ing all the rain a-way. When you come a - round, you bring bright - er days.

G D/G Dm7/G C Am7 1. Am7/D G(9) D.C.
You're the per - fect one for me, and you for-ev-er will be. And I will love you so for al - ways.

2. Am7/D G(9) G D/G Dm/G C Am7 Am7/D G(9)
Repeat ad lib. and fade
al - ways. Ooh, ooh, hoo. I will love you so for al - ways.

ALWAYS AND FOREVER

Words and Music by
ROD TEMPERTON

Slowly
Dmaj7
Bm9
Gmaj7
Dmaj7
Al - ways and for - ev - er,
each mo-ment with you
is just like a dream to me
There'll al - ways be sun - shine
when I look at you;
some-thing I can't ex - plain

Em7
Em7/A A9 Dmaj7
Bm9
Gmaj7
that some-how came true.
And I know to - mor-row
will still be the same,
'cause we've got a
just the things that you do.
And if you get lone-ly
phone me and take
a sec - ond to

Chorus:
Dmaj7
Em7
Em7/A A9
Dmaj7
Gmaj7 D/F♯
Em7
life of love
that won't ev - er change.
And
give to me
that mag - ic you make.
And
ev - 'ry day
love me your own spe - cial way.
Melt all my

Em7/A
Dmaj7
F♯m7
Gmaj7 D/F♯
Em7
F♯m7
heart a - way
with a smile.
Take time to tell me
you real - ly care
and
and

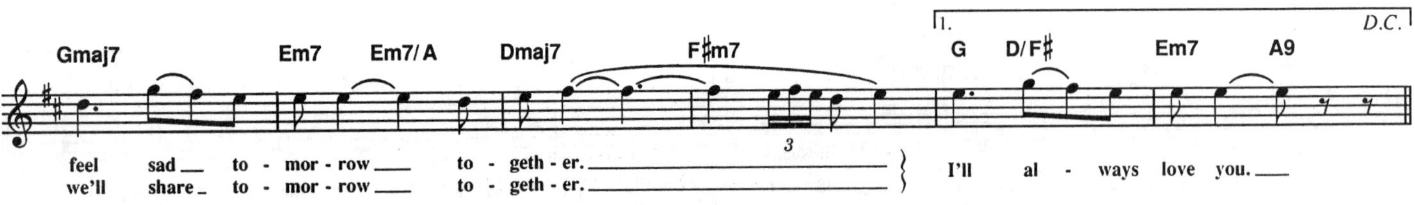
Gmaj7
Em7
Em7/A
Dmaj7
F♯m7
1.
G D/F♯
Em7
A9
D.C.
feel sad to - mor - row
to - geth - er.
we'll share to - mor - row
to - geth - er.
I'll al - ways love you.

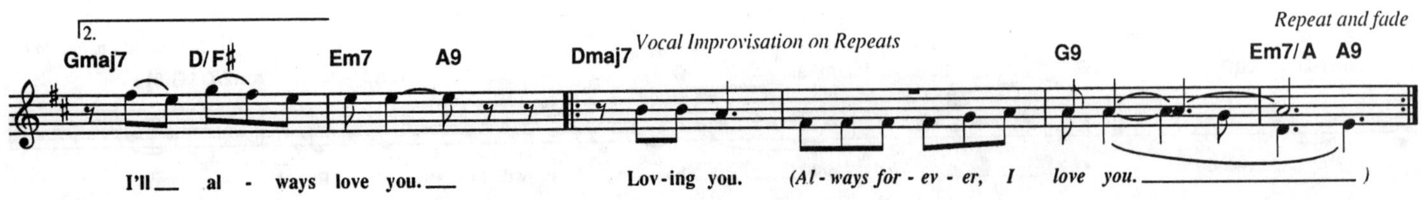
2.
Gmaj7 D/F♯
Em7 A9
Dmaj7
Vocal Improvisation on Repeats
G9
Repeat and fade
Em7/A A9
I'll al - ways love you.
Lov-ing you.
(Al - ways for - ev - er, I love you.)

ALWAYS IN MY HEART

(Siempre en Mi Corazón)

English Words by KIM GANNON
Spanish Words and Music by
ERNESTO LECUONA

Moderately

B♭ F+ B♭ F7(♯5) B♭ F+ B♭ N.C.
You are al - ways in my heart, e - ven tho' you're far a - way, I can hear the mu - sic
Siem-pre es-ta en mi co - ra - zón el re - cuer - do de tu a - mor, que al i - gual que tu can -

B♭ C♯dim7 Cm F7 Cm7
of the song of love I sang with you. You are al - ways in my heart, and when skies a - bove are
ción qui - to de mi al - ma su do - lor. Siem-pre es-ta en mi co - ra - zón la nos - tal - gia de tu

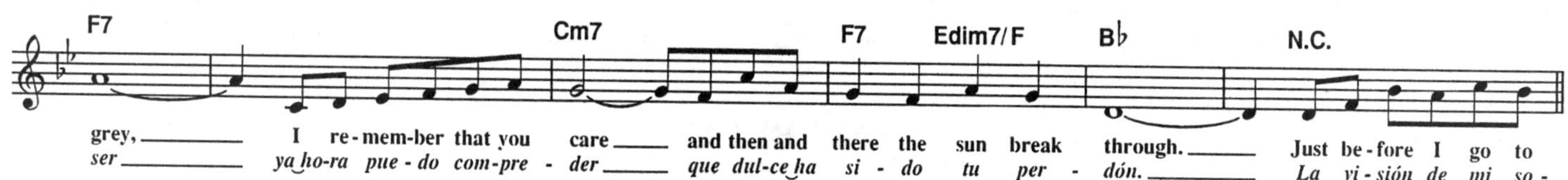
F7 Cm7 F7 Edim7/F B♭ N.C.
grey, I re - mem - ber that you care and then and there the sun break through. Just be - fore I go to
ser ya ho - ra pue - do com - pre - der que dul - ce ha si - do tu per - dón. La vi - sión de mi so -

B♭ F+ B♭ F7(♯5) B♭ F+ B♭ Dm7(♭5) G7 Dm7(♭5) G7
sleep there's a ren - dez - vous I keep and the dream I al - ways meet helps me for - get we're far a -
ñar me hi - zo ver con e - mo - ción que fué tu al - ma ins - pi - ra - ción don - de a pla - qué mi sed de a -

Cm N.C. Cm7(♭5) B♭/F B♭/D D♭dim7
part. I don't know ex - act - ly when, dear, but I'm sure we'll meet a - gain, dear, and, my dar - ling, till we
mar. Hoy tan so - lo es pe - ro ver - te y ya nun - ca más per - der - te, mien - tras tan - to que tu a -

F7/C F7 1. B♭ F+ N.C. 2. B♭
do you are al - ways in my heart. You are al - ways in my heart.
mor, siem - pre es - ta en mi co - ra - zón. Siem - pre es - ta en mi co - ra - zón.

ALWAYS LATE
(With Your Kisses)

Words and Music by
LEFTY FRIZZELL and
BLACKIE CRAWFORD

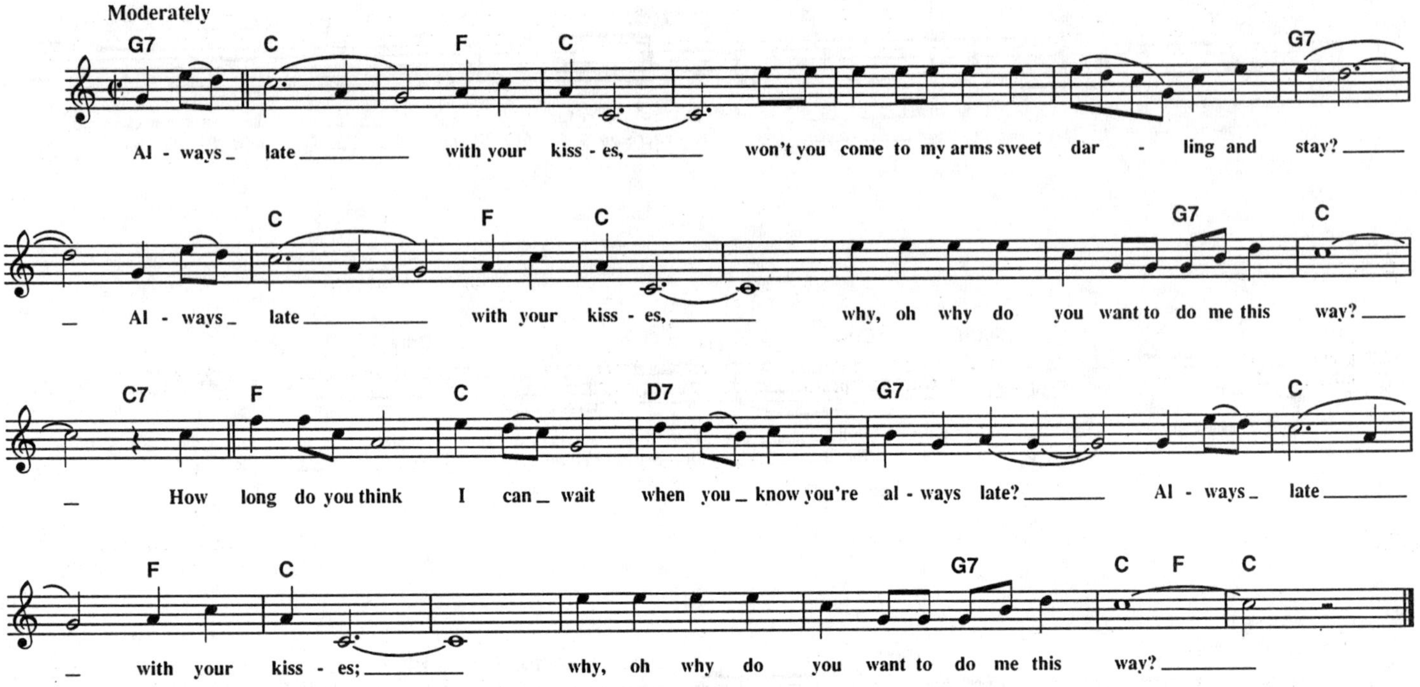

Moderately

G7 C F C G7
Al - ways _ late ___ with your kiss - es, ___ won't you come to my arms sweet dar - ling and stay? ___

C F C G7 C
_ Al - ways _ late ___ with your kiss - es, ___ why, oh why do you want to do me this way? ___

C7 F C D7 G7 C
_ How long do you think I can _ wait when you _ know you're al - ways late? ___ Al - ways _ late ___

F C G7 C F C
_ with your kiss - es; ___ why, oh why do you want to do me this way? ___

AM I BLUE?
(Yes, I'm Blue)

Words and Music by
DAVID CHAMBERLAIN

Moderate shuffle

F F♯dim7 Gm7 C7
Am I blue? ___ Yes, I'm ___ blue; ___ It start - ed the day I lost you. ___

To Coda

Gm7 C7sus C7
No - bod - y ev - er missed some - bod - y like I do. Am I blue? Am I blue? ___

F
C7
1. Just this morn - ing _ o - ver cof - fee, _ I sat there cry - ing 'cause you're gone. ___ I did - n't
2. Tried to call and _ say _ I'm sor - ry; _ I could - n't get you on the line. ___ You nev - er
1. D.S.
2. D.S. al Coda
F
know just how much I was gon - na miss you till I spent my first night a - lone. ___ Am I _ Am I
know just how much I'm wish - ing you would show up and say you changed your mind. ___
Coda
C7sus C7 F E F E F E F
Am I Blue? ___

AMAZING GRACE

TRADITIONAL

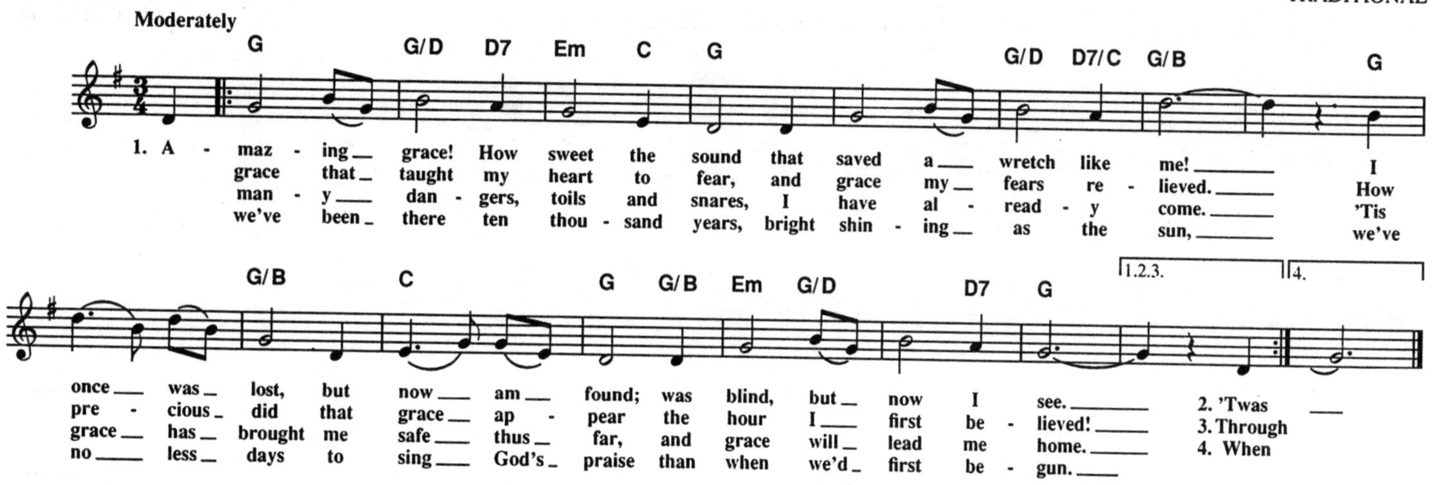
Moderately
G G/D D7 Em C G G/D D7/C G/B G
1. A - maz - ing grace! How sweet the sound that saved a wretch like me! I
grace that taught my heart to fear, and grace my fears re - lieved. How
man - y dan - gers, toils and snares, I have al - read - y come. 'Tis
we've been there ten thou - sand years, bright shin - ing as the sun, we've
G/B C G G/B Em G/D D7 G
1.2.3.
4.
once was lost, but now am found; was blind, but now I see. 2. 'Twas
pre - cious did that grace ap - pear the hour I first be - lieved! 3. Through
grace has brought me safe thus far, and grace will lead me home. 4. When
no less days to sing God's praise than when we'd first be - gun.

AMERICA

(My Country 'Tis of Thee)

Text by Rev. SAMUEL F. SMITH
TRADITIONAL MELODY

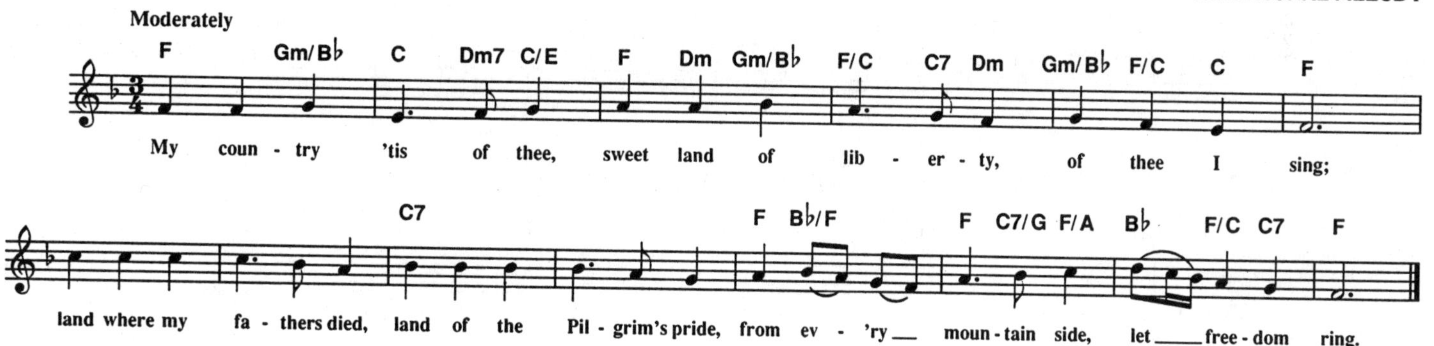
Moderately
F Gm/B♭ C Dm7 C/E F Dm Gm/B♭ F/C C7 Dm Gm/B♭ F/C C F
My coun - try 'tis of thee, sweet land of lib - er - ty, of thee I sing;
C7 F B♭/F F C7/G F/A B♭ F/C C7 F
land where my fa - thers died, land of the Pil - grim's pride, from ev - 'ry moun - tain side, let free - dom ring.

AMERICA THE BEAUTIFUL

Words by KATHERINE LEE BATES
Music by SAMUEL A. WARD

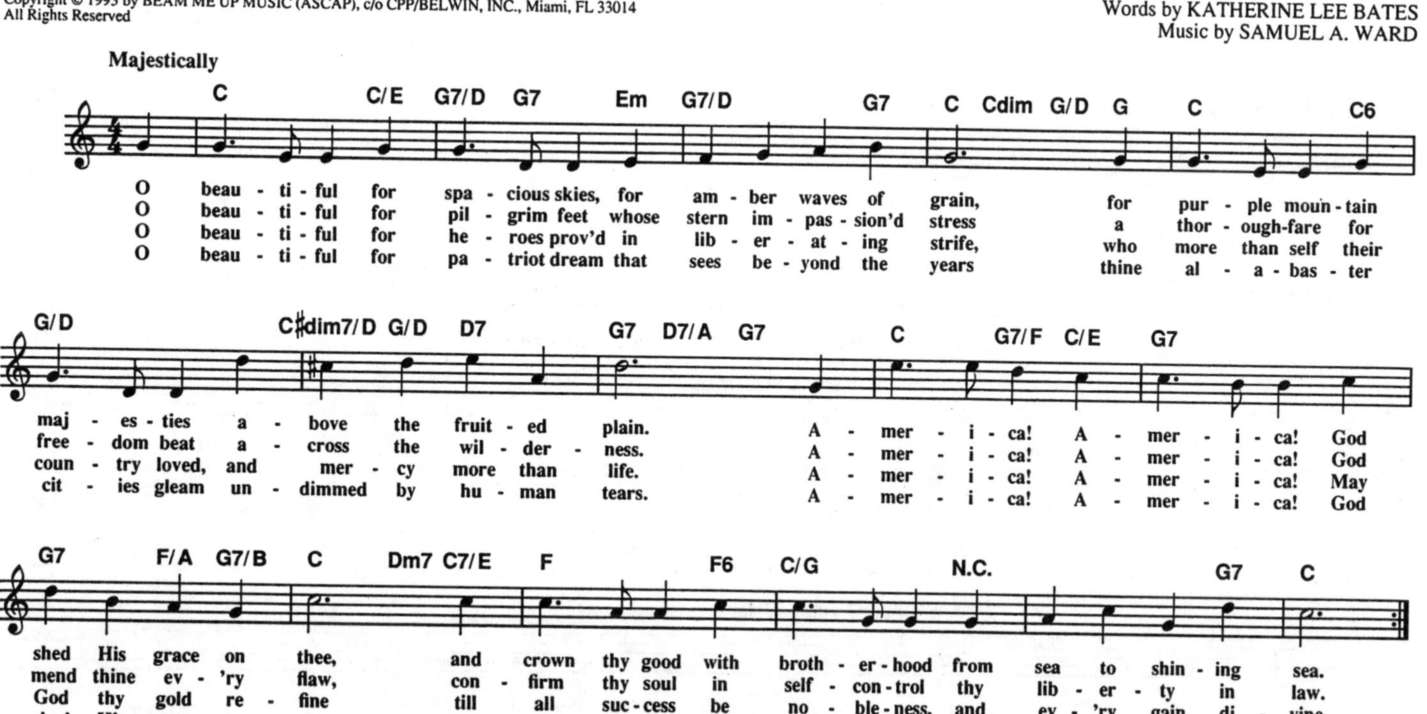
Majestically
C C/E G7/D G7 Em G7/D G7 C Cdim G/D G C C6
O beau - ti - ful for spa - cious skies, for am - ber waves of grain, for pur - ple moun - tain
O beau - ti - ful for pil - grim feet whose stern im - pas - sion'd stress a thor - ough-fare for
O beau - ti - ful for he - roes prov'd in lib - er - at - ing strife, who more than self their
O beau - ti - ful for pa - triot dream that sees be - yond the years thine al - a - bas - ter
G/D C♯dim7/D G/D D7 G7 D7/A G7 C G7/F C/E G7
maj - es - ties a - bove the fruit - ed plain. A - mer - i - ca! A - mer - i - ca! God
free - dom beat a - cross the wil - der - ness. A - mer - i - ca! A - mer - i - ca! God
coun - try loved, and mer - cy more than life. A - mer - i - ca! A - mer - i - ca! May
cit - ies gleam un - dimmed by hu - man tears. A - mer - i - ca! A - mer - i - ca! God
G7 F/A G7/B C Dm7 C7/E F F6 C/G N.C. G7 C
shed His grace on thee, and crown thy good with broth - er - hood from sea to shin - ing sea.
mend thine ev - 'ry flaw, con - firm thy soul in self - con - trol thy lib - er - ty in law.
God thy gold re - fine till all suc - cess be no - ble - ness, and ev - 'ry gain di - vine.
shed His grace on thee, and crown thy good with broth - er - hood from sea to shin - ing sea.

THE AMERICAN PATROL

By F.W. MEACHAM

Moderate swing
F6/9 C7
F6/9 G7 C7 F6/9
B♭ Dm7 Gm7 C7 F C7
F C7 F F7 B♭
F C♯dim Dm B♭ F C7 F

ANCHORS AWEIGH

Words and Music by
CAPTAIN ALFRED H. MILES (Ret.), CHARLES A. ZIMMERMAN
and GEORGE D. LOTTMAN

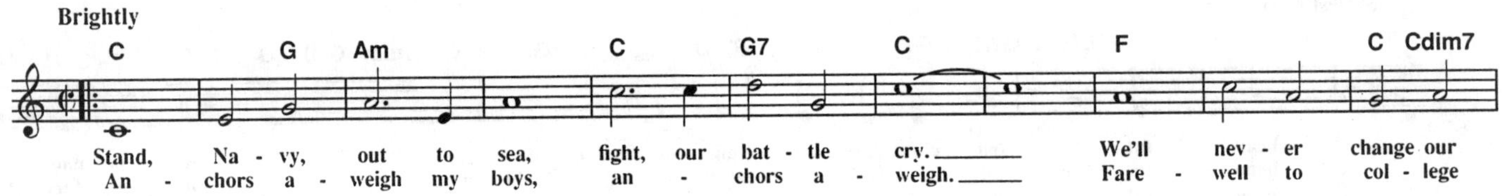
Brightly
C G Am C G7 C F C Cdim7
Stand, Na - vy, out to sea, fight, our bat - tle cry. We'll nev - er change our
An - chors a - weigh my boys, an - chors a - weigh. Fare - well to col - lege

G7 C D7 G7 F G7 C G Am C G7
course, so, vi - cious foe steer shy - y - y - y. Roll out the T. N. T. An - chors a -
joys, we sail at break of day, day, day, day. Through our last night on shore, drink to the

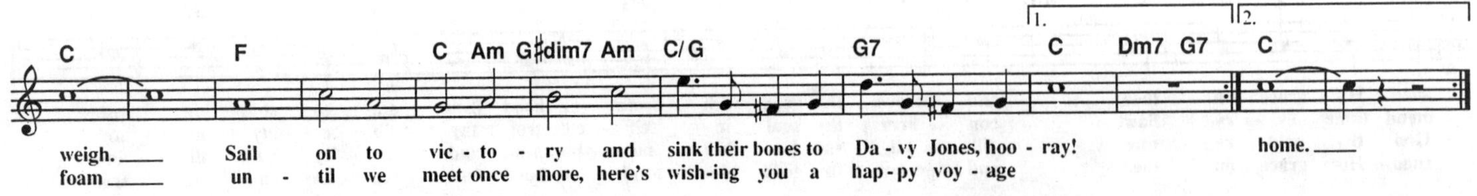
C F C Am G♯dim7 Am C/G G7 C Dm7 G7 C
1. 2.
weigh. Sail on to vic - to - ry and sink their bones to Da - vy Jones, hoo - ray! home.
foam un - til we meet once more, here's wish-ing you a hap - py voy - age

AN AMERICAN TRILOGY

Words and Music by
MICKEY NEWBURY

Moderately
C F F♯dim
How I wish I was in the land of cot - ton. Old things, they are not for - got - ten, look a -
C Am Dm7 G7 C F C
way, look a - way, look a - way Dix - ie - land. Oh, I wish I was in
F D7 Dm7/G C F C
Dix - ie, a - way, a - way. In Dix - ie - land, I take my stand to live and die in
Dm7 G7 Dm7 G7 C F
Dix - ie. 'Cause, Dix - ie - land, that's where I was born ear - ly, Lord, one
F♯dim C Am Dm7 G7 C F C
fros - ty morn - ing, look a - way, look a - way, look a - way Dix - ie - land. Glo - ry,
F C
glo - ry, hal - le - lu - jah! Glo - ry, glo - ry, hal - le - lu - jah!
E+ E7 Am G F Dm7 G7 Am7 F
Glo - ry, glo - ry, hal - le - lu - jah! His truth is march - ing on.
Dm C Gm7 C
So, hush, lit - tle chil - dren, don't you cry. You know your dad - dy's bound to
F C F Dm7 G7 C
die. But all my trials, Lord, soon be o - ver.

AMOR, AMOR, AMOR

English Words by NORMAN NEWELL
Spanish Words by RICARDO LOPEZ MENDEZ
Music by GABRIEL RUIZ

Tempo beguine
C
G7
A - mor, a - mor, a - mor. This word so sweet that I re - peat means I a - dore you.
A - mor, a - mor, a - mor. Na - ció de tí, na - ció de mí de la es - pe - ran - za.

Dm
G7
Bdim C6
A - mor, a - mor, my love. Would you de - ny this heart that I have placed be - fore you?
A - mor, a - mor, a - mor. Na - ció de Dios pa - ra los dos, na - ció del al - ma.

Bdim C6
Em
B7
Em
I can't find an - oth - er word with mean - ing so clear. My lips try to whis - per sweet - er things in your ear. But
Sen - tir que tus be - sos a - ni - da - ron en mí, I - gual que pa - lo - mas men - sa - je - ras de luz. Sa -

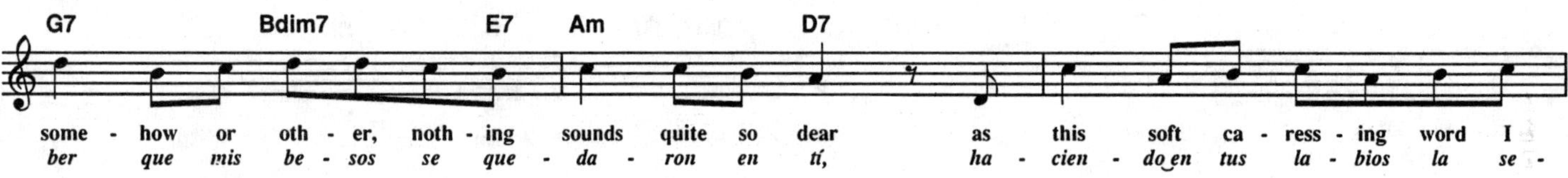
G7
Bdim7
E7
Am
D7
some - how or oth - er, noth - ing sounds quite so dear as this soft ca - ress - ing word I
ber que mis be - sos se que - da - ron en tí, ha - cien - do en tus la - bios la se -

a tempo
G7 Dm7 G7
C
know. A - mor, a - mor, my love. When you're a - way, there is no day, and nights are
ñal de la cruz. A - mor, a - mor, a - mor. Na - ció de tí, na - ció de mí, de la es - pe -

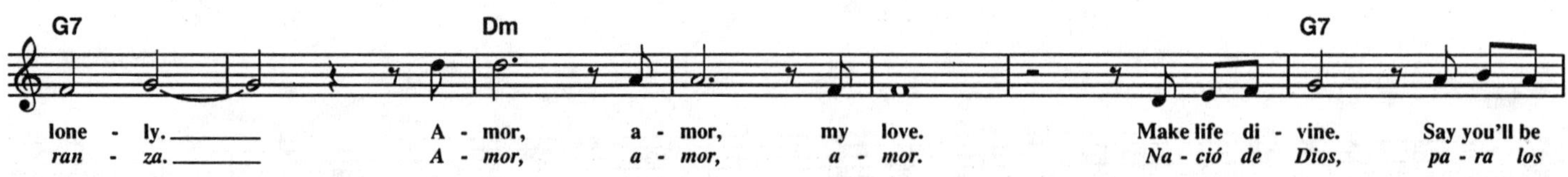
G7
Dm
G7
lone - ly. A - mor, a - mor, my love. Make life di - vine. Say you'll be
ran - za. A - mor, a - mor, a - mor. Na - ció de Dios, pa - ra los

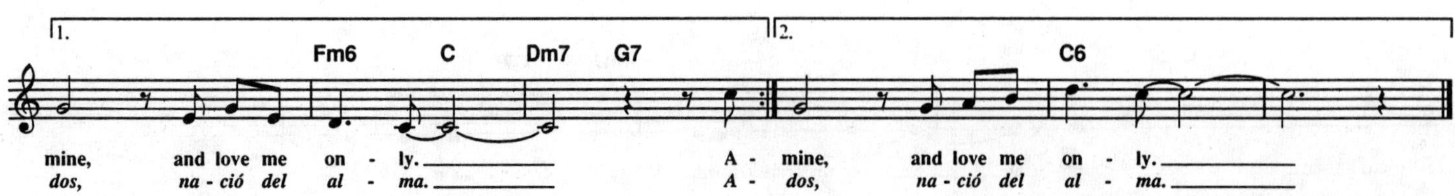
1.
Fm6
C
Dm7
G7
2.
C6
mine, and love me on - ly. A - mine, and love me on - ly.
dos, na - ció del al - ma. A - dos, na - ció del al - ma.

ANDANTE CANTABILE FROM 5TH SYMPHONY

PETER ILICH TSCHAIKOWSKY

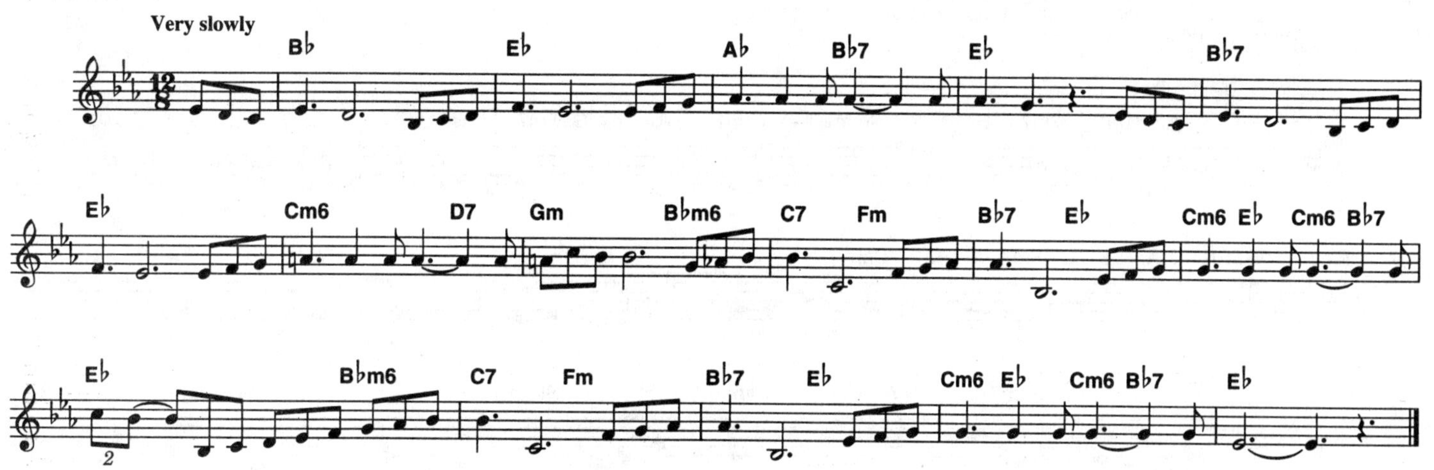
Very slowly
B♭ E♭ A♭ B♭7 E♭ B♭7
E♭ Cm6 D7 Gm B♭m6 C7 Fm B♭7 E♭ Cm6 E♭ Cm6 B♭7
E♭ B♭m6 C7 Fm B♭7 E♭ Cm6 E♭ Cm6 B♭7 E♭

ALL THROUGH THE NIGHT

Words and Music by
COLE PORTER

Moderato

F A Amaj7 A7 Am7 F♯dim F7 B♭ E♭9 E♭(♭9) E♭7 A♭

All ___ through the night ___ I de - light ___ in your love, ___
All ___ through the night ___ from a height ___ far a - bove, ___

1. G7(♯5) G7 G7(♭5) C(♭9) C7 C(♭9) F6 Gm7 C7 — 2. Emaj7

all ___ through the night ___ you're so close to me. ___ You ___

E7 E6 E♭(♭9) E♭6 Bdim A♭m6 A♭ C7 Fm D♭

_ and your love ___ bring me ec - sta - sy. ___ When dawn ___ comes to

B♭m6 C7 C7(♭5) C7 A♭7 A♭7(♭5) G♭ A♭7 D♭6 Edim A♭

wak - en me, you're nev - er there at all, ___ I know ___ you've for - sak - en

Bdim G7 C C7 F A Amaj7 A7 Am7 F♯dim F7

me Till the shad - ows fall; ___ but then ___ once a - gain ___ I can

B♭ B♭(♭5) B♭ B♭m N.C. F6 E7(♭5) A7 Gm7 C(♭9) C7 Fsus F

dream, ___ I've the right ___ to be close to you all through the night. ___

ANGELA

(Theme from "Taxi")

Music by
BOB JAMES

Moderate ballad
E♭ A♭maj9 Gm7 B♭/D A♭maj7/C Gm/B♭ A♭ E♭/G Fm7 A♭/B♭ E♭ E♭7 A♭maj9 E♭/G
Fm7 Gm/B♭ A♭ E♭/G Fm7 A♭/B♭
Chorus:
Cm7 E♭/B♭ F7/A A♭ F B♭ G
Cm7 B♭m7 A7(♭5) A♭maj7 B♭ Cm A♭maj7 B♭
Cm Fm7 Gm7 A♭maj7 Fm/B♭ Cm7 Fm7 Gm7 A♭maj7 Fm/B♭ Cm7 A7(♭5) A♭maj7 E♭/G
1. Fm7 E♭/G A♭ A♭/B♭
2. Fm7 E♭/G A♭ A♭/B♭
Bridge:
G11 G6 G11
G6 G7/F Em7 F/B Em7 Am7 C/G Fmaj7 Bm7(♭5) Em7 Am7
To Coda
Dm7 G7 Cmaj7 Fmaj7 Em7 E♭13 Dm11 D♭9(♯11) Cm E♭/B♭ F7/A
Instrumental solo
A♭maj7 G7 Cm7 B♭m7 A7(♭5) A♭maj7 Fm7 Gm7 Fm7 A♭/B♭
Repeat as needed
Last time D.S. al Coda
Coda
Cm7 E♭/B♭ F7/A A♭ F B♭ G
Cm7 B♭m7 A7(♭5) A♭maj7 B♭ Cm A♭maj7 B♭
Cm Fm7 Gm7 A♭maj7 Fm/B♭ Cm7 Fm7 Gm7 A♭maj7 Fm/B♭ Cm7 A7(♭5)
A♭maj7 E♭/G Fm7 E♭/G A♭ A♭/B♭ E♭ A♭maj9 Gm7 B♭/D A♭maj7/C Gm/B♭
A♭ E♭/G Fm7 A♭/B♭ E♭ E♭7 A♭maj9 E♭/G Fm7 Gm/B♭ A♭ E♭/G Fm7 A♭/B♭ Cm11

ANGELS FROM THE REALMS OF GLORY

Words by JAMES MONTGOMERY
Music by HENRY SMART

Moderately
C C/E G C/E F C/E G/B G7 C
1. An - gels from the realms of glo - ry, wing your flight o'er all the earth.
2. Shep - herds in the fields a - bid - ing, watch - ing o'er your flocks by night.
3. Sag - es, leave your con - tem - pla - tions; bright - er vi - sions beam a - far.
4. Saints be - fore the al - tar bend - ing, watch - ing long in hope and fear.

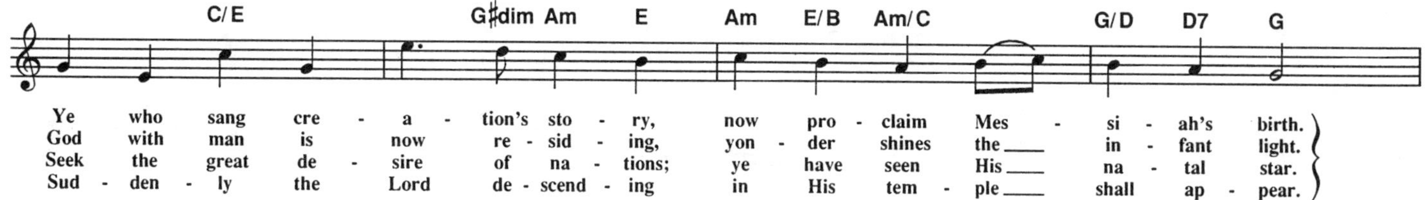
C/E G♯dim Am E Am E/B Am/C G/D D7 G
Ye who sang cre - a - tion's sto - ry, now pro - claim Mes - si - ah's birth.
God with man is now re - sid - ing, yon - der shines the in - fant light.
Seek the great de - sire of na - tions; ye have seen His na - tal star.
Sud - den - ly the Lord de - scend - ing in His tem - ple shall ap - pear.

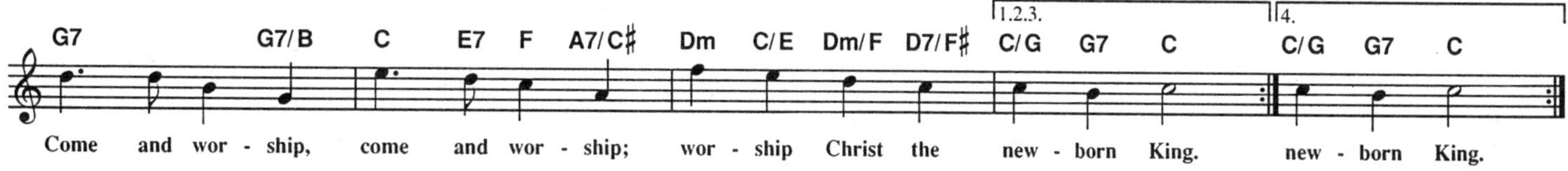
G7 G7/B C E7 F A7/C♯ Dm C/E Dm/F D7/F♯ C/G G7 C C/G G7 C
1.2.3. 4.
Come and wor - ship, come and wor - ship; wor - ship Christ the new - born King. new - born King.

ANGELS WE HAVE HEARD ON HIGH

TRADITIONAL

Joyously
Verse:
G D G D/F♯ G G/D D7 G
1. An - gels we have heard on high sweet - ly sing - ing o'er the plains.
2. Shep - herds why this ju - bi - lee? Why your joy - ous strains pro - long?
3. Come to Beth - le - hem and see Him whose birth the an - gels sing.
4. See Him in a man - ger laid, whom the choirs of an - gels praise.

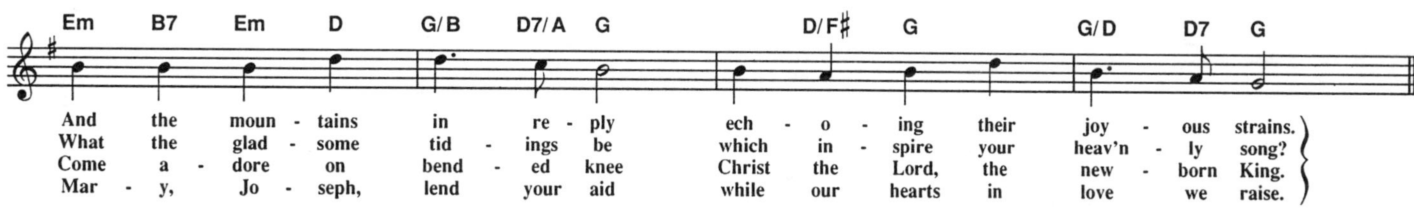
Em B7 Em D G/B D7/A G D/F♯ G G/D D7 G
And the moun - tains in re - ply ech - o - ing their joy - ous strains.
What the glad - some tid - ings be which in - spire your heav'n - ly song?
Come a - dore on bend - ed knee Christ the Lord, the new - born King.
Mar - y, Jo - seph, lend your aid while our hearts in love we raise.

Chorus:
E7 Am D7/F♯ G C/E D G D G C G/D D G E7
Glo - ri - a in ex - cel - sis De - o. Glo -

Am D7 G C/E D7 G D G C G/D D7 G G
1. 2. 3. 4.
ri - a in ex - cel - sis De - o. o.

AN AMERICAN IN PARIS

(In Miniature)

By GEORGE GERSHWIN

Allegretto grazioso
mp
f
p
mf
Blues tempo
poco rubato
poco rubato
Allegro
mf con anima
mp
Rubato
mf espress.

ANGEL

Words and Music by
MADONNA CICCONE and STEVE BRAY

Medium tempo

Am7 Bm7 Cmaj7 Am7 Bm7 Cmaj7
Why am I stand - in' on a cloud ev - 'ry time you're a - round __ and my
down a crowd - ed av - e - nue, oth - er faces seem like noth - in' next to you. And I

Am7 Bm7 Cmaj7 Am7 Bm7 Cmaj7
sad - ness dis - ap - pears ____ ev - 'ry time you are near? ____
can't hear the traf - fic rushin' by, just the poundin' of my heart and that's why.

Am7 Bm7 Cmaj7 Am7 Bm7 Cmaj7 Am7 Bm7 Cmaj7
You must __ be an an - gel. I can see it in your eyes, ___ full of won - der and sur - price. __

Bm7 Cmaj7 Am7 Bm7 Cmaj7 Am7 Bm7 Cmaj7
____ And just now I re - al - ize: ___ Oooh, ____ you're an an - gel. Oooh, _____ you're an

Am7 Bm7 Cmaj7 | 1. Am7 Bm7 Cmaj7 | 2.
an - gel. Oooh, you're an an - gel in dis - guise. I can see it in your eyes. Walk-in' an - gel in dis -

Am7 Bm7 Cmaj7 Am7 Bm7 Cmaj7 Bm7 Am7 Bm7 Cmaj7
guise. ____ I can see it in your eyes. _

Bm7 Am7 Bm7 Cmaj7 Bm7 Am7 Bm7 Cmaj7 Bm7

𝄋 Am7 Bm7 Cmaj7 Am7 Bm7 Cmaj7 Am7 Bm7 Cmaj7 *To Coda* ⊕ Am7 Bm7 Cmaj7
You're an an - gel. You're an an - gel, ba - by. You're an an - gel. You must __ be an an -

Am7 Bm7 Cmaj7 Am7 Bm7 Cmaj7
__ gel. ________ Now I be - lieve ___ that dreams __ come true, __ 'cause you came when I wished _

Am7 Bm7 Cmaj7 Am7 Bm7 Cmaj7 *D.C.* 𝄋 *al Coda* ⊕
__ for you. __ This just can't be co - in - ci - dence. __ The on - ly way __ that this __ makes __ sense _ is that:

⊕ **Coda**

Repeat and fade

Am7 Bm7 Cmaj7 Am7 Bm7 Cmaj7
__ gel, ba - by.

(THEME FROM) THE APARTMENT

By CHARLES WILLIAMS

Moderately slow

F
F6
Gm
C7
F/A
A♭dim7
Gm7
B♭m
A7(♯5)
A7

To Coda
1.
F7
B♭6
E♭7
A♭6
Adim7
C/G
Fdim7
F/C
G7

2.
C7(♭5)
C7
C7(♯5)
Gm7
C7
F
A♭
A♭+
D♭/A♭
D♭m/A♭
A♭
F7(♭9)
3

B♭m
E♭m/B♭
B♭m
G7(♭9)
C7(♭9)
A♭m
Fdim7
3

Dm/A
Meno mosso
3

D.C. al Coda
F/C
C13(♭9)
A♭dim7/C
F/C
B♭/C
C7
3

Coda
F/C
Bm7(♭5)
B♭m6
F/A
Dm
Gm
B♭m6
F6
3

From the Broadway Musical Production "APPLAUSE"

APPLAUSE

Copyright © 1970 by LEE ADAMS and CHARLES STROUSE
All rights administered by THE SONGWRITERS GUILD OF AMERICA
All Rights Reserved

Words by LEE ADAMS
Music by CHARLES STROUSE

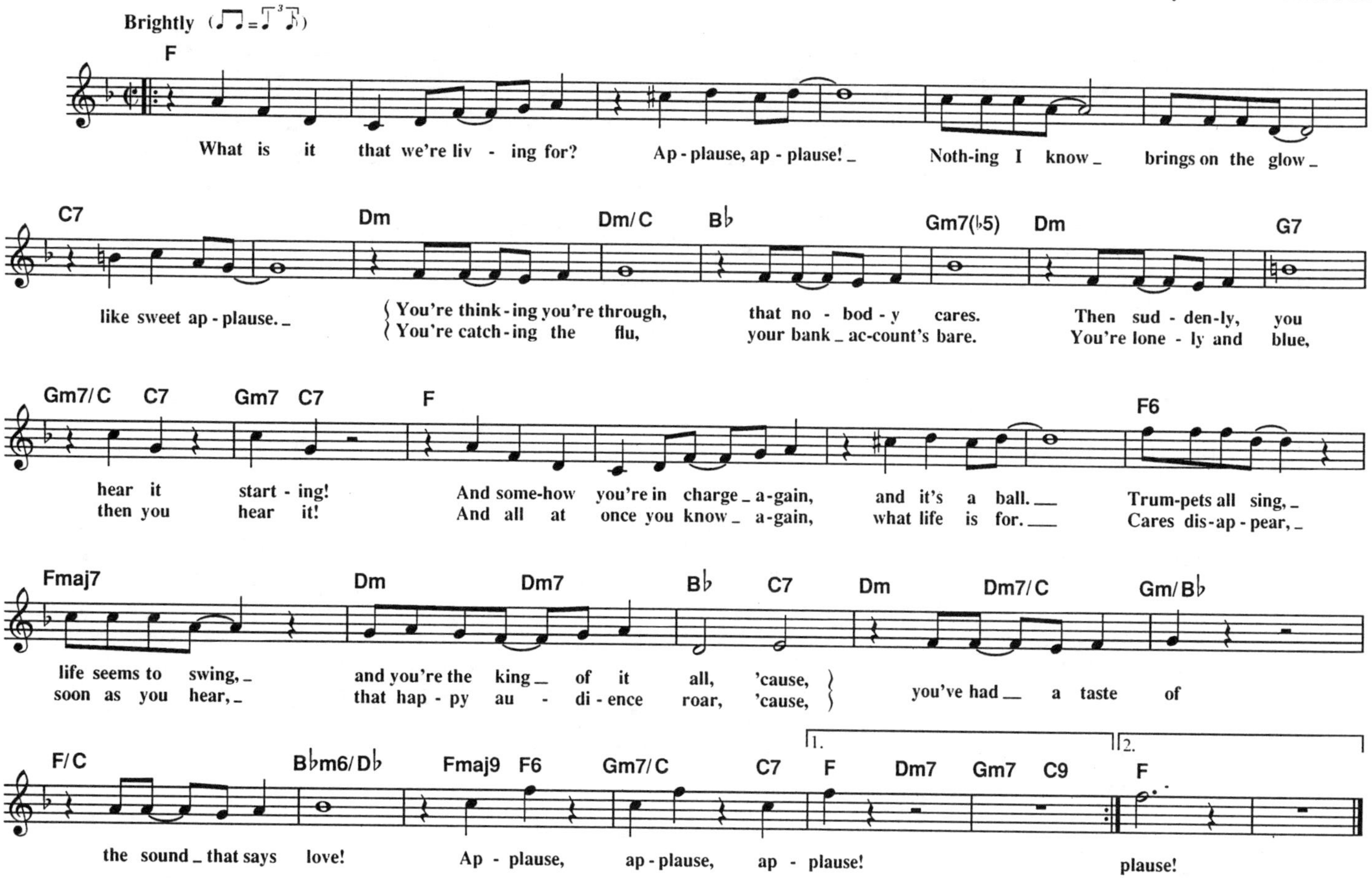

Brightly

What is it that we're liv - ing for? Ap - plause, ap - plause! Noth-ing I know brings on the glow like sweet ap - plause.

You're think - ing you're through, that no - bod - y cares. Then sud - den - ly, you hear it start - ing! And some-how you're in charge a-gain, and it's a ball. Trum-pets all sing, life seems to swing, and you're the king of it all, 'cause,

You're catch - ing the flu, your bank ac-count's bare. You're lone - ly and blue, then you hear it! And all at once you know a-gain, what life is for. Cares dis-ap - pear, soon as you hear, that hap - py au - di - ence roar, 'cause,

you've had a taste of the sound that says love! Ap - plause, ap - plause, ap - plause!

plause!

From the Motion Picture "AROUND THE WORLD IN 80 DAYS"

AROUND THE WORLD

Copyright © 1956 (Renewed 1984) CEBCO MUSIC,
c/o THE SONGWRITERS GUILD and LIZA MUSIC CORP.
All Rights Reserved

Words and Music by
HAROLD ADAMSON
and VICTOR YOUNG

Moderately
A - round the world I've searched for you. I trav-eled on when hope was gone to keep a ren - dez - vous. I
knew some - where, some - time, some - how, you'd look at me and I would see the smile you're smil - ing now. It
might have been in Count - y Down, or in New York, in Gay Pa - ree, or e - ven Lon - don Town. No
more will I go all a - round the world, for I have found my world in you.

AS TEARS GO BY
© 1964 by FORWARD MUSIC LTD., London, England
TRO-ESSEX MUSIC, INC., New York, controls all publication rights for the U.S.A. & Canada
All Rights Reserved
Words and Music by MICK JAGGER, KEITH RICHARDS and ANDREW LOOG OLDHAM
Moderately
It is the eve-ning of the day, I sit and watch the chil-dren play.
My rich-es can't buy ev-'ry-thing, I want to hear the chil-dren sing.
Smil-ing fac-es I can see, but not for me, I sit and watch As Tears Go By.
All I hear is the sound
of rain fall-ing on the ground. I sit and watch As Tears Go By.
It is the eve-ning of the day. I sit and watch the chil-dren play.
To Coda
Do-in' things I used to do, they think are new, I sit and watch As Tears Go By.
D.S. al Coda
Coda
Mm
AS TIMES GOES BY
© 1931 WARNER BROS. INC. (Renewed)
All Rights Reserved
Words and Music by HERMAN HUPFELD
Liltingly
You must re-mem-ber this, a kiss is still a kiss, A sigh is just a sigh;
when two lov-ers woo, they still say, "I love you," On that you can re-ly;
The fun-da-men-tal things ap-ply, As Time Goes By. And
No mat-ter what the fu-ture brings, As Time Goes
By.
Moon-light and love songs nev-er out of date, Hearts full of pas-sion,
jeal-ous-y and hate; Wo-man needs man and man must have his mate, That no one can de-ny
It's still the same old sto-ry, a fight for love and glo-ry, A case of do or die!
The world will al-ways wel-come lov-ers, As Time Goes By.

From the American Tribal Love-Rock Musical "HAIR"

AQUARIUS

Words by JAMES RADO and GEROME RAGNI
Music by GALT MacDERMOT

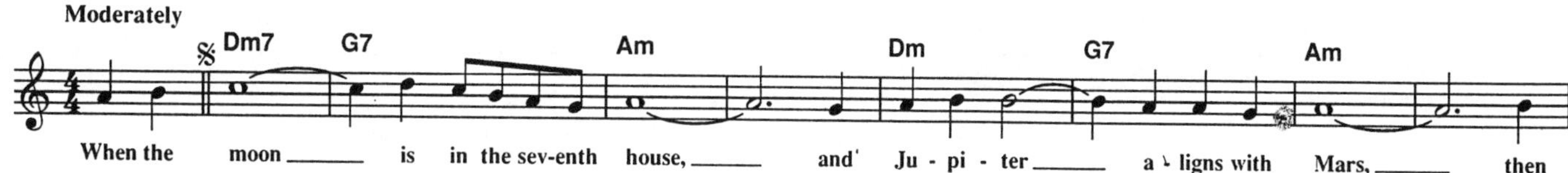
Moderately
Dm7 G7 Am Dm G7 Am
When the moon is in the sev-enth house, and Ju - pi - ter a - ligns with Mars, then

Dm7 G7 Am F G7 C N.C.
peace will guide the plan - ets and love will steer the stars. This is the dawn-ing of the

B♭ Dm G7
age of A - quar - i - us, the age of A - quar - i - us. A - quar - i - us,

Dm Fine C7 F
A - quar - i - us. Har - mo - ny and un - der - stand - ing,

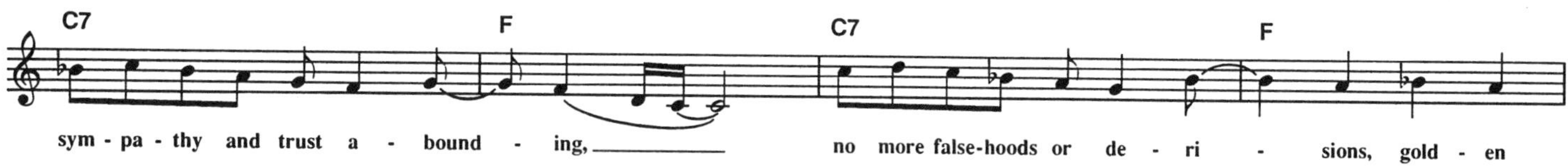
C7 F C7 F
sym - pa - thy and trust a - bound - ing, no more false-hoods or de - ri - sions, gold - en

C7 F A7/E Dm Gm
liv - ing dreams of vi - sions, mys - tic crys - tal rev - e - la - tion, and the mind's true lib - er -

Am Gm Dm D.S. 𝄋 al Fine
a - tion. A - quar - i - us. A - quar - i - us. When the

ARRIVEDERCI, ROMA

Words by CARL SIGMAN
Music by R. RASCEL

Moderately
G Cm D7 G B7 C E7 Am N.C.
Ar - ri - ve - der - ci, Ro - ma. Good - bye, good - bye to Rome. Cit - y of a

D7 Am7 D7 Am7 D7 Am7
mil - lion moon - lit plac - es, cit - y of a mil - lion warm em - brac - es, where I found the one of all the

D7 Cm D7 G B♭7 Am7 D7 G Cm D7 G
fac - es far from home. Ar - ri - ve - der - ci, Ro - ma. it's time for

B7 C E7 Am N.C. D7 Am7 D7
us to part. Save the wed - ding bells for my re - turn - ing, keep my lov - er's

Am7 D7 Am7 D7 Am7 D7 G
arms out-stretched and yearn - ing. Please be sure the flame of love keeps burn - ing in her (his) heart.

ARTZA ALINU

TRADITIONAL

Brightly
1. 2.
Em Am Em Am Em C Am7 B7 Em Em G
Ar - tza a - li - nu, ar - tza a - li - nu, ar - tza a - li - nu. nu. K'-var ha-rash - nu

B7 Em Am Em
v' - gam za - ra - nu, k' - var ha - rash - nu, v' - gam za - ra nu. A - val od lo ka - tzar - nu,

A7 Em Am B7 Em Am9 B7 Em6
a - val od lo ka - tzar - nu. A - val od lo ka - tzar - nu, a - val od lo ka - tzar - nu.

From the Film "THE FLEET'S IN"

ARTHUR MURRAY TAUGHT ME DANCING IN A HURRY

J. MERCER and
V. SCHERTZINGER

C G7sus G7 C F7 F♯dim7 C/G G9(♯5)
Ar - thur Mur-ray taught me danc-ing in a hur - ry.
Mur-ray then ad - vised me not to wor - ry,

C A♭9 G7 C♯dim7 G7
I had a week to spare. He showed me the ground - work, the walk a - round work, and
it - 'd come out all right. To my way of think - in', it came out stink - in'. I

1. Dm7 G+ G7 C Dm7 G7
told me to take it from there. Ar - thur
2. Fm G+ G7 C Dm7 C
don't know my left from my right. The

F♯dim7 G9(♯5) G9 C Dm7 G7 C F♯dim7 G9(♯5) G9
peo-ple a - round me can all sing a - one and a - two and a - three. But an - y re - sem - blance to

C Cm G A♭ Am7 D7 G7 C G7sus G7
waltz - ing is just co - in - ci - den - tal with me, 'cause Ar - thur Mur-ray taught me danc-ing in a

C F7 F♯dim7 C/G G7(♯9) C A♭9 G7 C♯dim7
hur - ry. And so I take a chance. To me it re - sem - bles the

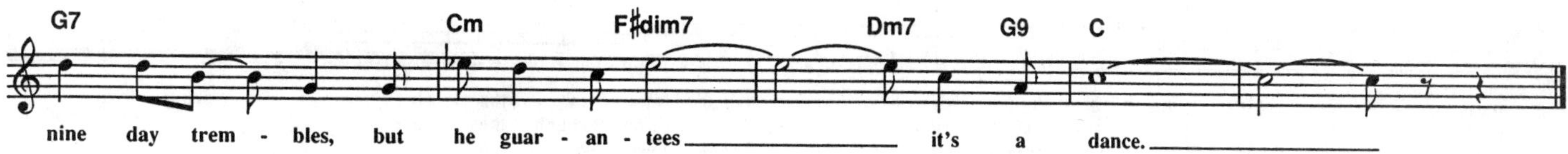
G7 Cm F♯dim7 Dm7 G9 C
nine day trem - bles, but he guar - an - tees it's a dance.

ARTIST'S LIFE

JOHANN STRAUSS

Waltz tempo

C C+ Dm
C G7 C
E7 Am C+ Dm
C G7 C

Fine

G G+ Am D7 Gdim7 G
B7 E7 Am Em B7 Em
Am G 1. D7 G 2. D7 G

D.C. al Fine

AURA LEE

TRADITIONAL

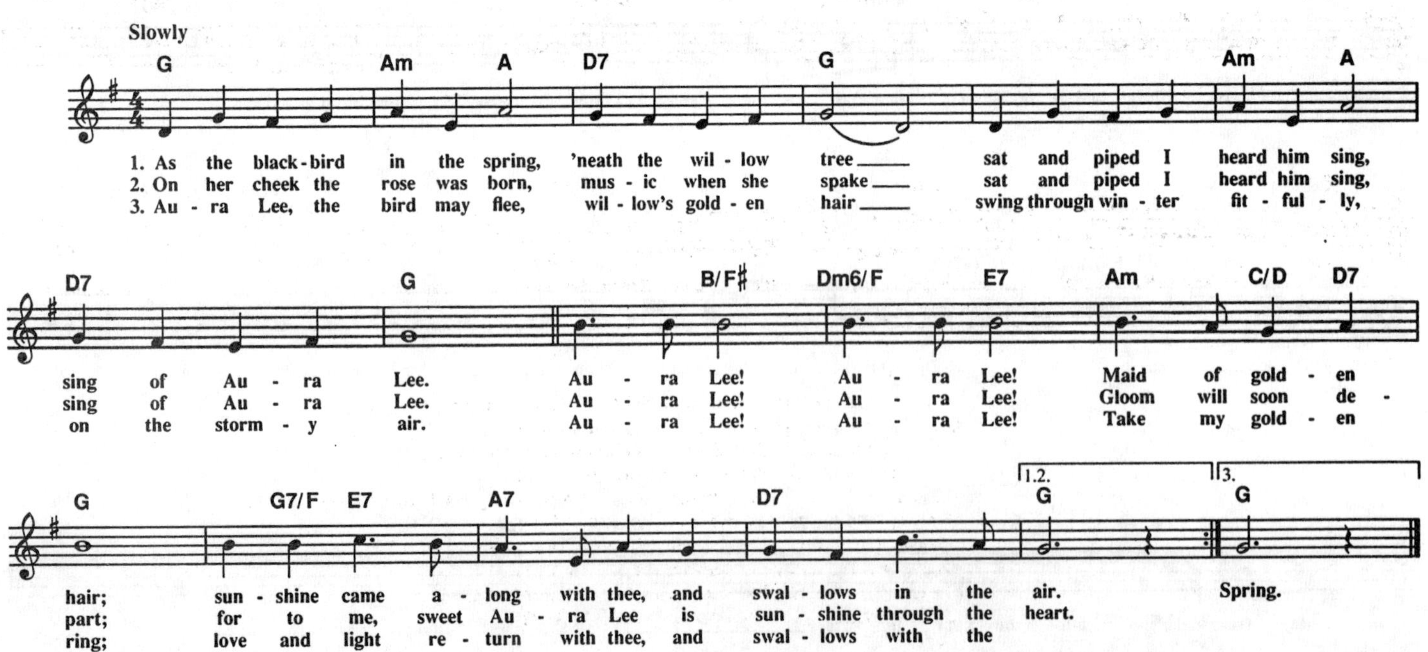
Slowly
G Am A D7 G Am A
1. As the black-bird in the spring, 'neath the wil - low tree sat and piped I heard him sing,
2. On her cheek the rose was born, mus - ic when she spake sat and piped I heard him sing,
3. Au - ra Lee, the bird may flee, wil - low's gold - en hair swing through win - ter fit - ful - ly,
D7 G B/F♯ Dm6/F E7 Am C/D D7
sing of Au - ra Lee. Au - ra Lee! Au - ra Lee! Maid of gold - en
sing of Au - ra Lee. Au - ra Lee! Au - ra Lee! Gloom will soon de -
on the storm - y air. Au - ra Lee! Au - ra Lee! Take my gold - en
G G7/F E7 A7 D7 1.2. G 3. G
hair; sun - shine came a - long with thee, and swal - lows in the air. Spring.
part; for to me, sweet Au - ra Lee is sun - shine through the heart.
ring; love and light re - turn with thee, and swal - lows with the

AS

Words and Music by
STEVIE WONDER

Moderate rock
Bmaj7 B7 Emaj7 Bmaj7 B7 Emaj7
Do do do do do, mm do do do do do. 1. As a-round
Verse:
Bmaj7 B7 Emaj7 Bmaj7
the sun the earth knows she's re-volv-ing, and the rose-buds know to bloom in ear-ly May;
can't re-veal the mys-'try of to-mor-row, but in pass-ing will grow old-er ev-'ry day;
time knew to move on since the be-gin-ing, and the sea-sons know ex-act-ly when to change;
day I know I'm liv-ing, but to-mor-row, could make me the past, but that I must-n't fear;
Amaj7 Bmaj7 B7 Emaj7 E6
just as hate knows love's the cure, you can rest your mind as-sure that
just as all that's born is new, you know what I say is true, that
just as kind-ness knows no shame, know through all your joy and pain that
for I know deep in my mind the love of me I've left be-hind, 'cause
1.3. G♯m A♯m7 D♯ G♯m C♯9 C♯m F♯7
I'll be lov-ing you al-ways.
2.4. G♯m A♯m7 D♯
2. As now I'll be lov-ing you al-ways.
4. As to-
Chorus:
G♯m A♯m B C♯ G♯m A♯m
(Un-til the rain-bow burns the stars out in the sky.) Al-ways. (Un-til the o-cean cov-ers
(Un-til the dol-phin flies and par-rots live at sea.) Al-ways. (Un-til we dream of life and
1.3.4.5.6.7.etc. fade after 7th time
B C♯
ev-'ry moun-tain high.) Al-ways.
2. B F(2)
life be-comes a dream.)
Emaj7 Bmaj7 Emaj7 Amaj7
Did you know that true love asks for noth-ing? Her ac-cep-tance is the way we pay.
Emaj7 Bmaj7 C♯m7 D♯sus D♯ F♯sus F♯
Did you know that life has giv-en love a guar-an-tee to last through for-ev-er and an-oth-er day?
D.S.
3. Just as

Chorus 2:
Always (Until the day is night, and night becomes the day.)
Always (Until the trees and seas just up and fly away.)
Always (Until the day that eight times eight times eight is four.)
Always (Until the day that is the day that are no more.)
Did you know you're loved by somebody? (Until the day starts turning right to left.)
Always (Until the earth just for the sun denies itself.)
I'll be loving you forever (Until dear Mother Nature says her work is through.)
Always (Until the day that you are me and I am you.)
Always (Until the rainbow burns the stars out in the sky.)
(Until the ocean covers every mountain high) Always.
(Fade)

ASHES OF LOVE

By JACK ANGLIN,
JOHNNIE WRIGHT and JIM ANGLIN

Moderately

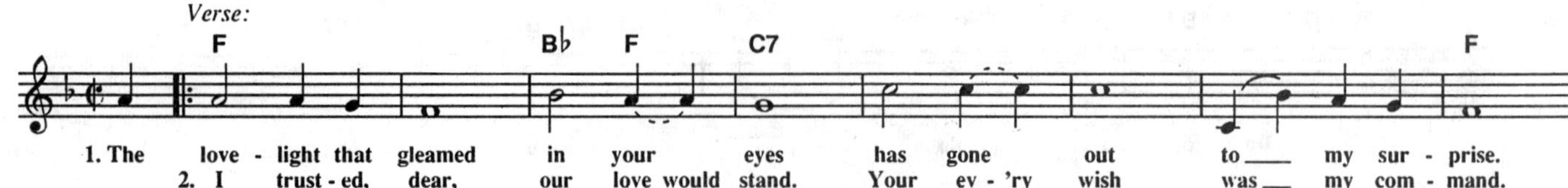
Verse:
F Bb F C7 F
1. The love - light that gleamed in your eyes has gone out to ___ my sur - prise.
2. I trust - ed, dear, our love would stand. Your ev - 'ry wish was ___ my com - mand.

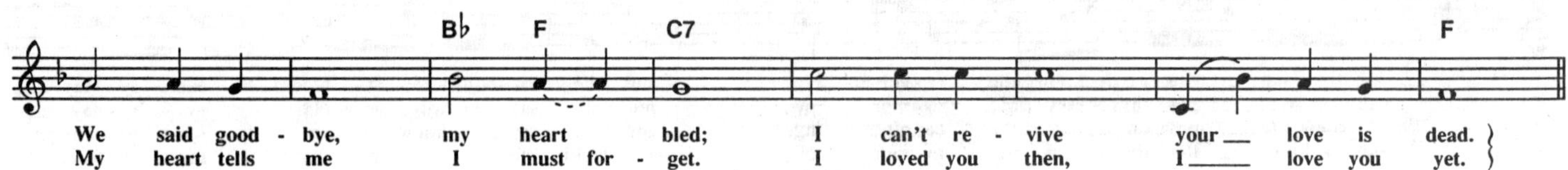
Bb F C7 F
We said good - bye, my heart bled; I can't re - vive your ___ love is dead.
My heart tells me I must for - get. I loved you then, I ___ love you yet.

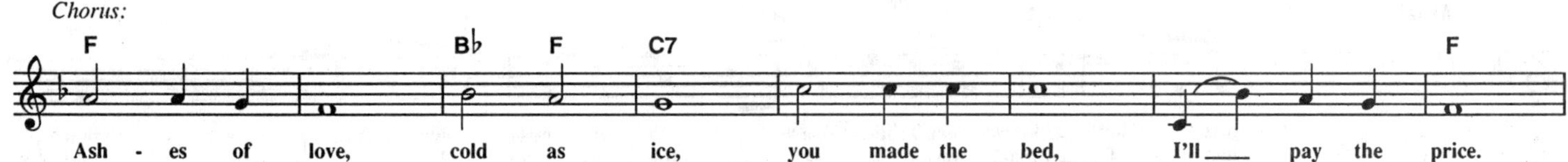
Chorus:
F Bb F C7 F
Ash - es of love, cold as ice, you made the bed, I'll ___ pay the price.

1. 2.
Bb F C7 F F
Our love is gone, there's no doubt; ash - es of love, the flame _ burned _ out. flame _ burned _ out.

AULD LANG SYNE

Words by ROBERT BURNS
Music TRADITIONAL

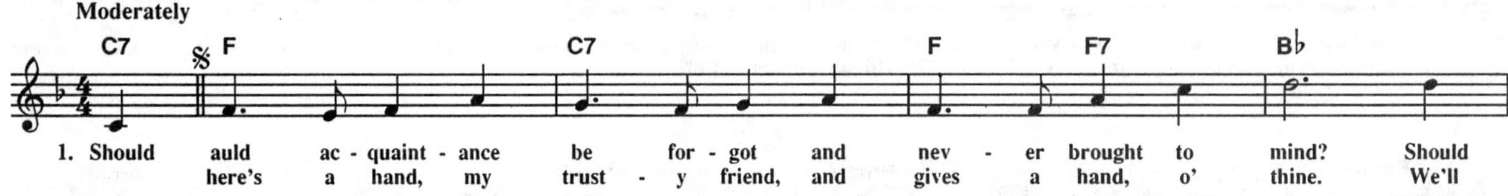
Moderately
C7 F C7 F F7 Bb
1. Should auld ac - quaint - ance be for - got and nev - er brought to mind? Should
here's a hand, my trust - y friend, and gives a hand, o' thine. We'll

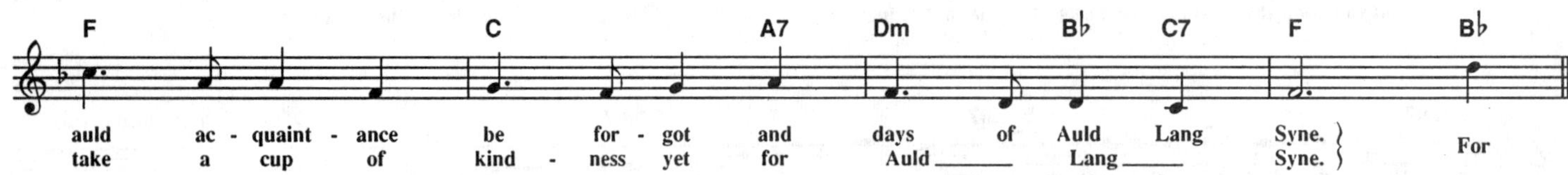
F C A7 Dm Bb C7 F Bb
auld ac - quaint - ance be for - got and days of Auld Lang Syne.
take a cup of kind - ness yet for Auld ___ Lang ___ Syne.
For

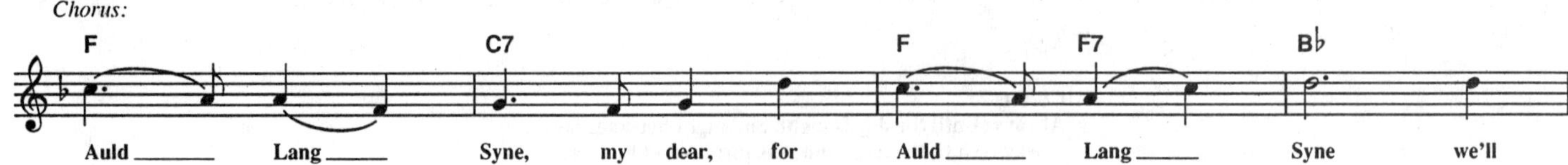
Chorus:
F C7 F F7 Bb
Auld ___ Lang ___ Syne, my dear, for Auld ___ Lang ___ Syne we'll

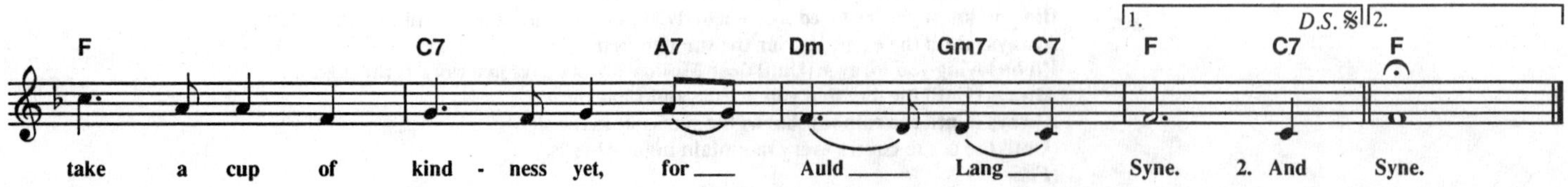
1. D.S. 2.
F C7 A7 Dm Gm7 C7 F C7 F
take a cup of kind - ness yet, for ___ Auld ___ Lang ___ Syne. 2. And Syne.

From the 20th Century Fox Motion Picture "ORCHESTRA WIVES"

AT LAST

Words by MACK GORDON
Music by HARRY WARREN

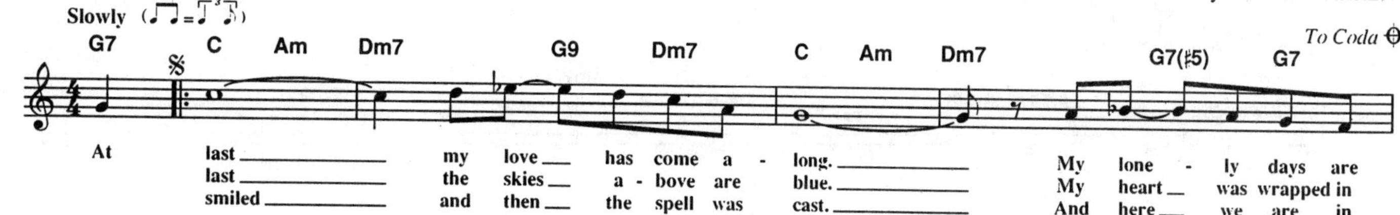
Slowly
G7 C Am Dm7 G9 Dm7 C Am Dm7 G7(♯5) G7
To Coda
At last my love has come a - long. My lone - ly days are
last the skies a - bove are blue. My heart was wrapped in
smiled and then the spell was cast. And here we are in

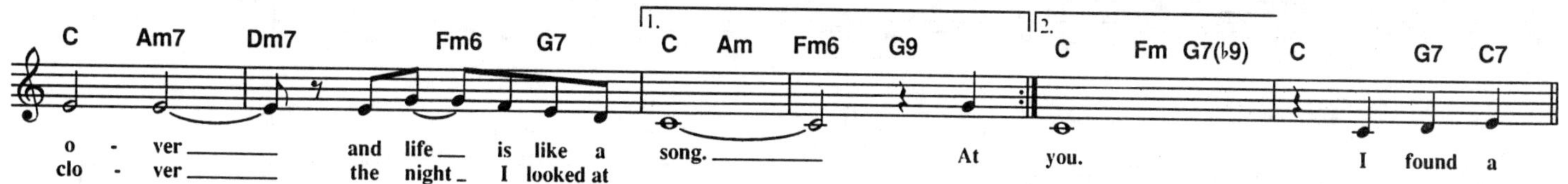
C Am7 Dm7 Fm6 G7 C Am Fm6 G9 C Fm G7(♭9) C G7 C7
1. 2.
o - ver and life is like a song. At you. I found a
clo - ver the night I looked at

Fmaj7 G7(♭9) Cmaj7 C6 B F♯m7(♭5) B7(♭9) Em Am6 Cm6 D7 Gmaj7 G6 C
dream that I can speak to, a dream that I can call my own, I found a thrill to press my cheek to, a

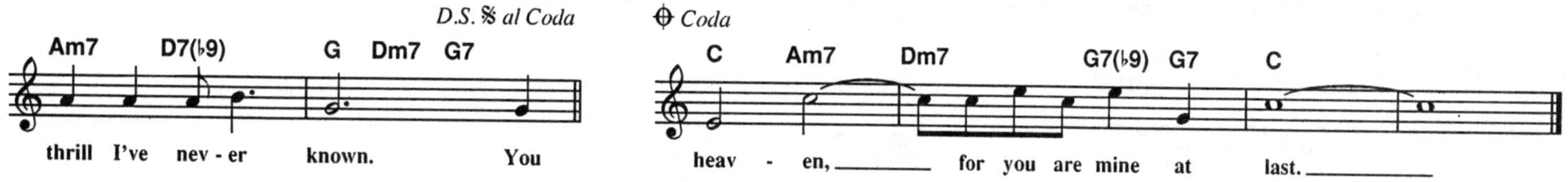
D.S. al Coda
Coda
Am7 D7(♭9) G Dm7 G7 C Am7 Dm7 G7(♭9) G7 C
thrill I've nev - er known. You heav - en, for you are mine at last.

AWAY IN A MANGER

By J.R. MURRAY

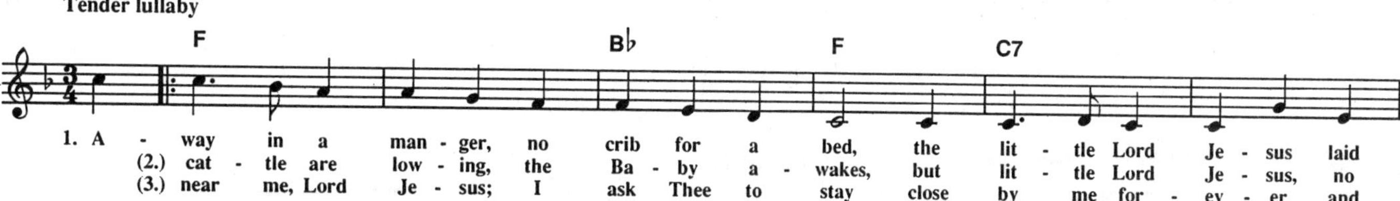
Tender lullaby
F B♭ F C7
1. A - way in a man - ger, no crib for a bed, the lit - tle Lord Je - sus laid
(2.) cat - tle are low - ing, the Ba - by a - wakes, but lit - tle Lord Je - sus, no
(3.) near me, Lord Je - sus; I ask Thee to stay close by me for - ev - er and

F B♭
down His sweet head. The stars in the sky looked down where He
cry - ing He makes. I love Thee, Lord Je - sus; look down from the
love me I pray. Bless all the dear chil - dren in Thy ten - der

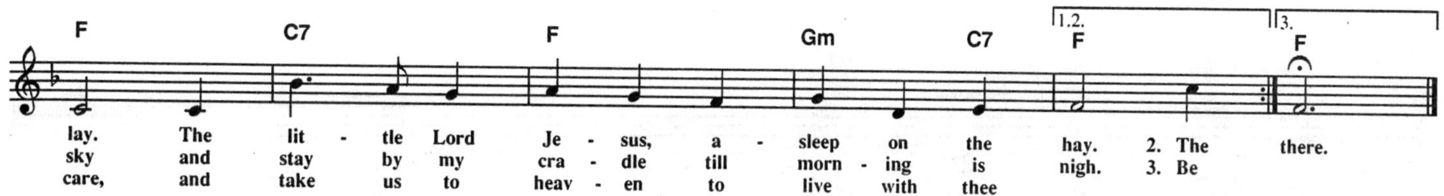
F C7 F Gm C7 F F
1.2. 3.
lay. The lit - tle Lord Je - sus, a - sleep on the hay. 2. The there.
sky and stay by my cra - dle till morn - ing is nigh. 3. Be
care, and take us to heav - en to live with thee

AVE MARIA
(Bach - Gounod)

From The First Prelude of
JOHANN SEBASTIAN BACH
Adapted by CHARLES GOUNOD

Andante con moto
G
Am7/G
(Keyboard)
D7/F♯
G
Am7/G D7/F♯ G Em/G A7/G
A - ve Ma - ri - a, gra - ti - a ple - na,
(A - ve Ma - ri - a, Thou high - ly fa - vored,
D7/F♯ G/F♯ Em7 A7 D
Do - mi - nus te - cum, be - ne - di - cta tu in
God is with thee. Bless - ed, bless - ed art thou, art
Ddim7 Am/C Cdim7 G/B C/B
mu - li - e - ri - bus et be - ne - di - ctus fru - ctus
thou a - bove all wom - en. Bless - ed be thine off - spring. Bless - ed be thy
Am D7 G G7 Cmaj7
ven - tris tu - i Je - sus. Sanc - ta Ma - ri - a,
Son, the Son of God, the Lord most high! Bless - ed Ma - ri - a!
C♯dim7 Gm(♯7)/D Am7(♭5)/E♭ D7 G/D
Sanc - ta Ma - ri - a, Ma - ri - a, o - ra pro - no - bis,
Bless - ed Ma - ri - a, Ma - ri - a! Pray, oh, pray for us,
D7sus D7 Edim7/D G/D D7sus
no - bis pec - ca - to - ri - bus, nunc et in ho - ra, in ho - ra
for us wretch-ed sin - ners. Now and when the hour of our death, our
D7 G7 C/G D7/G G
mor - tis nos - trae. A - men! A - men!
death o'er takes us. A - men! A - men!)

Theme from the Paramount Motion Picture "BEVERLY HILLS COP"

AXEL F

By HAROLD FALTERMEYER

Moderately fast
N.C.
(Bass only:)
F♯ E B F♯ E B F♯ D E
F♯ E/F♯ F♯ N.C.
(Bass only:)
1.3.
2. To Next Strain
4.
Fine
A3 A3/F♯
A3/G A3/E A3
A3/F♯ Asus/G Asus/E
F♯ E B F♯ E B F♯ D E
F♯ E/F♯ F♯ D E F♯ E/F♯ F♯
D.S. 𝄋 al Fine

AVE MARIA
(Schubert)

Text by REV. BURTON AMES
Music by FRANZ SCHUBERT

Lento
A♭ A♭7 D♭/A♭ D♭dim/A♭ A♭
(accomp. simile)
(A♭) Fm6 A♭/E♭ E♭7 Fm B♭m E♭7 A♭ A♭+ Fm/A♭
A - ve Ma - ri - a! Gra - ti - a ple - na, Ma - ri - a, gra - ti - a
A - ve Ma - ri - a! Maid - en mild. Ah! lis - ten to a maid-en's
Dm7(♭5)/G G7 Edim Fm Fm6 E♭/G F7/C
ple - na, Ma - ri - a, gra - ti - a ple - na, A - ve, A - ve! Do - mi -
prayer; for Thou canst hear a - mid the wild, 'tis Thou, 'tis Thou canst save a -
E♭/B♭ B♭7 E♭ E♭7 A♭/E♭
nus, Do - mi - nus te - cum, Be - ne - di - cta tu in mu - li - e - ri - bus, et
mid de - spair. We slum - ber safe - ly till the mor - row, 'tho
E♭7 Fm E♭ C B♭m
be - ne - di - ctus, et be - ne - di - ctus fru - ctus ven - tris, ven - tris
e'en by men out - cast, re - vil'd: Oh maid - en, see a maid - en's sor - row, oh
B♭m/D♭ Fdim E♭ E♭7 A♭ Fm6 A♭/E♭ E♭7 A♭ A♭7 D♭/A♭ D♭dim/A♭ A♭
tu - i, Je - sus. A - ve Ma - ri - a!
Moth - er, hear a sup - pli - ant child! A - ve Ma - ri - a!
Fm6 A♭/E♭ E♭7 Fm B♭m E♭7 A♭ A♭+ Fm/A♭
A - ve Ma - ri - a! Ma - ter De - i, O - ra pro - no - bis pec - ca -
A - ve Ma - ri - a! Un - de - fil'd! The flint - y couch where - on we're
Dm7(♭5)/G G7 Edim Fm Fm6 E♭/G F7/C
to - ri - bus, O - ra, o - ra pro - no - bis, O - ra, o - ra pro - no -
sleep - ing shall seem with down of ei - der pil'd, if Thou a - bove sweet watch art
E♭/B♭ B♭7 E♭ E♭7 A♭/E♭
bis pec - ca - to - ri - bus, nunc et in ho - ra mor - tis, in
keep - ing, The murk - y cav - ern's air so heav - y shall

E♭7 Fm E♭ C B♭m
ho - ra mor - tis no - strae, in ho - ra mor - tis, mor - tis no - strae, in
breathe of balm, _ if Thou _ hast smil'd; O Maid - en hear, a maid - en's plead - ing, O
B♭m/D♭ Fdim E♭ E♭7 A♭ Fm6 A♭/E♭ E♭7 A♭ A♭7 D♭/A♭ D♭dim/A♭ A♭
ho - ra mor - tis no - strae. A - ve Ma - ri - a!
Moth - er, hear _ a sup-pliant child! A - ve Ma - ri - a!
Fm6 A♭/E♭ E♭7 Fm B♭m E♭7 A♭ A♭+ Fm/A♭
A - ve Ma - ri - a! Gra - ti - a ___ ple - na, Ma - ri - a, ___ gra - ti - a
A - ve Ma - ri - a! Stain - less ___ styl'd! Each fiend of ___ air of earth - ly
Dm7(♭5)/G G7 Edim Fm Fm6 E♭/G F7/C
ple - na, Ma - ri - a, gra - ti - a ___ ple - na. A - ve, ___ A - ve! Do - mi -
es - sence, from this their wont - ed haunt _ ex - il'd, shall ___ flee be - fore _ Thy ho - ly
E♭/B♭ B♭7 E♭ E♭7 A♭/E♭
nus, ___ Do - mi - nus ___ te - cum; Be - ne - di - cta tu in mu - li - e - ri - bus et
pres - ence! We bow, be - neath our cares o're - la - den, to
E♭7 Fm E♭ C B♭m
be - ne - di ___ ctus, et be - ne - di - ctus fru - ctus ven - tris, ven - tris
Thy dear gui - dance rec - on - cil'd; then hear, oh Maid, a sim - ple maid - en and
B♭m/D♭ Fdim E♭ E♭7 A♭ Fm6 A♭/E♭ E♭7 A♭ A♭7
tu - i, Je - sus. A - ve Ma - ri - a!
for a fa - ther hear _ a child! A - ve Ma - ri - a!
D♭/A♭ D♭dim/A♭ A♭

AZURE

By DUKE ELLINGTON
and IRVING MILLS

Slowly

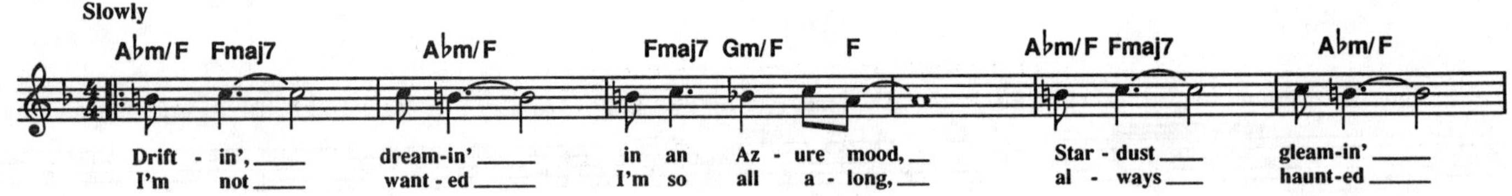
Abm/F Fmaj7 Abm/F Fmaj7 Gm/F F Abm/F Fmaj7 Abm/F
Drift - in', dream-in' in an Az - ure mood, Star - dust gleam-in'
I'm not want - ed I'm so all a - long, al - ways haunt-ed

Fmaj7 Gm/F F F7 A Bb Am/C C#dim7 Dm Cm7 F7 A Bb Am/C F7 G7 G7(b5) C7
thru my sol - i - tude. Here in my se - clu - sion, you're a blue il - lu - sion
by the dreams I own. But, thought I'm tor - ment - ed I must be con - tent - ed

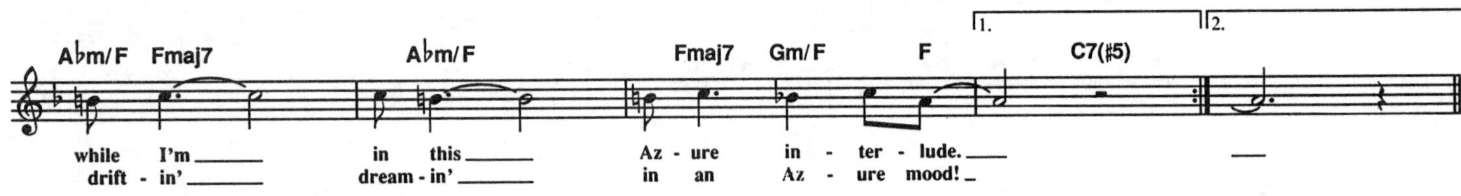
Abm/F Fmaj7 Abm/F Fmaj7 Gm/F F C7(#5)
1. 2.
while I'm in this Az - ure in - ter - lude.
drift - in' dream - in' in an Az - ure mood!

Abm/F Fmaj7 Abm/F Fmaj7 Gm/F F Abm/F Fmaj7 Abm/F
Drift - in' dream-in' in an Az - ure mood. Star - dust gleam-in'

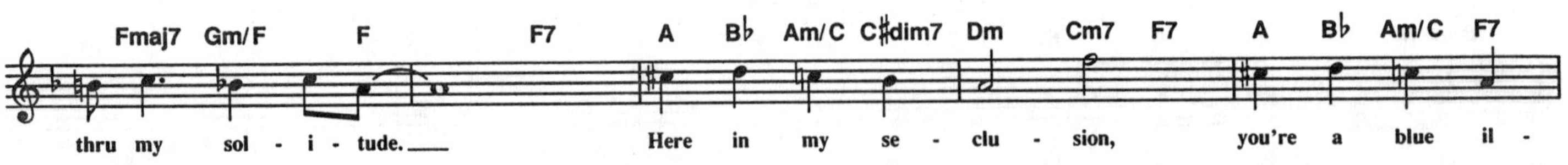
Fmaj7 Gm/F F F7 A Bb Am/C C#dim7 Dm Cm7 F7 A Bb Am/C F7
thru my sol - i - tude. Here in my se - clu - sion, you're a blue il -

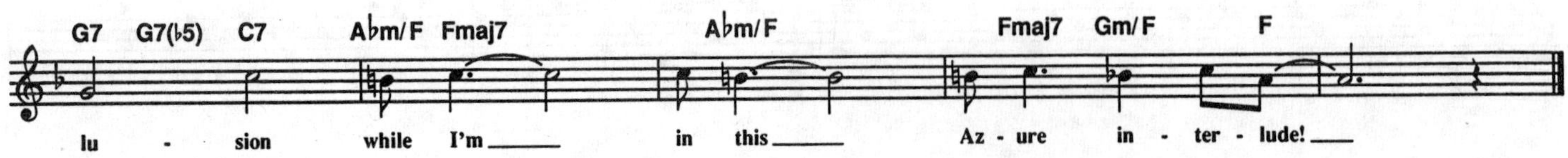
G7 G7(b5) C7 Abm/F Fmaj7 Abm/F Fmaj7 Gm/F F
lu - sion while I'm in this Az - ure in - ter - lude!

BABE

Words and Music by
DENNIS DE YOUNG

Moderately
Verse:
D6 Em7 G/A A D6
1. Babe, I'm leav-ing, I must be on my way, the time is draw-ing near. My train is go-ing. I
2. Babe, I'm leav-ing, I'll say it once a-gain, and some-how try to smile. I know the feel-ing we're
Em7 G/A A Bm Gmaj7 A
see it in your eyes, the love, the need, your tears. But I'll be lone-ly with-out you,
try-ing to for-get, if on-ly for a-while. 'Cause I'll be lone-ly with-out you,
Gmaj7 A G/A A D6 Em7 G/A
To Coda
and I'll need your love to see me through. So, please be-lieve me, my heart is in your hands, and I'll be miss-ing
and I'll need your love to see me through. But please be-lieve me, my heart is in your hands, 'cause I'll be miss-ing
Chorus:
D6 G/A D A/D G/D Bm A
you. 'Cause you know it's you, babe, when-ev-er I get wea-ry and I've had e-nough, feel like
Bm A D A/D G/D Bm A Bm A
giv-ing up. You know it's you, babe, giv-ing me the cour-age and the strength I need. Please be-lieve that it's
Gmaj7 D6 Em7 D6 G/A A G/A A
1. To Next Strain
2. D.C. al Coda
true. Babe, I love you.
Bridge:
B♭ C/B♭ B♭ C/B♭ D/A G/A D/A G/A
B♭ C/B♭ B♭ C/B♭ G/A A G/A A
D.S.
You know it's
Coda
D6 Em7 D6 Em7 D6 G/A D6
you. Babe, I love you. Babe, I love you. Ooh, babe.

BABY, COME TO ME

Words and Music by
ROD TEMPERTON

Moderately

Verse:

Am7 D/A Am7 D/A F/G G F/G G

1. Think-in' back in time, _ when love was on - ly in the mind, _ I re - a - lize
2. Spend-in' ev - ery dime _ to keep you talk - in' on the line; _ that's how it was. And

Am7 D/A Am7 D/A F/G G F/G G Am7

ain't no sec - ond chance; _ you've got to hold on to ro - mance. _ Don't let it slide. _____ There's a
all those walks to - geth - er out in an - y kind of weath - er just be - cause. _____ There's a

B♭maj7 Am7 A♭maj7 G11 F/G G

spe - cial kind of mag - ic _ in the air _____ when you find an - oth-er heart _ that needs to share.
brand new way of look - ing _ at your life, _____ when you know that love is stand - ing by your side.
Ba - by,

Chorus:

Cm7 Fm9 A♭/B♭ Fm Gm7 E♭maj9 G7(♭9)

come to me; _ let me put my arms a - round _ you. This was meant to be, _ and I'm oh, so glad I found you. Need you
(you.)

Cm7 Fm9 A♭/B♭ Fm Gm7 | 1. Dm7 G7(♭9) Cm

ev - 'ry day; _ got to have your love a - round _ me. Ba - by, al - ways stay, 'cause I can't go back to liv - in' with-out you.

Cm/B♭ B♭ *D.C.* | 2. Dm7 G7(♭9) Csus C *To Next Strain* | 3.4.etc. Dm7 G7(♭9) *Repeat ad lib. and fade*

can't go back to liv - in' with-out you. _____ The can't go back to liv - in' with-out

Bridge:

A♭maj7 Cm7 A♭/B♭ E♭maj7

night can _ get cold; there's a chill _____ to ev-'ry eve - ning when you're all a - lone. _ Don't

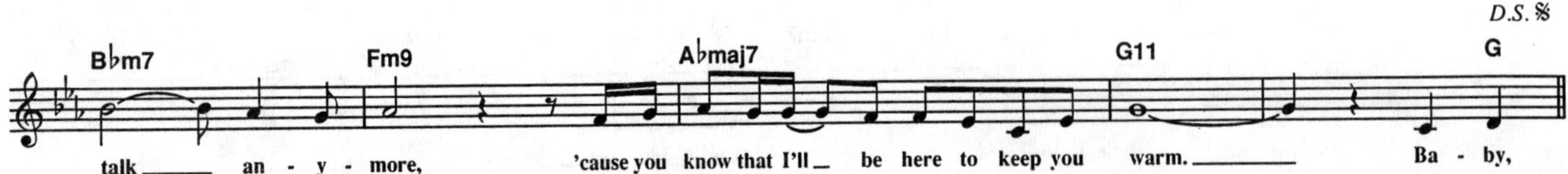
D.S. 𝄋
B♭m7
Fm9
A♭maj7
G11
G
talk _____ an - y - more, 'cause you know that I'll _ be here to keep you warm. _____ Ba - by,

BABY FACE

Words and Music by
BENNY DAVIS and HARRY AKST

Quickly
C C♯dim7 G7
Ba - by face, you've got the cut - est lit - tle ba - by face. There's not an - oth - er one could
C Gm6/B♭ A7 D7 G7
take your place, ba - by face. My poor heart is jump - in', you sure have start - ed some-thin'.
C E7 Bm7 E7 Am C7
Ba - by face, I'm up in heav - en when I'm in your fond em - brace. I did - n't
F F♯dim7 C A7 D7 D+ G7 C
need a shove, 'cause I just fell in love with your pret - ty ba - by face.

BABY I LOVE YOUR WAY

Words and Music by
PETER FRAMPTON

Moderately

Verse:

G Bm Em C F7

Shadows grow so long before my eyes and they're moving across the page.
Moon appears to shine and light the sky with the help (of) some firefly.
I can see the sun set in your eyes brown and grey and blue besides.

G Bm Em C

Suddenly the day turns into night far away from the city.
(I) wonder how they have the power to shine? *(shine shine)* (I can) see them under the pine.
Clouds are stalking islands in the sun, (I wish I could) buy one out of season.

F7 Bm7 E7 Am7 D7

(But) Don't hesitate 'cause your love won't wait.

Chorus:

G D Am G

Ooh, baby, I love your way. Wanna

D Am G D Am

tell you I love your way. Wanna be with you night and day.

1.2. *D.C.* 3.4.*etc.* *Repeat ad lib. and fade*

(You're So Square) BABY, I DON'T CARE

Words and Music by
JERRY LEIBER and MIKE STOLLER

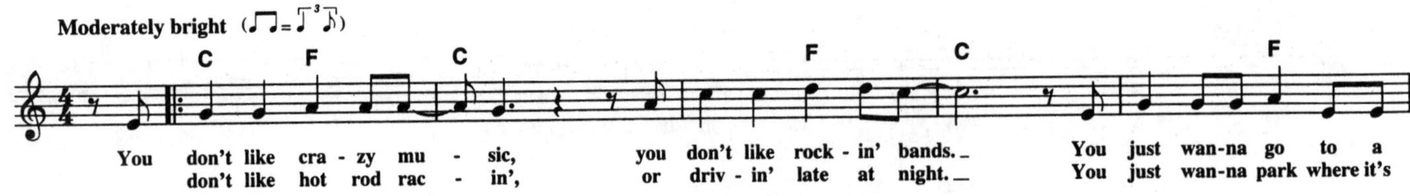
Moderately bright
C F C F C F
You don't like cra - zy mu - sic, you don't like rock - in' bands. You just wan-na go to a
don't like hot rod rac - in', or driv - in' late at night. You just wan-na park where it's

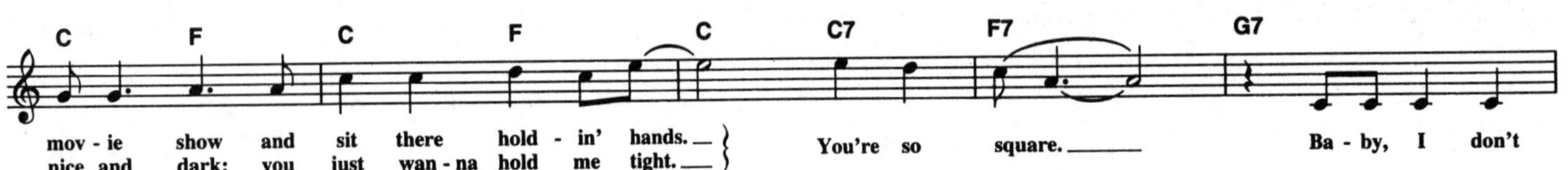
C F C F C C7 F7 G7
mov - ie show and sit there hold - in' hands. You're so square. Ba - by, I don't
nice and dark; you just wan - na hold me tight.

1. 2.
C C F F♯dim7
care. You care. You don't know an - y dance steps that are
(Instrumental)

C C7 F F♯dim7 G7
new. But no one else can love me like you do. I

C F C F C F
don't know why my heart flips; I on - ly know it does. I won - der why I

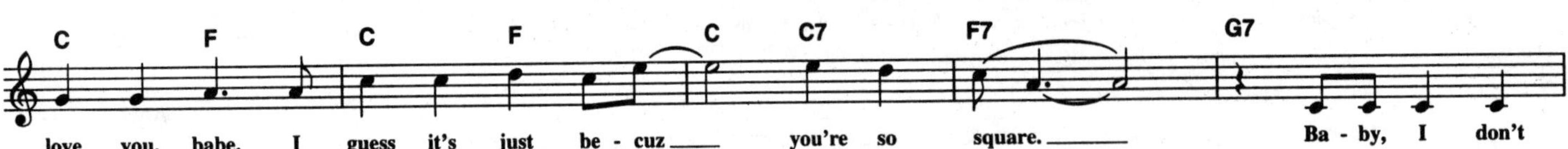
C F C F C C7 F7 G7
love you, babe, I guess it's just be - cuz you're so square. Ba - by, I don't

To Coda
C
care. Ba - by, I don't care. Ba - by, I don't care. Ba - by, I don't

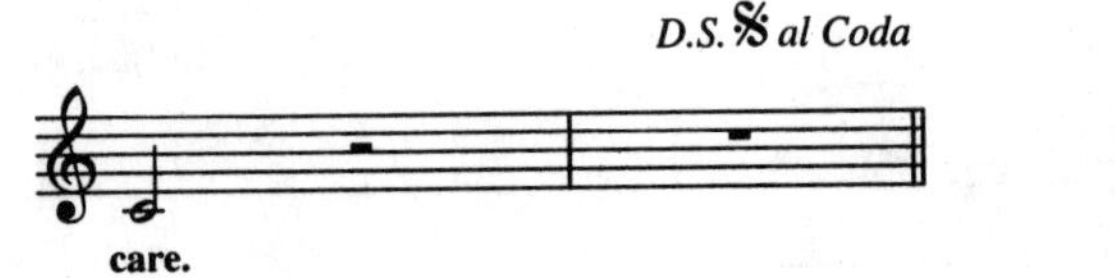
D.S. al Coda
care.

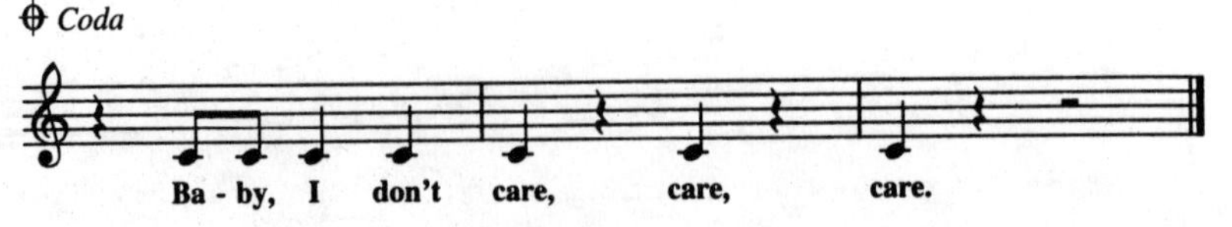
Coda
Ba - by, I don't care, care, care.

BABY, IT'S YOU

By BURT BACHARACH, MACK DAVID
and BARNEY WILLIAMS

Moderate rock
E♭6/9 Cm E♭6/9 Cm E♭6/9
(Sha la la la la la la. Sha la la la la la la. Sha la la la la la
Verse:
Cm A♭ E♭
la. Sha la la la la.) It's not the way you smile that touched my heart.
A♭ E♭ Cm
It's not the way you kiss that tears me a - part. Man-y, man-y, man-y
Fm 1. E♭ Cm
nights go by, I sit a - lone at home and I cry o - ver you. What can I do?
A♭ B♭7 N.C. E♭6/9 Cm
Can't help my - self, 'cause ba - by, it's you. (Sha - la la la la la la.) Ba - by, it's
E♭6/9 Cm 2. E♭ Cm A♭ B♭7
you. (Sha la la la la la la. Sha la la la do when it's true. Don't want no - bod - y, no-bod - y,
N.C. E♭6/9 Cm E♭6/9 Cm
'cause ba - by, it's you. (Sha la la la la la la.) Ba - by, it's you. (Sha la la la la la la.) Don't leave me all a -
E♭6/9 Cm E♭6/9 Cm E♭
lone. (Sha la la la la la la.) Come on home. (Sha la la la la la la.) 'Cause ba - by, it's you.

Verse 2:
You should hear what they say about you.
They say you've never, never been true.
Doesn't matter what they say.
I know I'm gonna love you any old way.
What can I do when it's true?
Don't want nobody, nobody,
'Cause baby, it's you.

From the Paramount Motion Picture "HATARI"

BABY ELEPHANT WALK

By HENRY MANCINI

Moderately

F
B♭7

F
C
B♭

F
1.
2.
B♭
Am
Gm
F
F7
F

B♭
F
B♭
F
B♭

F
C
B♭
F

B♭7

F
C
B♭
F
F7

BALLERINA

Words by
BOB RUSSEL
Music by
CARL SIGMAN

Moderately

Dance, Bal-le-ri-na, dance, and do your pir-ou-ette in rhy-thm with your ach-ing heart.
Whirl, Bal-le-ri-na, whirl, and just ig-nore the chair that's empty in the sec-ond row.
Dance, bal-le-ri-na, dance, you mustn't once for-get a danc-er has to dance the part.
This is your mo-ment, girl, al-though he's not out there ap-plaud-ing as you steal the show.
Tacet
Once you said his love must wait its turn, You want-ed fame in-stead, I guess that's your con-cern, we live and learn. And love is gone, Bal-leri-na, gone. So on with your ca-reer, you can't af-ford a back-ward glance. Dance on and on and on. A thou-sand peo-ple here have come to see the show, as 'round and 'round you go, so Bal-le-ri-na dance, dance, dance.

BESIDE A BABBLING BROOK

Words by GUS KAHN
Music by WALTER DONALDSON

Moderato
I'd be more than sat-is-fied if I could hide a-way Be-side A Bab-bling Brook,
Rip-pling wa-ters call me far a-way to a qui-et sha-dy nook. Thru the woods I long to hike, to
lin-ger where the world is like a sto-ry-book, Like a la-zy dai-sy gaz-in' at the sky,
Let me live and love and let the world go by, I'd be more than sat-is-fied if
I could hide a-way Be-side A-Bab-bling Brook. Brook.

BABY DREAM YOUR DREAM

From the Musical "SWEET CHARITY"

Music by
CY COLEMAN
Lyrics by
DOROTHY FIELDS

Moderate swing

C6 C+5 Am7

Ba - by, dream your dream; close your eyes and try it. Dream of fur - ni - ture;
dream we sign the lease; leave a small de - pos - it; three and one half rooms
Ev - 'ry Sat - ur - day we'll spend all our mon - ey, join the P. T. A.;

C7 F *To Coda* C/E 1. D7 G7

dream that I can buy it. That fan - cy bed you prayed for, not on - ly bought but paid for;
with a walk - in clos - et. We'll ask the lo - cal jet set
they will love you, hon - ey. Life will be

2. Bm7(♭5) E7 Am7 Am7(maj7) Am7 D7 Gm7 Gm7(maj7) Gm7 C

to dine on our din - ette set. Right a - cross the street there's a friend - ly bank. You

F Fmaj7 F6 F Dm7-5 G7+5 G7 *D.C. al Coda*

make a friend - ly loan, and the bank says thank you.

Coda E7+9 Am7

fro - zen peach - es and cream,

D7-5 D7 Dm7 G7 Em7-5 A7 D7-5 G7 C6 D9 D♭9 Cmaj9

ba - by; dream your dream, dream your dream.

IL BACIO

(The Kiss)

By LUIGI ARDITI

Bright waltz tempo

D
A7
D
To Coda
A7
D A D
E7
A
E7
1. A
2. A
D.S. al Coda
Coda
D♯°7
Em
C7
D
A7
D
3

BACK IN THE SADDLE AGAIN

Words and Music by
GENE AUTRY and RAY WHITLEY

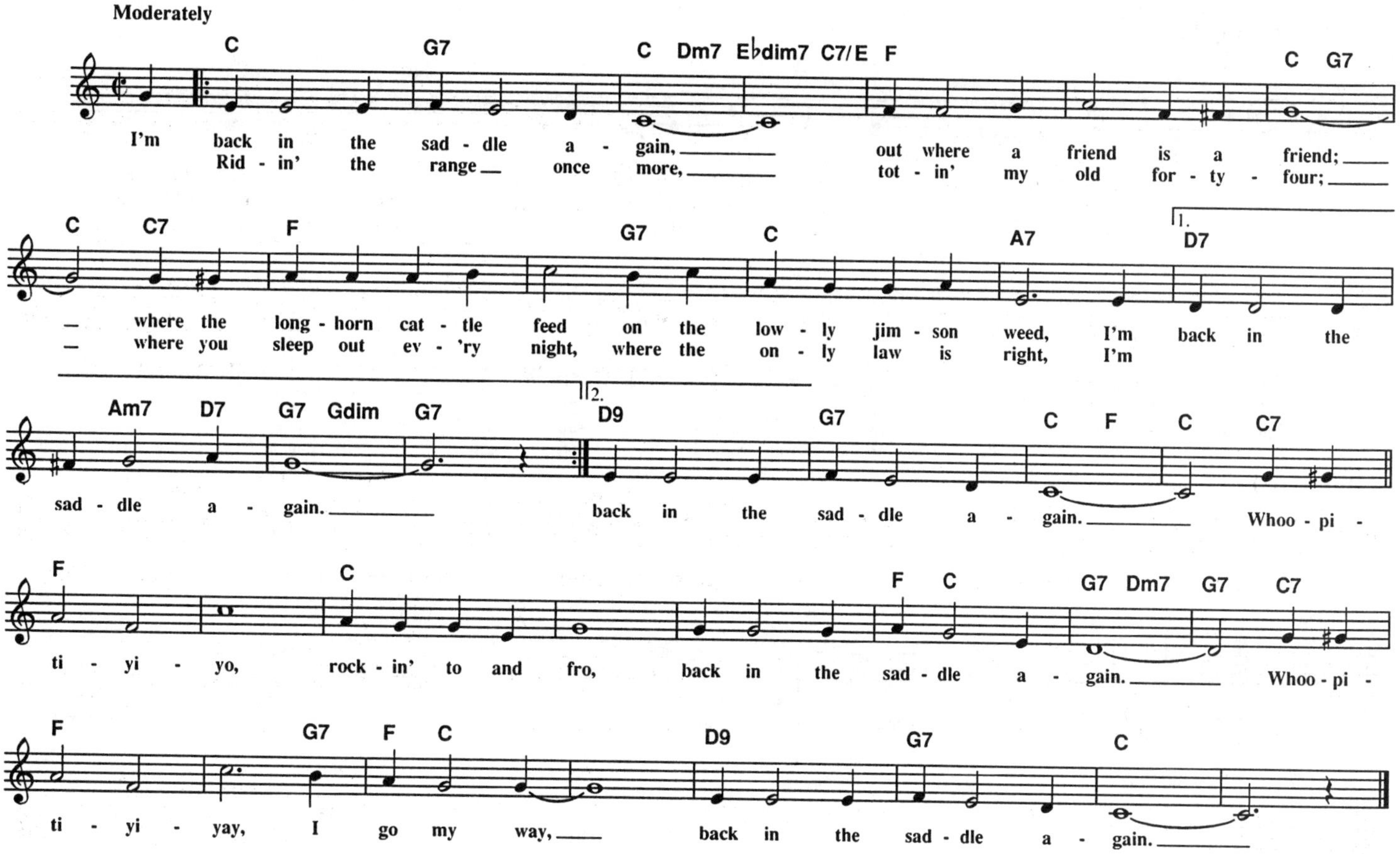

Moderately

C G7 C Dm7 E♭dim7 C7/E F C G7

I'm back in the sad - dle a - gain, out where a friend is a friend;
Rid - in' the range once more, tot - in' my old for - ty - four;

C C7 F G7 C A7 1. D7

where the long - horn cat - tle feed on the low - ly jim - son weed, I'm back in the
where you sleep out ev - 'ry night, where the on - ly law is right, I'm

Am7 D7 G7 Gdim G7 2. D9 G7 C F C C7

sad - dle a - gain. back in the sad - dle a - gain. Whoo - pi -

F C F C G7 Dm7 G7 C7

ti - yi - yo, rock - in' to and fro, back in the sad - dle a - gain. Whoo - pi -

F G7 F C D9 G7 C

ti - yi - yay, I go my way, back in the sad - dle a - gain.

BAD MOON RISING

Words and Music by
J.C. FOGERTY

Moderately bright
Verse:
F C B♭ F C B♭
I see the bad moon a - ris - ing. I see trou - ble on the
I hear hur - ri - canes a - blow - ing. I know the end is com - ing
Hope you got your things to - geth - er. Hope you are quite pre - pared to
F C B♭ F
way. I see earth - quakes and light - nin'. I see
soon. I fear riv - ers o - ver - flow - ing. I hear the
die. Looks like we're in for nas - ty weath - er. One eye is
C B♭ F Chorus: B♭ F
bad times to - day.
voice of rage and ruin.
tak - en for an eye.
Don't go a - round to - night, well, it's bound to take your life.
C B♭ 1.2. F D.C. 3. F 4. F
There's a bad moon on the rise.

BAD TO ME

By JOHN LENNON and PAUL McCARTNEY

Freely
E♭ Cm Gm
3
If you ev - er leave me, I'll be sad and blue. Don't you ev - er leave me, I'm

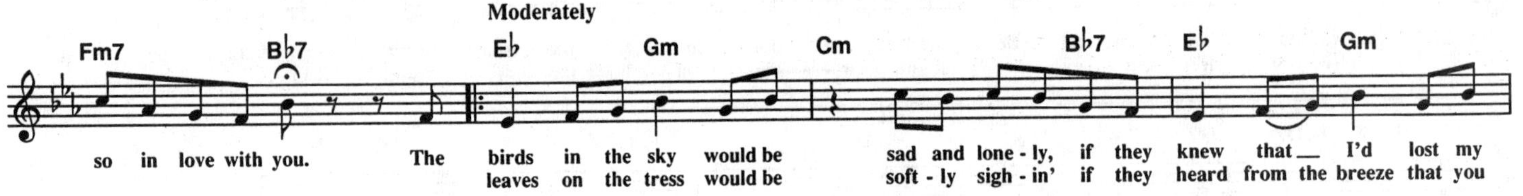
Moderately
Fm7 B♭7 E♭ Gm Cm B♭7 E♭ Gm
so in love with you. The birds in the sky would be sad and lone - ly, if they knew that I'd lost my
leaves on the tress would be soft - ly sigh - in' if they heard from the breeze that you

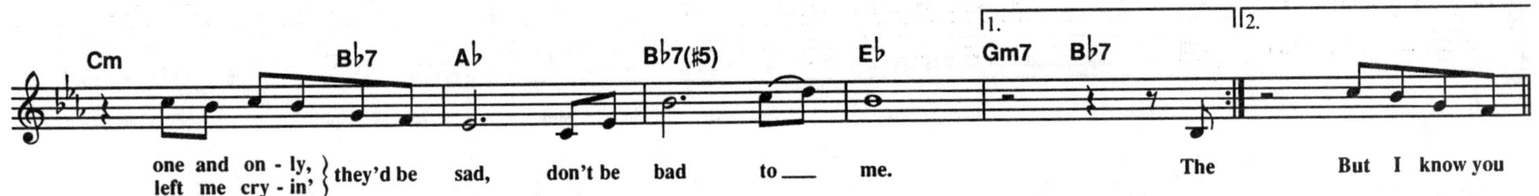
1. 2.
Cm B♭7 A♭ B♭7(♯5) E♭ Gm7 B♭7
one and on - ly, they'd be sad, don't be bad to me. The But I know you
left me cry - in'

A♭ B♭7 Gm C7
won't leave me 'cos you told me so, and I've no in - ten - tion of let - ting you go

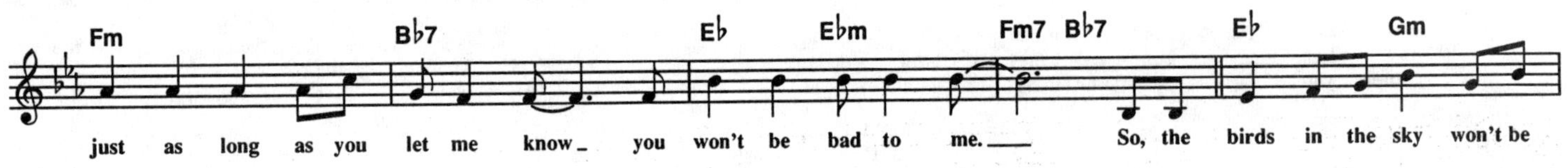
Fm B♭7 E♭ E♭m Fm7 B♭7 E♭ Gm
just as long as you let me know you won't be bad to me. So, the birds in the sky won't be

Cm B♭7 E♭ Gm Cm B♭7 A♭
sad and lone - ly, 'cos they know that I got my one and on - ly. They'll be glad you're not

B♭7(♯5) B♭m6 C7 A♭ B♭7 B♭7(♯5) E♭ Gm Cm B♭7 E♭
bad to me. They'll be glad you're not bad to me.

Theme from "GILLIGAN'S ISLAND" TV Series

THE BALLAD OF GILLIGAN'S ISLE

Words and Music by
SHERWOOD SCHWARTZ and
GEORGE WYLE

Lively

Dm C Dm C
Just sit right back and you'll hear a tale, a tale of a fate - ful trip that

Dm C B♭ C Dm C
start - ed from this trop-ic port_ a - board this ti - ny ship. The mate was a might - y sail - in' man,_ the

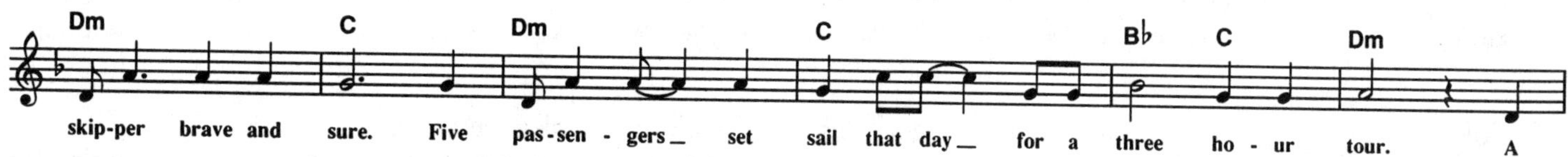
Dm C Dm C B♭ C Dm
skip-per brave and sure. Five pas-sen - gers_ set sail that day_ for a three ho - ur tour. A

B♭ C Dm B7 Em D Em D
three hour_ tour. The weath - er start - ed get - tin' rough,_ the ti - ny ship was tossed. If

Em D C D Em C D Em
not for the cour-age of the fear-less crew,_ the Min-now would be lost. The Min - now would be lost. The

Fm E♭ Fm E♭ Fm
ship's a - ground on the shore of this un - chart - ed des - ert isle, with Gil - li - gan,___ the

E♭ Fm E♭
skip - per too,___ the mil - lion - aire___ and his wife,___ the

Fm E♭ Fm E♭ Fm
mov - ie___ star___ and the rest_ are here on Gil - li - gan's Isle!___

BALLIN' THE JACK

Words by JIM BURRIS
Music by CHRIS SMITH

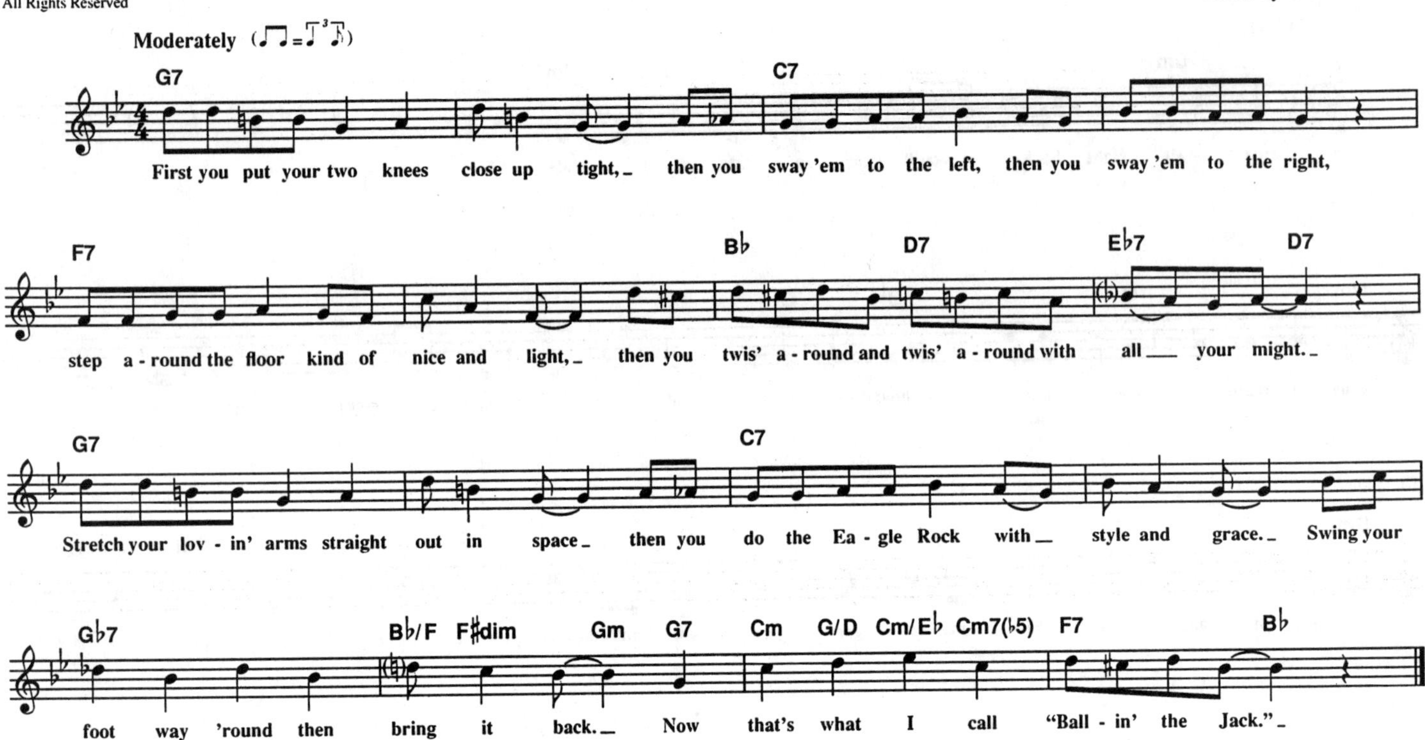
Moderately
G7 C7
First you put your two knees close up tight, then you sway 'em to the left, then you sway 'em to the right,
F7 B♭ D7 E♭7 D7
step a-round the floor kind of nice and light, then you twis' a-round and twis' a-round with all your might.
G7 C7
Stretch your lov-in' arms straight out in space then you do the Ea-gle Rock with style and grace. Swing your
G♭7 B♭/F F♯dim Gm G7 Cm G/D Cm/E♭ Cm7(♭5) F7 B♭
foot way 'round then bring it back. Now that's what I call "Ball-in' the Jack."

THE BAND PLAYED ON

Words by JOHN F. PALMER
Music by CHARLES B. WARD

Moderately

G D7
Ca-sey would waltz with a straw-ber-ry blonde, and the band played on.

G
He'd glide 'cross the floor with the girl he a-dored and the band

D7 G7 C
played on. But his brain was so load-ed it near-ly ex-plod-ed, the

Am E7 Am C C♯dim7
poor girl would shake with a-larm. He'd ne'er leave the girl with the

G/D Em A7 D7 1. G 2. G
straw-ber-ry curls, and the band played on. on.

BARCAROLLE

OFFENBACH

Moderately

C
G7
C

G7
To Coda
C
G7

C
G7
C

C7
F
D7

G
Gdim
G
Gdim
G7
D.C. al Coda

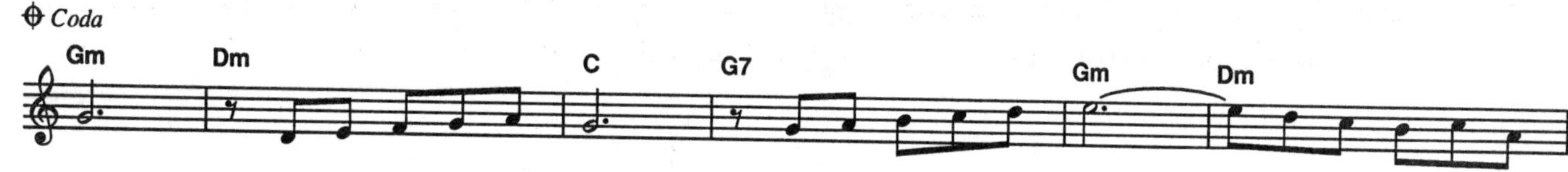
Coda
Gm
Dm
C
G7
Gm
Dm

C
G7
C
G7
C
G7

C
C
F
C

BAREFOOT IN THE PARK

Words and Music by
JOHNNY MERCER and
NEIL HEFTI

Moderately

Gm7 C7 Gm7 C7 F B♭7 Am7 D7
Go - ing bare - foot in the park where it says, "Keep off the grass," is - n't

Gm7 C7 Gm7 C7 Gm7 C7(♭9) Fmaj7 F6 B7 B♭ A7(♭9)
rec - om - mend - ed for the ver - y old. But when you're young and

Dm7 G7(♭9) C Cmaj7 Am Am7 Dm7 Bdim7 C
you're in love the world is beau - ti - ful and I'm not a bit a - fraid of

Dm7 Cmaj7 C7 Bm7 E7 Am7 D7 G Gm7
you catch - ing cold. Run - ning bare - foot through the park, stroll - ing bare - head - ed

C7 F Dm7 Gm7 B♭maj7 Fmaj7 Gm7 C7(♭9) Fmaj7
in the rain just to look for a dai - sy seems kind o' cra - zy to do.

B7 B♭maj7 B♭m6 F F+ B♭6 Bdim F A
But come a - long, my bare - foot love, to the fields that shine with

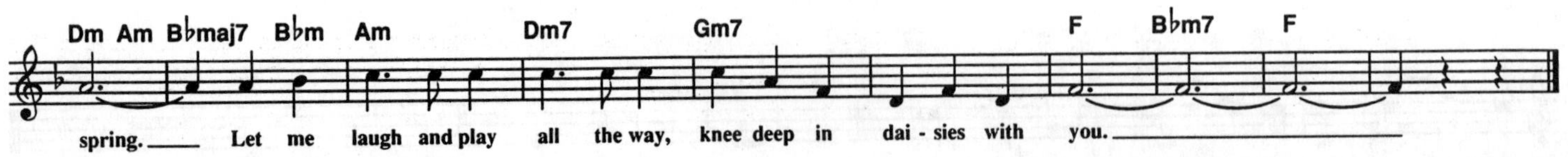
Dm Am B♭maj7 B♭m Am Dm7 Gm7 F B♭m7 F
spring. Let me laugh and play all the way, knee deep in dai - sies with you.

BATMAN THEME

Words and Music by
NEAL HEFTI

Bat rock tempo

G7

Bass riff continues throughout

G7

Bat - man, Bat - man,

C7 G7 D7 C7 G7 *To Coda*

Bat - man, Bat - man, Bat - man, Bat - man, Bat - man.

G Bb C

G Bb D C G

1. 2. *D.S. al Coda*

Coda

D7 C7 G7

Bat - man, Bat - man, Bat - man.

G Gm7(4)

Da da da da da da da da da da da da da da da da da, Bat - man!

BEAUTIFUL DREAMER

Words and Music by STEPHEN C. FOSTER

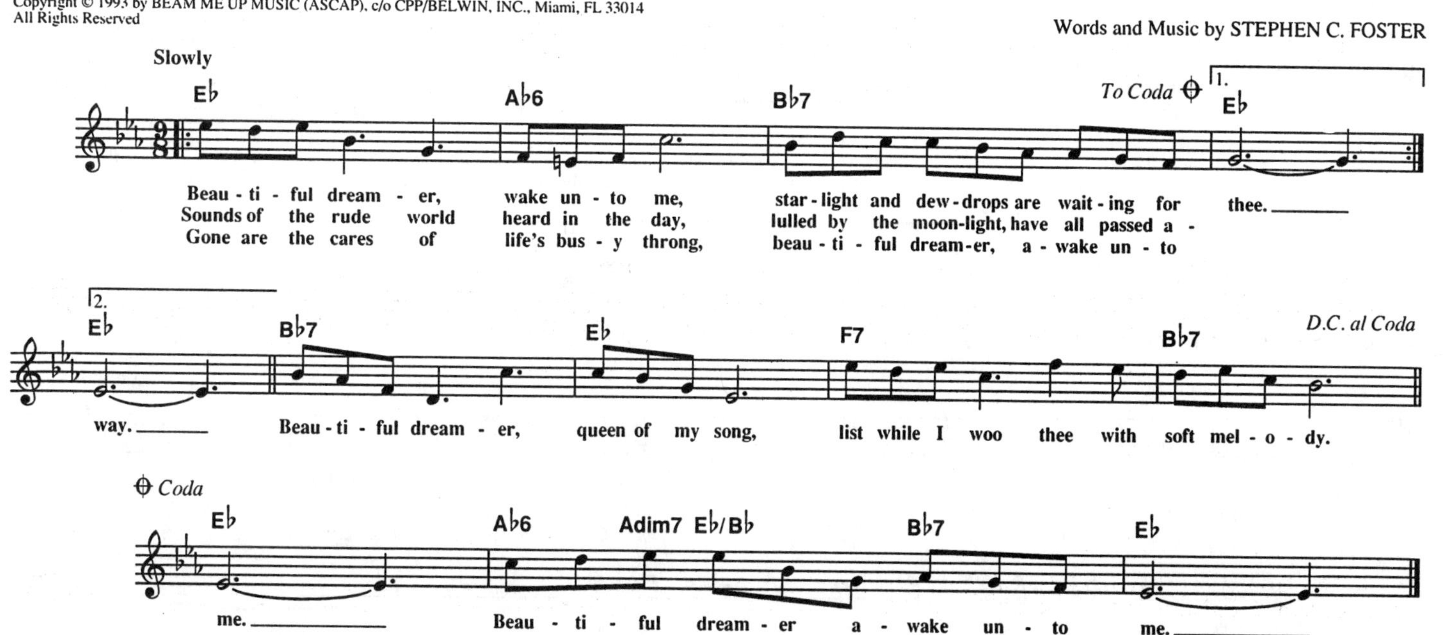
Slowly
Eb Ab6 Bb7 To Coda 1. Eb
Beau - ti - ful dream - er, wake un - to me, star - light and dew - drops are wait - ing for thee.
Sounds of the rude world heard in the day, lulled by the moon - light, have all passed a -
Gone are the cares of life's bus - y throng, beau - ti - ful dream - er, a - wake un - to
2. Eb Bb7 Eb F7 Bb7 D.C. al Coda
way. Beau - ti - ful dream - er, queen of my song, list while I woo thee with soft mel - o - dy.
Coda
Eb Ab6 Adim7 Eb/Bb Bb7 Eb
me. Beau - ti - ful dream - er a - wake un - to me.

THE BATTLE HYMN OF THE REPUBLIC

Words by JULIA WARD HOWE
U.S.A. CAMPMEETING TUNE

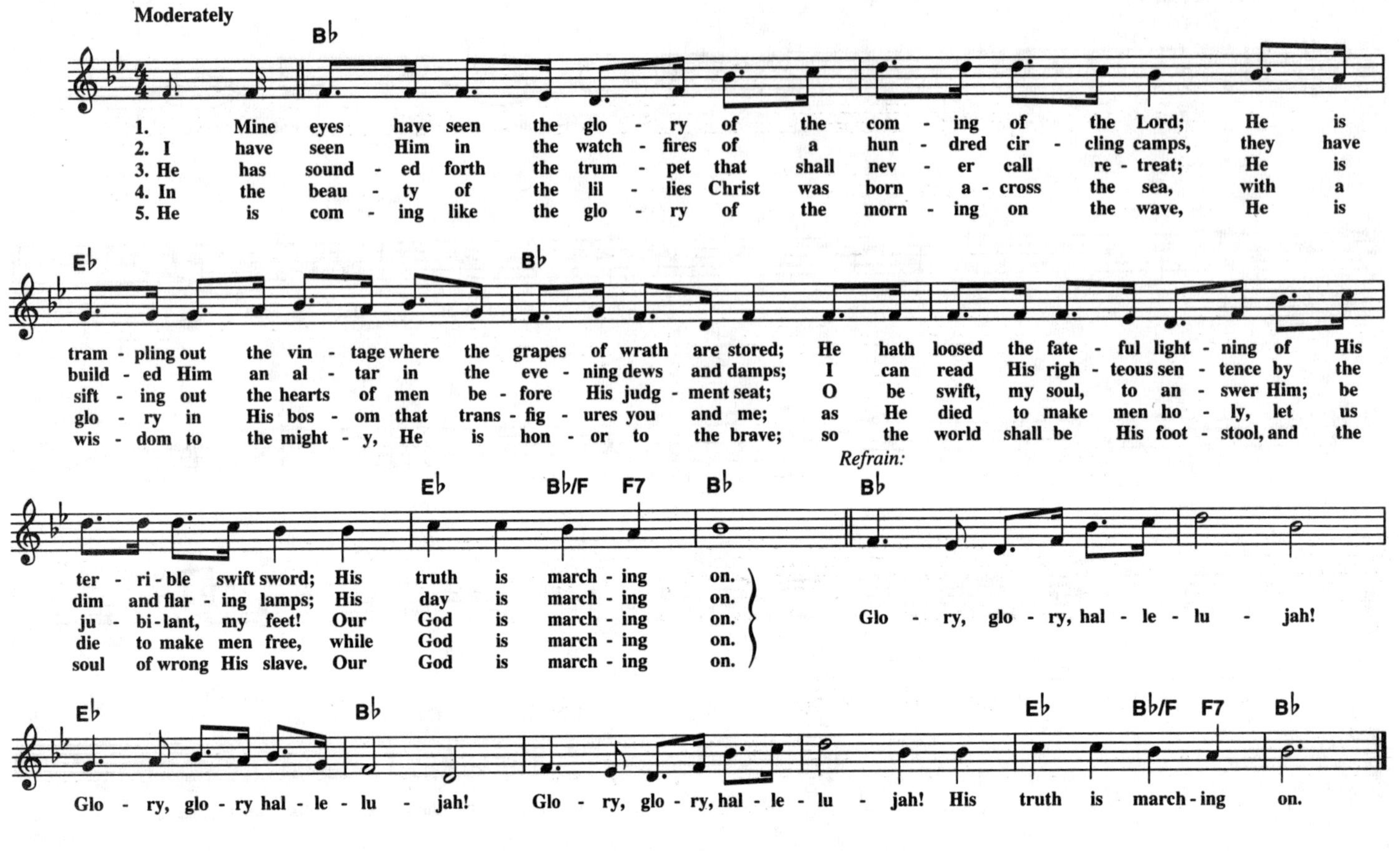
Moderately
B♭
1. Mine eyes have seen the glo - ry of the com - ing of the Lord; He is
2. I have seen Him in the watch - fires of a hun - dred cir - cling camps, they have
3. He has sound - ed forth the trum - pet that shall nev - er call re - treat; He is
4. In the beau - ty of the lil - lies Christ was born a - cross the sea, with a
5. He is com - ing like the glo - ry of the morn - ing on the wave, He is
E♭ B♭
tram - pling out the vin - tage where the grapes of wrath are stored; He hath loosed the fate - ful light - ning of His
build - ed Him an al - tar in the eve - ning dews and damps; I can read His righ - teous sen - tence by the
sift - ing out the hearts of men be - fore His judg - ment seat; O be swift, my soul, to an - swer Him; be
glo - ry in His bos - om that trans - fig - ures you and me; as He died to make men ho - ly, let us
wis - dom to the might - y, He is hon - or to the brave; so the world shall be His foot - stool, and the
E♭ B♭/F F7 B♭ Refrain: B♭
ter - ri - ble swift sword; His truth is march - ing on.
dim and flar - ing lamps; His day is march - ing on.
ju - bi - lant, my feet! Our God is march - ing on.
die to make men free, while God is march - ing on.
soul of wrong His slave. Our God is march - ing on.
Glo - ry, glo - ry, hal - le - lu - jah!
E♭ B♭ E♭ B♭/F F7 B♭
Glo - ry, glo - ry hal - le - lu - jah! Glo - ry, glo - ry, hal - le - lu - jah! His truth is march - ing on.

BEFORE THE NEXT TEARDROP FALLS

Words and Music by
BEN PETERS and VIVIAN KEITH

Moderately slow
F F7 B♭ F B♭
If he brings you hap - pi - ness, then I wish you both the best. It's your hap - pi - ness that
hurts to let you go, dar - ling, I want you to know that I'll stand by you if
C7 F C7 F F7 B♭ F B♭
mat - ters most of all. But if he ev - er breaks your heart, if the tear-drops ev - er start, I'll be
ev - er you should call. And if I should ev - er hear that he made you shed a tear,
ev - er leaves you blue, just re - mem - ber I love you,
To Coda 1. 2.
F C7 F B♭ C7 F B♭ F F7 B♭
there be - fore the next tear - drop falls. Tho' it falls. I'll be there an - y
C7 F G7 C7 D.S. al Coda
time you need me by your side, to dry a - way ev - 'ry tear - drop that you cried. If he
Coda
F B♭ F C7 F B♭ F C7 F
falls. Yes, I'll be there be - fore the next tear - drop falls.

From the M-G-M Musical Production "THE TOAST OF NEW ORLEANS"

BE MY LOVE

By SAMMY CAHN and
NICHOLAS BRODSZKY

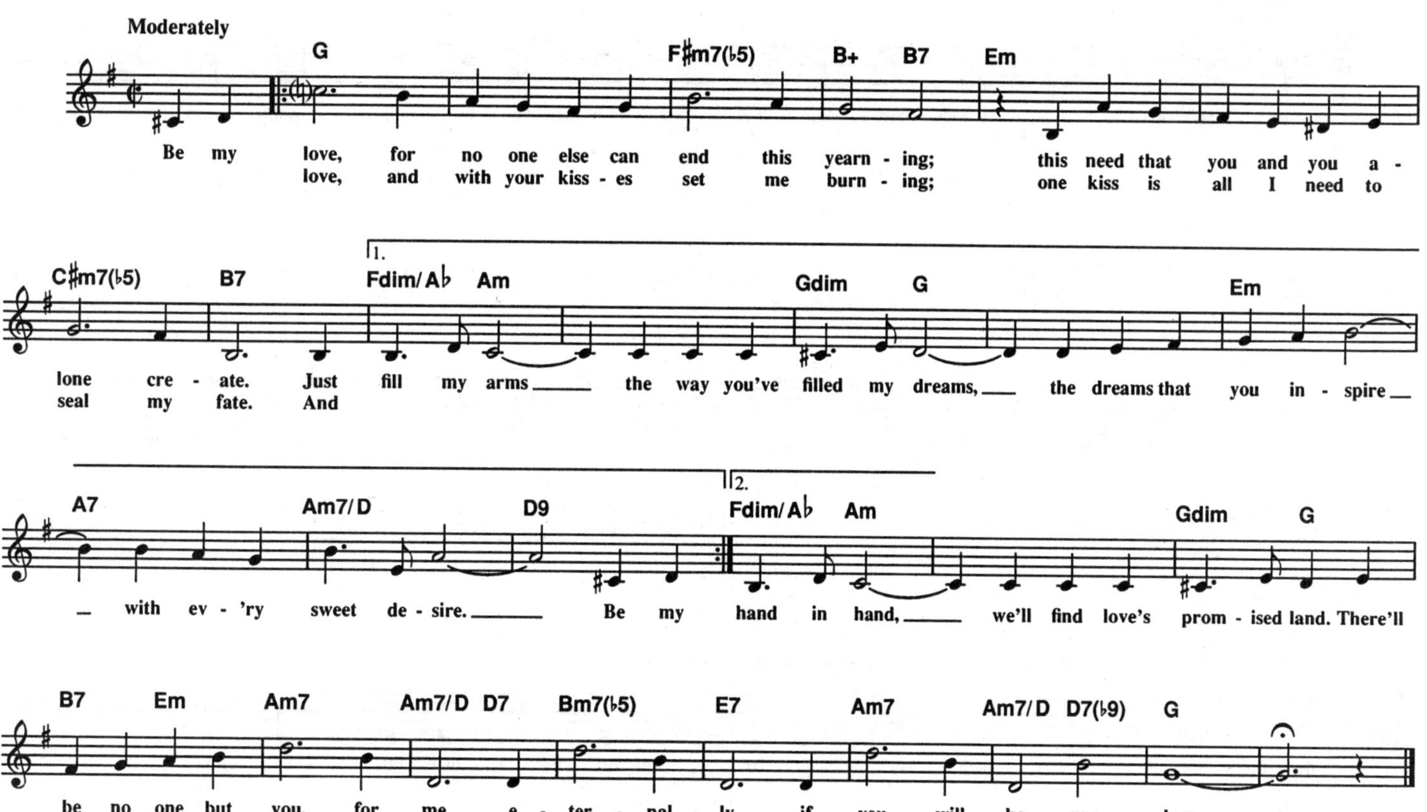
Moderately
G F♯m7(♭5) B+ B7 Em
Be my love, for no one else can end this yearn - ing; this need that you and you a -
love, and with your kiss - es set me burn - ing; one kiss is all I need to
C♯m7(♭5) B7 1. Fdim/A♭ Am Gdim G Em
lone cre - ate. Just fill my arms the way you've filled my dreams, the dreams that you in - spire
seal my fate. And
A7 Am7/D D9 2. Fdim/A♭ Am Gdim G
with ev - 'ry sweet de - sire. Be my hand in hand, we'll find love's prom - ised land. There'll
B7 Em Am7 Am7/D D7 Bm7(♭5) E7 Am7 Am7/D D7(♭9) G
be no one but you, for me e - ter - nal - ly, if you will be my love.

BECAUSE

Words by EDWARD TESCHEMACHER
French Words and Music by GUY d'HARDELOT

Slowly
B♭ B♭maj7 F7 G/B Cm Cm7 Cm7/F F7
Be - cause you come to me with naught save love, and hold my hand and lift mine eyes a - bove. A
cause God made thee mine I'll cher - ish thee, and thru light and dark-ness thru all time to be. And

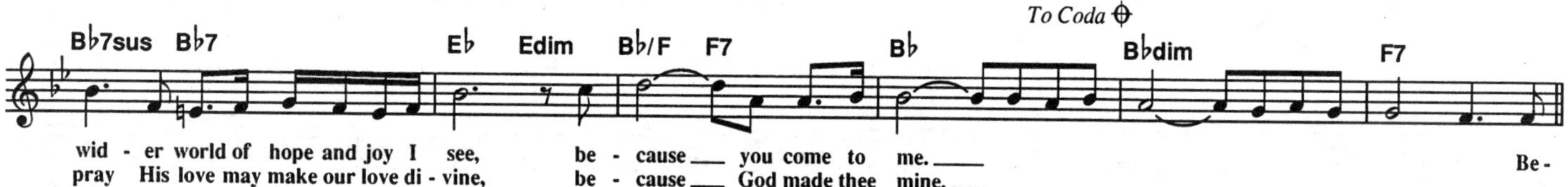
To Coda
B♭7sus B♭7 E♭ Edim B♭/F F7 B♭ B♭dim F7
wid - er world of hope and joy I see, be - cause you come to me.
pray His love may make our love di - vine, be - cause God made thee mine. Be -

B♭7 E♭ C7/E C7 Fm D7/F♯ D7 Gm
cause you speak to me in ac-cents sweet, I find the ros - es wak-ing 'round my feet. And I am led through tears and joy to thee, Be-

D.S. al Coda
Coda
B♭+ Cm7/F F7 Cm7/F F7 Gm E♭m/G♭ Cm7/F F7 B♭
cause you speak to me. Be-

BE-BOP-A-LULA

Words and Music by
GENE VINCENT and
TEX DAVIS

Moderately slow rock shuffle
Chorus:
C7
Be - bop - a - lu - la, she's my ba - by. Be - bop - a - lu - la, I don't mean may - be.

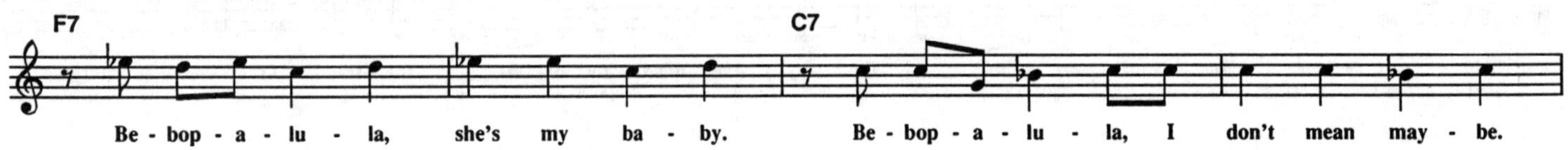
F7
C7
Be - bop - a - lu - la, she's my ba - by. Be - bop - a - lu - la, I don't mean may - be.

G7
F7
C7
Be - bop - a - lu - la, she's my ba - by love, my ba - by love, my ba - by love.

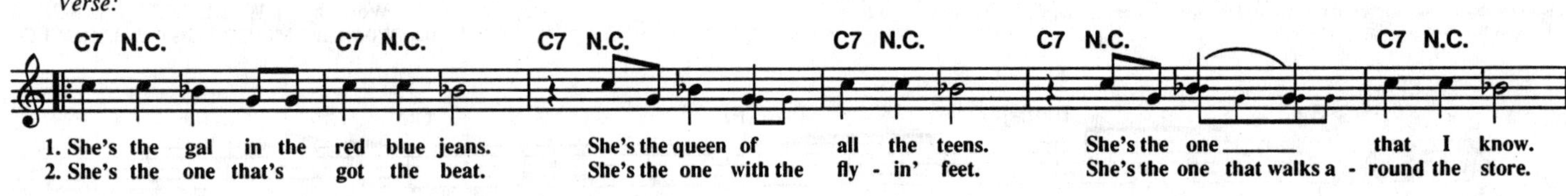
Verse:
C7 N.C.
1. She's the gal in the red blue jeans. She's the queen of all the teens. She's the one that I know.
2. She's the one that's got the beat. She's the one with the fly - in' feet. She's the one that walks a - round the store.

C7 N.C.
F7
C7
She's the one that loves me so.
She's the one that gets more and more.
Be - bop - a - lu - la, she's my ba - by. Be - bop - a - lu - la, I

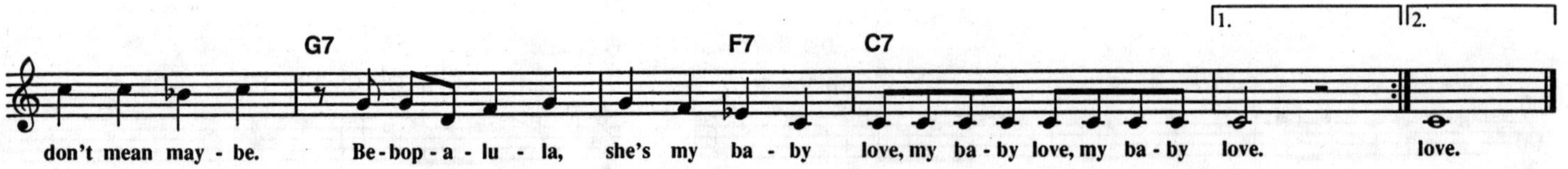
G7
F7
C7
1.
2.
don't mean may - be. Be - bop - a - lu - la, she's my ba - by love, my ba - by love, my ba - by love. love.

BEAT IT

© 1982 MIJAC MUSIC
All Rights Administered by WARNER-TAMERLANE PUBLISHING CORP.
All Rights Reserved
Written and Composed by
MICHAEL JACKSON
Moderately fast
They told him, "Don't you ev - er come a - round here. Don't wan - na see your face; you bet - ter dis - ap - pear." The fi - re's in their eyes and their words are real - ly clear. So beat it. just beat it.
They're out to get you. Bet - ter leave while you can. Don't wan - na be a boy; you wan - nar be a man. You wan - na stay a - live; bet - ter do what you can. So beat it, just beat it.
You bet - ter run; you bet - ter do what you can. Don't wan - na see no blood. Don't be a ma - cho man. You wan - na be tough; bet - ter do what you can. So beat it. But you wan - na be bad.
You have to show them that you're real - ly not scared. You're play - in' with your life. This ain't no truth or dare. They'll kick you, then they beat you, then they'll tell you it's fair. So beat it. But you wan - na be bad.
Just beat it, beat it. No ___ one wants to be de - feat - ted. Show - in' how funk - y and strong _ is your fight. It ___ does - n't mat - ter who's _
1.
___ wrong or right. Just beat it, just beat it, just beat it, just beat it.
2.
D.S. 𝄋 and fade
___ wrong or right. Just

BEEP BEEP

Words and Music by
DONALD CLAPS and CARL CICCHETTI

Tempo starts very slow, getting faster with each Refrain
Fm C7 Fm C7 Fm C7 Fm
1. While rid - ing in my Cad - il - lac, What, to my sur - prise; A
(2. I) pushed my foot down to the floor, To give the guy the shake; But the
(3. My) car want in - to pass - ing gear And we took off with dust; And
(4.___) Now we're do - ing a hun-dred and ten, It cer-tain- ly was a race; For a
(5.___) Now we're do - ing a hun-dred and twen- ty, As fast as I could go; The
C7 Fm C7 Fm C7 Fm Last Time To Coda
lit - tle Nash Ram-bler was fol - low - ing me, A - bout one third my size. The
lit - tle Nash Ram-bler stayed right be - hind, He still had on his brake. He
soon we were do - in' nine - ty, Must have left him in the dust. When I
Ram-bler to pass a Cad - dy, Would be a big dis - grace. For the
Ram - bler pulled a - long side of me, As if I were go - ing slow. The
B♭ C7 Fm C7 Fm (Horn effect)
guy must have want- ed it to pass me up, As he kept on toot - ing his horn; (BEEP! BEEP!) I'll
must have thought his car had more guts, As he kept on toot - ing his horn; (BEEP! BEEP!) I'll
peeked in the mir - ror of my car, I could- n't be-lieve my eyes;___ That
guy who want - ed to pass me, He kept on toot - ing his horn; (BEEP! BEEP!) I'll
C7 Fm C7 Fm C7 Fm C7 Fm
show him that a Cad - il - lac is not a car to scorn.
show him that a Cad - il - lac is, not a car to scorn.
lit - tle Nash Ram - bler was right be - hind, you'd think that guy could fly.
show him that a Cad - il - lac is not a car to scorn.
BEEP,
Fm C7 Fm C7 Fm C7 Fm D.S. al Coda
(BEEP, BEEP) (BEEP, BEEP) (BEEP, BEEP)
BEEP, BEEP, BEEP, His horn went, "BEEP, BEEP, BEEP."
2. I
3. My
4. ___
5. ___
Coda
B♭m C7 Fm C7 Fm
fel - low rolled down his win - dow And yelled for me to hear, "Hey,
B♭m C7 Fm C7 B♭m
bud - dy, how can I get this car out of
Fm6 C7 Fm C7 Fm C7 Fm C7 Fm
sec - ond gear?"___

BELLE OF THE BALL

Words by MITCHELL PARISH
Music by LEROY ANDERSON

Moderate waltz

E♭ Fm7 B♭7 E♭ G7
Danc - ing so light - ly and smil - ing so bright - ly, to - night you're the belle of the ball.

Cm G7 Cm F7 Fm7(♭5)
Is it a won - der the { fel - lows are / whole world is } un - der the spell of the belle of the ball?

E♭ A♭6 E♭ F♯dim Fm7 B♭7 E♭
You are the girl of { their / my } dreams. Ev - 'ry - one seems to a - dore you.

D7 Gm C7 Fm7 B♭7 A♭ B♭7 B♭dim B♭7 E♭dim
And you can tell at a glance there is ro - mance wait - ing some - where for you.

E♭ Fm7 B♭7 E♭ G7
So have a gay time, the mu - sic of May - time will end with the break of the dawn.

Cm G7 Cm F7 Fm7(♭5)
You and your laugh - ter will lin - ger long af - ter the sound of the mu - sic is gone.

E♭ E♭dim A♭m6 E♭ Cm G7 Cm F7 D7
{ We / I } will re - mem - ber the night you were the fair - est of all. { In our hearts / In my heart } you'll be

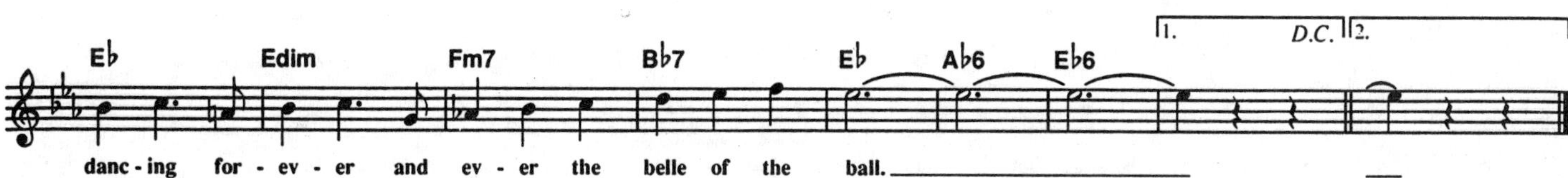
E♭ Edim Fm7 B♭7 E♭ A♭6 E♭6
1. D.C. 2.
danc - ing for - ev - er and ev - er the belle of the ball.

THE BELLS OF AVALON

Words by MITCHELL PARISH
Music by JOSEPH CHERNEY

Moderate waltz
C G7 C
I hear the bells of Av - a - lon re - mind - ing me that you are gone. An - oth - er
F C G7 C C7 F C C7
day has trav - elled on in - to a night of dreams.___ You gave me a mem - o - ry,
Fm C F C G7 C
then you wan - dered on. I won - der if you hear the bells, my dear, the bells of Av - a - lon.___

BE MY LITTLE BABY BUMBLE BEE

Words by STANLEY MURPHY
Music by HENRY I. MARSHALL

Moderato

E7 A7 D7
Be my lit - tle ba - by bum - ble bee,_ (buzz a - round, buzz a - round keep a - buzz-in' 'round.) Bring home all the

G G♯dim D7 E7 A7
hon - ey, love,___ to me, (lit - tle bee, lit - tle bee, lit - tle bee.) Let me spend the hap-py hours_ rov - ing with you

D7 G♯dim D7
'mongst the flow'rs_ and when we get where no one else can see, (cud - dle up, cud - dle up, cud - dle up.)

E7 A7 D7
Be my lit - tle ba - by bum - ble bee, (buzz a - round, buzz a - round, keep a - buzz-in' 'round,) we'll be just as

C7 B7 B7(♭5)/F E7
hap - py as can be, (you and me, you and me, you and me,) Hon - ey, keep a - buz - zin' please,_ I've

A7 G G7(♯5) Em A7 D7 G Cm G
got a doz - en cou - sin bees,_ but I want you___ to be my ba - by bum - ble bee.___

BENJAMIN

By DAVE BRUBECK

Brightly
Am7 Bm7 Cmaj7 Bm7 Am7 Bm7 Cmaj7 Bm7 Am7 Bm7 Cmaj7 Bm7

Am7 D G2 F G F G

F G F E♭maj13 B♭sus E♭maj13 D♭maj13

E♭maj13 D♭maj13 E♭maj13 Am7 D7 G F Em7

F/G C Bm7 Am7 G Bm/F♯ Am/E D G F

G F G F G E7 Am7 Bm7

Cmaj7 Bm7 Am7 Bm7 Cmaj7 Bm7 Am7 Bm7 Cmaj7 Bm7 Am7 D G2

BESAME MUCHO

Music and Spanish Lyric by
CONSUELO VELAZQUEZ
English Lyric by SUNNY SKYLAR

Moderately

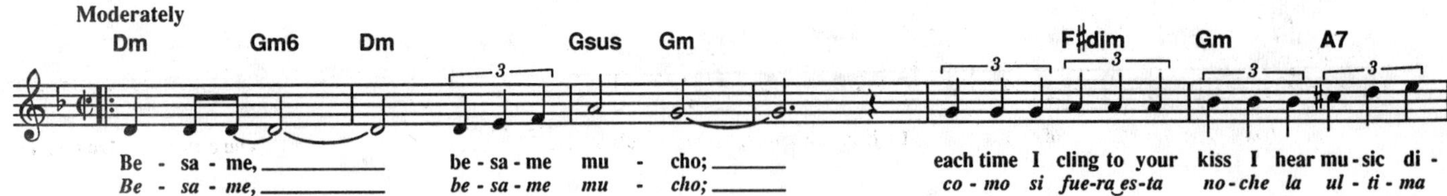
Dm Gm6 Dm Gsus Gm F♯dim Gm A7
Be - sa - me, be - sa - me mu - cho; each time I cling to your kiss I hear mu - sic di -
Be - sa - me, be - sa - me mu - cho; co - mo si fue-ra es-ta no - che la ul - ti - ma

Dm A7 Dm D7 C2/E D7/F♯ D7(♭9) Gsus Gm Dm
vine. Be - sa - me mu - cho, hold me, my dar - ling, and
vez. Be - sa - me mu - cho, que ten - go mie - do - per -

E7(♭9) A7 Dm Gm6 Dm Gm Dm
say that you'll al - ways be mine. This joy is some-thing new, my arms en - fold - ing you;
der - te, per - der - te o - tra vez. Quie - ro te - ner - te muy cer - ca, mi - rar - me en tus

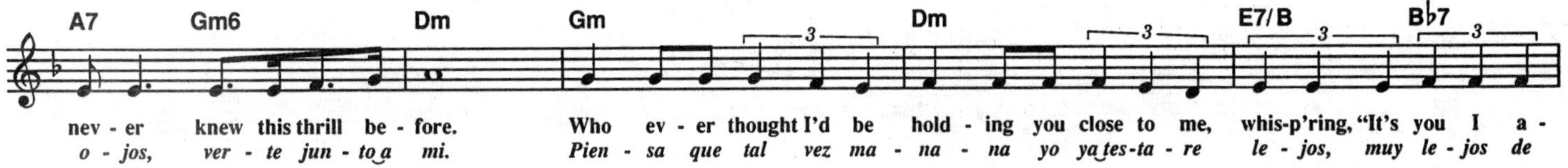
A7 Gm6 Dm Gm Dm E7/B B♭7
nev - er knew this thrill be - fore. Who ev - er thought I'd be hold - ing you close to me, whis-p'ring, "It's you I a -
o - jos, ver - te jun - to a mi. Pien - sa que tal vez ma - na - na yo ya es - ta - re le - jos, muy le - jos de

A7 Dm Gm6 Dm Gsus Gm F♯dim
dore?" Dear - est one, if you should leave me, each lit - tle dream would take
ti. Be - sa - me, be - sa - me mu - cho, co - mo si fue - ra es - ta

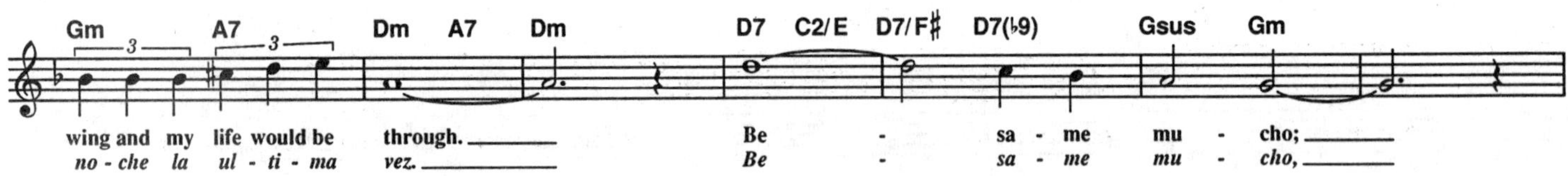
Gm A7 Dm A7 Dm D7 C2/E D7/F♯ D7(♭9) Gsus Gm
wing and my life would be through. Be - sa - me mu - cho;
no - che la ul - ti - ma vez. Be - sa - me mu - cho,

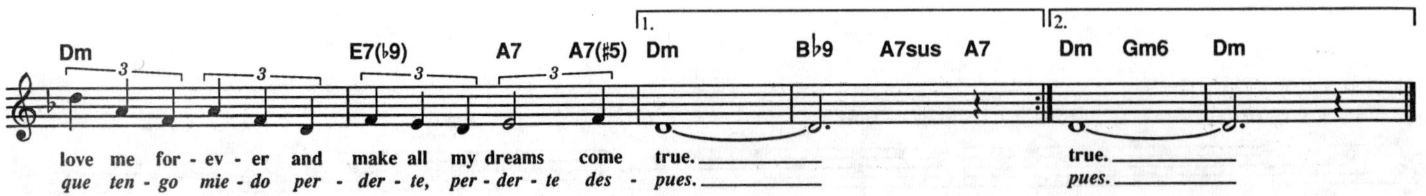
1. 2.
Dm E7(♭9) A7 A7(♯5) Dm B♭9 A7sus A7 Dm Gm6 Dm
love me for - ev - er and make all my dreams come true. true.
que ten - go mie - do per - der - te, per - der - te des - pues. pues.

THE BEST IS YET TO COME

Music by CY COLEMAN
Lyric by CAROLYN LEIGH

Moderately
Abmaj7 Ab7 Ab6 Ab+ Ab Abmaj7 Ab7
Out of the tree of life I just picked me a plum. You came a-long and ev-

Ab6 Ab+ Ab F7 Bbm7 Eb7
-'ry-thing's start-in' to hum. Still it's a real good bet the best is yet to

Ab Dm7(b5) G7 Cmaj7 C7 C6 C+ C
come. The best is yet to come and babe, won't it be fine.

Cmaj7 C7 C6 C+ C A7
You think you've seen the sun, but you ain't seen it shine.

Dm7 G7 Dm7 G7 C Dm7 Ebdim7 C/E Dm7 G7
Wait 'til the warm-up's un-der way. Wait 'til our lips have met. Wait 'til you see that

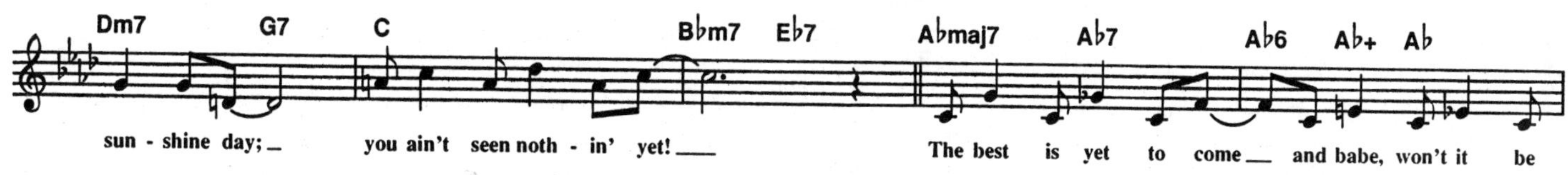
Dm7 G7 C Bbm7 Eb7 Abmaj7 Ab7 Ab6 Ab+ Ab
sun-shine day; you ain't seen noth-in' yet! The best is yet to come and babe, won't it be

F7 Bb7 Eb7 Ab
fine. The best is yet to come, come the day you're mine.

BETWEEN THE DEVIL AND THE DEEP BLUE SEA

Words by TED KOEHLER
Music by HAROLD ARLEN

Moderate swing

F C7 F C7 F7 B♭
I don't want you, but I'd hate to lose you. You've got me in be - tween _ the

F C7 F C7 F C7 F7
dev - il and the deep blue sea. ___ I for - give you, 'cause I can't for - get you. You've got me

B♭ F C7 F A Bm7 E9
in be - tween _ the dev - il and the deep blue sea. ___ I ought to cross you off my list. ___

A Adim A E7 C Fm6
But when you come knock-ing at my door, _ fate seems to give my heart a twist, _ and

A♭7 Fm6 G7 C7 F C7 F
I come run - ning back for more. I should hate you, but I guess I

C7 F7 B♭ F C7 F
love you. You've got me in be - tween _ the dev - il and the deep blue sea. ___

From the Paramount Picture "MONTE CARLO"

BEYOND THE BLUE HORIZON

Words by LEO ROBIN
Music by RICHARD A. WHITING
and W. FRANKE HARLING

Moderately
B♭ B♭dim7 B♭ E♭m F7 B♭ B♭dim7 B♭ G9
Be - yond the blue ho - ri - zon waits a beau - ti - ful day. ___ Good -
Cm7 E♭m6 B♭ B♭dim7 C7 F7 F+
bye to things that bore me, joy is wait - ing for me. I
B♭ B♭dim7 B♭ E♭m F7 B♭ Bdim7 G7
see a new ho - ri - zon, my life has on - ly be - gun. ___ Be -
Cm E♭m6 B♭/F B♭dim7 B♭6 Cm7 F7 B♭
yond the blue ho - ri - zon lies a set - ting sun. ___

THE BIBLE TELLS ME SO

Words and Music by
DALE EVANS

Moderately

G D7 G7 Dm7 G7 C G
Have faith, hope and char - i - ty, that's the way to live suc - cess - ful - ly. How do I know? The

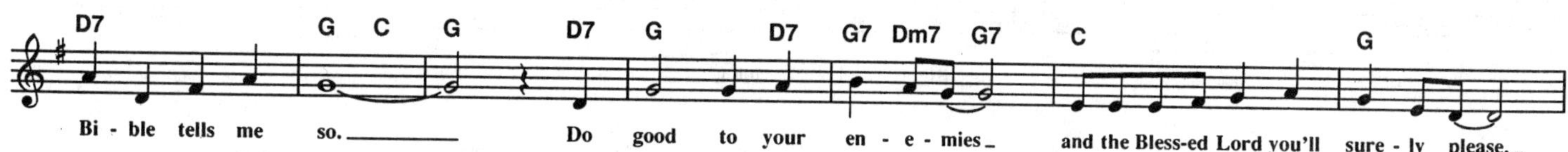
D7 G C G D7 G D7 G7 Dm7 G7 C G
Bi - ble tells me so. Do good to your en - e - mies and the Bless-ed Lord you'll sure - ly please.

D7 G C G C G C♯dim7/G
How do I know? The Bi - ble tells me so. Don't wor - ry 'bout to - mor - row, just be real good to -

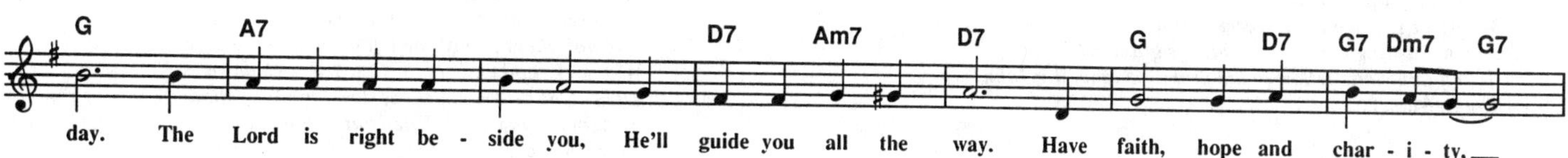
G A7 D7 Am7 D7 G D7 G7 Dm7 G7
day. The Lord is right be - side you, He'll guide you all the way. Have faith, hope and char - i - ty,

C G D7 G
that's the way to live suc - cess - ful - ly. How do I know? The Bi - ble tells me so.

A BICYCLE BUILT FOR TWO

(Daisy Bell)

TRADITIONAL

Moderately

G C G D7 G Em
Dai - sy, Dai - sy, give me your an - swer, do. I'm half cra - zy,

A7 D7 G
all for the love of you. It won't be a sty - lish mar - riage, I can't af -

C G D7 G D7 G D7 G D7 G
ford a car - riage. But you'll look sweet, on the seat of a bi - cy - cle built for two.

BIG BAD JOHN

Words and Music by
JIMMY DEAN

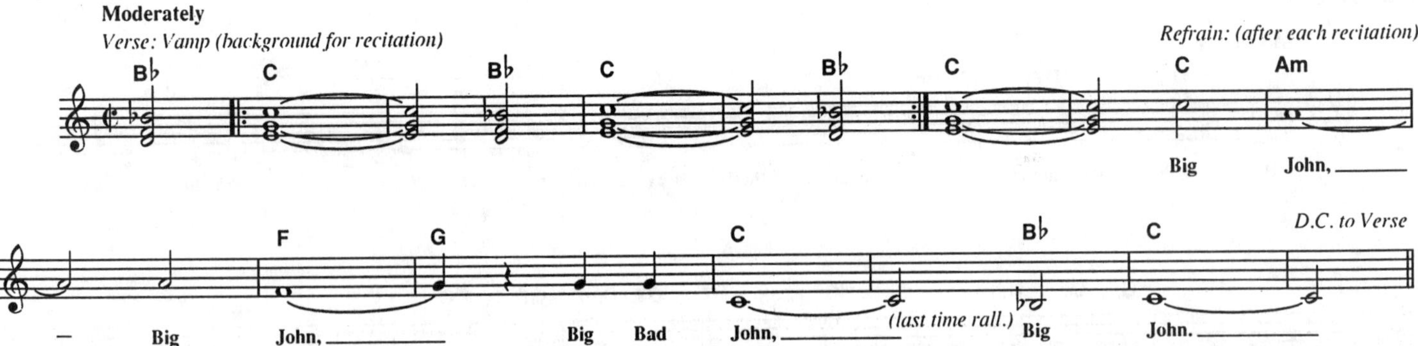
Moderately
Verse: Vamp (background for recitation)
Refrain: (after each recitation)
B♭ C B♭ C B♭ C C Am
Big John, — Big John,
F G C B♭ C
Big Bad John, (last time rall.) Big John.
D.C. to Verse

Verse 1:
Spoken:
Every morning at the mine you could see him arrive,
He stood six-foot-six and weighed two-forty-five.
Kind of broad at the shoulder and narrow at the hip,
And everybody knew you didn't give no lip to Big John!
(To Refrain:)

Verse 2:
Nobody seemed to know where John called home,
He just drifted into town and stayed all alone.
He didn't say much, a-kinda quiet and shy,
And if you spoke at all, you just said, "Hi" to Big John!
Somebody said he came from New Orleans,
Where he got in a fight over a Cajun queen.
And a crashing blow from a huge right hand
Sent a Louisiana fellow to the promised land. Big John!
(To Refrain:)

Verse 3:
Then came the day at the bottom of the mine
When a timber cracked and the men started crying.
Miners were praying and hearts beat fast,
And everybody thought that they'd breathed their last 'cept John.
Through the dust and the smoke of this man-made hell
Walked a giant of a man that the miners knew well.
Grabbed a sagging timber and gave out with a groan,
And, like a giant oak tree, just stood there alone. Big John!
(To Refrain:)

Verse 4:
And with all of his strength, he gave a mighty shove;
Then a miner yelled out, "There's a light up above!"
And twenty men scrambled from a would-be grave,
And now there's only one left down there to save; Big John!
With jacks and timbers they started back down
Then came that rumble way down in the ground,
And smoke and gas belched out of that mine,
Everybody knew it was the end of the line for Big John!
(To Refrain:)

Verse 5:
Now they never re-opened that worthless pit,
They just placed a marble stand in front of it;
These few words are written on that stand:
"At the bottom of this mine lies a big, big man; Big John!"
(To Refrain:)

BIG MIDNIGHT SPECIAL

Arranged by WILMA LEE COOPER

Moderately
Chorus:
G7 C G D7
Big mid - night spe - cial, shine your light on me. Big mid - night spec - ial, shine your
1.2.3.4.5.6. To Next Strain 7. Fine Verse:
G G7 G C
ev - er - lov - in' light on me. 1. Woke up this me. morn - in', heard the whis - tle
2. I've never had the blues so in my life be -
G D7 G G7 D.S. 𝄋
blow. The jail - or said, "Come boy, it's time to go."
fore till my ba - by left me at the sta - tion door.
Big mid - night

Verse 3:
They put him in a Pullman, guards around his door.
Said, "You're off to Atlanta to serve ten years more."
(To Chorus:)

Verse 4:
He looked all around him in the Pullman car.
Saw the men wearin' cloth hats, smokin' big cigars.
(To Chorus:)

Verse 5:
Took him off in Atlanta, at the end of the line.
Said, "You start serving time, boy, for your awful crime."
(To Chorus:)

Verse 6:
That whistle makes me lonesome on that midnight train.
But he knows I'm a-waitin' till it brings him home again.
(To Chorus:)

THE BIG ROCK CANDY MOUNTAIN

TRADITIONAL

Happily

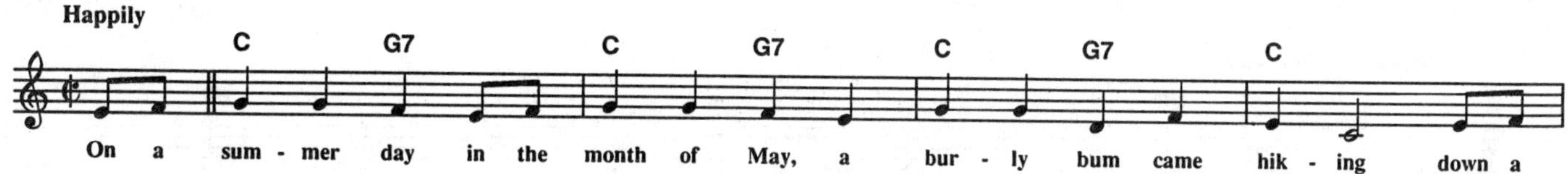
C
G7
C
G7
C
G7
C
On a sum - mer day in the month of May, a bur - ly bum came hik - ing down a

G7
C
G7
C
G7
C
shad - y lane through the sug - ar cane. He was look - ing for his lik - ing. As he

G7
C
G7
C
roamed a - long, he sang a song of the land of milk and hon - ey, where a

G7
C
G7
C
G7
C
G7
bum can stay for man - y'a day and he won't need an - y mon - ey. Oh, the

C
C7
F
C
buzz - in' of the bees in the cig - ar - ette trees near the so - da wa - ter foun - tain; at the

G7
C
G7
C
lem - on - ade springs where the blue - bird sings, in the Big Rock Can - dy Moun - tain.

BILLBOARD MARCH

FIGHT SONG

March tempo

F
G7
C7
F

G7
C7
F

From the Musical Comedy "SWEET CHARITY"

BIG SPENDER

Music by CY COLEMAN
Lyrics by DOROTHY FIELDS

Moderately
Dm
B♭
E7
The min-ute you walked in the joint. I could see you were a man of dis-tinc-tion, a real big spend-er,

A7
Dm
B♭7
A7(♯5)
good look-ing, so re-fined. Say would-n't you like to know what's go-ing on in my mind? So, let me get

Dm
B♭
E7
Dm
right to the point. I don't pop my cork for ev-'ry guy I see. Hey! Big spend-er,

To Coda
B♭7
A7
Dm
spend a lit-tle time with me.

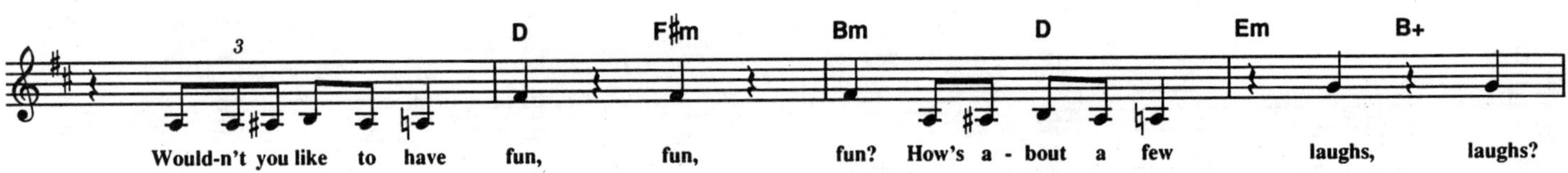
D
F♯m
Bm
D
Em
B+
Would-n't you like to have fun, fun, fun? How's a-bout a few laughs, laughs?

D.S. al Coda
Em7
B♭9
A9
B♭9
A13
I can show you a good time. Let me show you a good time. The min-ute you

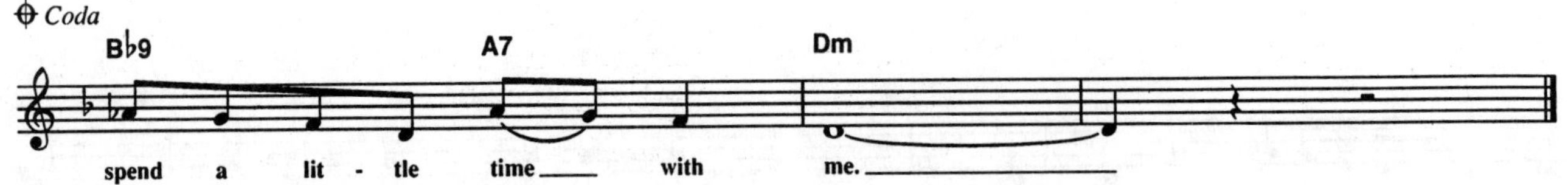
Coda
B♭9
A7
Dm
spend a lit-tle time with me.

BILL BAILEY, WON'T YOU PLEASE COME HOME?

Words and Music by
HUGHIE CANNON

Brightly

G C♯dim G G♯dim D7/A D7
Won't you come home, Bill Bai - ley, won't you come home? She moans the whole day long.

D9(♯5) G
I'll do de cook - ing, dar - ling, I'll pay de rent. I knows I've done you wrong.

C♯dim G Bdim Am/C E7/B Am
'Mem-ber dat rain - y eve dat I drove you out, wid noth - in' but a fine tooth comb? I

C C♯dim G/D E7 A7 D9 D7 G A7 D7 G
1. 2.
knows I'se to blame, well, ain't dat a shame? Bill Bai - ley, won't you please come home? home?

BIRTH OF THE BLUES

Words and Music by
B. G. DeSYLVA and LEW BROWN
Music by RAY HENDERSON

Moderately

C C♯dim Dm6 D♯dim C6/E E7(♭9)
They heard the breeze in the trees sing - ing weird mel - o - dies,
jail came the wail of a down - heart - ed frail,
nursed it, re - hearsed it, and gave out the news
F F♯dim G Em E♭dim G7/D G7 C C7 Cdim Dm7(♭5) C C/G Adim Bdim
1.
and they made that the start of the blues. And from a
and they played that as part of the blues.
that the South land gave birth to the blues!
2.3. Fine
C B7(♯5) E7 F7 E7 F7 E7 F7
From a whip - por - will out on a hill, they took a new
E7 A7 B♭7(♯9) A7 E♭9 D9 D7(♭9) G9 G6 Adim Bdim
D.S. al Fine
note, pushed it through a horn 'til it was worn in - to a blue note! And then

A BIRD IN A GILDED CAGE

Words by ARTHUR J. LAMB
Music by HARRY VON TILZER

Moderately

B♭
Cm
F7
She's on - ly a bird in a gild - ed cage, a beau - ti - ful sight to
sad when you think of her wast - ed life, for youth can - not mate with

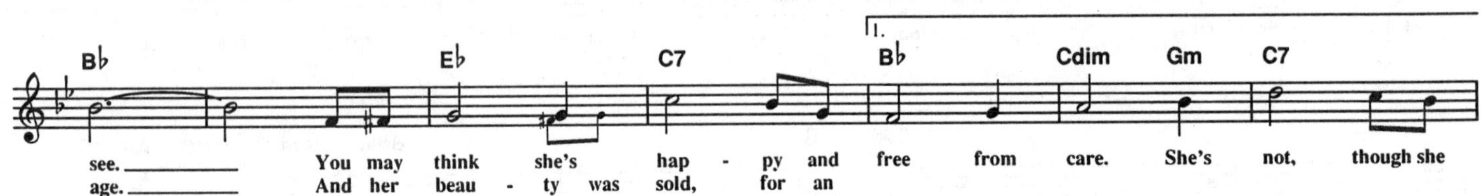
B♭
E♭
C7
1.
B♭
Cdim
Gm
C7
see. You may think she's hap - py and free from care. She's not, though she
age. And her beau - ty was sold, for an

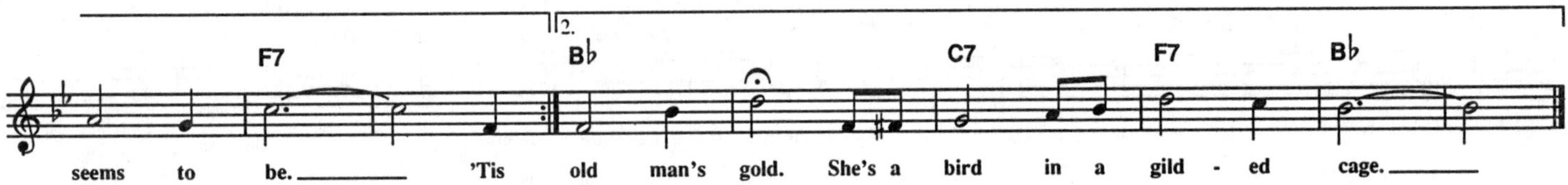
F7
2.
B♭
C7
F7
B♭
seems to be. 'Tis old man's gold. She's a bird in a gild - ed cage.

BLACK IS THE COLOR OF MY TRUE LOVE'S HAIR

AMERICAN

Slowly

Em
Em7/D
Cmaj7
Em
Bm7
Em9
Em
1. Black, black, black is the col - or of my true love's hair. Her lips are like a
2. I go to the Clyde for to mourn and weep, but sat - is - fied I

Am
Cmaj7
D
Am
Em
rose so fair. The pur - est eyes and the neat - est hands, I love the ground where -
nev - er can sleep; I'll write to you in a few short lines, I'll suf - fer death ten

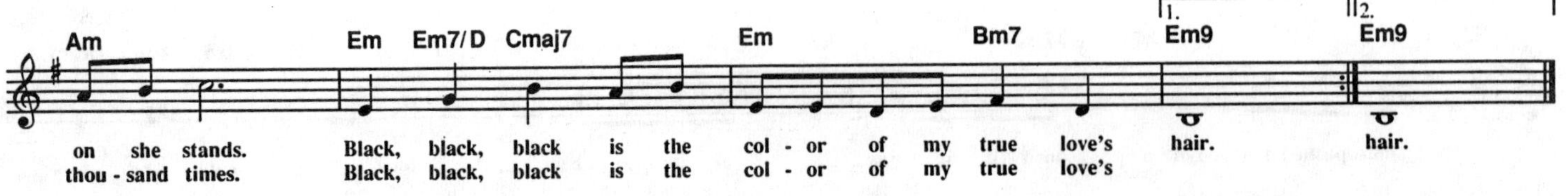
Am
Em
Em7/D
Cmaj7
Em
Bm7
1.
Em9
2.
Em9
on she stands. Black, black, black is the col - or of my true love's hair. hair.
thou - sand times. Black, black, black is the col - or of my true love's

BIRD OF BEAUTY

Words and Music by
STEVIE WONDER

Moderate bossa nova
Bm Bbm Am D7 Gmaj7
Oh do do do do do do
do do do do do do.
do do do do do do. 1. Si-mon
Bm Bbm Am D7 Gmaj7 Bm Bbm Am D7
says that now your mind de-sires a va-ca-tion, free to join in fun and plen-ty re-cre-
says that your mind is re-quest-ing fur-lough, let it find the an-swers to things that you've al-ways wanted
bem vo-cê deve des-can-car a sua-mente, naõ faz mal o que vai a-con-te-cer da-
Gm7 E7 A7
a-tion. There a-waits you a tick-et at Please Have a Good Time Sta-tion,
to know. There's a tour of man-y plac-es that you've al-ways want-ed to go,
qui pra fren-te. Vai can-tar a-le-gri-a que sa-co-de de re-pen-te,
Eb D
'cause what is, is gon-na stay, 'til ole Fa-ther Time de-cides to change. 2. Si-mon
and to me that sure sounds best 'cause it means hap-pi-ness for
vo-cê co-ra-caõ as-sim taõ fe-liz ja vai can-tar car-
D Db C Cm G/D G7 C Cm
you. There is so much in life for you to feel un-found in white, red, or yel-
na-val.
G/D G7 C Bm E/D A7
-low pills. A mind ex-cur-sion can be such a thrill, you please sat-is-fy, take a
Ab7 Gmaj7
chance and ride the bird of beau-ty of the sky. Do do do do do do
do do do do do do. 3. Do do
D.S. 𝄋
Gmaj7 Ab9 Gmaj7
sky. The bird of beau-ty of the sky.
Repeat ad lib. and fade

BLUE BAYOU

Words and Music by
ROY ORBISON and JOE MELSON

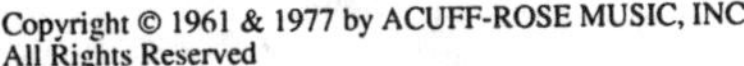

Moderately

Verse:
F
C7
1. I feel so bad, I've got a wor - ried mind. I'm so lone - some all the time since I left my

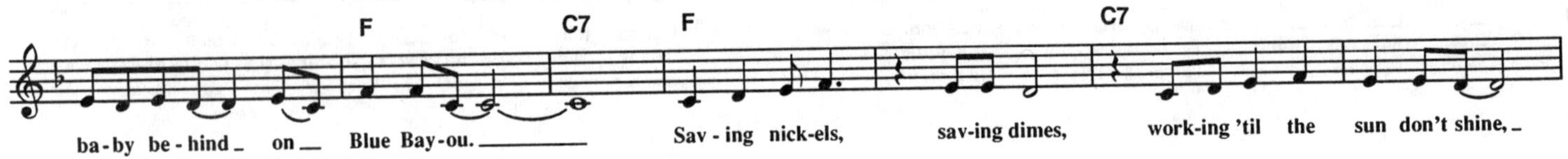
F
C7
F
C7
ba - by be - hind on Blue Bay - ou. Sav - ing nick - els, sav - ing dimes, work - ing 'til the sun don't shine,

F
E♭
F
Chorus:
C7
look - ing for - ward to hap - pi - er times on Blue Bay - ou. I'm go - ing back some day, come what may, to Blue Bay - ou,

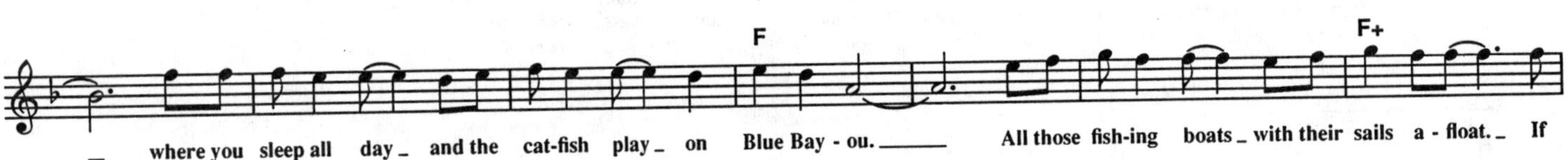
F
F+
where you sleep all day and the cat - fish play on Blue Bay - ou. All those fish - ing boats with their sails a - float. If

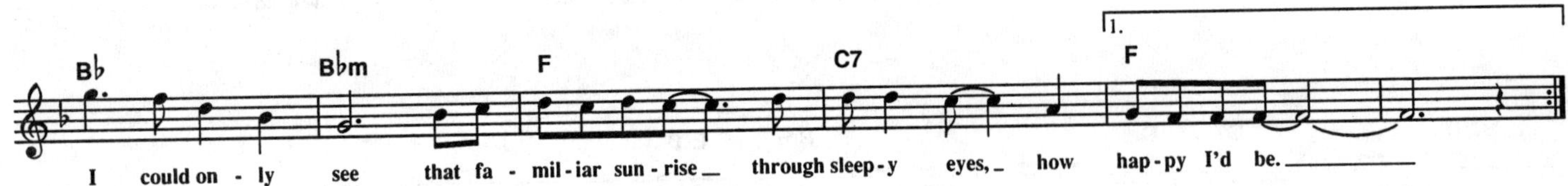
B♭
B♭m
F
C7
1.
F
I could on - ly see that fa - mil - iar sun - rise through sleep - y eyes, how hap - py I'd be.

2.
F
C7
F
hurt - in' in - side. I'll nev - er be blue, my dreams come true on Blue Bay - ou.

Verse 2:
Go to see my baby again
And to be with some of my friends.
Maybe I'd be happy then on Blue Bayou.
Saving nickels, saving dimes,
Working 'til the sun don't shine.
Looking forward to happier times on Blue Bayou.

Chorus 2:
I'm going back some day, gonna stay on Blue Bayou,
Where the folks are fine and the world is mine on Blue Bayou.
Ah, that girl of mine by my side, the silver moon and the evening tide.
Oh, some sweet day gonna take away this hurtin' inside.
I'll never be blue, my dreams come true
On Blue Bayou.

BLUE DANUBE WALTZ

JOHANN STRAUSS

Moderate waltz
C
G7
C
F
G7
C
F
G7
C
Fine
D7
G
D7
Cdim
Em
Am
D7
G
D.C. al Fine

BLUE EYES CRYING IN THE RAIN

Words and Music by
FRED ROSE

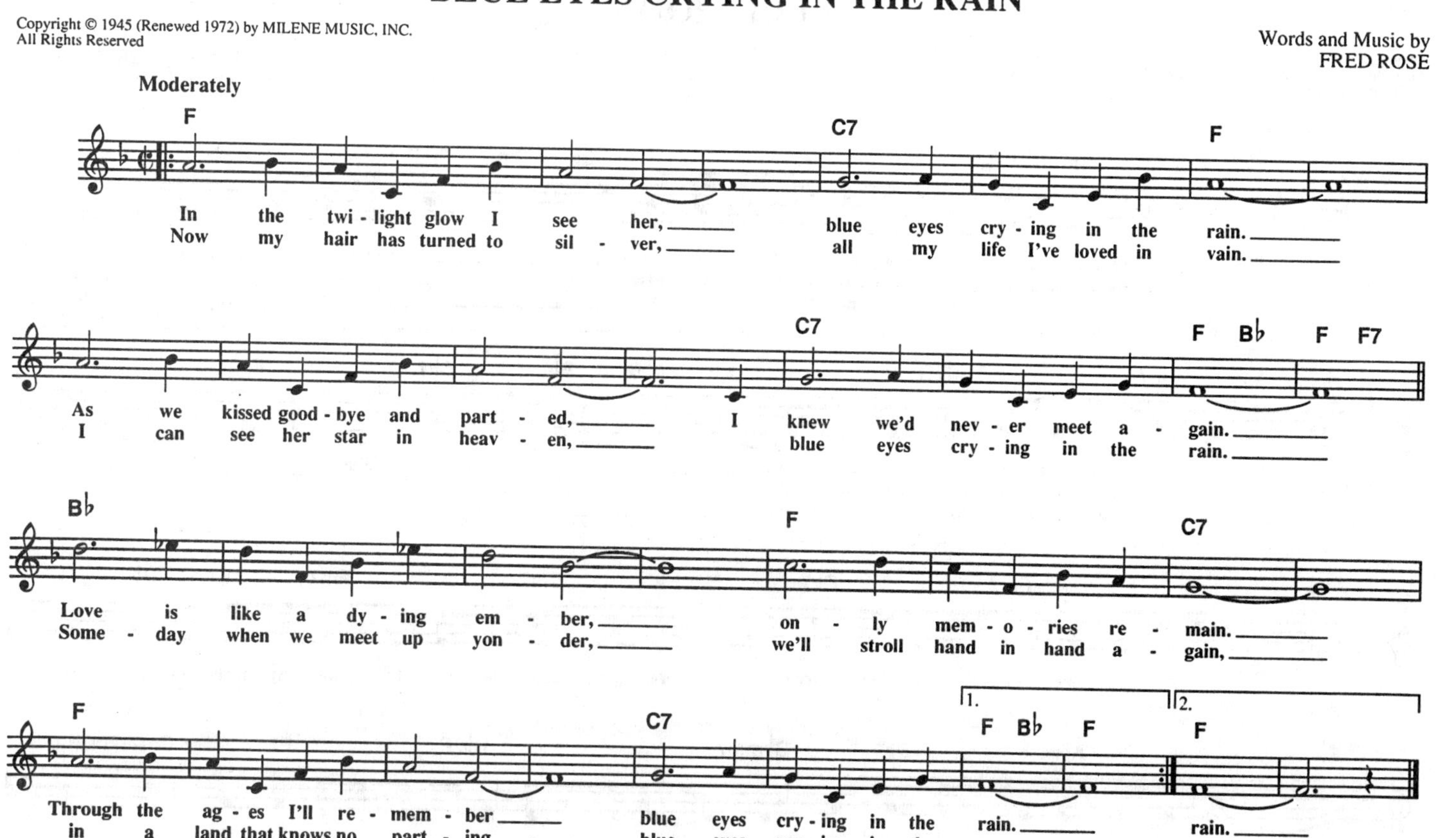
Moderately
F
C7
F
In the twi - light glow I see her, blue eyes cry - ing in the rain.
Now my hair has turned to sil - ver, all my life I've loved in vain.
C7
F Bb F F7
As we kissed good - bye and part - ed, I knew we'd nev - er meet a - gain.
I can see her star in heav - en, blue eyes cry - ing in the rain.
Bb
F
C7
Love is like a dy - ing em - ber, on - ly mem - o - ries re - main.
Some - day when we meet up yon - der, we'll stroll hand in hand a - gain,
F
C7
1.
F Bb F
2.
F
Through the ag - es I'll re - mem - ber blue eyes cry - ing in the rain.
in a land that knows no part - ing, blue eyes cry - ing in the rain.

BLUE HAWAII

Words and Music by
LEO ROBIN and RALPH RAINGER

Refrain - slowly and voluptuously
Bb Eb Bb G+ C7 F7
Night and you and blue Ha - wa - ii, the night is heav - en - ly and you are
Bb F7 Bb Eb Bb G+ C7
heav-en to me. Love - ly you and blue Ha - wa - ii, with all this love - li - ness
F7 Bb Eb6/Bb Bb Bb7(#5) Eb Bb
there should be love. Come with me while the moon is on the sea. The
C7 Cm7/F F7 F9 F7(b9) Bb Eb Bb
night is young and so are we. Dreams come true in blue Ha - wa - ii
G+ C7 F7 Bb Eb/Bb 1. Bb F7 2. Bb
and mine could all come true this mag - ic night of nights with you. you.

Featured in the Film "HOLLYWOOD HOTEL" (Warners 1937)

BLUE MOON

Lyrics by LORENZ HART
Music by RICHARD RODGERS

Moderately
Bb7 Eb Cm Fm7 Bb7 Eb Cm Fm7 Bb7
Blue moon you saw me stand-ing a - lone with - out a dream in my heart,
moon you knew just what I was there for. You heard me say - ing a pray'r
moon now I'm no long - er a - lone with - out a dream in my heart,
Eb Cm Fm7 Fm7/Bb 1.3. Eb Ab6 Eb Fine Bb7 2. Eb Ab6
with - out a love of my own. Blue for.
for some - one I could real - ly care
with - out a love of my own.
Eb Fm7 Bb7 Eb Cm7 Fm7 Bb7
And then there sud - den - ly ap - peared be - fore me the on - ly one my arms will ev - er
D.S. al Fine
Eb Abm Db9 Gbmaj7 Bb/F F7 Gm7 Bb7
hold. I heard some - bod - y whis-per, "Please a - dore me." And when I looked, the moon had turned to gold! Blue

BLUE MONDAY

By DAVE BARTHOLOMEW
and ANTOINE DOMINO

Slow blues

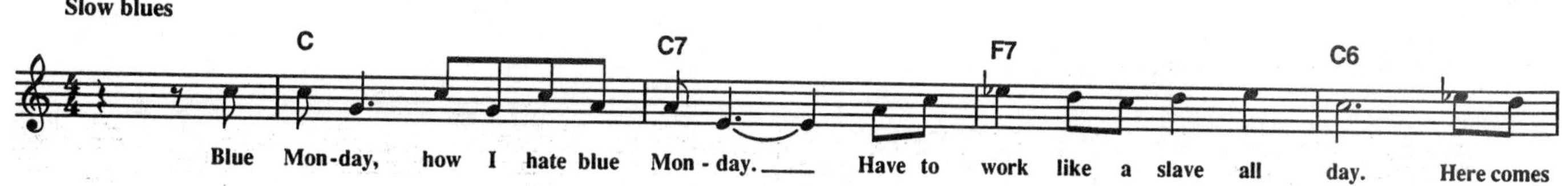
C
C7
F7
C6
Blue Mon-day, how I hate blue Mon - day. Have to work like a slave all day. Here comes

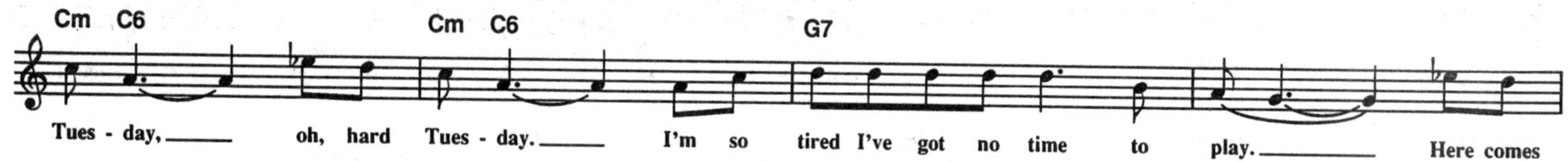
Cm C6
Cm C6
G7
Tues - day, oh, hard Tues - day. I'm so tired I've got no time to play. Here comes

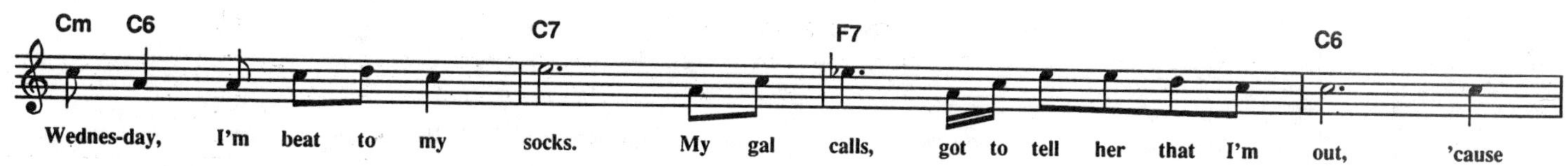
Cm C6
C7
F7
C6
Wednes-day, I'm beat to my socks. My gal calls, got to tell her that I'm out, 'cause

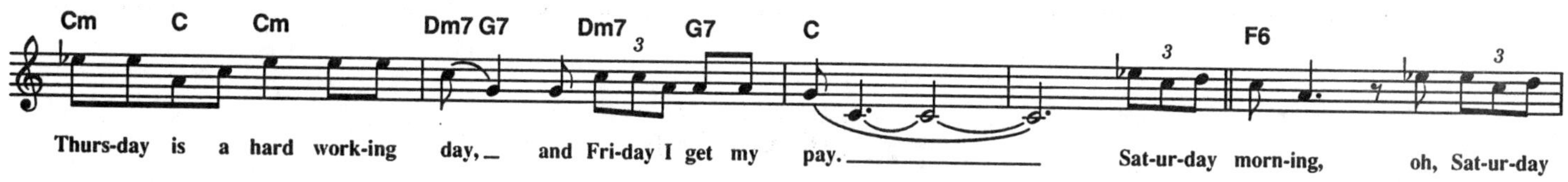
Cm C Cm
Dm7 G7
Dm7 G7
C
F6
Thurs-day is a hard work-ing day, and Fri-day I get my pay. Sat-ur-day morn-ing, oh, Sat-ur-day

F♯dim
C
C7
F6
F♯dim
morn-ing, all my tired-ness has gone a - way. Got my mon-ey and my hon-ey, and I'm

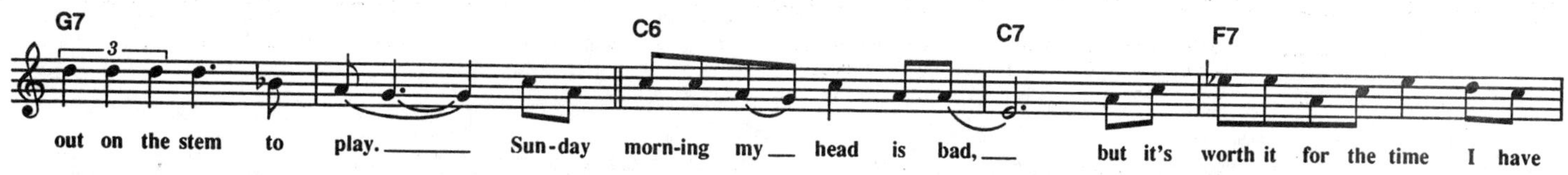
G7
C6
C7
F7
out on the stem to play. Sun-day morn-ing my head is bad, but it's worth it for the time I have

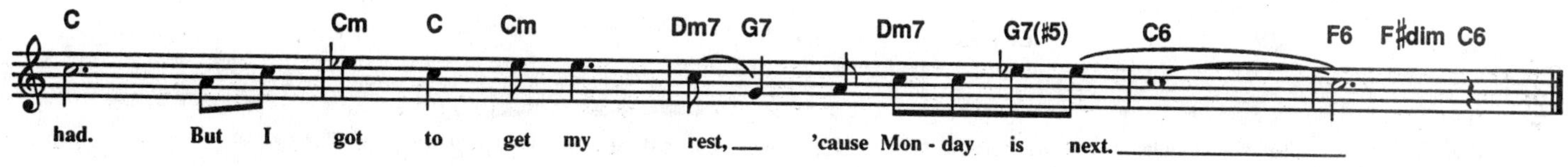
C
Cm C Cm
Dm7 G7
Dm7 G7(♯5)
C6
F6 F♯dim C6
had. But I got to get my rest, 'cause Mon - day is next.

BLUE MOON OF KENTUCKY

Words and Music by
BILL MONROE

Brightly
G G7 C7 G
I said, "Blue moon of Ken - tuck - y, to keep on shin - ing, shine on the one that's
D7 G G7 C7
gone and left me blue." I said, "Blue moon of Ken - tuck - y to keep on shin - ing,
G D7 D7(♯5) D7 G G7 C
shine on the one that's gone and left me blue." Well, it was on one moon - light
C7 G G7 C C7 G D7 G G7
night, stars shin-in' bright, whis - per on high; love said, "Good-bye." Blue moon of Ken - tuck-y, keep on
C7 G Gdim7 D7 D7(♯5) D7 G G/B C7 C♯dim7 G/D G
shin - ing, shine on the one that's gone and left me blue.
BLUE ON BLUE
Copyright © 1963 (Renewed 1991) by FAMOUS MUSIC CORPORATION
All Rights Reserved
Words by HAL DAVID
Music by BURT F. BACHARACH
Moderately slow
Verse:
F7 B♭ Gm E♭ Cm F7 B♭
1. I walk a - long the street we used to walk. Two by two lov - ers pass and as they're pass-ing by,
(2.) lone - ly night we meet in dreams. As I run to your side you wait with o - pen arms.
Gm C7 E♭ B♭ E♭ B♭
I could die 'cause you're not here with me. Now the trees are bare, there's sad - ness in the air and
O - pen arms that now are closed to me. Through a vale of tears your vi - sion dis - ap - pears and
Chorus:
Cm7 F7 B♭ E♭ B♭ E♭ B♭
I'm as blue as I can be. I'm as blue as I can be. Blue on blue, heart-ache on heart-ache, blue on blue now that we are through.
E♭ B♭ E♭ F F7 B♭ F7
Blue on blue, heart-ache on heart-ache and I find I can't get o - ver los-ing you. 2. Night af - ter

THE BLUE SKIRT WALTZ

Words by MITCHELL PARISH
Music by VACLAV BLAHA

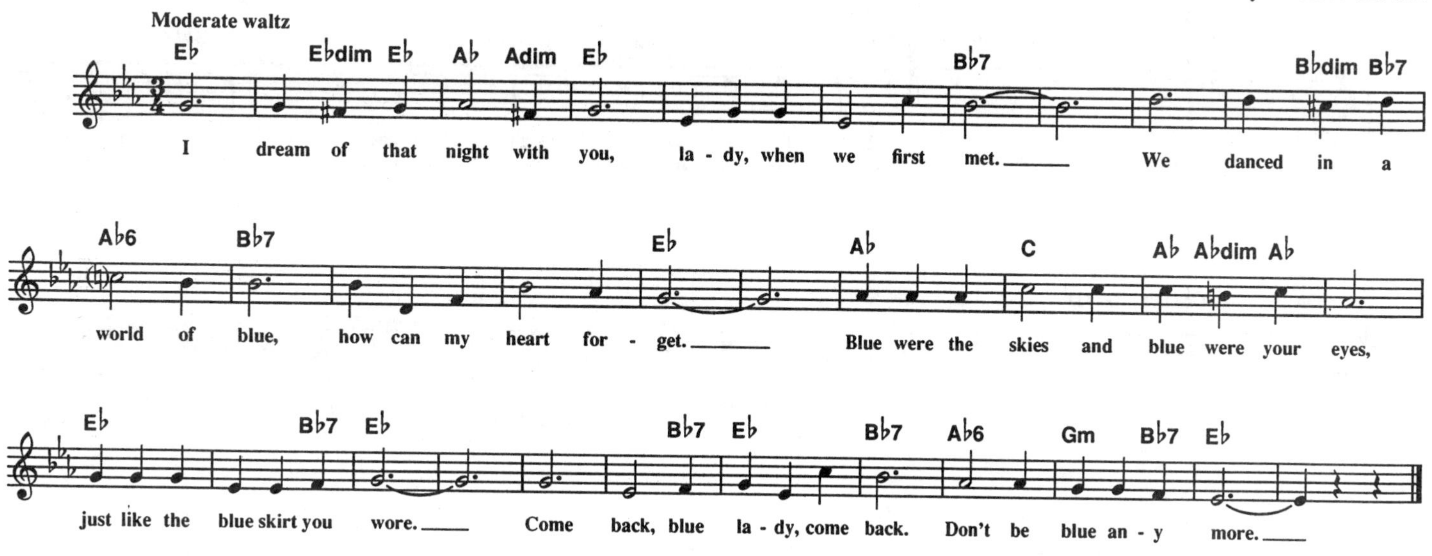
Moderate waltz
E♭ E♭dim E♭ A♭ Adim E♭ B♭7 B♭dim B♭7
I dream of that night with you, la - dy, when we first met. We danced in a
A♭6 B♭7 E♭ A♭ C A♭ A♭dim A♭
world of blue, how can my heart for - get. Blue were the skies and blue were your eyes,
E♭ B♭7 E♭ B♭7 E♭ B♭7 A♭6 Gm B♭7 E♭
just like the blue skirt you wore. Come back, blue la - dy, come back. Don't be blue an - y more.

BLUE TANGO

Words by MITCHELL PARISH
Music by LEROY ANDERSON

Tango

A7 D G D F♯m A7 D G D
Here am I with you in a world of blue, and we're danc - ing to the
G D G Adim A7 D G D F♯m A7
tan - go we loved when first we met. While the mu - sic plays, we re - call the days when our

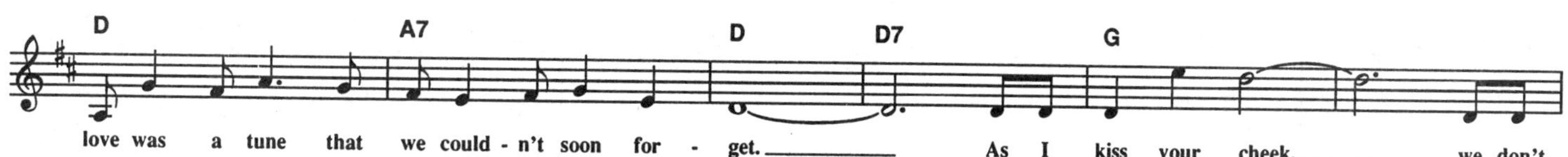
D A7 D D7 G
love was a tune that we could - n't soon for - get. As I kiss your cheek, we don't

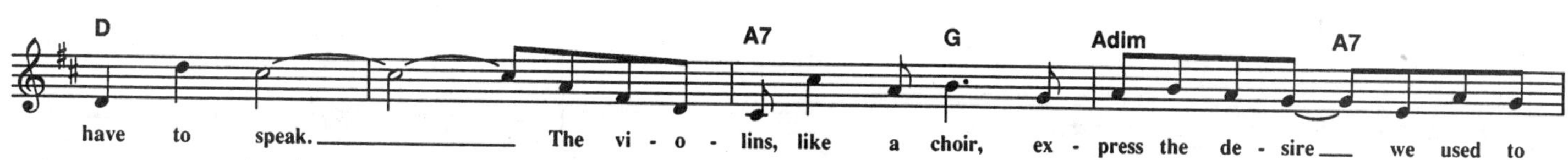
D A7 G Adim A7
have to speak. The vi - o - lins, like a choir, ex - press the de - sire we used to

D D7 G D
know not long a - go. So just hold me tight in your arms to - night,

A7 G Adim A7 D G D
and this blue tan - go will be our thrill - ing mem - o - ry of love.

BOOGIE ON REGGAE WOMAN

By STEVIE WONDER

Moderately
Vamp:
Ab Gb/Ab Db/Ab
Verse:
Ab Gb/Ab Db/Ab Ab Gb/Ab Db/Ab
1. I like to see you boo - gie right a - cross the floor.
2. I'd like to see both of us fall deep - ly in love.
Db Cb/Db Gb/Db Db /C /Cb Bb Eb
I like to do it to you till you hol - ler for more.
I'd like to see you and me un - der the stars a - bove.
Ab Gb/Ab Db/Ab Ab Gb/Ab Db/Ab Ab Gb/Ab Db/Ab
I like to reg - gae,
I'd like to see both of us
Ab Ab7(#9) Db Cb/Db Gb/Db Db /C /Cb Bb
but you dance too fast for me.
fall deep - ly in love.
I'd like to make love to you
I'd like to see you in the raw
Eb Ab Gb/Ab Db/Ab Ab /Gb /F
so you can make me scream.
un - der the stars a - bove.
1. Boog - ie on reg - gae
2. So boog - ie on reg - gae
Chorus:
Bb7 Db Gb Ab A Bb7
wo - man; what is wrong with me? Boog - ie on reg - gae wo - man;
wo - man; what is wrong with you? Boog - ie on reg - gae wo - man;
wo - man; let me do it to you. Boog - ie on reg - gae wo - man;
1. D.S. 𝄋
2.3. Repeat ad lib. and fade
Eb Ab Gb/Ab Db/Ab Ab Gb/Ab Db/Ab Ab /Gb /F
ba - by, can't you see?
what you try'n' to do?
what you try'n' to do?
3. Boog - ie on reg - gae

BORN TO LOSE

Words and Music by
TED DAFFAN

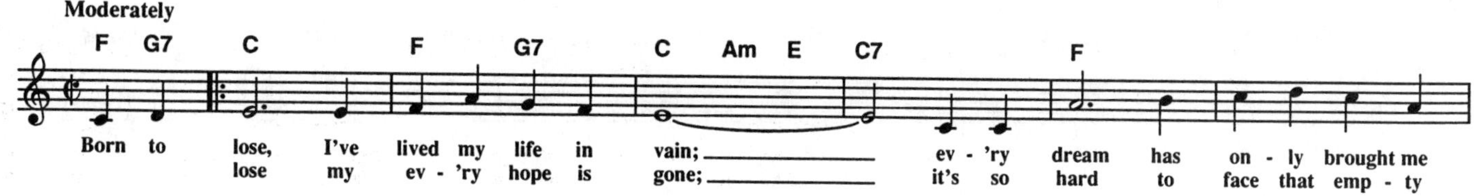
Moderately
F G7 C F G7 C Am E C7 F
Born to lose, I've lived my life in vain; ev - 'ry dream has on - ly brought me
lose my ev - 'ry hope is gone; it's so hard to face that emp - ty

C G7 C G7 C Gm7 C7 F G7 Dm7 G7
pain. All my life I've al - ways been so blue; born to lose and now I'm los - in'
dawn. You were all the hap - pi - ness I knew; born to lose and now I'm los - in'

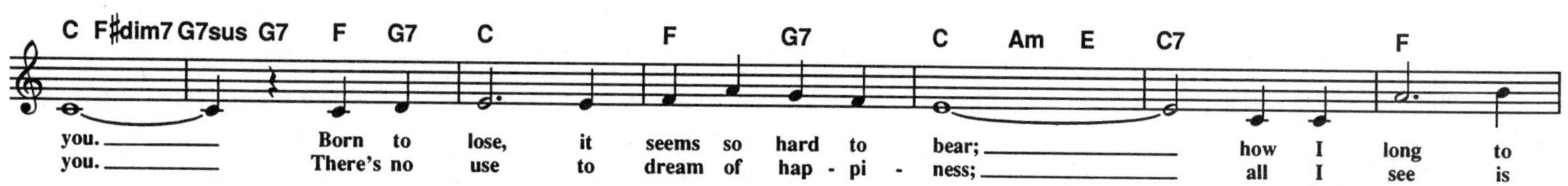
C F♯dim7 G7sus G7 F G7 C F G7 C Am E C7 F
you. Born to lose, it seems so hard to bear; how I long to
you. There's no use to dream of hap - pi - ness; all I see is

C G7 C G7 C Gm7 C7 F
al - ways have you near. You've grown tired and now you say we're through;
on - ly lone - li - ness. All my life I've al - ways been so blue;

G7 Dm7 G7
1. C F♯dim7 G7sus G7 F G7
2. C A♭7 C
born to lose, and now I'm los - in' you. Born to you.

BRAHMS' LULLABY

JOHANNES BRAHMS

Slowly
E♭ B♭7

E♭ A♭ E♭ B♭7 E♭ B♭7 E♭ A♭ E♭ B♭7 E♭ B♭7 E♭

BOSSA NOVA U.S.A.

By DAVE BRUBECK

Moderato

Gm7(♭5) C7(♭9) Fmaj7 F6 F6(9) Cm7(♭5) F7(♭9)

B♭maj7 B♭6 B♭6(9) Dm7(♭5) G7(♭9) Cmaj9 Cm7(♭5) F7(♭5) B♭maj9 B♭m7(♭5) E♭7

A♭maj7 D♭maj7 Gm7(♭5) C7(♭9 ♯11) Gm7(♭5) C7(♭9) Fmaj7 F6

Cm7(♭5) F7(♭9) B♭maj7 B♭6 F Fm Dm7(♭5) G7(♯11) Cmaj7 Cm7(♭5) F7(♭5 ♭9) B♭maj9

B♭m7(♭5) D♭m/E♭ A♭maj7 D♭maj7 Gm7(♭5) C13(♭9) 1. F6(9) 2. F6(9)

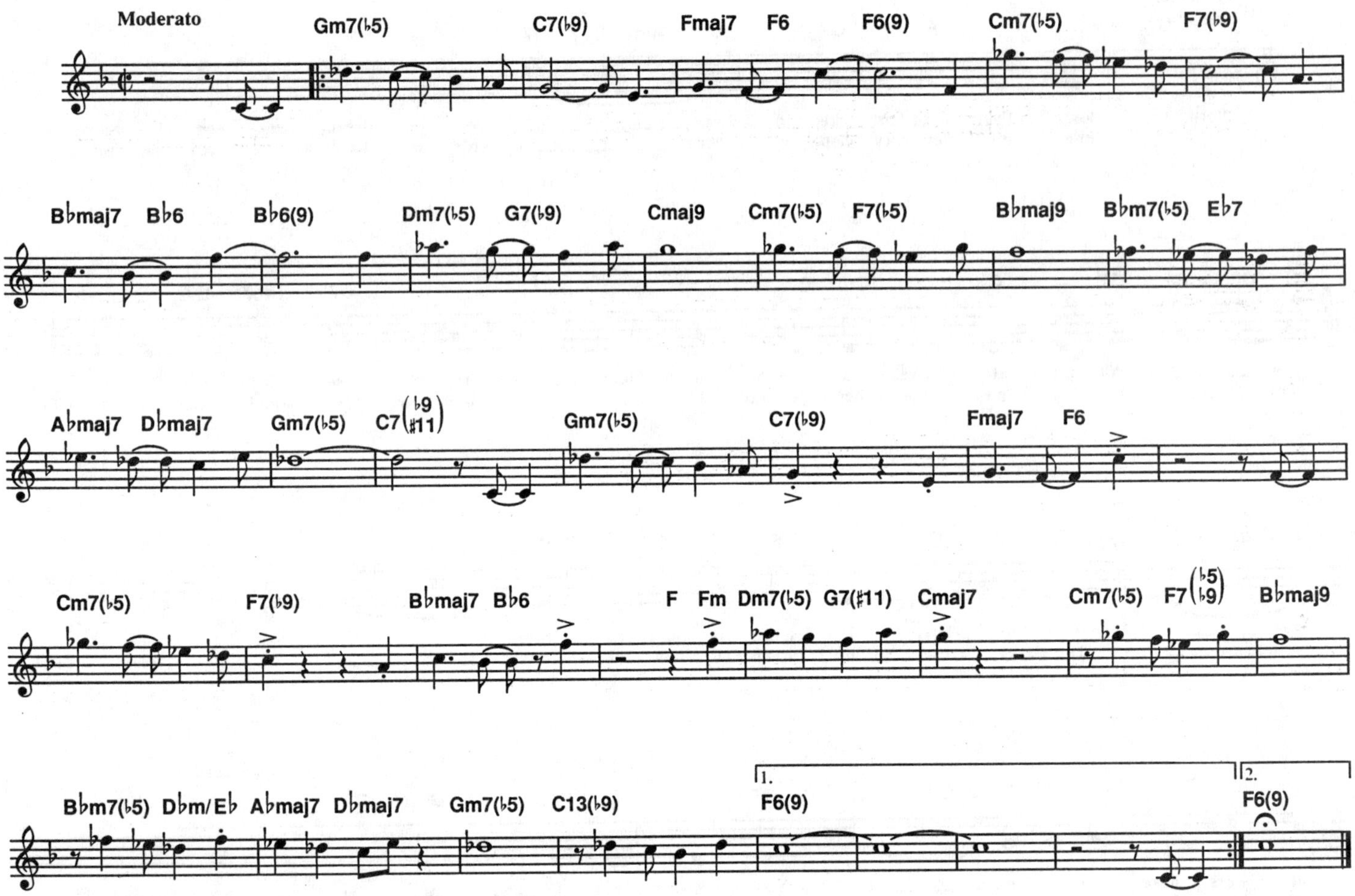

As Performed by Judy Garland in the 1944 M-G-M Production "MEET ME IN ST. LOUIS"

THE BOY NEXT DOOR

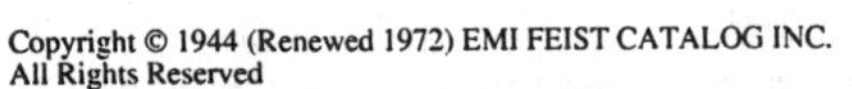

Words and Music by
HUGH MARTIN and RALPH BLANE

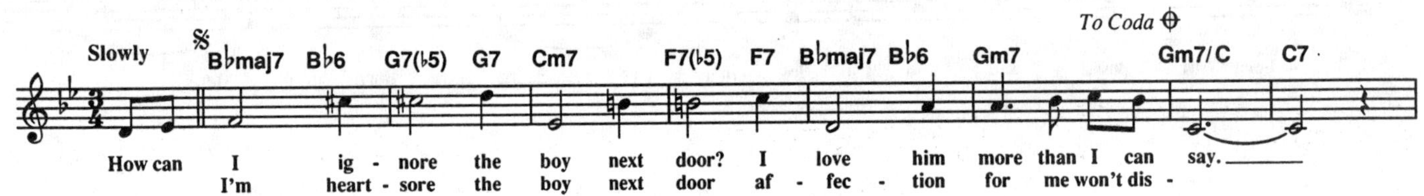
To Coda
Slowly
B♭maj7 B♭6 G7(♭5) G7 Cm7 F7(♭5) F7 B♭maj7 B♭6 Gm7 Gm7/C C7
How can I ig - nore the boy next door? I love him more than I can say.
I'm heart - sore the boy next door af - fec - tion for me won't dis -

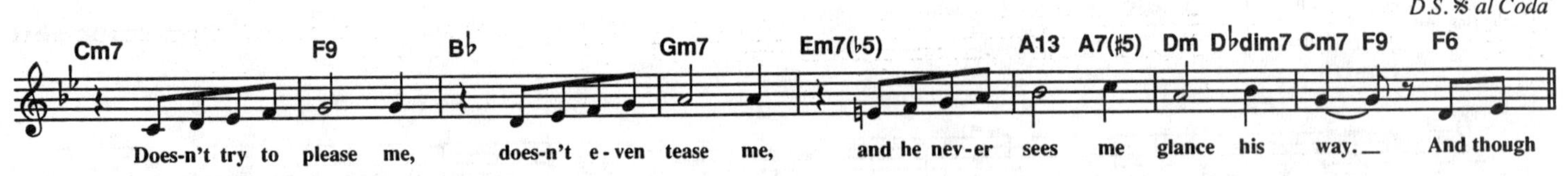
D.S. al Coda
Cm7 F9 B♭ Gm7 Em7(♭5) A13 A7(♯5) Dm D♭dim7 Cm7 F9 F6
Does-n't try to please me, does-n't e-ven tease me, and he nev-er sees me glance his way. And though

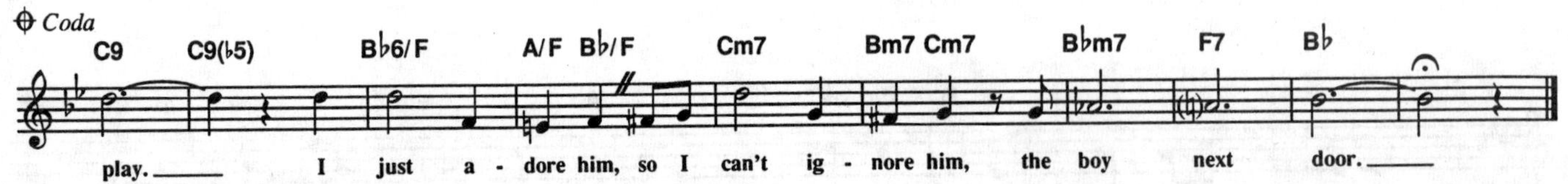
Coda
C9 C9(♭5) B♭6/F A/F B♭/F Cm7 Bm7 Cm7 B♭m7 F7 B♭
play. I just a - dore him, so I can't ig - nore him, the boy next door.

BOTTLE OF WINE

Words and Music by TOM PAXTON

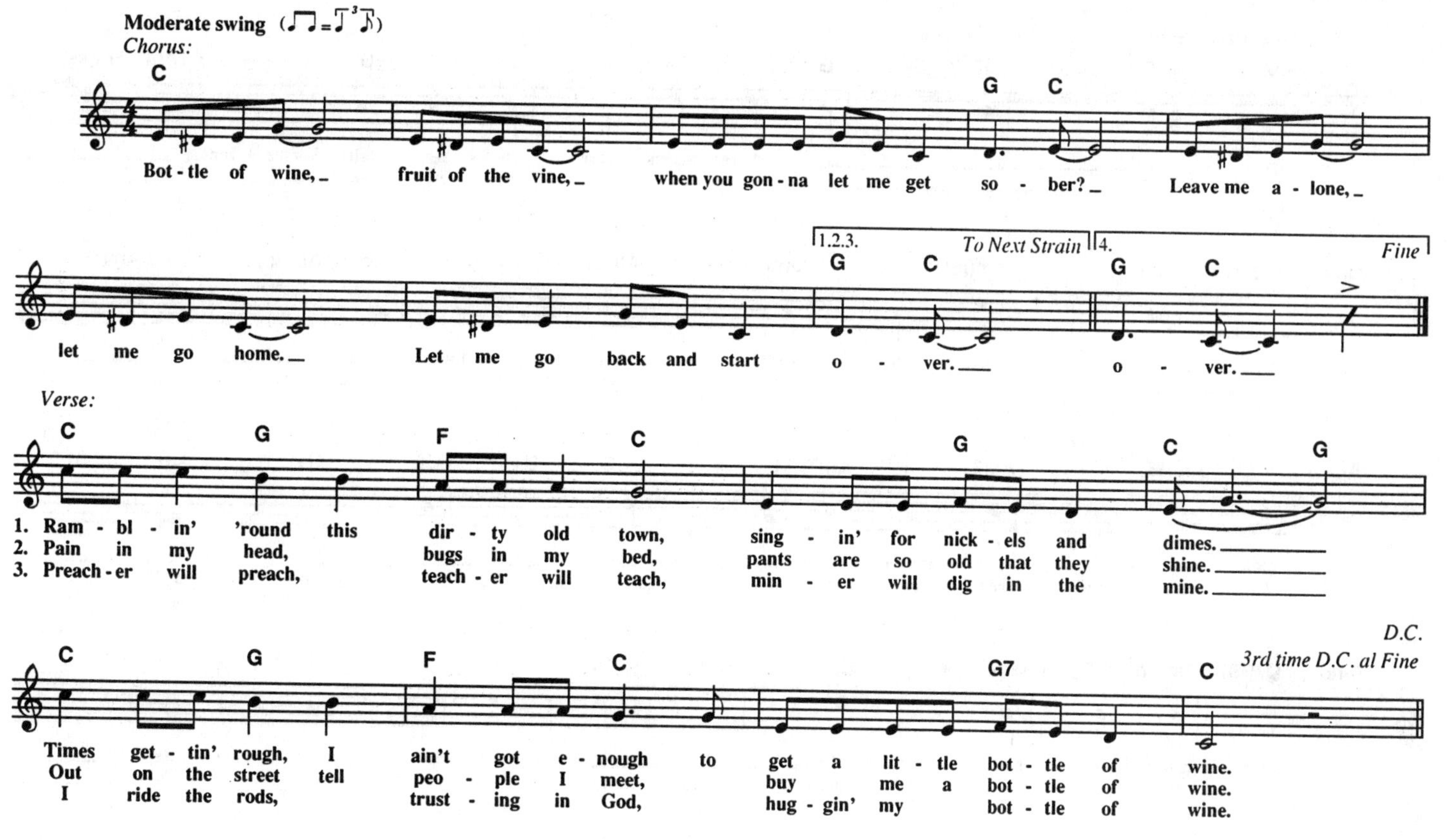
Moderate swing
Chorus:
C G C
Bot - tle of wine, fruit of the vine, when you gon - na let me get so - ber? Leave me a - lone,
let me go home. Let me go back and start o - ver.
1.2.3. To Next Strain
4. Fine
Verse:
1. Ram - bl - in' 'round this dir - ty old town, sing - in' for nick - els and dimes.
2. Pain in my head, bugs in my bed, pants are so old that they shine.
3. Preach - er will preach, teach - er will teach, min - er will dig in the mine.
F G7
D.C.
3rd time D.C. al Fine
Times get - tin' rough, I ain't got e - nough to get a lit - tle bot - tle of wine.
Out on the street tell peo - ple I meet, buy me a bot - tle of wine.
I ride the rods, trust - ing in God, hug - gin' my bot - tle of wine.

BREAD AND BUTTER

Words and Music by
JAY TURNBOW and LARRY PARKS

Moderate rock
C F G7
1. I like bread and but - ter, I like toast and jam. That's what my ba - by
feeds me, I'm her lov - in' man. He likes bread and but - ter, he likes toast and jam.
That's what his ba - by feeds him, he's her lov - in' man.
1.2.
3.
with some oth - er man.

Verse 2:
She don't cook mashed potatoes,
Don't cook T - bone steak.
Don't feed me peanut butter.
She knows that I can't take
No more bread and butter,
No more toast and jam.
He found his baby eatin'
With some other man.

Verse 3:
Got home early one mornin'
Much to my surprise,
She was eatin' chicken and dumplin's
With some other guy.
No more bread and butter,
No more toast and jam.
I found my baby eatin'
With some other man.

BRAZIL

Brazilian Samba by ARY BARROSO
Text in English by S.K. RUSSELL

Moderately bright
D7 G G+ G6 G+ G G+ G6 G+ Am Am(♯5)
Bra - zil, where hearts were en - ter - tain - ing June,
O a - bre a cor - ti - na do pas - sa - do,
Am6 Am(♯5) Am Am(♯5) Am6 Am(♯5) Am Am(♯5) Am6 Am(♯5)
we stood be - neath an am - ber moon
ti - ra mae pre - ta do ser - ra - do
Am Am(♯5) Am6 Am7(♭5) G G+ G6 G+ Am Am(♯5)
and soft - ly mur - mured, "Some day soon". We kissed
bo - ta o rei gon - go no con - ga Bra - sil!
Am6 D7(♭9) Gmaj7 G7 G♭7 F7 E7 Dm/F E7
and clung to - geth - er. Then to - mor - row was an - oth - er day.
Bra - sil! Deixa, can - tar de no - vo o tro - va - dor.
Dm/F E7 Dm F7 E7
The morn - ing found me miles a - way, with still a
A me - ren - co - rea luz da lua to - da a can -
Am Am(♯5) Am6 Am(♯5) Am Am(♯5)
mil - lion things to say. Now
cao do meu a - mor. Quero
Am Cm G(2) B♭dim7
when twi - light dims the sky a - bove, re - call - ing thrills of our love,
ver a "sa do - na" ca - mi - nhando, pe - los sa - loes ar - ras - tan -
Am7 Am E♭9(♯11) D9 G G+ G6 G+ Am Am(♯5)
there's one thing I'm cer - tain of: re - turn
do, o seu ves - ti - do ren - da - do, Bra - sil!
Am6 Am G G+ G6 G+ Am Am(♯5) Am6 Am G G+ G6 G+ G G+ G6 G6/9
I will to old Bra - zil.
Bra - sil! pra mim pra - mim.

BREAK MY MIND

Words and Music by
JOHN D. LOUDERMILK

Moderately
G
C
G
1. Ba - by, oh, ba - by, tell the man at the tick-et stand that you've changed my mind.

C
G
Let me run on out and tell the cab to keep his me - ter fly - in'. 'Cause if you

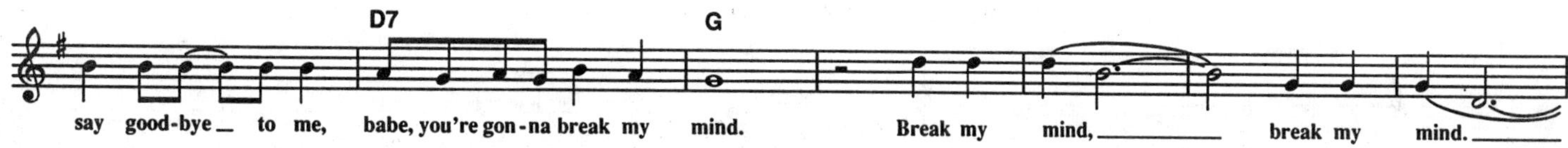
D7
G
say good-bye to me, babe, you're gon - na break my mind. Break my mind, break my mind.

D7
G
G7
No, I just can't stand to hear them big jet en - gines whine. Break my mind, break my

C
Cm
G
D7
G
1.
mind. If you leave, you're gon - na leave a bab - bl - in' fool be - hind.

2.
D7
G
If you leave, you're gon - na leave a bab - bl - in' fool be - hind.

Verse 2:
Baby, oh, baby,
Let me take your suitcase
Off the scales in time.
Tell the man that you've suddenly developed
A thing about flyin'.
'Cause if you say goodby to me, babe, you're
Gonna break my mind.

From the Film "BREAKFAST AT TIFFANY'S"

BREAKFAST AT TIFFANY'S

HENRY MANCINI

Moderately
F
D7sus
D7
3
Gm7
Am7
B♭m7 E♭7
A♭
Fm
G7sus
G7
3
To Coda ⊕
Em7
E♭7
3
Dm7
G7
Gm7
C7
Fm7
B♭7
Gm7
G♭9

C♭maj7
B♭9
E♭maj7
E♭m
A♭7
Fm7
B♭7(♭9)

E♭m7
A♭7(♭9)
D♭maj7
D.C. al Coda
Gm7 C7
⊕ Coda
E♭7
A♭
Fm
Dm7
G7
D♭maj7
C

BRIDAL CHORUS
(From "Lohengrin")

RICHARD WAGNER

Slowly
B♭
F7
B♭
E♭
B♭
C7
F
B♭

F7
B♭
To Coda ⊕
Dm
Gm
Cm
F7
B♭
Cm
F7
B♭

F
Cm
G
D7
G
D7
G
D7

G
Em
A7
D
G
Gm
B♭
F7
B♭

Gm
F
Dm
A7
D.C. al Coda
D
⊕ Coda
Cm
F7
B♭

From the Broadway Musical Production "BRIGADOON"

BRIGADOON

Words by ALAN JAY LERNER
Music by FREDERICK LOEWE

Slowly
C F C C♯dim Dm C F G7 C E7
Brig - a - doon, Brig - a - doon, bloom - ing un - der sa - ble skies. Brig - a - doon, Brig - a -
Am6 Am7 C A7(♭5) G6 D7 G Dm Dm7 G6 Dm7 A7
doon, there my heart for ev - er lies. Let the world grow cold a - round us, let the
D7 G7 C F C F Fm6 C C6 Fmaj7 G7 F C
heav - ens cry a - bove. Brig - a - doon, Brig - a - doon, in thy val - ley there'll be love.

From the Broadway Musical Production "DAMES AT SEA"

BROADWAY BABY

Words by GEORGE HAIMSOHN
Music by JIM WISE

Brightly
G G+ G6 E♭9 D7 G G+ G6 E7(♭9) Am F/A Am6
I found me a Broad - way ba - by, she's a hit with me. What a smash, my
With my ne - on Broad - way beau - ty, who could be a - fraid? Me and my Ri -
Cm6/E♭ D7 1. Bm7 B♭dim Am7 D7 2. Bm7 G/B
Broad - way ba - by, stand-ing room on - ly is on the mar - quee. we'll lead the Eas - ter Pa -
al - to cut - ie,
E7 Bm7/F♯ Gm6 E7/G♯ A7 Am7 D7 G
rade. To - geth - er we'll climb that stair - way, we'll soar up to the

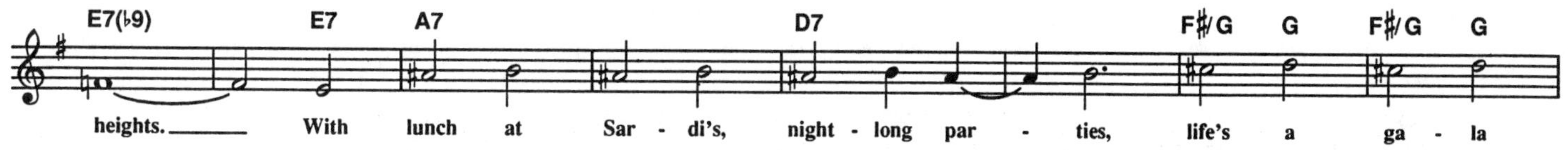
E7(♭9) E7 A7 D7 F♯/G G F♯/G G
heights. With lunch at Sar - di's, night - long par - ties, life's a ga - la

Bm7 E7 A7 D7 G
ball with my razz - ling, dazz - ling, Broad - way ba - by doll.

BUBBLES IN THE WINE

By FRANK LOESSER, BOB CALAME
and LAWRENCE WELK

Bright swing

C
E♭dim
Dm7
G7
My heart gets a lit - tle gay, like bub-bles in the wine ev - 'ry time I dance with you. Your

C
E♭dim
Dm7
G7
C7
arms take me far a - way like bub-bles in the wine, just as if I'd had a few. Oh, may-be it's that

F
D7
moon, or may-be it's that tune, play-ing as we gen - tly sway. Or may-be it's the fact that I love you.

Dm7
G7
C
E♭dim
Dm7
Can't real-ly say, how I get this way. My heart whis-pers a re - frain, like bub-bles in the wine, ev - 'ry time you're

G7
C7
F
close to me. I need - n't drink cham - pagne, a feel - ing quite in - sane lights me up and

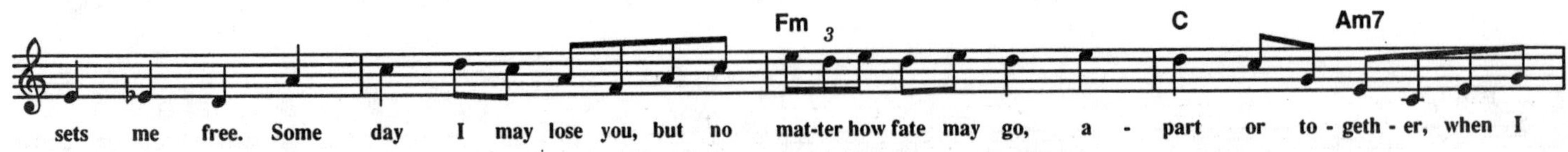
Fm
C
Am7
sets me free. Some day I may lose you, but no mat-ter how fate may go, a - part or to - geth - er, when I

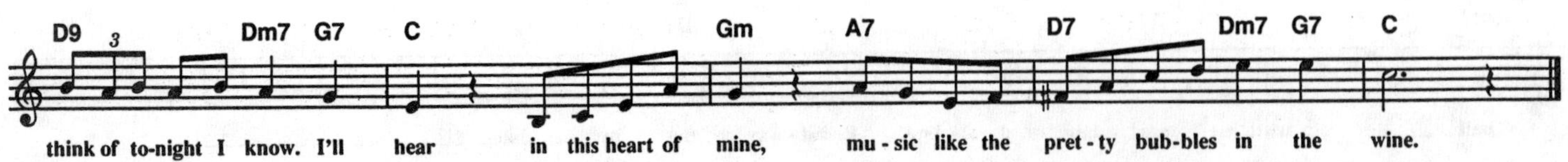
D9
Dm7 G7
C
Gm
A7
D7
Dm7 G7
C
think of to-night I know. I'll hear in this heart of mine, mu - sic like the pret - ty bub-bles in the wine.

BUFFALO GALS

Pre-Civil War Minstrel Song

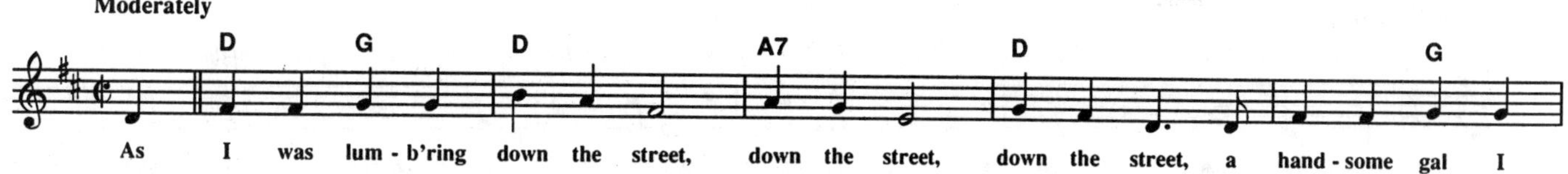
Moderately
D G D A7 D G
As I was lum - b'ring down the street, down the street, down the street, a hand - some gal I

D A7 D A7 D A7
chanced to meet. Oh, she was fair to view. Buf - fa - lo gals, won't you come out to-night, won't you come out to-night, won't you

D A7 D A7 D
come out to - night? Buf - fa - lo gals, won't you come out to - night, and dance by the light of the moon.

BUGLE CALL RAG

By JACK PETTIS, BILL MEYERS
and ELMER SCHOEBEL

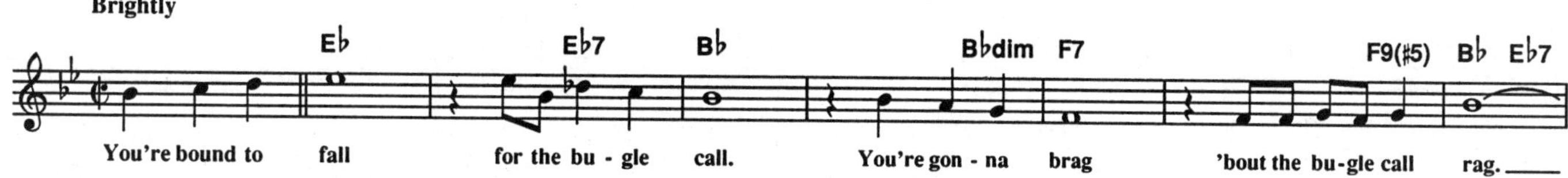
Brightly
E♭ E♭7 B♭ B♭dim F7 F9(♯5) B♭ E♭7
You're bound to fall for the bu - gle call. You're gon - na brag 'bout the bu-gle call rag.

B♭ B♭7 Fm7 B♭7 E♭ E♭7 B♭
Thin or fat, young or old, shake their should-ers bold. You're bound to fall for the bu - gle call.

B♭dim F7 F9(♯5) B♭ E♭7 B♭ Gm B♭7 E♭7
You're gon - na brag 'bout the bu-gle call rag. Hold me ba - by, let's syn - co-pate

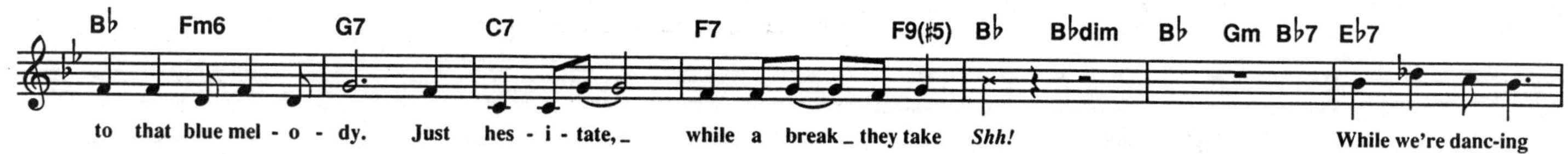
B♭ Fm6 G7 C7 F7 F9(♯5) B♭ B♭dim B♭ Gm B♭7 E♭7
to that blue mel - o - dy. Just hes - i - tate, while a break they take Shh! While we're danc-ing

B♭ Fm6 G7 C7 F7 F9(♯5) B♭ A♭ A6 B♭6
please hold me tight, step live-ly don't lag. Swing a - long to that bu-gle call rag.

BUTTONS AND BOWS

Words and Music by
JAY LIVINGSTON and RAY EVANS

Brightly

F F6 F F6 F F6 F F6 B♭
East is east and west is west and the wrong one I have chose; let's go where you'll
bur - y me in the prai - rie, take me where the ce - ment grows; let's move down to

F B♭ C9 F F6 F F6 F B♭
keep on wear - in' those frills and flow - ers and but - tons and bows, rings and things and
some big town where they love a gal by the cut of her clothes, and you'll stand out in

1. 2.
C7 F F7 B♭
but - tons and bows. Don't I'll love you in buck - skin, or skirts that you've home -
but - tons and bows.

F G9 Dm7 G7 C7
spun. But I'll love 'ya lon - ger, stron - ger where yer friends don't tote a gun. My

F F6 F F6 F F6 F F6 B♭ F B♭ C9
bones de - nounce the buck - board bounce and the cac - tus hurts my toes. Let's va - moose where gals keep us - in' those

F F6 F F6 F B♭ C7 F
silks and sat - ins and lin - en that shows, and you're all mine in but - tons and bows. Gim - me

Gm7 C7 Fmaj7 F6 Gm7 C7 Fmaj7 F6
east - ern trim - min' where wom - en are wom - en in high silk hose and peek - a - boo clothes, and

Gm7 C7 Fmaj7 F6 Gm7 C7 F
French per - fume, that rocks the room and you're all mine in but - tons and bows.

BUTTON UP YOUR OVERCOAT

Copyright © 1928 STEPHEN BALLENTINE MUSIC PUB. CO. c/o, THE SONGWRITERS GUILD OF AMERICA. (Ballentine share only)
All Rights Reserved
Words and Music by B.G. DeSYLVA, LEW BROWN and RAY HENDERSON
Moderate swing
G C/G G Bm7(♭5) E7 A7 G♯dim7 D7/A
But-ton up your o-ver-coat when the wind is free. Take good
But-ton up your o-ver-coat when the wind is free. Take good
G♯dim7 D7/A G6 Cmaj7/D D7 G C/G G Bm7(♭5) E7
care of your-self you be-long to me! Eat an ap-ple ev-'ry day;
care of your-self you be-long to me! Wear your flan-nel un-der-wear
A7 G♯dim7 D7/A G♯dim7 D7/A G6 G7 Dm7/G G7
get to bed by three. Take good care of your-self, you be-long to me! Be care-ful
when you climb a tree. Take good care of your-self, you be-long to me! Don't sit on
C C6 C G Gmaj7 G6 Em7 A7
cross-ing streets, oo-oo! Don't eat meats, oo-oo! Cut out sweets, oo-oo!
hor-nets' tails, oo-oo, or on nails, oo-oo, or third rails oo-oo!
D7 Em7 D9/F♯ Gmaj7 Am7 C♯7 G C/G G Bm7(♭5) E7 A7
You'll get a pain and ru-in your tum-tum! Keep a-way from boot-leg hootch when you're on a
You'll get a pain and ru-in your tum-tum! Don't go out with col-lege boys when you're on a
G♯dim7 D7/A G♯dim7 D7/A G C7 1. G Adim7 B♭dim7 2. G
spree. Take good care of your-self, you be-long to me. me.
spree. Take good care of your-self, you be-long to
BYE BYE BLACKBIRD
Copyright © 1926 (Renewed 1953) OLDE CLOVER LEAF MUSIC, c/o THE SONGWRITERS GUILD OF AMERICA
All Rights Reserved
Words by MORT DIXON
Music by RAY HENDERSON
Moderately
F F+ F6 F Gm7 C9 F F/A A♭dim7 Gm7 C7
Pack up all my care and woe, here I go, sing-ing low. Bye, bye black-bird.
Gm Gm(♯5) Gm6 Gm C7 Gm7 C7 Gm7 C7 Fmaj7 F6
Where some-bod-y waits for me, sug-ar's sweet, so is she. Bye, bye black-bird.
F7 Am7(♭5) D7 Gm Gm7(♭5) C7
No one here can love and un-der-stand me. Oh, what hard luck sto-ries they all hand me.
F F+ F6 F Gm7 C7 Am7(♭5) D7 Gm7 C7 1. F Dm7 Gm7 C7 2. F B♭ B♭m F6
Make my bed and light the light, I'll ar-rive late to-night. Black-bird, bye, bye. bye.

BY THE BEAUTIFUL SEA

Words by HAROLD R. ATTERIDGE
Music by HARRY CARROLL

Bright tempo
Bb7 Bb+ Eb
By the sea, by the sea, by the beau - ti - ful sea, you and I, you and I, oh, how
Bb7 Bbdim Bb7 Bbdim Bb7 Bbdim Bb7 A Bb
hap - py we'll be. When each wave comes a - roll - ing in, we will duck or swim, and we'll
Eb N.C. Bb7 Bb+ Eb
float and fool a - round the wa - ter, o - ver and un - der and then up for air. Pa is rich, Ma is
Bb Eb7 Ab Ab6 Ebdim Gm Gm7
rich, so now what do we care? I love to be be - side your side, be - side the
C9 C7 F7 Bb7 1. Eb Bbdim Bb7 2. Eb
sea, be - side the sea - side, by the beau - ti - ful sea. By the sea.

BY THE LIGHT OF THE SILVERY MOON

Lyric by ED MADDEN
Music by GUS EDWARDS

Moderate swing
C Ebdim7 G7/D C C/E Ebdim7 Dm Dm/F E7 A7 Dm
1. Place park, scene dark, sil-v'ry moon is shin-ing thru the trees. Cast two, me, you,
2. Act two, scene new, ros-es bloom-ing all a-round the place. Cast three, you, me,
G7 C G7 C Ebdim7 G7/D C C/E Cm6/Eb G
sound of kiss-es float-ing on the breeze. Act one, be - gun, di - a - logue, "Where would you like to spoon?"
preach-er, with a sol-emn look-ing face. Choir sings, bell rings, preach-er, "You are wed for-ev-er - more."
D7 G Em Am7 Am7/D D7 1. G7 2. G7 Refrain C D7
My cue, with you un-der-neath the sil - v'ry moon. core. By the light of the sil-ver-y moon,
Act two all through, ev-'ry night the same en -
G7 C C#dim7 G7/D G7 C F A7/E Dm A/E Dm
I want to spoon, to my hon-ey I'll croon love's tune. Hon-ey moon, keep a shin-ing in June. Your sil - v'ry
C C7/Bb D7/A Fm/Ab Am Bb7 A7 D7 C/G G7 C 1. 2.
beams will bring love dreams. We'll be cud-dl-ing soon, by the sil-ver-y moon. By the

From the Broadway Musical Production "CABIN IN THE SKY"

CABIN IN THE SKY

Words by JOHN LATOUCHE
Music by VERNON DUKE

Moderately

G E7 Am7 F♯7 Bm7 B7 E7 F♯m7 E7 Am E7
There's a lit - tle cab - in in the sky, ba - by. For me and for you I

Cm6 D7 G D7 G E7 Am7 F♯7 Bm7 B7 E7 F♯m7 E7
feel that it's true some - how.____ Can't you see that cab - in in the sky, ba - by, an

Am E7 Cm6 D7 G B7 Em
a - cre or two of heav - en - ly blue to plow.____ We will be oh, so gay, eat fried

B7 E Em7 A7 Em7 A7 D7 Ddim Am7 D7 G E7
chick - en ev - 'ry day, as the an - gels go sail - ing by.____ That is why my

Am7 F♯7 Bm7 B7 E7 F♯m7 E7 Am E7 Am7 Am7/D D7 G
heart is fly - ing high, ba - by, 'cause I know we'll have a cab - in in the sky.____

THE CAISSONS GO ROLLING ALONG

(United States Field Artillery Song)

EDMUND L. GRUBER

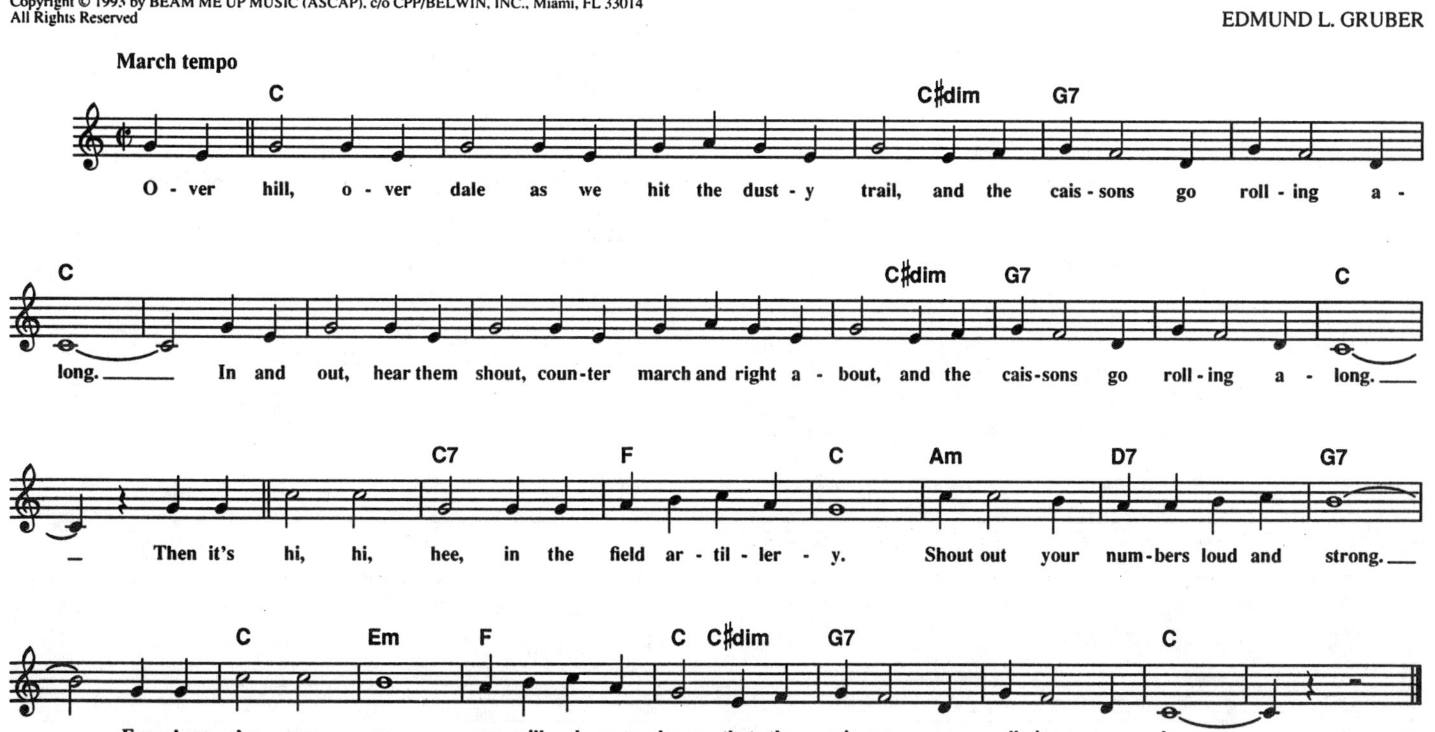
March tempo
C C♯dim G7
O - ver hill, o - ver dale as we hit the dust - y trail, and the cais - sons go roll - ing a -
C C♯dim G7 C
long.____ In and out, hear them shout, coun - ter march and right a - bout, and the cais - sons go roll - ing a - long.____
C7 F C Am D7 G7
____ Then it's hi, hi, hee, in the field ar - til - ler - y. Shout out your num - bers loud and strong.____
C Em F C C♯dim G7 C
____ For where - e'er you go, you will al - ways know that the cais - sons go roll - ing a - long.____

CALIFORNIA GIRLS
Copyright © 1965 and 1970 IRVING MUSIC, INC. (BMI)
All Rights Reserved
Words and Music by
BRIAN WILSON
Moderate rock shuffle
(Keyboard:)
1. Well,
Bb Ab/Bb Eb7
east coast girls are hip; I really dig those styles they wear. And the south-ern girls with the
west coast has the sun-shine, and the girls all get so tanned. I dig a French bi-ki-ni on Ha-
F7 Bb
way they talk, they knock me out when I'm down there. The mid-west farm-er's daugh-ters real-ly
wai-ian is-lands dolls by a palm tree in the sand. I been all around this great big world, and I've
Ab/Bb Eb7
make you feel al-right. And north-ern girls with the way they kiss, they keep their
seen all kinds of girls. But I could-n't wait to get back in the states, back to the
Chorus:
F7 Bb Cm7
boy-friends warm at night.
cut-est girls in the world.
I wish they all could be Cal-i-for-nia, I
Ab Bbm Gb Abm Bb
wish they all could be Cal-i-for-nia, I wish they all could be Cal-i-for-nia girls.
1. D.S. 𝄋 2. N.C.
2. The (Keyboard:) I
Bb Cm7 Repeat and fade
wish they all could be Cal-i-for-nia girls.
I wish they all could be Cal-i-for-nia; I
CAMPTOWN RACES
Copyright © 1993 by BEAM ME UP MUSIC (ASCAP), c/o CPP/BELWIN, INC., Miami, FL 33014
All Rights Reserved
Words and Music by
STEPHEN C. FOSTER
Brightly
Eb Bb7 Eb
De camp-town la-dies sing dis song, doo-dah! doo-dah! De camp-town race-track
came down dar wid my hat cav'd in, doo-dah! doo-dah! I go back home wid a
1. 2.
Bb7 Eb Fm Bb7 Eb Ab
nine miles long. Oh, doo-dah day! I Oh, doo-dah day! Gwine to run all night. Gwine to run all
pock-et-ful of tin.
Eb Ab Eb Fm7 Bb7 Eb
day, I'll bet my mon-ey on a bob-tail nag, some-bod-y bet on de bay.

CALIFORNIA HERE I COME

Words and Music by AL JOLSON,
B.G. DeSYLVA & JOSEPH MEYER

Brightly
C C+ F G7 Dm7 C♯dim G7 C
Cal - i - for - nia, here I come, right back where I start - ed from.
E♭dim7 G7 C E♭dim7 G7
Where bow - ers of flow - ers bloom in the sun, each morn - ing at dawn - ing bird - ies sing and
C C+ F G7 Dm7 C♯dim G7 Em7 A7 Gm6 A7
ev - 'ry - thing. A sun - kissed miss said, "Don't be late." That's why I can hard - ly wait.
Dm A7 Dm F♯dim C E7 Am D7 Dm G7 C F7 C
O - pen up that Gold - en Gate, Cal - i - for - nia, here I come!

From the Paramount Picture "PAPA'S DELICATE CONDITION"

CALL ME IRRESPONSIBLE

Words by SAMMY CAHN
Music by JAMES VAN HEUSEN

Moderately

F F6 F♯dim7 Gm Gm6 G♯dim Fmaj7 F

Call me ir - re - spon - si - ble, call me un - re - li - a - ble; throw in
Call me un - pre - dict - a - ble, tell me I'm im - prac - ti - cal; rain - bows

A7 *To Coda* ⊕ A7(♯5) Cm7 Am7(♭5) D7 Gm Gm(♯7) Gm7 B7/C C7 Am7(♭5)

un - de - pend - a - ble too. Do my fool - ish al - i - bis bore
I'm in - clined to pur -

D7 G7 C11 Gm C7 *D.C. al Coda* ⊕ *Coda* D7

you? Well, I'm not too clev - er, I just a - dore you. sue.

Gm7 Gm(♯5) Gm7 B7/C C7 Am7(♭5) D7 Gm7

Call me ir - re - spon - si - ble. Yes, I'm un - re - li - a - ble, but it's

B7/C C7 A7(♭5) D7(♭9) Gm7 C7(♭9) F6/9

un - de - ni - a - bly true; I'm ir - re - spon - si - bly mad for you!

From the Paramount Picture "AMERICAN GIGOLO"

CALL ME

Lyrics by DEBORAH HARRY
Music by GIORGIO MORODER

Moderate disco beat
Dm
B♭7
Dm
1. Col - or me your col - or, ba - by, col - or me your car.
2. Cov - er me with kiss - es, ba - by, cov - er me with love.
Col - or me your col - or, dar - ling, I know who you are.
Roll me in de - sign - er sheets, I'll nev - er get e - nough.
G
A
Come up off your col - or chart, I know where you're com - ing from.
E - mo - tions come, I don't know why, cov - er up love's al - i - bi.
Call me
Chorus:
F
G
B♭
on the line, call me, call me an - y, an - y time. Call me
I love you, can't you call me an - y day or night.
al - right, when you're read - y we can share the wine.
Call
1.
2.
G F
F C
me.
me.
Em
Am G
Ooh, he speaks the
Bm7
lan - guag - es of love.
Ooh. a - mo - re, chia - ma - mi, spoken: chia - ma - mi.
Ooh. ap - pelle moi,
C
G7
mon cher - ie. spoken: Ap - pelle moi,
an - y time an - y place, an - y - where, an - y - way,
an - y time an - y place, an - y - where,
an - y day.
Call me
in my life, call me, call me an - y, an - y time. Call me
Repeat ad lib. and fade
CARA MIA
Copyright © 1954 EMI FEIST CATALOG INC. Renewed 1982
Copyright © Renewal Prop. SEPTEMBER MUSIC CORP.
Rights for U.S.A. Controlled by SEPTEMBER MUSIC CORP.
Rights for the rest of the world Controlled by EMI FEIST CATALOG INC.
All Rights Reserved
Italian Lyric by GAGIS
Original Words and Music by
TULIO TRAPANI and LEE LANGE
Moderately slow
F
Am
B♭
B♭m6
G7
C7(♭9)
Ca - ra Mi - a why must we say good - bye? Each time we part my heart wants to die. My
Gm7
C7
1. To next strain
dar - ling, hear my pray'r, Ca - ra Mi - a fair. Here are my arms, you a - lone will share.
Ca - ra Mi - a mine say those words di - vine, I'll be your love till the end of
D.S. al Fine
2.
Fine
D♭
Fmaj7 F6
D♭7
C7
time. All I want is you for - ev - er - more, to have, to hold, to love, a - dore.

CAN CAN

By JACQUES OFFENBACH

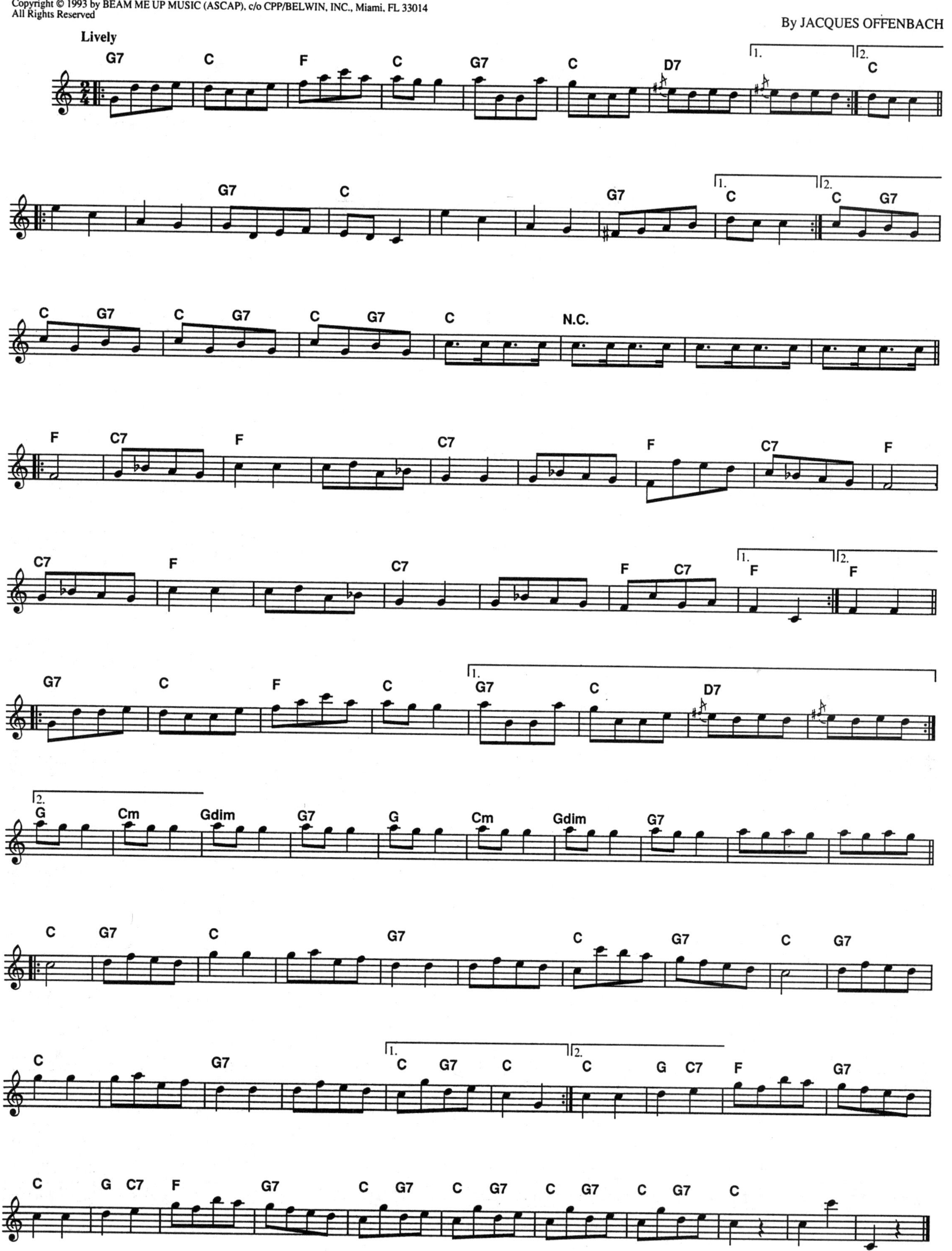
Lively
G7 C F C G7 C D7 1. 2. C
G7 C G7 1. C 2. C G7
C G7 C G7 C G7 C N.C.
F C7 F C7 F C7 F
C7 F C7 F C7 1. F 2. F
G7 C F C 1. G7 C D7
2. G Cm Gdim G7 G Cm Gdim G7
C G7 C G7 C G7 C G7
C G7 1. C G7 C 2. C G C7 F G7
C G C7 F G7 C G7 C G7 C G7 C G7 C

CAN'T YOU HEAR MY HEART BEAT

Copyright © 1965 SOUTHERN MUSIC PUBLISHING CO. LTD., London, England
Sole Selling Agent: SOUTHERN MUSIC PUBLISHING CO. INC., New York, N.Y.
All Rights Reserved
Words and Music by
CARTER-LEWIS
Moderately
1. Ev - 'ry time I see you look - in' my way, ba - by, ba - by, can't you hear my heart beat?
2. When I feel you put your arms a - round me, ba - by, ba - by, can't you hear my heart beat?
3. All my friends are cry - ing out to meet you. Ba - by, ba - by, can't you hear my heart beat?
In the park or walk - in' down the high - way, ba - by, ba - by, can't you hear my heart beat?
Then I'm glad, I'm might - y glad you found me. Ba - by, ba - by, can't you hear my heart beat?
Now's the time to go and see the preach - er. Ba - by, ba - by, can't you hear my heart beat?
When you move up clos - er to me, I get a feel - ing that's ooo, eee, yeah.
When you asked me to meet your ma, I know that ba - by, we'd be go - ing far, yeah.
Wed - ding bells are go - ing to chime. And ba - by, ba - by you're gon - na be mine, yeah.
Can't you hear the pound - in' of my heart beat? You're the one I love, you're the one I love.
you're the one I love, you're the one I love, you're the one I love.
CANDY
Copyright © 1944 (Renewed 1972) EMI FEIST CATALOG INC.
Copyright assigned to HARRY VON TILZER PUBLISHING COMPANY and KRAMER-WHITNEY, INC. in the USA
All Rights Reserved
Words and Music by MACK DAVID,
JOAN WHITNEY and ALEX KRAMER
Slowly
Can - dy, I call my sug - ar Can - dy be - cause I'm sweet on Can - dy
and Can - dy's sweet on me. He / She un - der - stands me, my un - der - stand - ing Can - dy and Can - dy's al - ways
hand - y when I need sym - pa - thy. I wish that there were four of him / her so
I could love much more of him. / her. He / She has tak - en my com - plete heart, got a sweet tooth for my sweet - heart, Can - dy.
It's gon - na be just dan - dy the day I take my Can - dy and make him / her mine all mine.

CANADIAN SUNSET

Words by NORMAN GIMBEL
Music by EDDIE HEYWOOD

Smoothly
F F6 F F6
Once, I was a - lone. So lone - ly and then
Cold, cold was the wind. Warm, warm were your lips,
G9 B♭dim7 B♭9 E♭7 F6 Gm7 C7
you came out of no - where, like the sun up from the hills.
out there on that ski trail where your kiss filled me with
F6 Gm7 C9 Gm7 C7(♭9) F F6 Gm7 D7(♭9)
thrills. A week-end in Can - a - da, a change of scene was the most
C9 Gm7 C7(♭9) C9 F6 Gm7 C9 Gm7 C7(♭9) F Am
I bar - gained for. And then I dis - cov - ered you, and in your eyes I found a
E7 Am F♯dim7 Gm7 C7 F F6 F
love that I could-n't ig - nore. Down, down came the sun. Fast, fast beat my
F6 G9 B♭9 E♭7 F6
heart. I knew, as the sun set, from that day, we'd nev - er part.

CARNIVAL OF VENICE

JULIUS BENEDICT

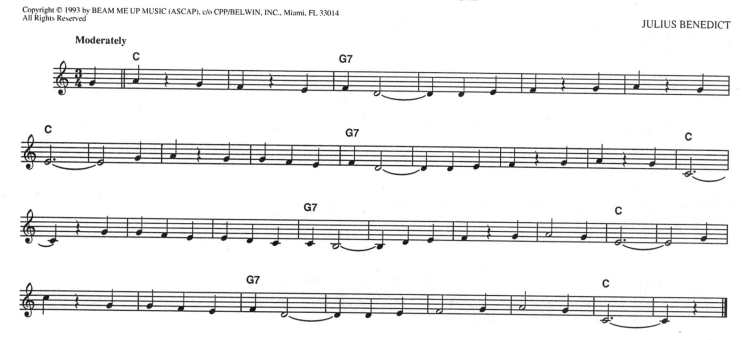

Moderately

C G7

C G7 C

G7 C

G7 C

CANON IN D

JOHANN PACHELBEL

Moderato grazioso
N.C.
D A Bm F♯m G D G A D A
Bm F♯m G D G A D A Bm F♯m G D G A G Asus A7
1. 2.
D A Bm F♯m G D G A D A Bm F♯m
G D G A D A Bm F♯m G D G A
2nd time only
1st time only
D A Bm D/F♯ G D
G A D A Bm D/F♯
G D G A D A Bm F♯m
G D G A D A Bm F♯m G D
G A D A Bm D/F♯ G D G Asus A D A
Bm D/F♯ G D G A D A Bm D/F♯ G D G A D

CARAVAN

By
DUKE ELLINGTON, IRVING MILLS
and JUAN TIZOL

Brightly
Edim C7 Edim C7 Edim C7 Edim C7 Edim C7 Edim C7
Night and stars a - bove that shine so bright,
Edim C7 Edim C7 Edim C7 Edim C7 Edim C7
the mys - t'ry of their fad - ing light that shines up -
Edim C7 Fm6 Edim C7 Edim C7
on our Car - a - van. Sleep
Edim C7 Edim C7 Edim C7 Edim C7 Edim C7
up - on my shoul - der as we creep a - cross the
Edim C7 Edim C7 Edim C7 Edim C7 Edim C7
sands so I may keep this mem - 'ry of our Car - a -
Fm6 F7 F7(♭9) F+
van. This is so ex - cit - ing.
B♭7 Fm B♭7 E♭7 Gdim
You are so in - vit - ing, rest - ing in my arms as I
A♭ C7 Fm6 E♭dim C7 Edim C7 Edim C7 Edim C7
thrill to the mag - ic charms of you be - side me,
Edim C7 Edim C7 Edim C7 Edim C7 Edim C7 Edim C7
here be - neath the blue. My dream of love is com - ing true
Edim C7 Edim C7 Edim C7 Fm6
with - in our des - ert Car - a - van.

CAROLINA MOON

Words and Music by
BENNY DAVIS & JOE BURKE

Moderately slow

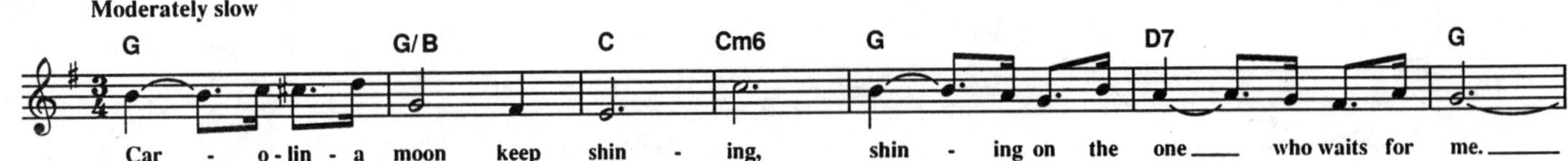
G G/B C Cm6 G D7 G
Car - o-lin - a moon keep shin - ing, shin - ing on the one who waits for me.

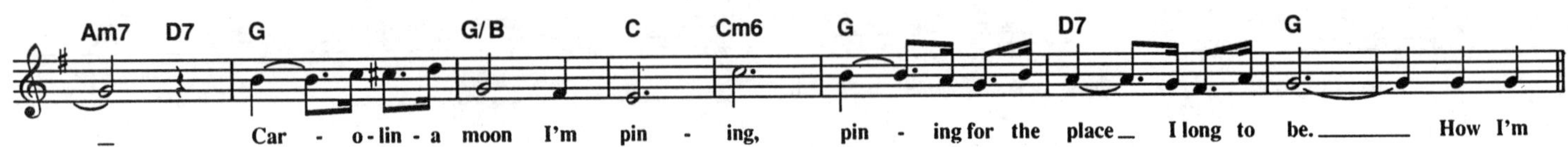
Am7 D7 G G/B C Cm6 G D7 G
Car - o-lin - a moon I'm pin - ing, pin - ing for the place I long to be. How I'm

C G A7 Am7 D7(♯5)
3 3 3 3
hop-ing to-night you'll go, go to the right win - dow, scat-ter your light, say I'm all right, please do.

G G/B C Cm6 G A7 D7 G C G6
Tell her that I'm blue and lone - ly, dream - y Car - o - lin - a moon.

CARRY ME BACK TO OLD VIRGINNY

Words and Music by
JAMES BLAND

Moderately

G C G G7 C G C A7 D
Car - ry me back to old Vir - gin - ny. There's where the cot - ton and the corn and 'ta - toes grow.

G C G G7 C G C G D7 G D7 G
There's where the birds war - ble sweet in the spring-time. There's where the old dark - ey's heart am longed to go.

D7 G D7 G B7 Em A7 D7
There's where I la - bored so hard for the mas - sa, day af - ter day in the fields of yel - low corn.

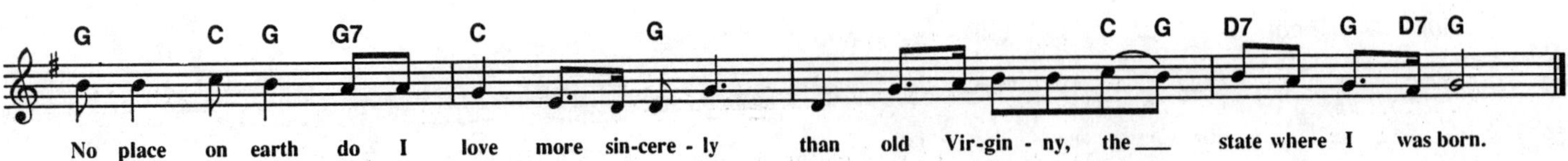
G C G G7 C G C G D7 G D7 G
No place on earth do I love more sin-cere - ly than old Vir-gin - ny, the state where I was born.

From the Broadway Musical Production "AIN'T MISBEHAVIN'"

(Get Some) CASH FOR YOUR TRASH

Words by ED KIRKEBY
Music by
THOMAS "FATS" WALLER

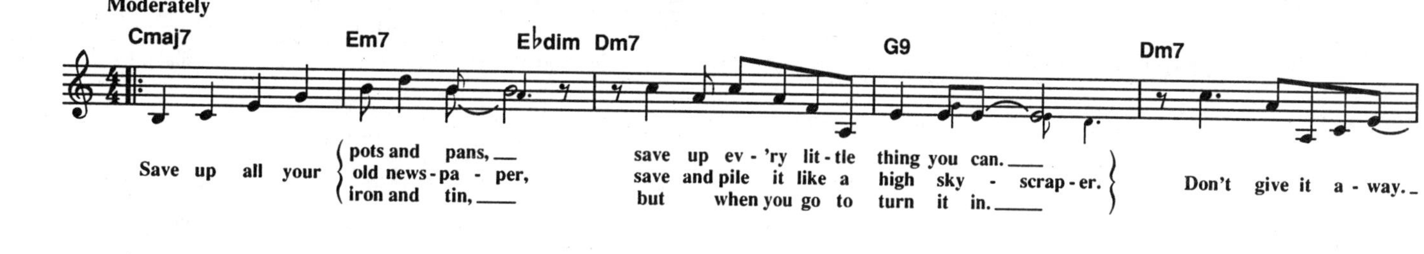
Moderately
Cmaj7 Em7 E♭dim Dm7 G9 Dm7
Save up all your pots and pans, save up ev-'ry lit-tle thing you can.
old news-pa-per, save and pile it like a high sky-scrap-er.
iron and tin, but when you go to turn it in.
Don't give it a-way.

To Coda 1. 2.
G9 C F9 C G7 C D♭9(♭5) C7 D♭9(♭5) C7
Get some cash for your trash.
In be-tween we'll do some lov-in',

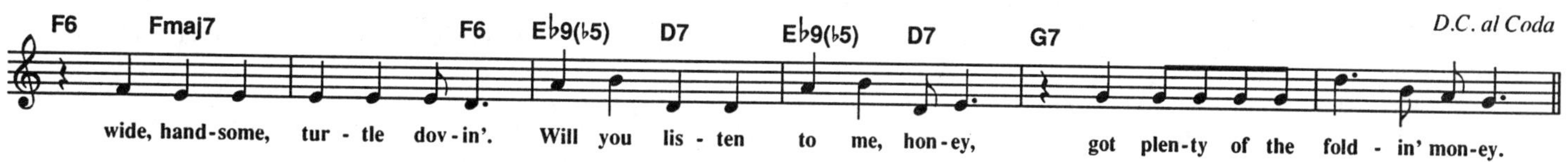
D.C. al Coda
F6 Fmaj7 F6 E♭9(♭5) D7 E♭9(♭5) D7 G7
wide, hand-some, tur-tle dov-in'. Will you lis-ten to me, hon-ey, got plen-ty of the fold-in' mon-ey.

Coda
C G+ C F9 C G+ C D9 G11 C
Get some cash for your trash. Get some cash, get some cash, get some cash for your trash.

From the 20th Century-Fox CinemaScope Production "A CERTAIN SMILE"

A CERTAIN SMILE

Lyrics by PAUL FRANCIS WEBSTER
Music by SAMMY FAIN

Moderately slow
To Coda
Gm7 C7 F6/9 Gm7 C9 F Fmaj7
A cer-tain smile, a cer-tain face, can lead an un-sus-pect-ing heart on a mer-ry chase.
while, and when love goes, you try to hide the tears in-side with a cheer-ful pose.

D.S. al Coda
F6 Em7 A7 Em7/A A7 Dm G9 Cmaj7 Dm7 G7 Gm7/C C9
A fleet-ing glance can say so man-y love-ly things. Sud-den-ly you know why my heart sings. You love a-

Coda
F7 Cm7/F F7 A/B♭ B♭ Am7(♭5) D7(♭9) Gm7 B♭m6 F/C Dm Gm7 C9 F6/9
But in the hush of night ex-act-ly like a bit-ter-sweet re-frain, comes that cer-tain smile to haunt your heart a-gain.

CATHY'S CLOWN
Copyright © 1960 by ACUFF-ROSE MUSIC, INC.
All Rights Reserved
Words and Music by
DON EVERLY
Moderately slow rock
Chorus:
Don't want your love ___ an - y - more. Don't want your kiss - es, that's for sure.
To Coda
I die each time I hear this sound. Here he comes ___ that's Cath - y's clown.
Verse:
1. I've got to stand tall. You know a man ___ can't crawl. For when he knows you tell
2. When you see me shed a tear, and you know that it's sin - cere, don't you think it's kind of
lies and he lets them pass by, then he's not a man at all. Don't want your
sad that you're treat-ing me so bad, or don't you e - ven care?
D.S. D.S. al Coda
Don't want your
Coda
Repeat and fade
That's Cath - y's clown. That's Cath - y's clown; that's Cath - y's
CHANTILLY LACE
Copyright © 1958 by GLAD MUSIC
Sole Selling Agent by PEER INTERNATIONAL CORPORATION
All Rights Reserved
Words and Music by
J.P. RICHARDSON
Moderately bright shuffle
1.3. Chan - til - ly lace ___ and a pret - ty face ___ and a pon - y tail ___ hang-in' down; ___ wig - gle in her
2. Instr. ad lib.
walk and a gig - gle in her talk makes the world go 'round. ___ Ain't noth - in' in this world like a
Spoken: Oh, you sweet thing. Do I what?
big eyed girl ___ to make me act so fun - ny, make me spend my mon - ey, make me feel real loose like a
Will I what? Oh baby, you know what I
long - necked goose like a girl. Oh, ba - by, that's what I like. ___
like.
3. Chan - til - ly lace ___ girl. Oh, ba - by, that's what I like. ___

Theme Song from the Stanley Donen Production, a Universal Release

CHARADE

Words by JOHNNY MERCER
Music by HENRY MANCINI

Moderate waltz

Am — E7
When we played our cha - rade ___ we were like chil - dren pos - ing; ___
Oh, what a hit we made, ___ we came on next to clos - ing; ___

Bm7(♭5) — E7 — Bm7(♭5) — E7 — Bm7(♭5) — E7(♯5) — E7 — Am
play - ing at games, act - ing out names, guess - ing the parts we played. ___
best on the bill, lov - ers un - til love left the mas - que - rade. ___

Dm7 — G7 — Cmaj7 — Am7 — Dm — G7 — C — C♯dim
Fate ___ seemed to pull the strings; I turned and you were gone. ___

Dm7 — G7 — Cmaj7 — Am — D7 — D9 — Bm7(♭5) — E7
While ___ from the dark - ened wings the mu - sic box played on. ___

Am7 — E7
Sad lit - tle ser - e - nade ___ song of my heart's com - pos - ing; ___

Bm7(♭5) — E7 — Bm7(♭5) — E7 — Bm7(♭5) — E7(♯5 ♭9) — E7 — Am
I hear it still, I al - ways will, best on the bill, ___ cha - rade. ___

CHARLIE BROWN THEME

By VINCE GUARALDI

Easy swing
C6/9
F6/9
F♯dim7
G9
Em7
A7(♭9)
Dm7
G13
C6/9
F6/9
F♯dim7
C
B♭13
Am7
Dm7
G9
C6/9
1.
Dm7
G7(♭9 ♯5)
2.
A7(♯5)
Dm7
G9
C6/9
Cmaj9

CHARLOTTE'S WEB
Words and Music by
RICHARD M. SHERMAN and ROBERT B. SHERMAN
Copyright © 1971, 1972 by ENSIGN MUSIC CORPORATION
All Rights Reserved
Moderately
1. Fra - gile and mag - i - cal sha - dows, si - lent - ly start to ap - pear love - ly and lyr - i - cal, sil - ver - y mir - a - cle Char - lotte's Web.
2. Care - ful - ly spin - ning her trac - ings, la - cy and grace - ful - ly sheer o - ver and un - der the in - fin - ite won - der of Char - lotte's Web.
Why is she spin - ning and weav - ing a - way, all night long?
What is she try - ing so hard to con - vey with her si - lent song?
Some - times when some - bod - y loves you, mir - a - cles some - how ap - pear. And there in the warp and the woof is the proof of it: Char - lotte's Web.
From the 20th Century-Fox Motion Picture "WHAT PRICE GLORY"
CHARMAINE
Words and Music by
ERNO RAPEE and
LEW POLLACK
Copyright © 1926 (Renewed 1954) EMI MILLER CATALOG INC.
All Rights Reserved
Slowly
I won - der why you keep me wait - ing, Char - maine cries in vain.
I won - der when blue - birds are mat - ing, will you come back a - gain?
I won - der if I keep on pray - ing, will our dreams be the same?
I won - der if you ev - er think of me, too? Char - maine's wait - ing, just wait - ing for you.

From the 20th Century-Fox Motion Picture "SUN VALLEY SERENADE"

CHATTANOOGA CHOO CHOO

Words by MACK GORDON
Music by HARRY WARREN

Moderate

Par - don me boy, is that the Chat - ta - noo - ga Choo Choo? Track twen - ty - nine, boy you can gim - me a shine.
I can af - ford to board a Chat - ta - noo - ga Choo Choo. I've got my fare and just a tri - fle to spare.
There's gon - na be a cer - tain par - ty at the sta - tion, sat - in and lace; I used to call fun - ny

To Coda

You leave the Penn - syl - va - nia sta - tion 'bout a quar - ter to four, read a mag - a - zine and then you're in Bal - ti - more. Din - ner in the din - er, noth - ing could be fin - er than to have your ham 'n' eggs in Car - o - li - na.
When you hear the whis - tle blow - in' eight to the bar then you know that Ten - nes - see is not ver - y far. Shov - el all the coal in, got - ta keep it roll - in'. Woo, woo, Chat - ta - noo - ga, there you are.

D.C. al Coda

Coda

face. She's gon - na cry un - til I tell her that I'll nev - er roam. So Chat - ta - noo - ga Choo Choo, won't you choo choo me home.

CATCH US IF YOU CAN

Words and Music by
DAVE CLARK and LENNY DAVIDSON

Moderately, with a beat
Here they come a - gain, mm, catch us if you can, mm. Time to get a move on, mm,
Now we got - ta run, mm, no more time for fun, mm. When we're get - tin' an - gry, mm,
We will yell with all of our might: Catch us if you can, Catch us if you can,
Catch us if you can, catch us if you can.
(snap fingers)
Fine

CHATTANOOGIE SHOE SHINE BOY

By HARRY STONE
& JACK STAPP

Moderate swing
C C7 F7 C G7 C C7 F C D7 G7 C C7 F7 C G7 C C
Have you ev - er passed the cor - ner of Fourth and Grand_ where a lit - tle ball of rhy - thm has a shoe-shine stand?_ Peo - ple gath - er 'round and they clap_ their hand._ He's a great big bun - dle of joy._ He pops a boog-ie woog-ie rag, the Chat-ta - noog-ie shoe-shine boy.
He charg - es you a nick - el just to shine one shoe._ He makes the old - est kind of leath - er look like new._ You feel as though you want to dance when he gets through._ He's a great big bun - dle of joy._ He pops a boog-ie woog-ie rag, the Chat-ta - noog-ie shoe-shine boy.
It's a won - der that the rag don't tear the way he makes it pop._ You ought to see him fan the air_ with his hop-pi - ty, hip-pi - ty, hip-pi - ty, hop-pi - ty, hop-pi - ty, hip-pi - ty hop. He o - pens up for bus'-ness when the clock strikes nine._ He likes to get 'em ear - ly when they're feel - in' fine._ Ev - 'ry-bod - y gets a lit - tle rise_ and shine_ with the great big bun-dle of joy._ He pops a boog-ie woog-ie rag, the Chat-ta - noog-ie shoe-shine boy. Have you
D.S. 𝄋
CHINATOWN, MY CHINATOWN
Copyright © 1993 by BEAM ME UP MUSIC (ASCAP), c/o CPP/BELWIN, INC., Miami, FL 33014
All Rights Reserved
Words by WILLIAM JEROME
Music by JEAN SCHWARTZ
Moderately fast
C G7 Am E7 Am D7 G7 C G7 C7 C+ F Fm6 C Gm6 A7 D7 Dm7 G7 C C♯dim7 Dm Gm6 G7 C
Chi - na - town, my Chi - na - town,_ where the lights are low._ Hearts that know no oth - er land,_ drift - ing to and fro._ Dream - y, dream - y, Chi - na - town,_ al - mond eyes of brown,_ hearts seem light and life seems bright_ in dream - y Chi - na - town. town._

From the United Artists Musical Production "CHITTY CHITTY BANG BANG"

CHITTY CHITTY BANG BANG

Words and Music by
RICHARD M. SHERMAN and
ROBERT B. SHERMAN

Brightly
Chit-ty Bang Bang, Chit-ty Chit-ty Bang Bang, Chit-ty Bang Bang, Chit-ty Chit-ty Bang Bang,
Chit-ty Bang Bang, Chit-ty Chit-ty Bang Bang! Oh, you, pret-ty Chit-ty Bang Bang, Chit-ty Chit-ty Bang Bang, we love you!
Oh, you, pret-ty Chit-ty Bang Bang, Chit-ty Chit-ty Bang Bang, we love you!
And our pret-ty Chit-ty Bang Bang, Chit-ty Chit-ty Bang Bang, loves us too! High, low, an-y-where we go, on
And in. Chit-ty Chit-ty Bang Bang, Chit-ty Chit-ty Bang Bang, what we'll do! Near, far, in our mo-tor car, oh,
Chit-ty Chit-ty we de-pend. Bang Bang, Chit-ty Chit-ty Bang Bang, our fine four-fen-dered friend. You're un-cat-e-
what a hap-py time we'll spend. Bang Bang, Chit-ty Chit-ty Bang Bang, our fine four-fen-dered friend. You're sleek as a
gor-i-cal, a fuel burn-ing or-a-cle, a fan-tas-ma-gor-i-cal ma-chine! You're more than spec-
thor-ough-bred. Your seats are a feath-er bed. You'll turn ev-'ry-bod-y's head to-day! We'll glide on our
tac-u-lar, to use the ver-nac-u-lar, you're wiz-ard, you're smash-ing, you're keen! Oh, Chit-ty, you, Chit-ty,
mo-tor trip, with pride in our own-er-ship, the en-vy of all we sur-vey! Oh, Chit-ty, you, Chit-ty,
pret-ty Chit-ty Bang Bang, Chit-ty Chit-ty Bang Bang, we love you! And Chit-ty, our Chit-ty, pret-ty Chit-ty Bang Bang, Chit-ty Chit-ty Bang Bang,
pret-ty Chit-ty Bang Bang, Chit-ty Chit-ty Bang Bang, we love you! And Chit-ty, in Chit-ty, pret-ty Chit-ty Bang Bang, Chit-ty Chit-ty Bang Bang,
loves us too! High Chit-ty, low Chit-ty, an-y-where we go, on Chit-ty Chit-ty Chit-ty we de-pend. Bang bang, Chit-ty
what we'll do! Near Chit-ty, far Chit-ty, in our mo-tor car, oh, what a hap-py time we'll spend. Bang bang, Chit-ty Chit-ty
Bang Bang, our fine four-fen-dered friend! friend! Bang Bang, Chit-ty Chit-ty Bang Bang, our
Bang Bang, our fine four-fen-dered
fine four-fen-dered friend!
(Chit-ty Chit-ty Bang Bang, Chit-ty Chit-ty Bang Bang, fine four-fen-dered chit-ty chit-ty friend.)

CHRISTMAS TIME IS HERE
(From "A Charlie Brown Christmas")

By LEE MENDELSON
and VINCE GUARALDI

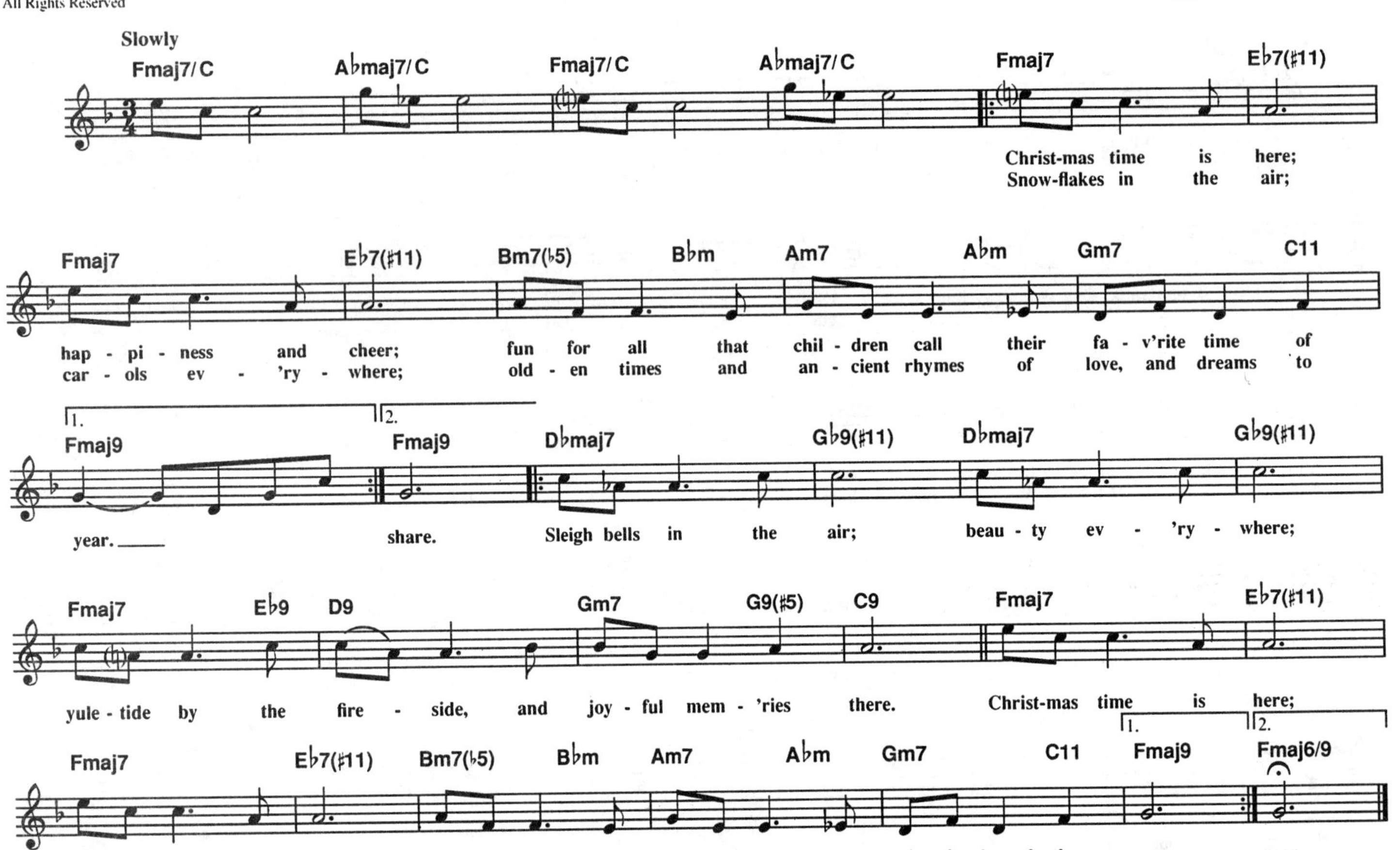
Slowly
Fmaj7/C Abmaj7/C Fmaj7/C Abmaj7/C Fmaj7 Eb7(#11)
Christ-mas time is here;
Snow-flakes in the air;
Fmaj7 Eb7(#11) Bm7(b5) Bbm Am7 Abm Gm7 C11
hap - pi - ness and cheer; fun for all that chil - dren call their fa - v'rite time of
car - ols ev - 'ry - where; old - en times and an - cient rhymes of love, and dreams to
1. Fmaj9 2. Fmaj9 Dbmaj7 Gb9(#11) Dbmaj7 Gb9(#11)
year. share. Sleigh bells in the air; beau - ty ev - 'ry - where;
Fmaj7 Eb9 D9 Gm7 G9(#5) C9 Fmaj7 Eb7(#11)
yule - tide by the fire - side, and joy - ful mem - 'ries there. Christ-mas time is here;
Fmaj7 Eb7(#11) Bm7(b5) Bbm Am7 Abm Gm7 C11 1. Fmaj9 2. Fmaj6/9
fam-'lies draw - ing near. Oh, that we could al - ways see such spir - it through the year. year.

THE COVENTRY CAROL
(Lullay, Thou Little Tiny Child)

TRADITIONAL

Gently, like a lullaby
Gm D Gm F Gm D Gm D/F# Gm
1. Lul - lay, Thou lit - tle ti - ny Child, bye - bye, lul -
2. O sis - ters, too, how may we do for to pre -
3. Her - od the King in his rag - ing charg - ed he
4. Then woe is me, poor child for Thee, and ev - er
Cm D7 Gm Bb F/A Gm F Bb Cm Cm/Eb
loo, lul - lay. Lul - lay, Thou lit - tle ti - ny
serve this day? This poor Young - ling for whom we
hath this day his men of might in his own
morn and day. For Thy part - ing nor say, nor
D Gm D/F# Gm Cm D 1.2.3. G 4. G
Child, bye - bye, lul - loo, lul - lay. lay.
sing, bye - bye, lul - loo, lul - lay.
sight, all chil - dren young to slay.
sing, bye - bye, lul - loo, lul -

CIAO, CIAO, BAMBINO

English Lyric by MITCHELL PARISH
Original Italian Text by MODUGNO - VERDE
Music by DOMENICO MODUGNO

Moderately

E♭dim Dm Dm(♯7) Dm7 Dm6 Dm Dm(♯7) Dm7 G7 G+ C(9) C Cmaj7
Ciao, ciao, Bam - bi - no, the rain is fall - ing. Once more, I kiss you
trem - bling up - on your face, dear, or are they tear - drops

C6 C(9) C Cmaj7 C6 C Cmaj7 C6 Em Em(♯7) Em7 B7
1.
and then good - bye. Our love was just like a fair - y sto - ry, but all it's glo - ry
for the love we knew? Ciao, ciao, Bam - bi - no, my heart is call - ing.

Em E♭dim G7 Em7 E♭dim Dm7 G7 Dm7 G7 C
2.
must pass us by. Are rain-drops While rain is fall - ing, I cry with you.

CIRIBIRIBIN
(Chiribiribee)

English Lyric by HOWARD JOHNSON
Music by A. PESTALOZZA

Brightly

F
Ci - ri - bi - ri - bin, a mel - o - dy your heart can toss up to the

C7 F
sky; Ci - ri - bi - ri - bin, a song to sing when - ev - er things have gone aw - ry;

B♭
Ci - ri - bi - ri - bin, when you feel sad just hum it for a lit - tle while. Ci - ri - bi - ri -

Fdim F C7 F
bin, soon as you be - gin, Ci - ri - bi - ri - bin, the world will smile.

CITY OF NEW ORLEANS

Words and Music by
STEVE GOODMAN

Moderately bright country beat

Verse:

1. Rid - in' on___ the Cit - y of___ New Or - leans, Il - li - nois___ Cen - tral

Mon - day morn - in' rail.___ Fif-teen cars_ and fif - teen rest - less rid - ers, three con -

duc - tors and twen-ty-five sacks of mail.___ All a - long the south-bound Od - ys - sey,_ the train pulls out of Kan -

- ka - kee_ and rolls a - long_ the hous - es, farms_ and fields._ Pass-in' towns_ that have__ no name_ and

freight-yards_ full of old___ black men,_ and the grave - yards_ of the rust - ed au - to-mo-biles.___ *(last time)*

Chorus:

{Good morn - ing, / Good-night} A -

mer - i - ca,_ how are___ you? Say, "Don't you know_ me? I'm your na - tive son." I'm the train they call the

Cit-y of__ New Or - leans. I'll be gone_ five hun-dred miles_ when the day_ is done. 2. Deal-in'

3. done. I'll be gone__ five hun - dred miles__ when the day_ is done.

Verse 2:
**Dealin' card games with the old men in the club car,
Penny a point ain't no one keeping' score.
Pass the paper bag that holds the bottle;
Feel the wheels grumblin' 'neath the floor;
And the sons of Pullman porters, and the sons of engineers
Ride their father's magic carpet made of steel.
Mothers with their babes asleep are rockin' to the gentle beat
And the rhythm of the rails is all they feel.**
(To Chorus:)

Verse 3:
**Nighttime on the City of New Orleans,
Changin' cars in Memphis, Tennessee;
Halfway home, we'll be there by mornin',
Thru the Mississippi darkness rollin' down to the sea.
But all the towns and people seem to fade into a bad dream,
And the steel rail still ain't heard the news;
The conductor sings his songs again;
The passengers will please refrain,
This train's got the disappearin' railroad blues.**
(To Chorus:)

CLAIR DE LUNE

CLAUDE DEBUSSY

D♭/F G♭dim7 D♭/F A♭7/E♭ G♭6/D♭ A♭7/C G♭6/B♭ F7/A
D♭6/A♭ G♭6 D♭6/F A♭7/E♭ D♭ G♭6 To Coda G♭6
D♭7/F B♭m E♭m7
A♭7 Adim7 G♭/B♭ Cm7(♭5) G♭/D♭ E♭m6
D♭/F D♭m6/F♭ E♭m7(4) A♭7 D♭ Fm F♭/A♭ D♭ Fm F♭/A♭ D♭ E♭9 A♭9 G♭ Fm
A♭9 G♭ Fm E♭m D+ E♭m A♭+ D♭ Fm F♭/A♭ D♭ Fm E/G♯ E6/B /C♯ /E
F♯m/G♯ /F♯ /E♯ F♯m7/E Dmaj7 A/C♯ Bm7 A6 A/G♯ F♯m7 G♭6/A♭ A♭9
G♭6/A♭ A♭9 G♭/A♭ A♭7 G♭/A♭ A♭7 G♭6/A♭ A♭9 G♭6/A♭ A♭9 G♭6 G♭m6 G♭m6(4)
D.C. al Coda
Coda
D♭7/A♭ B♭m D♭/F E♭m7 A♭9 A♭7
D♭ Fm D♭ Fm F♭/A♭ D♭ Fm D♭ Fm F♭/A♭ D♭

CLARINET POLKA

TRADITIONAL

Bright polka tempo

Bb F7 Bb F7

To Coda 1. Bb 2. Bb To Next Strain 3. Bb Fine C7

F C7 F C7

F C7 1. F 2. F D.S. al Coda

Coda Bb Eb Bb7

1. Eb 2. D.S. al Fine Eb

CLASSICAL GAS

Music by MASON WILLIAMS

Freely
Am G G/F♯ Em Am G G/F♯ Em Am G Am G/B C Am

Moderately fast
To Coda
a tempo
D.S. al Coda
Coda
rit.

CLEMENTINE

FOLK SONG

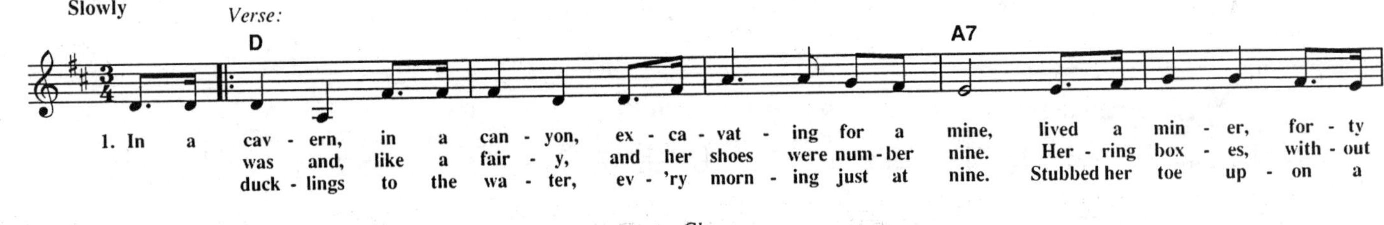
Slowly
Verse:
D
A7
1. In a cav - ern, in a can - yon, ex - ca - vat - ing for a mine, lived a min - er, for - ty
was and, like a fair - y, and her shoes were num - ber nine. Her - ring box - es, with - out
duck - lings to the wa - ter, ev - 'ry morn - ing just at nine. Stubbed her toe up - on a

Chorus:
D
A7
D
nin - er, and his daugh - ter Clem - en - tine.
top - es, san - dals were for Clem - en - tine.
splin - ter, fell in - to the foam - ing brine.
Oh my dar - ling, oh my dar - ling, oh my dar - ling Clem - en -

1.-6.
7.
A7
D
A7
D
D
tine; you are lost and gone for - ev - er, dread - ful sor - ry, Clem - en - tine! 2. Light she tine!
3. She drove

Verse 4:
Ruby lips above the water,
Blowing bubbles soft and fine,
But alas, I was no swimmer,
So I lost my Clementine.
(To Chorus:)

Verse 5:
There's a churchyard on the hillside,
Where the flowers grow and twine,
There grow roses 'mongst the posies,
Fertilized by Clementine.
(To Chorus:)

Verse 6:
Then the miner, forty-niner,
Soon began to peak and pine;
Thought he ought to join his daughter,
Now he's with his Clementine.
(To Chorus:)

Verse 7:
In my dreams she still doth haunt me,
Robed in garments soaked in brine;
Though in life I used to hug her,
Now she's dead I draw the line.
(To Chorus:)

THE CLOSER I GET TO YOU

Words and Music by
JAMES MTUME and
REGGIE LUCAS

Slowly
Amaj7 Dmaj9 C♯m7 F♯m7 Amaj7 Dmaj9 C♯m7 F♯m7
The clos-er I get to you, the more you make me see;
Ly-ing here next to you, time just seems to fly.
Amaj7 Dmaj9 C♯m7 F♯m7 Amaj7 Dmaj9 C♯m7 A7
by giv - ing me all you've got, your love has cap - tured me.
Need-ing you more and more; let's give love a try.
Dmaj7 C♯m7 Em7 A7 Dmaj7
O - ver and o - ver a - gain, I try to tell my - self that we could nev - er be more than
Sweet-er and sweet - er love grows, and heav - en's there for those who fool the tricks of
1. D.C. 2. D.C. and fade
C♯m7 Em7 A7 Dmaj7 C♯m7 Bm7 E7sus Bm7 E7sus
friends, and all the while in - side I knew it was real, the way you make me feel. spe - cial way.
time. With the hearts of love they find true love in a

THE CLOSER YOU GET

Words and Music by
MARK GRAY and
JAMES P. PENNINGTON

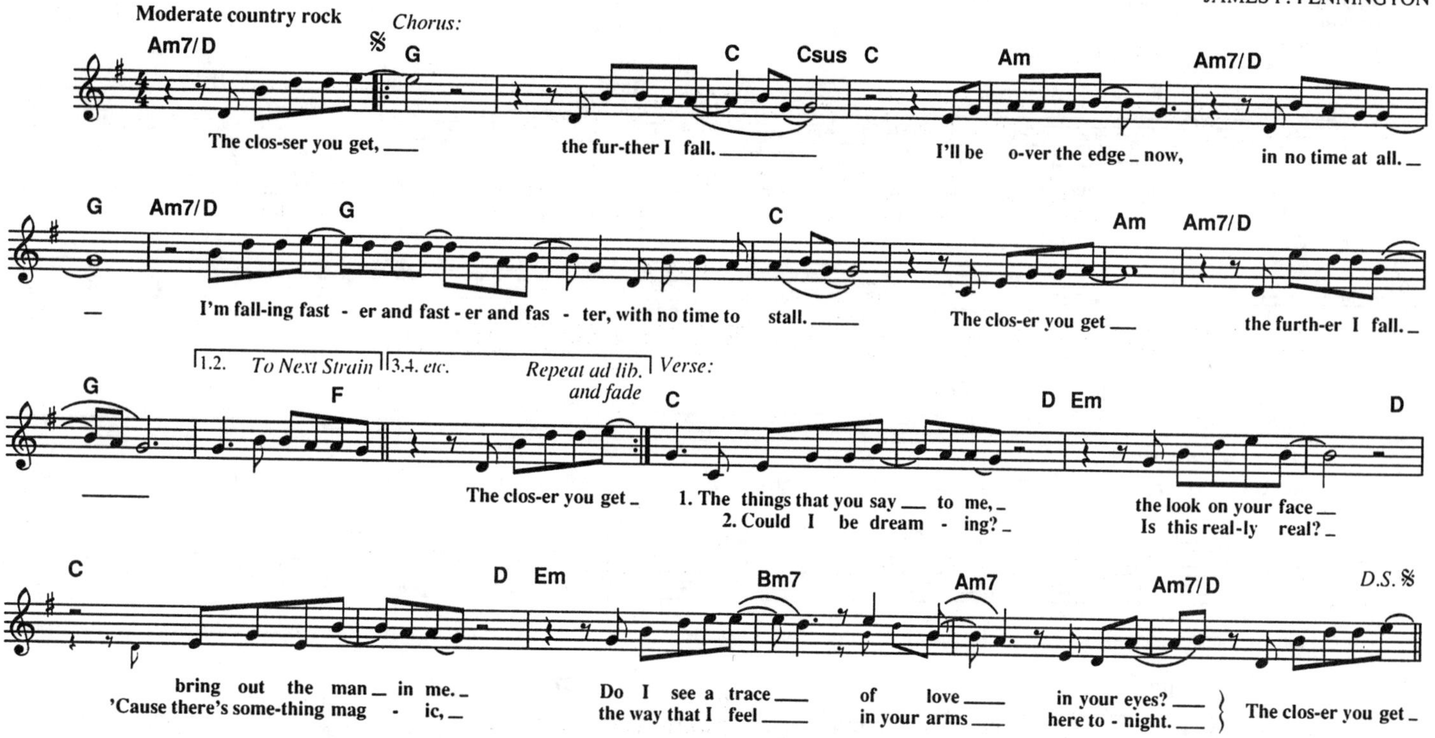

Moderate country rock

Chorus:

The clos-ser you get, the fur-ther I fall. I'll be o-ver the edge now, in no time at all. I'm fall-ing fast - er and fast - er and fas - ter, with no time to stall. The clos-er you get the furth-er I fall.

1.2. *To Next Strain* 3.4. *etc.* *Repeat ad lib. and fade*

The clos-er you get

Verse:

1. The things that you say to me, the look on your face bring out the man in me. Do I see a trace of love in your eyes?
2. Could I be dream - ing? Is this real-ly real? 'Cause there's some-thing mag - ic, the way that I feel in your arms here to - night.

The clos-er you get

D.S. 𝄋

COCKTAILS FOR TWO

Words and Music by
ARTHUR JOHNSTON and
SAM COSLOW

Moderately

In some se - clud - ed ren - dez - vous that o - ver - looks the av - e - nue with some-one shar-ing a de - light - ful chat of this and that and cock-tails for two. As we en - joy a cig - a - rette, to some ex - qui - site chan-son - nette, two hands are sure to sly - ly meet be-neath a ser - vi-nette, with cock-tails for two. My head may go reel - ing, but my heart will be o - be - di - ent with in - tox - i - cat-ing kiss - es for the prin - ci - pal in - gre - di - ent. Most an - y af - ter-noon at five we'll be so glad we're both a - live. Then may-be for-tune will com - plete her plan that all be-gan with cock-tails for two.

From the Film "COCOANUT GROVE"

COCOANUT GROVE

HARRY OWENS

Smooth swing
There's a co-coa-nut grove where life is en-tranc-ing, and there, sweet-heart, we'll find ro-manc-ing and love for two by the light of a south sea is-land moon. There's co-coa-nut grove where your hap-py lov-er will do his part and soon dis-cov-er a ren-dez-vous in the shel-ter of a trop-i-cal la-goon. Palm trees will be sway-ing while steel gui-tars are play-ing. Be-lieve what I'm say-ing, dear. I swear it's true. There's a co-coa-nut grove where I'll be con-fess-ing the sim-ple truth that you've been guess-ing, sweet-heart, I love but you.

COLD, COLD HEART

Words and Music by
HANK WILLIAMS

Moderately
1. I tried so hard, my dear, to show that you're my ev-'ry dream. Yet you're a-fraid each thing I do is just some e-vil scheme. A mem-'ry from your lone-some past keeps us so far a-part. Why can't I free your doubt-ful mind and melt your cold, cold heart? An-oth-er love be-fore my time made your heart sad and blue. And so my heart is pay-ing now for things I did-n't do. In an-ger, un-kind words are said that make the tear-drops start. Why can't I free your doubt-ful mind and melt your cold, cold heart? 2. You'll
nev-er know how much it hurts to see you sit and cry. You know you need and want my love, yet you're a-fraid to try. Why do you run and hide from life? To try it just ain't smart. Why can't I free your doubt-ful mind and melt your cold, cold heart? There was a time when I be-lieved that you be-longed to me. But now I know your heart is shack-led to a mem-o-ry. The more I learn to care for you, the more we drift a-part. Why can't I free your doubt-ful mind and melt your cold, cold heart?

From the Broadway Musical "BARNUM"

THE COLORS OF MY LIFE

Music by CY COLEMAN
Lyrics by MICHAEL STEWART

Slowly
C11 F Fmaj7 F6 C11 F Fmaj7 F6 F B♭maj7
(Boy) The col - ors of my life are boun - ti - ful and bold, the pur - ple glow of
(Girl) The col - ors of my life are soft - er than a breeze, the sil - ver gray of
Am7(♭5) Am7(♭5)/D D7 Gm(9) Gm Gm7 B♭/C C7 C11 F Fmaj7
in - di - go, the gleam of green and gold. The splen-dor of a sun - rise, the daz-zle of a flame,
ei - der-down, the dap-pled green of trees. The am - ber of a wheat field, the ha-zel of a seed,
F6 F B♭maj7 Am7(♭5) Am7(♭5)/D D7 Gm7 C7sus C7 C11 F C11
the glo - ry of a rain - bow, I'd put 'em all to shame. No qui - et browns and grays, I'll take my days in -
the crys-tal of a rain - drop are all I'll ev - er need. Your reds are much too bold, in gold I find no
F B♭maj7 Am7(♭5) Am7(♭5)/D D7(♭5) D7 Gm E7
stead, and fill them till they o - ver - flow with rose and cher-ry red. And should this sun - lit world
worth. I'll fill my days with sage and brown, the col - ors of the earth. And if from by my side
Am C7sus C7 C11 F B♭/C C7 F C11
grow dark one day, the col-ors of my life will leave a shin-ing light to show the way. The col-ors of my
my love should roam, the col-ors of my life will shine a qui - et light to lead him home. The col-ors of my
F B♭/C F G/F Gm/F F
life will leave a shin-ing light to show the way.
life will shine a qui - et light to lead him home.
CUTE
© 1958 WB MUSIC CORP. (Renewed)
All Rights Reserved
Music by NEAL HEFTI
Moderately
Dm7 Em7 A7(♭9 ♯5) Dm7 G9 C6 A7 A7(♭9) Dm7 Em7 A7(♭9 ♯5)
Dm7 G9 Gm7 C7 Gm7 C9 Fmaj7 Em7 F6 Dm7(♭5) C F7 E7 Am7
Am6 B7 Emaj7 Em7(♭5) A7 Dm7 Em7 A7(♯5) Dm7 G9 C6

COLUMBIA, THE GEM OF THE OCEAN
(The Red, White and Blue)

Words by DAVID T. SHAW
Music by THOMAS BECKET

Maestoso
O Co - lum - bia, the gem of the o - cean, the home of the brave and the free, the shrine of each pa - triot's de - vo - tion, a world of - fers hom - age to thee. Thy man - dates make he - roes as - sem - ble, when Lib - er - ty's form stands in view. Thy ban - ners make tyr - an - ny trem - ble when borne by the red, white and blue.
war winged its wide des - o - la - tion, and threat - ened the land to de - form, the ark then of free - dom's foun - da - tion, Co - lum - bia, rode safe thro' the storm; with the gar - lands of vic - t'ry a - round her, when so proud - ly she bore her brave crew, with her flag proud - ly float - ing be - fore her, the boast of the red, white and blue.
star span - gled ban - ner bring hith - er, o'er Co - lum - bia's true sons let it wave; may the wreaths they have won nev - er with - er, nor its stars cease to shine on the brave. May the ser - vice, u - nit - ed, ne'er sev - er, but hold to their col - ors so true, the ar - my and na - vy for - ev - er. Three cheers for the red, white and blue.
Chorus:
When borne by the red, white and blue, when borne by the red, white and blue, thy ban - ners make tyr - an - ny trem - ble when borne by the red, white and blue. When
The boast of the red, white and blue, the boast of the red, white and blue, with her flag proud - ly float - ing be - fore her, the boast of the red, white and blue. The
Three cheers for the red, white and blue, three cheers for the red, white and blue, the ar - my and na - vy for - ev - er, three cheers for the red, white and blue.
From the Broadway Musical Production "BRIGADOON"
COME TO ME — BEND TO ME
Copyright © 1947 (Renewed 1975) ALAN JAY LERNER and FREDERICK LOEWE
World rights assigned to and controlled by EMI U CATALOG INC.
All Rights Reserved
Words by ALAN JAY LERNER
Music by FREDERICK LOEWE
Moderately
Verse:
Be - cause they've told me I can't be - hold ye 'til wed - din' mu - sic starts play - in' to ease my long - in', there's noth - in' wrong in me stand - in' out here an' say - in':
near me so ye can hear me, I've got to whis - per this soft - ly. For though I'm burn - in' to shout my yearn - in' the words come tip - toe - in' off me.
Chorus:
Oh, come to me, bend to me, kiss me good day. Dar - lin', my dar - lin', 'tis all I can say. Just come to me, bend to me, kiss me good day. Give me your lips an' don't take them a - way. Come, dear - ie, way.

COME BACK TO SORRENTO

(Torna A Surriento)

Words and Music by
ERNESTO di CURTIS

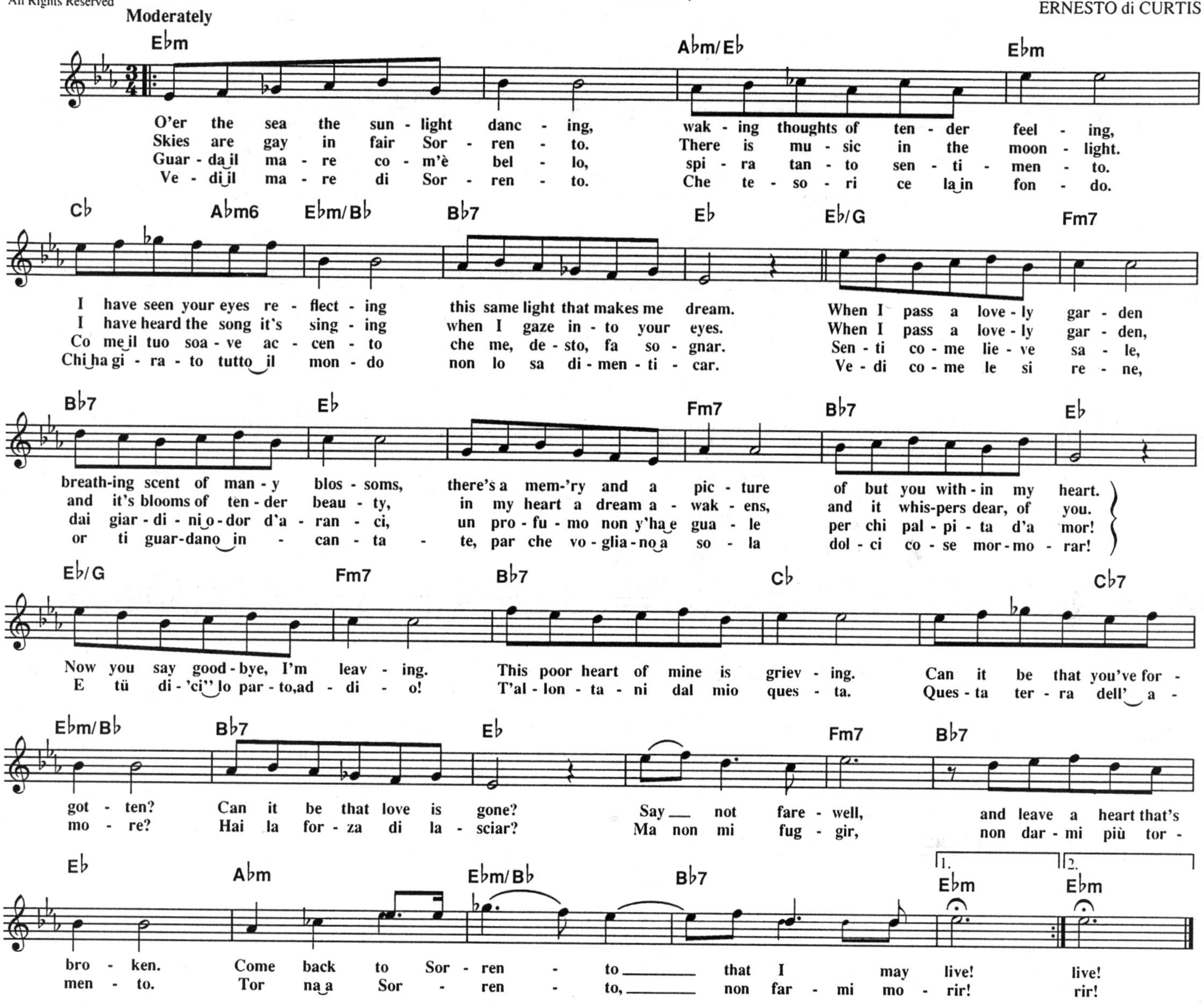

Moderately

Ebm Abm/Eb Ebm

O'er the sea the sun - light danc - ing, wak - ing thoughts of ten - der feel - ing,
Skies are gay in fair Sor - ren - to. There is mu - sic in the moon - light.
Guar - da il ma - re co - m'è bel - lo, spi - ra tan - to sen - ti - men - to.
Ve - di il ma - re di Sor - ren - to. Che te - so - ri ce la in fon - do.

Cb Abm6 Ebm/Bb Bb7 Eb Eb/G Fm7

I have seen your eyes re - flect - ing this same light that makes me dream. When I pass a love - ly gar - den
I have heard the song it's sing - ing when I gaze in - to your eyes. When I pass a love - ly gar - den,
Co me il tuo soa - ve ac - cen - to che me, de - sto, fa so - gnar. Sen - ti co - me lie - ve sa - le,
Chi ha gi - ra - to tutto il mon - do non lo sa di - men - ti - car. Ve - di co - me le si re - ne,

Bb7 Eb Fm7 Bb7 Eb

breath-ing scent of man - y blos - soms, there's a mem - 'ry and a pic - ture of but you with - in my heart.
and it's blooms of ten - der beau - ty, in my heart a dream a - wak - ens, and it whis - pers dear, of you.
dai giar - di - ni o - dor d'a - ran - ci, un pro - fu - mo non y'ha e gua - le per chi pal - pi - ta d'a mor!
or ti guar - dano in - can - ta - te, par che vo - glia - no a so - la dol - ci co - se mor - mo - rar!

Eb/G Fm7 Bb7 Cb Cb7

Now you say good - bye, I'm leav - ing. This poor heart of mine is griev - ing. Can it be that you've for -
E tü di - 'ci'' lo par - to, ad - di - o! T'al - lon - ta - ni dal mio ques - ta. Ques - ta ter - ra dell' a -

Ebm/Bb Bb7 Eb Fm7 Bb7

got - ten? Can it be that love is gone? Say not fare - well, and leave a heart that's
mo - re? Hai la for - za di la - sciar? Ma non mi fug - gir, non dar - mi più tor -

Eb Abm Ebm/Bb Bb7 1. Ebm 2. Ebm

bro - ken. Come back to Sor - ren - to that I may live! live!
men - to. Tor na a Sor - ren - to, non far - mi mo - rir! rir!

COMIN' THROUGH THE RYE

TRADITIONAL

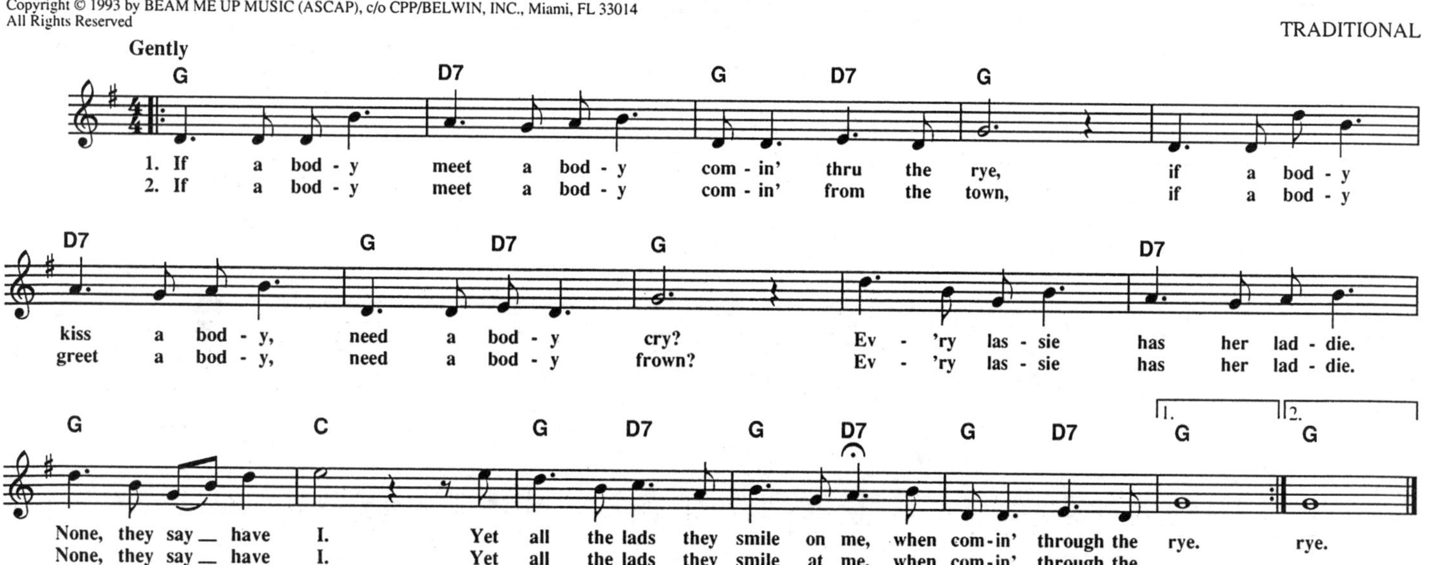
Gently
G D7 G D7 G
1. If a bod - y meet a bod - y com - in' thru the rye, if a bod - y
2. If a bod - y meet a bod - y com - in' from the town, if a bod - y
D7 G D7 G D7
kiss a bod - y, need a bod - y cry? Ev - 'ry las - sie has her lad - die.
greet a bod - y, need a bod - y frown? Ev - 'ry las - sie has her lad - die.
G C G D7 G D7 G D7 1. G 2. G
None, they say have I. Yet all the lads they smile on me, when com - in' through the rye. rye.
None, they say have I. Yet all the lads they smile at me, when com - in' through the

COME SATURDAY MORNING

Words by DORY PREVIN
Music by FRED KARLIN

Moderately slow

Eb Ab Ab6 Eb Db6 Db

Come Sat - ur - day morn - ing I'm go - ing a - way with my friend.
Come Sat - ur - day morn - ing I'm go - ing a - way with my friend.

Ab Db C7sus Fm

We'll Sat - ur - day spend till the end of the day. Just I and my
We'll Sat - ur - day laugh more than half of the day. Just I and my

Bb Fm Bbsus Bb7 Ebmaj7 Abmaj7

friend, we'll trav - el for miles in our Sat - ur - day smiles, and then we'll move
friend, dressed up in our rings and our Sat - ur - day things,

Gm7 Ab Gm Cm Fm7 Bb9 Eb

on. But we will re - mem - ber long af - ter Sat - ur-day's gone.

Ab Ab6 1. Eb Ab Ab6 2. Eb Ab Ab6 Eb

Come Sat - ur - day morn - ing. Come Sat - ur - day morn - ing.

COTTONTAIL

Music by DUKE ELLINGTON
Words by JOHN HENDRICKS

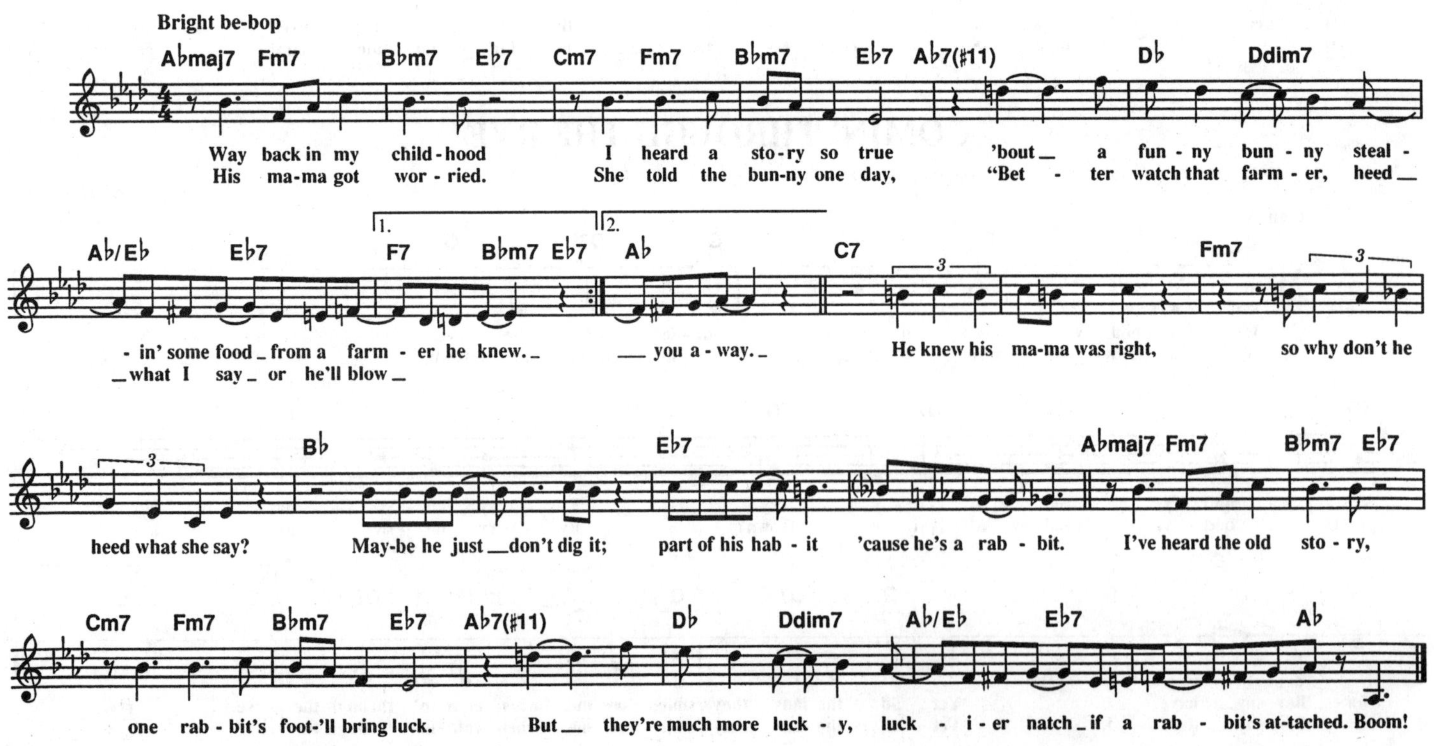
Bright be-bop
Abmaj7 Fm7 Bbm7 Eb7 Cm7 Fm7 Bbm7 Eb7 Ab7(#11) Db Ddim7
Way back in my child - hood I heard a sto - ry so true 'bout a fun - ny bun - ny steal -
His ma - ma got wor - ried. She told the bun-ny one day, "Bet - ter watch that farm - er, heed
Ab/Eb Eb7 1. F7 Bbm7 Eb7 2. Ab C7 Fm7
- in' some food from a farm - er he knew. you a - way. He knew his ma-ma was right, so why don't he
what I say or he'll blow
Bb Eb7 Abmaj7 Fm7 Bbm7 Eb7
heed what she say? May-be he just don't dig it; part of his hab - it 'cause he's a rab - bit. I've heard the old sto - ry,
Cm7 Fm7 Bbm7 Eb7 Ab7(#11) Db Ddim7 Ab/Eb Eb7 Ab
one rab - bit's foot-'ll bring luck. But they're much more luck - y, luck - i - er natch if a rab - bit's at-tached. Boom!

COME FLY WITH ME
© 1958 by MARAVILLE MUSIC CORP.
Copyright Renewed, assigned to MARAVILLE MUSIC CORP. & CAHN MUSIC CO.
All Rights on behalf of CAHN MUSIC CO. Administered by WB MUSIC CORP.
All Rights Reserved
Words by SAMMY CAHN
Music by JAMES VAN HEUSEN
Refrain (moderately, with a strong beat)
Come Fly With Me! Let's fly! Let's fly away! If you can use some exotic booze there's a bar in far Bombay, Come Fly With Me! Let's fly! Let's fly away! Come
Fly With Me! Let's float down to Peru! In Llama Land there's a one-man band and he'll toot his flute for you, Come Fly With Me! Let's take
Weather wise, it's such a lovely day! Just say the words and we'll beat the birds down to Acapulco Bay. It's perfect for a fly-
off in the blue! (Once I get you) Up there! Where the air is rarified, We'll just glide, starry-eyed. (Once I get you) Up there! I'll be holding you so near, You may hear Angels cheer, 'cause we're together.
ing honeymoon, they say, Come Fly With Me! Let's fly! Let's fly away!
To Coda
D.S. al Coda
Coda
COME GO WITH ME
© 1957 (Renewed) by GIL MUSIC CORP. & FEE BEE MUSIC
1650 Broadway, New York, N.Y. 10019
All Rights Reserved
Words and Music by
C.E. QUICK
Slow beat
Refrain:
1. Love, love me, darlin', Come and go with me, Please don't send me 'way beyond the sea;
2.3. Come, come, come, come, come, Come into my heart, Tell me, darlin', We will never part;
I need you, darlin', So Come Go With Me
Me
Fine
Yes, I need you, Yes, I really need you, Please say you'll never leave me. Well say, you never, Yes, you really never, You never give me a chance.
D.S. al Fine

COMING AROUND AGAIN

By CARLY SIMON

Moderately slow

C Am7 F(9) C

1. Ba - by sneez-es, Mom-my pleas-es, Dad - dy breez-es in. So good on pa - per,
2. You pay the gro - cer, fix the toas - ter; you kiss the host good - bye. Then you break a win - dow,

Am7 F(9) C F

so ro - man - tic, but so be - wil - der - ing.
burn the souf - fle, scream a lul - la - by.
I know no-thin' stays the same,

Dm B♭(9) F

but if you're will-ing to play the game, it's com-ing a - round a - gain. So

F/E♭ E♭ Am7(♭5)/C D/C F/A C/E (1. D.C.) C/E (2.) C

don't mind if I fall a - part; there's more room in a bro - ken heart, (bro - ken heart.) bro - ken heart. And

Am7 F C F

I be - lieve in love. But what else can I do; I'm so in love with you. I know

Dm B♭(9) F *Repeat and fade*

noth-ing stays the same, but if you're will-ing to play the game, it's com-ing a - round a - gain.

COUNTRY GARDENS

TRADITIONAL

Moderately
C F G7 C C7 F Fm C G7 C F G7 C
C7 F Fm C G7 C Cdim G7 C D7 G7 Am Cm6 D7 G D7 G
C F G7 C C7 F Fm G7 C F G7 C
F C G7 C F G7 C C7 F Fm G7 C

COMING OUT OF THE DARK

Words and Music by
GLORIA ESTEFAN, EMILIO ESTEFAN, JR.
and JON SECADA

Gospel rock
N.C.
(Keyboard:)
Verse:
E(2) D/E E(2) D/E
1. Why be a - fraid if I'm not a - lone? Life is nev-er eas - y, the rest is un - known.
2. Start-ing a - gain is part of the plan, and I'll be so much strong-er hold - ing your hand.
E D/E E
And up till now for me it's been hands a - gainst stone. I spend each and ev - 'ry
Step by step I'll make it through, I know I can. It may not make it
D/E A/C♯ Amaj7 A/B
mo - ment search - ing for what to be - lieve.
eas - i - er, but I have felt you near all the way.
Chorus:
E E7
Com-ing out of the dark I fin - 'lly see the light,
A/E Am6/E E C♯m7
now, and it's shin - ing on me.
A(2) A/B E E7
Com-ing out of the dark, I know the love that saved
1.
A/E Am6/E E D2/E E D2/E N.C.
me, you're shar - ing with me.
D.S.
2.
A/E A/B
me, you're shar - ing with me.
To Next Strain
3.4.etc.
A/E Am6/E E C♯m7
me you're shar - ing, you're shar - ing with me, shar - ing with me,
A(2) A/B
shar-ing with me, shar-ing with me.
Repeat ad lib. and fade
Bridge:
A E/G♯ F♯m7 E/G♯ F♯m/A Amaj7/B
For-ev - er stand on the rock of your love.
A E/G♯ F♯m7 A/B B♭7(♭5) A E/G♯
Ev - er, ev - er, ooh. Can't no-bod - y stop me! Watch me! Ev - er and ev - er
F♯m7 E/G♯ F♯m/A Amaj7/B E E/D A/C♯ A A/B
stand on the rock of your love is all it takes no mat-ter what we face. Com-ing out of the
D.S.S.

COMPADRE PEDRO JUAN

Words and Music by
LUIS ALBERTI

Bright merengue

G D7 G D7 G G D7 G6 D7 G6 D7 G6

Com - pa-dre Pe - dro Juan, bai - le el me - ren - gue. Com - pa-dre Pe - dro Juan, que es-tá sa - bro - so. A - que-lla ni - ña de los o - jos ver-des que tie-ne cuer-po flex - i - ble bai - le-la de em-pal - i - za. Com- co a-tra - pa - o.

pa-dre Pe - dro Juan, sa - que su da - ma. Com - pa-dre Pe - dro Juan, no pier-da el tiem - po. Se a - ca - ba-ra el me-ren - gue y si-no an - da con cui - da-o se que-da - rá co-mo peri -

(Bai - le) Com - pa-dre Juan, (bai - le) de me-dio lao. (Bai - le) Com - pa-dre Juan, (bai - le) de a - quí pa-llá.

(Bai - le) a - pam-bi-chao, (bai - le) de em - pal - i - za. (Bai - le) de a - lla pa - cá, (bai - le) me - dio jin-cao.

Montuno — *Repeat as needed* — *Last time*

Com -

G D7 G D7 G D7 G

pa-dre Pe - dro Juan, bai-le el me - ren - gue. Com-pa-dre Pe - dro Juan, que es-tá sa - bro - so. A - que-lla ni - ña de los o - jos ver-des que tie-ne cuer-po flex - i - ble bai - le-la de em-pa - li - za. Com- co a - tra - pao.

pa-dre Pe - dro Juan sa-que su da - ma. Com-pa-dre Pe - dro Juan no pier-dal tiem - po. Se a - ca - ba-rá el me-ren - gue y si-no an - da con cui - da-o se que-da - rá co-mo peri -

A CUP OF COFFEE, A SANDWICH AND YOU

Words by BILLY ROSE and AL DUBIN
Music by JOSEPH MEYER

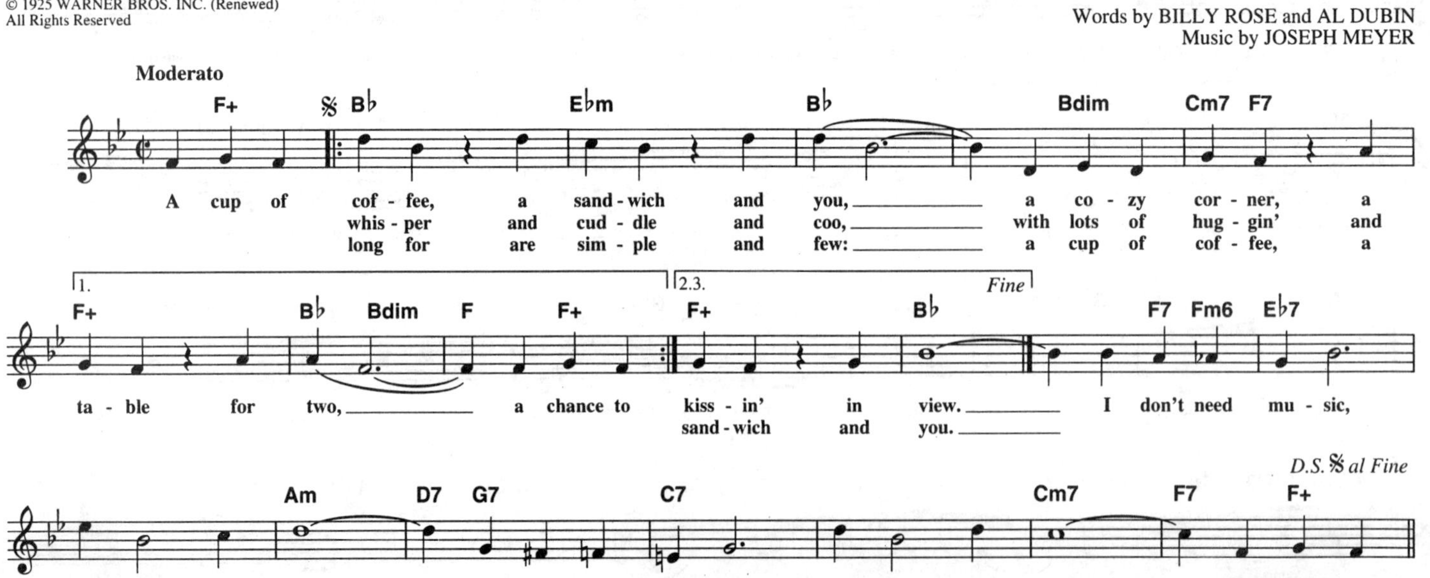
Moderato
F+ B♭ E♭m B♭ Bdim Cm7 F7
A cup of cof - fee, a sand-wich and you, a co - zy cor - ner, a
whis - per and cud - dle and coo, with lots of hug - gin' and
long for are sim - ple and few: a cup of cof - fee, a
F+ B♭ Bdim F F+ F+ B♭ F7 Fm6 E♭7
ta - ble for two, a chance to kiss - in' in view. I don't need mu - sic,
sand - wich and you.
Fine
D.S. al Fine
Am D7 G7 C7 Cm7 F7 F+
lob - ster or wine, when - ev - er your eyes look in - to mine. the things I

CONGA

Words and Music by
ENRIQUE E. GARCIA

Moderate salsa rock
N.C.
Come _ on, shake your bod - y, ba - by, do the con - ga, I know _ you can't con-trol your-self an - y lon - ger. Come _
_ on shake your bod-y, ba-by, do the con - ga, I know _ you can't con-trol your-self an - y lon - ger.
Em
Come _
Chorus:
D
Em
_ on, shake your bod - y, ba - by, do the con - ga, I know _ you can't con - trol your-self an - y lon - ger. Feel _
1.2.4.
To Next Strain
D
Em
_ the rhy - thm of the mu - sic get - ting stron - ger. Don't _ you fight it 'til you tried it, do that con - ga beat.
3.
Em
D
To Coda
Em
_ you fight it 'til you tried it, do the con - ga. Come _
Verse:
D
Em
1. Ev-'ry-bod - y _ gath-er 'round now. _ Let your bod - y feel _ the heat.
2. It's the rhy - thm _ of the is - land, _ and like sug-ar cane _ so sweet.
D
1.3.
Em
2.
D.S.
Don't you wor - ry _ if you can't dance; _ let the mu-sic move _ your feet.
If you want to _ do the con - ga, _ you've got to lis-ten to _ the beat.
Come on _
4.
D.S. al Coda
Come on _
Coda
N.C.
Em
Come _ on, shake your bod-y, ba-by, do that con - ga!

Verse 3:
Feel the fire of desire, as you dance the night away,
'Cause tonight we're gonna party, 'til we see the break of day.

Verse 4:
Better get yourself together, and hold on to what you've got.
Once the music hits your system, there's no way you're gonna stop.
(To Chorus:)

(From the Broadway Musical "PIPPIN")

CORNER OF THE SKY

Words and Music by
STEPHEN SCHWARTZ

Moderately
C Dm/C C B♭/C F C/E
1. Ev-'ry-thing has its sea - son, ev-'ry-thing has its time. Show me a rea - son and I'll soon
2. Ev-'ry man has his day - dreams, ev-'ry man has his goal. Peo-ple like the way dreams have of stick-
3. may-be some mist - y day, you'll wak-en to find me gone. And far a - way you'll hear me sing-
Dm B♭ E♭maj7 A♭ Dm7
show you a rhyme. Cats fit on the win - dow sill, chil - dren fit in the snow.
- ing to the soul. Rain comes af - ter thun - der, win - ter comes af - ter fall.
- ing to the dawn. And you'll won - der if I'm hap - py there, a lit - tle more than I've been. And the
Gm Gm/F E♭ B♭/D C B♭ Am7 C F Fmaj7 Gsus G
Why do I feel I don't fit in an-y - where I go?
Some-times I think I'm not af - ter an-y - thing at all.
an-swer will come back to you like laugh - ter on the wind.
Riv-ers be-long where they can ram - ble,
Em Em7 F C Dm/C G/B Am F C
ea-gles be-long where they can fly. I've got to be where my spir-it can run free, got to find my cor - ner
1. Gm C Dm/C C Dm/C
of the sky.
2. Gm C B♭/C F
of the sky.
C F Em Dm Fmaj7 Gsus C Dm/C
D.C.
3. And
3. Gm C Dm/C C Dm/C
of the sky.
C Dm/C C Dm/C C B♭/C F C

CORRINE, CORRINA

By MITCHELL PARISH, BO CHATMAN
and J. MAYO WILLIAMS

Moderately

A

Verse:

𝄋 (A) E7 A A7 D

1. I love Cor - ri - na, tell the world I do. I love Cor - ri - na,
dar-lin' where you been so long? Oh lit - tle dar - lin'
ri - na way a - cross the sea. Oh me, I left Cor - ri - na

A E7 A A7

tell the world I do. I pray ev-'ry night she'll learn to love me too.
where you been so long? I ain't had no lov-in' since you've been gone.
way a - cross the sea. If you see Cor - ri - na send her home to me.
Cor - ri - na, Cor -

Chorus:

𝄋𝄋 D D7 A E7 A

ri - na, Cor - ri - na, Cor - ri - na. Cor - ri - na, Cor - ri - na, I love you so.

To Coda ⊕ 1. D.S. 𝄋

2. Oh, lit - tle

2. A To Next Strain 3. A A7 D.S.S. 𝄋𝄋 al Coda

I love you so. I love you so. Cor - ri - na, Cor -

Bridge:

A E7 A A7 D E A D.S. 𝄋

3. I left Cor -

⊕ Coda

a tempo

Repeat ad lib. and fade

A E7 A E7

I love you so. {Oh, dar - lin', / Dar - lin',} don't you know, I love you

CUDDLE UP A LITTLE CLOSER, LOVELY MINE

Words by OTTO HAUERBACH
Music by KARL HOSCHNA

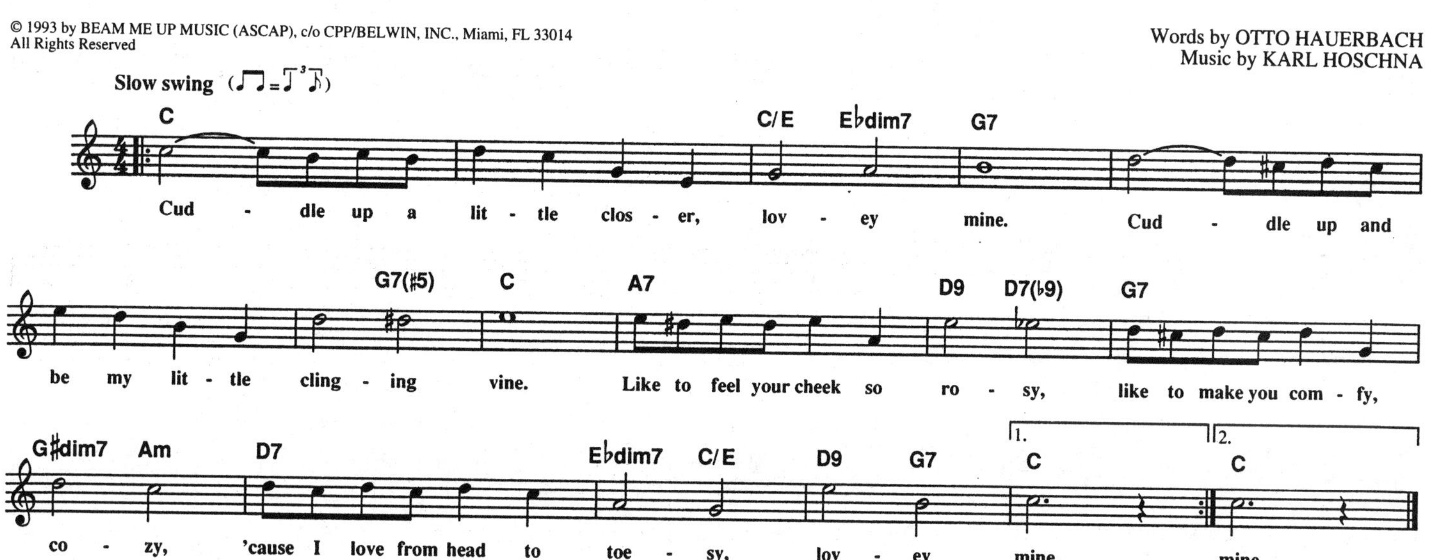
Slow swing
C C/E E♭dim7 G7
Cud - dle up a lit - tle clos - er, lov - ey mine. Cud - dle up and
G7(♯5) C A7 D9 D7(♭9) G7
be my lit - tle cling - ing vine. Like to feel your cheek so ro - sy, like to make you com - fy,
G♯dim7 Am D7 E♭dim7 C/E D9 G7 1. C 2. C
co - zy, 'cause I love from head to toe - sy, lov - ey mine. mine.

CRYING

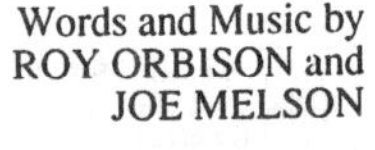
Words and Music by
ROY ORBISON and
JOE MELSON

Moderately slow rock

C
1. I was al - right for a - while. I could smile for a - while. But I saw you last night, _ you held my
2. I was o - ver you. But it's true, so ___ true. I love you e - ven more _ than I

C+ F Fm G9 C G7
hand real tight, _ as you stopped to say "Hel - lo." Oh you wished me well. _ You could-n't tell ___ that I'd been
did be - fore, _ but dar-ling what can I do? For you don't love me, _ and I'll al - ways be, ___

Chorus:

C Em C Em F G7
cry - ing o - ver you, _ cry - ing o - ver you. _ When you said "So long," left me
Yes, now you're ___ gone, and from

F G7 C C+ F/C Fm/C C
stand-ing ___ all a - lone, a - lone and cry - ing, _ cry - ing, _ cry - ing, _ cry - ing. It's hard to un - der -
this ___ mo-ment on I'll be

G7 C C
stand, but the touch of your hand ___ can start me cry - ing. ___ 2. I thought that cry - ing. ___

1. D.S. 𝄋 2.

CU-CU-RRU-CU-CU PALOMA

English Lyrics by
PAT VALANDO and RONNIE CARSON
Spanish Lyrics and Music by
TOMAS MENDEZ

Slowly
Verse:
G Gmaj7 G D7 G7 C Cmaj7
Please, pret-ty lit-tle dove, hur-ry to my love, tell {her / him} this for me. Since {she / he} is far a - way, ev-'ry day is
Di - cen que por las no - ches no-mas se le̮ i - ba̮ en pu - ro llo - rar. Di - cen que no co - mi - a, no-mas se
C6 C D♭ D7 G Gmaj7 G6 G♯dim
sad, blue as it can be. I could-n't e - ven start pour-ing out my heart to {her / him} in a let - ter. ___ You, pret-ty lit-tle bird, you can sing the
le̮ i-ba̮ en pu-ro to-mar. Ju-ran que̮ el mis-mo cie - lo se̮ ex-tre-me - ci - a̮ al o - ir su llan-to; ___ co - mo su-frio por e - lla que̮ has-ta̮ en su
D7 G Chorus: G7 C D7 G
words, you can tell {her / him} bet - ter. ___ Coo coo roo coo coo, ___ Pa - lo - ma, ___ tell {her / him} that I'm, oh ___ so lone - ly. ___
muer - te la fue lla - man-do. ___ ¡Ay, ay, ay, ay, ay, ___ can - ta - ba! ___ ¡Ay, ay, ay, ay, ay, ___ ge - mi - a! ___
G7 C D7 1. G 2. G
Coo coo roo coo coo, ___ Pa - lo - ma ___ tell {her / him} that I love ___ {her / him} on - ly. ___ on - ly. ___
¡Ay, ay, ay, ay, ay, ___ can - ta - ba, ___ de pa - sion mor-tal, ___ mo - ri - a. ___ ri - a. ___

CUTS BOTH WAYS

Words and Music by
GLORIA ESTEFAN

Slowly
B2
G♯m7
(Keyboard:)
Emaj7
C♯m7(♭5)/G
Verse:
B2
1. It cuts both ways. Our love is like a knife that
G♯m7
cuts both ways. It's driv-en deep into my
Emaj7
heart each time
C♯m7(♭5)/G
that I re-a-lize how it
To Coda
B2
cuts both ways.
Can't be to-geth-er can-not
G♯m7
live a-part. We're head-ing straight in-to a
Emaj7
bro-ken heart, but
C♯m7(♭5)/G
I can't stop. 'Cause I feel
Slower and soulfully
Chorus:
Emaj7
too much to let you go. I'm hurt-ing you, and it's hard I know to stay
D♯m7
and fight for what we've got,
G♯m7
know-ing it-'ll nev-er be good e-nough. 'Cause you and I
Emaj7
are dan-ger-ous. We want too much, and life ain't that way. Don't ask
D♯m7
for more, don't be a fool.
1.
C♯m7
Have-n't we al-read-y
C♯m7(♭5)/G
bro-ken ev-ery rule?
Slowly
D.S. 𝄋
2. It
2.
C♯m7
Have-n't we al-read-y
C♯m7(♭5)/G
bro-ken ev-ery rule?
F♯sus
Slowly
3. It
D.S. 𝄋 al Coda
Coda
B2
It cuts both ways.
Mm
Emaj7
it cuts both ways,
C♯m7(♭5)/G
B2
it cuts both
F♯ B
ways.

Verse 2:
It cuts both ways.
We're in too deep for sorry alibis.
Can't have regrets or even questions why
We can't say goodbye,
Because it cuts both ways.
No more illusions of the love we make.
No sacrifice would ever be too great
If you would just stay.
(To Chorus:)

Verse 3:
It cuts both ways.
Our love is like a knife that cuts both ways.
It's driven deep into my heart each time
I see we're livin' a lie, and it cuts both ways,
(To Coda)

DANCE LITTLE BIRD

Copyright © 1973, 1974, 1982 by INTERVOX MUSIC, Kontich, Belgium
All rights for U.S.A. controlled by SEPTEMBER MUSIC CORP., New York, N.Y.
All Rights Reserved
By TERRY RENDALL and WERNER THOMAS
Moderately
DAISY JANE
© 1975 WB MUSIC CORP.
All Rights Reserved
Words and Music by
GERRY BECKLEY
Moderately
Fly-in' me back to Memphis, got-ta find my Dai-sy Jane; well, the sum-mer's gone and I hope she's feel-in' the same.
Fly-in' me back to mem-phis, hon-ey, keep the ov-en warm; all the clouds are clear-in' and I think we're o-ver the storm.
Well, I left her just to roam the cit-y, think-in' it would ease the pain; I'm a cra-zy man and I'm play-in' my cra-zy game, game.
Well, I been pick-in' it up a-round me, Dai-sy, I think I'm sane, And I'm aw-ful glad and I guess you're real-ly to blame, blame.
Does she real-ly love me? I think she does? Like the stars a-bove me, I know be-cause when the sky is bright, ev-'ry-thing's all right.
Do you real-ly love me? I hope you do. Like the stars a-bove me, how I love you when it's cold at night, ev-'ry-thing's all right.

DANCE OF THE SUGAR-PLUM FAIRY

(From "The Nutcracker Suite")

Music by
PETER ILYICH TCHAIKOVSKY

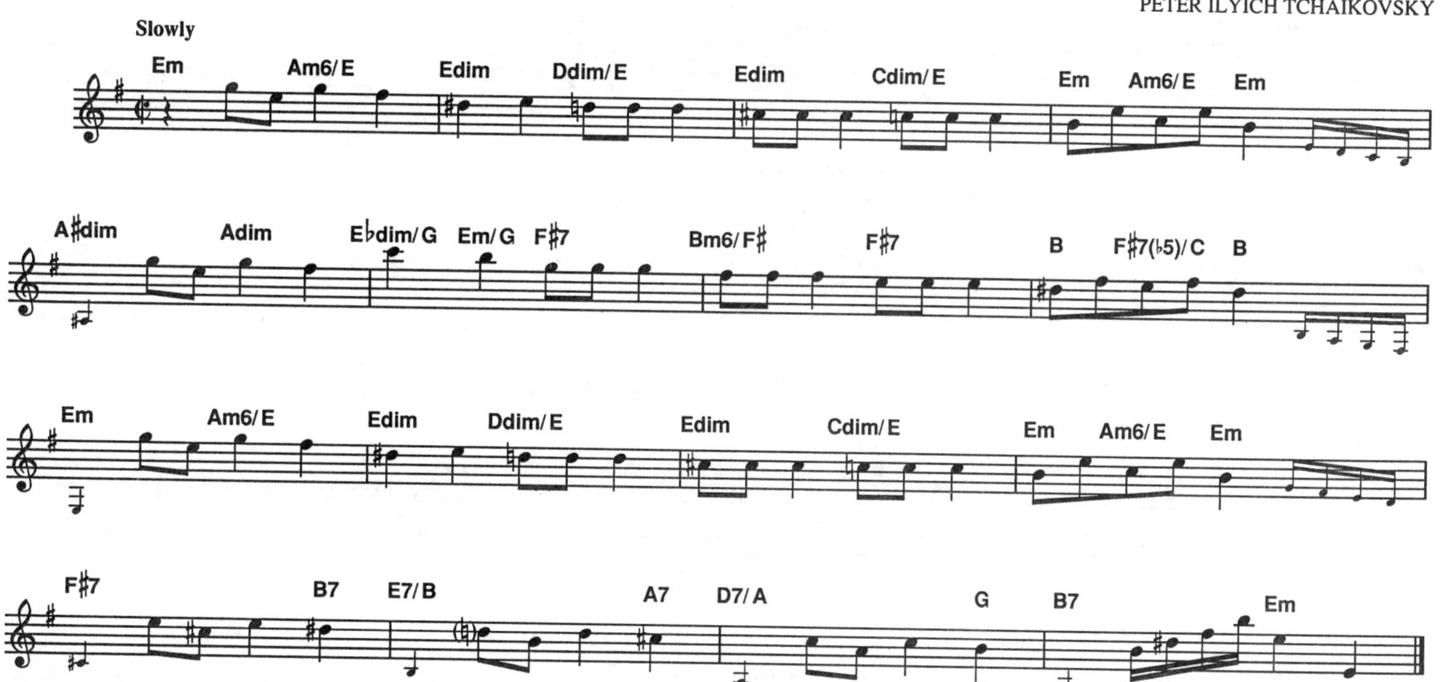
Slowly
Em Am6/E Edim Ddim/E Edim Cdim/E Em Am6/E Em
A♯dim Adim E♭dim/G Em/G F♯7 Bm6/F♯ F♯7 B F♯7(♭5)/C B
Em Am6/E Edim Ddim/E Edim Cdim/E Em Am6/E Em
F♯7 B7 E7/B A7 D7/A G B7 Em

DECK THE HALL

OLD WELSH AIR

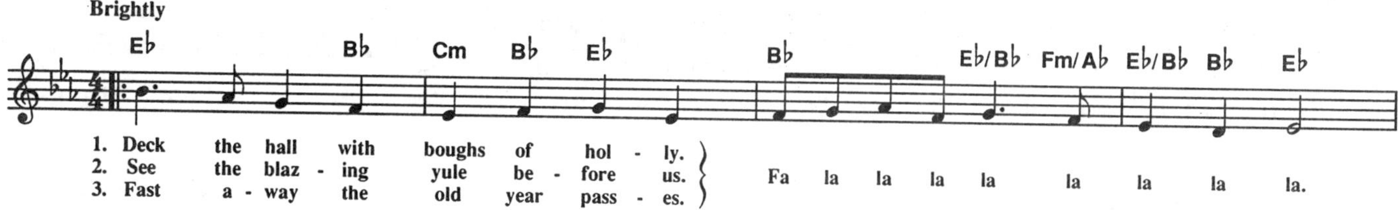
Brightly
E♭ B♭ Cm B♭ E♭ B♭ E♭/B♭ Fm/A♭ E♭/B♭ B♭ E♭
1. Deck the hall with boughs of hol - ly.
2. See the blaz - ing yule be - fore us.
3. Fast a - way the old year pass - es.
Fa la la la la la la la la.

B♭ Cm B♭ E♭ B♭ E♭/B♭ Fm/A♭ E♭/B♭ B♭ E♭
'Tis the sea - son to be jol - ly.
Strike the harp and join the cho - rus.
Hail the new, ye lads and lass - es.
Fa la la la la la la la la.

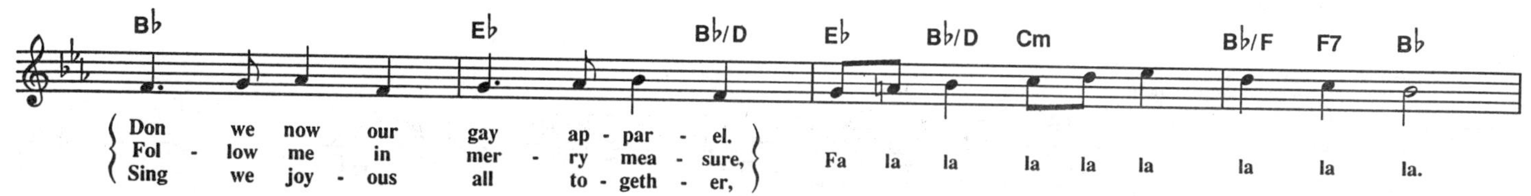
B♭ E♭ B♭/D E♭ B♭/D Cm B♭/F F7 B♭
Don we now our gay ap - par - el.
Fol - low me in mer - ry mea - sure,
Sing we joy - ous all to - geth - er,
Fa la la la la la la la la.

E♭ B♭ Cm B♭ E♭ A♭ E♭/G Fm/A♭ 1.2. E♭/B♭ B♭ E♭ 3. E♭/B♭ B♭ E♭
Troll the an - cient yule - tide car - ol.
while I tell of yule - tide trea - sure.
heed - less of the wind and weath - er.
Fa la la la la la la la la. la la la.

DANCIN' IN THE MOONLIGHT

Words and Music by
SHERMAN KELLY

Moderately
N.C.
Verse 1:
Cm7 Fm7
1. We get it on most ev-'ry-night,
Bb7 Eb Eb/D Cm7 Fm7 Bb7
when that moon gets big and bright. It's su-per-nat-u-ral de-light. Ev-'ry-bod-y's danc-
Eb Eb/D Cm7 Fm7 Bb7 Eb Eb/D Cm7
-in' in the moon-light.
Verse 2:
Fm7
Ev-'ry-bod-y here is out-a sight.
Bb7 Eb Eb/D Cm7 Fm7 Bb7
They don't bark and they don't bite. They keep things loose, they keep things light. Ev-'ry-bod-y's danc-
Eb Eb/D Cm7
-in' in the moon-light.
Chorus:
Fm7 Bb7 Eb Eb/D
Danc-in' in the moon-light, ev-'ry-bod-y's feel-in' warm and right.
1. To Next Strain
Cm7 Fm7 Bb7 Eb Eb/D Cm7
It's such a fine 'n' nat-'ral sight. Ev-'ry-bod-y's danc-in' in the moon-light. 3. We like our fun
2.3.etc. Repeat ad lib. and fade
Cm7
light.
Verse 3:
Fm7 Bb7 Eb Eb/D
Danc- and we nev-er fight. You can't dance 'n' stay up-tight, it's su-
D.S.
Cm7 Fm7 Bb7 Eb Eb/D Cm7
-per-nat-u-ral de-light. Ev-'ry-bod-y's danc-in' in the moon-light. Danc-

DAY IN - DAY OUT

Words by JOHNNY MERCER
Music by RUBE BLOOM

Moderately (with expression)

𝄋 C6 Dm7 G9 Dm7 G9 G+ C6 G7/D E♭dim7 C/E *To Coda* 𝄌

Day in, day out, the same old hoo - doo fol - lows me a -
rain, come shine, I meet you and to me the day is

Em7/G C/E E♭dim7 G7 Dm7 G7 Dm7 E♭7/B♭ G7/B

bout. The same old pound - ing in my heart when - ev - er I think of you, and dar - ling, I

E♭7/B♭ Dm7/A G7 Dm7 G7 C G+ C6 Dm7 G9 Dm7 G9 G+

think of you, day in and day out. Day out, day in, I

C6 G7/D E♭dim7 C/E Cm Cm6 G Dm7

need - n't tell you how my days be - gin. When I a - wake, I a - wak - en with a tin - gle,

G Dm7 G Bm Am7 D9(♯5) G9sus G9 Gm7 G7 G7(♯5) *D.S. 𝄋 al Coda*

one pos - si - bil - i - ty in view, that pos - si - bil - i - ty of may - be see - ing you. Come

𝄌 *Coda*

E7(♯5) E7 A7 A9 D7(♯5) D7 Fm6/G G9(♯5) Cmaj7 A7(♯5)

fine. Then I kiss your lips and the pound - ing be - comes the o - ceans

Dm7 G7(♯5) Cmaj7 A7(♭9) D7 Fm6/G G9(♯5) C

roar, a thou - sand drums; can't you see it's love, can there be an - y doubt,

A7/C♯ C♯dim Dm7 G7(♭9) 1. C Fm6 A♭7 Dm7 G+ 2. C Fm6 C

— When there it is; day in, day out? Day out?

DARK EYES
(Orche Tchornia)

RUSSIAN FOLK SONG

Moderately

G7 Cm G7
Eyes of mys - ter - y, ev - er taunt - ing me, ev - er haunt - ing me, like a
an - swer me, you can bring to me joy and ec - sta - sy for e -
Cm Fm Cm
mel - o - dy. Do you se - cret - ly hold ro - mance for me, or a
ter - ni - ty. Tell me ten - der - ly you'll no lon - ger be eyes of
G7 1. Cm 2. Cm
trag - e - dy? Dark Eyes, speak to me! When you speak to me!
mys - ter - y,

DANNY BOY

Words by FRED WEATHERLY
Music from AN OLD IRISH AIR

Slowly
C C7 F Dm G7 C Am
1. Oh Dan - ny Boy, the pipes the pipes are call - ing from glen to glen and down the moun - tain
come and all the flowers are dy - ing. If I am dead, as dead I well may
Dm G7 C C7 F C Dm G7 C
side. The sum-mer's gone and all the ros - es fall - ing. 'Tis you, 'tis you must go and I must bide.
be, you'll come and find the place where I am ly - ing, and kneel and say an A - ve there for me.
Cdim7 G7 C Em C Cdim7 G7 Am F Em Dm G7
But come ye back when sum-mer's in the mea - dow, or when the val - ley's hushed and white with snow. 'Tis I'll be
And I shall hear though soft you tread a - bove me. And all my grave will warm - er, sweet - er be. If you will
1.2. 3.
C7 F C Am Am/G Am/F♯ Fm C/E Am Dm7 G7 C
there in sun-shine or in shad - ow. Oh Dan-ny Boy, oh Dan - ny Boy I love you so. And when ye
bend and tell me that you love me, then I shall sleep in peace un - til you come to me.

THE DARKTOWN STRUTTERS' BALL

By SHELTON BROOKS

Moderately

C A7 D7 Am7 D7
I'll be down to get you in a tax - i, hon - ey. You bet - ter be read - y a - bout half past eight.

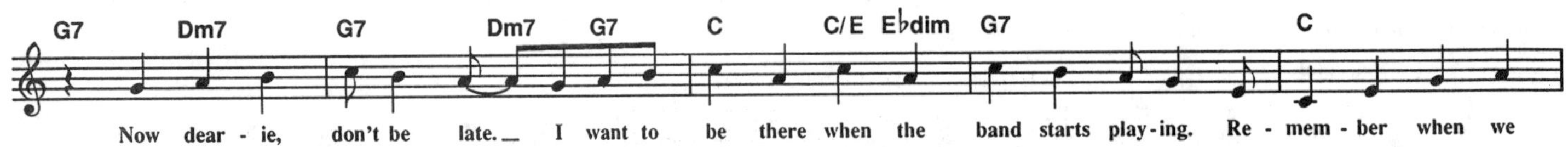
G7 Dm7 G7 Dm7 G7 C C/E E♭dim G7 C
Now dear - ie, don't be late. I want to be there when the band starts play - ing. Re - mem - ber when we

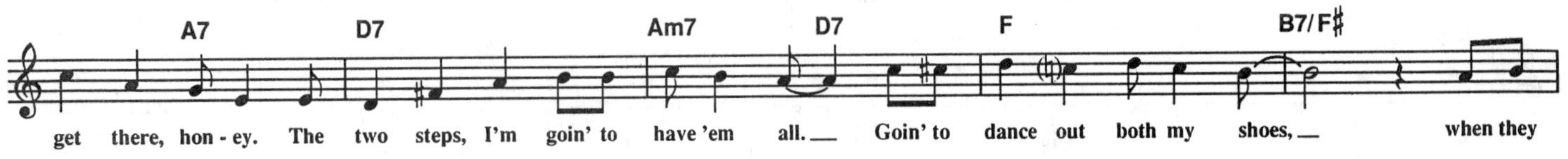
A7 D7 Am7 D7 F B7/F♯
get there, hon - ey. The two steps, I'm goin' to have 'em all. Goin' to dance out both my shoes, when they

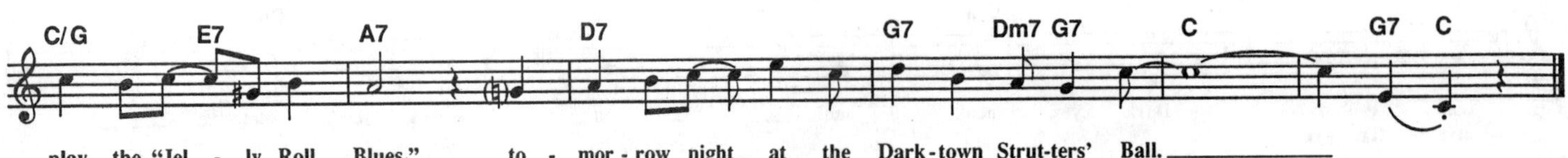
C/G E7 A7 D7 G7 Dm7 G7 C G7 C
play the "Jel - ly Roll Blues," to - mor - row night at the Dark - town Strut - ters' Ball.

DANCING ON THE CEILING
(He Dances On My Ceiling)

Words by LORENZ HART
Music by RICHARD RODGERS

Moderato
F A+ B♭6 G7 C Em Gm7 Cdim C
He danc - es o - ver - head on the ceil - ing, near my bed, in my
I try to hide in vain un - der - neath my coun - ter - pane; there's my
F B♭6 C7 F6 C7 F6
sight, through the night.
love up a - bove! I whis - per, "Go a - way, my lov - er, it's not fair,"
C7 F Cdim C7 F
But I'm so grate - ful to dis - cov - er he's still there. I love my
A+ B♭6 G7 C Em Gm7 C7 F
ceil - ing more since it is a danc - ing floor just for my love.

DAY BY DAY

Words and Music by
SAMMY CAHN, AXEL STORDAHL
and PAUL WESTON

Moderately slow

Am7 Bm Am7 D7 Am7 D7 G Bm7
Day by day, I'm fall - ing more in love with you, and day by day, my love seems to grow.

E9 Bm7/F♯ Gm E7/G♯ Am B7 Em Em(maj7) Em7 A7
There is - n't an - y end to my de - vo - tion. It's deep - er, dear, by

Em7 A7 Am7 D7(♭9) E7(♭9) Am7 Bm Am7 D7 Am7
far than an - y o - cean. I find that day by day you're mak - ing all my dreams come

D7 G Bm7(♭5) E7 E7(♭9) E6 Am7
true. So come what may, I want you to know, I'm yours a - lone

Bm Am7 D7 G Bm7(♭5)/F E7 E7(♭9/♯5) Am7 D9 D7(♭9) G6 C G
and I'm in love to stay, as we go through the years, day by day.

Theme Song from the Warner Brothers Production

DEAR HEART

Words by JAY LIVINGSTON and RAY EVANS
Music by HENRY MANCINI

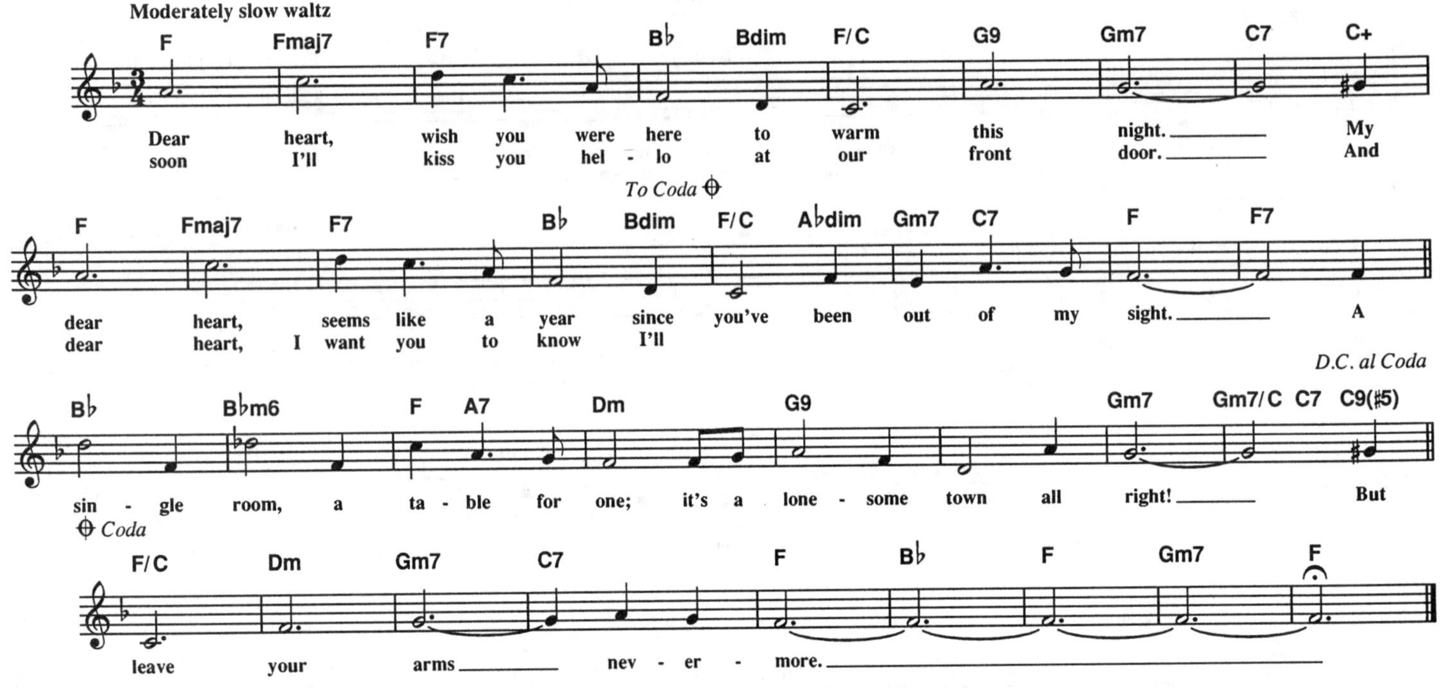
Moderately slow waltz
F Fmaj7 F7 B♭ Bdim F/C G9 Gm7 C7 C+
Dear heart, wish you were here to warm this night. My
soon I'll kiss you hel - lo at our front door. And
To Coda
F Fmaj7 F7 B♭ Bdim F/C A♭dim Gm7 C7 F F7
dear heart, seems like a year since you've been out of my sight. A
dear heart, I want you to know I'll
D.C. al Coda
B♭ B♭m6 F A7 Dm G9 Gm7 Gm7/C C7 C9(♯5)
sin - gle room, a ta - ble for one; it's a lone - some town all right! But
Coda
F/C Dm Gm7 C7 F B♭ F Gm7 F
leave your arms nev - er - more.

DEEP IN THE HEART OF TEXAS

Words by JUNE HERSHEY
Music by DON SWANDER

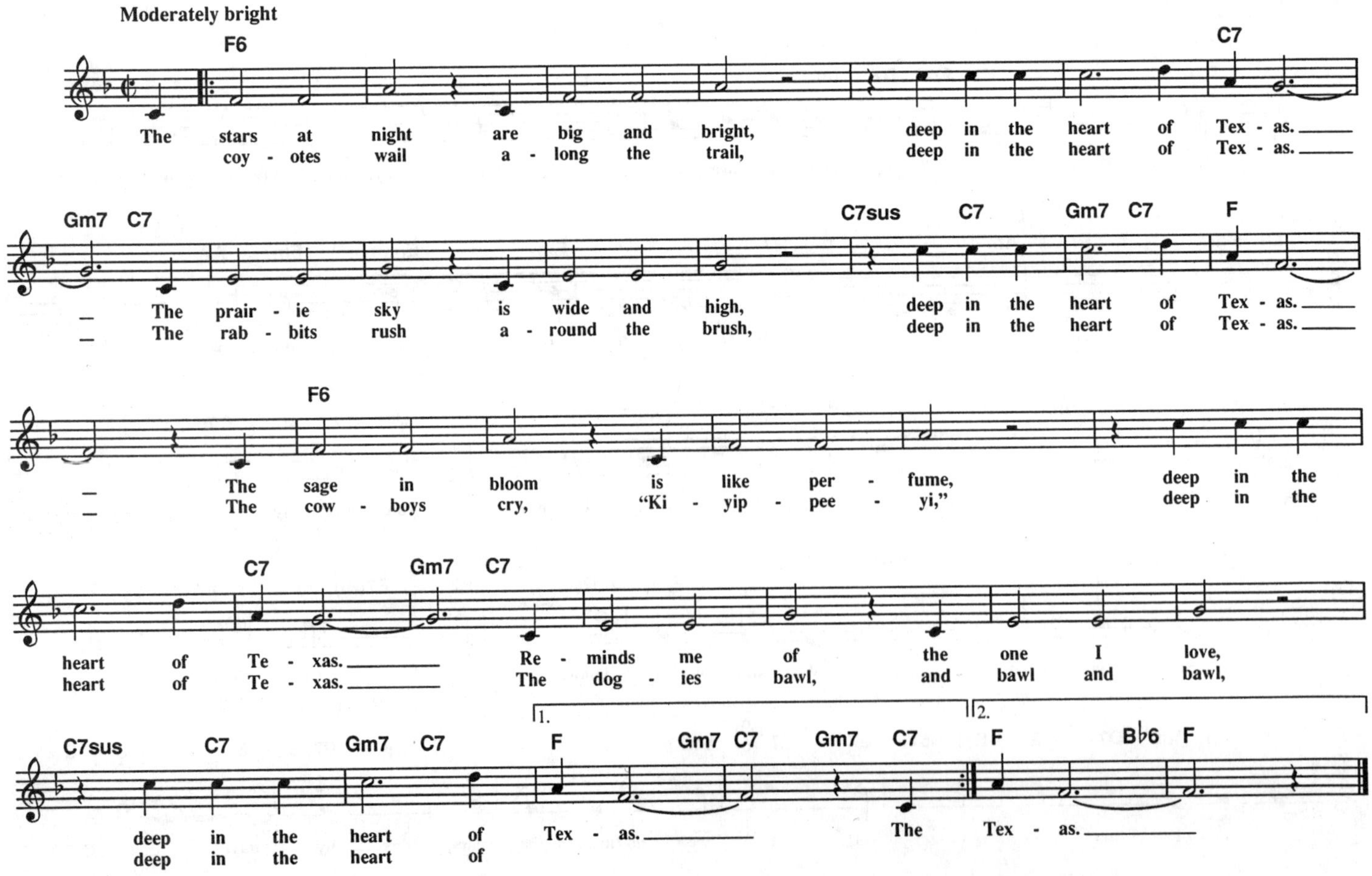

Moderately bright

F6 C7
The stars at night are big and bright, deep in the heart of Tex - as.
coy - otes wail a - long the trail, deep in the heart of Tex - as.

Gm7 C7 C7sus C7 Gm7 C7 F
The prair - ie sky is wide and high, deep in the heart of Tex - as.
The rab - bits rush a - round the brush, deep in the heart of Tex - as.

F6
The sage in bloom is like per - fume, deep in the
The cow - boys cry, "Ki - yip - pee - yi," deep in the

C7 Gm7 C7
heart of Te - xas. Re - minds me of the one I love,
heart of Te - xas. The dog - ies bawl, and bawl and bawl,

C7sus C7 Gm7 C7 1. F Gm7 C7 Gm7 C7 2. F B♭6 F
deep in the heart of Tex - as. The Tex - as.
deep in the heart of

DEEP IN A DREAM

Words by EDDIE DeLANGE
Music by JIMMY VAN HEUSEN

C C+ C6 C7 F F+
I dim all the lights and I sink in my chair, The smoke from my cig - a - rette
smoke makes a stair - way for you to de - scend, you come to my arms, may this
cig - a - rette burns me, I wake with a start, my hand is - n't hurt, but there's

F6 F7 B♭ B♭+ B♭6 A7 Dm Bdim B♭7
climbs through the air, The walls of my room fade a - way in the blue and I'm
bliss nev - er end, For we love a - new just as we used to do, When I'm
pain in my heart. A - wake or a - sleep ev - 'ry mem - 'ry I'll keep

1. Am D7 G7 Dm7-5 G7 | 2. 3. Am D7 D♭7 *Fine* C
Deep In A Dream of you. The Deep In A Dream of you. Then from the

A♭ E7/B B♭m7 E♭7 A♭/C A♭dim/C♭ B♭m7 E♭7
ceil - ing sweet mu - sic comes steal - ing, we glide through a lov - er's re - frain; You're so ap -

A♭ E7/B B♭m7 E♭7 A7/C Fm7 Dm7 G7 *D.C. al Fine*
peal - ing that I'm soon re - veal - ing my love for you o - ver a - gain. My

DEVOTED TO YOU

Words and Music by
BOUDLEAUX BRYANT

Slowly
F C7 F C7 F
Dar - ling, you can count on me, Till the sun dries up the sea.
I'll be yours thru end - less time, I'll a - dore your charms sub - lime.
Thru the years my love will grow, like a riv - er it will flow
B♭ Am Gm F B♭ C7 F Fine Gm
Un - til then I'll al - ways be
Guess by now you know that I'm De - vot - ed To You. I'll nev - er hurt you,
It can't die be - cause I'm so
Am Dm Gm C7 F Gm
I'll nev - er lie, I'll nev - er be un - true. I'll nev - er give you
Am Dm G7 C7 D.C. al Fine
rea - son to cry, I'd be un - hap - py if you were blue

DEEP PURPLE

Lyric by MITCHELL PARISH
Music by PETER DE ROSE

Slowly
F F♯dim Gm C7 F Cm6
When the deep pur - ple falls o - ver sleep - y gar - den walls, and the stars be - gin to flick - er in the
still of the night once a - gain I'll hold you tight. Though you're gone, your love lives on when moon-light
D7 C/E Fm D7/F♯ Gm B♭m Am7 1. A♭dim Gm7
sky, through the mist of a mem - o - ry you wan - der back to me, breath - ing my
beams. And as long as my heart will beat, lov - er, we'll
C9 C7(♯5) F D7/F♯ Gm7 C7 2. A♭dim Gm7 C7 F B♭9 F6
name with a sigh. In the al - ways meet here in my deep pur - ple dreams.

DELTA DAWN

Words and Music by
ALEX HARVEY and LARRY COLLINS

Moderately

Chorus:

F B♭ F
Del - ta Dawn, what's that flow - er you have on? Could it be a fad - ed rose from days gone

C F B♭ F C
by? And did I hear you say he was a - meet-in' you here to - day to take you to his man-sion in the

1. B♭ F *To Next Strain* 2. B♭ F *Fine* *Verse:* F E♭ F
sky. 1. She's sky. for - ty - one and her dad - dy still calls her ba - by.
young - er days they called her Del - ta Dawn.

E♭ F B♭ D/A Gm C7
All the folks a - round Browns - ville say she's cra - zy, 'cause she walks down - town with a suit - case in her
Pret - ti - est wom - an you ev - er laid eyes on, then a man of low de - gree stood by her

F E♭ 1. F 2. F *D.C. al Fine*
hand, look - in' for a mys - ter - ious dark - haired man. 2. In her bride.
side, and prom - ised her he'd take her for his

THE DESERT SONG

Words by OTTO HARBACH and OSCAR HAMMERSTEIN II
Music by SIGMUND ROMBERG

Tempo di Valse moderato
C G+ G9 Gdim G7 G6 Dm7 G7 Cmaj7 Cdim
Blue heav - en and you and I, and sand kiss - ing a moon - lit
Oh, give me that night di - vine, and let my arms in yours en -
C E7 Am 1. Am(♭5) Am D6 D7
sky. A des - ert breeze whis - p'ring a lul - la - by, on - ly stars a - bove you to
twine. The des - ert song, call - ing, it's voice en -
G9 G7 G9(♯5) G7(♯5) 2. D/F♯ C/G G7 C
see I love you. thrall - ing, will make you mine.

From the United Artists Motion Picture "THE DEVIL'S BRIGADE"

THE DEVIL'S BRIGADE MARCH
(I Want a Woman)

Words by AL STILLMAN
Music by ALEX NORTH

Brightly

C F C G7
I want a wom-an, an - y kind of a wom-an. Got - ta find me a wom-an right a - way, an - y - where. So broth-er,
I want a wom-an, an - y kind of a wom-an. Got - ta find me a wom-an right a - way, an - y - where. I mean she

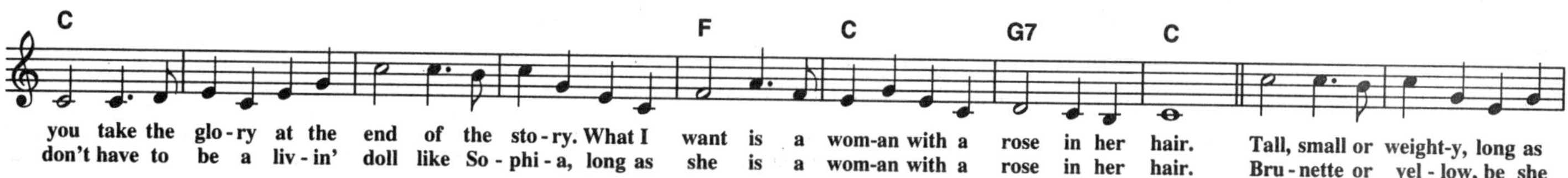
C F C G7 C
you take the glo - ry at the end of the sto - ry. What I want is a wom-an with a rose in her hair. Tall, small or weight-y, long as
don't have to be a liv - in' doll like So - phi - a, long as she is a wom-an with a rose in her hair. Bru - nette or yel - low, be she

D7 G D7 G7 C
she's un - der eight-y, I will give her a kiss that she nev - er will for - get. 'Cause all I want is a wom-an, an - y kind of a wom-an. And when
firm or like Jel - lo, I will give her a kiss with a prom-ise and a dare. I got-ta find me a wom-an, an - y kind of a wom-an, with a

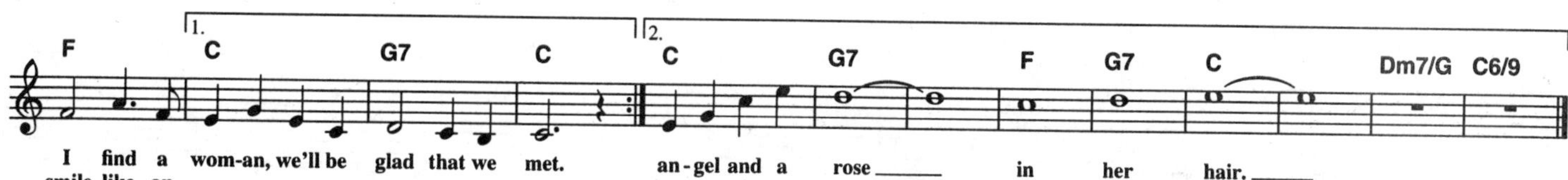
F 1. C G7 C 2. C G7 F G7 C Dm7/G C6/9
I find a wom-an, we'll be glad that we met. an - gel and a rose in her hair.
smile like an

From the United Artists Motion Picture "DIAMONDS ARE FOREVER"

DIAMONDS ARE FOREVER

Lyric by DON BLACK
Music by JOHN BARRY

Moderately

Dm Gm7 C7
Dia-monds are for-ev-er, they are all I need to please me. They can stim-u-late and tease me. They won't

Gm7 E♭maj7 C7 Dm
leave in the night, I've no fear that they might de - sert me.
Dia-monds are for-ev-er, hold one
Dia-monds are for-ev-er, spark-ling

Gm7 C7 Gm7 E♭maj7
up and then ca-ress it. Touch it, stroke it and un-dress it, I can see ev-'ry part, noth-ing hides in the heart to
round my lit-tle fin-ger. Un-like men, the dia-monds lin-ger; men are mere mor-tals who are not worth go-ing to your

C7 Am7 Dm Gm7 E♭6 E♭maj7
hurt me.
grave for.
I don't need love, for what good will love do me? Dia-monds nev-er lie to me, For when love's

A7 C♯dim7 C♯dim7 Dm
gone, they'll lus-tre on. (1.) on. (2.) Dia-monds are for-ev-er, for-ev-er, for-ev-er.

Gm7 E♭maj7 Dm
Dia-monds are for-ev-er, for-ev-er, for-ev-er, for-ev-er and ev-er.

From the 20th Century-Fox Motion Picture "SEVENTH HEAVEN"

DIANE

Words and Music by
ERNO RAPEE and LEW POLLACK

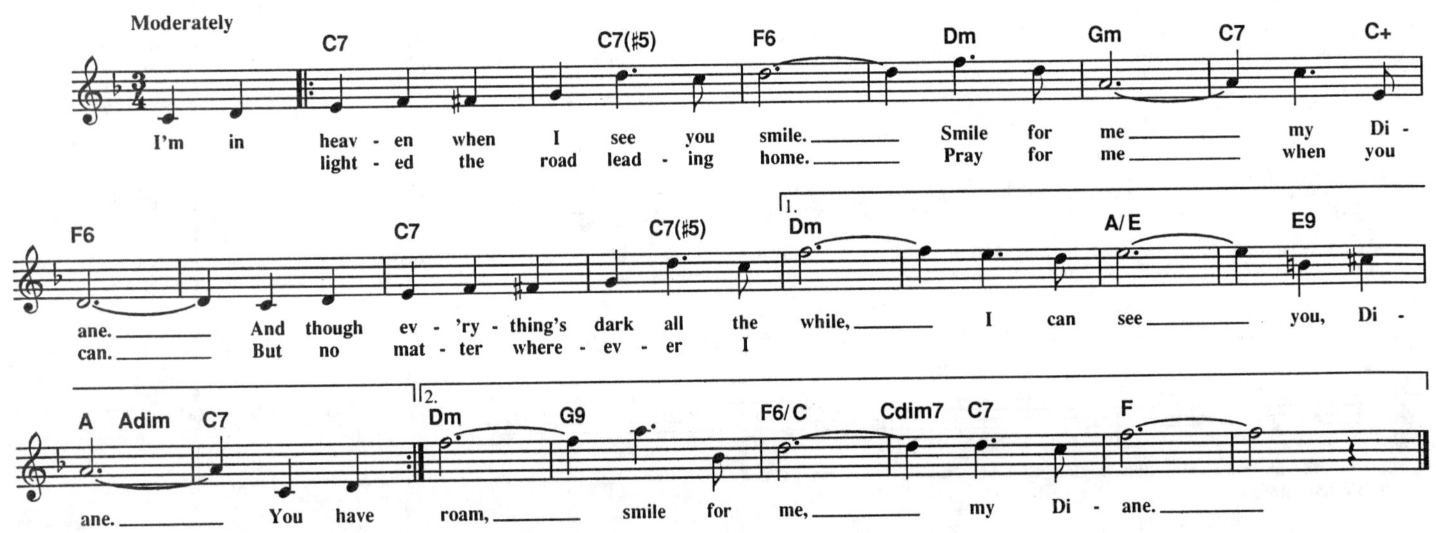
Moderately
C7 C7(♯5) F6 Dm Gm C7 C+
I'm in heav - en when I see you smile. Smile for me my Di -
light - ed the road lead - ing home. Pray for me when you
F6 C7 C7(♯5) Dm A/E E9
ane. And though ev - 'ry - thing's dark all the while, I can see you, Di -
can. But no mat - ter where - ev - er I
A Adim C7 Dm G9 F6/C Cdim7 C7 F
ane. You have roam, smile for me, my Di - ane.

DIRTY, DIRTY FEELIN'

Words and Music by
JERRY LEIBER and MIKE STOLLER

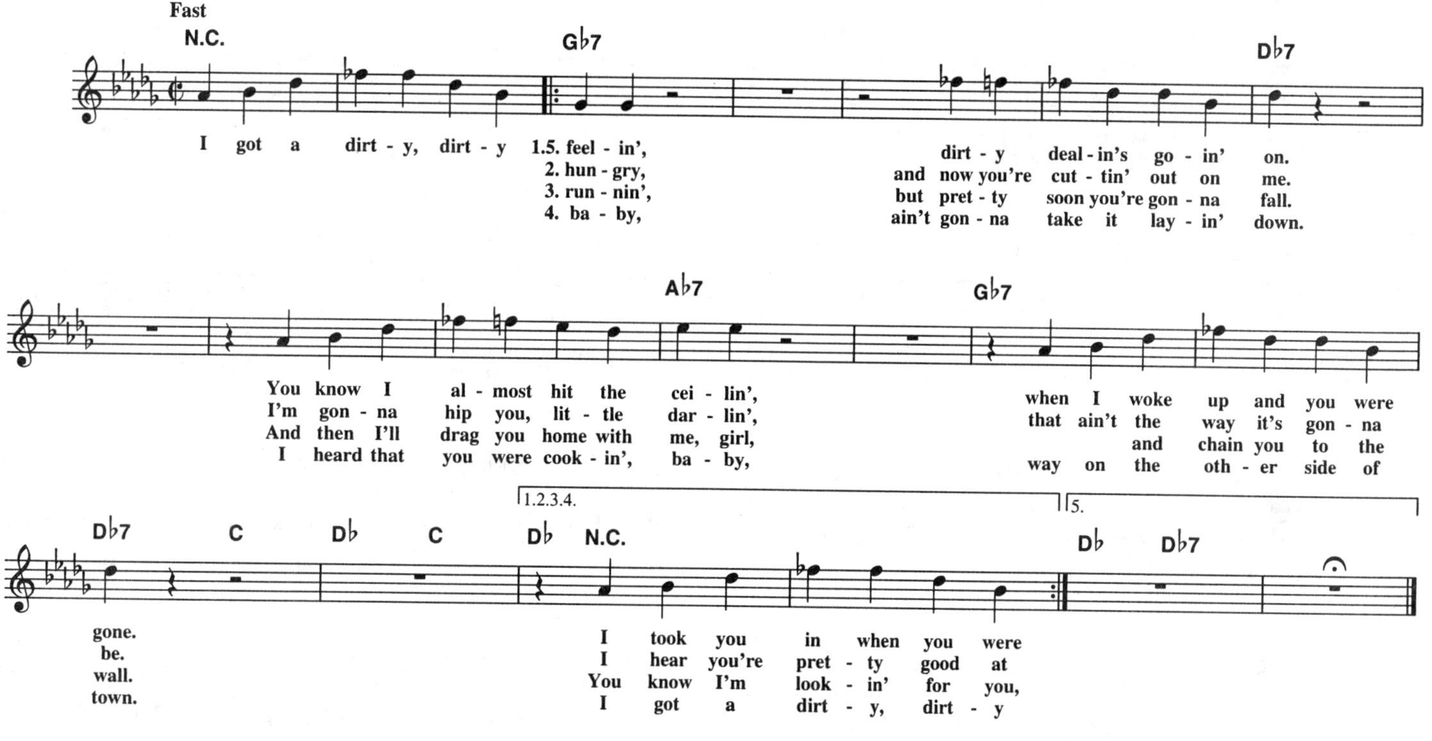
Fast
N.C.
G♭7
D♭7
I got a dirt - y, dirt - y 1.5. feel - in', dirt - y deal - in's go - in' on.
2. hun - gry, and now you're cut - tin' out on me.
3. run - nin', but pret - ty soon you're gon - na fall.
4. ba - by, ain't gon - na take it lay - in' down.
A♭7
G♭7
You know I al - most hit the cei - lin', when I woke up and you were gone.
I'm gon - na hip you, lit - tle dar - lin', that ain't the way it's gon - na be.
And then I'll drag you home with me, girl, and chain you to the wall.
I heard that you were cook - in', ba - by, way on the oth - er side of town.
D♭7 C D♭ C D♭ N.C.
1.2.3.4.
5.
D♭ D♭7
I took you in when you were
I hear you're pret - ty good at
You know I'm look - in' for you,
I got a dirt - y, dirt - y

DINAH

Words by SAM M. LEWIS and JOE YOUNG
Music by HARRY AKST

Moderate swing
G Gmaj7 G6 G+ D7
Din - ah, is there an - y - one fin - er in the state of Car - o - lin - a?
G D7 G
If there is and you know 'er, show 'er to me. Din - ah, with her Dix-ie eyes blaz-in', how I love to sit and
D7 G Em E♭+ Em7/D
gaze in - to the eyes of Din-ah Lee. Ev-'ry night why do I shake with fright?
A7 D7 Em A7 D7 G
Be - cause my Din-ah might change her mind a-bout me. Din - ah, if she wan-dered to
Gmaj7 G6 G+ D7 G C6 G6
Chi - na, I would hop an o - cean lin - er, just to be with Din - ah Lee!

DIDN'T WE ALMOST HAVE IT ALL

Words and Music by
MICHAEL MASSER and
WILL JENNINGS

Slowly
Verse:
Bb Fm/Ab G7sus G Cm G/B Cm F
1. Re-mem-ber when we held on in the rain, the nights we al-most lost it; once a-gain we can take the
2. The way you used to touch me felt so fine; we kept our hearts to-geth-er; down the line, a mo-ment in the
Bb Bb/A Gm Ebmaj7 F/Eb Dm7 Gm7 Cm7 Eb/F Bb C/D D
night in-to to-mor-row liv-ing on feel-ings. Touch-ing you, I feel it all a-gain.
soul can last for-ev-er, com-fort and keep us. Help me bring the feel-ing back a-gain.
Chorus:
G D/C C Bm7 Em7 Am7 D7sus G C D/F# G D/C C Bm7 Em7
Did-n't we al-most have it all, when love was all we had worth giv-ing? The ride with you was worth the fall, my friend;
Am7 Dsus G Eb/F F Bb F/Eb Eb Dm7 Gm7 Cm7 Eb/F
lov-ing you makes life worth liv-ing.
Chorus:
1.2.4. Did-n't we al-most have it all, the nights we held on till the
3. Did-n't we al-most have it all, when love was all we had worth
To Coda
1.
D.C.
Bb Eb/Bb F/Bb Bb F/Eb Eb Dm7 Gm7 Cm7 Eb/F Bb Eb/Bb F/Bb
morn-ing? You know we'll nev-er love that way a-gain; did-n't we al-most have it all?
giv-ing? The ride with you was worth the fall, my friend;
2.
To Next Strain
3.
D.S. al Coda
Bridge:
Cm7 D7(#5) D7 Cm7 Eb/F Bb Eb/Bb F Ebmaj7
Did-n't we al-most have it lov-ing you makes life worth liv-ing. all? Did-n't we have the best of
Dm7 F/G Gm/F Ebmaj7 Dm7 F/G Gm/F
times, when love was young and new? Could-n't we reach in-side and find the world of me and
D.S.
Ebmaj7 F(9)/Eb Ebmaj7 Dm7 Gm7 Cm7 Bb/D Ebmaj7 F7sus
you? We'll nev-er lose it a-gain, 'cause once you know what love is, you nev-er let it end.
Coda
Cm7 Eb/F Bb F/Eb Eb Dm7 Gm7 Cm7 F7sus F7 Bb(9)
Did-n't we al-most have it all? Did-n't we al-most have it all?

DIGGY LIGGY LO

(Duet Version)

By J.D. MILLER

Moderately
Chorus:
G C G D7
(Her) I'm Dig-gy Lig-gy Li. (Him) I'm Dig-gy Lig-gy Lo. (Both) We fell in love at the fais do do. The pop was
Verse:
G G C G
cold and the cof-fee cheau for Dig-gy Lig-gy Li and Dig-gy Lig-gy Lo. 1.There's the place we found ro - mance, where they do

D7 G
the Ca - jun dance, threw a kiss with ev - 'ry chance and showed our love with ev - 'ry glance. (Her) 1. I'm Dig-gy Lig-gy

Chorus 2, 3 & 4:
C F C G C G D7
Li. (Him) I'm Dig-gy Lig-gy Lo. (Her) I was your girl, you was my beau. No tru - er love you'll ev - er know than the love I

1. 2.3. 4.
D.S.
G G G
had for Dig-gy Lig-gy Lo. I'm Dig-gy Lig-gy Lo. (Her) I'm Dig-gy Lig-gy Lo.

Verse 2:
(Him) I finally went to see her pa.
Now, I got me a pappy-in-law.
We moved out where the bayou flows,
And now we've got a little Diggy Liggy Lo.

Chorus 2:
She's Diggy Liggy Li, I'm Diggy Liggy Lo.
She was my girl, I was her beau.
The only love she'd ever know
Was the love of Diggy Liggy Lo.

Chorus 3:
(Her) I'm Diggy Liggy Li.,
(Him) I'm Diggy Liggy Lo.
We fell in love at the fais do do.
The pop was cold the coffee cheau
For Diggy Liggy Li and Diggy Liggy Lo.

Chorus 4:
(Her) I'm Diggy Liggy Li,
(Him) I'm Diggy Liggy Lo.
Real Cajun love where the bayou flows.
Now the whole wide world can know
About the love of Diggy Liggy Lo.

From the Metro-Goldwyn-Mayer Musical Production "THE WIZARD OF OZ"

DING-DONG! THE WITCH IS DEAD

Words by E.Y. HARBURG
Music by HAROLD ARLEN

Brightly
Cmaj7 C6 C Cmaj7 C6 Dm7 G7(♯9) C Am7 Dm7 G9
Ding - dong, the witch is dead. Which old witch? The wick-ed witch, ding - dong, the wick-ed witch is dead.
Cmaj7 C6 C Cmaj7 C6 Dm7 D7(♭5) Gm7 C7
Wake up, you sleep - y head, rub your eyes, get out of bed. Wake up, the wick-ed witch is dead. She's
Am F Am6 F Gmaj7 G6 Em Am7 D9 Dm7 G7
gone where the gob-lins go be - low, be - low, be - low. Yo - ho, let's o - pen up and sing and ring the bells out.
Cmaj7 C6 C Am Dm7 G7 C
Ding - dong, the mer - ry - o, sing it high, sing it low. Let them know the wick-ed witch is dead.

DIXIE

Words and Music by
DANIEL C. EMMET

Brightly
C F C
I___ wish I was_ in the land of cot - ton, old times there are not for-got-ten. Look a - way, look a -
G7 C F C
way, look a - way, Dix-ie land. In_ Dix - ie land_ where_ I was born in, ear - ly on one frost - y morn-in', look a - way, look a - way, look a -
G7 C F D7 G7 C F C
way, Dix-ie land. Then I wish I was in Dix - ie, hoo - ray, hoo - ray. In Dix - ie land I'll take my stand to live and die in
G7 C G7 C G7 C G7 C G7 C
Dix - ie. A - way, a - way, a - way down south in Dix - ie; a - way, a - way, a - way down south in Dix - ie.
DIZZY
Copyright © 1968 by LOW-TWI INC.
All Rights Reserved
Words and Music by
TOMMY ROE and FREDDY WELLER
Moderate rock
Chorus:
C F A D G A D G
Diz - zy, I'm so diz - zy, my head is spin - nin'_ like a whirl - pool. It nev - er ends,_
To Coda
A D G A D Eb Ab Bb Ab
Verse:
Eb Ab
_ and it's you, girl, mak-in' it spin._ You're mak-in' me diz - zy. First time that I saw you, girl, I
Bb Ab Eb Ab Bb Ab Eb Ab Bb Ab Eb Ab
knew that I just had to make you mine._ But, it's so hard to talk to you with fel-lows hang-in' round you all the time._
Bb Eb Bb Ab Eb
1.
G
I want you for my sweet pet, but you keep play-in' hard to get, I'm go-in' a-round in cir-cles all the time.
2.
D.C. al Coda
G
time.
Coda
Repeat and fade
A D G A
_ You're mak-ing me diz - zy. You're mak-ing me
diz - zy. I'm so

DO NOTHIN' TILL YOU HEAR FROM ME

Words by BOB RUSSELL
Music by DUKE ELLINGTON

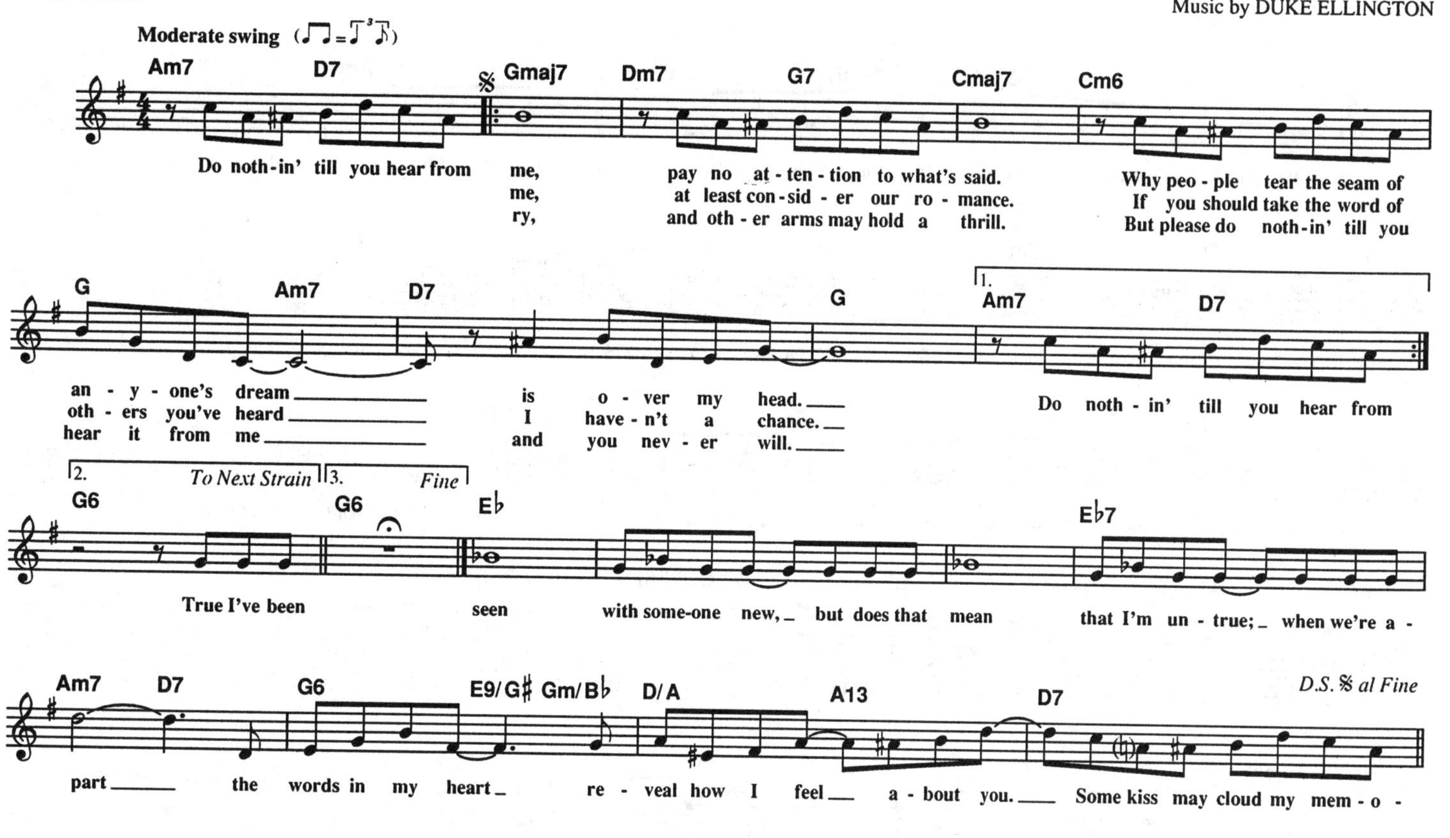
Moderate swing
Am7 D7 Gmaj7 Dm7 G7 Cmaj7 Cm6
Do noth-in' till you hear from me, pay no at-ten-tion to what's said. Why peo-ple tear the seam of
me, at least con-sid-er our ro-mance. If you should take the word of
ry, and oth-er arms may hold a thrill. But please do noth-in' till you
G Am7 D7 G 1. Am7 D7
an-y-one's dream is o-ver my head. Do noth-in' till you hear from
oth-ers you've heard I have-n't a chance.
hear it from me and you nev-er will.
2. To Next Strain 3. Fine
G6 G6 Eb Eb7
True I've been seen with some-one new, but does that mean that I'm un-true; when we're a-
Am7 D7 G6 E9/G# Gm/Bb D/A A13 D7 D.S. al Fine
part the words in my heart re-veal how I feel a-bout you. Some kiss may cloud my mem-o-

DO YOU EVER THINK OF ME

Words by HARRY D. KERR and JOHN COOPER
Music by EARL BURTNETT

Moderately
Eb Ebdim Eb Ebdim Eb Ebdim Eb Eb+ Ab/Eb Eb Ebdim Eb Bb7
When you have an-oth-er's arms a-bout you, do you ev-er think
Edim Bb7
of me? When you whis-per, "I can't live with-out you," do you
Eb F#dim Eb Eb7 Ebdim Eb9
ev-er think of me? And when your eyes dis-guise the same old lov-ing
Ab Eb+ Ab Abm Bb7 Eb Ebdim Eb Ebdim
lies you tell so ten-der-ly, deep in your heart, un-feel-ing.
Eb Ebdim Eb Eb+ Ab/Eb Eb Ebdim Eb Bb7 Eb
When some heart you're steal-ing, do you ev-er think of me?

DO YOU KNOW WHAT IT MEANS TO MISS NEW ORLEANS

Lyric by EDDIE DE LANGE
Music by LOUIS ALTER

Slowly

C6 G7(♯5) Cmaj7 Am7 Em7 Am7 D9
Do you know what it means_ to miss New Or - leans,_ and miss it each night_ and day? I

Dm7 D♯dim7 Em7 A7 Dm7 A♭7 G7
know I'm not wrong,_ the feel - in's get - tin' strong - er the long - er I stay_ a - way._ Miss the

C G7(♯5) Cmaj7 Am7 Em7 Am7 D9 Dm7 D♯dim7
moss-cov - ered vines,_ the tall su - gar pines_ where mock-in'-birds used_ to sing. And I'd like to see_ the

Em7 A7 Dm7 G7 C Cm7(♭5) F7 B♭m7 E♭9 A♭ F7
la - zy Mis - sis - sip - pi a hur - ry - in' in - to spring._ The moon - light on the bay - ou,_ a cre - ole

B♭m7 E♭9 A♭ Am7 D9 G6 Em7
tune_ that fills the air; I dream_ a - bout mag - nol - ias in June,_ and soon I'm

Am7 D9 Dm7 G7 C6 G7(♯5) Cmaj7 Am7 Em7 Am7
wish - in' that I_ was there._ Do you know what it means_ to miss New Or - leans_ when that's where you left_ your

D9 Dm7 D♯dim7 Em7 A7 D9 G7(♭9) C
heart? And there's some-thing more;_ I miss the one I care for more than I miss_ New Or - leans.

DOWN ON 33RD AND 3RD
(Thoity Thoid and Thoid)

Words and Music by
BEN RYAN

Valse moderato
G Gdim G B7/F♯ E7 B7/F♯ E7/G♯ A7
Down on the East side on thoi - ty thoid and thoid that's my home, sweet
D7 Am7 D7 Am7 D7 G D7/F♯ Edim G A7
home._
Some peo - ple think it's the home of black eyes, just be - cause
Folks buy pi - a - nos for one dol - lar down, then wait with
Fel - lers don't dress like that Miss Prince of Wales, six bucks they

D7 Edim Fdim D7 G Gdim G B7/F♯ E7
guys don't wear col - lars and ties. That's all the bunk, they just say that in fun,
sticks for the guy to come 'round. Gawd help col - lec - tors when they come to call,
pay for their suits thru the mails. They don't go in for that Eu - ro - pean stuff,
A7 D7 Edim Fdim D7 C♯dim A7/E E♭7 G G7
real East - side folks is the best folks what come, they'd give their shoit on - ly they ain't got
three flights of stairs is a hell - av - a fall, spesh - ly with hard mar - ble floors in the
they wear tight pants with a sev - en inch cuff, af - ter the rain they look En - glish e -
E7 Bm/D♯ E7/G♯ A7 D7 1.2. G D7 3. G
none, hall, nough, down on thoi - ty thoid and thoid. thoid.
DO YOU WANT TO KNOW A SECRET?
Copyright © 1963 NORTHERN SONGS LTD.
All Rights for the U.S. and Canada Controlled and Administered
by EMI UNART CATALOG INC. All Rights Reserved
Words and Music by
JOHN LENNON and
PAUL McCARTNEY
Freely
Fm B♭m Fm A♭ G♭ C7 Moderate rock
You'll nev-er know how much I real-ly love you. You'll nev-er know how much I real-ly care. (Bass)
F Am A♭m Gm C7 F Am A♭m Gm C7 F Am A♭m Gm G♭
Lis-ten, do you want to know a se-cret? Do you prom-ise not to tell? Whoa,
F Am A♭m Gm C7 F Am A♭m Gm C7 B♭
clos - er; let me whis-per in your ear, say the words you long to hear:
To Coda 1. 2. Bridge:
C7 Dm Gm C7 Gm C7 B♭ Dm Cm
I'm in love with you, ooh. I've known a se-cret 'bout a week or two.
D.S. al Coda
B♭ Dm Cm Gm C7
No - bod - y knows, just we two.
Coda
Repeat and fade
Gm C7 Dm Gm C7 Dm
Ooh. Ooh.

(Sittin' On)
THE DOCK OF THE BAY

Words and Music by
STEVE CROPPER and
OTIS REDDING

Moderate rock
1. Sit-tin' in the morn-ing sun; I'll be sit-tin' till the eve-nin' come, watch-in' the ships roll in, then I watch 'em roll a-way a-gain. Yeah,
(2.) left my home in Geor-gia; head-ed for the 'Fris-co Bay. I have noth-ing to live for; looks like noth-in' gon-na come my way. So,
3. Sit-tin' here restin' my bones, and this lon-li-ness won't leave me a-lone. Two thou-sand miles I roam just to make this dock my home. Now,
Chorus:
I'm sit-tin' on the dock of the bay, watch-in' the tide roll a-way. Sit-tin' on the dock of the bay wast-in' time.
To Coda
D.C.
2. I
Bridge:
Looks like noth-ing gon-na change; ev-'ry-thing still re-mains the same. I can't do what ten peo-ple tell me to do, so I guess I'll re-main the same.
D.C. al Coda
Coda
(whistle)
Repeat and fade
DOES THE SPEARMINT LOSE ITS FLAVOR
(On the Bedpost Over Night?)
Words by BILLY ROSE and MARTY BLOOM
Music by ERNEST BREUER
Copyright © 1924 (Renewed 1952) by MILLS MUSIC, INC., c/o EMI MUSIC PUBLISHING
All Rights Reserved
Brightly
Does the spear-mint lose its flav-or on the bed-post o-ver night? If you chew it in the morn-ing will it be too hard to bite? Can't you see I'm go-ing craz-y, won't some-bod-y put me right? Does the spear-mint lose its flav-or on the bed-post o-ver night? Does the
Does the spear-mint lose its flav-or on the bed-post o-ver night? If you pull it out like rub-ber will it snap right back and bite? If you paste it on the left side, will you find it on the right? Does the spear-mint lose its flav-or on the bed-post o-ver night? Does the
Does the spear-mint lose its flav-or on the bed-post o-ver night? Would you use it on the col-lar when your but-ton's not in sight? Put your hand be-neath your seat and you will find it there all right. Does the spear-mint lose its flav-or on the bed-post o-ver night?

DOES ANYBODY REALLY KNOW WHAT TIME IT IS?

By ROBERT LAMM

Moderate swing (♫ = ♩³♪)

Gmaj7 Cmaj7 Gmaj7 Cmaj7 D Em7 F6 Em7

Verse:

G F B♭maj7 E♭maj7 B♭maj7 E♭maj7 B♭maj7 E♭maj7 D Em7 F6 Em7

As I was walk - ing down the street one day, a man came up to me and asked me what the time was that was on my watch.
And I was walk - ing down the street one day. A pret - ty la - dy looked at me and said her dia - mond watch had stopped cold dead.
Then I was walk - ing down the street one day, be - ing pushed and shoved by peo - ple try'n to beat the clock. Oh no I just don't know.

I said,

Chorus:

Gmaj7 C Gmaj7 C Gmaj7 C

"Does an - y - bod - y real - ly know what time it is? Does an - y - bod - y real - ly care? If so, I can't im - a - gine why,

1.2. Gmaj7 C

we've all got time e - nough to cry."

3. Gmaj7 C D Em7 F6 Em7 Gmaj7

we've all got time e - nough to die."

DOODLIN'

By HORACE SILVER

In a walkin' groove (♫ = ♩³♪)
D♭
D♭7
G♭7
D♭
B♭7
E♭m7 Fm7 G♭ B♭m6 E♭m7 A♭7 D♭ D♭7 G♭ Gdim7 D♭
1.
2.

DOLL DANCE
Copyright © 1927 (Renewed 1955) EMI MILLER CATALOG INC.
All Rights Reserved
By NACIO HERB BROWN
Moderately bright
What a pe - cul - iar tune, thrill-ing me night and noon, what a pe-cul - iar tune.
Has such a fun - ny swing, it's such a catch-y thing, mak-in' me like a loon.
It teas - es me, pleas - es me.
It's in the air, it's ev-'ry-where, it's haunt-ing me, taunt-ing me. What a re-frain; play it a-gain. Mak-in' me
want to dance, mak-in' me want to prance; that mel-o-dy so queer.
Mak-in' me want to twirl, keep-in' my brain a-whirl. Rhy-thm is all I hear.
The doll dance is its name. It's gon - na drive you in - sane. Such a pe - cul - iar tune. You're gon-na hum it soon.
What a pe-cul - iar tune.
DON'T BE THAT WAY
Copyright © 1935, 1938 (Renewed 1963, 1966) EMI ROBBINS CATALOG INC.
World-wide Print Rights Controlled by CPP/BELWIN, INC., Miami, FL 33014
All Rights Reserved
Words by MITCHELL PARISH
Music by BENNY GOODMAN and EDGAR SAMPSON
Moderately
Don't cry, oh hon - ey, please don't be that way. Clouds in the sky should nev - er make you feel that way.
rain will bring the vi - o - lets of May. Tears are in vain, so hon - ey, please don't be that way.
heart, to - mor - row is an - oth - er day. Don't break my heart, oh, hon - ey, please don't be that way.
The
As
To Next Strain
Fine

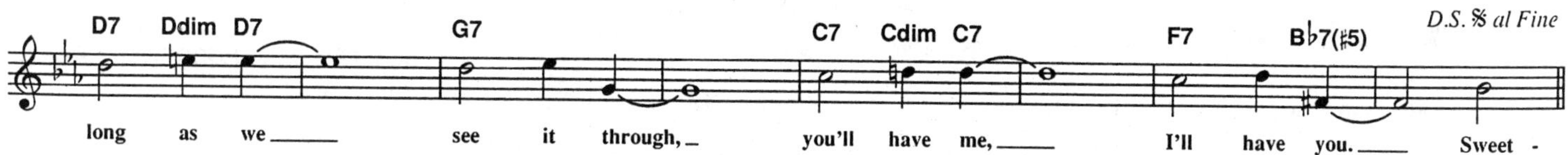
D7 Ddim D7 G7 C7 Cdim C7 F7 B♭7(♯5)
D.S. 𝄋 al Fine
long as we see it through, you'll have me, I'll have you. Sweet -

DON'T BLAME ME

Lyric by DOROTHY FIELDS
Music by JIMMY McHUGH

Moderately

C B♭ A A7 Dm7(♭5) G7 C Dm7(♭5) G7 Em7(♭5) A7
To Coda ⊕
Don't blame me for fall-ing in love with you. I'm un-der your spell, but how can I help it?
Can't you see when you do the things you do! If I can't con-ceal, the thrill that I'm feel-ing,
Blame your kiss, as sweet as a kiss can be. And blame all your charms that melt in my arms but
1. Dm7 G7(♯5) C G7
Don't blame me!
2. Dm7 G7 G7(♯5) C C7 F E7
don't blame me. I can't help it if that dog-goned
Am D7 Dm7 Dm7(♭5) G7
D.C. al Coda
moon a-bove makes me need, some-one like you to love!
⊕ Coda
Dm7 G7 C
don't blame me.

DON'T GET AROUND MUCH ANYMORE

Words by BOB RUSSELL
Music by DUKE ELLINGTON

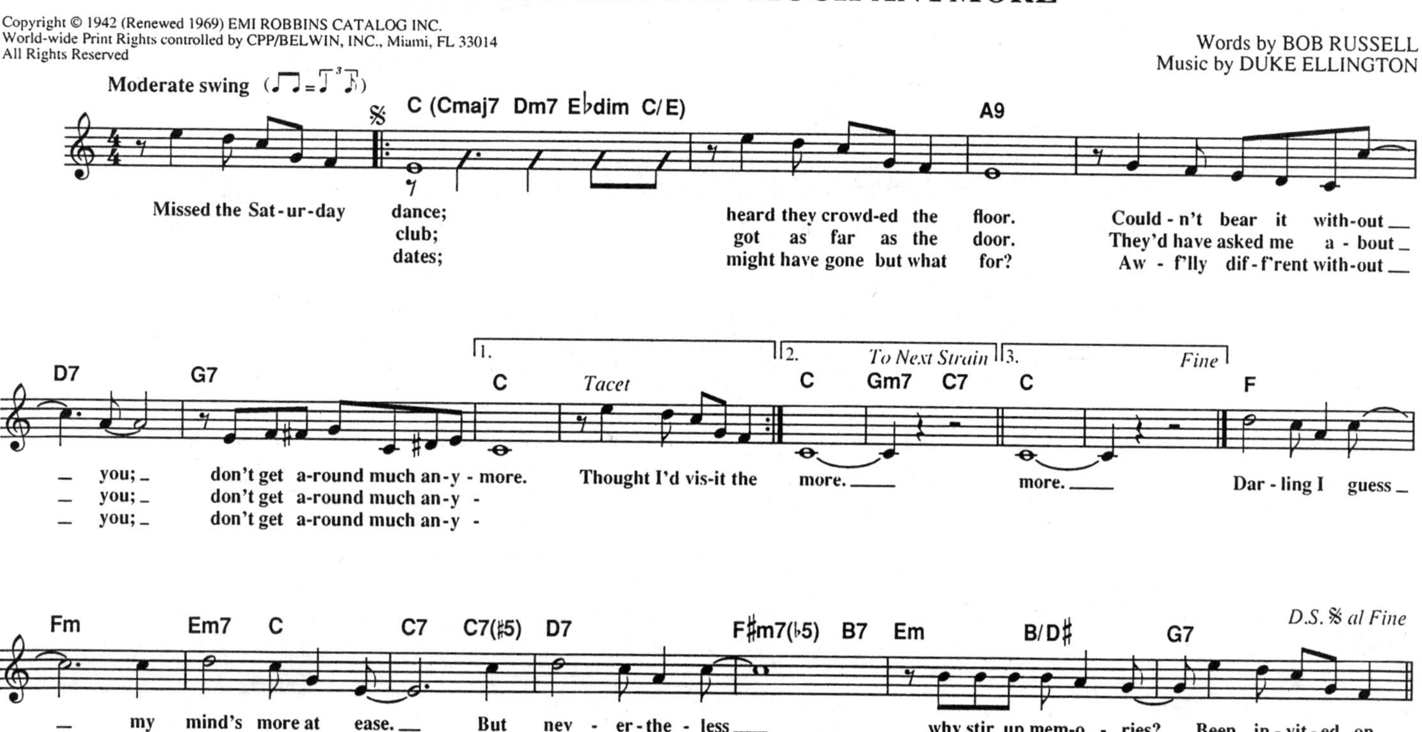
Moderate swing
C (Cmaj7 Dm7 E♭dim C/E) A9
Missed the Sat-ur-day dance; heard they crowd-ed the floor. Could-n't bear it with-out
club; got as far as the door. They'd have asked me a-bout
dates; might have gone but what for? Aw-f'lly dif-f'rent with-out
D7 G7 1. C Tacet 2. C Gm7 C7 To Next Strain 3. C Fine F
you; don't get a-round much an-y-more. Thought I'd vis-it the more. more. Dar-ling I guess
you; don't get a-round much an-y-
you; don't get a-round much an-y-
Fm Em7 C C7 C7(♯5) D7 F♯m7(♭5) B7 Em B/D♯ G7
D.S. 𝄋 al Fine
my mind's more at ease. But nev-er-the-less why stir up mem-o-ries? Been in-vit-ed on

DON'T CRY OUT LOUD

Words and Music by
PETER ALLEN and CAROLE BAYER SAGER

Moderately slow
Verse:
1. Ba - by cried the day the cir - cus came to town, 'cause she did-n't like parades just pass - ing by her. So she pain-ted on a smile and took up with some clown, and she danced with-out a net up on the wire. I know a lot a-bout her 'cause you see, ba - by is an aw - ful lot like me.
2. Ba - by saw the day they pulled the big top down, they left be-hind her dreams a - mong the lit - ter. And the dif-f'rent kind of love she thought she'd found, was noth - ing more than saw - dust and some glit - ter. But ba - by can't be bro - ken 'cause you see, she had the fin - est teach - er, that's me.
Chorus:
We don't cry out loud, we keep it in - side, learn how to hide our feel-ings. Fly high and proud and if you should fall re-mem-ber you al - most had it all.
I taught her don't cry out loud, just keep it in - side, learn how to hide your feel-ings. Fly high and proud and if you should fall re-mem-ber you
al - most had it. Don't cry out loud, keep it in - side, learn how to hide your feel-ings. Fly high and proud, and if you should fall re-mem-ber you al-most had it all. Keep it in-side just learn how to hide your feel-ings.
Repeat ad lib. and fade
DON'T FALL IN LOVE WITH A DREAMER
Words and Music by
KIM CARNES and
DAVE ELLINGTON
Copyright © 1980 ALMO MUSIC CORP., APPIAN MUSIC CO. and QUIXOTIC MUSIC CORP. (ASCAP)
All Rights Reserved
Slowly
Verse:
1. Just look at you sit-tin' there, you nev-er looked bet-ter than to-night. And it-'d be so eas-y to tell you I'd stay, like I've done so man-y times
2. I was so sure this would be the
3. See additional lyrics

D Bm Bm7/E A E/G♯ F♯m E
night you'd close the door _ and wan - na stay _ with me. ___ And it-'d be so eas - y to tell _ you I'd

D Bm A/C♯ D F♯m E *Chorus:* D
stay _ like I've done so man - y times. ___ Don't fall in love _ with a dream-

E C♯m7 F♯m Bm7 Bm7/A E/G♯ E
- er 'cause he'll al - ways take _ you in. ___ Just when you think _ you've real - ly changed _ him, he'll

A Bm7 A/C♯ D E7 C♯m7
leave you a - gain. ___ Don't fall in love _ with a dream - er 'cause he'll break _ you ev - 'ry time. _

F♯m D D/E 1. D/F♯ E/G♯ A E/G♯ F♯m E/G♯ *D.S.* 𝄋
— So, put out the light _ and just hold on ___ be - fore we say good - bye.

2. D/F♯ E/G♯ A D/A A D/A A E A E/G♯ F♯m E D D/E A
fore we say good - bye, ___ be-fore we say good - bye, good - bye.

Verse 3:
Now it's morning and the phone rings,
And ya say you've gotta get your things together,
You just gotta leave before you change your mind.
And if you knew what I was thinkin' girl,
I'd turn around, if you'd just ask me one more time.
(To Chorus:)

DON'T GIVE UP ON US

Words and Music by
TONY MACAULAY

Moderately slow
A Amaj7/G♯ D E/D C♯m F♯m7
Don't give up on us, ba - by. Don't make the wrong seem right. The fu-ture is-n't just one _ night. _
D A/C♯ D A/C♯ Bm7 D/E 𝄋 A Amaj7/G♯
It's writ-ten in the moon-light _ and paint-ed on the stars, _ we can't change ours. Don't give up on us, ba - by. We're still worth
up on us, ba - by. Lord knows we've
D E/D C♯m F♯m7 D A/C♯ D
one more try. And though we put a last one _ by, ___ just for a rain - y eve - ning _ when may - be stars are
come this far. Why can't we stay the way we _ are, ___ the an-gel and the dream - er, _ who some-times plays the
C♯sus C♯ Bm7 Bm7/A D/E A *Fine* A7 F Fmaj9
few. Don't give up on us, I ___ know we can still come through. I near-ly lost my head last night, _ you've got a
fool? Don't give up on us, I ___ know we can still come through.
Bm(4) Bm7 A C♯/G♯ F♯m D/E F E7sus D/E *D.S.* 𝄋 *al Fine*
right to stop be-liev - ing. _ There's still a lit-tle love left, e-ven so. Don't give

DON'T IT MAKE MY BROWN EYES BLUE

Words and Music by
RICHARD LEIGH

Moderately slow
C Am Dm7 G7 C Am7 Bm7(♭5) E7
Don't know when I've been so blue; don't know what's come o - ver you.
I'll be fine when you're gone, I'll just cry all night long.
I did - n't mean to treat you bad, did - n't know just what I had.
Am C/G D7/F♯ D7 F Em7 F G7
You've found some - one new, and don't it make my brown eyes blue.
Say it is - n't true, and
But hon - ey now I do, and
F F/G C Fine Am Em7 F C Am Em7
don't it make my brown eyes blue. Tell me no se - crets, tell me some lies. Give me no rea - sons, give me
D.C. al Fine
F C Am Em7 F C Dm7 Em F F/G
al - i - bis. Tell me you love me and don't let me cry. Say an - y - thing but don't say good - bye.

DON'T SIT UNDER THE APPLE TREE

(With Anyone Else but Me)

Words and Music by
LEW BROWN, CHARLIE TOBIAS
and SAM H. STEPT

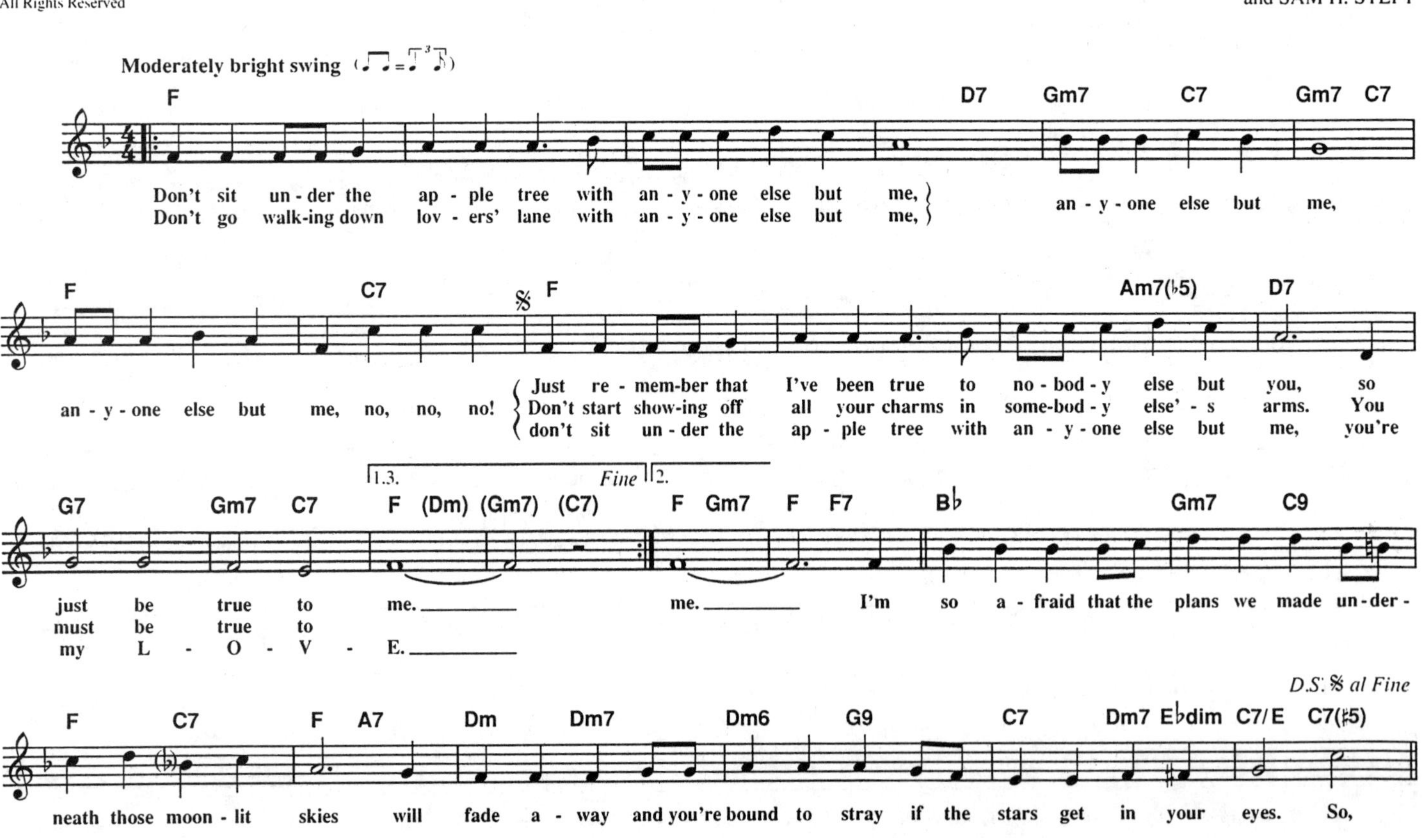
Moderately bright swing
F D7 Gm7 C7 Gm7 C7
Don't sit un - der the ap - ple tree with an - y - one else but me,
Don't go walk-ing down lov - ers' lane with an - y - one else but me,
an - y - one else but me,
F C7 F Am7(♭5) D7
an - y - one else but me, no, no, no!
Just re - mem-ber that I've been true to no - bod - y else but you, so
Don't start show-ing off all your charms in some-bod - y else' - s arms. You
don't sit un - der the ap - ple tree with an - y - one else but me, you're
G7 Gm7 C7 F (Dm) (Gm7) (C7) Fine F Gm7 F F7 B♭ Gm7 C9
just be true to me. me. I'm so a - fraid that the plans we made un - der -
must be true to
my L - O - V - E.
D.S. al Fine
F C7 F A7 Dm Dm7 Dm6 G9 C7 Dm7 E♭dim C7/E C7(♯5)
neath those moon - lit skies will fade a - way and you're bound to stray if the stars get in your eyes. So,

DON'T LET THE STARS GET IN YOUR EYES

Words and Music by
SLIM WILLET

Moderately
G
D7
Don't let the stars get in your eyes, don't let the moon break your heart.

G
Love blooms at night, in day - light it dies. Don't let the stars get in your eyes. Oh, keep your heart for me, for some day I'll re -

D7
G
1.2. To Next Strain
3. Fine
G
turn, and you know you're the on - ly one I'll ev - er love. Too man - y
nights, too man - y
miles, too man - y

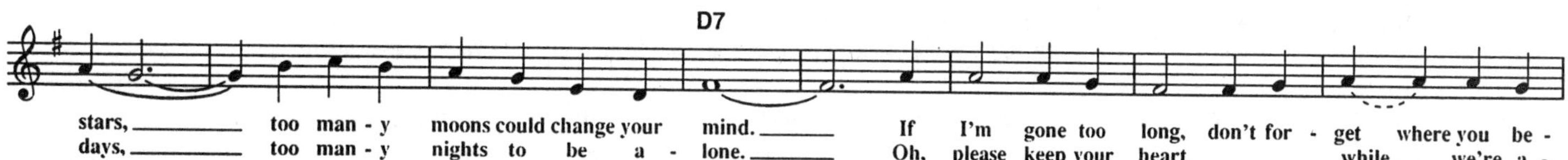
D7
stars, too man - y moons could change your mind. If I'm gone too long, don't for - get where you be -
days, too man - y nights to be a - lone. Oh, please keep your heart while we're a -

1.
G
D.S. 𝄋
2.
G
D.S. 𝄋 al Fine
long. When the stars come out, re - mem - ber you are mine. Don't let the gone. Don't let the
part. Don't lin - ger in the moon-light while I'm

DOWN BY THE OLD MILL STREAM

Words and Music by
TELL TAYLOR

Slowly
G
B♭dim
D7
Am7/D
D7
G
Bm
Down by the old mill stream, where I first met you, with your eyes of

C
E7/B
Am
D7
G
B♭dim
D7
B7/D♯
blue, dressed in ging - ham, too. It was there I knew that you loved me

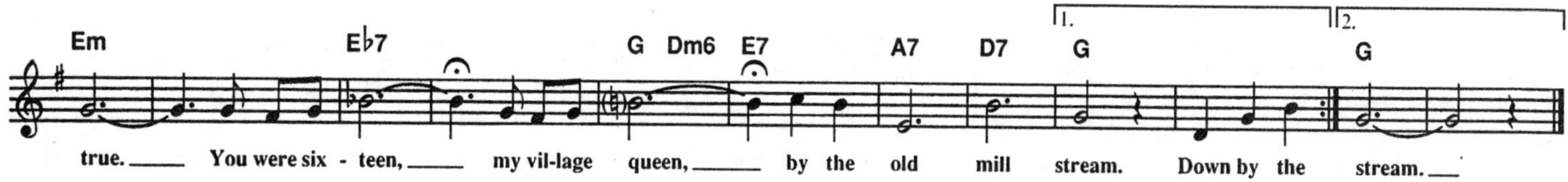
Em
E♭7
G
Dm6
E7
A7
D7
1.
G
2.
G
true. You were six - teen, my vil-lage queen, by the old mill stream. Down by the stream.

DON'T WANNA LOSE YOU

Words and Music by
GLORIA ESTEFAN

Moderately slow

Verse:

Fmaj7 Bbmaj7 Fmaj7 Bbmaj7 Fmaj7 Dm7 Ebmaj9

1. Some-times it's hard to make things clear, and know when to face the truth._ And I know__ that the mo-ment is

Fmaj7 Bb/C Fmaj7 Bbmaj7 Fmaj7 Bbmaj7 Fmaj7 Dm7 Ebmaj9

here.__ I'll o-pen my heart and show you in-side. My love has no pride or fear_ with you;_ I've got noth-ing to

Fmaj7 Bb/C Fmaj7 Bbmaj7 Fmaj7 Bbmaj7 Fmaj7 Dm7

hide.__ So o-pen your eyes and see who I am,________ and not who you want_for me_____ to be._

Chorus:

Ebmaj9 Fmaj7 Bb/C Fmaj7 Bbmaj7 Fmaj7 Bbmaj7

_ I am on-ly my-self,___ my-self.___ I don't wan-na lose_you now._ We're gon-na get through_some-how._

Fmaj7 Dm7 F/Eb C7sus Fmaj7 Bb/C Fmaj7 Bbmaj7 Fmaj7 Bbmaj7

Don't wan-na lose_you_now_ or ev-er._ Ba-by, I've fi-n'lly found_ cour-age to stand_my ground._ But if you

Fmaj7 Dm7 F/Eb C7sus [1. Fmaj7 Bb/C D.S. 𝄋] [2.3.etc. Fmaj7 Bb/C *Repeat and fade*]

want me, I'll be__ a-round_ for-ev-er.__ 2. We all make mis-ev-er,__ for-ev-er,_ yeah, yeah._ I

Verse 2:
We all make mistakes, or lose our way.
We stood the test of time.
I know it's the way it will stay.
It's all up to you to tell me to go,
'Cause it won't be me to walk away
When you're all that I know.
Now I know . . .
(To Chorus:)

DON'T WORRY 'BOUT ME

Words by TED KOEHLER
Music by RUBE BLOOM

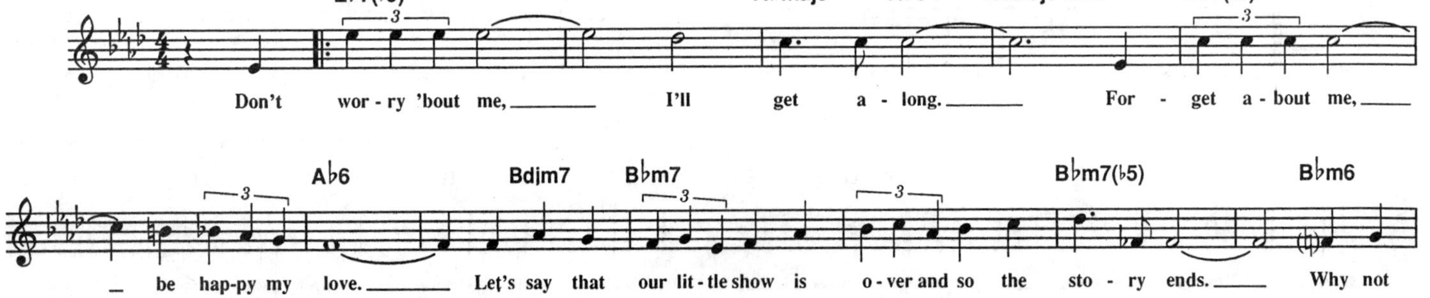
Moderately
Eb7(b9) Abmaj9 Ab6 Abmaj9 Ab6 Eb7(b9)
Don't wor-ry 'bout me,_______ I'll get a-long.________ For-get a-bout me,______
Ab6 Bdim7 Bbm7 Bbm7(b5) Bbm6
_ be hap-py my love._______ Let's say that our lit-tle show is o-ver and so the sto-ry ends._____ Why not

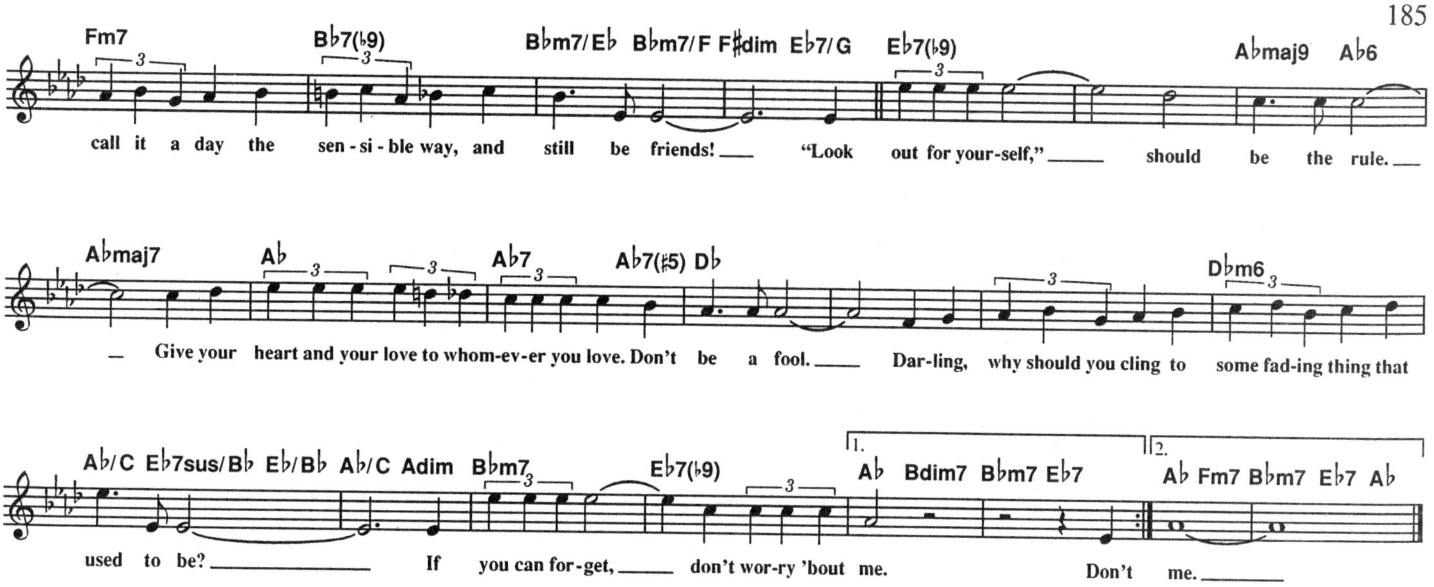

Fm7 | Bb7(b9) | Bbm7/Eb Bbm7/F F#dim Eb7/G | Eb7(b9) | Abmaj9 Ab6

call it a day the sen-si-ble way, and still be friends! "Look out for your-self," should be the rule.

Abmaj7 | Ab | Ab7 | Ab7(#5) Db | Dbm6

Give your heart and your love to whom-ev-er you love. Don't be a fool. Dar-ling, why should you cling to some fad-ing thing that

Ab/C Eb7sus/Bb Eb/Bb | Ab/C Adim | Bbm7 | Eb7(b9) | 1. Ab Bdim7 Bbm7 Eb7 | 2. Ab Fm7 Bbm7 Eb7 Ab

used to be? If you can for-get, don't wor-ry 'bout me. Don't me.

DON'T YOU KNOW I CARE

(Or Don't You Care to Know)

Words by MACK DAVID
Music by DUKE ELLINGTON

Slowly

Ddim | Eb Bb7(b9) Bb7(b9/#5) | Bbm9/Eb Eb9 | F11 Bb9 | Eb | Fm7 E9

Don't you know I care or don't you care to know If you know I

Eb C7 | Fm7 Bb7(b9/#5) | Eb Bb7(b9) | Eb Bb7(b9) Bb7(b9/#5) | Bbm9/Eb Eb9

care, how can you hurt me so? Dar-ling, you are part

F11 Bb9 | Eb | Fm7 E9 | Eb C7 | Fm7 E9 | Eb

of ev'-ry breath I take. Will you break my heart or give my heart a break? I

Gm | Am7(b5) D7 | Gm Gb7 | Cb | Ebm

can't fig-ure out what love's all a-bout, and where I fit in-to your scheme. Am I wast-ing time? Please

F7(b9) | Cb9 | Bb9 Bb7(b9) | Eb Bb7(b9) Bb7(b9/#5) | Bbm9 Eb9 | F11 Bb9

tell me, 'cause I'm down to my last dream? Won't you please be fair? Love me or let me go.

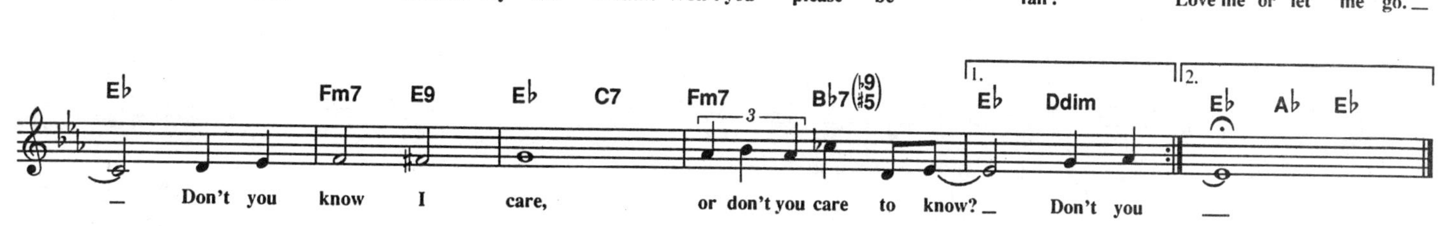
Eb
Fm7 E9
Eb C7
Fm7 Bb7(b9/#5)
1. Eb Ddim
2. Eb Ab Eb
Don't you know I care, or don't you care to know? Don't you

DON'T YOU WORRY 'BOUT A THING

Words and Music by
STEVIE WONDER

Moderate Latin rhythm
Vamp
Last time
1. Ev - 'ry - bod - y's got a thing, but some don't know how to han - dle it. You're al - ways reach - in' out in vain, just tak - ing the things not worth hav - ing.
say your style of life's a drag, and that you must go oth - er plac - es. But just don't you feel too bad when you get fooled by smil - ing fa - ces.
3. Ad lib. vocals 8va...
'ry - bod - y needs a change, a chance to check out the new. But you're the on - ly one to see the chang-es you take your-self through.
But don't you wor-ry 'bout a thing.
Don't you wor-ry 'bout a thing, ma - ma. 'Cause I'll be stand-in'
on the side when you check it out.
on the side
on the side
in the wings
To Coda
2. You when you check it out,
off your trip.
when you get
Don't you wor-ry 'bout a
To Next Strain
D.S. al Coda
4. Hey ev - thing.
(Sung 8va)
D.S.
Don't you wor - ry 'bout a
Coda
when you check it out.
Don't you wor-ry 'bout a thing.
Repeat ad lib. and fade
Don't you wor-ry 'bout a

DOWN BY THE RIVERSIDE

Words and Music by
DAZZ JORDAN

Moderately
I met my lit - tle bright-eyed doll down by the riv - er - side, down by the
asked her for a lit - tle kiss,
wed my lit - tle bright-eyed doll

F
riv - er - side, down by the riv - er - side. I met my lit - tle bright-eyed doll
I asked her for a lit - tle kiss
I'd wed my lit - tle bright-eyed doll
down by the
C7 F F F7 F B♭ F
1. 2. To Next Strain 3. Fine
riv - er - side, down by the riv - er - side. I side. She said, "Have side.
B♭ B♭7 F C7 Gm7 C7 F F7
pa - tience lit - tle man, I'm sure you'll un - der - stand I hard - ly know your name." I said, "If
B♭ B♭7 F G7 C7 D.C. al Fine
I can have my way, may - be some sweet day my name and yours will be the same." I'd

DOWN IN THE BOONDOCKS

Words and Music by
JOE SOUTH

Solid rock

Chorus:

G C D C
Down in the boon-docks, down in the boon-docks, peo-ple put me down 'cause that's the side of town I was

G C
born in. I love her, she loves me, but I don't fit in her so - ci - e - ty,

D C Bm Am G *To Coda* ⊕ *Verse:* G C
Lord, have mer-cy on the boy from down in the boon - docks. 1. Ev - 'ry night I watch the lights from the house up on the
2. *See additional lyrics*

G Em B7 Em Am7
hill. I love a girl who lives up there, and I guess I al - ways will. But I don't dare knock

D7 Am7 D7 Am7 D7 Am7
on her door, 'cause her dad-dy is my boss man. So I have to try to be con - tent, just to see her when - ev - er I

1. *D.C.* 2. *D.C. al Coda* ⊕ *Coda* *Repeat and fade*
D7 D7 D C Bm Am G
can. time. Lord, have mer-cy on the boy from down in the boon - docks.

Verse 2:
One fine day I'll find a way to move from this old shack.
I'll hold my head up like a king, and never, never will look back.
Until that morning, I'll work and slave and I'll save every dime.
But tonight she'll have to steal away to see me one more time.
(To Chorus:)

DOWN IN THE VALLEY
Copyright © 1993 by BEAM ME UP MUSIC (ASCAP), c/o CPP/BELWIN, INC., Miami, FL 33014
All Rights Reserved
TRADITIONAL FOLK SONG
Slowly
Down in the val - ey, val-ley so low, hang your head o - ver, hear the wind blow.
Hear the wind blow, love, hear the wind blow. Hang your head o - ver and hear the wind blow.
DOWN ON THE CORNER
Copyright © 1969 by JONDORA MUSIC
All Rights Reserved
Words and Music by
JOHN C. FOGERTY
Brightly
N.C.
Verse:
Ear-ly in the eve - nin' just a-bout sup-per-time, o-ver by the court-house, they're start-ing to un-wind. Four kids on the cor - ner try-ing to bring you up.
Roos-ter hits the wash - board and peo-ple just got to smile. Blink-y thumps the gut bass and so-los for a - while. Poor Boy twangs the rhy - thm out on his ka-la-ma-zoo.
You don't need a pen - ny just to hang a-round. But if you've got a nick - el, won't you lay your mon-ey down? O - ver on the cor - ner, there's a hap-py noise.
Wil-ly picks a tune out and he blows it on the harp.
Wil-ly goes in-to a dance and dou-bles on ka-zoo.
Peo-ple come from all a-round to watch the mag-ic boy.
Chorus:
Down on the cor-ner, out in the street, Wil-ly and the Poor Boys are play-in'. Bring a nick - el, tap your feet.
1.2. D.S.
3. Repeat ad lib. and fade
DREAM LOVER
Copyright © 1929 (Renewed 1956) by FAMOUS MUSIC CORPORATION
All Rights Reserved
Words by CLIFFORD GREY
Music by VICTOR SCHERTZINGER
Moderately
Dream lov-er, fold your arms a - round me. Dream lov-er, your ro-mance has found me. I'm held in your spell, know-ing so well dreams nev - er tell. We two can leave the world be - hind us. No - bod-y in-dis-creet can find us. Dream lov-er of mine, se-crets di - vine I am shar-ing with you.

THE DREAM OF OLWEN

Copyright © 1947 (Renewed) by LAWRENCE WRIGHT MUSIC CO., LTD., LONDON.
Exclusively published in the Western Hemisphere by MILLS MUSIC, INC., c/o EMI MUSIC PUBLISHING All Rights Reserved
Words by WINIFRED MAY
Music by CHARLES WILLIAMS
Moderately
Ol - wen, I hear you call to me at moon-rise a-cross a gol - den sea. Soft - ly, the waves make mel - o - dy to echo my song of mem - o - ry. Ol - wen, come to me, I im-plore. Tell me, where shall I find you? Ol - wen, till the stars shine no more, true un-to you I shall be.
Ol - wen it is your face I see that wak - ens in ev-'ry place for me, mu - sic of van - ished ecs - ta - cy, that ech - oes in - to e - ter - ni - ty. Ol - wen, in the wings of the wind, fond - ly your voice is fall - ing, call - ing from a world a-part. And strange-ly you seem to an-swer the dream in my heart.
To Next Strain
Fine
Deep in the blue that veils the night, the light in the west has fad - ed. But I must pur - sue, till dawn breaks through, the dream I am dream - ing of you, be - lov - ed.
D.C. al Fine
DRINKING CHAMPAGNE
Copyright © 1967 by ACUFF-ROSE MUSIC, INC. All Rights Reserved
Words and Music by BILL MACK
Country shuffle
I'm drink-ing cham-pagne, feel-ing no pain till ear - ly morn-ing. Din-ing and danc-ing with ev-'ry pret-ty girl I can find. I'm hav-ing a fling with a pret-ty young thing till ear-ly morn-ing, know-ing to-mor-row I'll wake up with you on my mind. Guilt-y wake up with you on my mind.
wake up with you on my mind.
Fine
con-science, I guess, though I must con - fess, I nev-er loved you much when you were mine. So, I'll keep So, I'll keep
To Next Strain
D.S. 𝄋
D.S. 𝄋 al Fine

DRINK TO ME ONLY WITH THINE EYES

TRADITIONAL

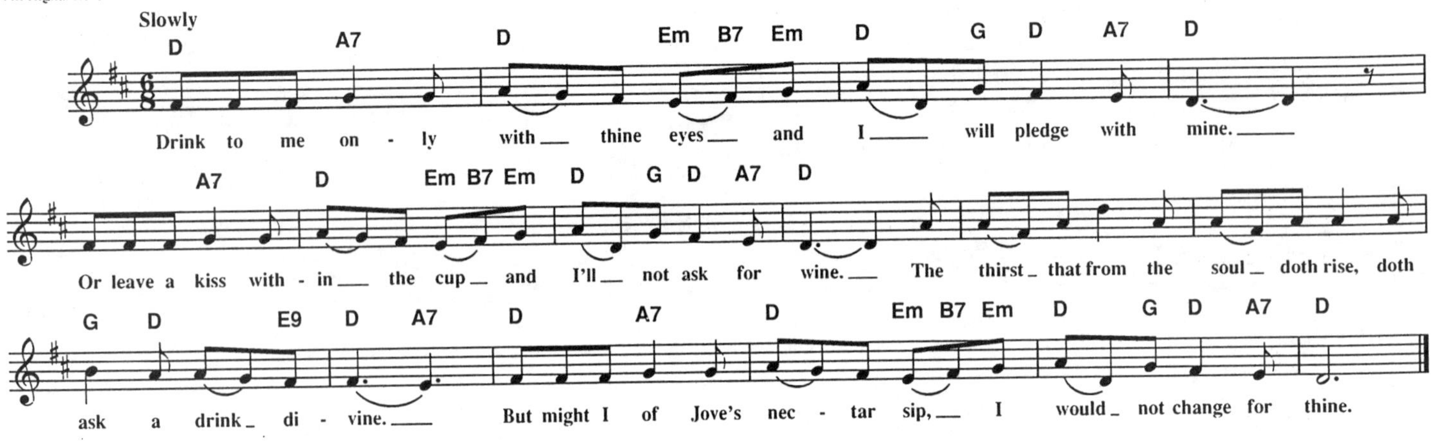
Slowly
D A7 D Em B7 Em D G D A7 D
Drink to me on - ly with thine eyes and I will pledge with mine.
A7 D Em B7 Em D G D A7 D
Or leave a kiss with - in the cup and I'll not ask for wine. The thirst that from the soul doth rise, doth
G D E9 D A7 D A7 D Em B7 Em D G D A7 D
ask a drink di - vine. But might I of Jove's nec - tar sip, I would not change for thine.

THE DRUNKEN SAILOR

TRADITIONAL FOLK SONG

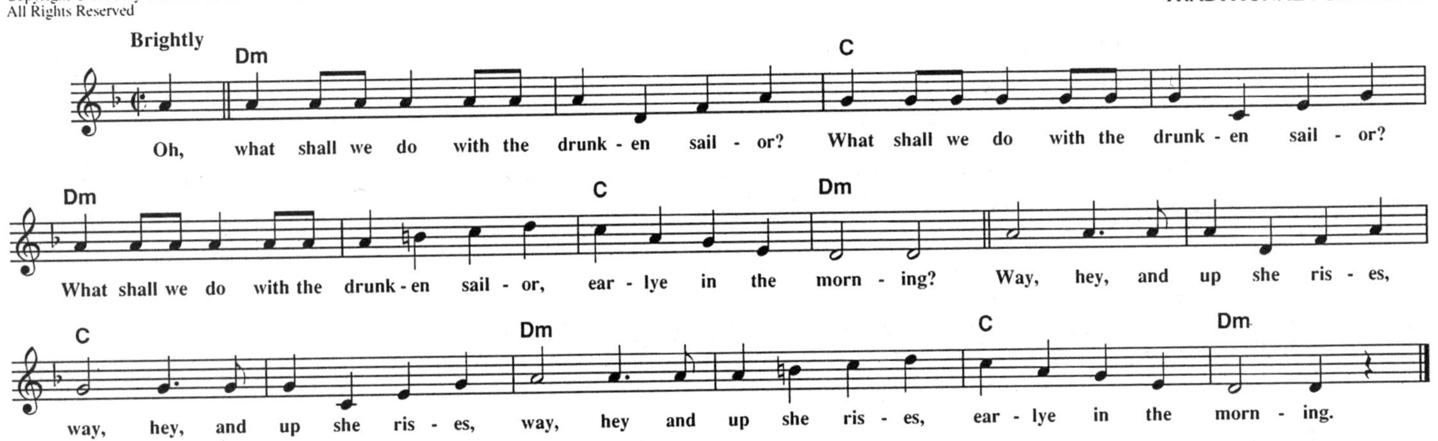
Brightly
Dm C
Oh, what shall we do with the drunk - en sail - or? What shall we do with the drunk - en sail - or?
Dm C Dm
What shall we do with the drunk - en sail - or, ear - lye in the morn - ing? Way, hey, and up she ris - es,
C Dm C Dm
way, hey, and up she ris - es, way, hey and up she ris - es, ear - lye in the morn - ing.

DUKE'S PLACE
(C Jam Blues)

Lyrics by
RUTH ROBERTS, BILL KATZ
and ROBERT THIELE
Music by
DUKE ELLINGTON

Moderately fast swing
F7 B♭9
Ba-by, take me down to Duke's Place. Wild-est box in town is Duke's Place.
Sax-es do their tricks in Duke's Place. Fel - las swing their chicks in Duke's Place.
Gm7 C7sus C7 F Dm7 Gm7 C7 Gm7 C7 F7
Love that pia-no sound in Duke's Place.
Come on, get your kicks in Duke's Place.
1. 2.
You find your-self a seat, and when you wan-na eat, you
B♭9 F7
look a-round and yell, "Wait - er." You fill your cup chock full of dreams and drink it up. You're jet-tin' a - long with your
C13 F Dm7 Gm7 C9 F7
girl - ie. It's af-ter three o - clock, but ba-by, it's ear - ly. If you've nev-er been to Duke's Place,

Moderately fast swing
B♭9
Gm7
C7sus
C7
F
F9(13)
take your toot-sies in-to Duke's Place. Life is in a spin in Duke's Place.

EARLY MORNIN' RAIN

Words and Music by
GORDON LIGHTFOOT

Moderato

F Fmaj7 F6 F C

In the ear - ly morn - in' rain. with a
Out on run - way num - ber nine, big seven -
Hear the might - y en - gines roar, see the
This old air - port's got me down, it's no

Gm C6 F F6 F

dol - lar in my hand, with an ach - in' in my
o - seven set to go, well, I'm stand - in' on the
sil - ver bird on high, she's a - way and west - ward
earth - ly good to me, 'cause I'm stuck here on the

Gm Gm6 Gm F

heart, and my pock - ets full of sand,
grass, where the cold wind blows.
bound, far a - bove the clouds she'll fly,
ground, as cold and drunk as I can be.

Gm Gm6 Gm

I'm a long way from home, and I
Well, the liquor tast - ed good, and the
where the mornin' rain don't fall, and the
you can't jump a jet plane like you

C7 F

miss my loved one so in the ear - ly morn - in'
wom - en all were fast, well, there she goes, my
sun al - ways shines, she'll be fly - in' o'er my
can a freight train, so I'd best be on my

Fmaj7 F6 Fmaj7 Gm C6 F B♭ F *D.C.*

rain and no place to go.
friend, she's roll - in' now at last.
home in a - bout three hours time.
way in the ear - ly mornin' rain.

Featured in the Paramount Picture "EASY LIVING"

EASY LIVING

By LEO ROBIN and
RALPH RAINGER

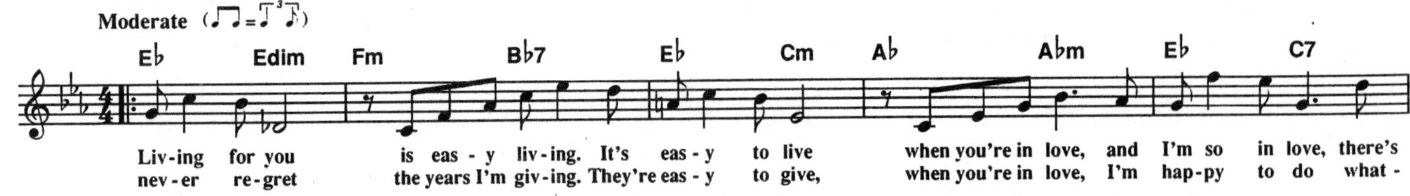
Moderate
Eb Edim Fm Bb7 Eb Cm Ab Abm Eb C7
Liv-ing for you is eas - y liv-ing. It's eas - y to live when you're in love, and I'm so in love, there's
nev - er re-gret the years I'm giv-ing. They're eas - y to give, when you're in love, I'm hap-py to do what -

1. 2.
Fm Bb9 Bb7(#5) Eb Edim Fm7 Bb7 Fm Bb9 Eb Fm7 F#dim Eb
noth - ing in life but you. I ev - er I do for you. For

B7 Gb7 B7 Gb7 B7
you, may - be I'm a fool but it's fun. Peo - ple say you rule me with one wave of your hand;

Abm Fm7 Bb7 Bb+ Eb Edim Fm Bb7
dar - ling it's grand. They just don't un - der - stand. Liv - ing for you is eas - y liv - ing. It's

Eb Cm Ab Abm Eb C7 Fm Bb9 Eb
eas - y to live when you're in love. And I'm so in love, there's noth-ing in life but you.

From the Broadway Musical Production "ANNIE"

EASY STREET

Words by MARTIN CHARNIN
Music by CHARLES STROUSE

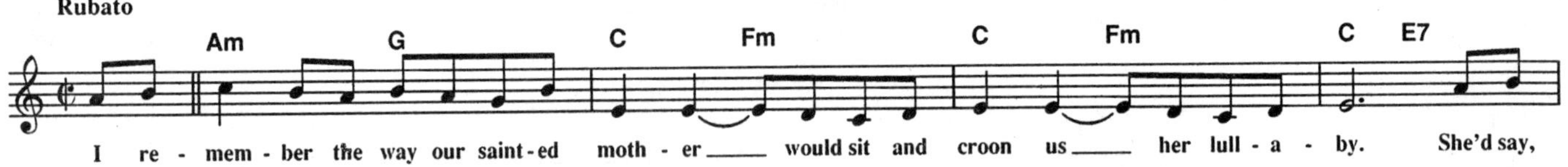
Rubato
Am G C Fm C Fm C E7
I re - mem - ber the way our saint - ed moth - er would sit and croon us her lull - a - by. She'd say,

Am G C Fm C E/B Am E Am G
"Kids, there's a place that's like no oth - er; you got - ta get there be-fore you die. You don't get there by play-in' from the

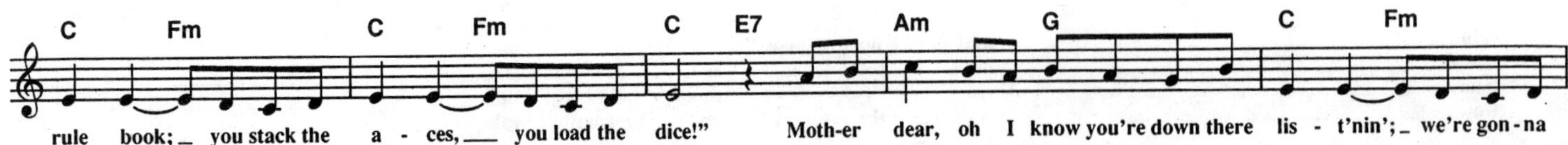
C Fm C Fm C E7 Am G C Fm
rule book; you stack the a - ces, you load the dice!" Moth-er dear, oh I know you're down there lis - t'nin'; we're gon-na

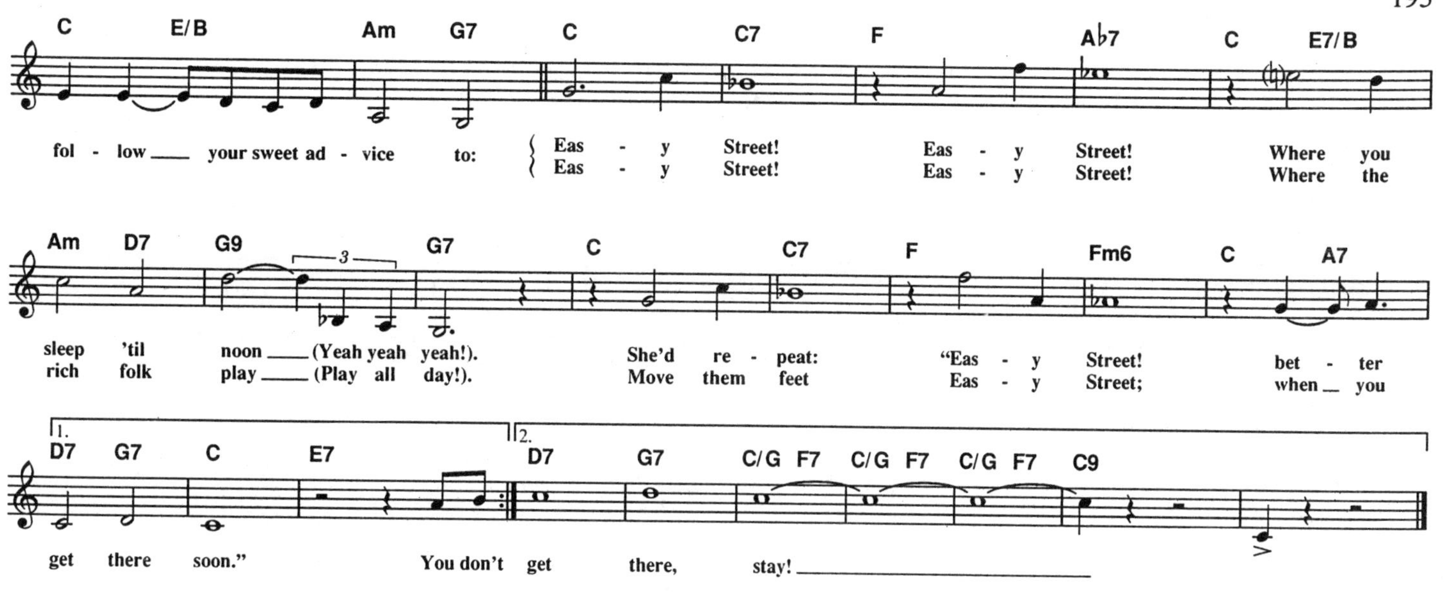
fol - low your sweet ad - vice to:
Eas - y Street! Eas - y Street! Where you sleep 'til noon (Yeah yeah yeah!).
Eas - y Street! Eas - y Street! Where the rich folk play (Play all day!).
She'd re - peat: "Eas - y Street! bet - ter get there soon."
Move them feet Eas - y Street; when you
You don't get there, stay!

From the Broadway Musical Production "HAIR"

EASY TO BE HARD

Words by JAMES RADO
and GEROME RAGNI
Music by GALT MacDERMOT

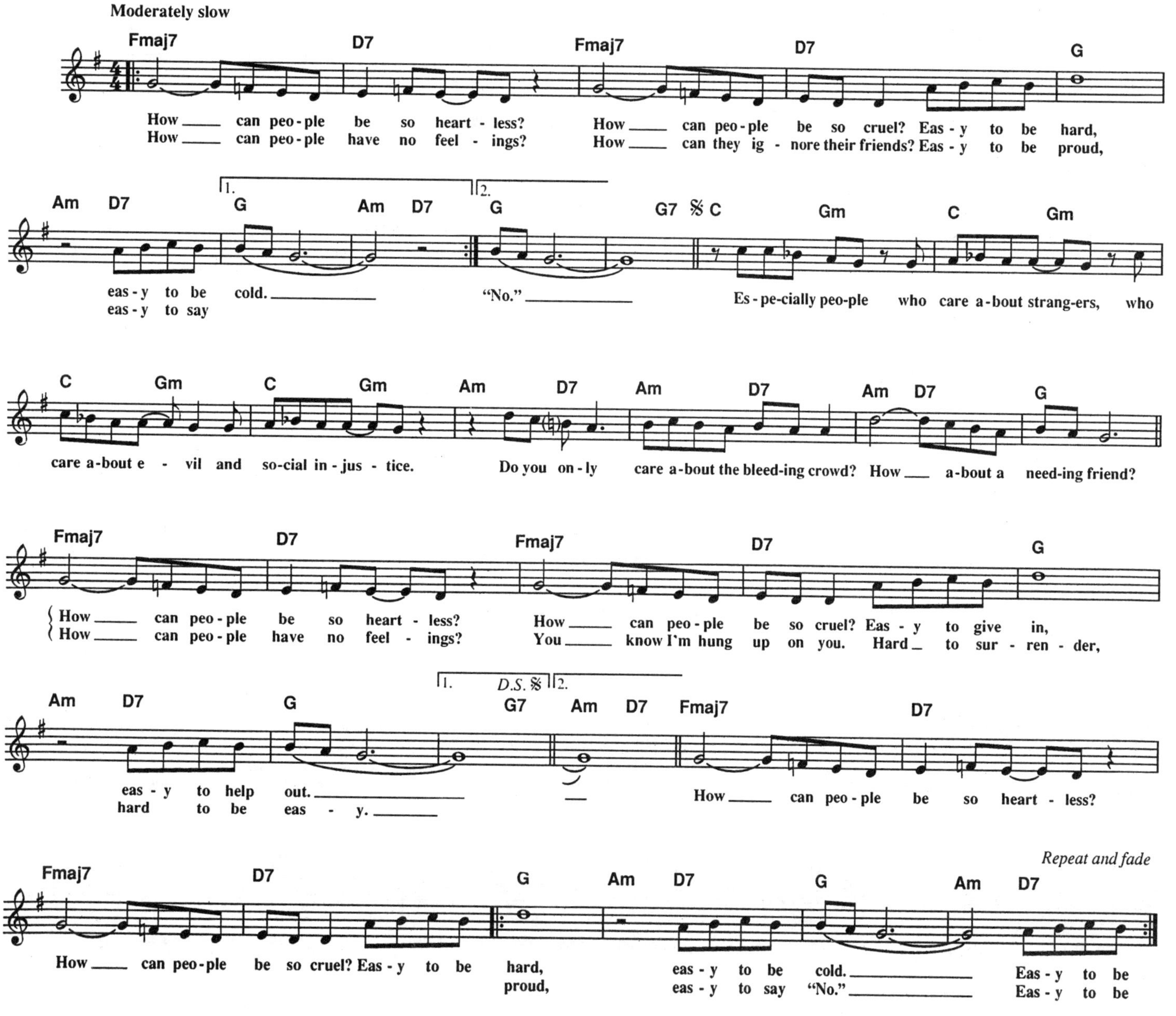

Moderately slow

How can peo-ple be so heart - less? How can peo-ple be so cruel? Eas - y to be hard, eas - y to be cold.
How can peo-ple have no feel - ings? How can they ig - nore their friends? Eas - y to be proud, eas - y to say "No."

Es - pe-cially peo-ple who care a-bout strang-ers, who care a-bout e - vil and so-cial in - jus - tice. Do you on - ly care a-bout the bleed-ing crowd? How about a need-ing friend?

How can peo-ple be so heart - less? How can peo-ple be so cruel? Eas - y to give in, eas - y to help out.
How can peo-ple have no feel - ings? You know I'm hung up on you. Hard to sur - ren - der, hard to be eas - y.

D.S. 𝄋

How can peo-ple be so heart - less? How can peo-ple be so cruel? Eas - y to be hard, eas - y to be cold. Eas - y to be
proud, eas - y to say "No." Eas - y to be

Repeat and fade

From the M-G-M Motion Picture "SWEET BIRD OF YOUTH"

EBB TIDE

Lyric by CARL SIGMAN
Music by ROBERT MAXWELL

Slowly
G7 Cmaj7 Am7 Dm7 G7 C B♭6
First the tide rush-es in, plants a kiss on the shore, then rolls out to sea, and the
rush to your side like the on - coming tide with one burn-ing thought; will your
1. 2.
A7 Dm7(♭5) G7 A7 A7/E A7(♭5)/E♭ Dm E7
sea is ver - y still once more. So I arms o-pen wide? At last we're face to face and as we
Am Am7/G Fm6 C/G C+/G♯ Am7 Dm7 G7 C Am7
rit. a tempo
kiss through an em-brace I can tell, I can feel, you are love, you are real, real - ly mine in the rain in the
Fm6 Dm7 G7 Cmaj7 Am7 Dm7 G7 Cmaj7 Am7 Dm7 G7 Cmaj7
dark, in the sun. Like the tide at its ebb I'm at peace in the web of your arms.
ELMER'S TUNE
Words and Music by
ELMER ALBRECHT, SAMMY GALLOP
and DICK JURGENS
Copyright © 1944 (Renewed 1969) EMI ROBBINS CATALOG INC.
All Rights Reserved
Moderately
G7 C6/9
Why are the stars al - ways wink-in' and blink-in' a - bove? What makes a fel - low start think-in' of
la - dy of eight - y go out on the loose? Why does a gan - der me - an - der in
gur - dies, the bird - ies, the cop on the beat; the can - dy mak - er, the bak - er, the
To Coda
1.
Dm7 G7(♯5) C6/9 G7 D7 G9 G+ C
fall - in' in love? It's not the sea - son, the rea - son is plain as the moon; it's just El - mer's tune. What makes a
search of a goose? What puts the kick in a chick-en, the mag-ic in June?
man on the street; the cit - y charm-er, the farm-er, the man in the moon,
2.
D7 G9 C6/9 F C F C
It's just El - mer's tune. Lis - ten, lis - ten, there's a lot you're li' - ble to be miss - in'.
D.S. al Coda
Coda
D7 G7 Dm7 G7 D7 G7 C6/9
Sing it, swing it, an - y old way and an - y old time. The hur-dy all sing El-mer's tune.

EL CHOCLO

A.G. VILLOLDO

Tango
Fm
C7
Fm
F7
B♭m
Fm
C7
To Coda
Fm
E♭7
A♭
Cm7
Bdim
E♭7
A♭
C7
Fm
G7
1.
C
N.C.
2.
C7
F
C7
F
D7
Gm
1.
G7
C7
2.
G7
Gm7
C7
F
D.S. al Coda
Coda
Fm
C7
Fm
Lively
Cm
A cum-ba, cum-ba, cum-ba, cum-ban - che-ro. A bon-go, bon-go, bon-go, bon-go - se - ro. Pri-qui -
B♭
A♭
Gm
Fm
E♭
Dm(♭5)
F♯dim
G7
ti que va - so - nan-do el cum-ban - che - ro bon-go - se - ro que se va, bon-go-se - ro que se va. A
1.
Cm
B♭
A♭7
G7
2.
To Next Strain
Cm
3.
Fine
Cm
C7
Fm
va. va. Y sue - ña a - si el tam - bor, bi - ri - qui - ti, bum-bum -
G7
D.S. al Fine
bá. Y vuel - ve a re - pi - car, bi - ri - qui - ti, bum-bum - ba. A

EL CUMBANCHERO

Spanish Words and Music by
RAFAEL HERNANDEZ

ELUSIVE BUTTERFLY
Copyright © 1965, 1966 EMI UNART CATALOG INC.
All Rights Reserved
Words and Music by
BOB LIND
Moderately
1. You might wake up some morn - in', to the sound of some-thing mov - ing past your win - dow in the wind. And if you're quick e - nough to rise, you'll catch the fleet - ing glimpse of some - one's fad - ing shad - ow.
2. Out on the new hor - i - zon, you may see the float - ing mo - tion of a dis - tant pair of wings. And if the sleep has left your ears, you might hear foot-steps run - ning through an o - pen mead - ow.
Don't be con - cerned, it will not harm you; it's on - ly me pur - su - ing some-thing I'm not sure of. A-cross my dream, with nets of won - der, I chase the bright e - lus - ive but - ter - fly of love.
1.
2.
love.
ELVIRA
Copyright © 1965 & 1981 by ACUFF-ROSE MUSIC, INC.
All Rights Reserved
Words and Music by
DALLAS FRAZIER
Moderately
Verse:
El - vir - a, El - vi - ra. My heart's on fi - re for El - vir - a.
1. Eyes that look like heav-en, lips like cher - ry wine, that girl can sho' nuff make my lit - tle light shine. I get a fun - ny feel - ing up and down my spine, 'cause I know that my El - vir - a's mine.
Chorus:
I'm sing-in' El - vir - a, El - vir - a. My heart's on fi - re for El - vir - a. Gid-dy-up, a oom pa-pa oom pa-pa mow mow, gid-dy-up, a oom pa-pa oom pa-pa mow mow. Hi - yo Sil - ver, a - way.
2. To - way. El -
D.S. 𝄋 al fade

Verse 2:
Tonight I'm gonna meet her
At the Hungry House Café,
And I'm gonna give her all the love I can.
She's gonna jump and holler
'Cause I saved up my last two dollars,
And we're gonna search and find that preacher man.
(To Chorus:)

From "THE AMERICANIZATION OF EMILY"

EMILY

Lyrics by JOHNNY MERCER
Music by JOHNNY MANDEL

Moderately slow

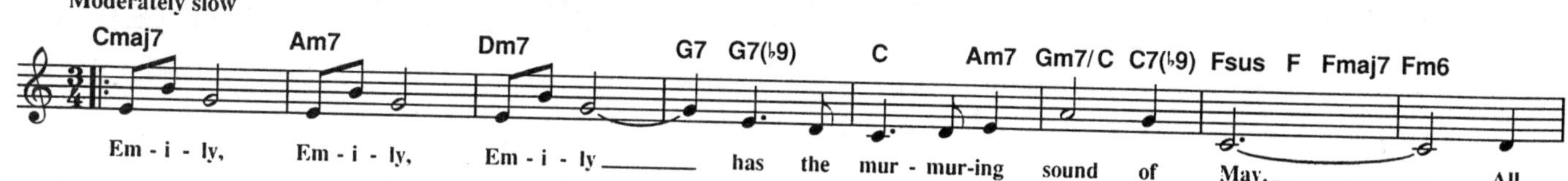
Cmaj7 Am7 Dm7 G7 G7(♭9) C Am7 Gm7/C C7(♭9) Fsus F Fmaj7 Fm6
Em - i - ly, Em - i - ly, Em - i - ly ___ has the mur - mur-ing sound of May. ___ All

A/C♯ F♯m7 Bm7 Bm7/E E7(♭9) Am7 D9 Dm7 G7(♯5 ♭9)
sil - ver bells, cor - al shells, car - ou - sels ___ and the laugh - ter of chil - dren at play say

Cmaj7 Am7 Dm7 G7 G7(♯5) Cmaj9 D♭9(♭5) C7 C7(♯5) Fmaj7 F(♯5) F6 Bm7/E E7(♭9)
Em - i - ly, Em - i - ly, Em - i - ly. ___ And we fade to a mar - vel - ous view, two

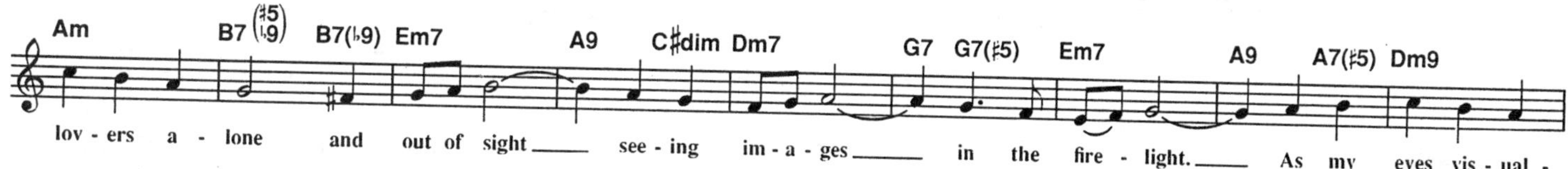
Am B7(♯5 ♭9) B7(♭9) Em7 A9 C♯dim Dm7 G7 G7(♯5) Em7 A9 A7(♯5) Dm9
lov - ers a - lone and out of sight ___ see - ing im - a - ges ___ in the fire - light. ___ As my eyes vis - ual -

Fm9(♯5) Fm6 Fm7 Em7 A9 A7(♯5 ♭9) Dm7 G9 G7(♯5)
1. C6 Am9 Dm7 G7(♭9)
2. C6/9
ize a fam - i - ly, ___ they see dream-i - ly, Em - i - ly too. ___ too. ___

EMPEROR WALTZ

JOHANN STRAUSS

Moderate waltz

C G7/D C G7/B /D C/E G7 C

G7/D C♯dim7 Dm F Cmaj7/G F Dm7 G7 C Dm/F

G7 C Dm/F
E7/G♯ Am
1. G7/B G7/D
2. G7 C

ENCHANTED SEA
Words and Music by FRANK METIS and RANDY STARR
Copyright © 1959 by VOLKWEIN BROS. INC.
All Rights Reserved
Moderately slow
There is a sea, the En-chant-ed Sea, that_ on-ly lov-ers know._ It sings a song as it flows a-long with_ waves that whis-per low._ When love is true, it will be_ end-less and deep as the deep blue sea. Your ten-der love brings the mag-ic of the En-chant-ed Sea to me._ There me.
EVERYDAY
Words and Music by NORMAN PETTY and CHARLES HARDIN
Copyright © 1957 (Renewed 1985) by PEER INTERNATIONAL CORPORATION
All Rights Reserved
Moderately
Oh, ev-er-y day_ it's a get-tin' clos-er; go-ing fast-er than a roll-er coast-er
ev-er-y-day_ seems a lit-tle fast-er. All my friends, they say, "Go on up and ask_ her."
Love like yours will sure-ly come_ my_ way. Yeah,
Oh, ev-er-y-day_ seems a lit-tle strong-er, and ev-er-y-day_ lasts_ a lit-tle long-er. Come what_ may,_ do you ev-er long for true love from me like I long_ for you, ba-by? Say ev-er-y day_ seems a lit-tle clos-er; go-ing fast-er than a roll-er coast-er. Love like yours will sure-ly come_ my_ way.
To Next Strain
Yes, a love like yours will sure-ly come my
(way.) day.
1.3.4. etc. Repeat and fade
Ooh, ev-er-y day. Ooh, ev-er-y
2. D.S.
Ooh,_

THE ENTERTAINER

By SCOTT JOPLIN

Not fast
N.C.
G
C
C7/G
F
C/E
/G
G7
Cm6/E♭
D7
C7/B♭
F/A
Fm/A♭
C/G
To Coda
Fm
/E
G/D
F♯dim7
D.S. al Coda
Coda
B♭
Dm
Gm
/B♭
G♯dim
E7
Am
D♭7
F/C
C7
F N.C.
Dm/F
E♭dim7
C/E N.C.
C N.C.

EVERYTHING OLD IS NEW AGAIN

Words and Music by
PETER ALLEN and
CAROLE BAYER SAGER

Moderate swing

C D9 C C/B♭ A7 D9
When trum-pets were mel-low and ev-'ry gal on-ly had one fel-low, no need to re-
your Long Is-land Jazz Age par-ties, wait-er, bring us some more Ba-car-dis, we'll or-der now what they
Don't throw the past a-way, you might need it some rain-y day. Dreams can come

G7sus G7 C C/B♭ F/A A♭7(♭5) G7 C *To Coda* 1. C7/B♭ F/A A♭7(♭5) G7 C
mem-ber when 'cause ev-'ry-thing old is new a-gain. Danc-in' at
or-dered then, 'cause ev-'ry-thing old is
true a-gain, when ev-'ry-thing old is

2. G7 C E7 B♭7(♭5) A7
new a-gain. Get out your white suit your tap shoes and tails, let's go back-wards when all

D13 G13 G7(♯5) *D.C. al Coda*
else fails. And mov-ie stars you thought were long dead now are framed be-side your bed.

Coda
G7 C C/B♭ F/A A♭7(♭5) G7 C E7
new a-gain. Get out your white suit, your tap shoes and tails.

A7 D13 G7 N.C. G7 E♭
Put it in back-ward when for-ward fails. But leave Gret-a Gar-bo a-lone, be a mov-ie star on your own. And don't throw the

F7 E♭ Gm7 C7 F7 B♭7 E♭ E♭/D♭ A♭/C B7(♭5)
past a-way, you might need it some rain-y day. Dreams can come true a-gain, when ev-'ry-thing old is

B♭7 E♭ E♭/D♭ A♭/C B7(♭5) B♭7 E♭ *freely* Cm7 F7 *a tempo* B♭7 E♭
new a-gain. I might fall in love with you a-gain.

EV'RY DAY OF MY LIFE

Words and Music by
JIMMIE CRANE and
AL JACOBS

Moderately

C C7(♯5) F G7 Dm7
Ev - 'ry day of my life, ___ I'll be in love with you. ___ Ev - 'ry day of my

G7 G7(♯5) Cmaj7 C6 Gm7 C7 F Dm G7 G9 Cmaj7
life, ___ I prom - ise I'll be true. ___ I'll nev - er make you cry, ___ and as the years go by ___

Am7 D7 Dm7 G7 C C7(♯5) F
— I'll al - ways try to do ___ what pleas - es you. ___ Ev-'ry day of my life, ___ I'll need you close to me, ___

G7 Dm7 G7 F7(♭5) E7 Gm6 A7 Dm Dm7 Fm6
— and if I have my way, ___ that's where you'll al - ways be. ___ I'll prove how much I love you

C/E Em7 A7 Dm G G7 G7(♭9) C
o - ver and o - ver a - gain, ev - 'ry mo-ment I live, ___ ev - 'ry day of my life. ___

FALLING IN LOVE AGAIN
(Can't Help It)

Words and Music by
FREDERICK HOLLANDER
Revised Lyric by SAMMY LERNER

Slow waltz
E♭ E♭7 A♭ A♭m E♭ Fm7 Fm7(♭5) B♭7 E♭ Adim B♭7
Fall - ing in love a - gain; nev - er want - ed to. What am I to do? Can't help it! ___
E♭ E♭7 A♭ A♭m E♭ Fm7 Fm7(♭5) B♭7 E♭ Am7(♭5) D7
Love's al - ways been my game. Play it how I may, I was made that way. Can't help it! ___
G7 Cm F7 B♭ Edim B♭7 B♭(♯5)
Men clus - ter to me, like moths a - round a flame. And if their wings burn, I know I'm not to blame.
E♭ E♭7 A♭ A♭m E♭ B♭m C7 Fm7 Fm7(♭5) B♭7 E♭
Fall - ing in love a - gain; nev - er want - ed to. What am I to do? Can't help it! ___

From the M-G-M Motion Picture "FAME"

FAME

Lyric by DEAN PITCHFORD
Music by MICHAEL GORE

Moderate dance beat
Fm Db/F Fm
Db/F Bbm7 C7
Verse:
Fm C7/G Fm/Ab Bbm7
Ba - by, look at me and tell me what you see.
Ba - by, hold me tight, 'cause you can make it right.
Eb Bb Db Eb C7/E Fm
You ain't seen the best of me yet. Give me time; I'll make you for - get the rest. I've got more
You can shoot me straight to the top. Give me love and take all I got to give. Ba - by, I'll
C7/G Fm/Ab Bbm7 Eb
in me, and you can set it free. I can catch the moon in my hand.
be tough. Too much is not e - nough. I can ride your heart till it breaks.
Chorus:
Bb C7sus C7 Fm Bbm7 Db/Eb Eb
Don't you know who I am?
Ooh, I got what it takes.
Re-mem-ber my name, fame! I'm gon - na live for - ev - er.
C7sus C7 Fm Bbm7 Db/Eb Eb C7sus C7
I'm gon - na learn how to fly high! I feel it com - in' to - geth - er. Peo - ple will see me and die.
Fm Bbm7 Db/Eb Eb C7sus C7 Fm
Fame! I'm gon - na make it to heav - en. Light up the sky like a flame; fame!
Bbm7 Db/Eb Eb C7sus C7 1. Fm
I'm gon - na live for - ev - er. Ba - by, re - mem - ber my name. (Re-mem-ber, re-mem-ber, re-mem-ber, re-mem-ber,
Db
re - mem - ber, re - mem - ber, re - mem - ber, re - mem - ber.)
Bbm7 C7 Fm Db Bbm7 C7 2. D.S. ad lib. and fade Fm
name, fame!

FASCINATION

Words by DICK MANNING
Music by F.D. MARCHETTI

Moderate waltz
C C/E E♭dim Dm A7
It was fas - ci - na - tion I know, and it might have end - ed right then at the start.
na - tion I know, see - ing you a - lone with the moon - light a - bove:
Dm Dm7/G G7
Just a pass - ing glance, just a brief ro - mance, and I might have gone on my way emp - ty heart - ed.
then I touched your
Dm G7 Dm7 G7 C
It was fas - ci - hand, and next mo - ment I kissed you. Fas - ci - na - tion turned to love.
FEELINGS
(¿Dime?)
Copyright © 1974, 1981 by EDITORA AUGUSTA LTDA.
All Rights Reserved
Spanish Lyrics by THOMAS FUNDORA
English Words and Music by MORRIS ALBERT
Moderately
Em Em/D♯ Em/D A7 Am7 D7 G F♯m7 B7
Feel-ings, noth-ing more than feel-ings, try-ing to for - get my feel-ings of love.
Em Em/D♯ Em/D A7 Am7 D7 G E7
Tear-drops rolling down on my face, try-ing to for - get my feel-ings of love.
C Am7 D7 Bm E7 Am D7 Bm E7
Feel - ings, for all my life I'll feel it. I wish I'd nev-er met you girl; you'll nev-er come a - gain.
C Am7 D7 Bm E7 Am D7 F♯m7 B7 B7(♭9)
Feel - ings, wo wo wo, feel - ings, wo wo wo, feel you a-gain in my arms.
To Coda
Em Em/D♯ Em7/D A7 Am7 D7 G E7(♯5) E7
Feel-ings, feel-ings like I've nev - er lost you, and feel-ings like I'll nev - er have you a-gain in my heart.
D.S. al Coda
C Am7 D7 Bm E7 Am D7 F♯m7 B7 B7(♭9)
Feel - ings, for all my life I'll feel it. I wish I'd nev-er met you, girl; you'll nev-er come a - gain.
Coda
Repeat and fade
C Am7 D7 Bm E7 Am D7 Bm E7
Feel - ings, wo wo wo, feel - ings, wo wo wo, feel - ings, a-gain in my arms.

FANTASIE IMPROMPTU
By FREDERIC CHOPIN
Moderately
To Coda
D.C. al Coda
Coda
FASCINATING RHYTHM
© 1924 WB MUSIC CORP. (Renewed)
All Rights Reserved
Words by IRA GERSHWIN
Music by GEORGE GERSHWIN
Moderately
Fas-ci-nat-ing Rhy-thm, you've got me on the go! Fas-ci-nat-ing, Rhy-thm, I'm all a-quiv-er.
once it did-n't mat-ter, but now you're do-ing wrong; When you start to pat-ter, I'm so un-hap-py.
What a mess you're mak-ing! The neigh-bors want to know why I'm al-ways shak-ing just like a fliv-er.
Won't you take a day off? De-cide to run a-long some-where far a-way off, and make it snap-py!
To Coda
Each morn-ing I get up with the sun, (Start a-hop-ping, nev-er stop-ping) to find at night, no work has been done.
I know that
D.C. al Coda
Coda
Oh, how I long to be the man I used to be! Fas-ci-nat-ing Rhy-thm, Oh, won't you stop pick-ing on me!

FINLANDIA

JEAN SIBELIUS

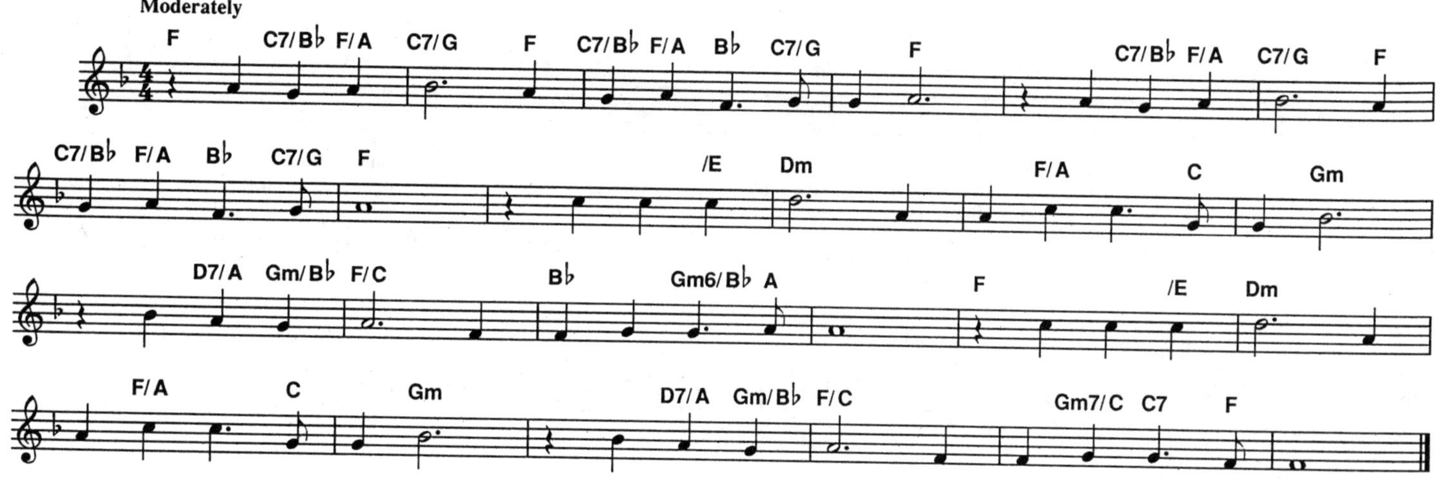
Moderately
F C7/B♭ F/A C7/G F C7/B♭ F/A B♭ C7/G F C7/B♭ F/A C7/G F
C7/B♭ F/A B♭ C7/G F /E Dm F/A C Gm
D7/A Gm/B♭ F/C B♭ Gm6/B♭ A F /E Dm
F/A C Gm D7/A Gm/B♭ F/C Gm7/C C7 F

THE FIRST NOEL

TRADITIONAL

Moderately slow

A7 D Bm A Em/G D/F♯ G D G

1. The first No - el, the an - gel did say, was to
2. (They) look - ed up and saw a star, shin - ing
3. (This) star drew nigh to the north - west; o - ver

D/F♯ D A7/E D/F♯ G A7/E D/F♯ D/A A7/C♯ D A7

cer - tain poor shep - herds in fields as they lay; in
in the East be - yond them far; and
Beth - le - hem it took its rest, and

D Bm A Em/G D/F♯ G D G D/F♯ D A7/E

fields where they lay keep - ing their sheep, on a cold win - ter's
to the earth it gave great light, and so it con -
there it did both stop and stay, right o - ver the

D/F♯ G A7/E D/F♯ D/A A7 D A7 D Bm F♯m D

night that was so deep.
tin - ued both day and night.
place where Je - sus lay.
No - el, No - el, No -

G D A/C♯ Bm D/A G D A7/E D/F♯ A7 D D

el, No - el, born is the King of Is - ra - el. 2. They 3. This el.

Verse 4:
Then entered in those Wise Men three,
Full rev'rently upon their knee,
And offered there in His presence,
Their gold and myrrh and frankincense.
Noel, Noel, Noel, Noel,
Born is the King of Israel.

From the Metro-Goldwyn-Mayer Musical Production "SINGIN' IN THE RAIN"

FIT AS A FIDDLE

Words by ARTHUR FREED
Music by AL HOFFMAN and AL GOODHEART

Moderate swing
Fm7 Bb7 Fm7 Bb7 Eb6 Ebmaj7
Fit as a fid - dle and read - y for love; I could jump o - ver the
Have - n't a wor - ry, I have - n't a care, feel like a feath - er that's
Hi did - dle did - dle, my ba - by's o - kay. Ask me a rid - dle, oh

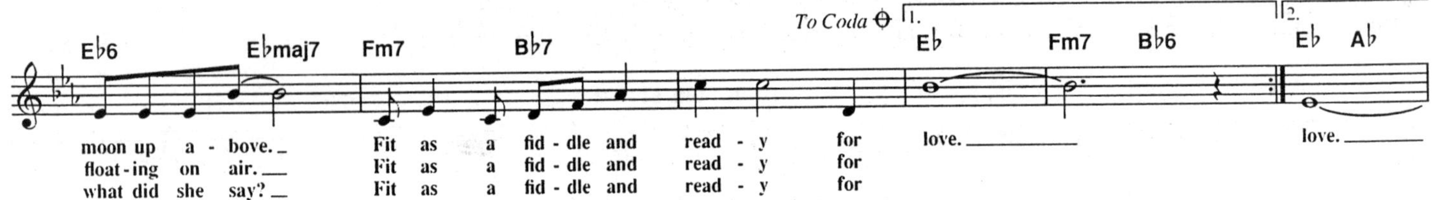
To Coda
Eb6 Ebmaj7 Fm7 Bb7 Eb Fm7 Bb6 Eb Ab
moon up a - bove. Fit as a fid - dle and read - y for love.
float - ing on air. Fit as a fid - dle and read - y for
what did she say? Fit as a fid - dle and read - y for
love.

Eb Ab7 Eb6 Eb7 Ab F7
Soon the church bells will be ring - ing, and I'll march with Ma and Pa. How those church bells will be

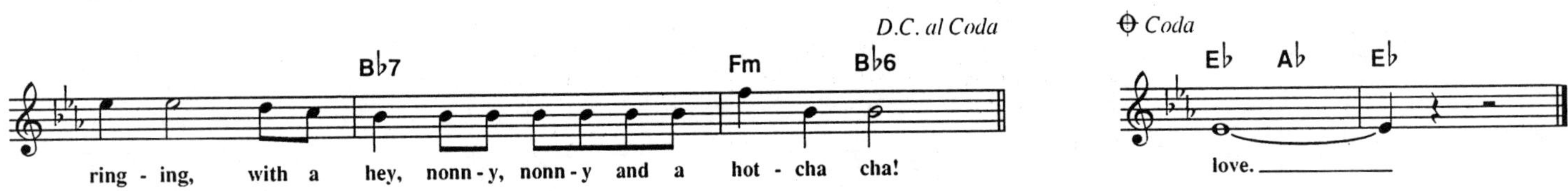
D.C. al Coda
Bb7 Fm Bb6
ring - ing, with a hey, nonn - y, nonn - y and a hot - cha cha!
Coda
Eb Ab Eb
love.

FIVE FOOT TWO, EYES OF BLUE

Words by SAM LEWIS and JOE YOUNG
Music by RAY HENDERSON

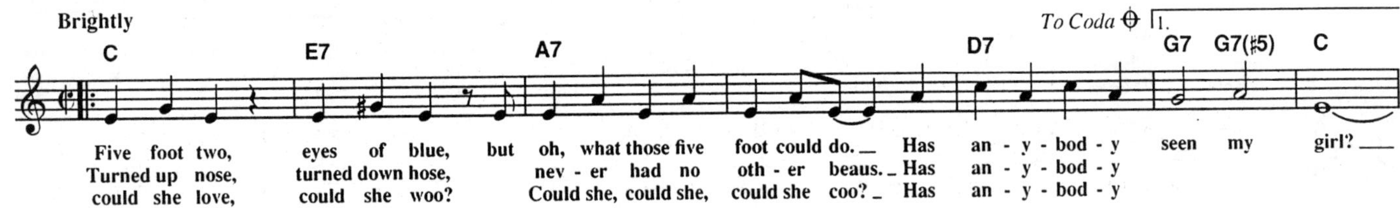
Brightly
To Coda
C E7 A7 D7 G7 G7(#5) C
Five foot two, eyes of blue, but oh, what those five foot could do. Has an - y - bod - y seen my girl?
Turned up nose, turned down hose, nev - er had no oth - er beaus. Has an - y - bod - y
could she love, could she woo? Could she, could she, could she coo? Has an - y - bod - y

D9 G7 G7 C6 F6/C C6 E7 A7 Em7 A7
seen my girl? Now if you run in - to a five foot two, cov - ered with fur,

D.C. al Coda
D7 G7 G7(#5)
dia - mond rings and all those things, bet - cha' life it is - n't her. But
Coda
G7 C6
seen my girl?

From the MGM/UA Motion Picture "THE SECRET OF NIMH"

FLYING DREAMS

Lyrics by PAUL WILLIAMS
Music by JERRY GOLDSMITH

Moderate waltz
Dream by night, wish by day; love be-gins this way. Lov-ing starts when o - pen hearts touch and stay.
Sleep for now; dream-ing's how lov-er's lives are planned; fu-ture songs and fly-ing dreams hand in hand. Love it seems made
fly - ing dreams so hearts could soar. Heav-en sent, these wings were meant to prove once more that love is the
key, love is the key. You and I touch the sky, the ea-gle and the dove. Night-in-gales, we keep our sails
filled with love. 1. (4.) And love, it seems made fly - ing dreams to bring you home to me. free. me.
2. Ev - er strong our fu - ture song; to sing it must be key. 4. And
3. Ev-'ry part is from the heart and love is still the
D.C.
FOR ME AND MY GAL
Copyright © 1917 (Renewed 1945) by MILLS MUSIC, INC.
All Rights Reserved
Words by EDGAR LESLIE
and E. RAY GOETZ
Music by GEO. W. MEYER
Moderately
The bells are ring - ing for me and my gal. The birds are sing - ing for me and my gal.
Ev-'ry-bod-y's been know - ing to a wed-ding they're go - ing. And for weeks they've been sew - ing,
ev-'ry Su - sie and Sal. They're con - gre - gat - ing for me and my gal. The Par - son's
wait - ing for me and my gal. And some-time I'm goin' to build a lit - tle home for two, for
three or four or more, in Love - land, for me and my gal. The bells are gal.

Paramount Pictures Presents a Daniel Melnick Production a Herbert Ross Film "FOOTLOOSE"

FOOTLOOSE

Written by
KENNY LOGGINS and
DEAN PITCHFORD

Bright rock
N.C.
Verse:
1. I been work-in' so hard; I'm punch-in' my card. Eight hours, for what?
Oh, tell me what I got. I've got this feel - in', that time's just hold-in' me down.
I'll hit the ceil - ing, or else I'll tear up this town.
Chorus:
1.3.4. To-night I got-ta cut loose, foot - lose; kick off your Sun-day shoes. Please, Lou - ise, pull me off of my
knees. Jack, get back; come on be-fore we crack. Lose your blues, ev-'ry-bod-y cut foot -
To Coda
To Next Strain
D.S. al Coda
loose.
ev-'ry-bod-y cut foot - ev-'ry-bod-y cut foot -
Bridge:
loose.
First, you've got to turn me a-round, sec-ond, and put your feet on the ground. Third, now take a hold of your soul.
D.S.
I'm turn-in' it
Coda
blues, ev-'ry-bod-y cut, ev-'ry - bod-y cut,
ev-'ry-bod-y cut, ev-'ry - bod-y cut, ev-'ry-bod-y cut, ev-'ry - bod-y cut, ev-'ry-bod-y, ev-'ry-bod-y cut foot - loose.

Verse 2:
You're playin' so cool,
Obeying every rule.
Dig way down in your heart.
You're burnin', yearnin' for some...
Somebody to tell you
That life ain't passin' you by.
I'm tryin' to tell you
It will if you don't even try;
You can fly if you'd only cut...
(To Chorus:)

Chorus 2:
Loose, footloose,
Kick off your Sunday shoes.
Ooh-ee, Marie,
Shake it, shake it for me.
Whoa, Milo,
Come on, come on let's go.
Lose your blues,
Everybody cut footloose.

FOR ALL WE KNOW

Words by SAM M. LEWIS
Music by J. FRED COOTS

Moderately

F G7 Gm7 C7 F D7
For all we know we may nev - er meet a - gain. Be - fore you go make this

Gm B♭m C7 G♯dim F/A A♭dim Gm7 C7
mo - ment sweet a - gain. We won't say "Good - night" un - til the last min - ute. I'll

F Dm7 Gm7 C7 F G7 Gm7
hold out my hand and my heart will be in it. For all we know this may on - ly be a dream.

C7 F D7 Gm B♭m C7 G♯dim F/A E7(♭5) E7(♭5) E7
We come and go like a rip - ple on a stream. So love me to - night; to -

A7 Am7(♭5) D7 Gm7 B♭m6 C7 Gm7 C9 F A♭dim Gm7 C9 F
1. 2.
mor-row was made for some, to - mor-row may nev - er come, for all we know. For know.

FOR HE'S A JOLLY GOOD FELLOW

TRADITIONAL

Brightly

D7 G C G D7 G G7
For he's a jol - ly good fel - low, for he's a jol - ly good fel - low, for he's a jol - ly good

C G/D D7 G C G C G
fel - low, which no - bod - y can de - ny. Which no - bod - y can de - ny, which no - bod - y can de - ny. For

C G D7 G C G/D D7 G
he's a jol - ly good fel - low, for he's a jol - ly good fel - low, for he's a jol - ly good fel - low, which no - bod - y can de - ny.

FOR LENA AND LENNY

By QUINCY JONES

Slow bounce
C
C♯dim7
Dm7
D♯dim7
C/E
E7(♯5)
Fmaj7
B♭7
E♭maj7
A7(♭9 ♭5)
1.
A♭maj7
Dm7/G
E9
A7
D7
Dm7
G9
2.
A♭maj7
Dm7/G
A♭dim7
C9
Am7
Gm7
C9
C9(♯5)
F
G♭dim7
G7(♯5)
C
C9
C9(♯5)
F
F♯dim7
A♭9
G7
C
C♯dim7
Dm7
D♯dim7
C/E
E7(♯5)
Fmaj7
B♭7
E♭maj7
A9(♭5)
A♭maj7
Dm7/G
G7(♭9)
C

From the United Artists Motion Picture "FOR YOUR EYES ONLY"

FOR YOUR EYES ONLY

Lyrics by MICHAEL LEESON
Music by BILL CONTI

Moderately slow
Verse:
G
C/G
G
C/G
1. For your eyes on-ly can see me through the night.
your eyes on-ly, the nights are nev - er cold.
For your eyes on - ly I nev-er need to hide.
You real - ly know me, that's all I need to know.
Cmaj7
Bm7
Em7
Cmaj7
Am7/D
You can see so much in me, so much in me that's new.
May-be I'm an o - pen book, be - cause I know you're mine.
I nev - er felt un - til I looked at you.
But you won't need to read be-tween the lines.
For your eyes
Chorus:
C/G
Gmaj7
Em7
Am7
Am7/D
C/G
Gmaj7
Em7
on - ly on - ly for you. You'll see what no one else can see, now I'm break-ing free. For your eyes on - ly, on - ly for you.
The
The

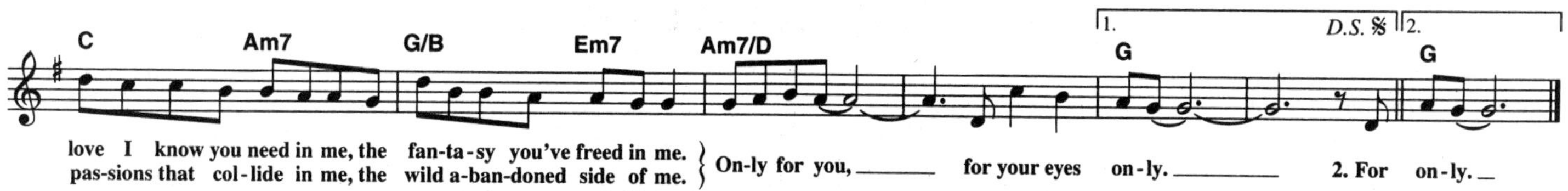
C Am7 G/B Em7 Am7/D
1. D.S. 𝄋 2.
G G
love I know you need in me, the fan-ta-sy you've freed in me.
pas-sions that col-lide in me, the wild a-ban-doned side of me.
On-ly for you, ___ for your eyes on-ly. ___ 2. For on-ly. _

FOREVER'S AS FAR AS I'LL GO

Words and Music by
MIKE REID

Slowly

Ab(2) Gm Cm Ab(2) Gm

Cm Ab(2)

Verse:

Eb Bb/Eb Eb Abmaj7 Ab6

1. I'll ad - mit I could feel it the first time that we touched. _ The look in ___ your eyes ___

Ab/Bb Bb Eb(2) Eb Cm7 Ab6 Ab

said you felt __ as much. _ But I'm not a man _ who falls so eas - i - ly. _ It's best that you know _

Chorus:

Abmaj7/Bb Bb Ab/Bb Bb Eb/G Ab Eb Eb(2)/G

where you stand _ with me. _ I will give you _ my heart _ faith - ful __ and true, _ and all the

Ab Gm Gm7 Cm7 Gm7 Ab(2) Ab

love it can hold, _ that's all I can do. ___ But I've thought a - bout ___ how long I'll _ love you,

Eb/Bb Fm(11) Eb/G Ab(2) Ab/Bb 1. Eb Ab/Eb

and it's on - ly fair _ that you know, ___ for - ev - er's _ as far _ as __ I'll __ go.

D.S. 𝄋 2.

Eb Ab/Eb Eb Eb/G Ab(2) Ab/Bb Bb Ab/Bb Bb Ab(2)

2. When there's go. For - ev - er's _ as far ___ as I'll go.

Repeat ad lib. and fade

Gm Cm Ab(2) Gm Cm Ab(2)

Verse 2:
**When there's age around my eyes and gray in your hair,
And it only takes a touch to recall the love we've shared.
I won't take for granted that you know my love is true.
Each night in your arms, I will whisper to you. . .**
(To Chorus:)

FORTUNATE SON

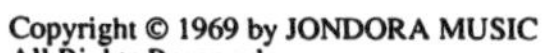
Copyright © 1969 by JONDORA MUSIC
All Rights Reserved

J.C. FOGERTY

Moderately bright

Verse:

G F C7 G

Some folks are born made to wave the flag. Ooh, they're red, white and blue.
Some folks are born sil - ver spoon in hand. Lord, don't they help them - selves.
Some folks in - her - it star span-gled eyes. Ooh, they send you down to war.

F C G

And when the band plays "Hail to the chief", they point the can - non right at you.
But when the tax man comes to the door, Lord, the house looks like a rum-mage sale.
And when you ask them, "How much should we give?" they on - ly ans - wer, "More! more! more!"

Chorus:

G D7 C7 G D7 *To Coda*

It ain't me, it ain't me_ I ain't no {1. sen - a - tor's / 2. mil-lion-aire's / 3. mil - i - ta-ry} son. It ain't me, it ain't me;_

C7 G | 1. G | 2. G Gdim7 C/G | 1. G | 2. G *D.C. al Coda*

I ain't no for-tun-ate one. one.

Coda

C7 G G D7 C7 G *Repeat ad lib. and fade*

I ain't no for-tu-nate one. It ain't me, it ain't me;_ I ain't no for-tun-ate one.

FRANKIE AND JOHNNY

Copyright © 1993 by BEAM ME UP MUSIC (ASCAP), c/o CPP/BELWIN, INC., Miami, FL 33014
All Rights Reserved

TRADITIONAL

Moderate blues

C G7 C Dm7/G C G7 C C7 F
Frank-ie and John - ny were lov - ers; oh, Lord-y how_ they could love! They swore to be true_ to each

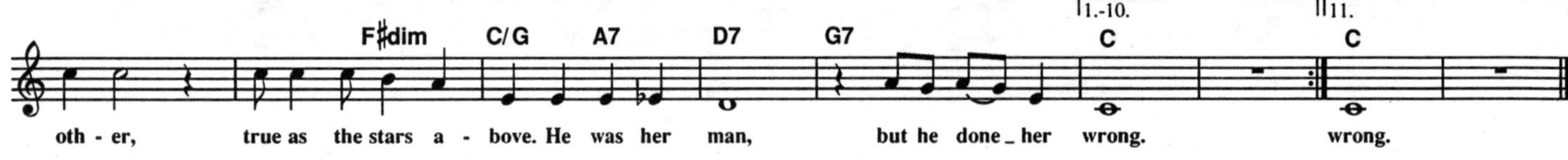
F♯dim C/G A7 D7 G7 1.-10. C 11. C
oth - er, true as the stars a - bove. He was her man, but he done_ her wrong. wrong.

Verse 2:
Frankie, she was a good woman,
As everybody knows;
Spent a hundred dollars
Just to buy her man some clothes.
He was her man, but he done her wrong.

Verse 3:
Frankie went down to the corner,
Just for a bucket of beer.
Said to the fat bartender,
"Has my lovin' Johnny been here?
He was my man, but he's doin' me wrong."

Verse 4:
"Now, I don't want to tell you no stories,
And I don't want to tell you no lies.
I saw your man about an hour ago
With a gal named Nellie Bly.
He was your man, but he's doin' you wrong."

Verse 5:
Frankie, she went down to the hotel,
Didn't go there for fun.
Underneath her long red kimono
She carried a forty-four gun.
He was her man, but he done her wrong.

Verse 6:
Frankie looked over the transom
To see what she could spy.
There sat Johnny on the sofa,
Just loving up Nellie Bly.
He was her man, but he done her wrong.

Verse 7:
Frankie got down from that high stool,
She didn't want to see no more.
Rooty-toot-toot, three times she shot
Right through that hardwood door.
He was her man, but he done her wrong.

Verse 8:
Sixteen rubber-tired hearses,
Sixteen rubber-tired hacks,
They take poor Johnny to the graveyard,
They ain't gonna bring him back.
He was her man, but he done her wrong.

Verse 9:
The judge said to the jury,
"It's as plain, as plain can be,
This woman shot her lover,
It's murder in the first degree."
He was her man, but he done her wrong.

Verse 10:
Frankie mounted to be the scaffold,
As calm as a girl can be,
And turning her eyes to heaven,
She said, "Good Lord, I'm comin' to Thee."
He was her man, but he done her wrong.

Verse 11:
This story has no moral,
This story has no end,
This story only goes to show
That there ain't no good in men!
He was her man, but he done her wrong.

FRENESI

English Lyrics by RAY CHARLES and S.K. RUSSELL
Spanish Words and Music by ALBERTO DOMINGUEZ

Moderately

Bbm7 Eb7 Bbm7 Eb7 Bbm7 Eb7

It was Fi - es - ta down in Mex - i - co, and so I stopped a - while to see the show.
Quie - ro que vi - vas só - lo pa - ra mí y que tú va - yas por don - de yo voy,

Bbm7 Eb7 Ab6 Abmaj7 Abdim Eb7 Ab6 N.C. Bbm7 Eb7

I knew that *fre - ne - si* meant "please love me", and I could say *"Fre-ne - si."* A love-ly se - ño - ri - ta caught my eye;
pa-ra que mi al-ma sea no - más de tí. bé - sa-me con fre-ne - sí. Da-me la luz que tie-ne tu mi - rar

Bbm7 Eb7 Bbm7 Eb7 Bbm7 Eb7 Ab6 Abmaj7 Abdim7 Eb7

I stood en-chant-ed as she wan - der'd by, and nev-er know-ing that it came from me, I gent - ly sighed, *"Fre-ne -*
y la an-sie-dad que en-tre tus la - bios ví, e - sa lo - cu - ra de vi - vir y a - mar, que es más que a - mor. fre-ne -

Ab6 N.C. Cmaj9 C6 Bbm6 Cmaj9 C6 N.C.

si." She stopped and raised her eyes to mine; her lips just plead-ed to be kissed. Her eyes were soft as can-dle -
si. Hay en el be - so que te dí, al - ma, pie - dad, co - ra - zón; di - me que sa - bes tu sen -

Cmaj9 C6 Db9 Dm7(b5) Bbm7 Eb9 N.C. Bbm7 Eb7 Bbm7 Eb7

shine; so how was I to re - sist? And now with-out a heart to call my own, a great-er hap-pi-ness I've
tir, lo mis - mo que sien-to yo. Quie-ro que vi - vas só - lo pa - ra mí y que tú va-yas por don -

Bbm7 Eb7 Bbm7 Eb7 Ab6 Abmaj7 Bbm7 Eb7 Ab6

nev - er known be - cause her kiss - es are for me a - lone; who would-n't say, *"Fre - ne - si?"*
de yo voy, pa - ra que mi al-ma sea no - más de tí, bé - sa me con fre - ne - sí.

FRERE JACQUES
(Brother John)

FRENCH FOLK SONG

Moderately
C G C G C G C G C
French: Frè - re Jac - ques, Frè - re Jac - ques, Dor - mez vous? Dor - mez vous?
English: Are you sleep - ing, are you sleep - ing, Broth - er John, Broth - er John?
G C G C G C 1. G C 2. G C
Son - nez les ma - ti - nes, son - nez les ma - ti - nes. Din, din, don! Din, din, don! Din, din, don!
Morn-ing bells are ring - ing, morn-ing bells are ring - ing. Ding, ding, dong! Ding, ding, dong! Ding, ding, dong!

FRIDAY ON MY MIND

Words and Music by
GEORGE YOUNG and
HARRY VANDA

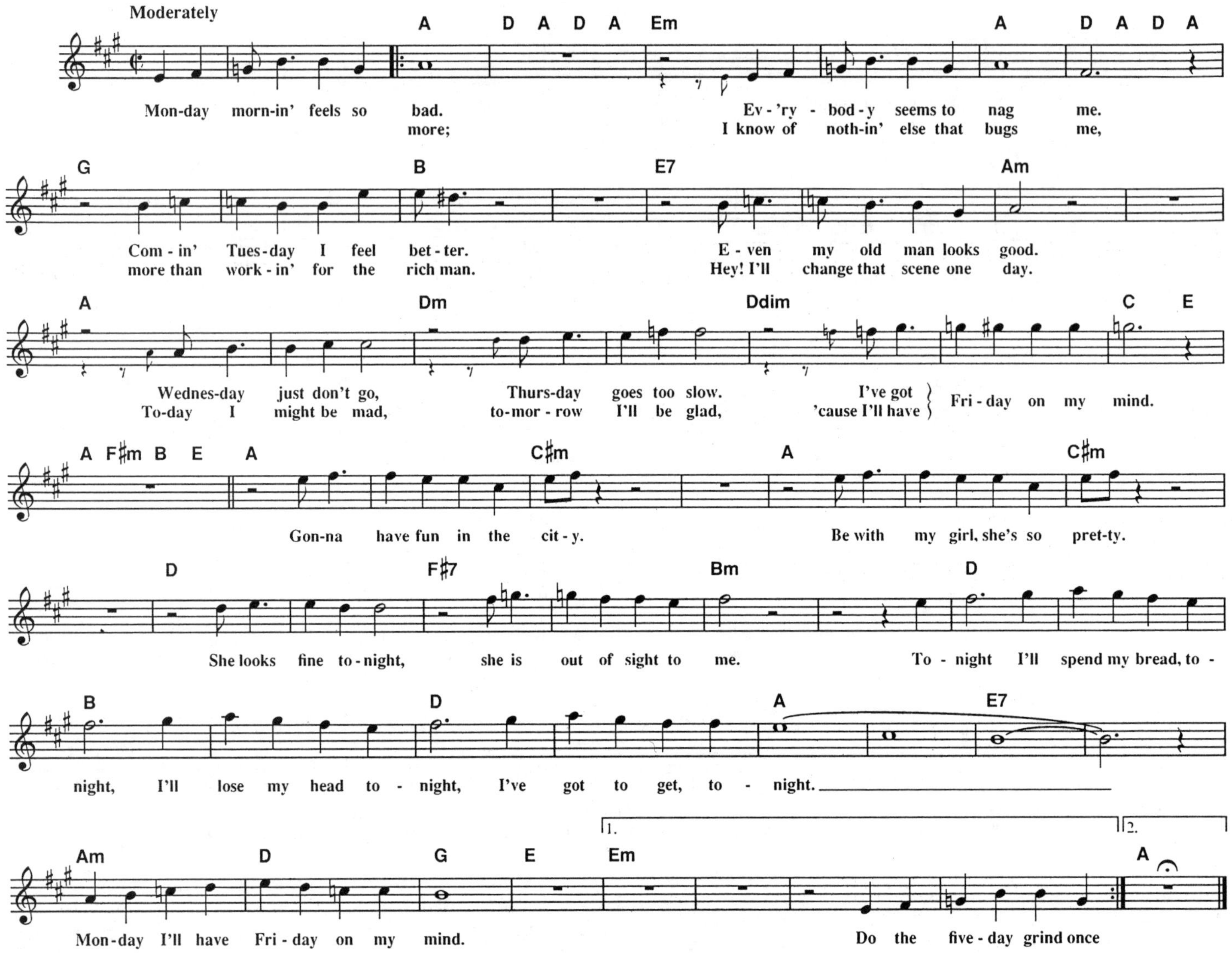

Moderately

A D A D A Em A D A D A

Mon-day morn-in' feels so bad. Ev-'ry-bod-y seems to nag me.
more; I know of noth-in' else that bugs me,

G B E7 Am

Com-in' Tues-day I feel bet-ter. E-ven my old man looks good.
more than work-in' for the rich man. Hey! I'll change that scene one day.

A Dm Ddim C E

Wednes-day just don't go, Thurs-day goes too slow. I've got / Fri-day on my mind.
To-day I might be mad, to-mor-row I'll be glad, 'cause I'll have / Fri-day on my mind.

A F♯m B E A C♯m A C♯m

Gon-na have fun in the cit-y. Be with my girl, she's so pret-ty.

D F♯7 Bm D

She looks fine to-night, she is out of sight to me. To-night I'll spend my bread, to-

B D A E7

night, I'll lose my head to-night, I've got to get, to-night.

Am D G E Em A

Mon-day I'll have Fri-day on my mind. Do the five-day grind once

FROM A DISTANCE

Lyrics and Music by
JULIE GOLD

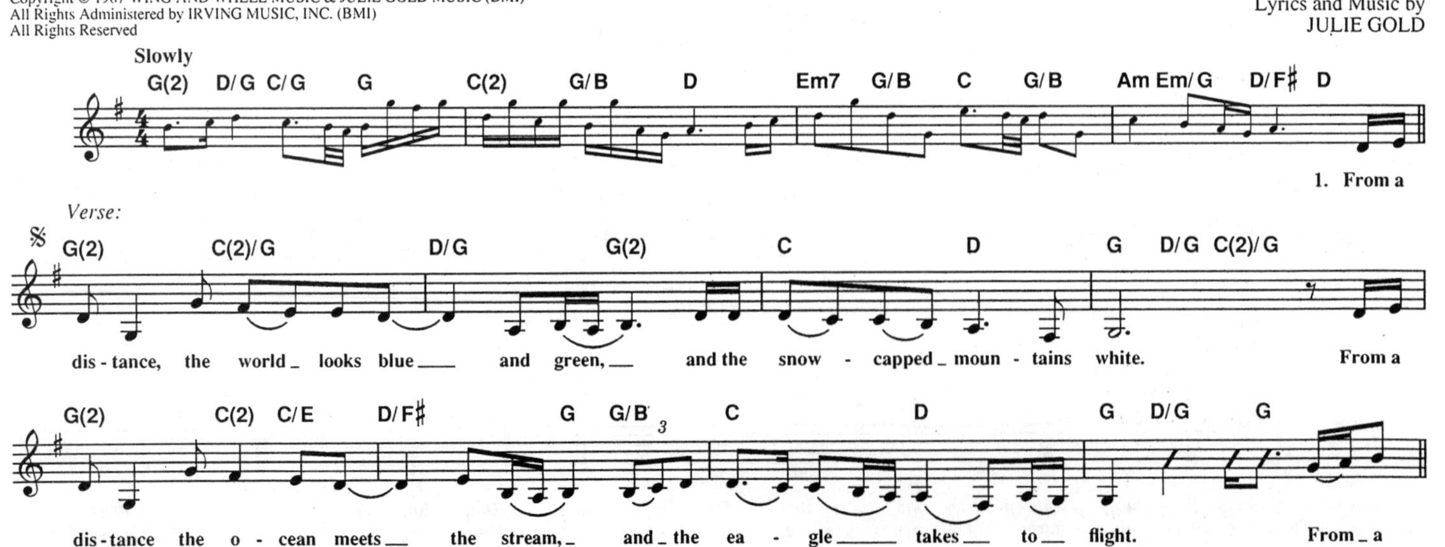
Slowly
1. From a
Verse:
dis-tance, the world looks blue and green, and the snow-capped moun-tains white. From a
dis-tance the o-cean meets the stream, and the ea-gle takes to flight. From a

dis-tance, there is har - mo-ny and it ech-oes through the land. It's the voice of hope, it's the
To Coda
voice of peace. It's the voice of ev - 'ry man.
D.S.
2. From a
Chorus:
man. God is watch-ing us. God is watch - ing us. God is watch-ing us from a dis - tance.
D.S. al Coda
3. From a
Coda
heart of ev - 'ry man. It's the hope of hopes, it's the
love of loves. This is the song of ev - 'ry man. And God is
Chorus:
watch-ing us. God is watch-ing us. God is watch-ing us from a dis - tance. Oh, God is
watch-ing us from a dis - tance.
rit.
slower

Verse 2:
From a distance, we all have enough,
And no one is in need.
There are no guns, no bombs, no diseases,
No hungry mouths to feed.
From a distance, we are instruments
Marching in a common band;
Playing songs of hope, playing songs of peace,
They're the songs of every man.
(To Bridge:)

Verse 3:
From a distance, you look like my friend
Even though we are at war.
From a distance I just cannot comprehend
What all this fighting is for.
From a distance there is harmony
And it echoes through the land.
It's the hope of hopes, it's the love of loves.
It's the heart of every man.

From the United Artists Motion Picture "FROM RUSSIA WITH LOVE"

FROM RUSSIA WITH LOVE

Words and Music by LIONEL BART

Moderately
From Rus-sia with love, I fly to you, much wis-er since my good-bye to you. I've travelled the
Rus-sia I flew, but there and then, I sud-den-ly knew you'd care a-gain. My run-ning a-
To Coda
world to learn I must re-turn from Rus-sia with love.
round is through; I fly to
I've seen plac-es, fac-es and smiled for a
mo-ment, but oh, you haunt-ed me so. Still my tongue-tied young pride would not let my love for you show,
in case you'd say no. To
D.S. al Coda
Coda
you, from Rus-sia with love.
FUN, FUN, FUN
Copyright © 1964 IRVING MUSIC, INC. (BMI)
All Rights Reserved
Words and Music by
BRIAN WILSON and MIKE LOVE
Bright rock
1. Well, she got her dad-dy's car, and she cruised through the ham-burg-er stand now. Seems she for-
girls can't stand her 'cause she walks, looks and drives like an ace now. She makes the
knew all a-long that your dad was get-tin' wise to you now. And since he
got all a-bout the li-brar-y like she told her old man now. And with her
In-dy Five Hun-dred look like a Ro-man char-i-ot race now. A lot-ta
took your set of keys you've been think-in' that your fun is all through now. But you can
ra-di-o blast-in', goes cruis-in' just as fast as she can now.
guys try to catch her, but she leads 'em on a wild-goose chase now.
come along with me, 'cause we got a lot-ta things to do now.
And she'll / we'll have fun, fun, fun till her / now that
dad-dy takes / dad-dy took the T-Bird a-way.
To Coda
2. Well, the
Solo ad lib.
D.S. al Coda
3. Well, you
Coda
And we'll have
fun, fun, fun now that dad-dy took the T-Bird a-way.
Repeat and fade
Ooo, ooo. Ooo,

FUNICULI, FUNICULA

(A Happy Heart)

By LUIGI DENZA
English Lyrics by
HOWARD JOHNSON

March tempo

E♭ B♭7 E♭ B♭7

Italian: *Sta - se - ra, Ni - na mia, io son mon - ta - to ___ Te lo di - rò? ___ Te lo di -*
English: Oh why ___ should an - y heart be filled with sad - ness? ___ We should be gay, ___ we should be

E♭ B♭7 E♭ B♭7

rò? ___ Co - là ___ do - ve di - spet - ti͜n cor in - gra - to ___ più far non può ___ più far non
gay. ___ Oh my, ___ the world should all be filled with glad - ness ___ in ev - 'ry way, ___ in ev - 'ry

E♭ Gm/D D7 Gm D7 Gm D7 Gm D7 Gm

può ___ Co - là ___ co - cen - te͜ è il fo - co, ma se fug - gi ___ Ti la - scia star ___ Ti la - scia star ___
way. ___ A song ___ can make most an - y - bod - y hap - py, ___ so let us sing, ___ yes let us sing. ___

B♭/F F7 B♭ F7 B♭ F7 B♭ F7 B♭

— E non ___ ti cor - re ap - pres - so, e non ti strug - gi ___ A ri - guar - dar, ___ A ri - guar - dar ___
— My song ___ is full of life and good and snap - py; ___ it's got the swing ___ and ev - ery - thing. ___

B♭7 E♭ G7/D

Le - sti, le - sti, via, mon - tiam su là le - sti, le - sti, via mon - tiam su là, fu - ni - cu - lì, fu - ni - cu -
Join the cho - rus, now's the time to start. Sing the cho - rus with a hap - py heart. Tra la la la la la la

Cm G7/B Cm A♭6 E♭/B♭ B♭7 1. E♭ 2. E♭

là fu - ni - cu - lì fu - ni - cu - là! via, mon - tiam su là, fu - ni - cu - lì fu - ni - cu - là. là. ___
la la la la, do your lit - tle part! Let the ech - o ring and sing it with a hap - py heart. heart. ___

FÜR ELISE

LUDWIG VAN BEETHOVEN

Brightly
N.C. Am E Am N.C. Am E
1. Am N.C. 2. Am C G Am E N.C.
Am E Am N.C. Am E Am

From the Motion Picture "THE TIME, THE PLACE & THE GIRL"

A GAL IN CALICO

Words by LEO ROBIN
Music by ARTHUR SCHWARTZ

Lightly with a lift

Eb Ebmaj7/D Eb6/C Ebmaj7/Bb Fm7 Bb9 Bb7(b9) Eb Ebmaj7/D

Met a gal in cal - i - co down in San - ta Fé; used to be her
Take my gal in cal - i - co down in San - ta Fé; guess I bet - ter

Eb6/C Ebmaj7/Bb Fm7 Bb9 Ebdim Eb Ab Eb Edim

Sun - day beau 'til I rode a - way. Do I want her, do I want her
let her know that I feel this way. Is she wait - in', is she wait - in'?

Bb7 Fm7 Bb9 D/Eb Eb Fm/BbEb G7/D G7(b5)/Db C7 F9 Bb9

love? Yes, sir - ee! Will I win her, will I win her love? Wait 'n see!
She bet - ter be. Am I hop - in' to be rop - in' her? Yes, sir - ee!

Eb Ebmaj7/D Eb6/C Ebmaj7/Bb Fm7 Bb9 Bb7(b9) Eb Ebmaj7/D

Work - in' with a Ro - de - o, go from town to town. See most ev - 'ry
Gon - na quit the Ro - de - o, gon - na set - tle down, buy a bolt of

Eb6/C Ebmaj7/Bb Fm7 Bb9 Ebdim Eb Ab Eb Bbm7 Eb7 Abmaj7 Fm7/Eb

kind - a gal, ev - 'ry kind - a gown. But who made my heart sing } Yip - pee Yi! Yip - pee
cal - i - co for a wed - din' gown. Then will I fence her in }

G7/D C7 F9(b5)/Cb Bb7 Eb Cm7 Fm7 Bb9 | 1. Eb Fm7 Eb Bb7 | 2. Eb Fm7 Bb7 Eb

Yo! My lit - tle gal in cal - i - co. co.

THE GANG THAT SANG "HEART OF MY HEART"

Words and Music by
BEN RYAN

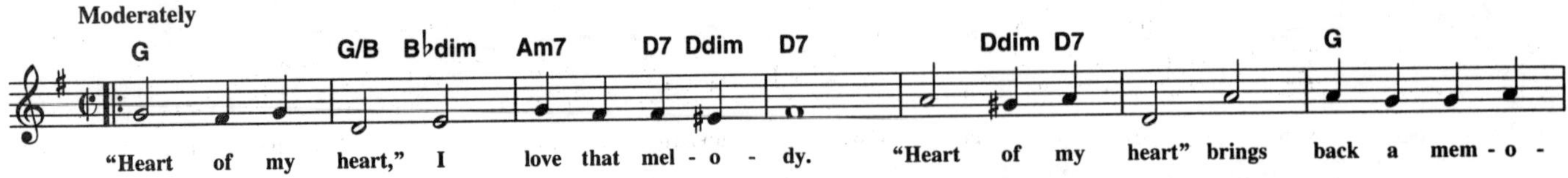
Moderately
G G/B Bbdim Am7 D7 Ddim D7 Ddim D7 G
"Heart of my heart," I love that mel - o - dy. "Heart of my heart" brings back a mem - o -

E7 A9 Gm6/Bb A7
ry. When we were kids on the cor - ner of the street, we were rough and read - y guys, but,

oh! how we could har - mo - nize. "Heart of my heart," meant friends were dear - er then.
Too bad we had to part. I know a tear would glis - ten if
once more I could lis - ten to that gang that sang "Heart of my heart." heart."
GEE WHIZ
Copyright © 1960 & 1973 EAST/MEMPHIS MUSIC
All Rights Reserved
Words and Music by
CARLA THOMAS
Slowly
Gee whiz, look at his eyes; gee whiz, how they hyp - no - tize. He's got
whiz, he's all the joy, gee whiz, I could find in a boy. He's
ev - 'ry - thing a girl could want; man, oh man, what a prize! Gee
aw - ful nice, it's par - a - dise; I hope I'm not his, be -
cause heav - en up a - bove knows how much I love that fel - low so.
An - gels sing of the love I bring; I hope our love will grow and grow. Oh, gee
whiz, I love that guy; gee whiz, my, my, oh my. There are things we could
do, I could say, "I love you;" but all I could say is, "Gee whiz."

GENTLE ON MY MIND

By JOHN HARTFORD

Moderately bright
C Cmaj7 C6 Cmaj7 Dm
It's know-ing that your door is al-ways o-pen and your path is free to walk, that makes me tend to
Dm7 G7 C Cmaj7 C6
leave my sleep-ing bag rolled up and stashed be-hind your couch. And it's know-ing I'm not shack-led by for - got-ten words and
Cmaj7 C Cmaj7 Dm Dm7 Dm6
bonds, and the ink stains that have dried up - on some line, that keeps you in the back-roads by the riv-ers of my
1. 2.
Dm7 Dm Dm(♯7) Dm7 G7 C C
mem-'ry, that keeps you ev-er gen-tle on my mind. 2. It's not mind.

Verse 2:
It's not clinging to the rocks and ivy planted on their columns now that binds me,
Or something that somebody said because they thought we fit together walkin'.
It's just knowing that the world will not be cursing or forgiving when I walk along
Some railroad track and find that you're moving
On the backroads by the rivers of my memory and for hours
You're just gentle on my mind.

Verse 3:
Though the wheat fields and the clothes lines and junkyards and the highways
Come between us,
And some other woman crying to her mother 'cause she turned and I was gone.
I still run in silence, tears of joy might stain my face and summer sun might
Burn me 'til I'm blind,
But not to where I cannot see you walkin' on the backroads by the rivers flowing
Gentle on my mind.

Verse 4:
I dip my cup of soup back from the gurglin' cracklin' caldron in some train yard,
My beard a roughing coal pile and a dirty hat pulled low across my face.
Through cupped hands 'round a tin can I pretend I hold you to my breast and find
That you're waving from the backroads by the rivers of my memory ever smilin',
Ever gentle on my mind.

CALCUTTA

By HEINO GAZE

Moderately
G D7 G
I've kissed the girls of Na-ples. They're pret-ty as can be. I've al - so kissed some French girls who came from Pa - ree. The
D7 G
Span-ish girls are love - ly, oh, yes, in - deed they are. But the la - dies of Cal - cut - ta are sweet-er by far. The
G7 C Cm G A7 D7
la - dies of Cal - cut - ta will steal your heart a - way. And af - ter it is stol - en, you'll say. I've
G D7 G
kissed the girls of Na - ples, I've kissed them in Pa - ree. But the la - dies of Cal - cut - ta do some-thing to me.

GEORGIA ON MY MIND

Lyrics by STUART GORRELL
Music by HOAGY CARMICHAEL

Moderately slow

E♭ G7 Cm Cm7/B♭ F/A A♭dim D♭7 E♭ D7

Geor - gia, __ Geor - gia, __ the whole day through; just an old sweet song keeps
Each day, __ Geor - gia, __ a song of you, comes as sweet and clear as

1. Fm7 B♭7 Gm7 Cm7 Fm7 B♭7 2. Fm7 Fm7/B♭ E♭ G7

Geor-gia on my mind. (Geor-gia on my mind. _) moon-light through _ the pines. ________

Cm6 Fm6 Cm7 A♭9 Cm6 A♭dim Cm7 F9 Cm Cm/B♭ Cm/A G7

Oth - er arms _ reach out to me; __ oth - er eyes __ smile ten - der - ly. ____ Still in peace - ful

Cm7 D7 Gm C7 Fm7 B♭7 E♭ G7

dreams I see __ the road leads back _ to you. _______ Geor - gia, ___ Geor - gia, ___

Cm Cm7/B♭ F/A A♭dim D♭7 E♭ D7 Fm7 Fm7/B♭ E♭

no peace I find; just an old sweet song keeps Geor-gia on __ my mind. _________

DO THAT TO ME ONE MORE TIME

Words and Music by
TONI TENNILLE

Moderately slow
F Dm B♭ C7
1. Do that to me one more _ time, __ once is nev - er e - nough __ with a man like you. ________
2. Pass that by me one more _ time, __ once just is - n't e - nough __ for my heart to hear. ________
F Dm B♭ C A/C♯
Do that to me one more _ time, __ I can nev - er get e - nough of a man like you. ______ Whoa, __
Tell it to me one more _ time, __ I can nev - er hear e - nough while I got 'cha near. ______ Whoa, __
Dm D♭+ F/C G7/B B♭/C C7
kiss ____ me ________ like you just _ did. ________ Oh, ba - by, do that to me once a - gain. _
say those words a - gain ____ like you just _ did. ________ Oh, ba - by, tell it to me once a - gain. _
1. F Dm B♭ C 2. F

GET HAPPY

Words and Music by
HAROLD ARLEN and TED KOEHLER

Moderate swing

E♭6 B♭7 E♭6 B♭7 E♭6 B♭7 A♭/B♭ E♭ E♭6 B♭7
For-get your trou-bles and just get hap - py. ___ You bet-ter chase all your cares a - way. ___ Sing Hal-le - lu-jah, come on, get

E♭6 B♭7 E♭ B♭7 A♭ E♭ A♭6 E♭7 A♭ E♭7 A♭6 E♭7 A♭6
hap - py, _ get read - y for the judge-ment day. _ The sun is shin-in', come on get hap - py. _ The Lord is wait-ing to take your hand. _ _ Shout Hal-le -

E♭7 A♭ E♭7 A♭ E♭7 A♭6 A♭9 D♭7 C7(♯5) F13
lu-jah! come on get hap - py. _ We're go - ing to the prom-ised land. We're head - in' _ 'cross the riv - er, _ wash your sins 'way _ in the

B♭7 A♭9 D♭7 C7(♯5) F7 B♭7 E♭6 B♭7 E♭6 B♭7 E♭6 B♭7
tide. It's all so peace-ful on the oth - er side. _ For-get your trou-bles and just get hap - py. _ You bet-ter chase all your cares a - way. _

A♭/B♭ E♭ E♭6 B♭7 E♭6 B♭7 E♭ B♭13 1. E♭ C♭7 B♭7 2. E♭
_ Shout Hal-le - lu-jah! come on, get hap - py _ Get read - y for the judge-ment day For-get your day.

From the Musical Production "WILDCAT"

GIVE A LITTLE WHISTLE

Lyric by CAROLYN LEIGH
Music by CY COLEMAN

Polka

Verse:

B♭ B♭maj7 B♭6 B♭maj7 B♭ B♭maj7 B♭6 B♭maj7 B♭m7 E♭9
From now on, I prom-ise to be - have. I'll pack my gear and dis - ap-pear from view! _ From now on, I'll

A♭6 B♭ Cm7 F7 B♭7
hud-dle in a cave, but if 'n case you miss the face that used to pes-ter you: Just
Chorus:
E♭6
give _ a lit-tle whis-tle, _
B♭9 E♭6 E♭7 B♭m7/F E♭7/G
ring _ a lit-tle bell. _ Crook _ your lit-tle fin - ger, hon - ey, give _ a lit-tle yell. _
1. I'll
2. I'll
A♭ A♭6 A♭maj7 A♭6 E♭ B♭/D C7sus C7 F7sus F7 B♭7 E♭6
leap o - ver fenc-es, I'll e - ven leave my sens-es, and I'll take, for your sake, to the air. _
streak like an ar-row through al - leys wide and nar-row, down a drain or a main thor-ough - fare. _
Just give _
C9 Fm7 B♭9 1. E♭6 F7 2. E♭6 F7 E♭6 B♭7(♭5) E♭
_ a lit-tle whis-tle. _ Say you want me and I'll be there! there! _

GIANT

(This Then Is Texas)
From the Movie "GIANT"

Words by
PAUL FRANCIS WEBSTER
Music by
DIMITRI TIOMKIN

Rousing march tempo

C Am F6 G7 C Em F G7

Just like a sleep - ing Giant Sprawl - ing in the sun, In
My Ma was born in Dal - las, Fa - ther in Fort Worth, You can
God made these lone - ly a - cres where I ride a - lone, But the

C D7 G G9/F C/E C F C/E Am7 D7 Dm7/G G7

one great hand the Ri - o Grande, In the oth - er Gal - ves - ton.
bet your boots I got my roots In the good old Tex - as earth.
dev - il cursed this land with thirst And he bleached it like a bone.

C Am F6 G7 C Em C7 F G7

Where oil wells laugh at An - gels and buz - zards wheel a - bove;
Just see the sil - ver dol - lars fall - ing from a - bove;
One day a wild tor - na - do, next a gen - tle dove;

Refrain with heart

C D7 G F G9/F Em

This then is Tex - as, Lone - Star State of Tex - as,

F G7sus4 G7 C Em F G7 1.2. C G7 3. C

This then is Tex - as, Land I love!
This is the Gi - ant, Land I love! love!

GIMME THAT OLD TIME RELIGION

TRADITIONAL

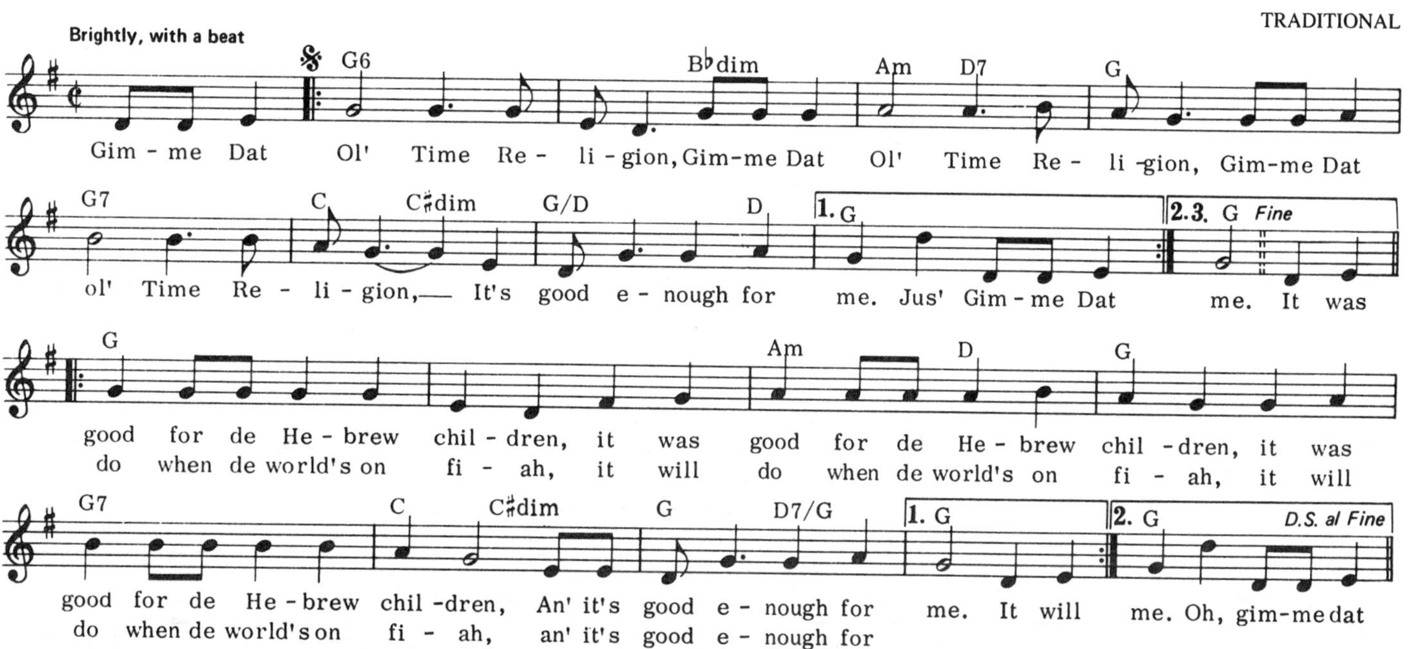
Brightly, with a beat
G6 B♭dim Am D7 G
Gim - me Dat Ol' Time Re - li - gion, Gim-me Dat Ol' Time Re - li - gion, Gim-me Dat
G7 C C♯dim G/D D 1. G 2.3. G Fine
ol' Time Re - li - gion, It's good e - nough for me. Jus' Gim - me Dat me. It was
G Am D G
good for de He - brew chil - dren, it was good for de He - brew chil - dren, it was
do when de world's on fi - ah, it will do when de world's on fi - ah, it will
G7 C C♯dim G D7/G 1. G 2. G D.S. al Fine
good for de He - brew chil - dren, An' it's good e - nough for me. It will me. Oh, gim-me dat
do when de world's on fi - ah, an' it's good e - nough for

(I Don't Stand) A GHOST OF A CHANCE

(With You)

Words by BING CROSBY
and NED WASHINGTON
Music by VICTOR YOUNG

Slowly
G7(♯5) Cmaj9 G7(♯5) Em7(♭5) A7 Fm6 Cmaj9 Am7 D7 G7(♯5)
I need your love so bad - ly. I love you, oh, so mad - ly, but I don't stand a ghost of a chance with
Cmaj9 Am7 Dm7(♭5) G7 Cmaj9 G7(♯5) Em7(♭5) A7 Fm6 Cmaj9 Am7
you! I thought at last I'd found you, but oth - er loves sur - round you. And "I don't stand a
D7 G7(♯5) C6/9 G7 G7(♯5) E♭7 Am C Am C
ghost of a chance with you!" If you'd sur-ren-der just for a ten-der kiss or two,
F♯m7(♭5) B7(♭9) E7 G7 G7(♭5) Cmaj9 G7(♯5)
you might dis-cov-er that I'm the lov-er meant for you, and I'd be true. But what's the good of schem-ing, I
Em7(♭5) A7 Fm6 Cmaj9 Am7 D7 G7(♯5) C6/9 F7 C6/9
know I must be dream-ing, for "I don't stand a ghost of a chance with you!"

GIVE MY REGARDS TO BROADWAY

GEORGE M. COHAN

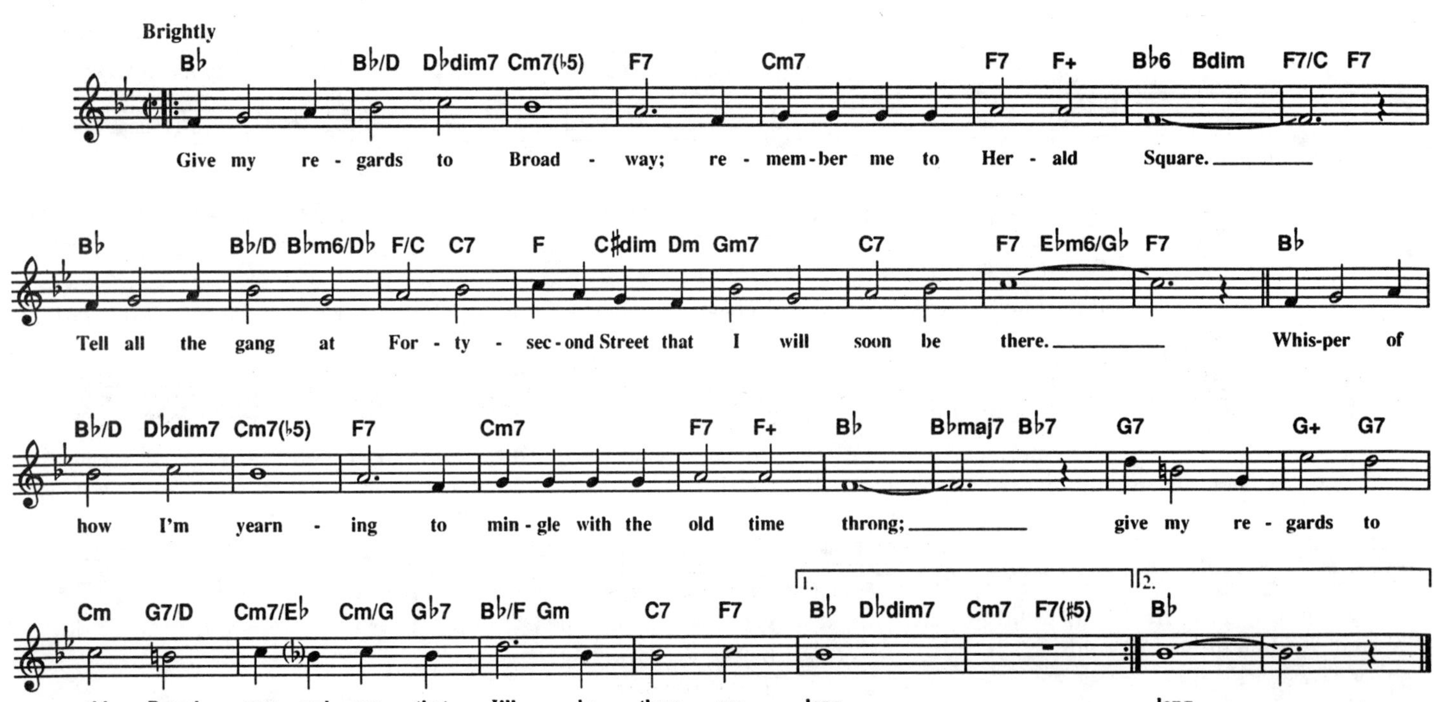
Brightly
B♭ B♭/D D♭dim7 Cm7(♭5) F7 Cm7 F7 F+ B♭6 Bdim F7/C F7
Give my re - gards to Broad - way; re - mem-ber me to Her - ald Square.
B♭ B♭/D B♭m6/D♭ F/C C7 F C♯dim Dm Gm7 C7 F7 E♭m6/G♭ F7 B♭
Tell all the gang at For - ty - sec-ond Street that I will soon be there. Whis-per of
B♭/D D♭dim7 Cm7(♭5) F7 Cm7 F7 F+ B♭ B♭maj7 B♭7 G7 G+ G7
how I'm yearn - ing to min-gle with the old time throng; give my re - gards to
1. 2.
Cm G7/D Cm7/E♭ Cm/G G♭7 B♭/F Gm C7 F7 B♭ D♭dim7 Cm7 F7(♯5) B♭
old Broad - way, and say that I'll be there, ere long. long.

GHOSTBUSTERS

Words and Music by
RAY PARKER, JR.

Moderate rock
Verse:
B A E B A E B A E B A E
1. If there's some-thing strange in your neigh - bor-hood,
2. see - ing things run-ning through your head,
who you gon-na call? Ghost - bust-ers!
If there's
An in -
some-thing wierd, and it don't look good,
vis-i-ble man sleep-ing in your bed,
who you gon-na call? Ghost - bust - ers!
Bm /A E7/G♯ E7
(spoken:) I ain't 'fraid of no ghost!
1.
(spoken:) I ain't 'fraid of no ghost!
3.
(spoken:)
2. If you're I ain't 'fraid of no ghost!
Chorus:
Who you gon-na call! Ghost - bust-ers!
If you're
all a - lone, pick up the phone and call Ghost - bust-ers!
To Coda
N.C.
(spoken:) I ain't 'fraid of no ghost! I hear it likes the gals . . . I ain't 'fraid of no ghost!
E7 E/A
Yeah, yeah, yeah, yeah. Bust - in' makes me feel good!
D.S. al Coda
Coda
Repeat and fade
Who you gon-na call? Ghost-bust-ers!

Chorus 2:
Who you gonna call? (Ghostbusters!)
You've had a dose of a freaky ghost, baby; *you better call Ghostbusters.*

Verse 3:
Don't get caught alone, oh no! *(Ghostbusters!)*
When it comes through your door,
Unless you just want some more, *I think you better call Ghostbusters.*

From the Paramount Motion Picture "SHIRLEY VALENTINE"

THE GIRL WHO USED TO BE ME

Lyric by ALAN & MARILYN BERGMAN
Music by MARVIN HAMLISCH

Slowly
Optional Intro.
It was al-ways, "Sit down, Shir-ley Val-en - tine." "Go 'way, Shir-ley Val-en - tine." And one day Shir-ley Val-en - tine just was-n't there an-y - more.
Verse:
A bird is born to fly, born for the mo-ment it takes to the sky and all its dreams are rid - ing on its wings. But if it falls the dreams are-n't bro - ken. As long as the wind is fair, the sky is al - ways there.
left with-out a sound. No-bod-y no-ticed she was-n't a - round. And on-ly the moon re - mem-bers her at all. The days go by. You start ask-ing ques-tions and won-der-ing
To Next Strain
Oh, the girl why, why did the dreams all go? I guess it's time to know. Oh, the girl
Chorus:
who used to be me, she could fly. She was free. You could read by the light of her smile. Yes, the girl who used to be me used to go danc - ing. She's been gone such a long, long while.
And she wrote all the words to her song. And I feel she's been gone too long. I'd like the chance to be the girl who used to be me.
D.S. 𝄋
2. She

GIVE ME THE NIGHT
Copyright © 1980 by RODSONGS c/o RONDOR MUSIC INTERNATIONAL
All Rights Reserved
Words and Music by ROD TEMPERTON
Moderate rock
Verse:
1. When-ev - er dark is fall - in', you know the spir - it of the par - ty starts to come a - live, until the day is dawn - in'. You can throw out all the blues and hit the cit - y lights, 'cause there's
eve - nin' ac - tion, a place to dine, a glass of wine, a lit - tle late ro - mance. It's a chain re - ac - tion. We'll see the peo - ple of the world com - in' out to dance,
Chorus:
mu - sic in the air, and lots of lov - in' ev - 'ry - where so give me the night. Give me the night.
2. You need the
So come on out to - night and we'll lead the oth - ers on a ride through par - a - dise. And if you feel all right, then we can be lov - ers 'cause I see that star - light look in your eyes. Well, don't you know we can fly? So give me the night.
Repeat ad lib. and fade
Give me the night.
GO TELL IT ON THE MOUNTAIN
Copyright © 1993 by BEAM ME UP MUSIC (ASCAP), c/o CPP/BELWIN, INC., Miami, FL 33014
All Rights Reserved
TRADITIONAL
Moderately
1. When I was a sin - ner, I prayed both night and day; I asked the Lord to aid me, and He showed me the way;
2. When I was a seek - er, I sought both night and day; I asked the Lord to help me, and He taught me how to pray,
3. Down in a low - ly man - ger the hum - ble Christ was born; and God sent out sal - va - tion that bless - ed Christ-mas morn.
Go tell it on the moun - tain, o - ver the hills and ev - 'ry - where; go tell it on the moun - tain, that Je - sus Christ is born.
born.

GIVING YOU THE BEST THAT I GOT

Words and Music by
ANITA BAKER, SKIP SCARBOROUGH
and RANDY HOLLAND

Moderate ballad
Dmaj7 A(2)/C♯ C Bm Am D/G F♯m7 B♭ Am7 Gm7 C/F D/E
Verse 1:
E/A A E/A A C♯m7
1. Ain't there some-thing I can give you in ex - change for ev-'ry - thing you give to me?
Dmaj9 Cmaj7 Bm7 Bm7/E
Read my mind and make me feel just fine, when I think my peace of mind is out of reach.
Verses 2 & 3:
E/A A E/A A C♯m7
The scales are some - times un - bal - anced, and you bear the weight of all that has to be.
2. Ev - 'ry - bod - y's got o - pin - ions 'bout the way they think our sto - ry's gon - na end.
Dmaj9 Cmaj7 Bm7 Bm7/E
I hope you see that you can lean on me and to - geth - er we can calm a storm-y sea.
Some folks feel it's just a su-per - fi-cial thrill; ev - 'ry - bod - y's gon-na have to think a - gain.
Dmaj9 A(2)/C♯ Cmaj7 Bm7 Bm7/E Dmaj9 A(2)/C♯
We love so strong and so un - self - ish - ly.
And I tell you now that I made a vow; I'm
They don't both-er me, so I'm gon-na keep on
To Coda
Cmaj7 Bm7 A/C♯ Dmaj9 A(2)/C♯ Cmaj7 Bm7
giv-ing you the best that I got, ba - by. Yes, I tell you now that I made a vow; I'm giv - ing you the best that I got,
giv-ing you the best that I got, ba - by. They don't both-er me, so I'm gon-na keep on giv - ing you the best that I got,
1. D.S. 2. Bridge:
Bm7/E Bm7/E A/E Bm7/E A/E
hon - ey. lis-ten, ba - by. Some-bod - y un - der - stands you; some-bod - y
D.S. al Coda
Bm7/E C13 Bm7 C♯m7 Dmaj9 D/E
gave his heart to me. I stum-bled my whole life long, al - ways on my own now I'm home.
Coda
Repeat and fade
Bm7/E Dmaj9 A(2)/C♯ Cmaj7 Bm7 Bm7/E
giv-in' it to you, ba - by. Giv-ing you the best that I got.

Verse 3:
My weary mind is rested,
And I feel as if my home is in your arms.
Fears are all gone, I like the sound of your song,
And I think I want to sing it forever.

We love so strong and unselfishly,
And I made a vow, so I tell you now;
I'm giving you the best that I got, baby.
I bet everything on my wedding ring;
I'm giving you the best that I got, givin' it to you, baby.
(To Coda:)

GO DOWN, MOSES

Moderately
When Is - rael was in E - gypt's land. Let my peo - ple go! Op -
press'd so hard they could not stand. Let my peo - ple
go! Go down, Mo - ses, way down in E - gypt's land;
Tell old Pha - roah, let my peo - ple go!
GLOW WORM
© 1993 BEAM ME UP MUSIC (ASCAP), c/o WARNER BROS. PUBLICATIONS U.S. INC., Miami, FL 33014
All Rights Reserved
TRADITIONAL
Moderately
When the night falls si-lent-ly the night falls si-lent-ly, on for-ests dream-ing, lov - ers wan - der
forth to see, they wan-der forth to see the bright stars gleam-ing. And lest they should lose their way, lest they should lose their way, the glow-worms
night - ly light their ti - ny lan-terns gay, their ti-ny lan-terns gay, and twin-kle bright-ly. Here and there, and ev-'ry-where, from
mos - sy dell and hol - low, float-ing, glid-ing through the air, they call on us to fol - low!
Refrain:
Shine lit-tle glow-worm,
glim-mer, glim-mer; shine lit-tle glow-worm, glim-mer, glim-mer! Lead us, lest too far we wan-der, love's sweet voice is call-ing yon-der.
Shine lit-tle glow-worm, glim-mer, glim-mer, shine lit-tle glow-worm, glim-mer, glim-mer! Light the path be - low a-bove, and lead us on to love.

GOD REST YE MERRY, GENTLEMEN

TRADITIONAL

Moderately

Em B/D♯ Em C G C Em Am6/C B

1. God rest ye mer - ry, gen - tle - men; let noth - ing you dis - may. Re -
2. (In) Beth - le - hem, in Is - ra - el, this bless - ed Babe was born, and
3. (From) God our heav'n - ly Fa - ther, a bless - ed an - gel came; and
4. (The) shep - herds at those tid - ings re - joic - ed much in mind; and

Em B/D♯ Em C G C Em Am6/C B E

mem - ber, Christ our Sav - ior was born on Christ - mas Day to
laid with - in a man - ger up - on this bless - ed morn; to
un - to cer - tain shep - herds brought tid - ings of the same; how
left their flocks a - feed - ing, in temp - est, storm and wind; and

Am G C/E G7/B C G B7 Em D G/D D7 Em D/F♯

save us all from Sa - tan's pow'r when we were gone a - stray.
which His Moth - er Mar - y did noth - ing take in scorn.
that in Beth - le - hem was born the Son of God by name.
went to Beth - le - hem straight - way, the Son of God to find.
O ___

G C/G G Am6 Em/B B7 Em A7/E D Em D/F♯

tid - ings of com - fort and joy, com - fort and joy! O ___

G G/B C G Am6 Em/B B | 1.2.3. Em | 4. Em

tid - ings of com - fort and joy. ___ 2. In 3. From 4. The | joy. ___

From the Paramount Picture "GOLDEN EARRINGS"

GOLDEN EARRINGS

Words by JAY LIVINGSTON and RAY EVANS
Music by VICTOR YOUNG

Moderately
Cm G7/D Cm/E♭ Adim A♭7(♭5) G7sus G7 Cm7 D7 G7 Fm6/A♭ Cm/G G7sus G7 Cm A♭7
There's a sto-ry the gyp-sy knows is true, that when your love wears gold-en ear-rings, she be-longs to you. An
old love sto-ry that's known to ver-y few, but if you wear those gold-en ear-rings, love will come to
Cm Fm Fm7 B♭7 E♭ Cm7 E♭m7 A♭7 F7/A Fm7/A♭
you. By ___ the burn-ing fire _ they will glow _ with ev-'ry coal. You ___ will hear de-sire _ whis-per low ___ in-side your
G7sus G7 Cm G7/D Cm/E♭ Adim A♭7(♭5) G7sus G7 Cm7 D7 G7 Fm6/A♭ Cm/G G7sus G7 Cm
soul. So be my gyp-sy, make love your guid-ing light, and let this pair of gold-en ear-rings cast their spell to-night.

GOLDEN LADY

Copyright © 1973 by JOBETE MUSIC CO., INC. and BLACK BULL MUSIC, INC.
All Rights Reserved

Words and Music by
STEVIE WONDER

Moderately
Verse:
Ebmaj9 Fm9 Gm7 Am7 Am7/D
1.Look - ing in your eyes, kind of heav - en eyes.
2.Look - ing at your hands, hands can un - der - stand.
3. (Instrumental solo . . .
Ebmaj9 Fm9 Gm7 Am7 Am7/D
Bridge:
Ebmaj7
Clos - ing both my eyes wait - ing for sur - prise. 1. To see the heav - en in your eyes is not
Wait - ing for the chance just to hold your hand. 2.3. A touch of rain and sun-shine made the flow -
. . .end solo
Bbmaj7 Abm7 Abm7/Db Gbmaj9 F#m7
so far, 'cause I'm not a - fraid to try and go it, to know the love and the beau-ty nev - er known
- ers grow in - to a love - ly smile that's bloom - ing. And it's so clear to me that here's a / you're my dream
To Coda
Chorus:
B9 Am9 Am7/D Gm Gm(maj7)
be - fore. I'll leave it up to you to show it.
come true. There's no way that I'll be los - ing. And Gold - en La - dy, Gold -
1.3. 2.
Gm7 Gm6 Abmaj7 Gmaj9 Fm9
en La - dy, I'd like to go there. Take me right a - way.
D.C. 4.
Bb13 Gmaj9 Fm9 Bb13
Take me right a - way.
D.C. al Coda
Coda
Am7/D Bbm7/Eb Abm Abm(maj7) Abm7 Abm6 Amaj7
Repeat ad lib. and fade
- ing. And Gold - en La - dy, Gold - en La - dy, I'd like to go there.

GOOD NIGHT LADIES

Copyright © 1993 by BEAM ME UP MUSIC (ASCAP), c/o CPP/BELWIN, INC., Miami, FL 33014
All Rights Reserved

TRADITIONAL

Brightly
Bb F7 Bb Bb7 Eb Bb F7
Good - night, la - dies, good - night, la - dies! Good - night la - dies, we're going to leave you
Bb F Bb F F7 Bb
now. Mer - ri - ly we roll a - long, roll a - long, roll a - long. Mer - ri - ly we roll a - long, o'er the deep blue sea.

From the United Artists Film "GOLDFINGER"

GOLDFINGER

Lyrics by LESLIE BRICUSSE
and ANTHONY NEWLEY
Music by JOHN BARRY

Slowly

F D♭ F B♭ E 1.
Gold - fin - ger, he's the man, the man with the Mi - das touch, a spi - der's
cold fin - ger beck-ons you to en - ter his web of sin

C C7 2. E Am Am(♯5) Am6 Am(♯5) Em
touch. Such a but don't go in. Gold - en words he will pour in your

B7 Em B7(♯9) E Cm Gm6
ear, but his lies can't dis-guise what you fear, for a gold - en girl knows when he's kissed her; it's the kiss of

D♭dim F D♭ F B♭ E
death from Mis - ter Gold - fin - ger. Pret-ty girl, be - ware of this heart of gold, this heart is

1. Am Am(♯5) Am6 Am(♯5) 2. Am Am(♯5) Am6 Am Am(♯5) Am6 Am(♯5)
cold. Gold - en cold. He loves on - ly gold, on - ly

Am Am(♯5) Am6 Am(♯5) Am Am(♯5) 1. Am6 Am(♯5) 2. Am6 Am(♯5) Am6
gold. He loves gold, he loves on - ly he loves gold.

From the United Artist's Motion Picture "ROCKY"

GONNA FLY NOW

Words by CAROL CONNORS
and AYN ROBBINS
Music by BILL CONTI

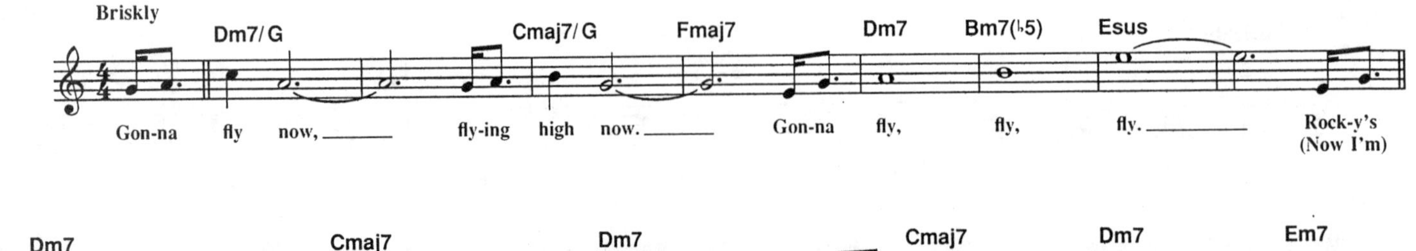
Briskly
Dm7/G Cmaj7/G Fmaj7 Dm7 Bm7(♭5) Esus
Gon-na fly now, fly-ing high now. Gon-na fly, fly, fly. Rock-y's
(Now I'm)

Dm7 Cmaj7 Dm7 Cmaj7 Dm7 Em7
read - y to make a move, yeah. Rock-y's read - y, he just can't lose, yeah. Ev-'ry nerve a wire
(Now I'm) (I)

Fmaj7 Esus Dm7 Cmaj7 Dm7
sweat-in' blood, like fire. Bod-y's ach - in' from the hurt it's tak - in', mus-cles scream-in' like a burn-in'

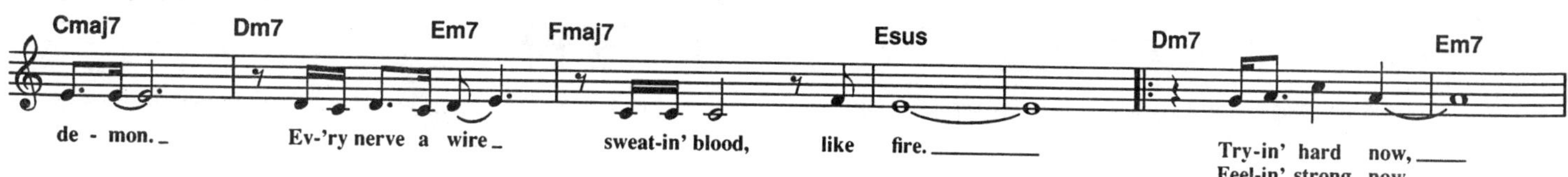
Cmaj7 Dm7 Em7 Fmaj7 Esus Dm7 Em7
de - mon. Ev-'ry nerve a wire sweat-in' blood, like fire.
Try-in' hard now,
Feel-in' strong now,

Fmaj7 B♭maj7 Asus Dm7 Cmaj7
it's so hard now. Try-in' hard now. Rock-y pow - er by the ho - ur.
won't be long now. Get-tin' strong now. (Fists like thun - der gon-na put you un - der.)
Pump-in'

Dm7 Cmaj7 Dm7 Em7 Fmaj7 Esus Dm7/G
i - ron, God ya know he's (I'm) try - in'. Ev-'ry nerve a wire sweat-in' blood, like fire. Gon-na fly now,

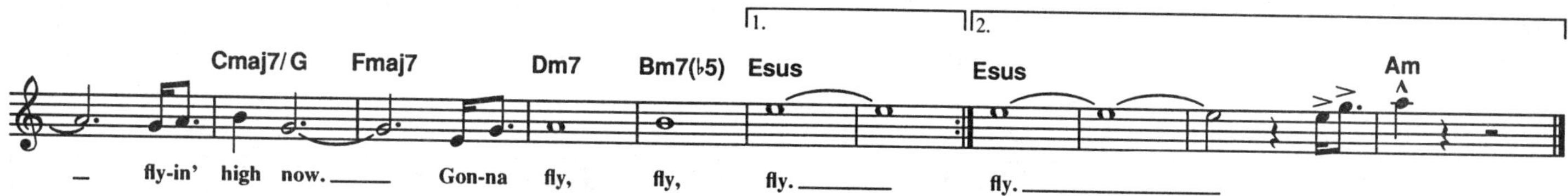
1. 2.
Cmaj7/G Fmaj7 Dm7 Bm7(♭5) Esus Esus Am
fly-in' high now. Gon-na fly, fly, fly. fly.

GOOD NIGHT SWEETHEART

American Version by RUDY VALLEE
Words and Music by
RAY NOBLE, JIMMY CAMPBELL
and REG CONNELLY

Moderately slow
C Cdim C Cdim C Cdim C F/C C G7 F♯7 G7 F♯7/G G7 F♯7/G G7
Good night sweet-heart, till we meet to - mor - row. Good night sweet-heart, sleep will ban - ish
good night sweet-heart, though I'm not be - side you. Good night sweet-heart, still my love will

1.
Dm7 G7 Am Dm7 G7 Cmaj7 Am
sor - row. Tears and part - ing may make us for - lorn. But with the dawn, a
guide you. Dreams en - fold you,

2.
Dm7 G7 D7 D♯dim C/E C♯dim G7/D G7 C Fm C
new day is born. So I'll say in each one I'll hold you. Good night sweet-heart, good night.

GOOD MORNING STARSHINE

Copyright © 1966, 1967, 1968, 1970 JAMES RADO, GEROME RAGNI, GALT MacDERMOT, NAT SHAPIRO and EMI U CATALOG INC.
All Rights Reserved

Words by JAMES RADO and GEROME RAGNI
Music by GALT MacDERMOT

Moderate rock

Good mor-ning Star - shine. The earth says "Hel - lo". You twin-kle a - bove us, we twin-kle be - low.

Good morn-ing Star - shine. You lead us a - long. My love and me as we sing our ear - ly morn-ing sing - ing song.

Glid-dy glup gloo-py, nib - by nab-by noo-py la la la lo lo. Sab-ba sib-by sab-ba, noo - by ab-ba nab - ba le le lo lo.

Too-by oo-by wal-la, noo-by ab-ba nab-ba, ear-ly morn-ing sing-ing song. Good morn-ing

Sing-ing a song, hum-ming a song, sing-ing a song, Lov-ing a song, laugh-ing a song, sing the song

Repeat ad lib. and fade

Sing the song, song the sing. Song, song, song, sing, sing, sing, sing song.

GOOD KING WENCESLAS

Copyright © 1993 by BEAM ME UP MUSIC (ASCAP), c/o CPP/BELWIN, INC., Miami, FL 33014
All Rights Reserved

Words by JOHN MASON NEALE
Music TRADITIONAL

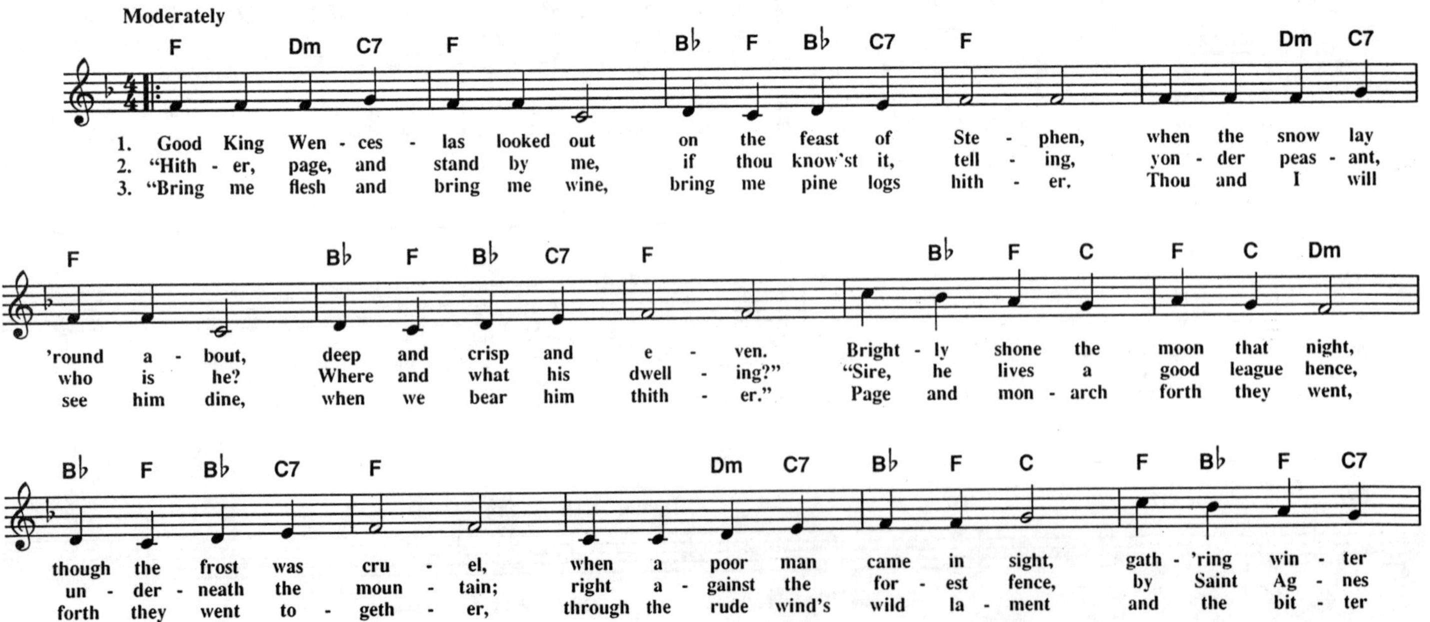
Moderately
1. Good King Wen - ces - las looked out on the feast of Ste - phen, when the snow lay 'round a - bout, deep and crisp and e - ven. Bright - ly shone the moon that night, though the frost was cru - el, when a poor man came in sight, gath - 'ring win - ter
2. "Hith - er, page, and stand by me, if thou know'st it, tell - ing, yon - der peas - ant, who is he? Where and what his dwell - ing?" "Sire, he lives a good league hence, un - der - neath the moun - tain; right a - gainst the for - est fence, by Saint Ag - nes
3. "Bring me flesh and bring me wine, bring me pine logs hith - er. Thou and I will see him dine, when we bear him thith - er." Page and mon - arch forth they went, forth they went to - geth - er, through the rude wind's wild la - ment and the bit - ter

F Bb F F D7 G Em D7 G
1.2. 3.
fu - el. er. 4. "Sire, the night is dark - er now,
foun - tain." 5. In his mas - ter's steps he trod,
weath -
C G C D7 G Em D7 G C G C D7
and the wind blows strong - er. Fails my heart, I know not how, I can go no
where the snow lay dint - ed. Heat was in the ver - y sod which the Saint had
G C G D G D Em C G C D7 G
long - er." "Mark my foot - steps, my good page, tread thou in them bold - ly.
print - ed. There - fore Chris - tian men, be sure, wealth or rank pos - sess - ing;
Em D7 C G D G C G D Em C G G
1. 2.
Thou shalt find the win - ter's rage freeze thy blood less cold - ly." ing.
ye who now will bless the poor shall your - selves find bless -

GRADUATION DAY

Words and Music by
JOE SHERMAN and NOEL SHERMAN

Moderately

C Dm7 C F C Dm7 C E♭dim Dm7 G7
It's a time for joy, a time for tears, a time we'll treas - ure thru the years; we'll re - mem - ber

C A7(♭9) Dm7 G9 C G7 C Dm7 C F C Dm7 C E♭dim
al - ways grad - u - a - tion day. At the sen - ior prom, we danced till three, and then you gave your heart to me.

Dm7 G7 C A7(♭9) Dm7 G9 C Gm7 C7 Fmaj7 F F♯dim Gm7 C7
We'll re - mem - ber al - ways grad - u - a - tion day. Tho we leave in sor - row all the joys we've

Fmaj7 F6 Am7 D7 Gmaj7 G G♯dim Am7 D7 G7 C Dm7 C F
known, we can face to - mor - row know - ing we'll nev - er walk - a - lone. When the I - vy Walls are far be - hind, no

C Dm7 C E♭dim Dm7 G7 C A7(♭9) Dm7 G9 C A♭7 G7 C F9 Cmaj7
1. 2.
mat - ter where our path may wind, we'll re - mem - ber al - ways grad - u - a - tion day! It's a day!

From the United Artists Motion Picture "THE GOOD, THE BAD AND THE UGLY"

THE GOOD, THE BAD AND THE UGLY

(Il Buona, Il Brutto, Il Cattivo)

By ENNIO MORRICONE

Brightly

Dm G Dm C Dm Am Dm G

Dm 1. 2. Dm Am B♭ F Dm Am C

To Coda ⊕

Am Dm G Dm G Dm G Dm G B♭ Am G F Em F C B♭

A♭ A7 Dm Dm G Dm C Dm

Am Dm G Dm N.C. G B♭ F

D.S. 𝄋 al Coda ⊕ *Coda*

C Am Dm A♭ A7

Dm G Dm C Dm

GRANDMA GOT RUN OVER BY A REINDEER!

Words and Music by
RANDY BROOKS

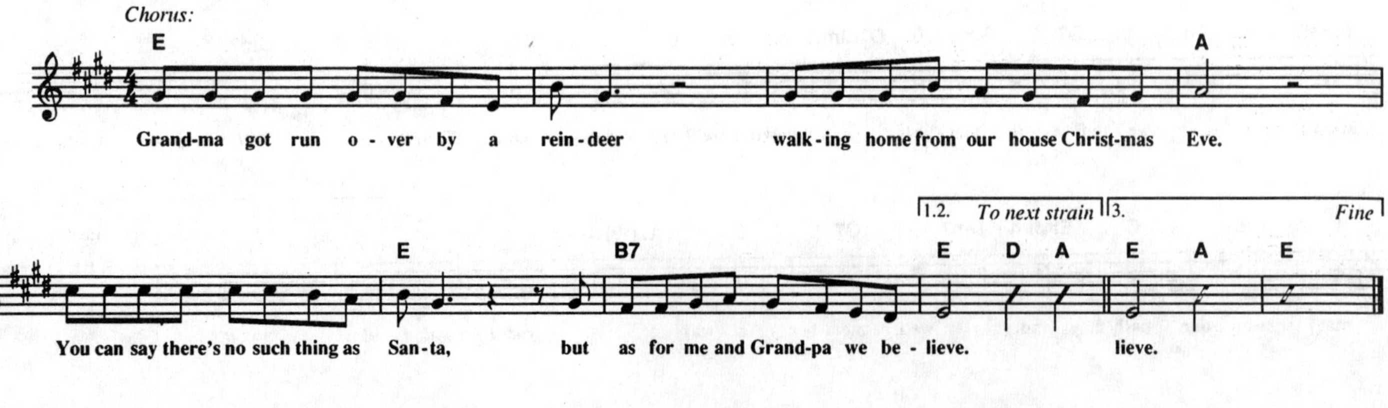

Moderately bright

Chorus:

E A

Grand-ma got run o - ver by a rein - deer walk - ing home from our house Christ-mas Eve.

1.2. *To next strain* 3. *Fine*

E B7 E D A E A E

You can say there's no such thing as San - ta, but as for me and Grand-pa we be - lieve. lieve.

Verse:

E B E E7

1. She'd been drink-ing too much egg-nog, and we begged her not to go, but she for-got her med-i-

A B7 E C♯m G♯m B7

ca-tion, and she stag-gered out the door in-to the snow. When we found her Christ-mas morn-ing at the scene of the at-

E E7 A B7 E *D.C.*

tack, she had hoof-prints on her fore-head, and in-crim-i-nat-ing Claus marks on her back.

Verse 2:
Now we're all so proud of Grandpa,
He's been taking this so well.
See him in there watching football,
Drinking beer, and playing cards with Cousin Mel.
It's not Christmas without Grandma.
All the family's dressed in black,
And we just can't help but wonder:
Should we open up her gifts or send them back?
(To Chorus:)

Verse 3:
Now the goose is on the table,
And the pudding made of fig,
And the blue and silver candles,
That would just have matched the hair in Grandma's wig.
I've warned all my friends and neighbors,
Better watch out for yourselves.
They should never give a license
To a man who drives a sleigh and plays with elves.
(To Chorus:)

From the United Artists Motion Picture "THE GREAT ESCAPE"

THE GREAT ESCAPE MARCH

Words by AL STILLMAN
Music by ELMER BERNSTEIN

March tempo

B♭ E♭ F7 B♭

Ma-bel, I love you, Ma-bel; love you as much as I am a-ble. But, oh, I'm cra-zy
Car-rie, I need you, Car-rie, but I don't think that we will mar-ry, 'cause that would hin-der

E♭ F7 B♭ Cm F7 𝄋 B♭ E♭ F7

for lit-tle Dai-sy. She is the one girl for me.
my love for Lin-da. She is the one girl for me.
Fick-le, I may be fick-le, but it's a

B♭ E♭ F7 B♭ *Fine*

dol-lar to a nick-el, that when I'm kiss-in' the one I'm kiss-in', she is the one girl for me!

B♭ E♭ B♭

1st time: Whistle . . .
2nd time: I love Ma-til-da, she is ver-y nice, ooh, but that Hil-da takes me to par-a-dise. I love Ma-

E♭ F7 B♭ 1. *D.C.* F7 Fdim F7 2. *D.S. 𝄋 al Fine* F7 Fdim F7

Whistle . . .
til-da, but Hil-da is ver-y nice, she is the one girl for me!

GOOD VIBRATIONS

Words and Music by
BRIAN WILSON and
MIKE LOVE

Moderate swing rock

Dm C B♭ A

I, ___ I love the col - or-ful clothes she wears, ___ and the way the sun-light plays up-on ___ her hair. ___
Close ___ my eyes; ___ she's some - how clos - er now. ___ Soft - ly smile; I know she must ___ be kind. ___

Dm C B♭ A C7

I ___ hear the sound of a gen - tle word ___ on the wind that lifts her per-fume through the air. ___
Then ___ I look in her eyes. ___ She goes with me to a blos-som world.

Chorus:

F B♭/F F7 B♭/F F B♭/F F7 B♭/F *(a tempo)* F B♭/F F7 B♭/F F B♭/F

I'm pick-ing up good vi - bra-tions. She's giv-ing me ex - ci - ta - tions. I'm pick-ing up good vi - bra-tions. She's giv-ing me

F7 B♭/F G C/G G7 C/G G C/G G7 C/G A D/A A7 D/A

ex - ci - ta - tions. I'm pick-ing up good vi - bra-tions. She's giv-ing me ex - ci - ta - tions. I'm pick-ing up good vi - bra-tions.

1. *D.C.* 2. *To next strain* 3. *etc.* *Repeat and fade*

A D/A A7 D/A A7 D/A A7 D/A A9 D/A A9 D/A A9 D/A

She's giv-ing me ex - ci - ta - tions. ex - ci - ta - tions. ex - ci - ta - tions.

A9 D/A A9 D/A A9 D/A

A little slower

E F♯m B E

Got - ta keep ___

1.2.3. 4. *D.S.*

F♯m B B E D/E

___ those a - lov - in' good vi - bra - tions a - hap-p'nin' with her. hap-p'nin' with her.

GREAT DAY

Words by EDWARD ELISCU and BILLY ROSE
Music by VINCENT YOUMANS

Moderately
1. To next strain 2. Fine
E♭ A♭ E♭/B♭ B♭7 E♭6
When you're down ___ and out, lift up your head ___ and shout,
It's not far ___ a - way, hold up your hands ___ and say,
"There's gon-na be ___ a great day." ___
E♭ Fm7 E♭/B♭ B♭7 E♭ E♭7/D♭
An - gels in ___ the sky prom - ise that bye ___ and bye there's gon - na be ___ a great day. ___
D.C. al Fine
A♭/C E♭7/G A♭ B♭7/A♭ E♭ Cm7 B♭/F E♭/F F7 A♭/B♭ Fm7 B♭7
Ga - bri - el will warn you ___ some ear - ly morn you ___ will hear his horn root - y toot - in'.

GOODBYE, MY CONEY ISLAND BABY

Words and Music by
LES APPLEGATE

Moderately

We all fall for some girl that dress-es neat, some girl that's got big feet. We meet her on the street. Then we'll join the ar-my of mar-ried boobs, to the al-tar, just like lead-ing lambs to slaugh-ter. When it's o-ver, oh boy we get it good; bach-'lor days we then re-call, rich man, poor man, beg-gar man, thief, doc-tor, law-yer, mer-chant chief. We all are bound for ma-tri-mo-ny. Good-bye, my Con-ey Is-land ba-by. Fare-well my own true love. I'm gon-na go a-way and leave you, nev-er to see you an-y-more. I'm goin' to sail up-on that fer-ry boat, nev-er to re-turn a-gain. So good-bye, fare-well, so long for-ev-er. Good-bye, my Con-ey Isle, good-bye, my Con-ey Isle, good-bye, my Con-ey Is-land babe. Oh, babe.

From the Batjac Production "THE ALAMO" a United Artists Release

THE GREEN LEAVES OF SUMMER

By PAUL FRANCIS WEBSTER
and DIMITRI TIOMKIN

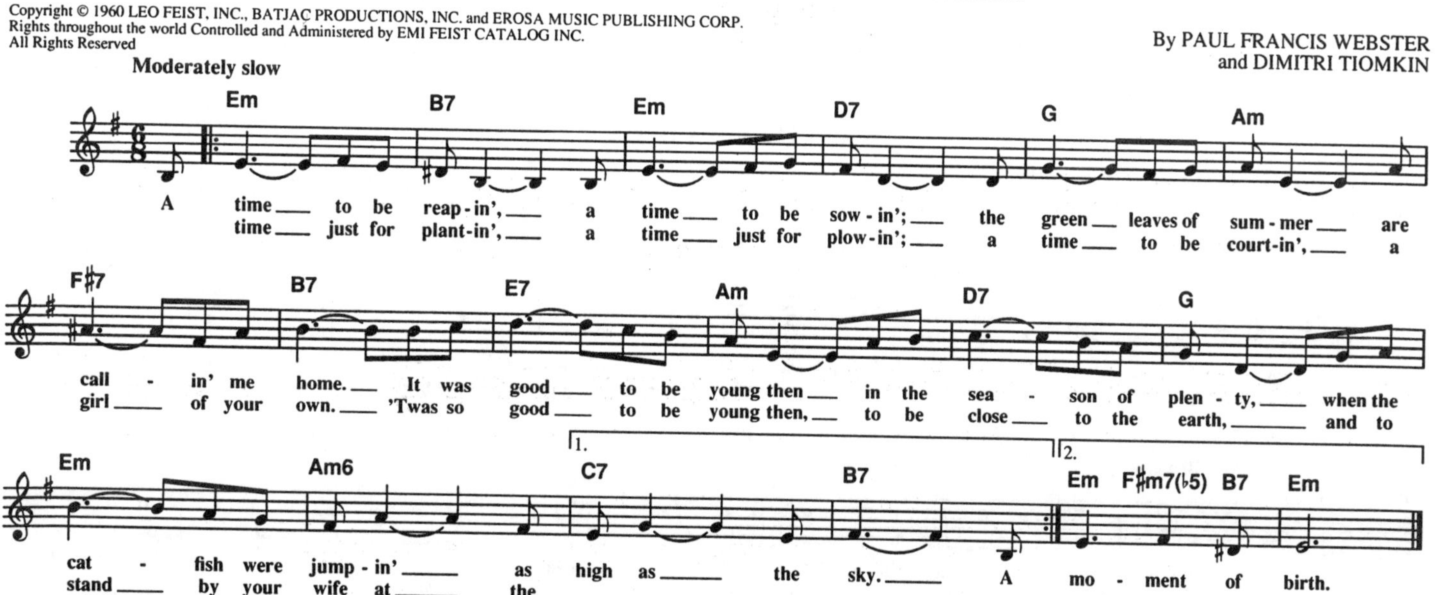
Moderately slow
A time to be reap-in', a time to be sow-in'; the green leaves of sum-mer are call-in' me home. It was good to be young then in the sea-son of plen-ty, when the cat-fish were jump-in' as high as the sky. A mo-ment of birth.
time just for plant-in', a time just for plow-in'; a time to be court-in', a girl of your own. 'Twas so good to be young then, to be close to the earth, and to stand by your wife at the

THE GOOD LIFE

Words by JACK REARDON
Music by SACHA DISTEL

Slowly, with feeling

Ab Gm7 C7
Oh, the good life ___ full of fun ___ seems to be ___ the i - deal, ___ yes, the

Fm Dm7(b5) G Am7 Gdim7 G Bbm7
good life ___ lets you hide ___ all the sad - ness you feel, ___ you won't real - ly ___ fall in

Gb7 Ab C7 Fm
love ___ for you can't take the chance. ___ So be hon - est ___ with your - self, don't try to

Bbm7 Eb7 Ab Gm7
fake ro - mance. ___ It's the good life ___ to be free ___ and ex - plore ___ the un - known, ___

C7 Fm Dm7(b5)
Like the heart aches ___ when you learn ___ you must face ___ them a - lone, ___

G Am7 Gdim7 G Bbm7 Gb7 Ab
please re - mem - ber ___ I still love you, ___ and in case you ___ did-n't

F7 Bbm7 Eb11 Eb7(b9) Ab
know, ___ well, just wake up, ___ kiss the good life ___ hel - lo. ___

GRANADA

English Lyric by DOROTHY DODD
Music by AGUSTIN LARA

Moderately
Am
Gra - na - da ___ tie - rra so - ña-da por mi ___ mi can - tar se vuel - ve gi - ta - no cuna-do es pa - ra
Gra - na - da ___ I'm fall - ing un-der your spell. ___ And if you could speak, what a fas-cin - at - ing tale you would

Broadly
E F E F
ti ___ mi can - tar ___ he-cho de fan - ta - si - a ___ mi can - tar ___ flor de me - lan-co - lí - a que yo
tell, ___ of an age ___ the world has long for - got - ten, ___ of an age ___ that weaves a si - lent mag - ic in Gra -

A tempo
E /G♯ /B /D /B /D Am/C /A G/B /G F/A /F E7 /G♯ /B /D /B /D
ven - go a dar.
na - da to - day.
Am/C /A G/B /G F/A /F E
Tempo di Habanera
N.C.
G7 C D7 G C
Gra - na - da tie - rra en-san - gren-
The dawn in the sky greets the
/E E♭dim G7
ta - da en tar - des de to - ros. Mu - jer que con - ser va el em - bru - jo de
day with a sigh for Gra - na - da, for she can re - mem - ber the splen - dour that
Dm7 G7 C6
los o - jos mo - ros. de sue - ño re - bel de y gi - ta - na cu - bier - ta de
once was Gra - na da. It still can be found in the hills all a - round as I
Em B7/D♯ Em
flo - res y be - so tu bo - ca de gra - na ju - go - sa man-
wan - der a - long, en - tranc'd by the beau - ty be - fore me, en - tranc'd by a
B7/D♯ Em G7 C
za - na que me ha - bla de a - mo - res. Gra - na - da ma - no - la can - ta - da en
land full of sun - shine and flow - ers and song. And when day is done and the sun starts to
/E E♭dim G7
co - plas pre - cio - sas. No ten - go o - tra co - sa que dar - te que un
set in Gra - na - da, I en - vy the blush of the snow - clad Si -
Dm7 G7 C6 C C7 F Fm
ra - mo de ro - sas. De ro - sas de sua - ve fra - gan - cia que le die - ran
er - ra Ne - va - da. For soon it will wel - come the stars while a thou - sand gui -
Broadly
A tempo
C/G Fm/A♭ Fm C Fm/A♭ C
mar - co a la Vir - gen mo - re - na Gra - na - da tu tie - rra es - tá lle - na de
tars play a soft hab - an - er - a; the moon - lit Gra - na - da will live a - gain the
G7 C Fm C Fm C Fm C G7 C
lin - das mu - je - res, de san - gre y de sol.
glo - ry of yes - ter - day, ro - man - tic and gay.

THE GREAT PRETENDER

Words and Music by
BUCK RAM

Slowly

Eb Bb7 Eb Eb7 Ab Eb Eb7

Oh, yes, I'm the great pre - tend - er, __ pre - tend - in' __ I'm __ do - in' well. My
yes, I'm the great pre - tend - er, __ a - drift in __ a world __ of my own. I

Ab Bb7 Eb Eb/G Ab Fm7 | 1. Eb Bb7 Eb Bb7 | 2. Eb Bb7

need __ is such, __ I pre - tend too much. I'm lone - ly, but no __ one can tell. Oh, left me __ to dream __ all a -
play __ the game, __ but to my real shame, you've

Eb Eb7 Ab Eb Eb7 Ab Eb/Bb Bb7

lone. Too real __ is this feel - ing of make - be-lieve; too real __ when I feel __ what my heart __ can't con-ceal. Oh, __

Eb Bb7 Eb Eb7 Ab Eb Eb7 Ab Bb7

yes, I'm the great pre - tend - er __ just laugh - in' and gay __ like a clown. I seem __ to be __ what I'm

Eb Eb/G Ab Fm7 Eb/Bb Ab6 G Bb7 Eb Ab6 Bb7 Eb

not, __ you see. __ I'm wear - in' __ my heart __ like a crown, pre - tend - in' __ that you're __ still a - round. __

GREEN ONIONS

Music by
BOOKER T. JONES, STEVE CROPPER,
LEWIS STEINBERG and AL JACKSON, JR.

Moderate blues rock
Fm Ab Bb Fm Ab Bb Fm Ab Bb Fm Ab Bb (Bb) Db Eb
Bb Db Eb Fm Ab Bb Fm Ab Bb C7 Eb F Bb Db Eb
Fm Ab Bb Fm Ab Bb Fm Ab Bb Fm Ab Bb Fm Ab Bb
Fm Ab Bb (Bb) Db Eb Bb Db Eb Fm Ab Bb Fm Ab Bb C7 Eb F
Bb Db Eb Fm Ab Bb 1. Fm Ab Bb 2. Fm Ab Bb Fm Ab Bb Fm Ab Bb
Repeat and fade

From the Columbia Picture "THE GREATEST" - A Columbia/EMI Presentation

THE GREATEST LOVE OF ALL

Words by LINDA CREED
Music by MICHAEL MASSER

Slowly
Verse:

A A+ A6 A7
1.3. I be - lieve that chil - dren are our fu - ture; teach them well and let __ them lead __ the way.
be. 2. Ev - 'ry - bod - y's search - ing for a he - ro; peo - ple need some - one __ to look up __ to.

D D+ D6 D+ C♯m7 F♯m7
Show them all the beau - ty they pos - sess in - side. Give them a sense of pride, to make it
I nev - er found an - y - one who ful - filled my need. A lone - ly place to be, and so I

1.3.
Bm7 E7 E7/D C♯m7 F♯m7 Bm7 D/E
eas - i - er; __ let the chil - dren's laugh - ter re - mind us how __ we used to

1st time: D.C. 3rd time: To next strain

2.
Bm7 D/E D(9) A/C♯ Bm7 Bm7/E
learned to de - pend on me. I de - cid - ed long __ a - go __ nev - er to walk in an - y - one's shad - ow.
(be.)

D(9) A/C♯ Bm7 Bm7/E D(9) A/C♯
If I fail, if I suc - ceed, __ at least I lived __ as I be - lieve. No mat - ter what they take from me, they

Chorus:

Bm7 Bm7/E C♯m7 F♯m7 Bm7 E7 E7/D
can't take a - way my dig - ni - ty. Be - cause the great - est love of all __ is hap - pen - ing to

C♯m7 F♯m7 Bm7 E7 E7/D C♯m7 F♯m7 Bm7 D/E A7
me. I found the great - est love of all __ in - side of me. The great - est

F♯m7 Bm7 Em7 A7 A7/G F♯m7 Bm7 Em7 A7 A7/G F♯m7 Bm7
love __ of all is eas - y to a - chieve. Learn - ing __ to love your - self is the

1. *D.C.* 2.
Em7 G/A D D E7 E7/D C♯m7 F♯m7 Bm7 E7 E7/D
great - est love of all. all. And if by chance that spe - cial place that you've been dream - ing

C♯m7 F♯m7 Bm7 E7 E7/D C♯m7 F♯m7 Bm7 D/E D(9) A/C♯ Bm7 Bm7/E A
of leads you to a lone - ly __ place, find your strength in love. ______

GREEN EYES

Music by NILO MENENDEZ
Spanish Lyrics by ADOLFO UTRERA
Translation by E. RIVERA and E. WOODS

Moderato *Chorus:*

Ebmaj7 Eb Eb6 Ebmaj7 Eb
Your green eyes with their soft lights, your eyes that prom-ise sweet nights bring to my soul a long - ing

Edim Bb7/F Bb7 Ab/Bb Bb7
a thirst for love di - vine. In dreams I seem to hold you to find you and en - fold you. Our lips meet, and our

C+ C7 F7 Bb7 Ebmaj7 Eb Eb6 Ebmaj7
hearts too, with a thrill so sub - lime. Those cool and lim-pid green eyes, a pool where-in my love lies

Gdim C7 Fm C7 Fm Ab6 Abmaj7 Adim
so deep, that in my search - ing for hap-pi-ness, I fear that they will ev-er haunt me. All through my life they'll

Eb Eb9/Db C7 F7 Bb7 1. Eb Cm Gdim Bb7 2. Eb
taunt me. But will they ev-er want me? Green eyes, make my dreams come true. Your green eyes with their true.

GREEN TAMBOURINE

Words and Music by SHELLEY PINZ and PAUL LEKA

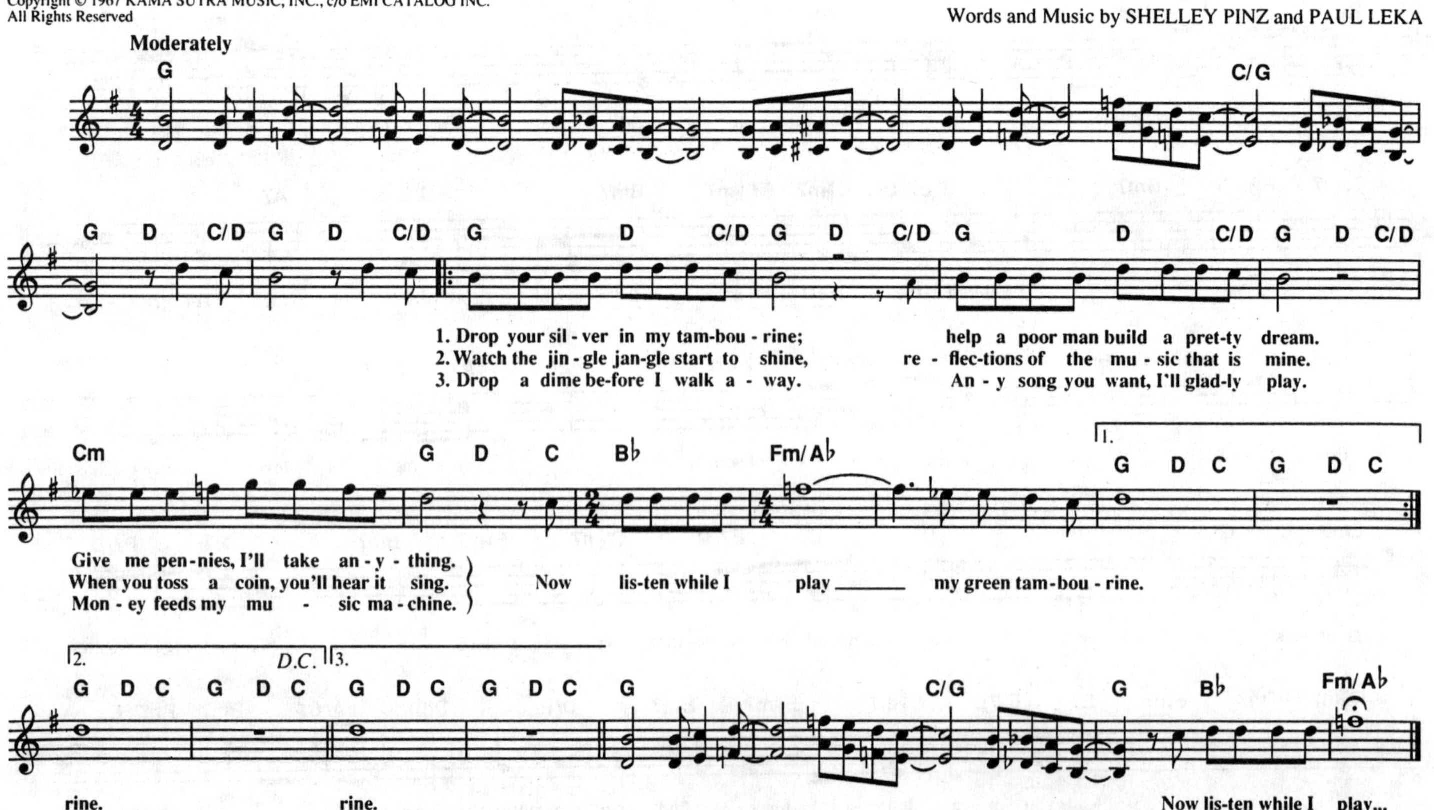
Moderately
G C/G
G D C/D G D C/D G D C/D G D C/D G D C/D G D C/D
1. Drop your sil - ver in my tam-bou - rine; help a poor man build a pret-ty dream.
2. Watch the jin - gle jan-gle start to shine, re - flec-tions of the mu - sic that is mine.
3. Drop a dime be-fore I walk a - way. An - y song you want, I'll glad-ly play.
Cm G D C Bb Fm/Ab 1. G D C G D C
Give me pen-nies, I'll take an - y - thing.
When you toss a coin, you'll hear it sing.
Mon - ey feeds my mu - sic ma - chine.
Now lis-ten while I play my green tam-bou - rine.
2. G D C G D C D.C. 3. G D C G D C G C/G G Bb Fm/Ab
rine. rine. Now lis-ten while I play...

GREENSLEEVES

TRADITIONAL

Slowly

Em D D♯dim Em F♯7 B Em
A - las, my love, you do me wrong to cast me off dis - cour - teous - ly, and I have loved you,

D Em B7 Em Am Em G D D♯dim
oh, so long, de - light - ing in your com - pa - ny. Green - sleeves was all my joy;

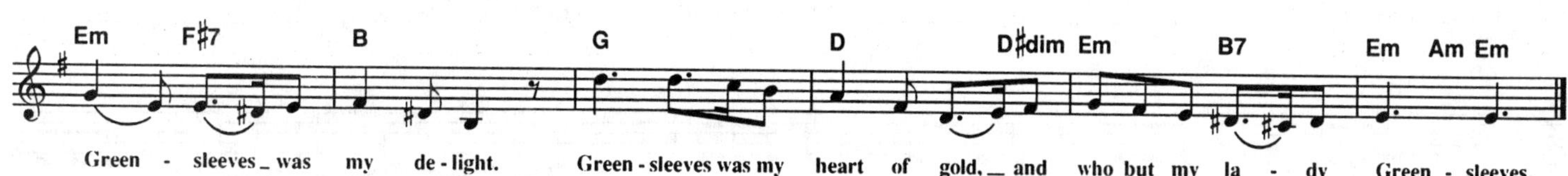
Em F♯7 B G D D♯dim Em B7 Em Am Em
Green - sleeves was my de - light. Green - sleeves was my heart of gold, and who but my la - dy Green - sleeves.

GUANTANAMERA

Original words and music by JOSE FERNANDEZ DIAS (Joseito Fernandez). Music adaptation by PETE SEEGER. Lyric adaptation by HECTOR ANGULO, based on a poem by JOSE MARTI

Moderately
Chorus:

Em7 A7 D G A7 D G
Guan - ta - na - me - ra, gua - ji - ra Guan - ta - na - me - ra. Guan - ta - na - me -

1.2.3. To Next Strain
4. Fine
Verse:
A7 D G A7 A7 D G
ra, gua - ji - ra Guan - ta - na - me - ra! 1. Yo soy un ra! hom - bre sin - ce - ro,

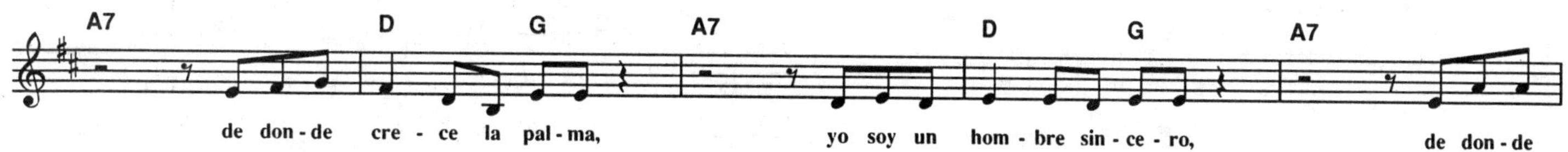
A7 D G A7 D G A7
de don - de cre - ce la pal - ma, yo soy un hom - bre sin - ce - ro, de don - de

D.C.
D G A7 D G A7 D G A7
cre - ce la pal - ma, y an - tes de mo - rir - me quie - ro, e - char mis ver - sos del al - ma.

Verse 2:
Mi verso es de un verde claro,
Y de un carmin encendido,
Mi verso es de un verde claro,
Y de un carmin encendido,
Mi verso es un cierro herido,
Que busca en el monte amparo.
(To Chorus:)

Verse 3:
Con los pobres de la tierra,
Quiero yo mi suerte echar,
Con los pobres de la tierra,
Quiero yo mi suerte echar,
El arroyo de la sierra,
Me complace mas que el mar.
(To Chorus:)

GUADALAJARA

Spanish Words and Music by
PEPE GUIZAR

Moderately
C7 F C7 F N.C.
Gua-da-la-
ja-ra Gua-da-la-ja-ra Gua-da-la-ja-ra Gua-da-la-ja-ra
tie-nes el al-ma de pro-vin-cia-na hue-les a lim-pio a ro-sa tem-pra-na a ver-de
ja-ra fres-ca del ri-o son mil pa-lo-mos tu ca-se-ri-o. Gua-da-la-ja-ra Gua-da-la-ja-ra sa-bes a
pu-ra tie-rra mo-ja-da
Ay! Co-lo-mi-tos le-ja-nos
Ay! o-ji-tos de a-gua her-ma-nos
Ay! co-lo-mi-tos i-nol-vi-da-bles i-nol-vi-
da-bles co-mo la tar-des en que la llu-via des-de la lo-ma ir-nos ha ci-a has-ta Za-po-pam.
N.C. Tempo ad lib.
Gua-da-la-ja-ra, Gua-da-la-ja-ra!

GUILTY

Words and Music by
GUS KAHN, HARRY AKST
and RICHARD A. WHITING

Moderately slow
B♭ G7 Cm7 A7 B♭maj7 B♭7(♯5) E♭maj7 E♭m6 B♭/D D♭dim
Is it a sin, is it a crime, lov-ing you, dear, like I do?
May-be I'm wrong dream-ing of you, dream-ing the lone-ly night through.
If it's a crime, then I'm

Cm7 F7 Cm7 F+ B♭ Cm7 F7 Cm7 F7 B♭ A7(♭9/♯5) Dm Dm(♯7) Dm7
1. 2.
guil-ty, guil-ty of lov-ing you. guil-ty of dream-ing of you. What can I do,

Em7(♭5) A7 Dm Dm7 Em9 A7 F/C Gm7/C C9 F6/C F♯dim
what can I say, af-ter I've tak-en the blame? You say we're through, you'll go your way; but

Gm7 C9 Cm7/F F7(♭9) B♭ G7 Cm7 A7 B♭maj7 B♭7(♯5)
I'll al-ways feel just the same. May-be I'm right, may-be I'm wrong, lov-ing you dear like I

E♭maj7 E♭m6 B♭/D D♭dim Cm7 F7 Cm Cm7/F F7(♭9) B♭
do. If it's a crime, then I'm guil-ty, guil-ty of lov-ing you.

HAIL TO THE CHIEF

JAMES SANDERSON

Majestically
B♭ F7 B♭ C7 F7 B♭

F7 B♭ E♭ B♭ F7 B♭ F7

B♭ Gm F7 B♭ E♭ B♭ E♭ B♭ F7 B♭

From the American Tribal Love-Rock Musical "HAIR"

HAIR

Words by JAMES RADO and GEROME RAGNI
Music by GALT MacDERMOT

Freely

Cm
Abmaj7 Cm
Eb
Cm
Ab
Cm
Eb
Gm
Eb
Gm
Bb

She asks me why, I'm just a hair-y guy. I'm hair-y noon and night. Hair, that's a fright. I'm hair-y high and low. Don't ask me why, don't know.

Moderate rock
Verse:
Gm
Eb
Gm
Bb
Cm
Ab
Cm
Eb
Cm
Ab

It's not for lack of bread, like the Grate-ful Dead. 1. Dar-lin', give me a head of hair, _ long beau-ti-ful hair, _ shin - ing, gleam-ing,

Cm
Eb
Gm
Eb
Gm
Bb
Gm
Eb
Gm
Bb7

steam-ing, flax-en, wax-en. Give me down to there hair, shoul-der length or lon-ger. Here, ba - by, there, mom-ma, ev - 'ry-where, dad-dy, dad-dy.

Chorus:
To Coda
1.
2.
Cm
Ab
Cm
Eb
Bb7
Eb7
Ab
Bb7
Eb
Bb11
Eb
Bb11

Hair, hair, hair, hair, hair, hair, hair, _ hair. Flow it, show it, long ___ as God can grow it, my ___ hair. 2. Let it hair. I want it

Bridge:
Dm
G7
Dm
G7
Gm
Cm
Gm
Cm

long, straight, curl - y, fuz - zy, snag-gy, shag-gy, rat - ty, mat - ty, oil - y, greas-y, fleec - y, shin-ing, gleam-ing, steam-ing, flax - en, wax - en,

Cm7
F7
Cm7
F7
Cm
F7
Cm
F7
Bb7

knot-ted, pol-ka dot-ted, twist-ed, bead-ed, braid-ed, pow-dered, flow-ered and con-fet-tied, ban-gled, tan-gled, span-gled and spa - ghet - tied. ___

D.S. al Coda
Coda
Eb
Bb7
Eb7
Ab
Bb7
Eb

_ 3. They'll be hair. Flow it, show it, long ___ as God can grow it, my ___ hair.

Verse 2:
Let it fly in the breeze and get caught in the trees.
Give a home to the fleas in my hair,
A home for fleas, (yeah) a hive for bees, (yeah) a nest for birds.
There ain't no words for the beauty, the splendor,
The wonder of my . . . ***(To Chorus:)***

Verse 3:
They'll be gaga at the gogo
When they see me in my toga,
My toga made of blond, brilliantined, biblical hair;
My hair like Jesus wore it.
Hallelujah, I adore it; Hallelujah, Mary loved her son.
Why don't my mother love me? ***(To Chorus:)***

THE HAPPY FARMER

ROBERT SCHUMANN

Brightly
F
Bb
F
C7
F
C
G7
C
C7
F
Bb
F
C7
F
1.
C7
F
2.
C7
F

HAIL! HAIL! THE GANG'S ALL HERE

Words and Music by
THEODORE MORSE and ARTHUR SULLIVAN

Brightly
G
D7
Am7 D7
Am7 D7
Hail! Hail! The gang's all here! What the heck do we care? What the heck do we care?
G
D7
Am7 D7 G
Hail! Hail! The gang's all here! What the heck do we care now?

HAPPY DAYS ARE HERE AGAIN

Words by JACK YELLEN
Music by MILTON AGER

Allegro moderato
C G+ C Cmaj7 C
Hap - py days are here a - gain! the skies a - bove
Al - to - geth - er shout it now! There's no one who
G+ C Cdim G7
are clear a - gain. Let us sing a song of cheer a - gain,
can doubt it now, so let's tell the world a - bout it now,
C F C G7
1.
2.3.
Fine
Am6 E E/G♯
hap - py days are here a - gain! your cares and
A6 G♯m B7/F♯ E/G♯ B7/F♯ E Cm6/E♭ G/D G/B C6 Bm D7/A G7
D.C. (1st Chorus) al Fine
trou - bles are gone; there'll be no more from now on.

H & T BLUES

By THAD JONES

G
Cdim
G
G7
C7
G
D7
G

HALF AS MUCH

Words and Music by
CURLEY WILLIAMS

Moderately

D
If you loved me half as much as I love you, ___ you would-n't wor - ry

A7 D D7 G
me half as much as you do. ___ You're nice to me when there's no one else a - round. ___ You on - ly

E7 A7 D
build me up to let me down. ___ If you missed me half as much as I miss you, ___ you would-n't

A7 D D7 G
stay a - way half as much as you do. ___ I know that I would nev - er be this blue. ___

A7 1. D 2. D A7 D7
_ If you on - ly loved me half as much as I love you. ___ If you you. ___

HANUKAH SONG

Words by A. EVRONIN
TRADITIONAL FOLK SONG

Moderately

Cm G Cm G Cm
Y' - mey ha-Cha-nu-kah Cha-nu - kat mik-da-shey nu b' - gil uv-sim-chah m'-ma - lim et li-bey - nu

A♭ G Cm A♭ G Cm
lai - la va-yom s'vi-vo - ney - nu yi-sov suf - ga-ni-yot no - chai bam la-rov ha - i - ru had -

F9 A♭ G Cm Fm G Cm Fm G A♭ G
li - ku ne - rot Cha-nu-kah ra - bim al ha-ni-sim ___ v' - al ha-nif-la-ot ___ a - sher chol-l'-lu ha-ma-ka -

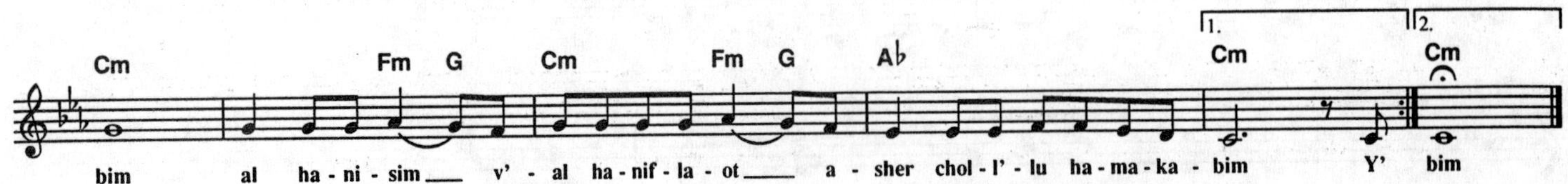
Cm Fm G Cm Fm G A♭ 1. Cm 2. Cm
bim al ha - ni - sim ___ v' - al ha-nif-la-ot ___ a - sher chol-l'-lu ha-ma-ka - bim Y' bim

HANDY MAN

Words and Music by
OTIS BLACKWELL
and JIMMY JONES

Moderate rock
(Keyboard:)
Hey girls, gath-er 'round.
Lis-ten to what I'm put-tin' down.
Hey ba-by, I'm your hand-y man.
I'm not the kind who use a pen-cil or rule.
I'm hand-y with love, and I'm no fool.
I fix bro-ken hearts; I know that I tru-ly can.
If your bro-ken heart should need re-pair, then I am the man to see.
I whis-per sweet things; you tell all your friends.
They'll come run-nin' to me.
Here is the main thing that I want to say:
I'm bus-y twen-ty-four hours a day.
I fix bro-ken hearts; I know that I tru-ly can.
Come-a, come-a, come-a, come-a, come, come.
Yeah, yeah, yeah.
Come-a, come-a, come-a, come-a, come, come.
D.S. 𝄋
come-a, come, come.
Yeah, yeah, yeah.

HAPPY BIRTHDAY

Words and Music by
STEVIE WONDER

Moderate rock
C F/C C B♭
You know it does-n't make _ much sense. _ There ought-a be a law _ a - gainst _
E♭/B♭ B♭ Am G/A Am G Dm7/G
an - y one who takes _ of - fense _ at a ____ day in your ___ cel - e - bra - tion. 'Cause we
C F/C C B♭ E♭/B♭ B♭ Am
all know in _ our minds _ that there ought-a be _ a time _ that we can set _ a - side _
G/A Am G Dm7/G F
to show ___ just how much ___ we love _ you. And I'm sure you would _ a - gree. _ What could
G F Dm/G Chorus: C F/C
fit more per - fect - ly ___ than to have a world _ par - ty ___ on the day you came to be? _ Hap - py birth - day _ to ya,
C F/C C F/C C F/C C F/C C
hap - py birth - day _ to ya, hap - py birth - day. _ Hap - py birth - day _ to ya, hap - py birth - day _ to ya, hap - py
1. D.S. 𝄋 2. To Next Strain 3.4. etc. Repeat ad lib. and fade Bridge:
F/C C F/C C F/C C Dm7
birth - day. _ 2. I just birth - day. ______ birth - day. _ Hap - py Why has there nev - er been _ a hol -
Am7 Dm7 A♭ B♭ C D.S. 𝄋
- i - day _ where peace is cel - e - brat - ed all through-out _____ the world? _____ 3. The

Verse 2:
I just never understood
How a man who died for good
Could not have a day that would
Be set aside for his recognition.
Because it should never be,
Just because some cannot see
The dream as clear as he,
That they should make it become an illusion.
And we all know everything
That he stood for time will bring.
For in peace our hearts will sing
Thanks to Martin Luther King.
Happy Birthday...
(To Chorus:)

Verse 3:
The time is overdue
For people like me and you
Who know the way to truth
Is love and unity to all God's children.
It should be a great event,
And the whole day should be spent
In full remembrance
Of those who lived and died
For the oneness of all people.
So let us all begin.
We know that love can win.
Let it out, don't hold it in.
Sing as loud as you can.
Happy birthday...
(To Chorus:)

From the Paramount T.V. Series "HAPPY DAYS"

HAPPY DAYS

Lyrics by NORMAN GIMBEL
Music by CHARLES FOX

Brightly

F Dm Gm C A Dm B♭ C
Sun-day, Mon-day, Hap-py Days; Tues-day, Wednes-day Hap-py Days; Thurs-day, Fri-day, Hap-py Days; Sat-ur - day,
B♭ C B♭ B C F Dm B♭ C F Dm
what a day, rock-in' all week with you. This day is ours. Won't you be mine? This day is ours.
To Coda
B♭ C F F7 B♭ A A♭
Oh, please be mine. 1. Hel-lo sun - shine, good-bye rain. She's wear-in' my school ring on a chain.
2. Gon - na cruise her 'round the town, show ev-'ry - bod-y what I've found.
G G7 C C7 1. 2. D.C. al Coda
She's my stead - y, I'm her man, I'm gon-na love her all I can. - er ends.
Rock 'n' roll with all my friends, hop-ing the mu - sic nev-

Coda

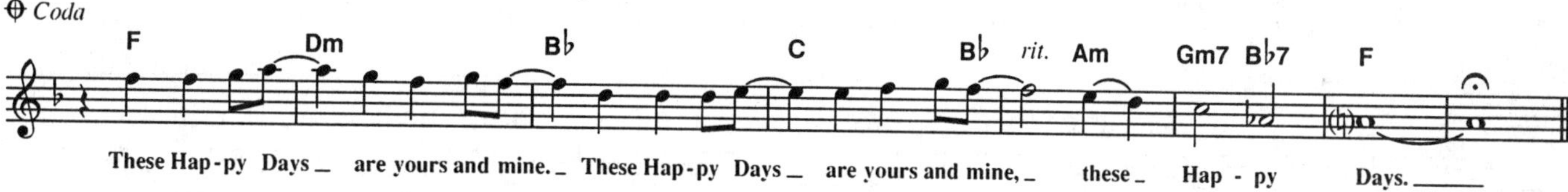
F Dm B♭ C B♭ rit. Am Gm7 B♭7 F
These Hap-py Days are yours and mine. These Hap-py Days are yours and mine, these Hap - py Days.

HAPPY TRAILS

Words and Music by
DALE EVANS

Moderately

E♭ Edim7 B♭7
Hap - py trails to you un - til we meet a - gain. Hap - py

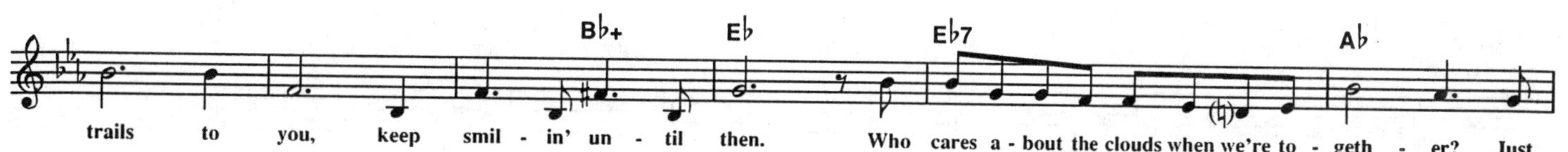
B♭+ E♭ E♭7 A♭
trails to you, keep smil - in' un - til then. Who cares a - bout the clouds when we're to - geth - er? Just

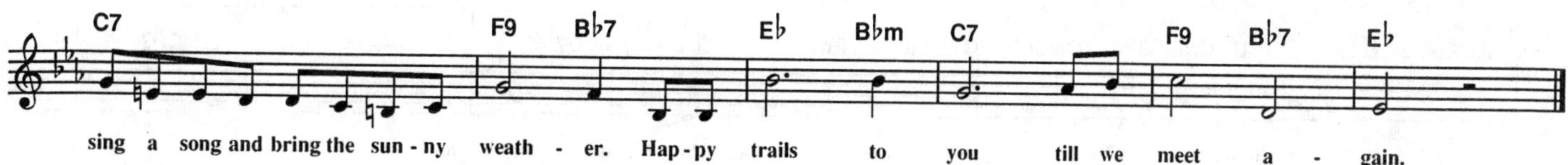
C7 F9 B♭7 E♭ B♭m C7 F9 B♭7 E♭
sing a song and bring the sun - ny weath - er. Hap - py trails to you till we meet a - gain.

HARK! THE HERALD ANGELS SING

Words by CHARLES WESLEY
Music by FELIX MENDELSSOHN

Moderately

G D G/B G G/D D G/B Bm C G/D D G

1. Hark! The her - ald an - gels sing, "Glo - ry to the new - born King!
2. Christ by high - est heav'n a - dored; Christ the ev - er - last - ing Lord!
3. Hail the heav'n born Prince of Peace! Hail the Son of Right - eous - ness!

D Em G/D A7/C♯ Bm A7/C♯ D Gmaj7 A7 D

Peace on earth and mer - cy mild, God and sin - ners re - con - ciled."
Late in time be - hold Him come, off - spring of a Vir - gin's womb.
Light and life to all He brings, ris'n with heal - ing in His wings.

N.C. G/D D7/F♯ G G/D D N.C. G/B D7/F♯ G G/D D

Joy - ful all ye na - tions rise; join the tri - umph of the skies;
Veiled in flesh the God - head see; hail the in - car - nate De - i - ty.
Mild He lays His glo - ry by, born that man no more may die.

C E7 Am E7 Am D7/C G/B G/D D G

with an - gel - ic host pro - claim, "Christ is born in Beth - le - hem!"
Pleased as man with man to dwell, Je - sus, our Em - man - u - el!
Born to raise the sons of earth; born to give them sec - ond birth.

C E7 Am E7/G♯ Am D7/C G/B | 1.2. G/D D G | 3. G/D D G

Hark! The her - ald an - gels sing, "Glo - ry to the new - born King!" new - born King!"

HARRIGAN

GEO. M. COHAN

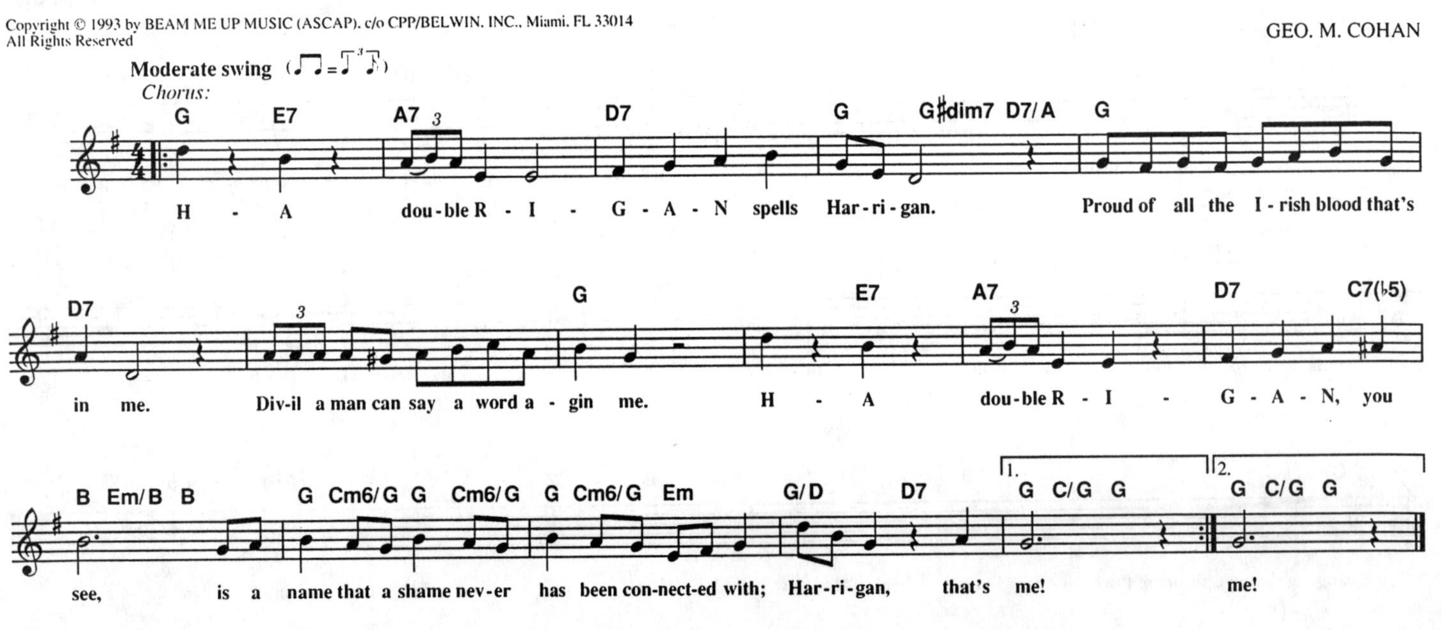
Moderate swing
Chorus:
G E7 A7 D7 G G♯dim7 D7/A G
H - A dou-ble R - I - G - A - N spells Har-ri-gan. Proud of all the I-rish blood that's
D7 G E7 A7 D7 C7(♭5)
in me. Div-il a man can say a word a - gin me. H - A dou-ble R - I - G - A - N, you
B Em/B B G Cm6/G G Cm6/G G Cm6/G Em G/D D7 1. G C/G G 2. G C/G G
see, is a name that a shame nev-er has been con-nect-ed with; Har-ri-gan, that's me! me!

HALF PAST JUMPIN' TIME

© 1943 WB MUSIC CORP. (Renewed)
All Rights Reserved

By NEAL HEFTI

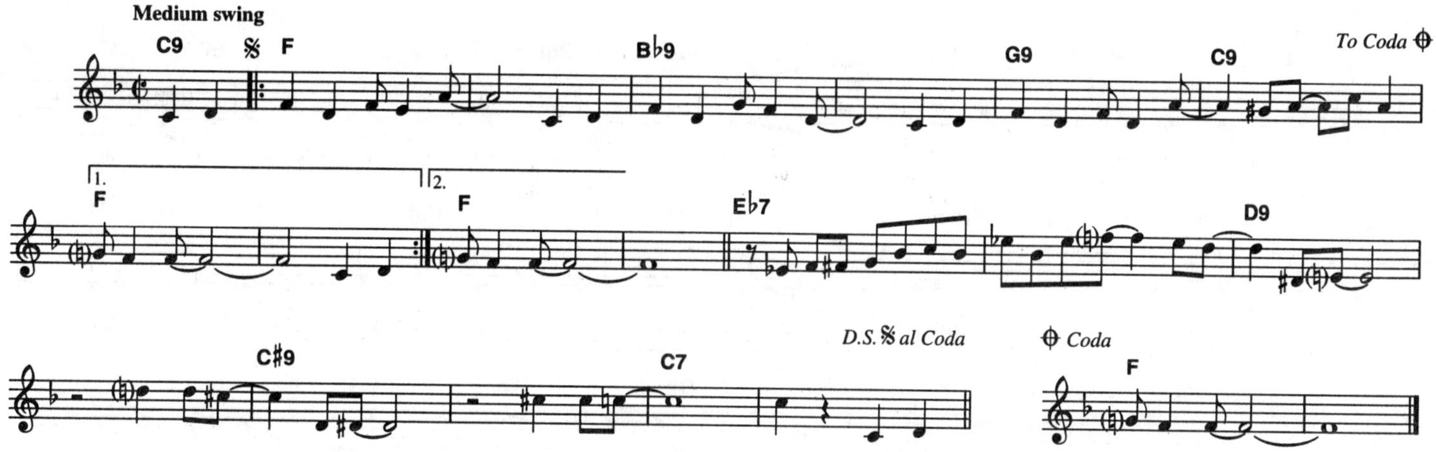
Medium swing
C9 F Bb9 G9 C9
To Coda
F F Eb7 D9
C#9 C7
D.S. al Coda
Coda
F

HALLELUJAH!

© 1927 WARNER BROS. INC.(Renewed)
Rights for Extended Renewal Term in the United States Controlled by WB MUSIC CORP., RANGE ROAD MUSIC, INC., QUARTET MUSIC, INC. and LEO ROBIN MUSIC
All Rights Reserved

Words by LEO ROBIN and CLIFFORD GREY
Music by VINCENT YOUMANS

Moderato
Sing "Hal - le - lu - jah! Hal - le - lu - jah!" and you'll shoo the
sue ya, "Hal - le - lu - jah" Gets you through the
lu - jah! Hal - le - lu - jah!" Helps to shoo the
blues a - way; when cares pur -
dark - est day.
clouds a - way.
Fine
Sa - tan lies a -
wait - in' and cre - at - in' skies of gray, but Hal - le -
D.S. al Fine

HAWAIIAN WAR CHANT
(Ta-Hy-Wa-Hu-Wai)

Copyright © 1936, 1940 (Renewed 1964, 1968) EMI MILLER CATALOG INC.
All Rights Reserved

English Lyric by RALPH FREED
Music by JOHNNY NOBLE and LELEIOHAKU

Moderately
G
Ta - hu - wa - i la - a ta - hu - wa - i wa - i - la, e - hu he - ne la a pi - li ko - o lu - a la,
C G D7 G C G D7 G
pu - tu - tu - i lu - a i - te to - e la, ha - nu li - po i - ta pa - a lai. Au we ta hu - a la.

HATIKVAH

JEWISH

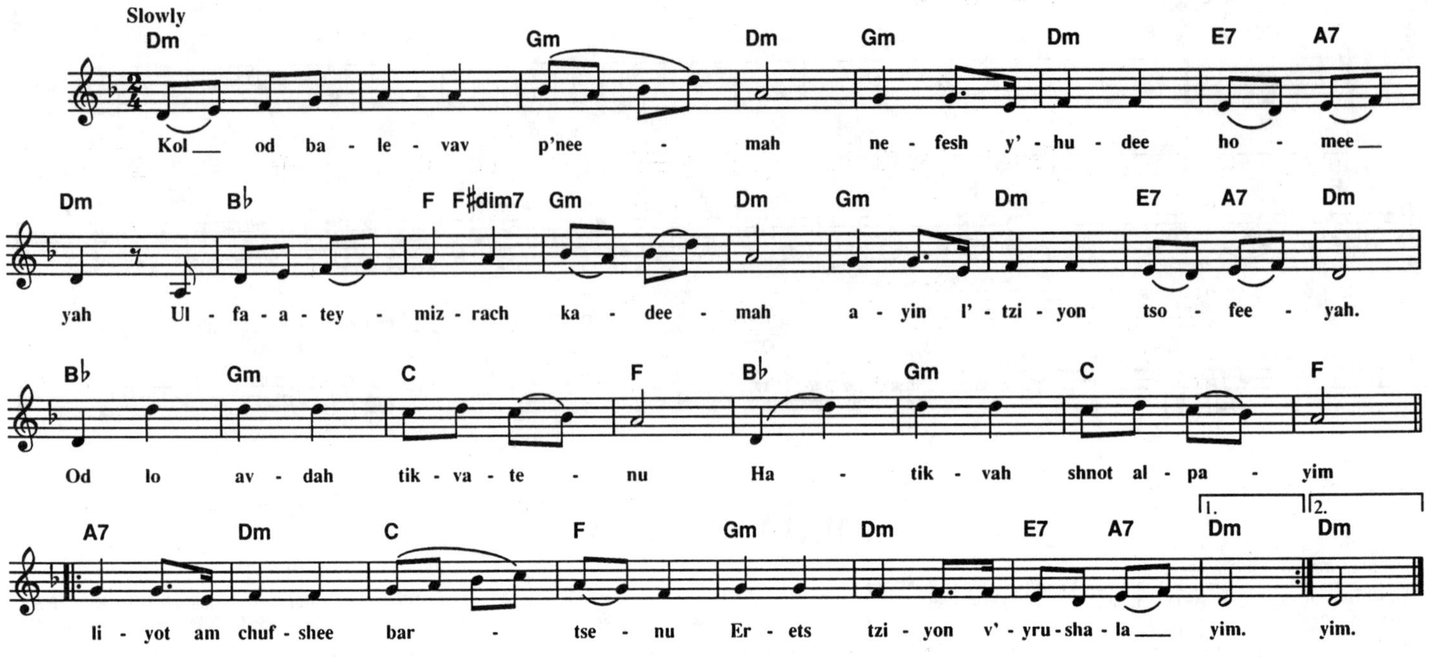
Slowly
Dm Gm Dm Gm Dm E7 A7
Kol od ba - le - vav p'nee - mah ne - fesh y' - hu - dee ho - mee
Dm B♭ F F♯dim7 Gm Dm Gm Dm E7 A7 Dm
yah Ul - fa - a - tey - miz - rach ka - dee - mah a - yin l' - tzi - yon tso - fee - yah.
B♭ Gm C F B♭ Gm C F
Od lo av - dah tik - va - te - nu Ha - tik - vah shnot al - pa - yim
A7 Dm C F Gm Dm E7 A7 1. Dm 2. Dm
li - yot am chuf - shee bar - tse - nu Er - ets tzi - yon v' - yru - sha - la yim. yim.

HAVAH NAGILAH

JEWISH

Brightly

D Gm

Ha - vah na - gi - lah, Ha - va na - gi - lah, Ha - va na - gi - lah,

D Cm D Cm

vey nis - 'm chayh. Ha - vah n' - ra - ne - nah, ha - vah n' - ra - ne - nah, Ha - vah n' - ra - ne - nah

D Cm D Gm Gm(♯7) Gm7 Gm6 Gm(♯5) Gm

vay - nis - m - chay. U - ru, u - ru, a - chim. U - ru a - chim b' lev sa - me - ach, U - ru a - chim, b'

D7 1.

lev sa - me - ach, u - ru a - chim, b' lev sa - me - ach, u - ru a - chim, b' lev sa - me - ah. U - ru a - chim

Gm *D.C.* 2. Gm 3.

b'lev sa me - ach. u - ru a - chim, b'lev sa me - ach. u - ru a - chim, u - ru a - chim,

Freely Faster Gm Cm Gm D7 Gm

b'lev sa me - ach.

HARD HEARTED HANNAH

(The Vamp of Savannah)

Words and Music by
JACK YELLEN, MILTON AGER,
BOB BIGELOW and CHARLES BATES

Moderato
E♭ D7 D♭6 C7 F F7
Hard heart-ed Han-nah, the vamp of Sa-van-nah, the mean-est gal in town;
B♭6 A7 B♭7 E♭ B7 B♭7
leath-er is tough, but Han-nah's heart is tough-er; she's a gal who loves to see men suf-fer!
talk of your cold, re-frig-er-a-ting mam-mas, broth-er, she's the Pol-ar bear's pa-jam-as! To
E♭ D7 D♭6 C7 Fm G7 Cm E♭7/B♭ A♭6
tease 'em and thrill 'em, to tor-ture and kill 'em is her de-light, they say,
I saw her at the sea shore with a
An ev-'ning spent with Han-nah sit-ting
B7/A E♭ B♭m/D♭ C7 F7
great big pan; there was Han-nah pour-ing wa-ter on a drown-ing man; she's
on your knees, is like trav-lin' thru A-las-ka in your B. V. D's; she's
hard heart-ed Han-nah, the
Fm7 B♭7 E♭ Edim B♭7 E♭ B♭7(♯5) E♭
vamp of Sa-van-nah G. A. They call her A.

HAVE YOU EVER SEEN THE RAIN?

J.C. FOGERTY

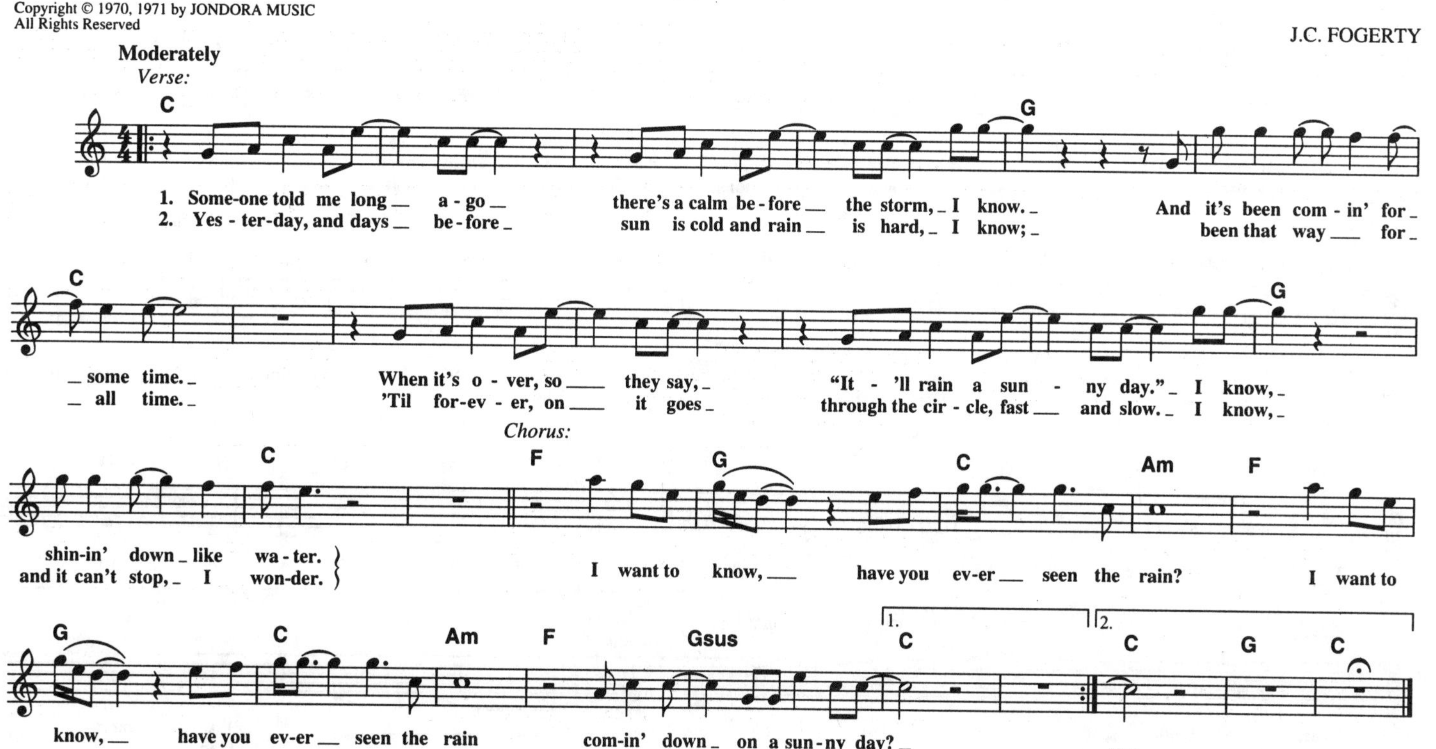
Moderately
Verse:
C G
1. Some-one told me long a-go there's a calm be-fore the storm, I know. And it's been com-in' for
2. Yes-ter-day, and days be-fore sun is cold and rain is hard, I know; been that way for
C G
some time. When it's o-ver, so they say, "It'll rain a sun-ny day." I know,
all time. 'Til for-ev-er, on it goes through the cir-cle, fast and slow. I know,
Chorus:
C F G C Am F
shin-in' down like wa-ter.
and it can't stop, I won-der.
I want to know, have you ev-er seen the rain? I want to
G C Am F Gsus C C G C
know, have you ev-er seen the rain com-in' down on a sun-ny day?

HAVE YOURSELF A MERRY LITTLE CHRISTMAS

Words and Music by
HUGH MARTIN
and RALPH BLANE

Slowly

C Am7 Dm7 F/G G7 C Am7 Dm7 G7 C Am7

Have your - self a mer - ry lit - tle Christ - mas. Let your heart be light. From now on our
Have your - self a mer - ry lit - tle Christ - mas. Make the Yule - tide gay. From now on our

1. Dm7 G7 E7 A7 D7 G7 | 2. Dm7 E7 Am Gm7 C7

trou - bles will be out of sight. ____ | trou - bles will be miles a - way. ____

Fmaj7 Fm(maj7) Em7 E♭dim7 Dm7 G7(♯5) Cmaj7 F♯m7(♭5) B7 Em E♭7

Here we are as in old - en days, hap - py gold - en days of yore. Faith - ful friends who are dear to us gath - er

G/D Am7 D7 Dm7 G7 C Am7 Dm7 F/G G7 C Am7 Dm7 G7 C Am7

near to us once more. Through the years we all will be to - geth - er if the fates al - low. Hang a shin - ing

Bm7(♭5) E7(♭9) Am C7(♯5) Fmaj7 C/E Dm7 Dm7/G G7 C6(9)

star up - on the high - est bough, ____ and have your - self a mer - ry lit - tle Christ - mas now. ____

HERE WE COME A-CAROLING

(The Wassail Song)

TRADITIONAL

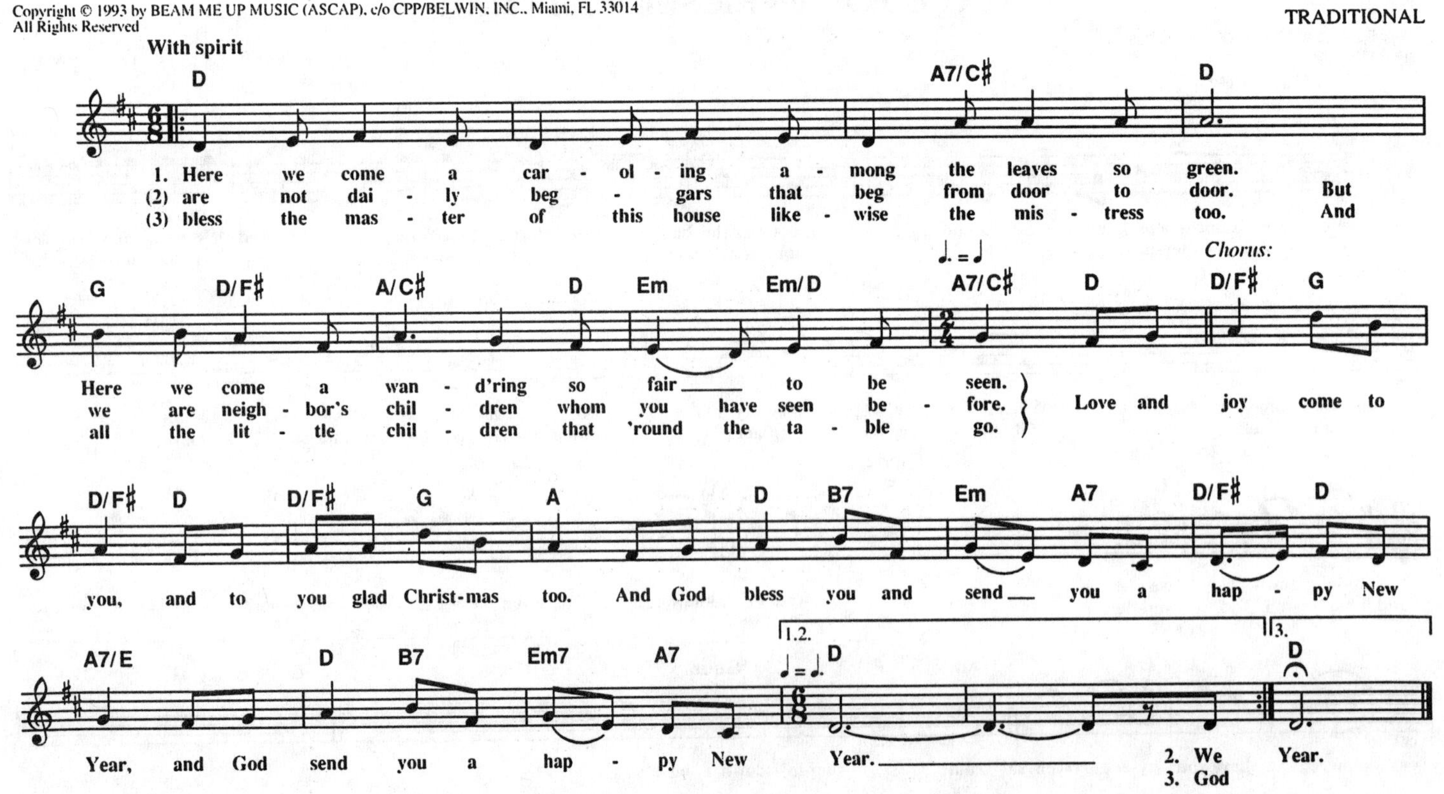
With spirit
D A7/C♯ D
1. Here we come a car - ol - ing a - mong the leaves so green.
(2) are not dai - ly beg - gars that beg from door to door. But
(3) bless the mas - ter of this house like - wise the mis - tress too. And
G D/F♯ A/C♯ D Em Em/D A7/C♯ D D/F♯ G
Here we come a wan - d'ring so fair ____ to be seen.
we are neigh - bor's chil - dren whom you have seen be - fore.
all the lit - tle chil - dren that 'round the ta - ble go.
Chorus:
Love and joy come to
D/F♯ D D/F♯ G A D B7 Em A7 D/F♯ D
you, and to you glad Christ - mas too. And God bless you and send ____ you a hap - py New
A7/E D B7 Em7 A7 1.2. D 3. D
Year, and God send you a hap - py New Year. ____
2. We
3. God
Year.

From the Broadway Musical "DAMN YANKEES"

HEART

Words and Music by
RICHARD ADLER and
JERRY ROSS

Moderately

E♭m6/G♭ Gm7 C7 C+ F D7 Gm7

You've got - ta have heart; all you real - ly need is heart. When the odds are say - in' you'll nev - er win, _
hope; must - n't sit a - round and mope. Noth - in's half as bad as it may ap - pear; _

1. Gm7(♭5) C7 F F♯dim C7/G E♭m6/G♭ 2. Gm7(♭5) C7(♭9) F B♭m6 F N.C.

that's when the grin _ should start. You've got - ta have wait-'ll next year _ and hope. When your luck is bat - tin'

Cm7 F7 B♭ N.C. Dm7 G7

ze - ro, ____ get your chin up off the floor. Mis - ter, you can be a he - ro; ____ you can o - pen an - y

C7 Gm7 C7 E♭m6/G♭ Gm7 C7 C+ F D7

door, there's noth - in' to it but to do it. You've got - ta have heart, miles 'n' miles 'n' miles of heart. Oh, it's fine to be a

Gm7 Gm7(♭5) Cm6 /E♭ D7 Gm7 C7 F Gm7/C C9(♯5) F

gen - ius, of course, _ but keep that old horse _ be - fore the cart; first, you've got - ta have heart. ____

HELLO! MA BABY

Words by IDA EMERSON
Music by JOSEPH E. HOWARD

Brightly

F G7 C7

Hel - lo ma ba - by, hel - lo ma hon - ey, hel - lo, ma rag - time gal! Send me a kiss by wire;

F Fdim F F♯dim C7/G F D7 G7

ba - by, my heart's on fire! If you re - fuse me, hon - ey, you'll lose me, then you'll be left a - lone; oh, ba - by,

C7 F♯dim C7
1. F F♯dim Gm C7
2. F
tel - e - phone, and tell me I'm your own. Hel - lo! Hel - lo! Hel - lo there! own. ____

HEART AND SOUL

Words by FRANK LOESSER
Music by HOAGY CARMICHAEL

Moderately
F Dm7 Gm7 C7 F Dm7 Gm7 C7 F Dm7 Gm7 C7
Heart and soul, I fell in love with you heart and soul, the way a fool would do, mad - ly, be-cause you held me

F Dm7 Gm7 C9 F Dm7 Gm7 C7 F Dm7 Gm7 C7
tight and stole a kiss in the night. Heart and soul, I begged to be a-dored; lost con - trol, and tum-bled o - ver-board,

F Dm7 Gm7 C7 F F7 B♭ A7 D7 G7 C7 F7
glad - ly, that mag-ic night we kissed, there in the moon-mist. Oh, but your lips were thrill - ing, much too

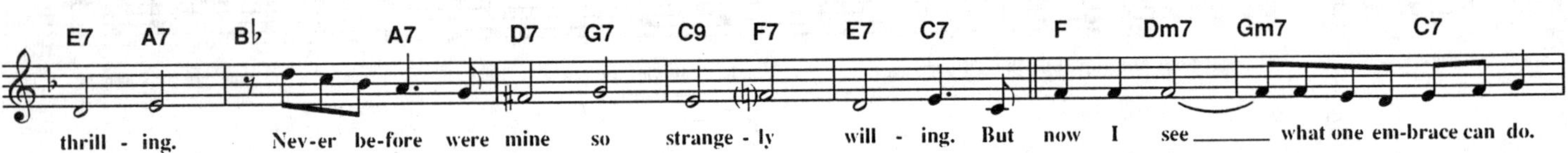
E7 A7 B♭ A7 D7 G7 C9 F7 E7 C7 F Dm7 Gm7 C7
thrill - ing. Nev-er be-fore were mine so strange - ly will - ing. But now I see what one em-brace can do.

F Dm7 Gm7 C7 F Dm7 Gm7 C7 A7 D7 Gm7 C7sus C7 F
Look at me, it's got me lov-ing you mad - ly. That lit-tle kiss you stole held all my heart and soul.

HELENA POLKA

Lively
F C7 F C7 F C7
F C7 F C7 To Coda F C
G7 C G7 C D.C. al Coda
Coda
F B♭ F7 B♭dim B♭
F7 B♭ F7 B♭

THE HEAT IS ON

Music by HAROLD FALTERMEYER
Words by KEITH FORSEY

Fast rock 'n' roll
C7
2nd time only
The heat is
C7
on, on the street, in-side your head,
F7
on ev - 'ry beat.
C7
And the beat's a - live, deep in - side.
Bbmaj7/C C
The pres-sure's high, just to stay a -
F7
live. 'Cause the heat is on.
C7
C F/A Bb Bb/D Eb F C
Oh, oh, oh, oh, oh, oh, oh, oh, caught up in the ac - tion, I'll be look-ing out for you. Oh, oh, oh, oh,
Gm7
oh, oh, oh, oh, tell me you can feel it; tell me you can feel it; tell me do you feel it?
1.3. To Next Strain
N.C.
The heat is
2.
C7
D.S.S.
The heat is
C7
on. The heat is on, on the street,
on, on the street. The heat is on, in-side your head.
on, the heat is on. The heat is on; the pres-sure's high.
F7
The heat is on, The heat is on,
The heat is on, on ev - 'ry beat. The heat is on.
The heat is on, the pres-sure's high. The heat is on,
1.3. To Next Strain
N.C.
The heat is . . . (drums)
2.
C7
The heat is On!
1.3.4. etc. Repeat ad lib. and fade
2. D.S.

HERE'S TO MY LADY

Words by JOHNNY MERCER
Music by RUBE BLOOM

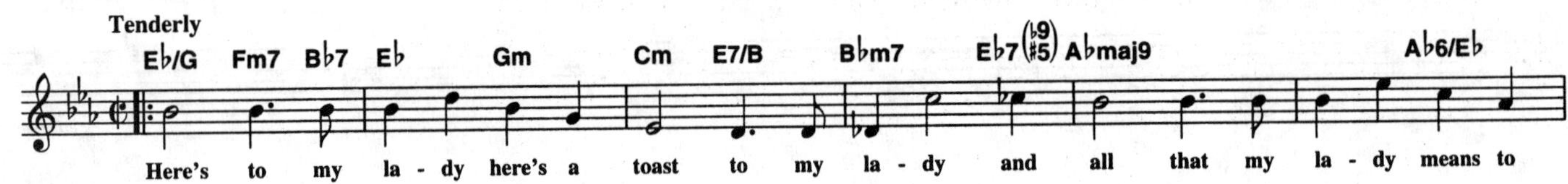
Tenderly
E♭/G Fm7 B♭7 E♭ Gm Cm E7/B B♭m7 E♭7(♭9 ♯5) A♭maj9 A♭6/E♭
Here's to my la - dy here's a toast to my la - dy and all that my la - dy means to

A♭m6 Fm7 B♭7 E♭ Dm7 G7 Cm Fm7 B♭7 E♭ Gm/D Cm Cm(maj7)
me. Like a hearth in the win - ter, a breeze in the sum - mer, a spring to re -

Cm7/F F7 B♭7 Fm7 B♭7 Fm7 B♭7(♯5) E♭ B♭7(♯5) E♭9 E♭7(♭9) Cm7 B♭m7 E♭7 A♭maj9 A♭6
mem - ber is she. Though the years may grow cold - er as peo - ple grow old - er it's

Cm Cm7 F9 Fm7/B♭ D♭7/C♭ B♭9 B♭6 B♭7 E♭/G Fm7 B♭7 E♭maj7 Gm Cm E♭7/B♭
shoul - der to shoul-der we'll be. But be it sun - shine or sha - dy, here's my love to my

F7/A A♭m6 E♭/G G♭7 Fm7 E7 1. E♭ Cm7 Fm7 B♭7(♭9 ♯5) 2. E♭ D♭9 E♭maj7
la - dy. I pray, may she al - ways love me. me.

From "BRIGADOON"

THE HEATHER ON THE HILL

Lyrics by ALAN JAY LERNER
Music by FREDERICK LOEWE

Moderately
E♭ Cm/B♭ A♭/B♭ B♭7 E♭ E♭7 A♭ C7/G Fm7 C7/G
The mist of May is in the gloom - in' and all the clouds are hold-in' still; so take my hand and let's go
The morn-in' dew is blink-in' yon - der, there's la-zy mu - sic in the rill, and all I want to do is
A♭6 A♭/B♭ E♭/B♭ Fm9/B♭ B♭7 1. E♭6 B♭7 2. E♭ Em(♯7) E B7
roam-in' through the heath - er on the hill. hill. There may be oth-er days as rich and rare; there may be
wan-der through the heath - er on the

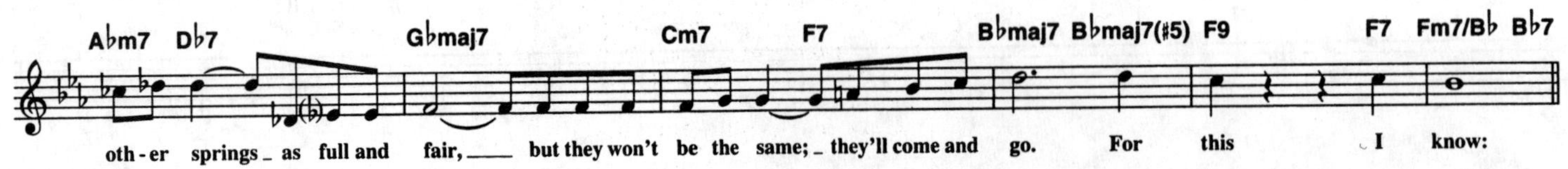
A♭m7 D♭7 G♭maj7 Cm7 F7 B♭maj7 B♭maj7(♯5) F9 F7 Fm7/B♭ B♭7
oth-er springs as full and fair, but they won't be the same; they'll come and go. For this I know:

Eb Cm/Bb Ab/Bb Bb7 Eb Eb7 Ab C7/G Fm7 C7/G
that when the mist is in the gloam - in', and all the clouds are hold-in' still, if you're not there, I won't go
Ab6 Ab/Bb Eb/Bb Abmaj7/Eb G7/D Cm Eb7/Bb Abm6 Eb/Bb Cm7 Fm7/Bb Bb Eb
roam - in' through the heath - er on the hill, the heath-er on the hill.
HEAVEN
Copyright © 1984 IRVING MUSIC, INC. (BMI), CALYPSO TOONZ and ADAMS COMMUNICATIONS (PROC)
All Rights Reserved
Words and Music by
BRYAN ADAMS and
JIM VALLANCE
Slow rock
Verse:
C Am7 G Dm Am Bb(2) Gsus G
1. Oh, think-in' a - bout all our young-er years; there was on - ly you and me; we were young and wild and free.
C Am7 G Dm Am Bb(2) F/A Gsus G
Now, noth-ing can take you a - way from me; we've been down the road be-fore but that's o - ver now; you keep me com-in' back for more.
Chorus:
F G Am C F G Am G
Ba-by, you're all that I want when you're ly - in' here in my arms. I'm find-ing it hard to be - lieve we're in heav-en. And
(ba-by,)
F G Am C F G Am 1. G C Am C/G F(2) D.C.
love is all that I need and I found it there in your heart. It is-n't too hard to see we're in heav-en.
2. G To Next Strain 3. G Repeat ad lib. and fade
heav - en. heav - en, heav - en.
Bridge:
Dm C/E F G
I've been wait - ing for so long for some - thing to ar -
Am G/B C Dm C/E F
rive; for love to come a - long. Now our dreams are com - in' true, through the good times and the
C Gsus G F G Am C F G Am G D.S.
bad. Yeah, I'll be stand-in' there by you. And

Verse 2:
Oh, once in your life you find someone
Who will turn your world around;
Bring you up when you're feelin' down.
Yeah, nothin' could change what you mean to me;
Oh there's lots that I could say;
But just hold me now,
'Cause our love will light the way.
(To Chorus:)

HELLO, I LOVE YOU

Words and Music by
THE DOORS

Moderate rock

Chorus:

Hel - lo, I love you, won't you tell me your name? _ Hel - lo, I love you, let me jump in your game. _ Hel - lo, I love you won't you tell me your name? _ Hel - lo, I love you, let me jump in your game. _

Verse:

1. She's walk-in' down the street, ___ blind to ev - 'ry eye she meets, _ do you think you'll be the guy ___ to make the queen of the an-gels sigh? _ Hel-

1. *D.S.* 𝄋

2. out this song. _

Side-walk crouch-es _ at her feet _ like a dog that begs for some-thing sweet. _ Do you hope to make her see, you fool? _ Do you hope to pluck this dus-ky jewel? _ Hel - lo, hel-lo ___ hel-lo, ___ hel-lo, _

Repeat and fade

Verse 2:
She holds her head so high
Like a statue in the sky.
Her arms are wicked and her legs are long.
When she moves, my brain screams out this song.

HELP ME RHONDA

Words and Music by
BRIAN WILSON

Moderate swing rock
1. Since you put me down, I've been out do - in' in my head. __ Come in late at night, _ and in the morn-in' I just lay in bed. __
(2.) gon - na be my wife, and I was gon - na be her man. __ But she let an - oth - er guy __ come be - tween us, and it ruined our plans. __
Well, Rhon-da, you look _ so fine, ___ and I know it would-n't take much time ___ for you to
Well, Rhon-da, you caught _ my eye, ___ and I'll give you lots of rea - sons why ___ you got - ta
help me Rhon - da, help __ me get her out of my heart. _
Chorus:
Help me Rhon-da, help, _ help me Rhon-da. Help me Rhon-da, help, _ help me Rhon-da.

C7
F
B♭
Help me Rhon-da, help, __ help me Rhon-da.
Help me Rhon-da, help, __ help me Rhon-da.
Help me Rhon-da, help, __ help me Rhon-da.
Dm7
F
B♭
C9
N.C.
1.
F
D.C.
Help me Rhon-da, help, __ help me Rhon-da.
Help me Rhon-da
yeah, get her out of my heart. _
2. She was
2.
F
N.C.
C7
F
Repeat and fade
Help me Rhon-da, help, __ help me Rhon-da.
Help me Rhon-da, help, __ help me Rhon-da.
HELP YOURSELF
(Gli Occhi Miei)
Copyright © 1968 by RADIO RECORD RICORDI R.R.R. s.r.l.
Rights for the United States of America and Canada controlled by FAMOUS MUSIC CORPORATION
All Rights Reserved
English Words by JACK FISHMAN
Original Italian Words by MOGOL
Music by C. DONIDA
Moderately
C
Verse:
Love is like can-dy on a shelf; __
We're al-ways told re-peat-ed-ly: __
My heart has love e-nough for two, __
G7
C
C7
F
you want a taste? Then help your-self. __
the ver-y best in life is free, __
more than e-nough for me and you. __
The sweet-est things are there for you. __
and if you want to prove it's true, __
I'm rich with love, a mil-lion-aire. __
C
G7
C
G7
C
1.
2.3
__ Help your-self, __ take a few. __ That's what I __ want you to do. __
__ ba-by, I'm __ tell-ing you __ this is what __ you should do. __
__ I've so much, __ it's un-fair. __ Why don't you __ take a share? __
Just help your-
Chorus:
C
Dm7 G7 Dm7 G7
self to my lips, __ to my arms. _ Just say the word _ and they are yours.
Just help your-self to the love __ in my heart. _
G7sus C
Dm7 G7
_ Your smile has o-pened up the door.
The great-est wealth that ex-ists __ in the world _ could nev-er buy __ what I can give.
Dm7
G7
G7sus
1.
C
D.S. 𝄋
2.
C
Just help your-self to my lips, __ to my arms, _ and then let's real-ly start to live. __
live. __

HERE AND NOW

Words and Music by
TERRY STEELE and DAVID ELLIOTT

Slowly
Verse:
G(2) F♯m7(♭5) B7(♭9) Em Gmaj7/D C(2) C/D
1. One look in your eyes and there I see just what you mean to me.
G(2) D/G G F♯m7(♭5) B7(♭9) Cmaj9 Bm7 Em7 E♭dim7 G/D C(2)
Here in my heart I be-lieve your love is all I ev-er need.
C G(2)/B E♭dim7 Em G(2)/B C(2) C/D F♯m7(♭5) A/B Bm7 Cmaj7
Hold-ing you close through the night, I need you. Here and now,
Chorus:
D/C D/F♯ G Bm7 C(2) F♯m7(♭5) A/B Bm7 Cmaj7
I prom-ise to love faith-ful-ly. (Faith-ful-ly.) You're all I need. Here and now,
To Coda
D/C D/F♯ G Bm7 Cmaj9 C(2) C/D
I vow to be one with thee. (You and me.) Your love is all I need.
G D/G G G(2)/B C(2) D7sus G D/G G G(2)/B C(2) C/D
D.C.
C(2) C/D
3. When Your love is all I need.
Bridge:
Cmaj7 D/C C/D G D/G
Start-ing here, start-ing now, I be-lieve in love. Start-ing here,
D.S. al Coda
Cmaj9 C/D F/G G/B Cmaj7
I'm start-ing right here, start-ing now, right now be-cause I be-lieve in your love so I'm glad to take the vow. Here and now
Coda
C(2) C/D G(2) D/G G G(2) D/G G/B Cmaj9 B♭6/9 C(2) B♭maj9 C(2) G(2)
Your love is all I need. Love is all I

Verse 2:
I look in you eyes and there I see
What happiness really means.
The love that we share makes life so sweet,
Together we'll always be.
This pledge of love feels so right,
And ooh, I need you.
(To Chorus:)

Verse 3:
When I look in your eyes, there I see
All that a love should really be.
And I need you more and more each day,
Nothing can take your love away.
More than I dare to dream,
I need you.
(To Chorus:)

HERE COMES SANTA CLAUS

(Right Down Santa Claus Lane)

Words and Music by
GENE AUTRY and
OAKLEY HALDEMAN

Moderately bright

F C7 Cdim7 C7
Here comes San - ta Claus, here comes San - ta Claus right down San - ta Claus lane.

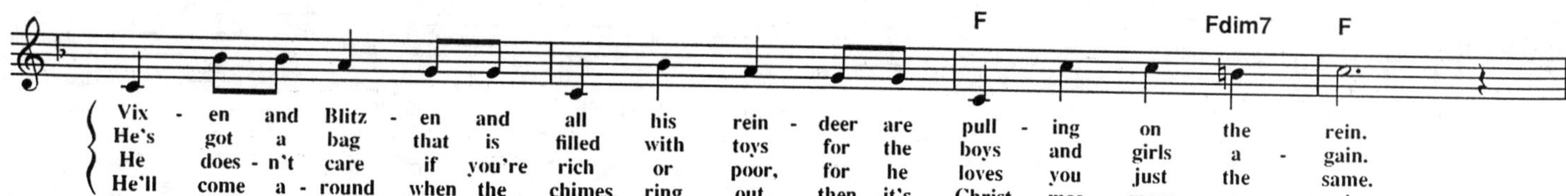
F Fdim7 F
Vix - en and Blitz - en and all his rein - deer are pull - ing on the rein.
He's got a bag that is filled with toys for the boys and girls a - gain.
He does - n't care if you're rich or poor, for he loves you just the same.
He'll come a - round when the chimes ring out, then it's Christ - mas morn a - gain

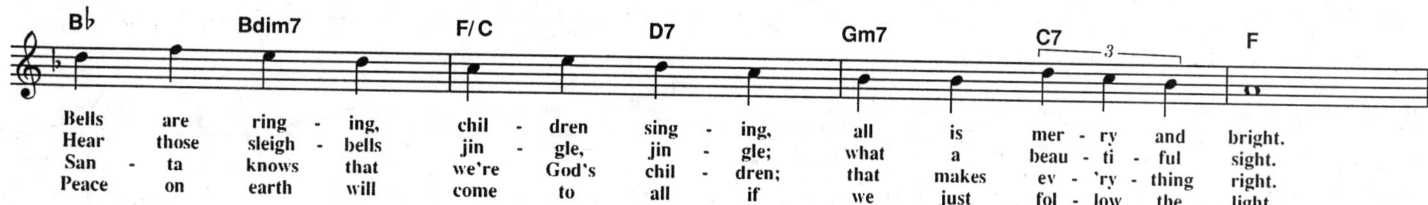
B♭ Bdim7 F/C D7 Gm7 C7 F
Bells are ring - ing, chil - dren sing - ing, all is mer - ry and bright.
Hear those sleigh - bells jin - gle, jin - gle; what a beau - ti - ful sight.
San - ta knows that we're God's chil - dren; that makes ev - 'ry - thing right.
Peace on earth will come to all if we just fol - low the light.

B♭ Bdim7 F/C D7 Gm7 C7 1.2.3. F 4. F
Hang your stock - ings and say your pray'rs,
Jump in bed, cov - er up your head,
Fill your hearts with a Christ - mas cheer
Let's give thanks to the Lord a - bove
'cause San - ta Claus comes to - night. night.

From the Videocraft T.V. Musical Spectacular "RUDOLPH, THE RED-NOSED REINDEER"

A HOLLY JOLLY CHRISTMAS

By JOHNNY MARKS

Moderately bright

C C♯dim7 G7/D G7 C♯dim7
Have a hol - ly, jol - ly Christ-mas. It's the best time of the year. I don't know if there'll be snow, but
hol - ly, jol - ly Christ-mas. And when you walk down the street, say hel - lo to friends you know, and

1.3. G7/D G7 C G7 2.4 G7/D G7 C F Em Dm7 C
have a cup of cheer. Have a ev - 'ry one you meet. Oh, ho, the mis - tle - toe hang where you can see.

Bdim7 Am D7 G7 C C♯dim7 G7/D G7
Some - bod - y waits for you; kiss her once for me. Have a hol - ly, jol - ly Christ-mas. And in case you did - n't hear:

C Am7 1. D7 G7 C D.S. 2. D7 G7 C Dm7 G7 C
Oh, by gol - ly, have a hol - ly, jol - ly Christ-mas this year. Have a Christ - mas this year.

HERE WE ARE

Words and Music by GLORIA ESTEFAN

Slowly
1.2.3.
4.
F♯m9 B7 B7
1. Here _ we
Verse:
E Emaj7 A/E A(2)/E E Emaj7
are face _ to face. We for - get time _ and place. Hold _ me now; don't _ let go ______ though it
A/E A/B B Amaj7 G♯m7
hurts, we __both know. _ The time we spend _ to - geth-er's gon - na fly, __________ and ev-'ry-thing you do _
Amaj7 G♯m7 C♯m /B Amaj7
_ to me _ is gon-na feel __ so right. __________ Ba - by, when you're lov - ing me _ I feel like I ___ could cry, _
G♯m7 F♯m9 F♯m7/B 1. F♯m9
'cause there's noth-ing I ___ can do _ to keep from lov-ing you. _
B7 F♯m9 F♯m7/B 2. E(2)
2. Here _ we ________ There's noth-ing I can
Bridge:
Am9 B7 Emaj7 Cmaj7 Amaj9/B Cmaj7 G/B
do; I'm help-less in __ your arms. __________ Oh ba-by, what you do; ___ I'm in love, _ this is it. _____ There's no turn-ing back _ this time. _
Am7 Am7/D G Gmaj7 C/G
__________ No, no, no. __________ 3. Here _ we are once _ a - gain. But this time we're on - ly friends. _
C(2)/G G Gmaj7 C/G C(2)/G C/D D
__ Fun - ny world; some-times lies ______ be-come the game when love's _ the prize. _ And though no _
Am7/D Bm7/D Cmaj7/D Bm7/D C/D G7
_one knows _ what's go - ing on _ in - side, __________ all the love I feel __for you _ is some-thing I should hide. ______ When I have you close _
Cmaj7 Bm7 Am7 Am/D
_ to me _ the feel-ing's so _ sub-lime __________ that there's noth-ing I ___ can do ___ to keep from lov-ing you. _

Am9 D7 *Repeat and fade*

Verse 2:
Here we are all alone;
Trembling hearts, beating strong;
Reaching out, a breathless kiss
I never thought could feel like this.
I want to stop the time from passing by.
I want to close my eyes and feel
Your lips are touching mine.
Baby, when you're close to me,
I want you more each time.
And there's nothing I can do
To keep from loving you.
(To Bridge:)

HERNANDO'S HIDEAWAY

Words and Music by
RICHARD ADLER and
JERRY ROSS

Tango

C7 Fm Gm7(♭5) C7

I know a dark se-clud-ed place, a place where no one knows your face, a glass of wine, a

Fm C7 Fm C7 Fm C7 Fm

fast em-brace, it's called Her-nan-do's Hide-a-way! O - lay!! All you see are sil-hou-ettes, and all you hear are

Gm7(♭5) C7 Fm C7 Fm C7 Fm

cas-ta-nets. And no one cares how late it gets, not at Her-nan-do's Hide-a-way! O - lay!!

C7 C7(♭9) C7 C7(♭9) Fm N.C. Fm C7 C7(♭9)

At the Gol-den Fin-ger-bowl or an-y place you go,

C7 C7(♭9) Fm N.C. F7 F7(♭9)
you will meet your Un-cle Max and ev-'ry-one you know.

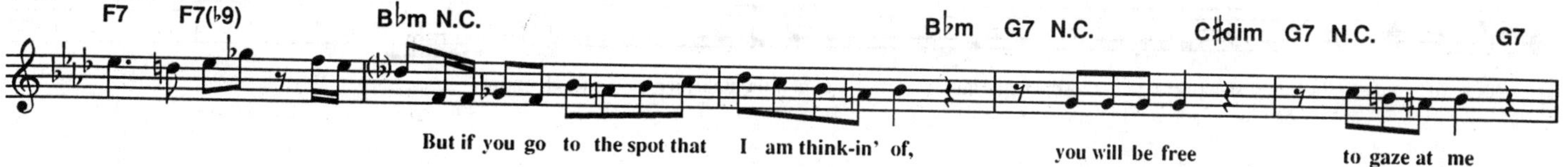
F7 F7(♭9) B♭m N.C. B♭m G7 N.C. C♯dim G7 N.C. G7
But if you go to the spot that I am think-in' of, you will be free to gaze at me

C7 B7 C7 C7(♭9) C7 Fm Gm7(♭5)
and talk of love! Just knock three times and whis-per low, that you and I were sent by Joe. Then
C7 Fm C7
1. Fm C7 Fm Gm7(♭5)
2. Fm6 C7 Fm
strike a match and you will know, you're in Her-nan-do's Hide-a-way! O - lay!! I way! O - lay!!

HE'S GOT THE WHOLE WORLD IN HIS HANDS

TRADITIONAL SPIRITUAL

Moderately
E♭
B♭7
E♭
1. He's got the whole world_ in His hands,_ He's got the whole world_ in His hands,_ He's got the

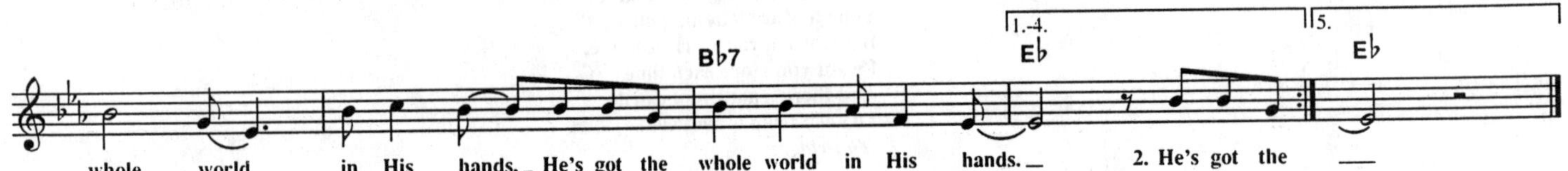
B♭7
1.-4.
E♭
5.
E♭
whole world_ in His hands,_ He's got the whole world in His hands._ 2. He's got the ___

Verse 2:
He's got the wind and the rain in His hands,
He's got the wind and the rain in His hands,
He's got the wind and the rain in His hands,
He's got the whole world in His hands.

Verse 3:
He's got the little tiny baby in His hands,
He's got the little tiny baby in His hands,
He's got the little tiny baby in His hands,
He's got the whole world in His hands.

Verse 4:
He's got you and me, brother, in His hands,
He's got you and me, sister, in His hands,
He's got you and me, brother, in His hands,
He's got the whole world in His hands.

Verse 5:
He's got everybody here in His hands,
He's got everybody here in His hands,
He's got everybody here in His hands,
He's got the whole world in His hands.

From the Motion Picture "DIRTY DANCING"

HEY! BABY!

Words and Music by
MARGARET COBB and
BRUCE CHANNEL

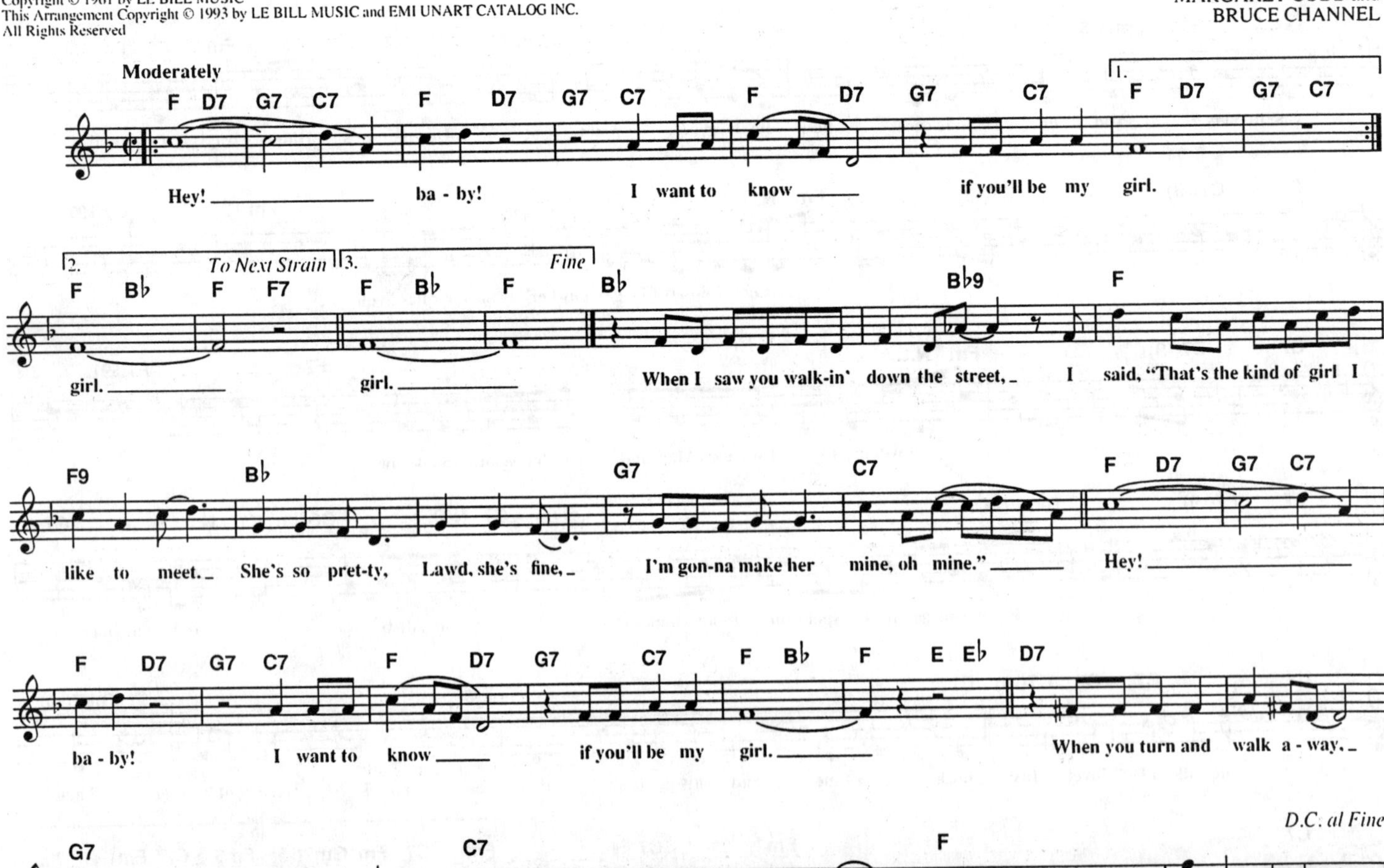
Moderately
F D7 G7 C7 F D7 G7 C7 F D7 G7 C7
1. F D7 G7 C7
Hey! ___ ba - by! I want to know ___ if you'll be my girl.
2. To Next Strain
3. Fine
F B♭ F F7 F B♭ F B♭ B♭9 F
girl. ___ girl. ___ When I saw you walk-in' down the street,_ I said, "That's the kind of girl I
F9 B♭ G7 C7 F D7 G7 C7
like to meet._ She's so pret-ty, Lawd, she's fine,_ I'm gon-na make her mine, oh mine." ___ Hey! ___
F D7 G7 C7 F D7 G7 C7 F B♭ F E E♭ D7
ba - by! I want to know ___ if you'll be my girl. ___ When you turn and walk a - way,_

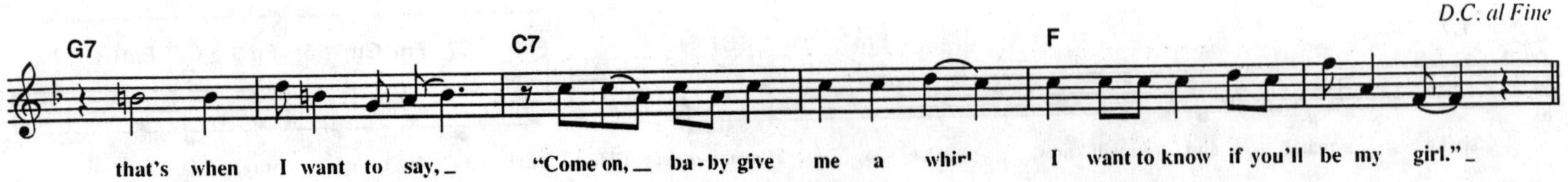
D.C. al Fine
G7
C7
F
that's when I want to say,_ "Come on,_ ba - by give me a whirl I want to know if you'll be my girl."_

HEY, GOOD LOOKIN'

Words and Music by
HANK WILLIAMS

Moderate country swing

C D7 G7

1. Hey, hey, good look-in'. What cha got cook-in'? How's a-bout cook-in' some-thin' up with
free and read-y so we can go stead-y. How's a-bout sav-in' all your time for

C G7 C D7

me? Hey, sweet ba-by, don't you think may-be we could find us a
me? No more look-in', I know I've been took-en. How's a-bout keep-in'

G7 C C7 F C F C

brand new rec-i-pe? I got a hot rod Ford and a two dol-lar bill and I know a spot right o-ver the hill.
stead-y com-pan-y? I'm gon-na throw my date book o-ver the fence and find me one for five or ten cents.

F C D7 G7 C

There's so-da pop and the danc-in's free, so if you wan-na have fun, come a-long with me.
I'll keep it 'til it's cov-ered with age, 'cause I'm writ-in' your name down on ev-'ry page. Hey, good look-in'.

D7 G7 1. C 2. C F C

What cha got cook-in'? How's a-bout cook-in' some-thin' up with me? 2. I'm me?

From the Musical Production "WILDCAT"

HEY, LOOK ME OVER

Lyric by CAROLYN LEIGH
Music by CY COLEMAN

March tempo
G B7 F♯m7/C♯ Ddim B7/D♯ E7 Am
Hey, look me o-ver, lend me an ear; fresh out of clo-ver, mort-gaged up to here. But
D7 Am7/E Fm6 D7/F♯ G B7/F♯ E7 A7 D7
don't pass the plate, folks, don't pass the cup. I fig-ure when-ev-er you're down and out, the on-ly way is
G B7 F♯m7/C♯ Ddim B7/D♯ E7 Am
up. And I'll be up like a rose-bud, high on the vine. Don't thumb your nose, bud, take a tip from mine. I'm a
Cmaj7 F9 G/B E7 Am7 D7 1. G 2. G
lit-tle bit short of the el-bow room, but let me get me some. And look out, Hear me shout, world, here I come. come.

HEY! PAULA

Words and Music by
RAY HILDERBRAND

Slowly
D9 D7(♭9) G Em7 Am7 D9 G Em7 Am7 D7
Hey! Hey! Paul - a, I wan - na mar - ry you. Hey! Hey! Paul - a, no one else will ev - er do. I've

G Em7 G Em7 Am7 Am7/D D7 G Am7 C
wait - ed so long for school to be through, Paul - a, I can't wait no more for you. My love, my

G D13 G Em7 Am7 D7 G Em7 Am7 D7
love. Hey! Paul, I've been wait - ing for you. Hey! Hey! Hey! Paul, I wan - na mar - ry you, too. If

G Em7 G Em7 Am7 Am7/D D7 G Am7 C G D13
you love me true, if you love me still, our love will al - ways be real. My love, my love.

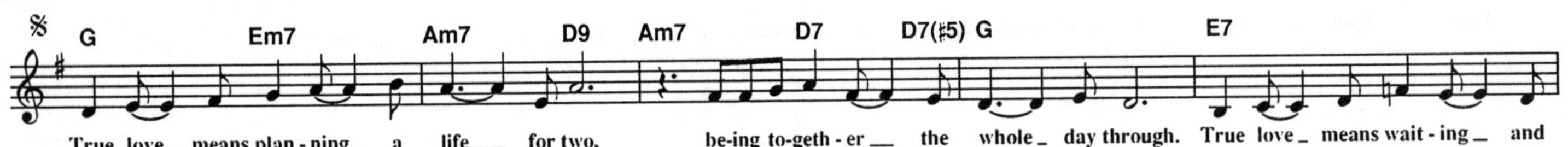
G Em7 Am7 D9 Am7 D7 D7(♯5) G E7
True love means plan - ning a life for two, be-ing to-geth - er the whole day through. True love means wait - ing and

1. To Next Strain 2. Fine
Am A7 Am7/D D7 G Am7 G D13 G A♭9(♯11) G6/9
hop - ing that soon, wish-es we've made will come true, my love, my love. Hey! Hey! love.

D.S. 𝄋 al Fine
G Em7 Am7 D7 G Em7 Am7 D7
Paul - a, I've been wait - ing for you. Hey! Hey! Paul, I want to mar - ry you too.

From the Warner Bros. Picture "THE PAJAMA GAME"

HEY THERE

Words and Music by
RICHARD ADLER and
JERRY ROSS

Slowly
E♭ Cm7 Fm7 B♭7 E♭ Cm7 Fm7 B♭7 C7 Fm7 B♭7
Hey there, you with the stars in your eyes, love nev - er made a fool of you. You used to be too

wise! Hey there, you on that high fly-ing cloud, though she won't throw a crumb to you, you
think some-day she'll come to you. Bet-ter for - get her, her with her nose in the air. She has you danc - ing
on a string. Break it and she won't care! Won't you take this ad - vice I hand you like a
broth-er? Or are you not see - ing things too clear? Are you too much in love to hear? Is it
all go - ing in one ear and out the oth - er? oth - er?
From the M-G-M Picture "LILI"
HI-LILI, HI-LO
Copyright © 1952 (Renewed 1980) METRO-GOLDWYN-MAYER INC.
All Rights Controlled and Administered by EMI ROBBINS CATALOG INC.
All Rights Reserved
Words and Music by
HELEN DEUTSCH and
BRONISLAU KAPER
Moderate waltz
A song of love is a sad song; hi - li - li, hi - li - li, hi - lo. A song of love is a
song of woe, don't ask me how I know. A song of love is a sad song, for I have loved and it's
so. I sit at the win-dow and watch the rain, hi - li - li, hi - li - li, hi - lo. To - mor-row I'll
prob - a - bly love a - gain, hi - li - li, hi - li - li, hi - lo. A li - li, hi - li - li, hi - lo.

HEY THERE LONELY GIRL

Words and Music by
EARL SHUMAN
and LEON CARR

Slowly

Chorus:
Cmaj7
Bm7
Am7
Gmaj7
Hey there lone - ly girl, lone - ly girl, let me make your bro - ken heart like new. Hey there

To Coda
Cmaj7
Bm7
Am7
G
C/G
G
N.C.
lone - ly girl, lone - ly girl, don't you know this lone - ly boy loves you?
1. Ev - er since he broke your
2. You think that on - ly his two

Verse:
Bm
C
D
N.C.
Bm
heart, you seem so lost each time you pass my way. Oh, how I long to take your hand, and say, "Don't
lips can kiss your lips and make your heart stand still. But once you're in my arms you'll see no one can

C D C/D D C/D D
1. D.S. 2. D.S. al Coda
cry; I'll kiss your tears a - way." Hey there Hey there
kiss your lips the way I will.

Coda
Am7 G
Don't you know this lone - ly boy loves you?

THE HOKEY POKEY

Words and Music by
LARRY LA PRISE, CHARLES P. MACAK
and TAFTT BAKER

Moderate swing

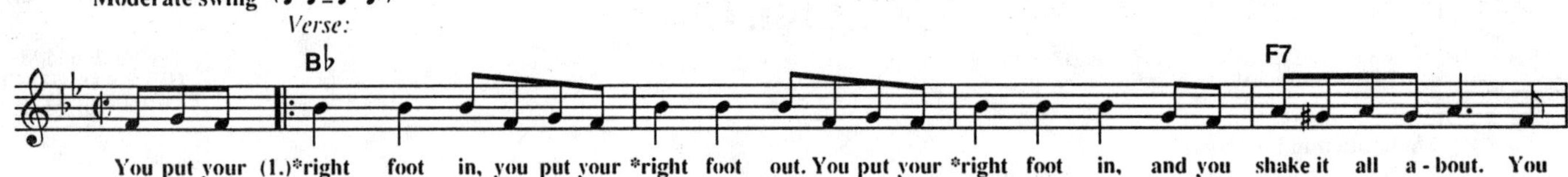
Verse:
B♭
F7
You put your (1.)*right foot in, you put your *right foot out. You put your *right foot in, and you shake it all a - bout. You

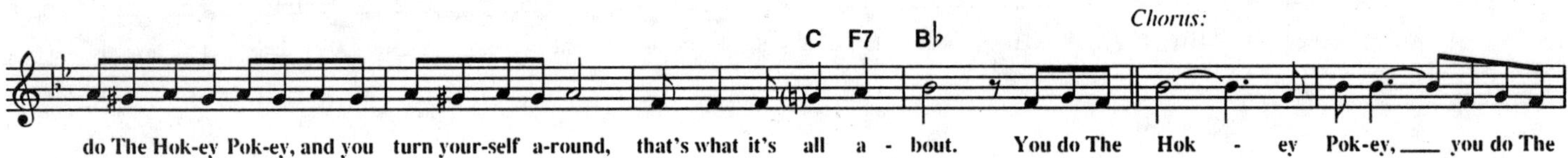
C F7 B♭
Chorus:
do The Hok-ey Pok-ey, and you turn your-self a-round, that's what it's all a - bout. You do The Hok - ey Pok-ey, you do The

F7
C F7 B♭
1.-9.
10.
B♭
Hok - ey Pok-ey. You do The Hok - ey Pok-ey. That's what it's all a - bout. You put your bout.
**(on your knees)
**(slap the floor)

Verses:
- ** 2nd time:* left foot
- ** 3rd time:* right arm
- ** 4th time:* left arm
- ** 5th time:* right elbow
- ** 6th time:* left elbow
- ** 7th time:* head
- ** 8th time:* right hip
- ** 9th time:* left hip
- **10th time:* whole self

***(last time only)*

HOLD ME, THRILL ME, KISS ME

Words and Music by
HARRY NOBLE

Slow swing
C Am Dm7 G7 C Am7 Dm7 G7 Am C+ Am7
Hold me, hold me. Nev-er let me go un-til you've told me, told me what I want to know. And then just hold me, hold me,
Dm7 G7 C Am Dm7 G7 C Am Dm7 G7
make me tell you I'm in love with you. (Hold me tight, nev-er let me go.) Thrill me, thrill me. Walk me down the lane where shad-ows
C Am7 Dm7 G7 Am Am(♯7) Am7 Dm7 G7 C Am
will be, will be, hid-ing lov-ers just the same as we'll be, we'll be, when you make me tell you I love you. (Will you
Dm7 G7 C F6 Fm6 C C+ C Dm7 G7 C
take me in your arms.) They told me, "Be sen-si-ble with your new love, don't be fooled think-ing this is the last you'll find." But
F♯m7(♭5) B7 Em Em(♯7) Em7 Am7 D9
they nev-er stood in the dark with you, love, when you take me in your arms and drive me slow-ly out of my mind.
C Am7 Dm7 G7 C Am7 Dm7 G7 E7
Kiss me, kiss me and when you do, I know that you will miss me, miss me if we ev-er say a-dieu, so
Am Am(♯7) Am7 Dm7 G7 C Am Dm7 G7 C
kiss me, kiss me. Make me tell you I'm in love with you. (Hold me tight, nev-er let me go.)
HONEY
Copyright © 1928 (Renewed 1956) EMI FEIST CATALOG INC.
All Rights Reserved
Words and Music by
SEYMOUR SIMONS
HAVEN GILLESPIE
RICHARD A. WHITING
Moderately
F B♭/F F G7 C7 Gm7 C7 A/C♯
I'm in love with you, hon-ey. Say you love me too, hon-ey. No one else will do, hon-ey. Seems
Dm G7 C7 Gm7/C C7 F B♭/F F A7 Dm F7
fun-ny, but it's true. Loved you from the start, hon-ey. Bless your lit-tle heart, hon-ey.
B♭ D♭7/C♭ F/C Cm6/E♭ D7 G7 C7 F Gm7 C7 F
Ev-'ry day would be so sun-ny, hon-ey, with you. you.

HOLD ON, I'M COMIN'

Words and Music by
ISAAC HAYES and
DAVID PORTER

Moderate rock
G Bb C G
1.3. Don't you
Verse:
G7 C7
ev - er feel sad. Lean on me when times are bad. When the day comes and you're
Chorus:
G Bb C
down in a riv-er of trou-ble, and I got to drown, just hold on, I'm com-in'. Hold on, I'm
1. D.S. 2.4.5. etc. Repeat and fade 3. Bridge:
G G G C7
com-in'. 2. I'm goin' my com-in'. Hold com-in'. Reach out to me for sat-is - fac - tion, yeah.
Bb C D7 G F Bb C D.C.
Call my name, now for quick re - ac - tion, hey, hey, hey, yeah.

Verse 2:
I'm goin' my way, your lover.
If you get cold, I'll be your cover.
Don't have to worry, 'cause I'm here.
No need to suffer, 'cause I'm here.
(To Chorus:)

HOME ON THE RANGE

FOLK SONG

Moderate waltz
G C G A7
Oh give me a home where the buf - fa - lo roam, where the deer and the an - te - lope
D7 G C Cm G D7 G
play, where sel - dom is heard a dis - cour - ag - ing word, and the skies are not cloud - y all day.
Chorus:
D7 G A7 D7 G
Home, home on the range, where the deer and the an - te - lope play, where sel - dom is
C Cm G D7 G
heard a dis - cour - ag - ing word, and the skies are not cloud - y all day.

From the Broadway Musical "AIN'T MISBEHAVIN'"

HONEYSUCKLE ROSE

Words by ANDY RAZAF
Music by THOMAS "FATS" WALLER

Moderately slow

Gm7 C7 Gm7 C7 Gm7 D♭9(♯5) C11 C9 F F7/A
Ev-'ry hon-ey bee fills with jeal-ous-y when they see you out with me. I don't blame them, good-ness knows,

B♭ D♭7 F C7/G F/A A♭dim Gm7 C9 Gm7 C9 Gm7 D♭9(♯5)
hon-ey-suck-le rose. When you're pass-ing by flow-ers droop and sigh, and I know the rea-son

C11 C9 F G♭maj7 G7 A♭6 A7(♯5) B♭ C7 F
why, you're much sweet-er, good-ness knows, hon-ey-suck-le rose.

F7 B♭dim7/F Bdim7/F F7 B♭6 F7(♭9) B♭dim7/F B♭6 G7 Cdim7/G C♯dim7/G G7
Don't buy sug-ar, you just have to touch my cup. You're my sug-ar,

C11 C7 Gm7 C9 Gm7 C9 Gm7 E♭9 D9
it's sweet when you stir it up. When I'm tak-in' sips from your tast-y lips, seems the hon-ey fair-ly

D♭9(♯5) C9 F F7/A B♭ C9 F F7/A B♭ Bdim F/C C7(♯5) F9
drips. You're con-fec-tion, good-ness knows, hon-ey-suck-le rose.

A HOT TIME IN THE OLD TOWN TONIGHT

Music by
THEODORE A. METZ

Brightly

G
When you hear them-a bells go ding ling ling, all join 'round and

sweet-ly you must sing. And when the verse is through, in the cho-rus all join

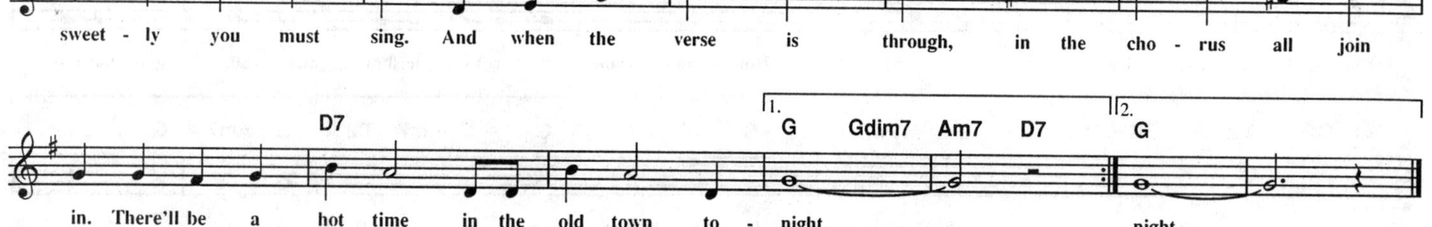
D7
1. G Gdim7 Am7 D7
2. G
in. There'll be a hot time in the old town to-night.
night.

HONKY TONK BLUES

Words and Music by
HANK WILLIAMS

Moderately
F
Bb7
1. I left my home _ down on a ru - ral route _ and told my folks _ I'm go - in' step - pin' out _ to get the honk - y tonk blues. _
2. I stopped in - to ev - 'ry place in town, _ this cit - y life _ has real - ly got me down. _ I got the honk - y tonk blues. _
(3.) tuck my wor - ries un - der - neath my arm _ and get right back _ to my Pap - py's farm _ and leave the honk - y tonk blues. _
F
C7
F
The jump - in' honk - y tonk blues. Lord, _ I got 'em, I got the honk - y tonk blues.
I got the honk - y tonk blues. Lord, _ I'm suf - ferin' with the
For - get the honk - y tonk blues. I don't want to be both - ered with the honk - y tonk blues. When
Bb7
I went to _ a dance, wore out my shoes, _ woke up this morn - in' wish - in' I could lose _ the jump - in' honk - y tonk blues. The wear - y
I get home _ a - gain to Ma and Pa, _ I know they're gon - na lay _ down the law _ a - bout the honk - y tonk blues. The jump - in'
F
C7
1.2.
F
3.
F
honk - y tonk blues. Lord, I'm suf - ferin' with the honk - y tonk blues. honk - y tonk blues.
honk - y tonk blues. Lord, I'm suf - ferin' with the honk - y tonk blues. 3. Gon - na

From the Tri-Star Motion Picture "The Fisher King"

HOW ABOUT YOU?

Lyric by RALPH FREED
Music by BURTON LANE

Moderately
G Gmaj7 G/B Bbdim Am7 D7 G Gmaj7 G/B F#/A# Bm7(b5) E7(#5)
I like New York in June. How a - bout you? _ I like a Gersh - win tune. How a - bout you? _
A7 Cm6 Am7(b5) D6 G6 B/F# B6/F# F#7sus F#7
I love a fire - side when a storm is due. _ I like po - ta - to chips, moon - light and mo - tor trips.
B Am7 D7 G Gmaj7 G/B Bbdim Am7 D7 G9 Dm7
How a - bout you? _ I'm mad a - bout good books, can't get my fill. _ And Frank - lin
G9 Dm7 Cmaj7 C6 Cm G/D Eb7/Db
Roose - velt's looks, give me a thrill. _ Hold - ing hands in a mov - ie show, when all the lights are low
Am/C Am B7(#5) B7 Em Em7 C D7
1.
G Am7 D9
2.
G Am7 G
may not be new, but I like it. How a - bout you? you? _

HONKY TONKIN'

Words and Music by
HANK WILLIAMS

Moderately

G *Verse:*

1. When you are sad and lone - ly and have no place to go, just come to see me, ba - by, and bring a - long some dough, and we'll go honk - y tonk - in', honk - y tonk - in', honk - y tonk - in', hon - ey ba - by. We'll go honk - y tonk - in' 'round this town. When you and your ba - by have a fall - in' out, just call me up, sweet ma - ma, and we'll go step - pin' out, and we'll go honk - y tonk - in', honk - y tonk - in', honk - y tonk - in', hon - ey ba - by. We'll go honk - y tonk - in' 'round this town. 2. We're

go - in' to the cit - y, to the cit - y fair. If you go to the cit - y then you will find me there and we'll go honk - y tonk - in', honk - y tonk - in', honk - y tonk - in', hon - ey ba - by. We'll go honk - y tonk - in' 'round this town. When you are sad and lone - ly and have no place to go, just come to see me, ba - by, and bring a - long some dough, and we'll go honk - y tonk - in', honk - y tonk - in', honk - y tonk - in', hon - ey ba - by. We'll go honk - y tonk - in' 'round this town.

HOW COME YOU DO ME LIKE YOU DO

By GENE AUSTIN and ROY BERGERE

Moderately
C F C Bb7(b5) A7 Eb7(b5) D7 G7 C
How come you do me like you do, do, do? How come you do me like you do?
F C Bb7(b5) A7 Eb7(b5) D7 G7 C7
Why do you try to make me feel so blue? I ain't done nuth - in' to you.
1. Do me right, or else just let me be, 'cause I can beat you do - in' what you're doin' to me.
2. If you rave, I'll have to get you told, for I can change your tem - p'ra - ture from hot to cold.
F6 Ab7 G7 C F
How come you do me like you
C E7 A7 D7 G7
do, do, do? How come you do me like you do?
1. C F6 C
2. C F6 C
do?

HOT ROD LINCOLN

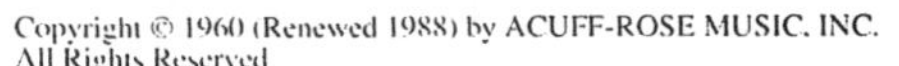

Words and Music by
CHARLES RYAN and
W.S. STEVENSON

My pappy said, "Son, you're gonna drive me to drinkin',
If you don't stop drivin' that hot rod Lincoln.

Bright rock
E
A
(Bass)
B7
E
1.
To Next Strain
Have you

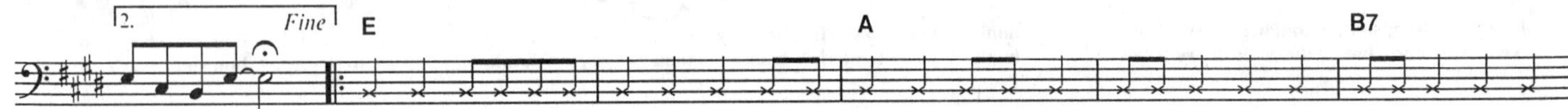
2.
Fine
E
A
B7
heard the sto-ry of the hot rod race, when the Fords and Lin-colns was set-tin' the pace. That sto-ry is true, I'm

E
1.-12.
13.
D.C. al Fine
here to say, 'Cause I was a-driv-in' that mod-el "A".
2. It's got a

Verse 2:
It's got a Lincoln motor and it's really souped up,
That model "A" body makes it look like a pup.
It's got 8 cylinders and uses 'em all,
Got overdrive, just won't stall.

Verse 3:
With a 4-barrel carb. and dual exhaust,
With 4-11 gears you can really get lost.
It's got safety tubes but I ain't scared.
The brakes are good, the tires, fair.

Verse 4:
Pulled out of San Pedro late one night,
The moon and the stars were shining bright.
We was drivin' up Grapevine Hill,
Passin' cars like they was standin' still.

Verse 5:
All of a sudden, in the wink of an eye,
A Cadillac sedan passed us by.
I said, "Boys, that's a mark for me."
By then the tail-light was all you could see.

Verse 6:
Now the fellas ribbed me for bein' behind,
So I thought I'd make the Lincoln unwind
Took my foot off the gas and man-a-live,
I shoved it on down into overdrive.

Verse 7:
I wound it up to a hundred and ten,
My speedometer said that I hit top then.
My foot was glued like lead to the floor.
That's all there is and there ain't no more.

Verse 8:
Now the boys all thought I lost my sense,
Them telephone poles looked like a picket fence.
They said, "Slow down, I see spots.
The lines on the road, just look like dots."

Verse 9:
Took a corner, sideswiped a truck,
I crossed my fingers just for luck.
My fenders was clickin' the guard-rail posts,
The guy beside me was white as a ghost.

Verse 10:
Smoke was comin' from out of the back,
When I started to gain on that Cadillac.
I knew I could catch him, I thought I could pass.
Don't you know by then we'd be low on gas.

Verse 11:
They had flames comin' from out of the side.
You can feel the tension, man, what a ride!
I said, "Look out, boys, I got a license to fly."
And that Caddy pulled over and let us by.

Verse 12:
Now all of a sudden she started to knockin',
Down in a dip she started to rockin'.
I looked in the mirror, a red light was blinkin',
The cops was after my hot rod Lincoln.

Verse 13;
They arrested me and they put me in jail,
I called my pappy to throw my bail.
He said, "Son, you're gonna drive me to drinkin',
If you don't stop drivin' that hod rod Lincoln."

HURT

Words and Music by JIMMIE CRANE and AL JACOBS

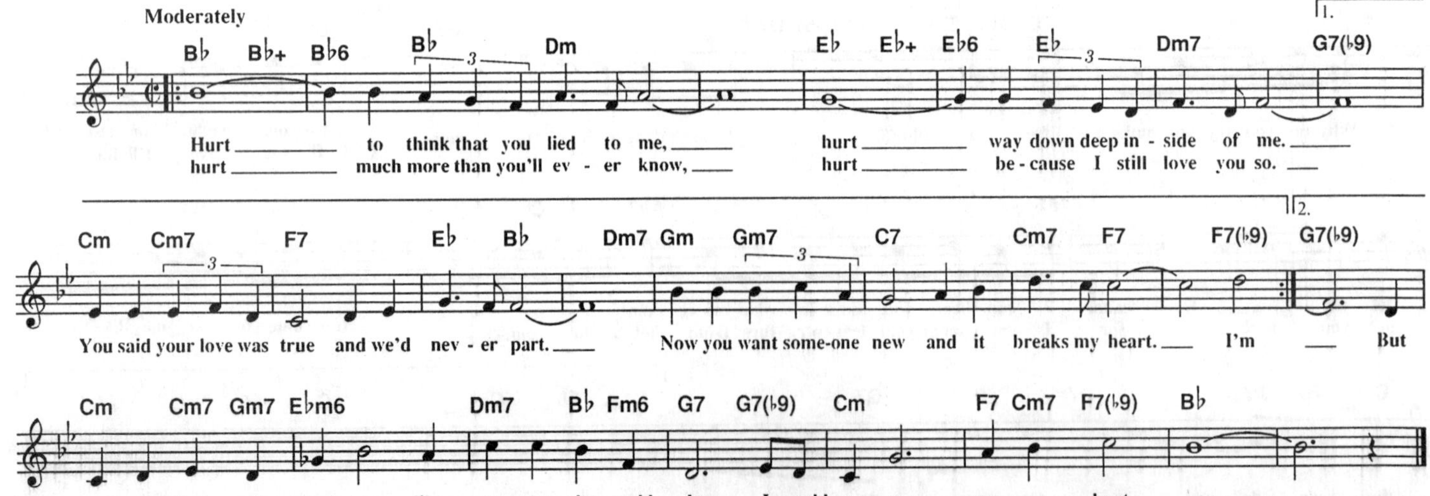
Moderately
B♭ B♭+ B♭6 B♭ Dm E♭ E♭+ E♭6 E♭ Dm7 G7(♭9)
1.
Hurt to think that you lied to me, hurt way down deep in-side of me.
hurt much more than you'll ev-er know, hurt be-cause I still love you so.
Cm Cm7 F7 E♭ B♭ Dm7 Gm Gm7 C7 Cm7 F7 F7(♭9) G7(♭9)
2.
You said your love was true and we'd nev-er part. Now you want some-one new and it breaks my heart. I'm But
Cm Cm7 Gm7 E♭m6 Dm7 B♭ Fm6 G7 G7(♭9) Cm F7 Cm7 F7(♭9) B♭
e-ven tho' you've hurt me like no one else could do, I would nev-er, nev-er hurt you.

THE HOUSE OF THE RISING SUN

Words and Music by
ALAN PRICE

Slow rock

Am C D F Am E7 Am E7 Am C D F Am C

1. There is a house in New Or-leans they call the ris - ing

E7 Am C D F Am E7 Am C D F Am E7 Am E7

sun. It's been the ru-in of man-y a poor boy, and God, I know I'm one. 2. My

Am C D F Am C E7 Am C

moth - er was a tail - or. She sewed my new blue jeans. My fa - ther was a
on - ly thing a gam-bler needs is a suit - case and a trunk. The on - ly time he'll
moth - er tell your chil - dren not to do what I have done; spend your lives in

D F Am E7 Am C D F Am E7 1.2. Am E7 3. Am

gam - bling man down in New Or - leans.
be sat - isfied is when he's on a drunk.
sin and mis - ery in the house of the ris - ing sun.

3. Now the
4. Oh

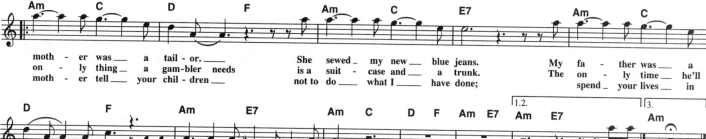

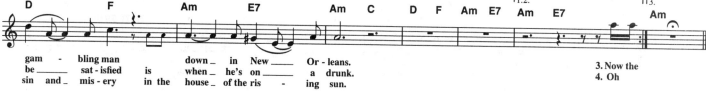

HOW LITTLE WE KNOW

Words by JOHNNY MERCER
Music by HOAGY CARMICHAEL

Beguine tempo
A♭maj7 A♭6 A♭maj7 A♭6 Adim B♭m7
May-be it hap - pens this way, may-be we real - ly be - long to - geth - er, but af - ter all,
May-be it's just for a day, love is as change - a - ble as the weath-er and af - ter all,
May-be you're meant to be mine, may-be I'm on - ly sup - posed to stay in your arms a - while,
E♭7 B♭m7 1. B♭dim E7(♭9) 2.3. B♭dim E♭7(♭9) A♭maj7 E♭dim A♭6 E♭7(♭9)
how lit - tle we know. Who knows why an A - pril breeze nev - er re-mains?
how lit - tle we know. Is this what I've wait - ed for? Am I the one?
as oth - ers have done.
To Coda
A♭maj7 Gm7 C7 Fmaj7 F♯dim F6 E♭m7 A♭7
Why stars in the trees hide when it rains? Love comes a - long, cast-ing a spell,
D♭maj7 D♭7 D♭6 Fm6 B♭9 E♭7 D.C. al Coda
Will it sing you a song, will it say a fare - well? Who can tell!
Coda
B♭7 E♭7 A♭6 B♭m7 E♭7 E♭7(♭9) A♭6
Oh, I hope in my heart that it's so, in spite of how lit - tle we know.

HOW 'BOUT US

Words and Music by
DANA WALDEN

Slowly
Verse:
Bb
Cm7(b5)/Bb
Bkgrd.: (Ooh, ooh, ooh.)
1. Mm, short and sweet; no sense in drag-ging on
past our needs. Let's don't keep it hang-ing on; if the fire's out, we should both be gone.
Chorus:
Cm7/Bb
Some peo-ple are made for each oth - er; some peo-ple can love one an-oth-er for life; how 'bout us?
Some peo-ple can hold it to-geth - er, man - age through all kinds of weath-er; but can
we? (Ooh, ooh, ooh.) but can we?
D.S.
(How 'bout us, how 'bout us ba - by? How 'bout us, how 'bout us, ba - by? How 'bout us, how 'bout us, ba - by, ooh?)
To Next Strain
Repeat ad lib. and fade
how 'bout us?
Bridge:
Gm
Dm
Fm
Cm7/F
D.S.S.
Are we gon-na make it girl, or are we gon-na drift, and drift, and drift to-geth-er?

Verse 2:
Now don't you get me wrong,
'Cause I'm not trying now to end it all.
It's just that I have seen
Too many lover's hearts lose their dream.
(To Chorus:)

HOW YA GONNA KEEP 'EM DOWN ON THE FARM
(After They've Seen Paree)

Words by SAM M. LEWIS and JOE YOUNG
Music by WALTER DONALDSON

Moderately fast

Bb Bb/D F7/C F7 F+ Bb6

How 'ya gon - na keep 'em down on the farm, af - ter they've seen Pa - ree?

/D D♭dim7 F7/C B♭ D♭7 F/C C7/G G♯dim7 F/A C7/G C7
— How 'ya gon - na keep 'em a - way from Broad - way, jazz - in' a - roun', and
F7 B♭ Bdim F7/C F7 D7
paint-in' the town? How 'ya gon - na keep 'em, a - way from harm? That's a mys - ter - y.
B♭7 E♭ C7/G E♭m6/G♭
They'll nev - er want to see a rake or plow, and who the deuce can par - ley - vous a cow?
Im - ag - ine Reu - ben when he meets his pa; he'll kiss his cheek and hol - ler "oo - la - la!"
B♭/F /D D♭dim7 F7/C F7 Cm7 F7 1. B♭ F7 2. B♭ Cm7 F7 B♭
How 'ya gon - na keep 'em, down on the farm, af - ter they've seen Pa - ree? ree?
A HUNDRED POUNDS OF CLAY
Copyright © 1961 (Renewed) GIL MUSIC CORP.
All Rights Reserved
Words and Music by BOB ELGIN, LUTHER DIXON and KAY ROGERS
With a beat
B♭ Gm Cm7 F7 B♭
He took a hun - dred pounds of clay and then He said, "Hey! Lis - ten. I'm gon - na fix this world to - day
hun - dred pounds of clay he made my life worth liv - in'. And I will thank Him ev - 'ry day
Gm Cm7 F7 E♭ F7 E♭ F7
— be - cause I know what's miss - sin'!" Then He rolled His big sleeves up and a brand new world be - gan. He cre -
— for ev - 'ry kiss you're giv - in'. And I thank Him ev - 'ry night for the arms that hold me tight. And He
B♭ Gm Cm9 F7 1. B♭ Gm Cm7 F7
at - ed a wom - an and a lot of lov - in' for a man. With just a
did it all with just a hun - dred pounds of
2. B♭ E♭ B♭ D♭dim7 Cm7
clay. Yes, He did! Oh, yes, He did! Now, can't you just see Him walk - in' 'round and 'round pick - in' clay up
F7 B♭ Bdim7 Cm7 F7 E♭ F7
off the ground, know - in' just what He should do to make a liv - ing dream like you, He rolled His big sleeves up and a
E♭ F7 B♭ Gm Cm9 F7 B♭ E♭ B♭
brand new world be - gan. He cre - at - ed a wom - an and a lot of lov - in' for a man.

HUMORESQUE

ANTONIN DVOŘÁK

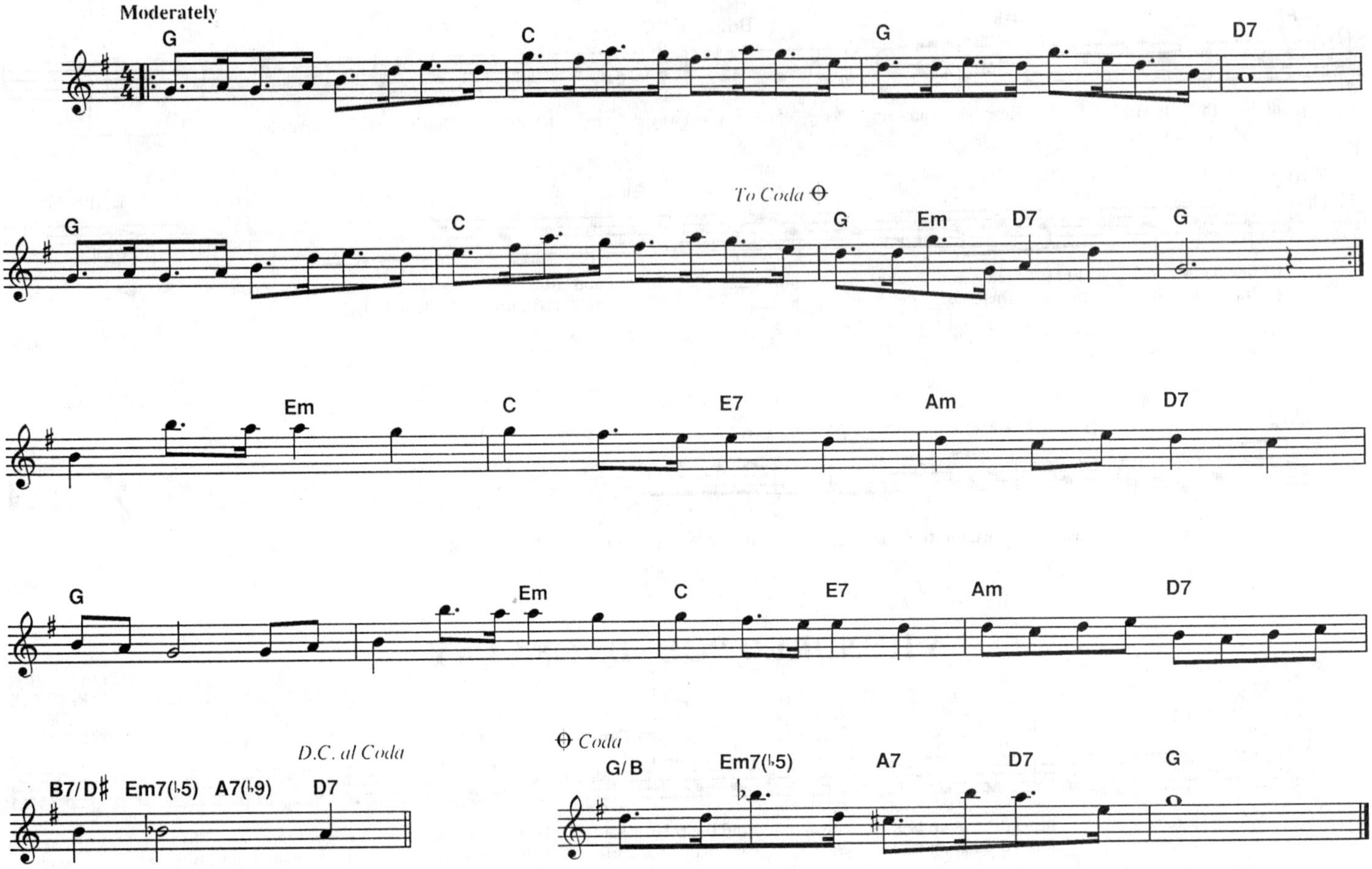

Moderately

G C G D7

To Coda 𝄌

G C G Em D7 G

Em C E7 Am D7

G Em C E7 Am D7

D.C. al Coda

B7/D♯ Em7(♭5) A7(♭9) D7

𝄌 *Coda*

G/B Em7(♭5) A7 D7 G

HUNGARIAN DANCE No. 5

JOHANNES BRAHMS

Brightly
Gm Cdim/G Gm Cm Gm D7 Gm
Cdim/G Gm E♭/G Dm/F Cm/E♭ B♭/D D7 Gm
G7 Cm F7 B♭ D7
rit.
E♭ Gm/B♭ D7 N.C. Gm Cm6/G Gm Cm6 D7 Gm
a tempo

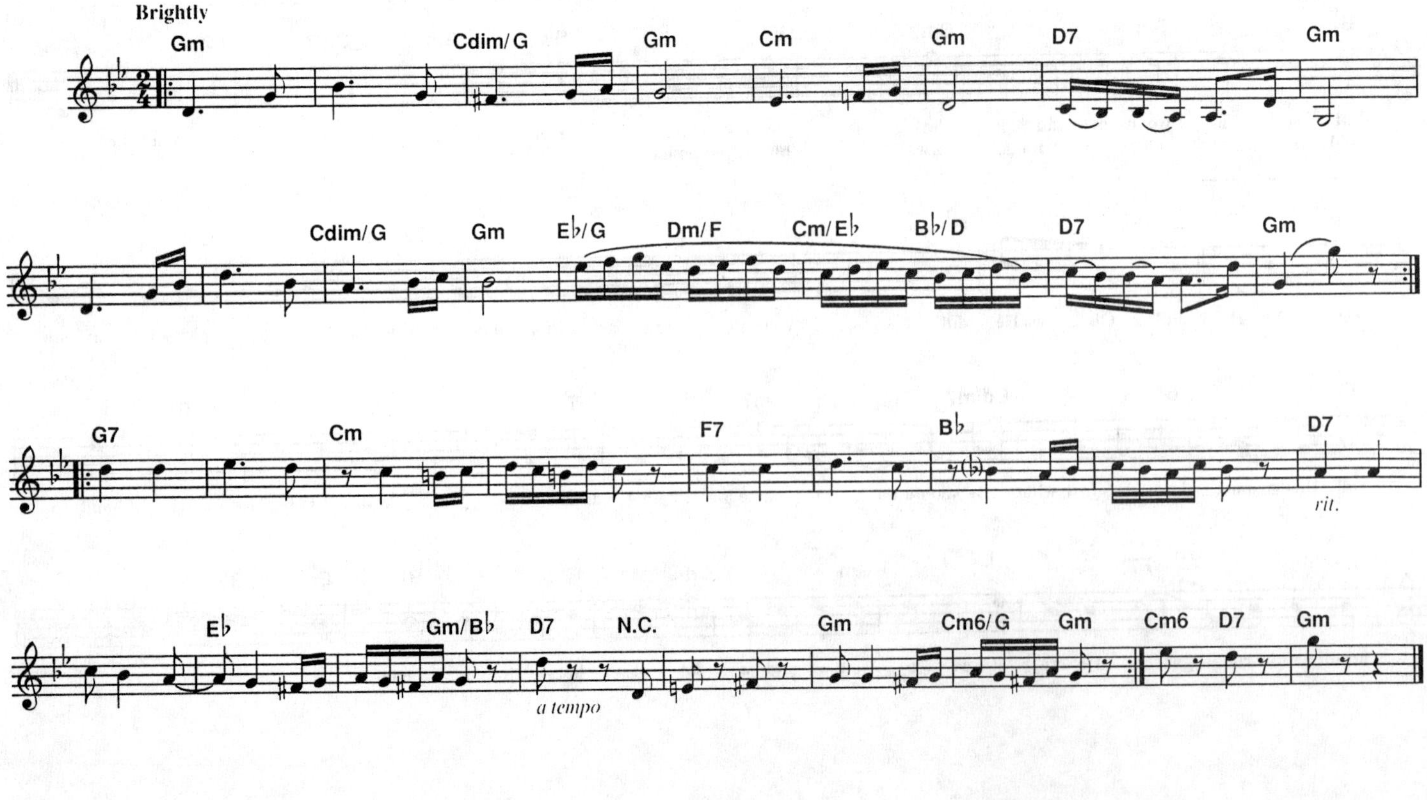

I AM WOMAN

Copyright © 1971 IRVING MUSIC, INC. and BUGGERLUGS MUSIC CO. (BMI)
All Rights Reserved
Words by HELEN REDDY
Music by RAY BURTON
Moderate rock
Verse 1:
1. I am wom-an, hear me roar_ in num-bers too big to ig-nore,_ and I know too much to go_ back to pre-tend._____ 'Cause I've
heard it all be-fore_ and I've been down there on the floor._ No one's ev-er gon-na keep_ me down a-gain. Oh,___
Chorus:
yes, I am wise,_ but it's wis-dom born of pain._____ Yes, I paid the price,_ but look how much_ I gained._ If I
To Coda
have to_ I can_do an-y-thing._ I am strong, I am in-vin-ci-ble,_ I am wom-an._
2. You can
3. I am
Verses 2 & 3:
bend but nev-er break_me, 'cause it on-ly serves to make_ me more de-ter-mined to a-chieve_my fi-nal goal._____ And I
wom-an, watch me grow___ see me stand-ing toe to toe_____ as I spread my lov-in' arms_ a-cross the land._____ But I'm
come back e-ven stron-ger, not a nov-ice an-y lon-ger, 'cause you've deep-ened the con-vic-tion in my soul. Oh,___
still an em-bry-o___ with a long, long way to go_____ un-til I make my broth-er un-der-
D.S. al Coda
stand. Oh,_____
Coda
wom-an!____ I am wom-an!____ I am wom-an!______
I GOT RHYTHM
© 1930 WB MUSIC CORP. (Renewed)
All Rights Reserved
Words by IRA GERSHWIN
Music by GEORGE GERSHWIN
Lively
To Coda
I___ got rhy-thm,_ I___ got mu-sic,_
I___ got dais-ies_ in___ green pas-tures,_
I___ got star-light,_ I___ got sweet dreams,_
I___ got my man_who could ask for an-y-thing
more? more? Old___ man trou-ble,_ I___ don't mind him,_ you___ won't
D.C. al Coda
find him_ 'round_ my door.
Coda
more, who could ask for an-y-thing more?

I CAN'T BELIEVE THAT YOU'RE IN LOVE WITH ME

Words and Music by
JIMMY McHUGH and
CLARENCE GASKILL

Moderately
C7(♯5) F6 Fm6 C D7 G7
Your eyes of blue, your kiss - es too, I nev - er knew what they could do. I can't be - lieve that

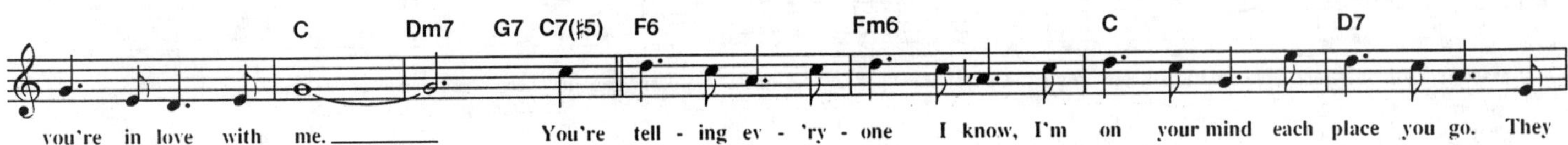
C Dm7 G7 C7(♯5) F6 Fm6 C D7
you're in love with me. You're tell - ing ev - 'ry - one I know, I'm on your mind each place you go. They

G7 C F9 C E7 E9 Em7 E7 A9
can't be - lieve that you're in love with me. I have al - ways placed you far a - bove

A7 D7 D9 Dm7 D7 G9 C7(♯5) F6 Fm6
me. I just can't i - mag - ine that you love me. And af - ter all is said and done, to

C D7 G7 C F9 C
think that I'm the luck - y one, I can't be - lieve that you're in love with me.

I CAN'T GIVE YOU ANYTHING BUT LOVE

Words by DOROTHY FIELDS
Music by JIMMY McHUGH

Moderately
G B♭dim Am7 D7 G Em7 A7 D7
I can't give you an - y - thing but love, ba - by. That's the on - ly thing I've plen - ty of, ba - by.

G7 C6/9 A7 D7 Am7 D7
Dream a-while, scheme a-while. We're sure to find, hap-pi-ness and I guess all those things you've al - ways pined for.

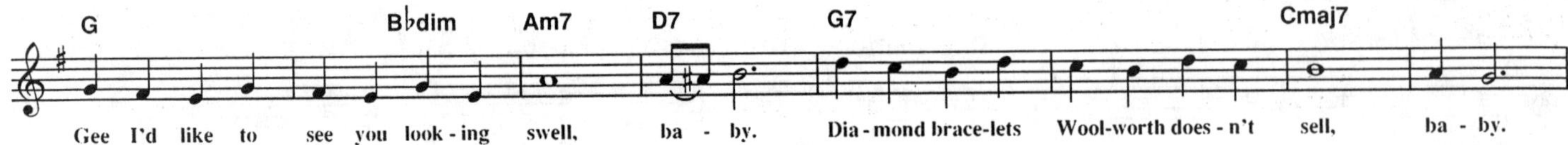
G B♭dim Am7 D7 G7 Cmaj7
Gee I'd like to see you look - ing swell, ba - by. Dia - mond brace-lets Wool-worth does - n't sell, ba - by.

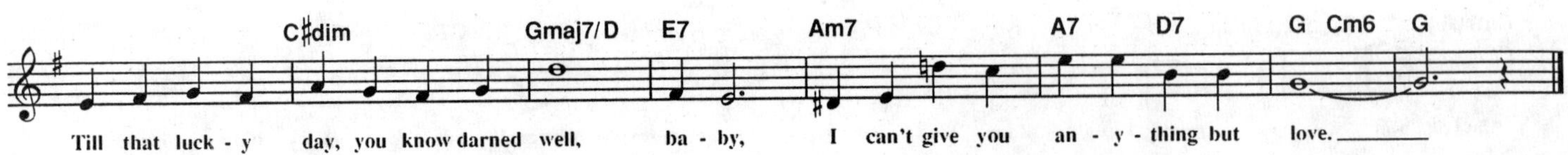
C♯dim Gmaj7/D E7 Am7 A7 D7 G Cm6 G
Till that luck - y day, you know darned well, ba - by, I can't give you an - y - thing but love.

I CAN'T HELP IT
(If I'm Still in Love with You)

Words and Music by
HANK WILLIAMS

Moderately

C7 F C7 F F7 B♭ F C7

To - day I passed you on the street and my heart fell at your feet. I can't help it if I'm

F C7 F C7 F F7 B♭ F

still in love with you. Some-bod - y else stood by your side and he looked so sat - is - fied. I can't

C7 F F7 B♭ F

help it if I'm still in love with you. { A pic - ture from the past came slow - ly steal - ing as I / It's hard to know an - oth - er's lips will kiss you and }

C7 F F7 B♭ F

brushed your arm and walked so close to you. Then sud - den - ly I got that old time feel - ing.
hold you just the way I used to do. Oh, heav - en on - ly knows how much I miss you.

C7 | 1. F C7 | 2. F C7 F

— I can't help it if I'm still in love with you. To - day I you.
— I can't help it if I'm still in love with

I CAN'T STOP LOVING YOU

Words and Music by
DON GIBSON

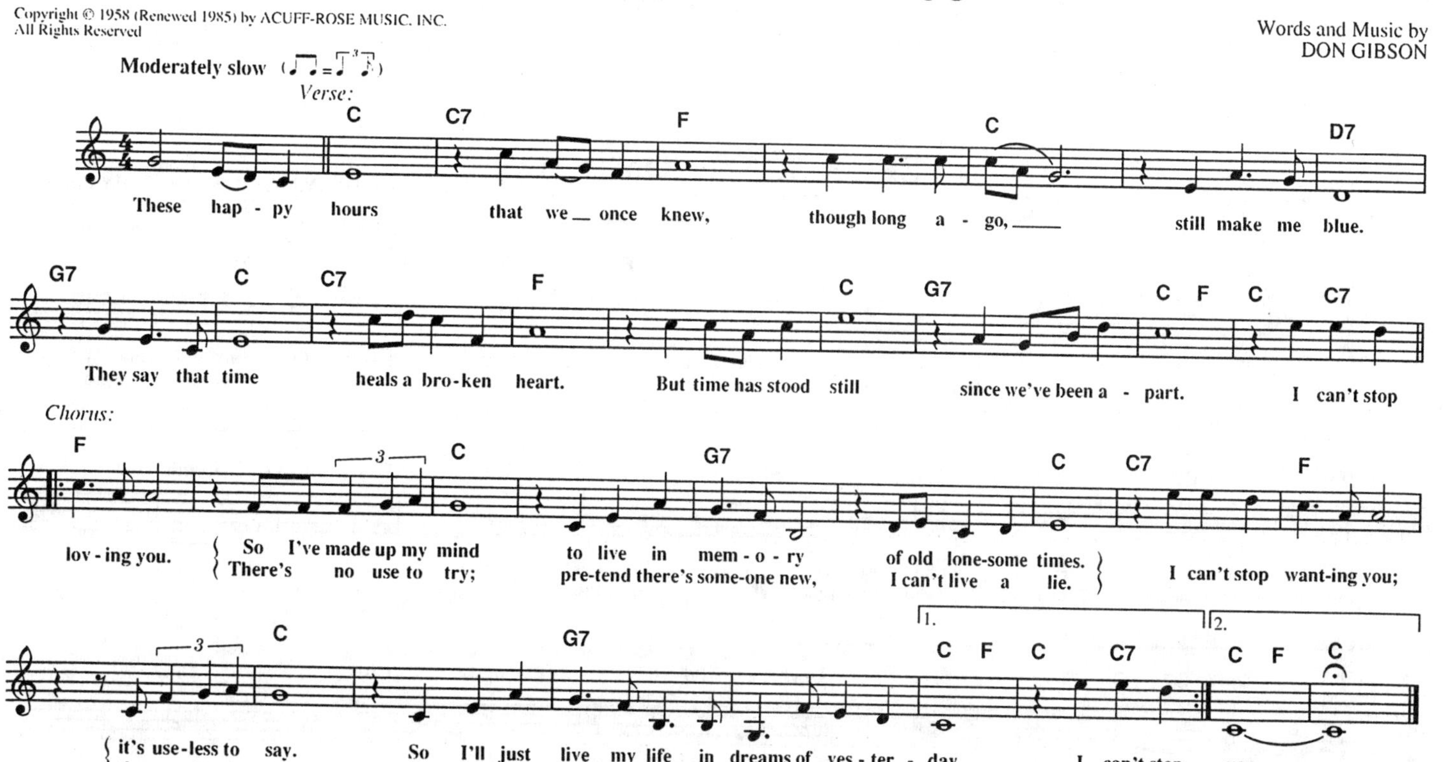
Moderately slow
Verse:
C C7 F C D7
These hap - py hours that we once knew, though long a - go, still make me blue.
G7 C C7 F C G7 C F C C7
They say that time heals a bro - ken heart. But time has stood still since we've been a - part. I can't stop
Chorus:
F C G7 C C7 F
lov - ing you. { So I've made up my mind to live in mem - o - ry of old lone-some times. / There's no use to try; pre-tend there's some-one new, I can't live a lie. } I can't stop want-ing you;
C G7 1. C F C C7 2. C F C
{ it's use-less to say. So I'll just live my life in dreams of yes - ter - day. / the way that I do. There's on - ly been one love for me, that one love is } I can't stop you.

From the 20th Century-Fox Technicolor Musical "THE DOLLY SISTERS"

I CAN'T BEGIN TO TELL YOU

Words by MACK GORDON
Music by JAMES V. MONACO
© 1945 WB MUSIC CORP. (Renewed)
All Rights Reserved
Broadly
I can't be - gin to tell you, how much you mean to me. My world will end if ev - er we were through.
I can't be - gin to tell you how hap - py I would be, if I could speak my mind like oth - ers do.
I make such pret - ty speech - es, when - ev - er we're a - part. But, when you're near, the words I choose re - fuse to leave my heart.
So, take the sweet - est phras - es the world has ev - er known, and make be - lieve I've said them all to you.
I you.
From the Walter Wanger Production "EVERY NIGHT AT EIGHT"
I FEEL A SONG COMIN' ON
Words and Music by
JIMMY McHUGH, DOROTHY FIELDS
and GEORGE OPPENHEIMER
Copyright © 1935 (Renewed 1953) EMI ROBBINS CATALOG INC.
All Rights Reserved
Brightly
I feel a song com - in', on, and I'm warn - ing ya, it's a vic - to - ri - ous, hap - py and glo - ri - ous new strain!
I feel a song com - in' on, it's a mel - o - dy full of the laugh - ter of chil - dren out af - ter the rain!
You'll hear a tune - ful sto - ry ring - in' thru ya! Love and glo -

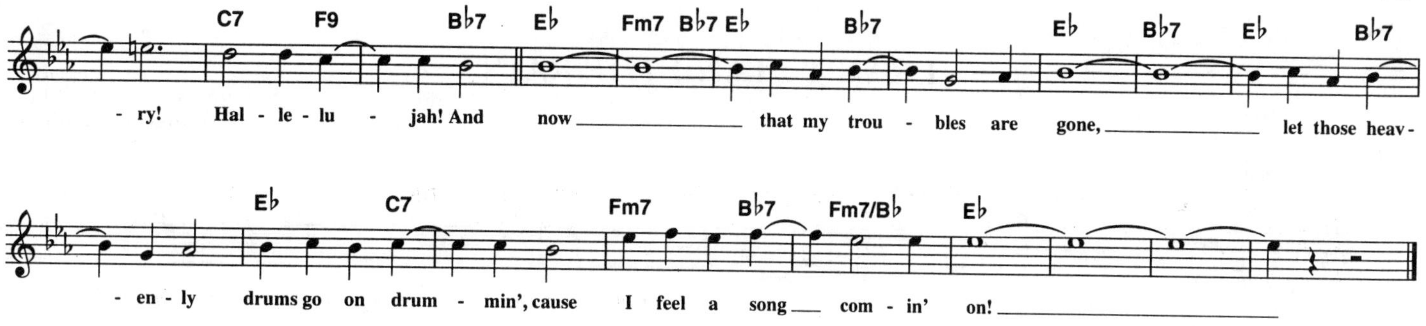

- ry! Hal - le - lu - jah! And now ___ that my trou - bles are gone, ___ let those heav -

- en - ly drums go on drum - min', cause I feel a song ___ com - in' on! ___

I CAN'T MAKE YOU LOVE ME

Lyrics and Music by
MIKE REID and ALLEN SHAMBLIN

Slowly

Verse:

1. Turn down the lights, _ turn down _ the bed, ___ turn down these voic - es in - side my head. _ Lay down with me, ___ tell me no _ lies. _ Just hold me close, ___ don't pa - tron-ize, ___ don't _ pa-tron - ize ___ me. _ 'Cause I can't

2. I'll close my eyes, _ then I ___ won't see ___ the love you don't feel ___ when you're hold - in' me. ___ Morn-in' will come ___ and I'll do what's _ right. _ Just give me till then ___ to give up this fight. _ And I will give up this fight. ___

To Next Strain

Chorus:

"Cause I can't make you love me _ if you _ don't. _ — I can't make your heart _ feel ___ some-thing it won't. _ Here in the dark ___ in these fi - nal hours, _ I will lay down my heart ___ and I'll feel _ the pow - er. ___ But you won't, no, _ you won't. 'Cause I can't make you love me ___ — if you don't.

D.S. 𝄋

poco rit.

I CAN'T STAND THE RAIN

Words and Music by
DON BRYANT, ANN PEEBLES
and BERNARD MILLER

Moderate disco

B♭

I can't stand the rain 'gainst my win - dow ho

bring-in' back sweet mem-o-ries. I can't stand the

B♭ E♭

rain a-gainst my win-dow ho be-cause he's not here with
rain a-gainst my win-dow ho bring-in' back sweet mem - o -

B♭ E♭ B♭

me. Hey, win-dow pane, do you re-mem - ber how sweet it used to be?
ries. I can't stand the rain 'gainst my win-dow 'cause he's not here with me.

A♭ B♭ D♭

When we were to - geth-er huh huh ev - 'ry-thing was so grand. Yes it was. Now that we've part -
Woah emp-ty pil-low huh huh where his head used to lay. Yeah. I know you've

C7 *To Coda* 1. F7 2. F7

- ed, and there's one sound that I just can't stand, I can't stand the nothin' to say hey hey.
got some sweet mem-o-ries but like a win-dow, you ain't got

B♭ A♭ B♭ D♭ B♭ *Play 3 times*

D.S. al Coda *Coda* F7 B♭

I can't stand the no-thin' to say hey hey.

Repeat and fade

I can't stand the rain. I can't, I can't, I can't, can't stand the rain.

I FOUGHT THE LAW

Words and Music by
SONNY CURTIS

Moderately bright

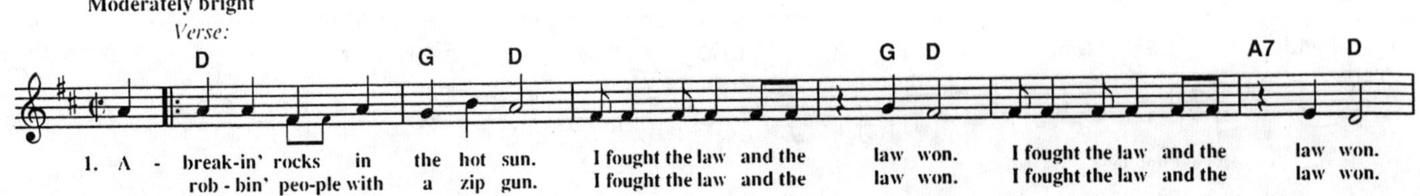
Verse:
D G D G D A7 D
1. A - break-in' rocks in the hot sun. I fought the law and the law won. I fought the law and the law won.
rob - bin' peo-ple with a zip gun. I fought the law and the law won. I fought the law and the law won.

A7 D G D G D A7 D
I miss my ba - by and the good fun. I fought the law and the law won. I fought the law and the law won.
I need-ed mon-ey 'cause I had none. I fought the law and the law won. I fought the law and the law won.
Chorus:
A7 D G D D7 G
I left my ba-by and I feel so bad. I guess my race is run. She's the best girl I've ev - er had.
D G D A7 D 1. A7 D A7 2. A7 D
I fought the law and the law won. I fought the law and the law won.
3 3
2. A -

(Last Night) I DIDN'T GET TO SLEEP AT ALL

Words and Music by
TONY MACAULAY

Moderately

Ab Fm7 Cm7
1. Oh, last night I did - n't get to sleep at all, no, no.
last night I got to think - ing may - be I, I, I
last night I did - n't get to sleep at all, no, no.

Fm Cm7 Dbmaj7 *To Coda*
I lay a - wake and watched un - til the morn - ing light washed a - way the dark - ness of the
should call you up and just for - get my fool - ish pride. I heard your num - ber ring - ing, I went
The sleep - ing pill I took was just a waste of time. I could - n't close my eyes 'cause you were

1. Eb7 Bbm7/Eb Eb7 2. Eb7 Fm Dbmaj7 Eb7 Ab
lone - ly night. 2. Oh, cold in - side, so last night I did - n't get to sleep at all.

Cm7 Fm7 Db Eb7 Ab
I know it's not my fault, I did my best. God knows this heart of mine could use a rest. But more and more I

Cm7 Fm7 Gbmaj7 Bbm7/Eb Eb7 *D.S. al Coda*
find the dreams I left be - hind are some - how too real to re - place. 3. Oh,

Coda

Eb7 Fm Dbmaj7
on my mind, and last night I did - n't get to sleep, did - n't get to sleep, no, I

Bbm7 Eb7 Ab Bbm7 Eb7 Ab
did - n't get to sleep at all. Did - n't get to sleep at all.

(EVERYTHING I DO) I DO IT FOR YOU

Lyrics and Music by
BRYAN ADAMS, R.J. LANGE
and M. KAMEN

Slowly
C G/C F/C Gsus G C
Verse 1:
1. Look in - to my eyes;
G/C F/C G/C C G/C
you will see what you mean to me. Search your heart, search your soul. And when you
F/C F C/G G Dm C Dm C Dm C
find me there, you'll search no more. Don't tell me it's not worth try - in' for. You can't tell me it's not worth dy - in'
Dm C/G Gsus C
Verse 2:
for. You know it's true, ev-'ry-thing I do, I do it for you. 2. Look in-to your heart;
G/C F Gsus C G/C
you will find there's noth - ing there to hide. Take me as I am, take my life. I would
F C G Dm C Dm Dm C
give it all, I would sac - ri - fice. Don't tell me it's not worth fight-ing for. I can't help it, there's noth-ing I want
Dm C G C Csus C B♭
more. You know it's true, ev-'ry-thing I do, I do it for you. There's no love like
E♭ B♭ F C G
your love, and no oth - er could give more love. There's no - where un-less you're there all the
D G F C Csus
time, all the way, yeah. (Inst. solo ad lib...
1. C 2. C Dm G Dm
...end solo) Oh, you can't tell me it's not worth try - ing for. I can't help it, there's noth-ing I want
G C G F Fm
more. Yeah, I would fight for you. I'd lie for you, walk the wire for you, yeah, I'd die for you.
C Gsus G F Dm C
You know it's true, ev-'ry-thing I do, oh, rit. I do it for you.

I DON'T HAVE THE HEART

Words and Music by
JUD FRIEDMAN and
ALLAN RICH

Moderate rock

N.C. G(2) A(2)/C♯ D G(2) A(2)/C♯ *Verse:* 𝄋 D(2)

1. Your face is
2. In - side I'm

A/C♯ G/B D/A A/G G(2) D/F♯ B♭maj9 Em7(♭5)/A

beam - ing. You say it's 'cause you're dream - ing of how good it's go - ing to be.
dy - ing to see you cry - ing. How can I make you un - der - stand?

D(2) A/C♯ G/B D/A A/G G(2)

You say you've been a - round, and now you've fi - nal - ly found
I care a - bout you, so much a - bout you.

Em7 D(2)/F♯ E7/G♯ Asus A/C♯ D A/C♯ Bm F♯m/A

ev - 'ry - thing you've want - ed and need - ed in me. I
I'm try - to say this as gent - ly as I can 'cause I } don't have the

𝄋𝄋 *Chorus:*

G(2) A(2)/C♯ G/B A/C♯ D A/C♯ Bm F♯m/A G(2) *To Coda* 𝄌

heart to hurt you, it's the last thing I want to do. But I don't have the heart to love

A(2)/C♯ G(2)/B G 1. D(2) Gm/B♭ A7sus A7 *D.S.* 𝄋

you not the way you want me to.

2. D(2) Em7 *Bridge:* F♯7sus F♯7 F♯7sus F♯7 Bm7

You're so trust - ing and o - pen, hop - ing that love will start.

Em7(♭5)/B♭ D/A A7sus A7 D/A A7sus A7 D A/C♯ Bm F♯m/A *D.S.S.* 𝄋𝄋 *al Coda*

But I don't have the heart. I don't have the heart. I don't have the

𝄌 *Coda*

A(2)/C♯ G/B A/C♯ D E B/D♯ C♯m G♯m/B

you, not the way that you want me too. I don't have the

Amaj7 B(2)/D♯ A(2)/C♯ B(2)/D♯ E *Repeat ad lib. and fade* B/D♯ C♯m G♯m/B

heart. I don't have the

(If Loving You Is Wrong)

I DON'T WANT TO BE RIGHT

Words and Music by
HOMER BANKS, RAYMOND JACKSON
and CARL HAMPTON

Moderately slow
Em G/D Cmaj7
If lov - in' you is wrong, I don't want to be right. If be - ing right means be - ing with - out you, I'd
Am I wrong to fall so deep-ly in love with you? Know-ing I got a wife and two little chil-dren de -
Am7 Bm7 C Bm7 Em Em/D
rath - er live a wrong-do - ing life. Your ma-ma and dad - dy say it's a shame, it's a down - right dis - grace. But
pend - ing on me, too; but am I wrong to hun - ger for the gen - tle-ness of your touch, know -
Cmaj7 Am7 Bm7 C Bm7 Am7
long as I got you by my side, I don't care what your peo-ple say. Your friends tell you it's no fu-ture in
ing I got some-one else at home who needs me just as much? And are you wrong to give your love
Em Am7 Em
lov - ing a mar - ried man. If I can't see you when I want to, I'll see you when I can. If
to a mar - ried man? And am I wrong for try'in to hold on to the best thing I ev - er had?
Chorus:
Cmaj7 Em Cmaj7 1. Em7 D.S.
lov - in you is wrong, I don't want to be right. If lov - in' you is wrong, I don't want to be right.
2. Em Em Cmaj7 Repeat ad lib. and fade
want to be right. I don't want to be right if it means be - ing with - out you.

I DON'T WANT TO WALK WITHOUT YOU

Words by FRANK LOESSER
Music by JULE STYNE

Moderately

Fm Fm7 B♭7 F7 B♭7 E♭ E♭maj7 E♭6 E♭
I don't want to walk with - out you, ba - by, walk with-out my arm a - bout you,

B♭m C7 F7 Fm7 B♭7 E♭ E♭+ Cm E♭7 Gm C♯dim D7
ba - by. I thought the day you left me be - hind, I'd take a stroll and get you right

Gm D7 Gm6 Adim B♭7 Adim B♭7 Edim7 Fm Fm7 B♭7 F7 B♭7
off my mind, but now I find that I don't want to walk with - out the sun - shine.

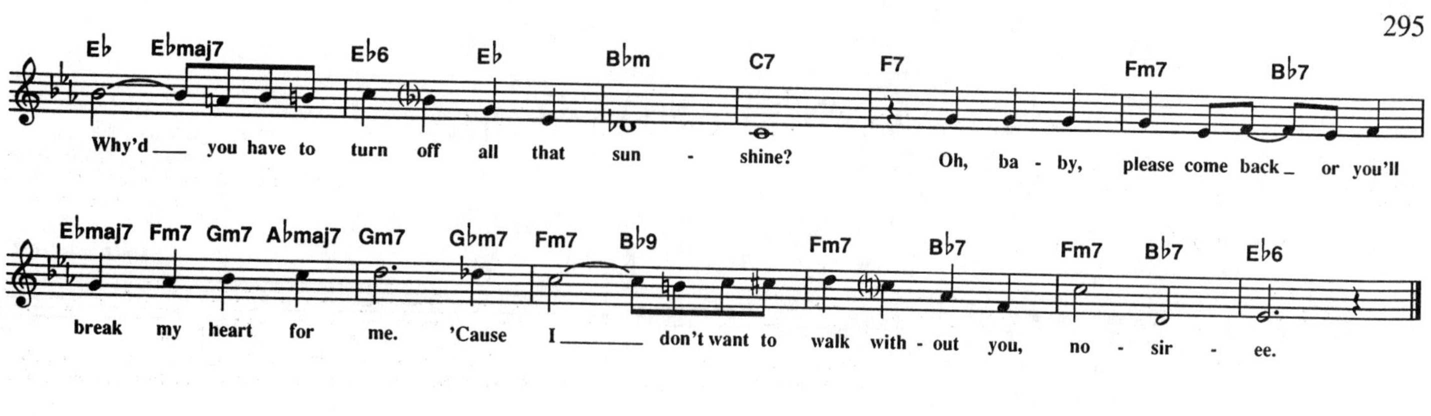
Eb Ebmaj7 Eb6 Eb Bbm C7 F7 Fm7 Bb7
Why'd you have to turn off all that sun - shine? Oh, ba - by, please come back or you'll
Ebmaj7 Fm7 Gm7 Abmaj7 Gm7 Gbm7 Fm7 Bb9 Fm7 Bb7 Fm7 Bb7 Eb6
break my heart for me. 'Cause I don't want to walk with - out you, no - sir - ee.

Performed in the R.K.O. Motion Picture "LAS VEGAS STORY"

I GET ALONG WITHOUT YOU VERY WELL

(Except Sometimes)

Words and Music by
HOAGY CARMICHAEL

Moderately slow

Bb Cm7 F7 Bb Dbdim7 Cm7 F7 Cm7
I get a-long with - out you ver - y well, of course I do, ex - cept when soft rains fall

F7 Cm7 F7 Cm7 F7 Bb Dbdim7 Cm7
and drip from leaves. Then I re - call the thrill of be - ing shel-tered in your arms, of course I do.

F7 Cm7 F7 Bb Cm7 F7 Bb Cm7 F7 Bb
But I get a - long with - out you ver - y well. I've for - got - ten you just like I should,

Dbdim7 Cm7 F7 Cm7 F7 Cm7 F7 Cm7
of course I have, ex - cept to hear your name or some-one's laugh that is the same, but I've for - got - ten

Bridge:

F7 Bb Bb7 Eb Bb Cm7
you just like I should. What a guy! What a fool am I to think my break-ing heart

F7 Bb Bb7 Eb Eb7 D7 Gm Gm7
could kid the moon. What's in store? Should I phone once more? No, it's best that I

C9 Cm7 F9 Bb Cm7 F7 Bb Dbdim7 Cm7 F7
stick to my tune. I get a-long with - out you ver - y well, of course I do, ex - cept per -

Cm7 F7 Cm7 F7 Cm7 F7 Bb
haps in spring, but I should nev - er think of spring, for that would sure - ly break my heart in two.

I DON'T WANNA CRY

Words and Music by
MARIAH CAREY and
NARADA MICHAEL WALDEN

Slowly
Verse:
F♯m Bm F♯m/A B5/G♯ F♯m Bm F♯m/A B5/G♯
1. Once a-gain we sit in si - lence after all is said and done.
F♯m Bm F♯m/A B5/G♯ F♯m Bm F♯m/A B5/G♯
On-ly emp-ti-ness in-side us; ba-by, look what we've be-come.
E Bm A E
We can make a mil-lion prom-is-es, but we still won't change. It is-n't right to stay to-geth - er when you
Bm7/E
Chorus:
A E/G♯
on-ly bring each oth - er pain. I don't wan-na cry, don't wan-na cry.
G Bm/F♯ F♯7/A♯ Bm A/C♯
Noth-ing in the world could take us back to where we used to be. Though I've giv - en you my heart and soul,
D E F♯m Bm A/C♯ Dmaj9
(giv-en you my heart and soul,) I must find a way of let - ting go, 'cause ba - by, I don't wan-na
F♯m Bm F♯m7/A B5/G♯ F♯m
1. Bm F♯m/C♯ C♯7sus D.C. 2. Bm F♯m/C♯ C♯7sus
cry.
Bridge:
E Bm A/C♯ E
All the mag - ic's gone, there's just a sha-dow of a mem-o-ry. Some-thing just went wrong. We can't go
Dmaj7/E E♭maj7/F F
Chorus:
B♭
on make-be-liev - ing, on make-be-liev - ing, 'Cause I don't wan-na cry,
F/A A♭ Cm/G G7/B
don't wan-na cry. Noth-ing in the world could take me back to where we used to be. Though I've giv-

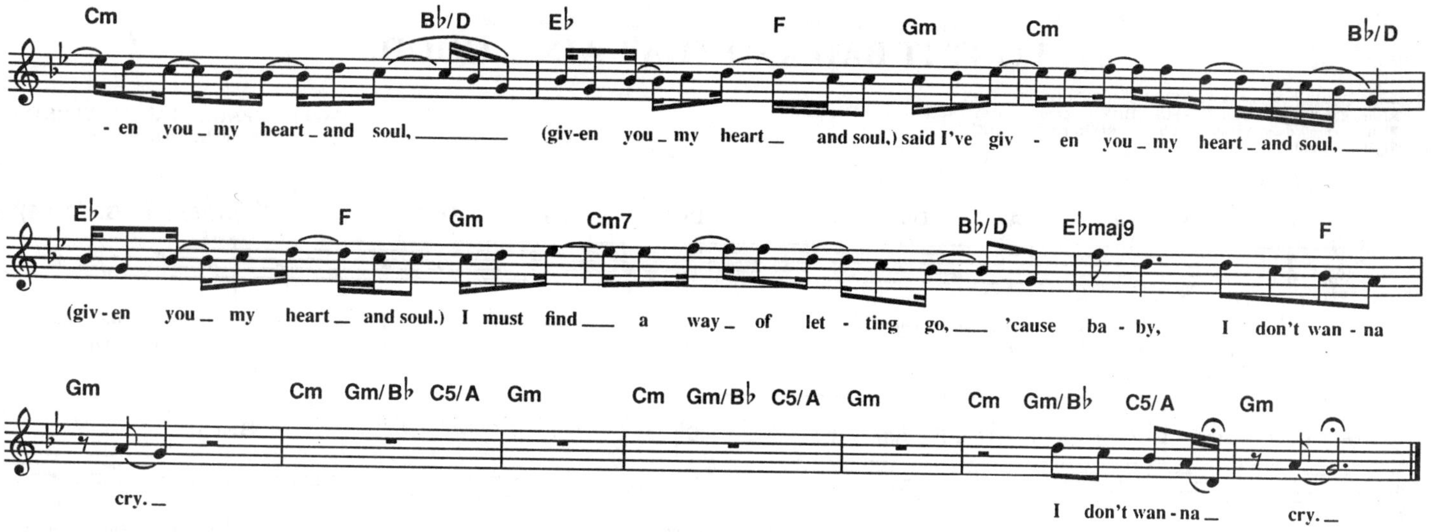

Cm Bb/D Eb F Gm Cm Bb/D

- en you _ my heart _ and soul, ___ (giv-en you _ my heart _ and soul,) said I've giv - en you _ my heart _ and soul, ___

Eb F Gm Cm7 Bb/D Ebmaj9 F

(giv - en you _ my heart _ and soul.) I must find ___ a way _ of let - ting go, ___ 'cause ba - by, I don't wan - na

Gm Cm Gm/Bb C5/A Gm Cm Gm/Bb C5/A Gm Cm Gm/Bb C5/A Gm

cry. _ I don't wan - na _ cry. _

Verse 2:
Too far apart to bridge the distance,
But something keeps us hanging on and on.
Pretending not to know the difference,
Denying what we had is gone.
Every moment we're together,
It's just breaking me down.
I know we swear it was forever,
But it hurts too much to stay around.
(To Chorus:)

I GET AROUND

Words and Music by
BRIAN WILSON

Bright rock

G E Am F D *

('Round, 'round, get a - round, I get a - round, _ yeah. Get a - round, 'round, 'round, I get a - round. _) I get a -

G E Am F

round ___ from town to town. _ I'm a real cool head; _ I'm mak - in' real good bread. ___

1.2. *To Next Strain* 3.4. *etc.* *Repeat and fade* *Verse:*

D D Am7 D Am D Am7 D

_ 1. I'm get - tin' ___ I get a - bugged driv - in' up and down the same old strip. _ I got - ta find a new place where the
2. We al - ways take my car _ 'cause it's nev - er been beat. _ And we've nev - er missed yet with the

Am7 D G Am7 D

kids are _ hip. _ My bud - dies and me _ are get - tin'
girls we _ meet. _ None of the guys go stead - y 'cause it

Am7 D Am7 D 3. Am7 D * *D.S.* 2. Am7 D *D.C.*

real well known. _ Yeah, the bad guys know us and they leave us a - lone. _ I get a - bt Sat - ur - day night. _
would - n't be fair ___ to leave your best girl home on a

*Chorus can be sung in falsetto

From the American Revue Theatre Production "JUMP FOR JOY"

I GOT IT BAD AND THAT AIN'T GOOD

Words by PAUL FRANCIS WEBSTER
Music by DUKE ELLINGTON

Slowly
Fdim F B♭/F F A7 Dm7 G9 Dm7 G9 Gm7 A7(♯5) D9 G7 C7(♭9)
Nev - er treats me sweet and gen - tle the way he should; I got it bad and that ain't
My poor heart is sen - ti - men - tal not made of wood; I got it bad and that ain't
1. F Dm7 Gm7 G♭7(♭5) 2. F B♭m6/F Fdim F7 B♭ B♭m6
good! good! But when the week-end's o - ver and Mon - day rolls a -
E/F F F6 Am7 D7 F♯dim Gm D♭7(♯5) C7 Fdim F B♭/F F
round, I end up like I start out just cry - in' my heart out. He don't love me
A7 Dm7 G9 Dm7 G9 Gm7 A7(♯5) D9 G7 C7(♭9) F B♭m/F F6
like I love him; no - bod - y could. I got it bad and that ain't good.

I HEAR YOU KNOCKING

Words and Music by
DAVE BARTHOLOMEW
and PEARL KING

Moderate rock shuffle
C C7 F7
You went a-way and left me long time a - go, and now you're knock-ing at my door. I hear you knock-ing,
bet-ter get back to your used to be, 'cause your kind of love aint good for me.

C F7 G7 C
but you can't come in. I hear you knock-ing; go back where you've been. I begged you not to go, but you
I told you way back in

C7 F7 C
said good-bye, and now you tell me all your lies. I hear you knock-ing, but you can't come in.
Fif - ty Two, that I would nev - er go with you.

F7 G7 1. D.S. 2. C F/C C G7 C
I hear you knock-ing; go back where you've been. 2. You

I GUESS I'LL HAVE TO CHANGE MY PLAN
© 1929 WARNER BROS. INC. (Renewed)
All Rights Reserved
Words by HOWARD DIETZ
Music by ARTHUR SCHWARTZ
Rather slow
I Guess I'll Have To Change My Plan, I should have re-alized there'd be an-oth-er man!
I o-ver-looked that point com-plete-ly Un-til the big af-fair be-gan;
Why did I buy those blue pa-ja-mas Be-fore the big af-fair be-gan?
Be-fore I knew where I was at, I found my-self up-on the shelf, and that was that I tried to reach the moon but when I got there, All that I could get was the air, My feet are back up-on the ground,
My boil-ing point is much too low, For me to try to be a fly Lo-tha-ri-o! I think I'll crawl right back and in-to my shell, Dwell-ing in my per-son-al Hell. I'll have to change my plan a-round,
I've lost the one girl I found. I found.
I HAVE BUT ONE HEART
('O MARENARIELLO)
© 1945 BARTON MUSIC CORP.
© 1973 JOHNNY FARROW, PAULINE SYMES PRIEST, DEBORAH LUCILLE SYMES, ELAINE SYMES
© Renewal Assigned 1966 to BARTON MUSIC CORP.
Renewal of Copyright Assigned 1974 to SANDS MUSIC CORP.
All Rights Reserved
Words by MARTY SYMES
Music by JOHNNY FARROW
Slowly
I Have But One Heart, this heart I bring you, I Have But One Heart to share with you. I have but one dream that I can cling to, You are the one dream I pray comes true. My dar-ling, un-til I saw you, I nev-er felt this way. And no-bod-y else be-fore you ev-er has heard me say: You are my one love, my life I live for you, I Have But One Heart to give to you.

From the Twentieth Century-Fox Motion Picture "THE LAST AMERICAN HERO"

I GOT A NAME

Words by NORMAN GIMBEL
Music by CHARLES FOX

Moderate

E♭ B♭/D Cm Cm7/B♭ A♭

1. Like the pine trees lin-ing the wind-ing road, I've got a name;
2. Like the north wind whis-tl-in' down the sky, I've got a song;
3. Like the fool I am and I'll al-ways be, I've got a dream;

B♭ E♭ B♭ Cm

I've got a name. Like the sing-ing bird and the croak-ing toad,
I've got a song. Like the whip-poor-will and the ba-by's cry,
I've got a dream. They can change their minds but they can't change me,

F7 B♭ Gm A♭ B♭7

I've got a name; I've got a name, and I car-ry it with me like my
I've got a song; I've got a song, and I car-ry it with me and I
I've got a dream; I've got a dream. Oh, I know I could share it if you'd

E♭ G Cm F7 B♭

dad-dy did, but I'm liv-ing the dream that he kept hid.
sing it loud; if it gets me no-where, I'll go there proud.
want me to; if you're go-in' my way, I'll go with you.

Gm A♭ Gm C7 A♭ B♭

Mov-in' me down the high-way, roll-in' me down the high-way, mov-in' a-head so life won't pass me by.

E♭ 1. 2.3. *Fine* E♭ *D.S. al Fine*

And I'm gon-na go there free.

I HONESTLY LOVE YOU

Words and Music by
PETER ALLEN and
JEFF BARRY

Slowly

Verse:

B♭ F/B♭ A♭/B♭ E♭

May-be I hang a-round here a lit-tle more than I should. We both know I got some-where else to go, but
You don't have to an-swer, I see it in your eyes. May-be it was bet-ter left un-said, but
If we both were born in an-oth-er place and time this mo-ment might be end-ing with a kiss, but

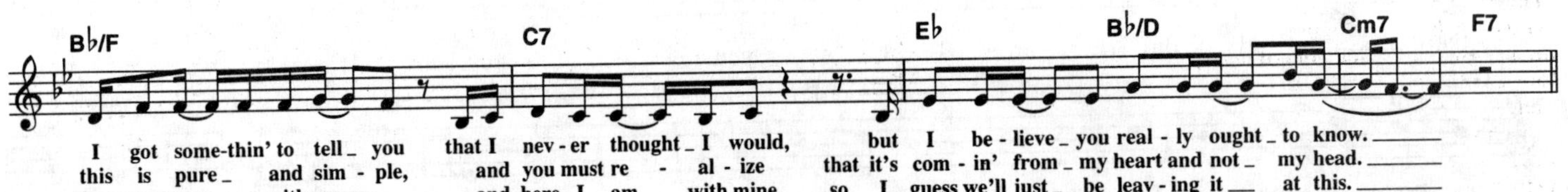
B♭/F
C7
E♭
B♭/D
Cm7
F7
I got some-thin' to tell you that I nev-er thought I would, but I be-lieve you real-ly ought to know.
this is pure and sim-ple, and you must re-al-ize that it's com-in' from my heart and not my head.
there you are with yours and here I am with mine, so I guess we'll just be leav-ing it at this.

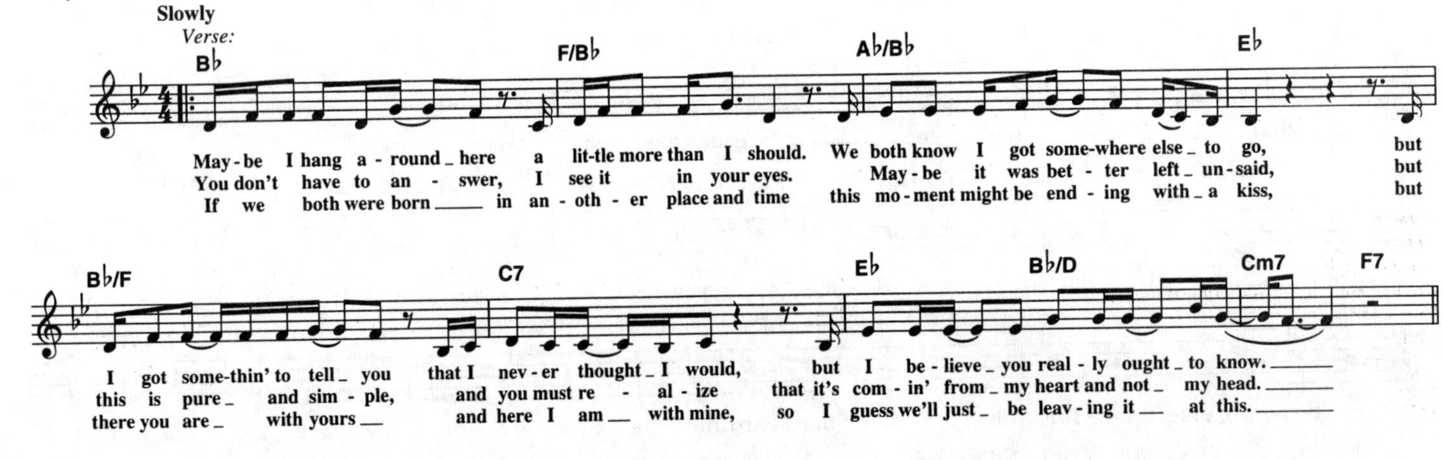

Chorus:
To Coda
I love you, I hon-est-ly love you. you.
I'm not tryin' to make you feel un-comf't-a-ble; I'm not tryin' to make you an-y-thing at all. But this
feel-ing does-n't come a-long ev'ry day, and you should-n't blow the chance when you got the chance to say, I love you.
D.C. al Coda
Coda
Spoken: I love you. I hon-est-ly love you. you. I hon-est-ly love you.
I KNEW YOU WHEN
Copyright © 1964 (Renewed 1992) by LOWERY MUSIC CO., INC.
All Rights Reserved
Words and Music by
JOE SOUTH
Moderately
(add bass)
Chorus:
Yeah! Yeah! Yeah! Yeah! Yeah! Yeah! Yeah! Yeah! I knew you when you were lone-ly. I knew you when you were
To Coda
Verse:
on-ly a boy all a-lone with-out love; I knew you when. 1. I knew you when you were sad and all a-lone. You did-n't have an-y-one
that you could call your own. I knew you when your heart be-longed to on-ly me, but that was man-y years a-go;
D.S.
D.S. al Coda
now your love is just a mem-o-ry. Yeah! Yeah! Yeah! Yeah! be-fore you came up in the world. Yeah! Yeah! Yeah! Yeah!
Verse 2:
I knew you when
We used to have a lot of fun,
But someone came and offered more;
Now I'm the lonely one.
I knew you when
I was just scared little girl.
I used to be your only love
Before you came up in the world.
(To Chorus:)
Coda
Repeat ad lib. and fade
love. Ah, ah. Ah,

I HEARD THE BELLS ON CHRISTMAS DAY

(Popular)

Words by HENRY WADSWORTH LONGFELLOW
Adapted by JOHNNY MARKS
Music by JOHNNY MARKS

Moderately slow
F F+ B♭/F C7/F Dm E7 Am Gm C7
I heard the bells on Christ-mas day. Their old fa - mil - iar car - ols play. And wild and sweet the
in des-pair, I bowed my head. "There is no peace on earth," I said. "For hate is strong, and

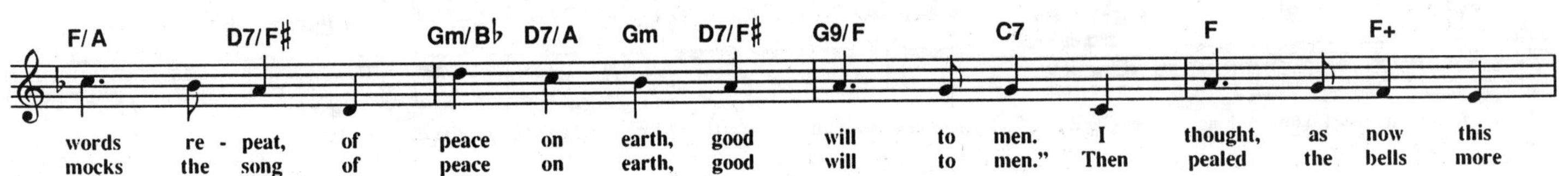
F/A D7/F♯ Gm/B♭ D7/A Gm D7/F♯ G9/F C7 F F+
words re - peat, of peace on earth, good will to men. I thought, as now this
mocks the song of peace on earth, good will to men." Then pealed the bells more

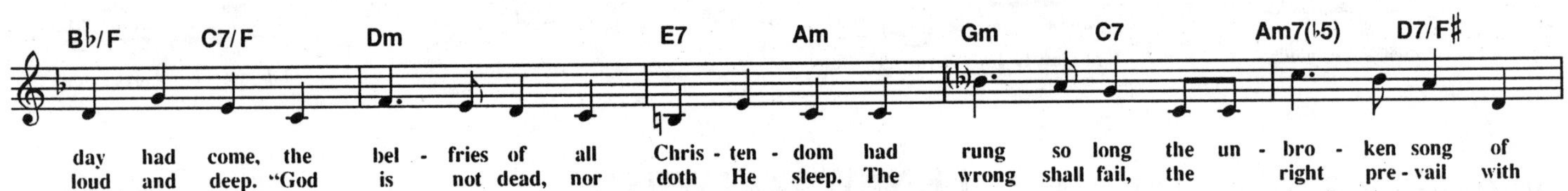
B♭/F C7/F Dm E7 Am Gm C7 Am7(♭5) D7/F♯
day had come, the bel - fries of all Chris - ten - dom had rung so long the un - bro - ken song of
loud and deep. "God is not dead, nor doth He sleep. The wrong shall fail, the right pre - vail with

1. 2.
Gm D7/A Gm/B♭ Bm7(♭5) Gm7/C C7 F Gm D7/A Gm/B♭ Bm7(♭5) Gm7/C C7 F
rit.
peace on earth, good will to men. And peace on earth, good will to men."

I HEARD THE BELLS ON CHRISTMAS DAY

(Traditional)

Words by HENRY WADSWORTH LONGFELLOW
Music by HENRY BISHOP

Moderately
E♭ E♭dim7 E♭ Edim7 B♭7/F Edim7 B♭7/F F♯dim7 E♭/G B♭7/A♭ E♭/G
1. I heard the bells on Christ - mas day. Their old fa - mil - iar car - ols play. And
thought how, as the day had come, the bel - fries of all Christ - en - dom had

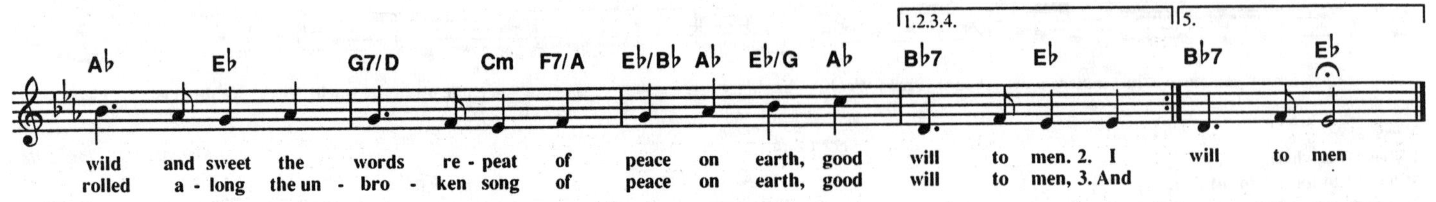
1.2.3.4. 5.
A♭ E♭ G7/D Cm F7/A E♭/B♭ A♭ E♭/G A♭ B♭7 E♭ B♭7 E♭
wild and sweet the words re - peat of peace on earth, good will to men. 2. I will to men
rolled a - long the un - bro - ken song of peace on earth, good will to men, 3. And

Verse 3:
And in despair I bowed my head:
"There is no peace on earth," I said,
"For hate is strong and mocks the song
Of peace on earth, good will to men."

Verse 4:
Then pealed the bells more loud and deep:
"God is not dead, nor doth He sleep;
The wrong shall fail, the right prevail,
With peace on earth, good will to men."

Verse 5:
Till, ringing, singing on its way,
The world revolv'd from night to day.
A voice, a chime, a chant sublime,
Of peace on earth, good will to men!

('TIL) I KISSED YOU

By DON EVERLY

Moderately

F Dm F Dm F Dm
1. Nev - er felt like this__ un - til I kissed you. How did I ex - ist__ un - til I
2. Things have real - ly changed_ since I kissed you. My life's not the same_ now that I

F Dm F C7
kissed you? Nev - er had you on my mind;__ now__ you're there all the time.__
kissed you. Mmm,_ you got a way a - bout_ you; now__ I can't live with-out you.

F Dm F Dm 1. F Dm
Nev - er knew what I missed un - til I kissed you. Uh huh, I kissed you, oh yeah.

2. F Dm F Dm
kissed you, oh yeah. You don't re - a - lize_ what you do to me.__ And I did-n't re - a - lize_ what a

F C7 F
kiss could be.__ Mmm,_ you got a way a - bout_ you; now__ I can't live with-out you. Nev - er

Dm F Dm F Dm F
knew what I missed un - til I kissed you. Uh huh, I kissed you, oh yeah, I kissed you.

I LOVE YOU

Lyric by HARLAN THOMPSON
Music by HARRY ARCHER

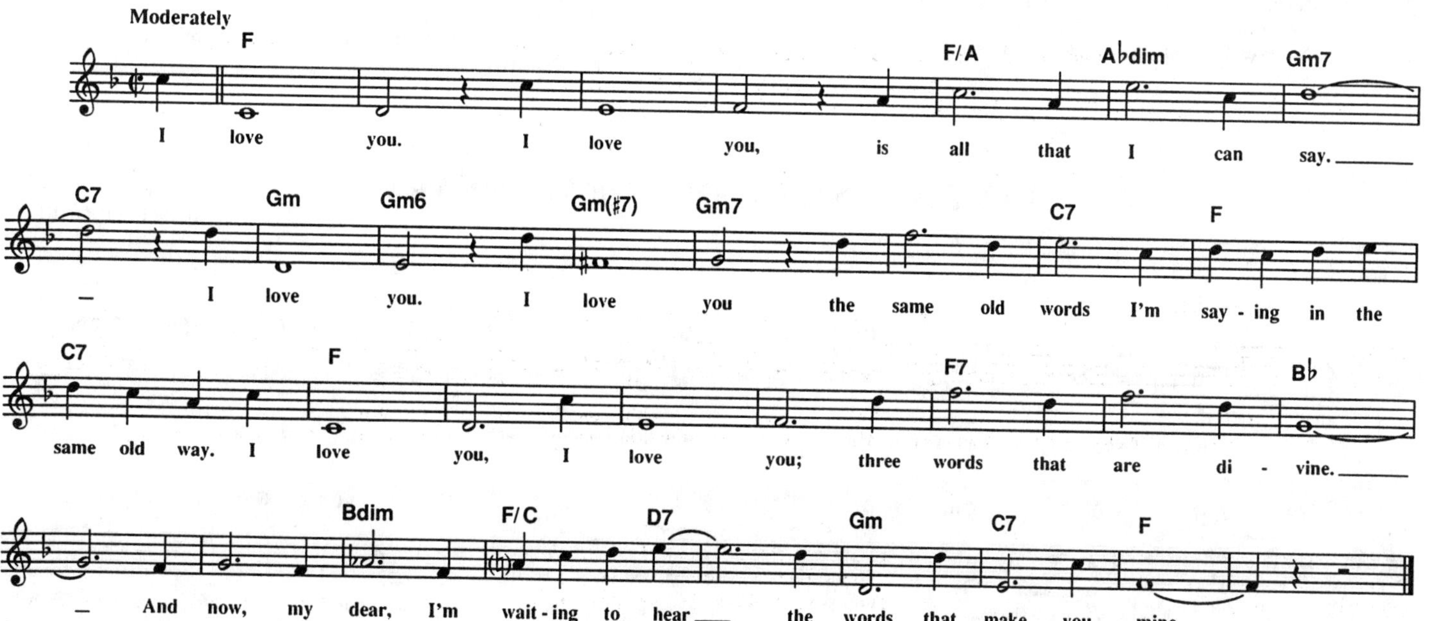
Moderately
F F/A A♭dim Gm7
I love you. I love you, is all that I can say.__
C7 Gm Gm6 Gm(♯7) Gm7 C7 F
I love you. I love you the same old words I'm say - ing in the
C7 F F7 B♭
same old way. I love you, I love you; three words that are di - vine.__
Bdim F/C D7 Gm C7 F
And now, my dear, I'm wait - ing to hear__ the words that make you mine.__

From the Motion Picture "THE WOMAN IN RED"

I JUST CALLED TO SAY I LOVE YOU

Words and Music by
STEVIE WONDER

Moderately *Verse:*

D

1. No New Year's Day to cel - e - brate; no choc-'late cov-ered can - dy hearts to give a - way.
rain; no flow - ers bloom; no wed - ding Sat - ur - day with-in the month of June.

Em Em(maj7) Em Em(maj7) Em7 Em(maj7) Em

No first of spring: no song to sing. In fact here's just an - oth - er or -
But what it is is some-thing true, made up of these three words that I

1.3. Em7/A A D — 2.4. Em7/A A D

- di - nar - y day. 2. No A - pril must say to you. I just called

Chorus:

Em7 A D Em A Bm7

to say I love you. I just called to say how much I care.

Em7 A Bm7 Em7 A7sus A7

I just called to say I love you. And I mean it from the bot - tom of my

1. D *D.S.* — 2. D — 3. D B♭ C(2) D

heart. 3. No sum-mer's heart. I just called heart of my heart. of my heart.

Verse 3:
No summer's high; no warm July:
No harvest moon to light one tender August night.
No autumn breeze; no falling leaves;
Not even time for birds to fly to southern skies.

Verse 4:
No Libra sun; no Halloween;
No giving thanks to all the Christmas joy you bring.
But what it is, though old so new
To fill your heart like no three words could ever do.
(To Chorus:)

I LET A SONG GO OUT OF MY HEART

Words by IRVING MILLS,
HENRY NEMO and JOHN REDMOND
Music by DUKE ELLINGTON

Moderately
E♭6/9 A♭7 E♭ Cm7 Gm7 C7 Gm7 C7 Fm/A♭ Gm Fm7 F♯dim
I let a song go out of my heart. It was the sweet-est mel - o - dy. I know I lost heav -
E♭/G A♭7 E♭ Cm7 Fm7(♭5) B♭7 E♭ A♭ E♭ Cm7 Gm7 C7
- en 'cause you were the song. Since you and I have drift-ed a-part, life does-n't mean a

thing to me. Please come back, sweet mu - sic, I know I was wrong. Am I too
late to make a - mends? You know that we were meant to be more than just
friends, just friends. I let a song go out of my heart. Be - lieve me, dar - ling,
when I say, I won't know sweet mus - ic un - til you re-turn some day.
I LOVE A PARADE
© 1931 WARNER BROS. INC. (Renewed)
All Rights Reserved
Words by TED KOEHLER
Music by HAROLD ARLEN
Tempo di marcia
I love a pa - rade, the tramp-ing of feet, I love ev - 'ry beat I hear of a
when I hear a band I just want to stand and cheer as they
drum. come. That rat - a - tat - tat, the blare of a
horn, that rat - a - tat - tat, a bright u - ni - form; the sight of a
drill, will give me a thrill, I thrill at the skill of an - y - thing mil - i -
tar - y. I love a pa - rade, a hand - ful of vets, a line of ca -
dets or an - y bri - gade, for I love a pa - rade.

I LOVE YOU TRULY

Words and Music by
CARRIE JACOBS-BOND

Slowly
F C7 C9 C7(♭9) F C7 C9 C7(♭9) F
I love you tru - ly, tru - ly, dear! Life with its sor - row, life with its tear,
A7 Dm Bdim F F6 F Gm C7 F
fades in - to dreams when I feel you are near. For I love you tru - ly, tru - ly, dear.

From the Musical Production "I MARRIED AN ANGEL"

I MARRIED AN ANGEL

Lyrics by ATHUR FREED
Music by HERB BROWN

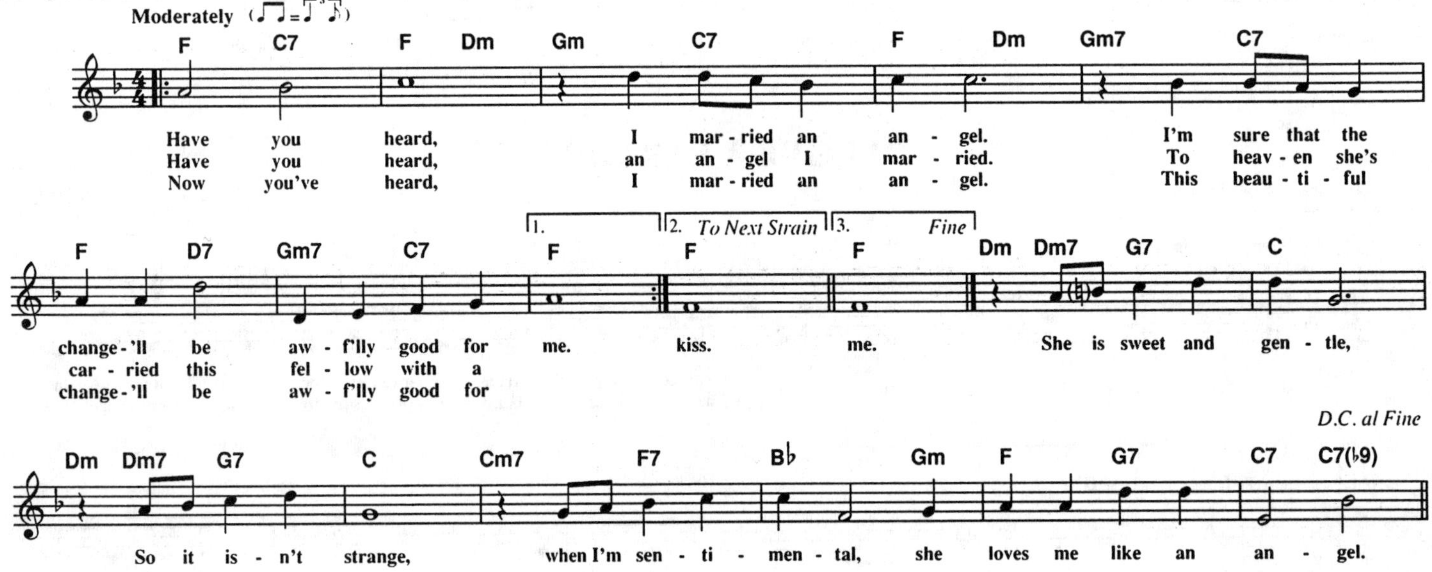

Moderately

F C7 F Dm Gm C7 F Dm Gm7 C7

Have you heard, I mar - ried an an - gel. I'm sure that the
Have you heard, an an - gel I mar - ried. To heav - en she's
Now you've heard, I mar - ried an an - gel. This beau - ti - ful

F D7 Gm7 C7 1. F 2. *To Next Strain* F 3. *Fine* F Dm Dm7 G7 C

change - 'll be aw - f'lly good for me. kiss. me. She is sweet and gen - tle,
car - ried this fel - low with a
change - 'll be aw - f'lly good for

D.C. al Fine

Dm Dm7 G7 C Cm7 F7 B♭ Gm F G7 C7 C7(♭9)

So it is - n't strange, when I'm sen - ti - men - tal, she loves me like an an - gel.

I REMEMBER YOU

Words by JOHNNY MERCER
Music by VICTOR SCHERTZINGER

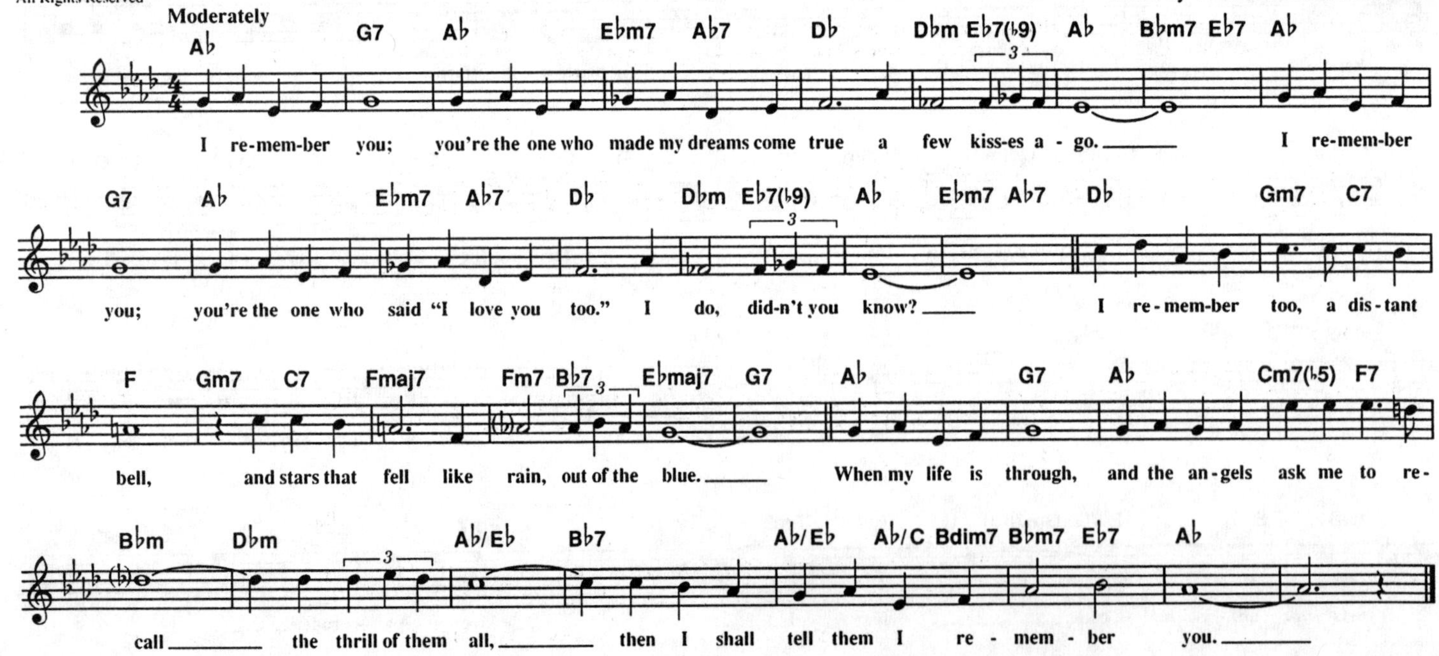

Moderately

A♭ G7 A♭ E♭m7 A♭7 D♭ D♭m E♭7(♭9) A♭ B♭m7 E♭7 A♭

I re-mem-ber you; you're the one who made my dreams come true a few kiss-es a - go. I re-mem-ber

G7 A♭ E♭m7 A♭7 D♭ D♭m E♭7(♭9) A♭ E♭m7 A♭7 D♭ Gm7 C7

you; you're the one who said "I love you too." I do, did-n't you know? I re - mem-ber too, a dis - tant

F Gm7 C7 Fmaj7 Fm7 B♭7 E♭maj7 G7 A♭ G7 A♭ Cm7(♭5) F7

bell, and stars that fell like rain, out of the blue. When my life is through, and the an-gels ask me to re-

B♭m D♭m A♭/E♭ B♭7 A♭/E♭ A♭/C Bdim7 B♭m7 E♭7 A♭

call the thrill of them all, then I shall tell them I re - mem - ber you.

I LOVE TO TELL THE STORY

By KATHERINE HANKEY and W.G. FISCHER

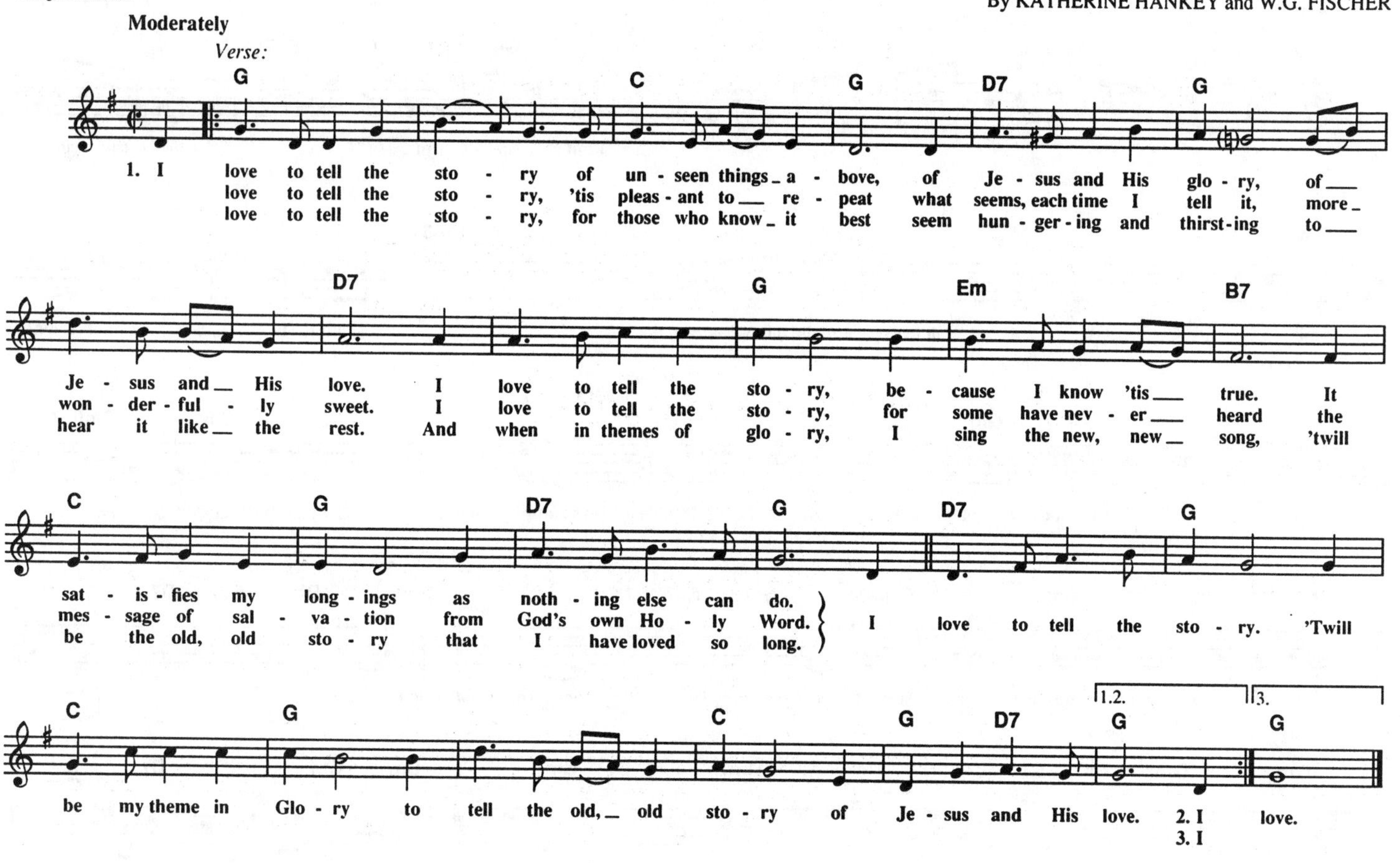
Moderately
Verse:
G C G D7 G D7 G Em B7 C G D7 G D7 G C G C G D7 G G
1. I love to tell the sto - ry of un - seen things a - bove, of Je - sus and His glo - ry, of Je - sus and His love. I love to tell the sto - ry, be - cause I know 'tis true. It sat - is - fies my long - ings as noth - ing else can do.
love to tell the sto - ry, 'tis pleas - ant to re - peat what seems, each time I tell it, more won - der - ful - ly sweet. I love to tell the sto - ry, for some have nev - er heard the mes - sage of sal - va - tion from God's own Ho - ly Word.
love to tell the sto - ry, for those who know it best seem hun - ger - ing and thirst - ing to hear it like the rest. And when in themes of glo - ry, I sing the new, new song, 'twill be the old, old sto - ry that I have loved so long.
I love to tell the sto - ry. 'Twill be my theme in Glo - ry to tell the old, old sto - ry of Je - sus and His love. 2. I 3. I love.
1.2. 3.

I SAW THE LIGHT

Words and Music by
HANK WILLIAMS

Moderately
Verse:
G C G G/D D7 G
1. I wan-dered so aim - less, life filled with sin. I would - n't let my dear Sav - iour in. Then Je - sus came like a strang - er in the night; praise the Lord, I saw the light.
2. Just like a blind man, I wan-dered a - long. Wor - ries and fears I claimed for my own. Then like the blind man that God gave back his sight; praise the Lord, I saw the light.
3. I was a fool to wan - der and stray. Straight is the gate and nar - row the way. Now I have trad - ed the wrong for the right; praise the Lord, I saw the light.
Chorus:
G C G D7 G D7 G
I saw the light. I saw the light. No more dark - ness, no more night. Now, I'm so hap - py, no sor - row in sight. Praise the Lord, I saw the light. I saw the light.
1.2. 3.

I PUT A SPELL ON YOU

Copyright © 1956 (Renewed 1984) EMI UNART CATALOG INC.
All Rights Reserved
Words and Music by
JAY HAWKINS
Slowly
I put a spell on you _ be - cause you're mine. _ You bet-ter stop the things that you do. I ain't ly - in', _ no, I ain't ly - in'. _ I just can't stand it, babe, _ the way you're al-ways run-nin' 'round, I just can't stand it, _ the way you al-ways put me down. I put a spell on you _ be - cause you're mine. _ I put a spell on you. _ I put a spell on you. _
From the M-G-M Motion Picture "FAME"
I SING THE BODY ELECTRIC
Copyright © 1979, 1980 METRO-GOLDWYN-MAYER INC., c/o EMI AFFILIATED CATALOG INC.
All Rights Reserved
Lyrics by DEAN PITCHFORD
Music by MICHAEL GORE
Moderately
1. I sing the bod - y e - lec - tric. I cel - e-brate the me yet to come. _ I toast to my own re - un - ion when I be-come one _ with the sun. _ And I'll look back on Ve - nus; I'll look back on Mars; _
sing the bod - y e - lec - tric. I glo - ry in the glow of re - birth, _ cre - at - ing my own to - mor - row when I shall em - bod - y the earth. _ And I'll ser - e - nade Ve - nus; I'll ser - e - nade Mars; _
and I'll burn with the fire _ of ten mil-lion stars. _ And in time, and in time we will all be stars. 2. I
stars.
Broadly
We are the em-per-ors now and we are the czars, _ and in time, and in time we will all be stars.

I SAW HER STANDING THERE

Words and Music by
JOHN LENNON and PAUL McCARTNEY

Moderately bright, with a beat

Bb7 Eb7 Bb7

Well, she was just sev - en - teen, and you know what I mean. And the way she looked was 'way be-yond com -
she looked at me, And I, I could see that be - fore too long, I'd fall in love with
(3rd time Inst. solo ad lib...

F7 Bb Bb7 Eb Gb Bb/F F7

pare. So how could I dance with an - oth - er, oh, when I saw her stand - ing
her. She would-n't dance with an - oth - er, oh when I saw her stand - ing

Bb7 1. 2.3. Eb7

there. Well, Well, my heart went boom when I crossed that room and I held her
there.
...end solo)

F7 Eb7 Bb7 Eb7

hand in mi - een. (mine.) Well, we danced through the night, and we held each oth - er tight.

Bb7 F7 Bb Bb7 Eb

And be - fore too long, I fell in love with her. Now I'll nev - er dance with an - oth - er,

Gb Bb F7 1. Bb *D.S.* 𝄋 2. Bb7 Bb/F

oh, since I saw her stand - ing there. there. Well, since I saw her

F7 Bb7 Bb/F F7 Eb Bb Bb9

stand - ing there Yeah, well, since I saw her stand - ing there.

I SAW THREE SHIPS

TRADITIONAL
Merrily
G C/G G C/G G D7
1. I saw three ships come sail - ing in on Christ - mas Day, on Christ - mas Day. I
2. what was in those ships all three on Christ - mas Day, on Christ - mas Day. And
3. Vir - gin Mary and Christ were there on Christ - mas Day, on Christ - mas Day. The
G C/G G C/G G 1.2. D7 G 3. D7 G
saw three ships come sail - ing in on Christ - mas Day in the morn - ing. 2. And mor - ning.
what was in those ships all three on Christ - mas Day in the morn - ing? 3. The
Vir - gin Mary and Christ were there on Christ - mas Day in the

I MAY BE WRONG
(But, I Think You're Wonderful!)

Words by HARRY RUSKIN
Music by HENRY SULLIVAN

Moderato

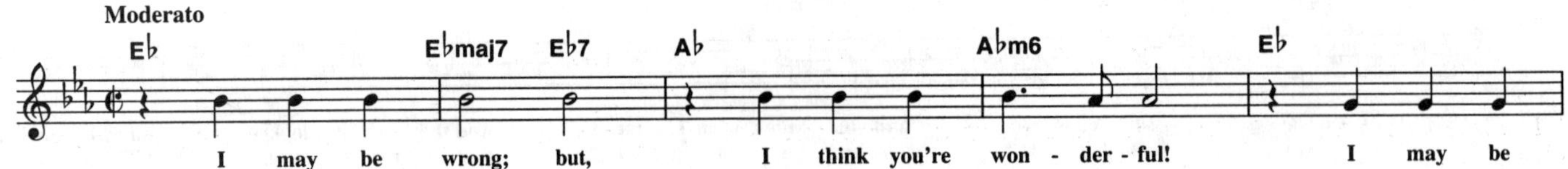
E♭ E♭maj7 E♭7 A♭ A♭m6 E♭
I may be wrong; but, I think you're won - der - ful! I may be

F9 B♭7 E♭ A♭6 E♭ E♭maj7 E♭7 A♭
wrong; but, I think you're swell! I like you style; say, I think it's

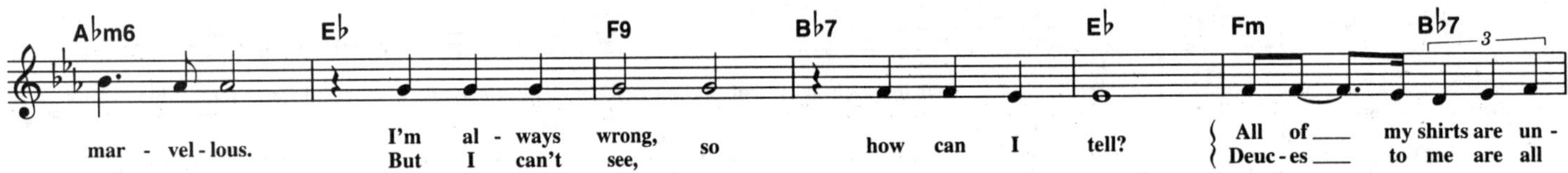
A♭m6 E♭ F9 B♭7 E♭ Fm B♭7
3
mar - vel - lous. I'm al - ways wrong, so how can I tell? All of ___ my shirts are un -
But I can't see, Deuc - es ___ to me are all

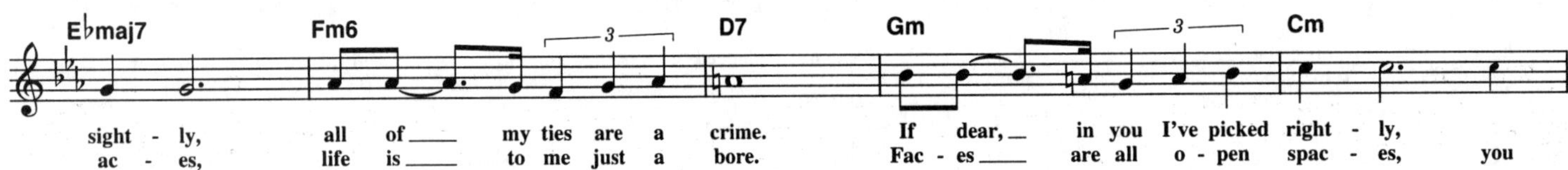
E♭maj7 Fm6 D7 Gm Cm
3
3
sight - ly, all of ___ my ties are a crime. If dear, __ in you I've picked right - ly,
ac - es, life is ___ to me just a bore. Fac - es ___ are all o - pen spac - es, you

Cm6/A F7 B♭ B♭7 E♭ E♭maj7 E♭7 A♭
it's the ver - y first time.
might be John __ Bar - ry - more.
You came a - long, say I think you're

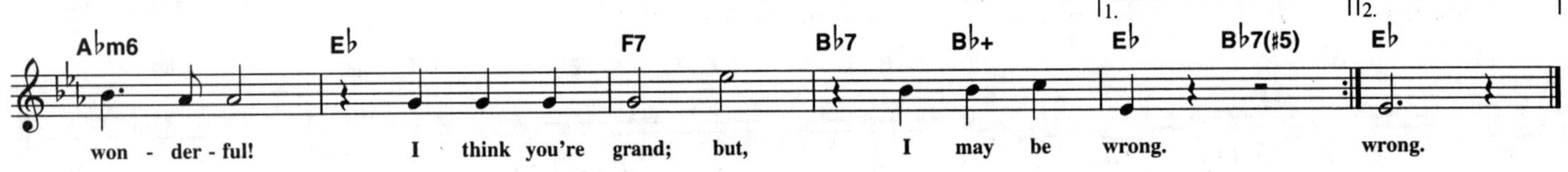
A♭m6 E♭ F7 B♭7 B♭+
1.
E♭ B♭7(♯5)
2.
E♭
won - der - ful! I think you're grand; but, I may be wrong. wrong.

I UNDERSTAND

Lyric by KIM GANNON
Music by MABEL WAYNE

Slowly

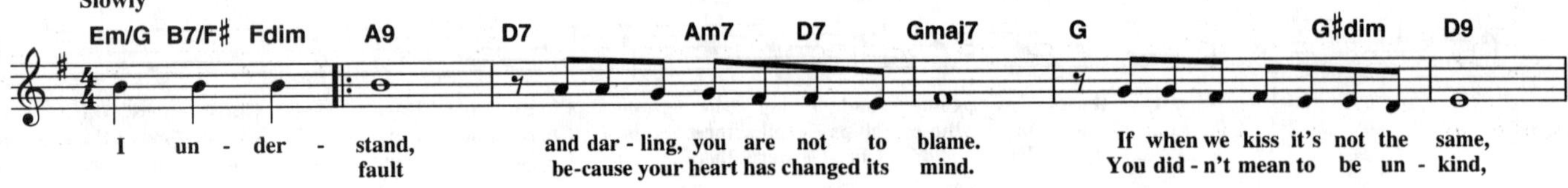
Em/G B7/F♯ Fdim A9 D7 Am7 D7 Gmaj7 G G♯dim D9
I un - der - stand, and dar - ling, you are not to blame. If when we kiss it's not the same,
fault be-cause your heart has changed its mind. You did - n't mean to be un - kind,

1.
D6 F♯ G D7 Em/G B7/F♯ Fdim7
2.
C♯7 D7 Dm7 G7 C B7
I un - der - stand. It's not your I un - der - stand. ___ For - get - ting you will be far from eas - y,

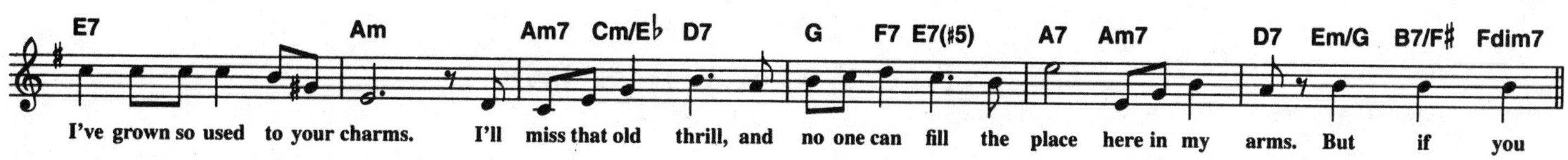
E7 Am Am7 Cm/E♭ D7 G F7 E7(♯5) A7 Am7 D7 Em/G B7/F♯ Fdim7
I've grown so used to your charms. I'll miss that old thrill, and no one can fill the place here in my arms. But if you

A9 D7 Am7 D7 Gmaj7 G Dm6 E7 Am7 D7 G F F♯ G
find our love was real-ly meant to be, then dar-ling, hur-ry back to me, and I'll un - der - stand.

I WANT A GIRL

(Just Like the Girl That Married Dear Old Dad)

Words by WILLIAM DILLON
Music by HARRY VON TILZER

March tempo

Verse:

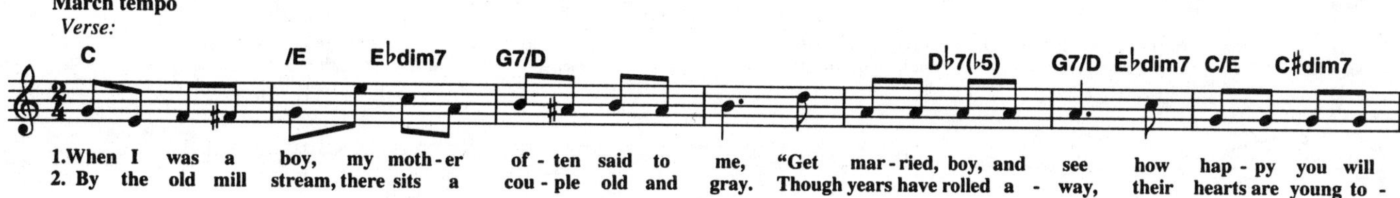
C /E E♭dim7 G7/D D♭7(♭5) G7/D E♭dim7 C/E C♯dim7
1.When I was a boy, my moth-er of - ten said to me, "Get mar-ried, boy, and see how hap - py you will
2. By the old mill stream, there sits a cou - ple old and gray. Though years have rolled a - way, their hearts are young to -

G7/D G7 C /E Cm6/E♭ G/D G/B D7/A D7 G E7
be." I have looked all o - ver, but no girl - ie can I find who seems to be just like the lit - tle
day. Moth - er dear looks up at Dad with love - light in her eye. He steals a kiss, a fond em - brace, while

Chorus:
Am D7 G G7/B B♭7 Dm/A B♭7/A♭ G7 Dm7/A B♭dim7 G7/B C
girl I have in mind. I will have to look a - round un - til the right one I have found.
eve - ning breez - es sigh. They're as hap - py as can be, so that's the kind of love for me.
I want a girl

F F/A A♭7(♭5) C/G Am7 D9 G7 C F F♯dim7 C/G A7
just like the girl that mar - ried dear old Dad. She was a pearl, and the on - ly girl that

D7 G7 C G7 G♯dim7 Am F7 E7
Dad - dy ev - er had. A good old - fash-ioned girl, with heart so true, one who loves no-bod - y else but

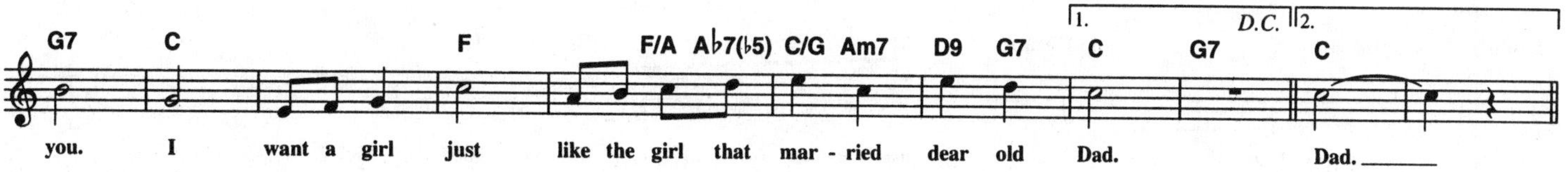
1. D.C. 2.
G7 C F F/A A♭7(♭5) C/G Am7 D9 G7 C G7 C
you. I want a girl just like the girl that mar - ried dear old Dad. Dad.

I WANT TO WALK YOU HOME

Words and Music by
ANTOINE DOMINO

Slow rock (♫ = ♩♪ triplet)

C F

1. I want to walk you home. Please let me walk you home. I want to walk you home.
hold your hand. Please let me hold your hand. I want to hold your hand.

C G7 F C

Please let me walk you home. You look so good to me. Oh, ooh-ee, I wish I was the luck-y guy who could
Please let me hold your hand. You look so good to me. Oh, ooh-ee, I saw you walk-in' all a-lone, that's

C

walk you right on down the aisle. I love the way you walk. I love to hear you talk. I love the
why I want to walk you home. So let me walk you home. Please let me walk you home. I want to

F C 1. G7

way you walk. I love to hear you talk. I'm not try-in' to be smart, I'm
walk you home. Please let me walk you home. You

F C

not try-in' to break your heart. But if I ask you for a date, will you tell me that I'm not too late? 2. I want to

2. G7 F C C

Repeat and fade

look so good to me. Oh, ooh - ee, I saw you walk-in' all a-lone. That's why I wan-na walk you home. That's

I'LL SEE YOU AGAIN

Words and Music by
NOEL COWARD

Tempo di valse
C A7 Dm Dm7 G7 C C/E
I'll see you a - gain, when-ev - er spring breaks through a - gain. Time may lie
D♯dim G7/D G7 Dm G7 D7 G+ C A7
heav - y be - tween, but what has been is past for - get - ting. This sweet
Dm Dm7 G7 C C7 F
mem - o - ry a - cross the years will come to me; tho' my world may go a -
Dm6/E E7 Am D♯dim C/E A7 Dm7 G7 C
wry, in my heart will ev - er lie just the ech - o of a sigh, good - bye!

I WANNA BE AROUND
© 1959 & 1963 WB MUSIC CORP.
All Rights Reserved
Words and Music by
JOHNNY MEERCER and
SADIE VIMMERSTEDT
Moderately
I wan - na be a - round, to pick up the piec - es, when
wan - na be a - round, to see how she does ___ it when
To Coda
some - bod - y breaks your heart; ___ Some some - bod - y twice as smart ___ as I, ___
she breaks your heart to bits; ___ Let's see if the puz - zle fits ___
A some - bod - y who ___ will swear to be true, ___ Like
you used to do ___ with me. ___ Who'll leave you to learn ___ that
D.S. al Coda
mis - 'ry loves com - pa - ny, ___ wait and see! ___ I
CODA
___ so fine. ___ And that's when I'll dis - cov - er that re -
venge is sweet; ___ As I sit there ap - plaud - ing from a front row seat, ___ When
some - bod - y breaks your heart like you broke mine. ___
I WANNA BE LOVED BY YOU
© 1928 WARNER BROS. INC. (Renewed)
All Rights Reserved
Words by
BERT KALMAR
Music by
HERBERT STOTHART and
HARRY RUBY
Moderato
1. 3. I Wan - na Be Loved By You,
2. I wan - na be kissed by you,
Just you, and no - bod - y else but you.
I Wan - na Be Loved By You a - lone, ___ poo - poo - pa - doop.
I wan - na be kissed by you a -
Fine
lone, poo - poo - pa - doop. I could - n't as - pire ___ to an - y - thing high - er, ___
D.C. al Fine
___ Then fill a de - sire ___ to make you my own; pa - pa - pad - ra, poo - poo - pa - doop.

I WILL ALWAYS LOVE YOU

Words and Music by
DOLLY PARTON

Freely
Verse 1:
N.C.
1. If I should stay, I would only be in your way. So I'll go, but I know I'll think of you ev'ry step of the way.
Slowly
Chorus:
A F♯m Dmaj7 E
And I will always love you.
A F♯m Dmaj7 E A(2)
I will always love you.
D A/C♯
You, my darling you.
Bm7 A/E Bm/E
Hmm.
Verses 2, 3, 4:
A Bm/A A E/G♯ F♯m C♯m/E D E A E/A
2. Bitter-sweet memories that is all I'm taking with me. So, goodbye. Please,
A E/G♯ F♯m C♯m/E
don't cry. We both know I'm not what you, you need.
To Coda
1. To Next Strain
Dmaj7 E
And I
2. D.S. al Coda
Dmaj7 E
4. I
Chorus:
A F♯m D E A F♯m D E
will always love you. I will always love you.
A D/A A C♯m/E Cm/E Bm/E
D.S.
Coda
Dmaj7 E N.C.
love. And
B G♯m Emaj7 F♯ B G♯m
I will always love you. I will al-
C♯m7 F♯ B G♯m Emaj7 F♯
ways love you. I will al - ways love you.
B G♯m C♯m7 F♯
I will al - ways love
B G♯m Emaj7 F♯ B G♯m
you. I will always love you.
Emaj7 F♯ N.C.
I, I will always love you.
ad lib.
a tempo
Emaj7 B(2)/D♯ E/F♯ F♯ B(2)
You, darling, I love you. Ooh, I'll always, I'll always love you.

Verse 3: Instrumental solo

Verse 4:
I hope life treats you kind
And I hope you have all you've dreamed of.
And I wish to you, joy and happiness.
But above all this, I wish you love.
(To Chorus:)

I WISH

Words and Music by
STEVIE WONDER

Brightly
Verse:
Look-ing back on when I was a lit - tle nap - py - head - ed boy,
Broth-er says he's tell - in' 'bout you play - in' doc - tor with that girl.
then my on - ly wor - ry was for Christ - mas what would be my toy.
Just don't tell. I'll give you an - y - thing you want in this whole wide world.
E - ven though we some - times would not get a thing, we were hap - py with the joy the day would bring.
Ma - ma gives you mon - ey for Sun-day School. You trade yours for can - dy af - ter church is through.
Sneak-in' out the back door to hang out with those hood-lum friends of mine,
Smok-in' cig - a - rettes and writ - ing some-thing nas - ty on the wall.
ooh;
greet-ed at the back door with, "Boy, I thought I told you not to go out - side."
Teach-er sends you to the prin - ci - pal's of - fice down the hall.
Tryin' the best to bring the wa-ter to your eyes, think-in' it might stop her from whoop-in' your be - hind.
You grow up and learn that kind-a thing ain't right. But while you were do - in' it, it sure felt out - ta sight.
I wish those
Chorus:
days could come back once more. Why did those days ev - er have to go? I wish those
days could come back once more. Why did those days ev - er have to go, 'cause I loved them so.
1.
Do do do do do do do do do do do do. Do do do do do do do do do do.
2.
Repeat and fade

I WONDER WHO'S KISSING HER NOW

TRADITIONAL

Waltz
Verse:
G
Cm/G
G
You have loved lots of girls in the sweet long a - go and each one has meant heav - en to you.
want to feel wretch-ed and lone - ly and blue, just im - ag - ine the girl you love best

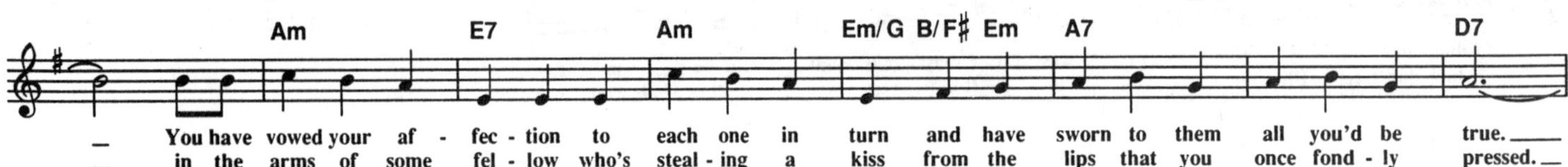
Am E7 Am Em/G B/F♯ Em A7 D7
You have vowed your af - fec - tion to each one in turn and have sworn to them all you'd be true.
in the arms of some fel - low who's steal - ing a kiss from the lips that you once fond - ly pressed.

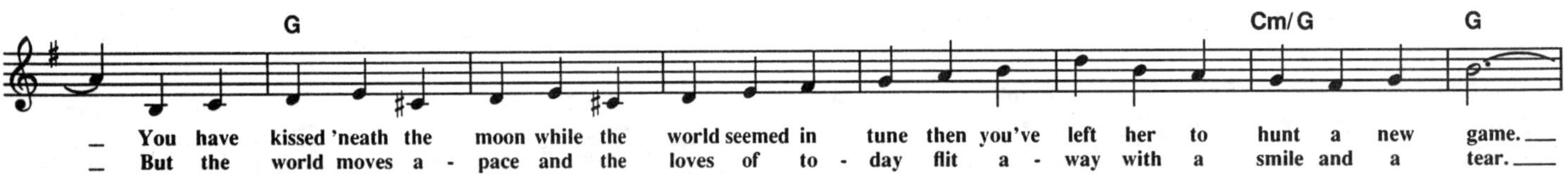
G Cm/G G
You have kissed 'neath the moon while the world seemed in tune then you've left her to hunt a new game.
But the world moves a - pace and the loves of to - day flit a - way with a smile and a tear.

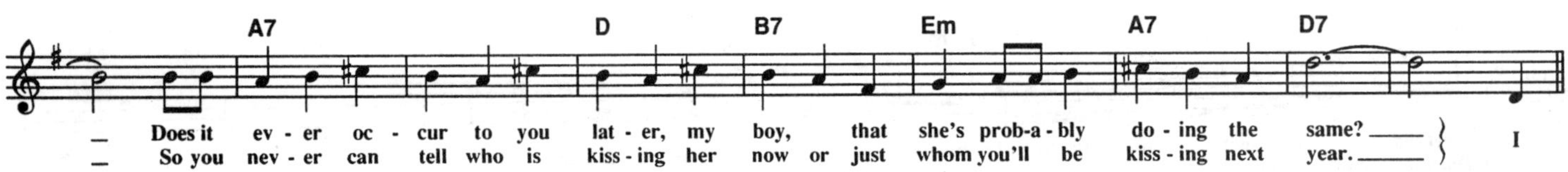
A7 D B7 Em A7 D7
Does it ev - er oc - cur to you lat - er, my boy, that she's prob-a - bly do - ing the same?
So you nev - er can tell who is kiss - ing her now or just whom you'll be kiss - ing next year.
I

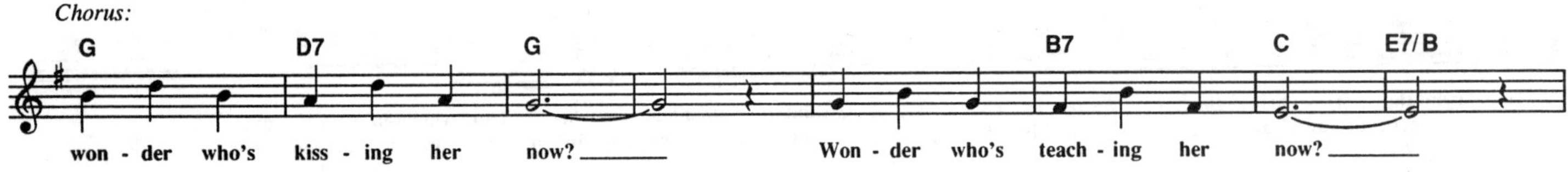
Chorus:
G D7 G B7 C E7/B
won - der who's kiss - ing her now? Won - der who's teach - ing her now?

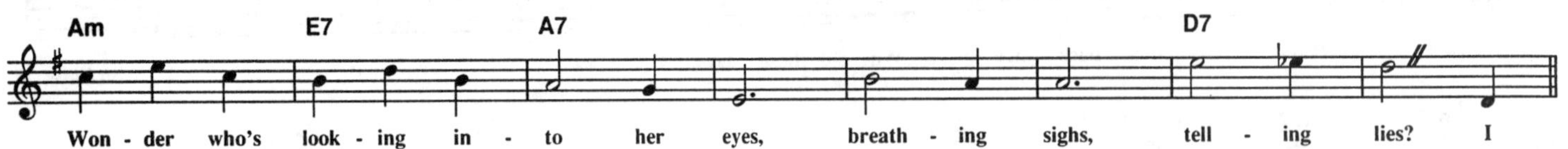
Am E7 A7 D7
Won - der who's look - ing in - to her eyes, breath - ing sighs, tell - ing lies? I

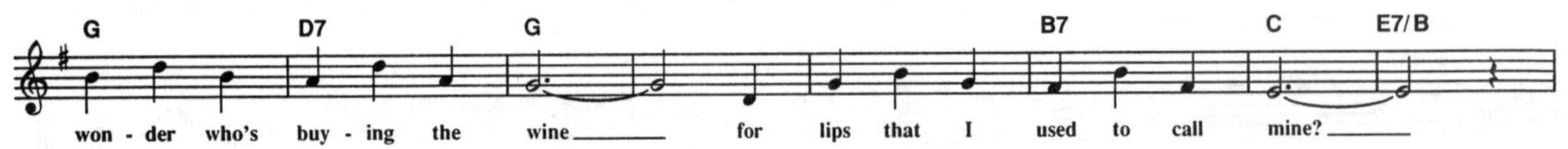
G D7 G B7 C E7/B
won - der who's buy - ing the wine for lips that I used to call mine?

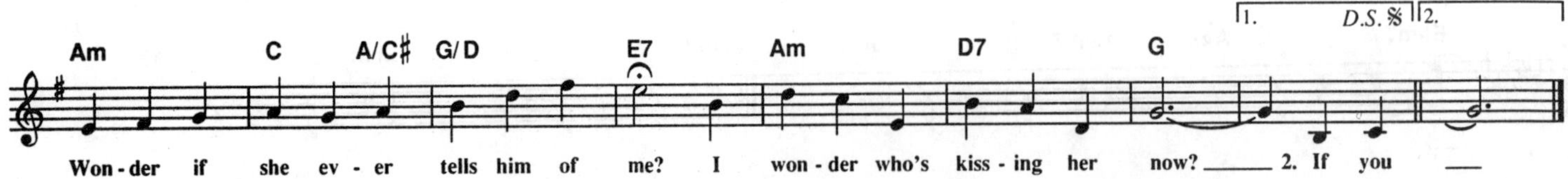
1. D.S. 𝄋 2.
Am C A/C♯ G/D E7 Am D7 G
Won - der if she ev - er tells him of me? I won - der who's kiss - ing her now? 2. If you

I WON'T LAST A DAY WITHOUT YOU

Lyrics by PAUL WILLIAMS
Music by ROGER NICHOLS

Moderately slow

G Bm7 C C/D Em9 Am7 Am7/D

1. Day af - ter day I must face a world of stran-gers where I don't be - long, I'm not that strong.
2. So man - y times when the cit - y seems to be with - out a friend-ly face, a lone - ly place.

G Bm7 C C/D Em9 Am7 Am7/D

It's nice to know that there's some-one I can turn to who will al-ways care, you're al-ways there.
It's nice to know that you'll be there if I need you, and you'll al-ways smile, it's all worth-while.

Chorus:

G F/G C(9) Am7 Am7/D G F/G C(9) Am7 Am7/D G F/G Cmaj7 G/B Am7 Am7/D

When there's no get-ting o-ver that rain-bow, when my small-est of dreams won't come true, I can take all the mad-ness the world has to give, but I won't last a day with-out

To Coda 𝄌

1. G G(9)/B C/D D — you.
2. G(9) — you.

Em7 A7 Dmaj7 Em7 A7 Bsus B C♯m7 F♯7

Touch me and I end up sing-ing, trou-bles seem to up and dis-ap - pear. You touch me with the love you're

B G♯m7 Amaj7 Bsus B Am7 D7

bring-ing. I can't real-ly lose when you're near. When there's

D.S. 𝄋 *al Coda*

𝄌 *Coda*

G G(9) C C/D D G

you.

IDA, SWEET AS APPLE CIDER

Words by EDDIE LEONARD
Music by EDDIE MUNSON

Moderately
C C♯dim G7 Dm7 G7 C E7/B
I - da, sweet as ap - ple ci - der, sweet - er than all I know.
A7 D7 G7
Come out in the sil - v'ry moon - light, of love we'll whis - per so soft and low.
C C♯dim G7 Dm7 G7 C E7/B
Seems I can't live with - out you. Lis - ten, oh hon - ey, do!
A7 D7 Dm7 D7 D7(♭5) G7 C
I - da, I i - do - lize you. I love you, I - da, 'deed I do.

I'D LIKE TO TEACH THE WORLD TO SING (In Perfect Harmony)

Words and Music by
B. BACKER, B. DAVIS, R. COOK and R. GREENAWAY

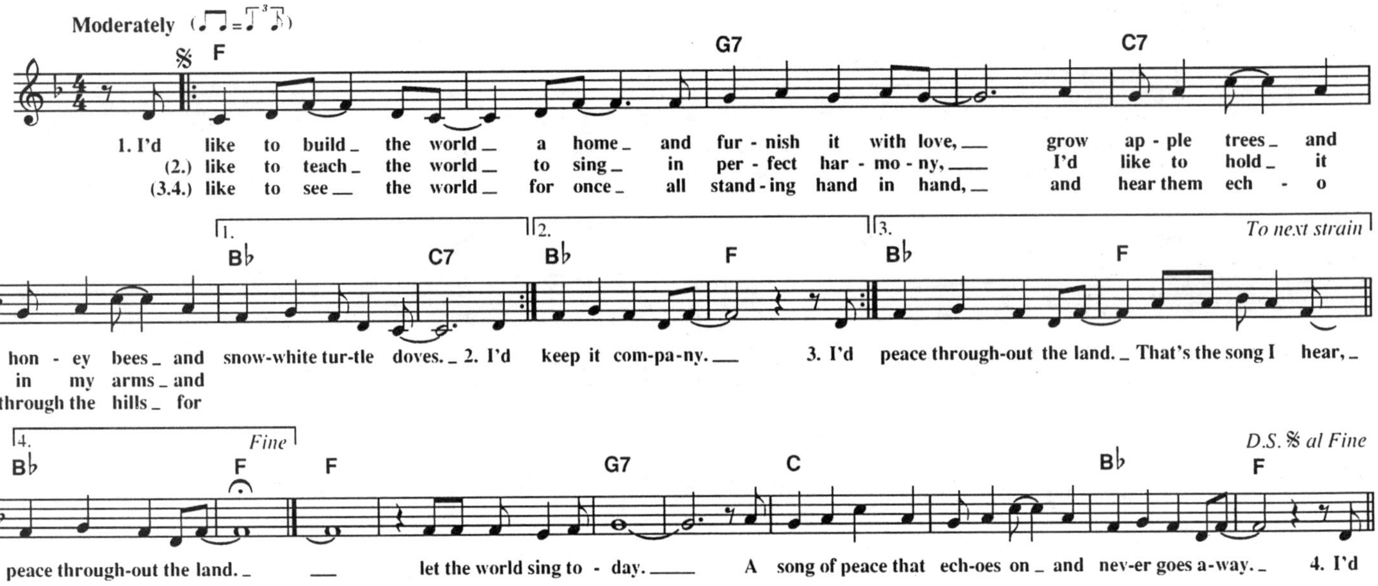

Moderately

1. I'd like to build the world a home and fur - nish it with love, grow ap - ple trees and hon - ey bees and snow-white tur-tle doves. 2. I'd
(2.) like to teach the world to sing in per - fect har - mo - ny, I'd like to hold it in my arms and keep it com-pa-ny. 3. I'd
(3.4.) like to see the world for once all stand - ing hand in hand, and hear them ech - o through the hills for peace through-out the land. That's the song I hear, *To next strain*

4. peace through-out the land. *Fine*

let the world sing to - day. A song of peace that ech-oes on and nev-er goes a-way. 4. I'd *D.S. al Fine*

I'D LOVE YOU TO WANT ME

Words and Music by
LOBO

Moderately

Verse 1:

When I saw you stand-in' there, I 'bout fell out my chair. And when you moved your mouth to speak, I felt the blood go to my feet.

Verses 2 & 3:

2. Now it took time for me to know what you tried so not to show. Some-thin' in my soul just cries, I feel the want in your blue eyes.
3. You told your - self years a - go you'd nev - er let your feel-ings show. The ob - li - ga - tion that you made for the ti - tle that they gave.

Chorus:

Ba - by, I'd love you to want me the way that I want you, the way that it should be. Ba - by, you'd love me to want you the way that I want to if you'd on - ly let it be. on - ly let it be.

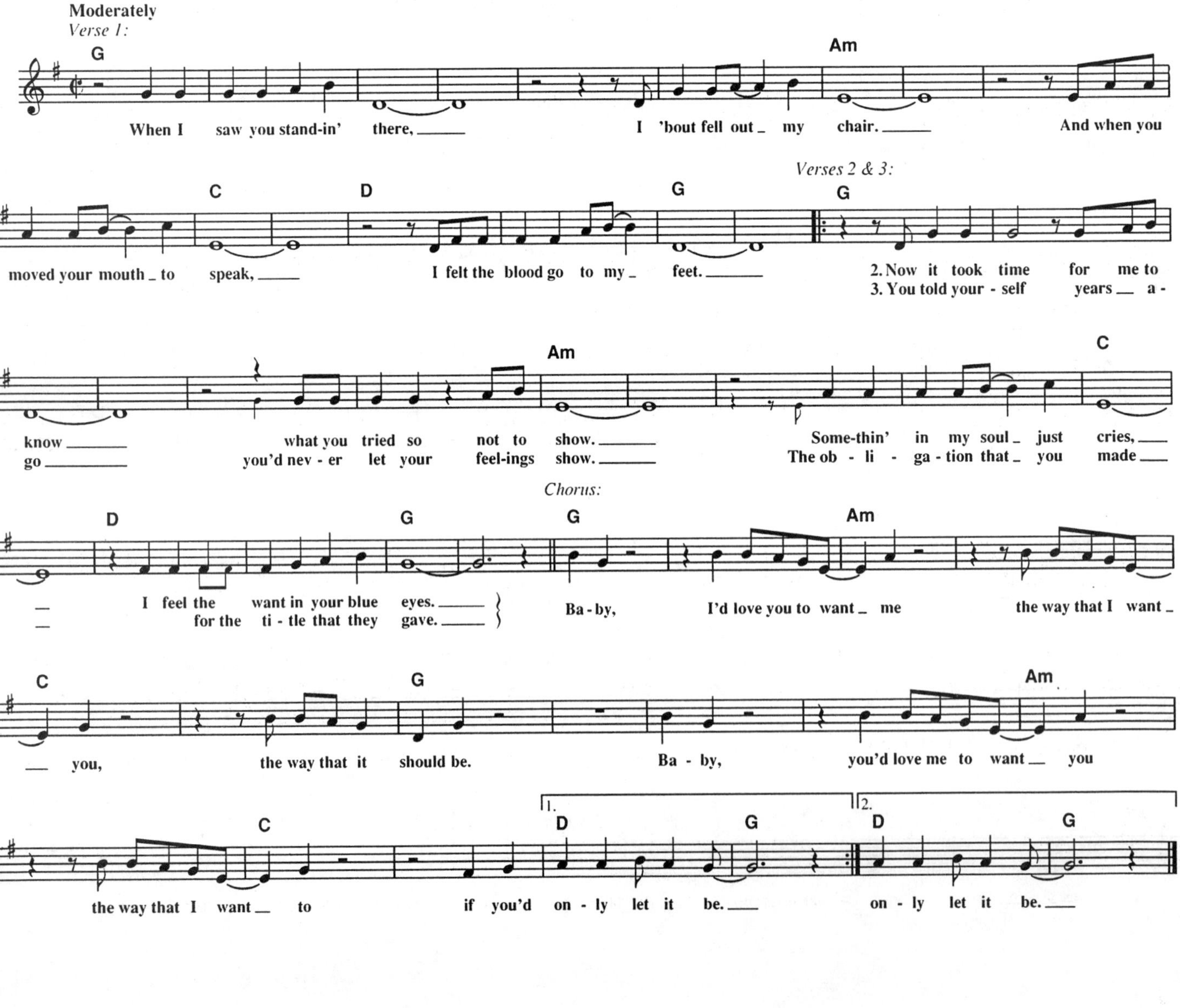

IF EVER YOU'RE IN MY ARMS AGAIN

Words and Music by
MICHAEL MASSER, TOM SNOW
and CYNTHIA WEIL

Moderately slow
D(2) G6/D
Ooo.
Verse:
D(2)
1. It all came so eas - y, all the lov - in' you gave _ me; the feel-ings we shared. _
I'm see - in' clear - ly how I still need you near _ me. I still love you so. _
G6/D D(2) G6/D
And I still can re-mem - ber how you touched me so ten - der. It told me you care. _
There's some-thing be-tween _ us that won't ev-er leave _ us. There's no let-ting go. _
C Fmaj7 F6 Dm Am C G
We had a once in a life - time, _ but I just could-n't see ___ un - til it was gone. _
We had a once in a life - time, _ but I just did - n't know it till my life fell a - part. _
C Fmaj7 F6 Dm Am C G A
A sec-ond once in a life - time; _ may be too much to ask. _ But I swear from now on... _
A sec-ond once in a life - time _ is - n't too much to ask. _ 'Cause I swear from now on... _
Chorus:
D D/F♯ Gmaj7 A F♯m7 Bm7 Em7 G A D D/F♯ Gmaj7 A
If ev - er you're in my arms a-gain, this time ___ I'll love ___ you much bet - ter. If ev - er you're in my arms a-gain,
F♯m7 Bm7 Em7 G/A A Dsus(2) D Dsus(2) D E7sus Em7
this time ___ I'll hold ___ you for - ev - er. This time will nev - er end. Ooo.
Esus(2) Em7/A G/A A
D.S. 𝄋
2. Now This time we'll nev - er end, ___
Bridge:
Bm7 Bm6 Bm7
nev-er end. ___
Bm6 G D/F♯ Em7
The best of ro - manc - in' de - serves se - cond chanc - es. I'll get to you some - how. 'Cause
G/A B E E/G♯ Amaj7 B G♯m7 C♯m7 F♯m7 A B
I prom-ise now. ___ (end.) If ev - er you're in my arms a - gain this time ___ I'll love ___ you much bet - ter.
E E/G♯ Amaj7 B G♯m7 C♯m7 F♯m7 A/B B
Repeat ad lib. and fade
If ev - er you're in my arms a - gain this time ___ I'll hold ___ you for - ev - er. This time we'll nev - er

IF I GIVE MY HEART TO YOU

Words and Music by
JIMMIE CRANE, AL JACOBS
and JIMMY BREWSTER

Slowly
N.C.
C Cmaj7 C6
Dm7
G7
If I give my heart to you, will you han-dle it with care? Will you al-ways treat me
you, will you give me all your love? Will you swear that you'll be
sure. Please don't an-swer 'til you do. When you prom-ise all these
To Coda
Dm7 G7 Dm7 G7 C C♯dim7 Dm7 G7 Dm7 G7 C F6
ten-der-ly and in ev-'ry way be fair? If I give my heart to by the light that shines a-bove?
true to me
things to me,
C F F♯dim7 C/G A9 Dm7
And will you sigh with me when I'm sad, smile with me when I'm glad, and al-ways be as you
D9 Dm7 Fm6 G7 N.C.
D.S. al Coda
are with me to-night? Think it o-ver and be
Coda
Dm7 G7 C Fm7 C6/9
then I'll give my heart to you.

IF YOU KNEW SUSIE

(Like I Know Susie)

Words and Music by
B.G. DE SYLVA and
JOSEPH MEYER

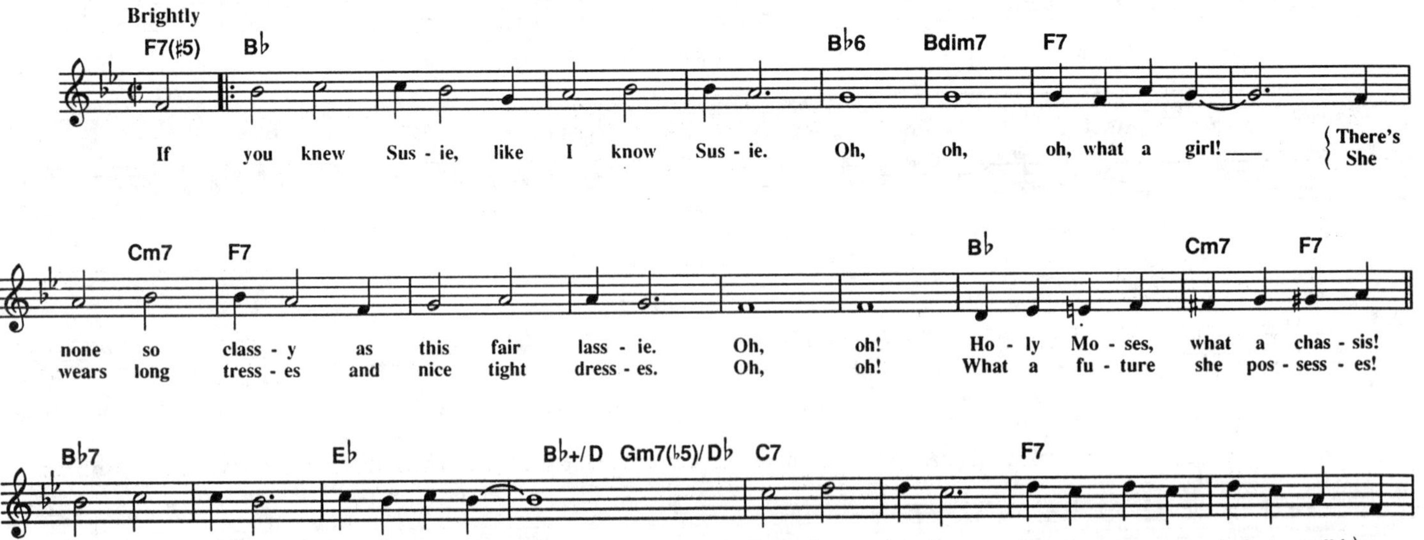
Brightly
F7(♯5) B♭ B♭6 Bdim7 F7
If you knew Sus-ie, like I know Sus-ie. Oh, oh, oh, what a girl! There's She
Cm7 F7 B♭ Cm7 F7
none so class-y as this fair lass-ie. Oh, oh! Ho-ly Mo-ses, what a chas-sis!
wears long tress-es and nice tight dress-es. Oh, oh! What a fu-ture she pos-sess-es!
B♭7 E♭ B♭+/D Gm7(♭5)/D♭ C7 F7
We went rid-ing, she did-n't balk. Back from Yon-kers, I'm the one who had to walk! If
Out in pub-lic, how she can yawn. In a par-lor, you would think the war was on!
B♭ C7 Cm7(♭5) F7 B♭ G♭7 F7 F7(♭9) B♭
you knew Sus-ie, like I know Sus-ie, oh, oh what a girl! If

IF I HAD YOU

By TED SHAPIRO, JIMMY CAMPBELL, and REG. CONNELLY

Moderately
I could show the world how to smile, I could be glad all of the while. I could change the grey skies to blue if I had you.
I could leave the old days be - hind, leave all my pals, I'd nev - er mind. I could start my life all a - new if I had
I could be a king, dear, un - crown'd, hum-ble or poor, rich or re - nowned. There is noth - ing I could - n't do if I had
To Coda
you.
I could climb the snow-capp'd moun-tains, Sail the might-y o - cean wide.
I could cross the burn - ing des - ert if I had you by my side.
D.C. al Coda
Coda
you.
IF I SAID YOU HAVE A BEAUTIFUL BODY WOULD YOU HOLD IT AGAINST ME
Copyright © 1979 by FAMOUS MUSIC CORPORATION and BELLAMY BROTHERS MUSIC
All Rights Reserved
Words and Music by DAVID BELLAMY
Moderately
Chorus:
If I said you have a beau-ti - ful bod - y, would you hold it a - gainst me?
If I swore you were an an - gel, would you treat me like the dev - il to - night?
If I was dy - ing of thirst, would your flow-ing love come quench me?
If I said you have a beau-ti-ful bod - y, would you hold it a - gainst me?
Verse:
Now, we could talk all night a - bout the weath-er; could tell you 'bout my friends out on the coast.
Now, rain can fall so soft a-gainst the win-dow; the sun can shine so bright up in the sky.
I could ask a lot of cra - zy ques - tions, or ask you what I real - ly want to know.
But dad-dy al-ways told me, don't make small talk. He said, "Come on out and say what's on your mind."
1. N.C. If I said
2. N.C. So, if I said
D.S. and fade

From the Broadway Musical Production "SWEET CHARITY"
IF MY FRIENDS COULD SEE ME NOW!
Copyright © 1965, 1969 by DOROTHY FIELDS and CY COLEMAN
All Rights throughout the World Controlled by NOTABLE MUSIC CO., INC.
In Co-publication with LIDA ENTERPRISES, INC.
All Rights Reserved
Music by CY COLEMAN
Lyric by DOROTHY FIELDS
Brightly
To-night at eight you should-a seen a chauf-feur pull up in a rent-ed lim-ou-sine!
My neigh-bors burned! They like to die! When I tell them who is get-tin' in and go-in' out is I! If they could
see me now, that lit-tle gang of mine, I'm eat-ing fan-cy chow and drink-ing fan-cy wine. I'd like those
see me now, my lit-tle dust-y group, trait-sin' 'round this mil-lion dol-lar chick-en coop. I'd hear those
see me now, a-lone with Mis-ter V. who's wait-in' on me like he was a mai-tre d'. I hear my
stum-ble bums to see for a fact the kind of top-drawer, first-rate chums I at-tract. All I can
thrift shop cats say: "Broth-er, get her! Draped on a bed-spread made from three kinds of fur." All I can
bud-dies say-ing, "Cra-zy what gives? To-night she's liv-ing like the oth-er half lives." To think the
say is, "Wow-ee! Look-a where I am. To-night I land-ed, pow! right in a pot of jam." What a
say is, "Wow! Wait till the riff and raff see just ex-act-ly how he signed this au-to-graph." What a
low-est brow, which there's no doubt is me. What a high-est brow, which I must say is he, should pick the
set up! Ho-ly cow!
build-up! Ho-ly cow!
step up! Ho-ly cow!
They'd nev-er be-lieve it, if my friends could see me now! 2.3. If they could
I'LL BE ON MY WAY
Copyright © 1969 NORTHERN SONGS LTD., London, England
All Rights Assigned to and Administered by EMI UNART CATALOG INC.
All Rights Reserved
Words and Music by
JOHN LENNON and
PAUL McCARTNEY
Moderately
The sun is fad-ing a-way, that's the end of the day.
Just one kiss, then I'll go. Don't hide the tears that don't show.
They were right, I was wrong. True love did-n't last long.
As the June light turns to moon-light,
I'll be on my way. way. To way. where the winds don't blow and gold-en riv-ers flow, this way will I go.
To next strain
Fine
D.S. al Fine

IF TOMORROW NEVER COMES

Words and Music by
GARTH BROOKS and
KENT BLAZY

Slowly
Verse:
G D/G C/G G Am7 D C/G G
1.Some-times late at night, _ I lie a - wake _ and watch _ her sleep - ing. _
Am/G G D Am7 D C G C/G
She's lost in peace - ful dreams, _ so I turn off the lights _ and lay there in the dark. ___
G Am7 D C/G G Am/G G
And the thought cross - es my mind, if I nev-er wake up in the morn - ing, __
D Am7 D C G C/G G
would she ev - er doubt __ the way __ I feel _ a - bout _ her in __ my heart. ______ If to - mor - row nev-er
Chorus:
C G
comes, will she know how much I loved her? ____ Did I try in ev - 'ry
D Am7 D C G Am7 G/B
way __ to show her ev - 'ry - day _______ that she's my on - ly one? ______________ And if my time on __ earth _ were
C D Em7 Bm7 Em
through, _ and she must face _ this world with - out me, __ is the love I gave _ her in __ the past _
Am7 D G D/G C/G G
_ gon-na be e - nough _ to last ___ if to-mor-row nev-er comes? ____
1. D.S.
2. 'Cause I've lost loved _ ones in my _
2.
G Am7 D C G/B Am7 G
So, tell that some-one that you love ________ just what you're think-ing of if to-mor-row _ nev-er comes. ____________

Verse 2:
'Cause I've lost loved ones in my life
Who never knew how much I loved them.
Now I live with the regret
That my true feelings for them never were revealed.
So I made a promise to myself
To say each day how much she means to me
And avoid that circumstance
Where there's no second chance to tell her how I feel. ('Cause)
(To Chorus:)

IF I COULD BE WITH YOU
(One Hour Tonight)

Words and Music by
HENRY CREAMER and JIMMY JOHNSON

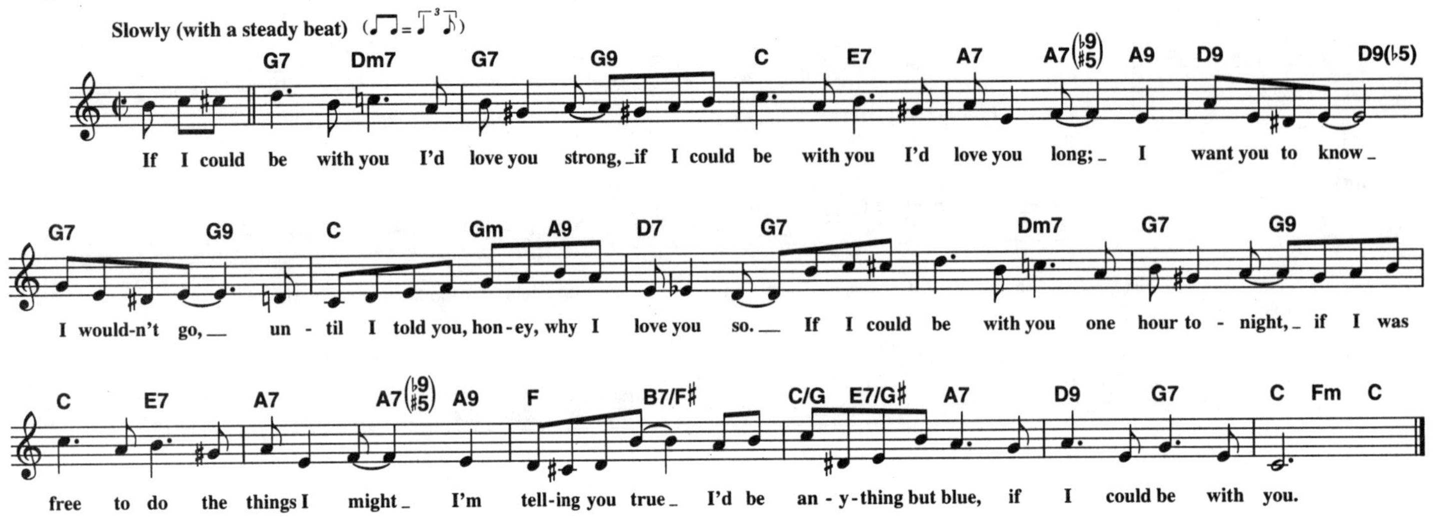
Slowly (with a steady beat)
G7 Dm7 G7 G9 C E7 A7 A7(♭9/♯5) A9 D9 D9(♭5)
If I could be with you I'd love you strong, if I could be with you I'd love you long; I want you to know
G7 G9 C Gm A9 D7 G7 Dm7 G7 G9
I would-n't go, un - til I told you, hon - ey, why I love you so. If I could be with you one hour to - night, if I was
C E7 A7 A7(♭9/♯5) A9 F B7/F♯ C/G E7/G♯ A7 D9 G7 C Fm C
free to do the things I might I'm tell-ing you true I'd be an - y - thing but blue, if I could be with you.

IF I LOVE AGAIN

Words by J.P. MURRAY
Music by BEN OAKLAND

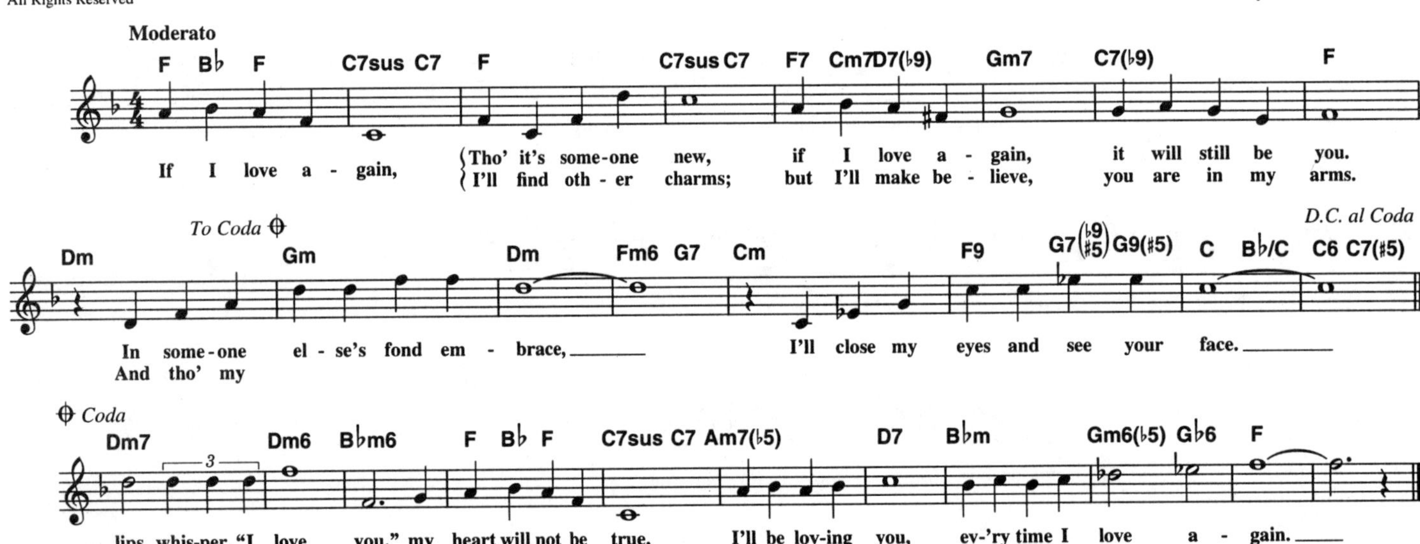
Moderato
F B♭ F C7sus C7 F C7sus C7 F7 Cm7 D7(♭9) Gm7 C7(♭9) F
If I love a - gain,
Tho' it's some-one new, if I love a - gain, it will still be you.
I'll find oth - er charms; but I'll make be - lieve, you are in my arms.
To Coda
D.C. al Coda
Dm Gm Dm Fm6 G7 Cm F9 G7(♭9/♯5) G9(♯5) C B♭/C C6 C7(♯5)
In some-one el - se's fond em - brace, I'll close my eyes and see your face.
And tho' my
Coda
Dm7 Dm6 B♭m6 F B♭ F C7sus C7 Am7(♭5) D7 B♭m Gm6(♭5) G♭6 F
lips whis-per, "I love you," my heart will not be true, I'll be lov-ing you, ev-'ry time I love a - gain.

I'LL BUILD A STAIRWAY TO PARADISE

Words by
B.G. DeSYLVA and IRA GERSHWIN
Music by
GEORGE GERSHWIN

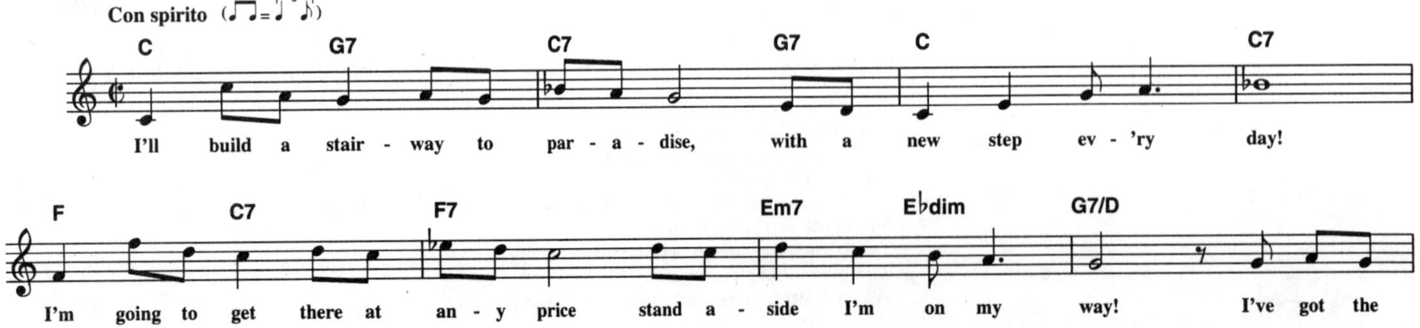
Con spirito
C G7 C7 G7 C C7
I'll build a stair - way to par - a - dise, with a new step ev - 'ry day!
F C7 F7 Em7 E♭dim G7/D
I'm going to get there at an - y price stand a - side I'm on my way! I've got the

blues and up above it's so fair. Shoes! Go on and carry me there!
I'll build a stairway to paradise, with a new step ev'ry day. day.
IF YOU REALLY LOVE ME
Copyright © 1970, 1971 by JOBETE MUSIC CO., INC.
All Rights Reserved
Words and Music by
STEVIE WONDER and
SYREETA WRIGHT
Moderately
Chorus:
Well, if you really love me, won't you tell me, yeah. And
(If you really love me, won't you tell me.)
if you really love me, won't you tell me, yeah. Then I won't have to be playing around.
Rubato
Verse:
1. You call my name, ooh, so sweet to make your kiss incomplete. When your mood is clear you quickly change your ways. Then you say I'm untrue. What am I s'posed to do, be a fool who sits alone waiting for you? But
2. I see the light of your smile calling me. All the while, you are saying, "Baby, it's time to go." First the feeling's alright, then it's gone from sight. So, I'm taking out this time to say...
a tempo
D.S.
Chorus:
Oh, if you really love me, won't you tell me, yeah.
(If you really love me, won't you tell me.)
And if you really love me, won't you tell me, baby, tell me. Then I won't have to be playing around, no.
Repeat ad lib. and fade

IF YOU SAY MY EYES ARE BEAUTIFUL

Words and Music by
ELLIOT WILLENSKY

Slowly and expressively
Verse:
E Emaj7 Amaj9 F♯m7 B9sus
1. If you say my eyes are beau - ti - ful, it's be - cause they're look - ing at you. And if
won - der why I'm smil - ing it's be - cause I'm hap - py with you, and the

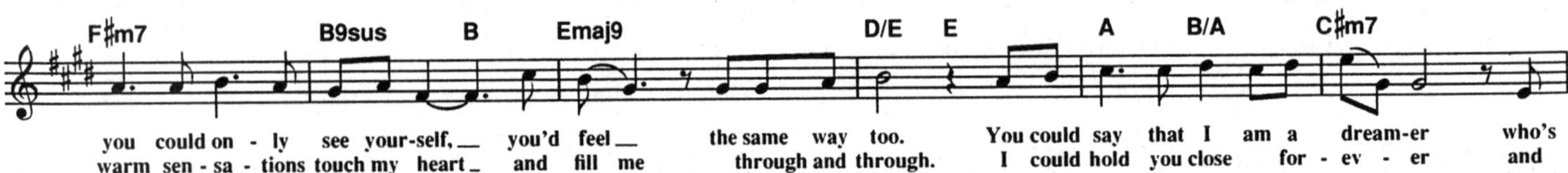
F♯m7 B9sus B Emaj9 D/E E A B/A C♯m7
you could on - ly see your-self, you'd feel the same way too. You could say that I am a dream-er who's
warm sen - sa - tions touch my heart and fill me through and through. I could hold you close for - ev - er and

To Coda
D♯m7(♭5) G♯sus C♯m7 C♯m7/B A B B/A G♯m7 C♯m11 F♯m7 B7sus B7 E(2) G♯m7 Amaj13 Bsus(2)
1.
had a dream come true. If you say my eyes are beau-ti-ful, it's be-cause they're look-ing at you. 2. If you
nev - er let you go. If you say my eyes are beau-ti-ful, it's be-cause I just love you

2.
Bridge:
E(2) C♯m7 F♯ F♯/B B C♯ D♯m G♯ G♯/C♯ C♯ D♯
so. Oh. Now my heart is an o - pen door. Won't you come in - side for more?

D.S. al Coda
Fm7 B♭7 B♭/E♭ E♭ D♯m G♯7sus B/C♯ C♯ B B/A B/G♯ B/F♯
You give love so sweet - ly now. Take my love, take me com-plete - ly now. Oh. 3. If you

Coda
A B B/A G♯m7 C♯m A B B/A G♯m7 C♯m
say my eyes are beau - ti - ful, if you say my eyes are beau - ti - ful, if you

A B B/A G♯m7 C♯m7 F♯m7 Bsus B7(♭9) C/E D/E A
say my eyes, my eyes are beau-ti - ful it's be - cause, (it's be-cause,) they're look - ing at you.

Verse 3:
If you say my eyes are beautiful.
It's because they're looking at you.
And my eyes are just the windows
For the feelings to come through.
And by far you are more beautiful
Than anything I ever knew.
If you . . .
(To Coda)

*Cue size notes indicate vocal harmony.

IF YOU'VE GOT THE MONEY, I'VE GOT THE TIME

Words and Music by
LEFTY FRIZZELL and
JIM BECK

Brightly
A7 Bm A7/C♯ D
1. If you've got the mon - ey, hon-ey I've got the time. We'll go honk-y tonk - in' and

D9 G A7
we'll have a time. We'll have more time, ba - by, all the way down the line. You got the mon-ey, hon-ey,

D
I've got the time. There ain't no need to tar - ry; let's start out to-night. We'll have fun, oh boy,

D9 G A7
oh boy, and we'll do it right. Bring a-long your Ca-dil-lac; leave my old wreck be-hind. If you've

1. 2.
D Bm A7/C♯ D.S. D G D G D G D A7 D
got the mon - ey, hon-ey, I've got the time. 2. We'll go I've got the time.

Verse 2:
We'll go honky tonkin';
Make ev'ry spot in town.
We'll go to the park where it's dark
And we won't fool around.
If you run short of money,
I'll run short of time.
You got no more money, honey,
I've no more time.
If you've got the money, honey,
I've got the time.
We'll go honky tonkin'
And we'll have a time.
Bring along your Cadillac;
Leave my old wreck behind.
If you've got the money, honey,
I've got the time.

I'LL SEE YOU IN MY DREAMS

Words and Music by
GUS KAHN and
ISHAM JONES

Moderately
C7 B♭ B♭m6 E♭7 F A♭dim E F6 D7 Am7
I'll see you in my dreams, hold you in my dreams. Some-one took you out of my arms.
Lips that once were mine, ten - der eyes that shine,
D7 G9 Gm7 C9 Am7(♭5) D7 D7(♭9) Em7(♭5) A7 Dm7 C B♭ Gm7(♭5) C7 F
Still I feel the thrill of your charms. they will light my way to - night. I'll see you in my dreams.

I'LL BE HOME FOR CHRISTMAS

Lyric by KIM GANNON
Music by WALTER KENT

Slowly and freely
Dm7 G7(♭9) Em7 E♭dim7 Dm7 G7 Cmaj7 F♯m7(♭5) E7(♭9)
I'm dream-ing to-night of a place I love e-ven more than I usu - al - ly do. And al-though I know it's a
Slowly with expression
Am7 D9 Dm7 G7 C E♭dim7 Dm7 G7 Dm7 G7 C6 Em7(♭5) A7
long road back, I prom-ise you: I'll be home for Christ - mas; you can plan on
Dm Em7(♭5) Dm/F Gm6 A7 Dm Dm7(♭5) G7 C G/B Am Am7 D7 Am7 D7(♭9) Dm7
me. Please have snow and mis - tle - toe, and pres - ents on the tree.
G7 C E♭dim7 Dm7 G7 Dm7 G7 C6 Em7(♭5) A7 Dm7
Christ - mas Eve will find me where the love - light gleams.
1. 2.
F6 Fm6 C Gm/B♭ A7 D7 Dm7 G7(♭9) C6 Dm7 G7 C6/9
I'll be home for Christ - mas, if on - ly in my dreams. dreams.

IT CAME UPON THE MIDNIGHT CLEAR

Words by EDMUND HAMILTON SEARS
Music by RICHARD STORRS WILLIS

Moderately
B♭ B♭+ E♭/B♭ B♭ E♭ B♭ E♭ C7 F F7/A
1. It came up - on the mid - night clear, that glo - rious song of old from
(2.) through the clo - ven skies they come with peace - ful wings un - furl'd. And
(3.) lo, the days are has - t'ning on by proph - ets seen of old. When
B♭ B♭+ E♭/B♭ B♭ E♭ B♭ E♭ Cm F7 B♭
an - gels bend - ing near the earth to touch their harps of gold. "Peace
still their heav'n - ly mu - sic floats o'er all the wear - y world. A -
with the ev - er - cir - cling years shall come the time fore - told, when
D D7/C Gm/B♭ D7/A Gm Gm/B♭ F/C C7 F F7
on the earth, good will to men. From heav'ns all gra - cious King." The
bove its sad and low - ly plains they bend on hov - 'ring wing. And
the new heav'n and earth shall own the Prince of Peace, their King. And the
1. 2.
B♭ B♭+ E♭/B♭ B♭ E♭ B♭ E♭ Cm F F7 B♭ B♭
world in sol - emn still - ness lay to hear the an - gels sing. 2. Still sing.
ev - er o'er its Ba - bel sounds, the bless - ed an - gels sing. 3. For
whole of world send back the song which now the an - gels

I'LL KEEP YOU SATISFIED

By JOHN LENNON and PAUL McCARTNEY

Moderately

Fm7 Bb7 Eb Fm7 Bb7 Eb Eb7

You don't need an - y - bod - y to hold you, here I stand with my arms o - pen wide. Give me love and re-mem-ber what

Ab Abm Eb Gm Bb7 Eb Fm7 Bb7 Eb Fm7 Bb7 Eb

I told you, I'll keep you sat - is - fied. You don't need an - y - bod - y to kiss you, ev-'ry day I'll be here by your side. Don't go

Eb7 Ab Abm Eb Gm Bb7 Eb Bb Ab Eb

'way, I'm a-fraid that I might miss you, I'll keep you sat - is - fied. You can al - ways get a sim-ple thing like love an - y

Cm Bb Ab Fm7 Bb7 Fm7 Bb7 Eb

time; that it's dif - f'rent with a boy like me and a love like mine. So, be - lieve ev-'ry-thing that I told you; and a -

Fm7 Bb7 Eb Eb7 Ab Abm6 Eb Gm Bb7 Eb Eb

gree that with me by your side, you don't need an - y - bod - y to hold you, I'll keep you sat - is - fied. You don't fied.

I'M A DING DONG DADDY FROM DUMAS

Words and Music by PHIL BAXTER

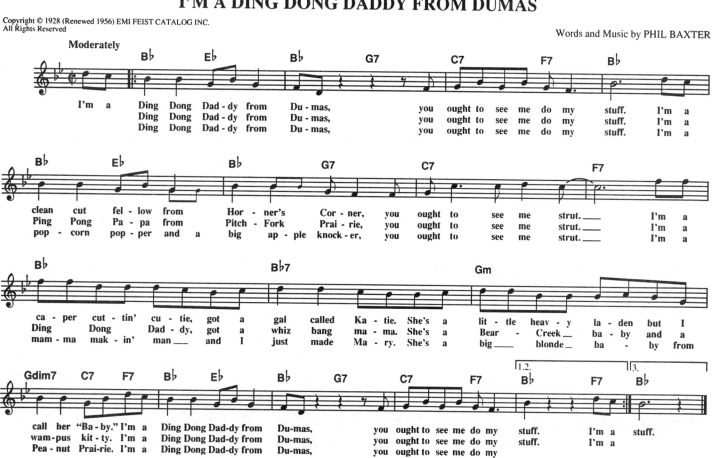

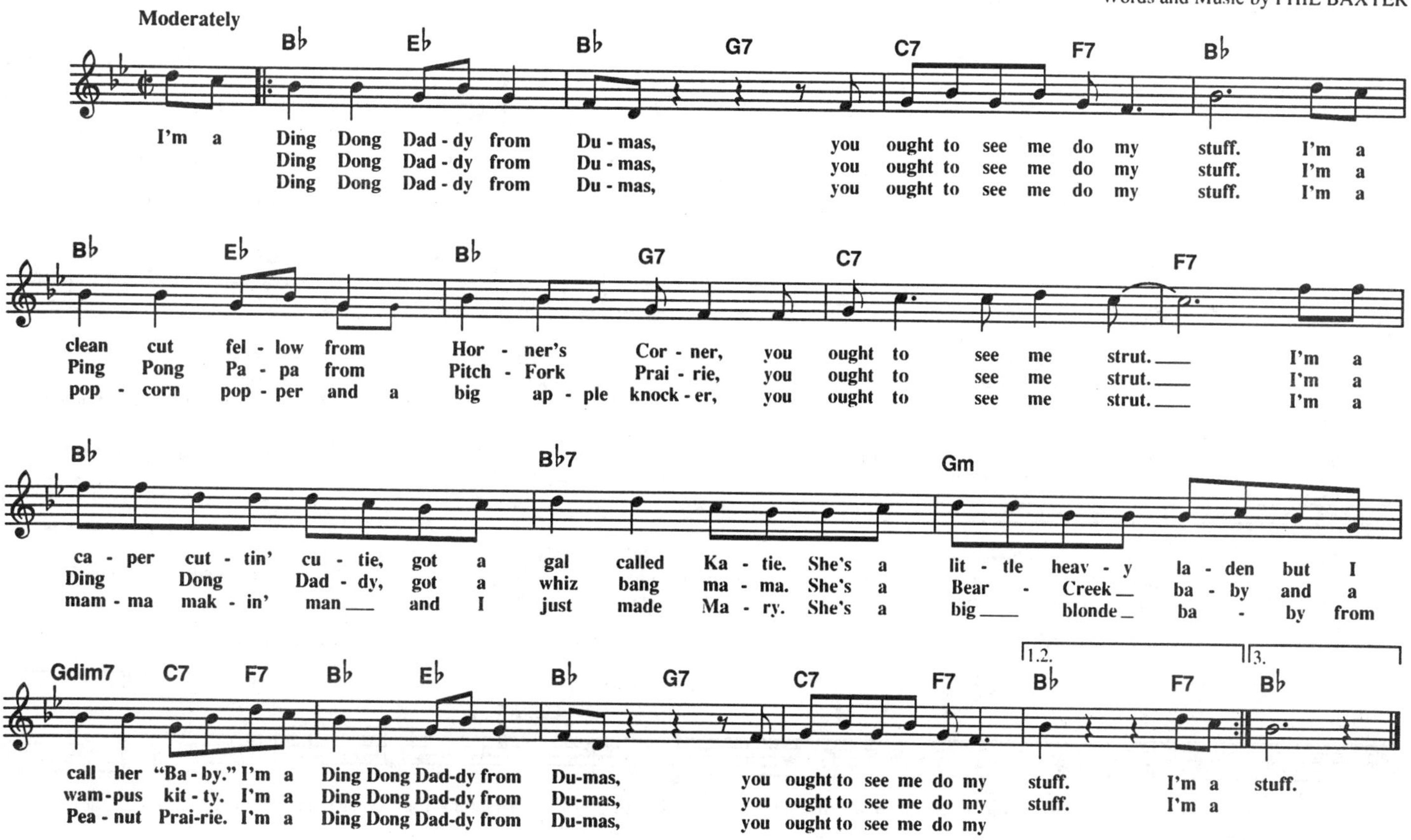

Moderately

Bb Eb Bb G7 C7 F7 Bb

I'm a Ding Dong Dad - dy from Du - mas, you ought to see me do my stuff. I'm a
Ding Dong Dad - dy from Du - mas, you ought to see me do my stuff. I'm a
Ding Dong Dad - dy from Du - mas, you ought to see me do my stuff. I'm a

Bb Eb Bb G7 C7 F7

clean cut fel - low from Hor - ner's Cor - ner, you ought to see me strut. I'm a
Ping Pong Pa - pa from Pitch - Fork Prai - rie, you ought to see me strut. I'm a
pop - corn pop - per and a big ap - ple knock - er, you ought to see me strut. I'm a

Bb Bb7 Gm

ca - per cut - tin' cu - tie, got a gal called Ka - tie. She's a lit - tle heav - y la - den but I
Ding Dong Dad - dy, got a whiz bang ma - ma. She's a Bear - Creek ba - by and a
mam - ma mak - in' man and I just made Ma - ry. She's a big blonde ba - by from

Gdim7 C7 F7 Bb Eb Bb G7 C7 F7 Bb F7 Bb

call her "Ba - by." I'm a Ding Dong Dad-dy from Du-mas, you ought to see me do my stuff. I'm a stuff.
wam-pus kit - ty. I'm a Ding Dong Dad-dy from Du-mas, you ought to see me do my stuff. I'm a
Pea - nut Prai-rie. I'm a Ding Dong Dad-dy from Du-mas, you ought to see me do my

I'LL NEVER LOVE THIS WAY AGAIN
Copyright © 1977 IRVING MUSIC, INC. (BMI)
All Rights Reserved
Words by WILL JENNINGS
Music by RICHARD KERR
Moderate ballad
1. You looked in - side my fan-ta-sies and made each one come true, some-thing no one else had ev - er found
fool will lose to - mor - row reach-ing back for yes ter - day; I won't turn my head in sor - row if you
a way to do. I've kept the mem'-ries one by one, since you took me in;
should go a - way. I'll stand here and re-mem-ber just how good it's been
I know I'll nev-er love this way a - gain.
Chorus:
I know I'll nev - er love this way a - gain, so I keep
hold - in' on be-fore the good is gone. I know I'll nev - er love this way a - gain, hold
on hold on, hold on.
2. A on.
I'LL TAKE YOU HOME AGAIN, KATHLEEN
Copyright © 1993 by BEAM ME UP MUSIC (ASCAP), c/o CPP/BELWIN, Miami, FL 33014
All Rights Reserved
T.P. WESTENDORF
Slowly
1. I'll take you home a - gain, Kath - leen, a - cross the o - cean wild and wide, to where your heart has ev - er been, since first you were my bon - ny bride.
know you love me, Kath-leen, dear, your heart was ev - er fond and true; I al - ways feel when you are near that life holds noth - ing dear but you.
that dear home be - yond the sea, my Kath - leen shall a - gain re - turn. And when thy old friends wel-come thee, thy lov - ing heart will cease to yearn.
The ros - es all have left your cheek, I've watched them fade a - way and die; your voice is sad when-e'er you speak and tears be - dim your lov - ing eye.
The smiles that once you gave to me, I scarce - ly ev - er see them now, tho man - y, man - y times I see a dark - 'ning shad-ow on your brow.
Where laughs the lit - tle sil - ver stream, be - side your moth-er's hum-ble cot, and bright - est rays of sun-shine gleam, there all your grief will be for - got.
Oh, I will take you back, Kath - leen, to where your heart will feel no pain. And when the fields are fresh and green, I'll take you to your home a - gain.
2. I
3. To
gain.

I'LL TAKE YOU THERE

Lyrics and Music by
ALVERTIS ISBELL

Moderately slow

C F G7 C F G7 C F G7 C F G7

I know a place, ain't no-bod-y cry-in' ain't no-bod-y wor-ried, ain't no smil-in' fac-es ly-in' to the

C F G7 C F G7 C F G7 C F G7 C F G7

rac - es. I'll take you there. I'll take you there. I'll take you there.

C F G7 C F G7 C

Repeat and fade

Let me take you now. I'll take you there. Let me take you there.
I'll take you there. I'll take you

I'M STILL IN LOVE WITH YOU

Lyrics and Music by
AL GREEN, WILLIE MITCHELL
and AL JACKSON

Moderately

C Cm7 Am7 Gmaj7 G7

Spend-ing my days think-ing a - bout you girl; be-ing here with you, be-ing

C Cm7 Am7 Gmaj7 G7

here with you I can't ex - plain my-self why I feel like I do, 'Tho it hurt me so to let you know. And I

C Cm7 Am7 Gmaj7 G7

look in your eyes and you let me know how you feel, let me know that love is real-ly real and it
look in your eyes all the years, how I see me lov-ing you and you lov-ing me it

Cm7 Am7 Cm7 Cmaj7 C Bm Am7 D7

To Coda

seems to me that I'm wrapped up in your love. Don't you know that I'm still in love, sho-nuff in love with you.
seems to me that I'm wrapped up in your love. Don't you know that I'm still in love, sho-nuff in love with you.

E♭ F G C Bm Am7 D7 Dm7 Em Dm7 G7

D.S. al Coda

Well, I know that I'm still in love, sho - nuff in love with you. When I

Coda

Cm7 Am7 Cm7 Cmaj7 C Bm Am7 D7

I, I, don't you know that I'm still in love, sho - nuff in love with you.

From the Broadway Musical Production "IRENE"

I'M ALWAYS CHASING RAINBOWS

Words by JOSEPH McCARTHY
Music by HARRY CARROLL

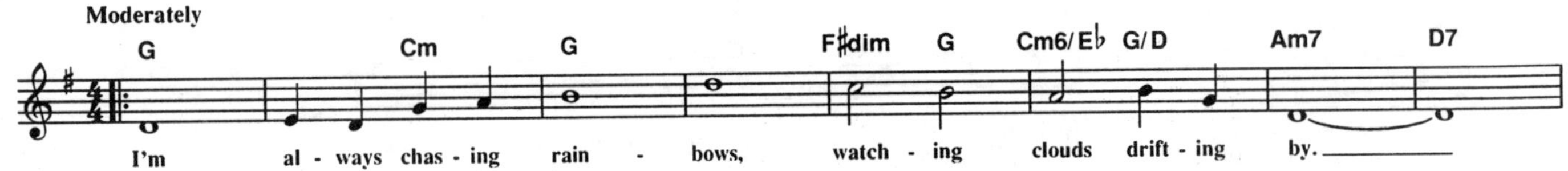
Moderately
G Cm G F♯dim G Cm6/E♭ G/D Am7 D7
I'm al - ways chas - ing rain - bows, watch - ing clouds drift - ing by.

E7 Bm7(♭5) Bm7/E E7 Am E7 Am A7 D7 Ddim D7
My schemes are just like all my dreams, end - ing in the sky.

G7 C E7
Some fel - lows look and find the sun - shine; I al - ways look and find the rain. Some fel - lows make a win - ning

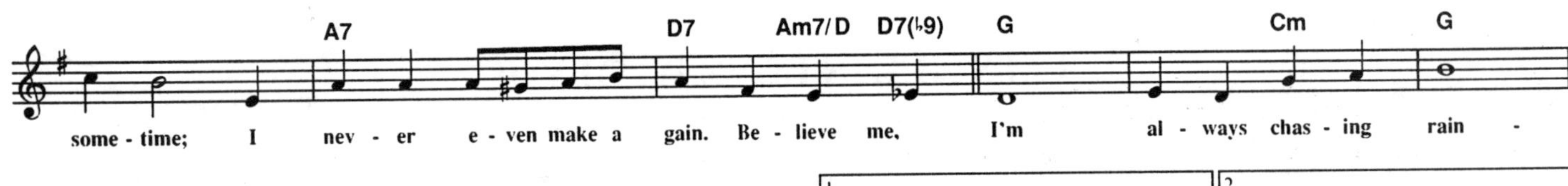
A7 D7 Am7/D D7(♭9) G Cm G
some - time; I nev - er e - ven make a gain. Be - lieve me, I'm al - ways chas - ing rain -

1. 2.
E7 Am Am7/D D7 G G♯dim Am7 D7 G E♭7 G
bows, wait - ing to find a lit - tle blue - bird in vain. vain.

I'M SO LONESOME I COULD CRY

Words and Music by
HANK WILLIAMS

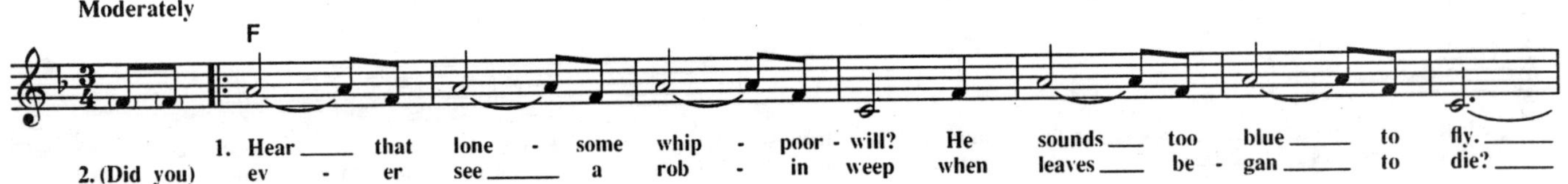
Moderately
F
1. Hear that lone - some whip - poor - will? He sounds too blue to fly.
2. (Did you) ev - er see a rob - in weep when leaves be - gan to die?

F7 B♭ F C7 F
The mid - night train is whin - ing low. I'm so lone - some I could cry. I've
That means he's lost the will to live. I'm so lone - some I could cry. The

F7 B♭
nev - er seen a night so long when time goes crawl - ing by. The moon just
si - lence of a fall - ing star lights up a pur - ple sky. And as I
1. 2.
F C7 F F
went be - hind a cloud to hide its face and cry. 2. Did you cry.
won - der where you are, I'm so lone - some I could

I'M GONNA SIT RIGHT DOWN AND WRITE MYSELF A LETTER

Words by JOE YOUNG
Music by FRED E. AHLERT

Moderately
I'm gon-na sit right down and write my-self a let - ter and make be-lieve it came from you. I'm gon-na
write words, oh, so sweet, they're gon-na knock me off my feet. A lot of kiss-es on the bot-tom, I'll be glad I got 'em. I'm gon-na
smile and say, "I hope you're feel-ing bet - ter" and close "with love" the way you do. I'm gon-na sit right down and
write my - self a let - ter and make be - lieve it came from you. I'm gon-na you.
Slowly
When I'm call - ing you oo - oo oo-oo - oo! Will you an - swer too oo -
oo oo-oo - oo? That means I of - fer my love to you to be your own. If you re -
fuse me, I will be blue and wait - ing all a - lone, but if when you hear my love call ring-ing
clear, and I hear your an - swer-ing ech - o, so dear, then I will know
our love will come true, you'll be - long to me, I'll be - long to you.

INDIAN LOVE CALL

Words by
OTTO HARBACH and
OSCAR HAMMERSTEIN II
Music by
RUDOLF FRIML

I'M LOOKING OVER A FOUR LEAF CLOVER

Words by MORT DIXION
Music by HARRY WOODS

Moderately
B♭
C7
F7
I'm look-ing o - ver a four leaf clo - ver that I o - ver - looked be - fore. One leaf is sun - shine, the

B♭
C7
F7
B♭
se - cond is rain, third is the ros - es that grow in the lane. No need ex - plain-ing, the one re - main - ing is

C7
E♭
Edim7
B♭/F
G7
C7
F7
B♭
some-bod - y I a - dore. I'm look-ing o - ver a four leaf clo - ver that I o - ver - looked be - fore.

IN A SENTIMENTAL MOOD

By DUKE ELLINGTON, IRVING MILLS
and MANNY KURTZ

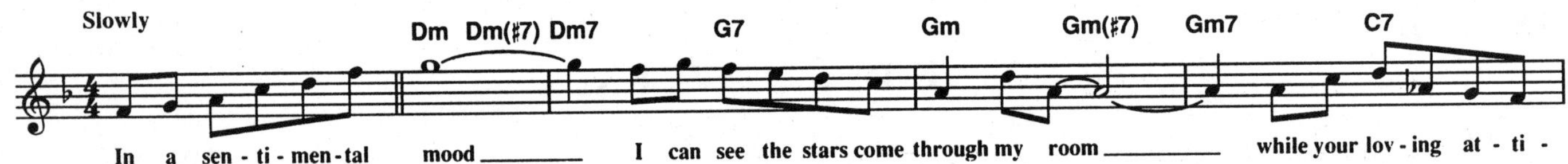
Slowly
Dm Dm(♯7) Dm7
G7
Gm
Gm(♯7)
Gm7
C7
In a sen - ti - men - tal mood I can see the stars come through my room while your lov - ing at - ti -

Dm
D7
Gm
G♭7
F
Dm Dm(♯7) Dm7
G7
tude is like a flame that lights the gloom. On the wings of ev - 'ry kiss drifts a mel - o - dy so

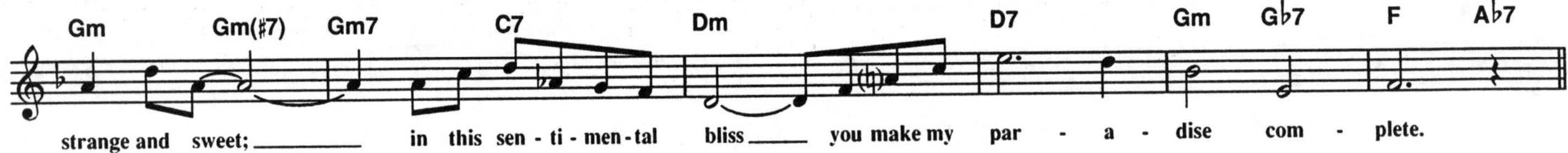
Gm
Gm(♯7)
Gm7
C7
Dm
D7
Gm
G♭7
F
A♭7
strange and sweet; in this sen - ti - men - tal bliss you make my par - a - dise com - plete.

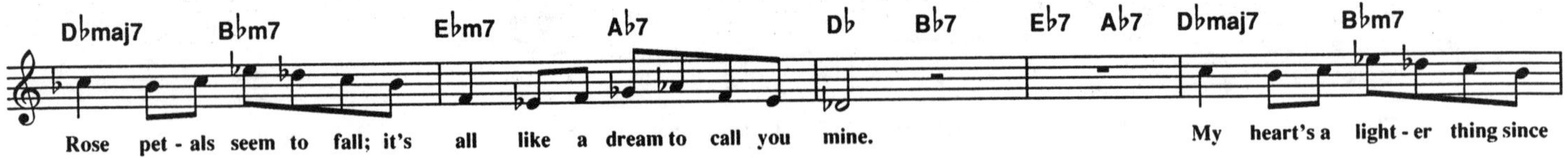
D♭maj7
B♭m7
E♭m7
A♭7
D♭
B♭7
E♭7
A♭7
D♭maj7
B♭m7
Rose pet - als seem to fall; it's all like a dream to call you mine. My heart's a light - er thing since

E♭m7
A♭7
C7
Dm Dm(♯7) Dm7
G7
you made this night a thing di - vine. In a sen - ti - men - tal mood I'm with - in a world so

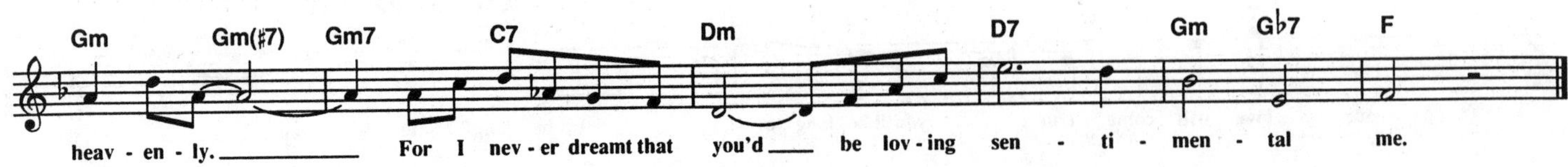
Gm
Gm(♯7)
Gm7
C7
Dm
D7
Gm
G♭7
F
heav - en - ly. For I nev - er dreamt that you'd be lov - ing sen - ti - men - tal me.

I'M SITTING ON TOP OF THE WORLD

Words by TED KOEHLER
Music by JIMMY McHUGH

Moderately

C+ F F7 B♭ F G7 C7

I'm sit - ting on top of the world, just roll - ing a - long, just roll - ing a -
quit - ting the blues of the world, just sing - ing a song, just sing - ing a
sit - ting on top of the world, just roll - ing a - long, just roll - ing a -

1.3. *Fine* 2.

F C+ F B♭ E7

long. I'm "Glo - ry Hal - le - lu - jah," I just phoned the Par - son, "Hey,
long. song.

Am Dm A+ Dm7 G9 C7 C+

D.S. 𝄋 *al Fine*

Par get read - y to call." Just like Hump - ty, Dump - ty, I'm go - ing to fall. I'm

I'M WALKIN'

Words and Music by
ANTOINE DOMINO and
DAVE BARTHOLOMEW

Moderate swing rock
F B♭7 F
I'm walk-in'; yes in - deed, and I'm talk - in' 'bout you and me.
lone - ly as I can be. I'm wait - in' for your com - pa - ny.
I'm hop - in'

1.3. 2.4.
C7 F F F7 B♭7
you'll come back to me, yeah. I'm me. What ya gon - na do when the

F B♭7 F B♭7 F
well runs dry? You're gon - na run a - way and hide. I'm gon - na run right by your side. For
You're gon - na sit right down and cry. What'ya gon - na do when I say, "Bye - bye"?

G7 C7 F B♭7
you pret - ty ba - by, I'll e - ven die.
All you're gon - na do is dry your eye.
I'm walk - in'; yes, in - deed. I'm talk - in' 'bout

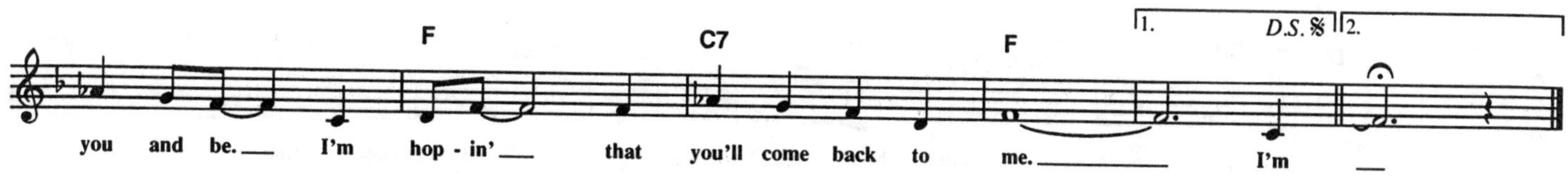
F C7 F
1. D.S. 𝄋 2.
you and be. I'm hop - in' that you'll come back to me. I'm

I'M THRU WITH LOVE

Words by GUS KAHN
Music by MATT MALNECK and FUD LIVINGSTON

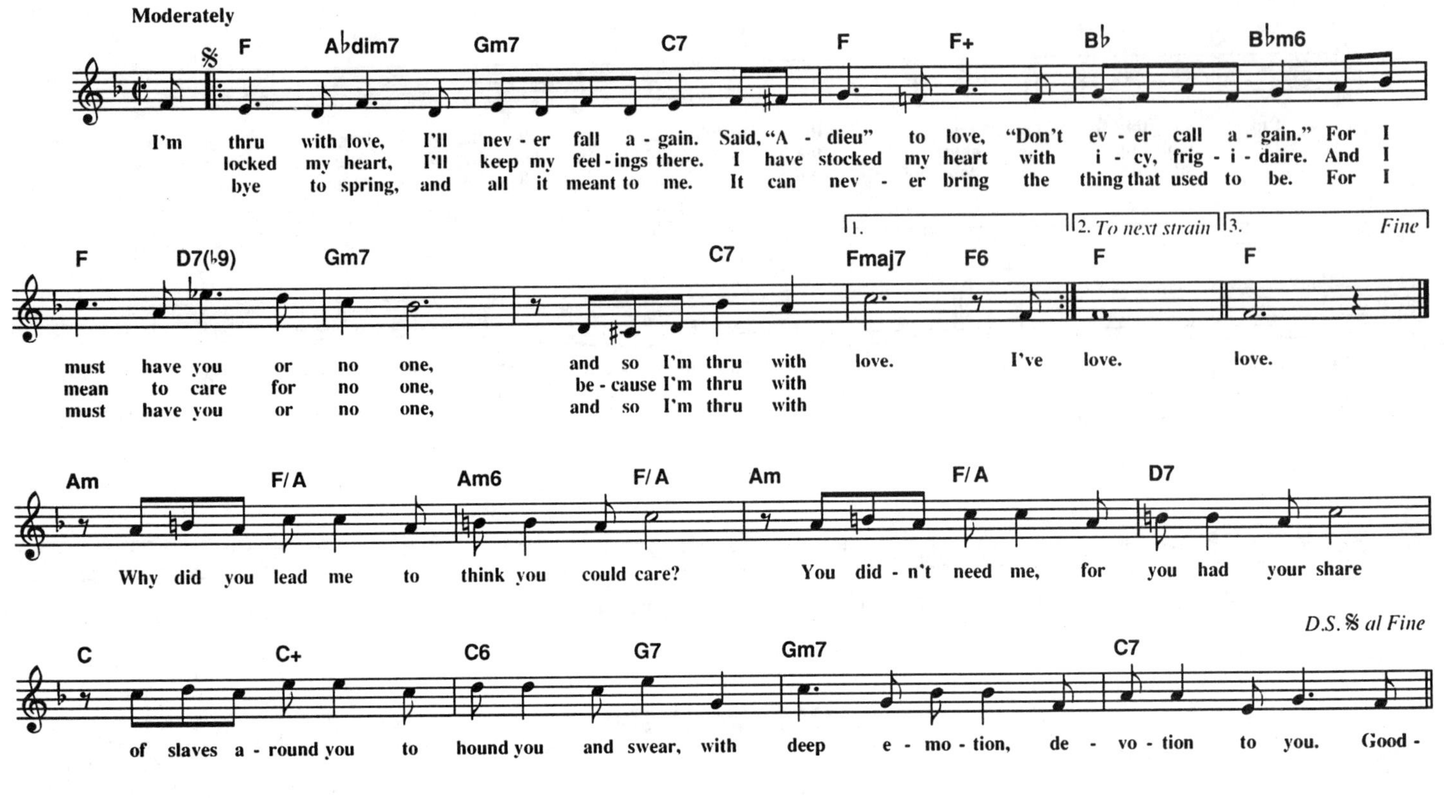
Moderately
F Abdim7 Gm7 C7 F F+ Bb Bbm6
I'm thru with love, I'll nev - er fall a - gain. Said, "A - dieu" to love, "Don't ev - er call a - gain." For I
locked my heart, I'll keep my feel - ings there. I have stocked my heart with i - cy, frig - i - daire. And I
bye to spring, and all it meant to me. It can nev - er bring the thing that used to be. For I
F D7(b9) Gm7 C7 Fmaj7 F6 F F
1. 2. To next strain 3. Fine
must have you or no one, and so I'm thru with love. I've love. love.
mean to care for no one, be - cause I'm thru with
must have you or no one, and so I'm thru with
Am F/A Am6 F/A Am F/A D7
Why did you lead me to think you could care? You did - n't need me, for you had your share
C C+ C6 G7 Gm7 C7
D.S. al Fine
of slaves a - round you to hound you and swear, with deep e - mo - tion, de - vo - tion to you. Good -

IN A MELLOW TONE

By DUKE ELLINGTON and MILT GABLER

Moderate swing
Bb7 Eb7 Abmaj7 Ebm7
In a mel - low tone, feel - in' fan - cy free. And I'm not a - lone,
Ab7 Dbmaj7 Db Ddim7 Abmaj7/Eb
I got com - pa - ny. Ev - 'ry - thing's O. K. the live long day.
F7 Bb7 Eb7 F7 Bb7
With this mel - low song I can't go wrong. In a mel - low tone,
Eb7 Abmaj7 Ebm7 Ab7 Dbmaj7
that's the way to live. If you mope and groan, some - thing's got - ta give. Just go your way,
Db7 Ddim7 Abmaj7/Eb F7 Bb7 Eb7 Ab (G7 Gb7 F7)
and laugh and play. There's joy un - known in a mel - low tone.

I GET A KICK OUT OF YOU

Words and Music by
COLE PORTER

Moderato
I get no kick from cham - pagne, Mere al - co -
hol does - n't thrill me at all, So tell me why should it be true,
That I Get A Kick Out Of You? Some get a
kick from co - caine I'm sure that if I had ev - en one
sniff it would bore me ter - rif - ic - 'ly too. Yet I Get A Kick
Out Of You. I get a kick ev - 'ry time I
see you're stand - ing there be - fore me. I get a
kick tho' it's clear to me You ob - vious - ly don't a -
dore me. I get no kick in a plane,
Fly - ing too high with some {gal guy} in the sky is my i - dea of noth - ing to
do. Yet I Get A Kick Out Of You.

IN MY MERRY OLDSMOBILE

Words by VINCENT BRYAN
Music by GUS EDWARDS

Moderate waltz

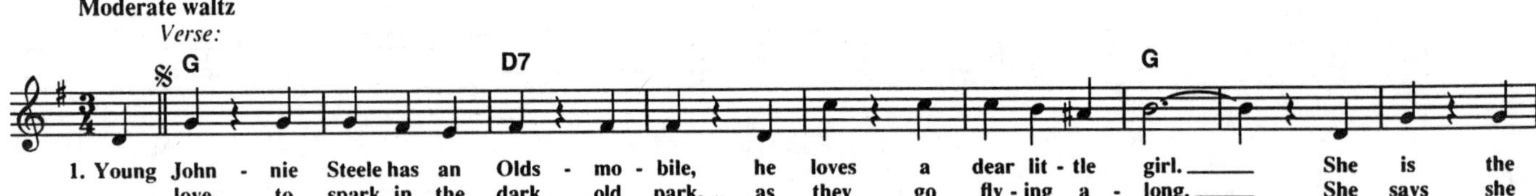
Verse:
G D7 G
1. Young John - nie Steele has an Olds - mo - bile, he loves a dear lit - tle girl. She is the
love to spark in the dark old park, as they go fly - ing a - long. She says she

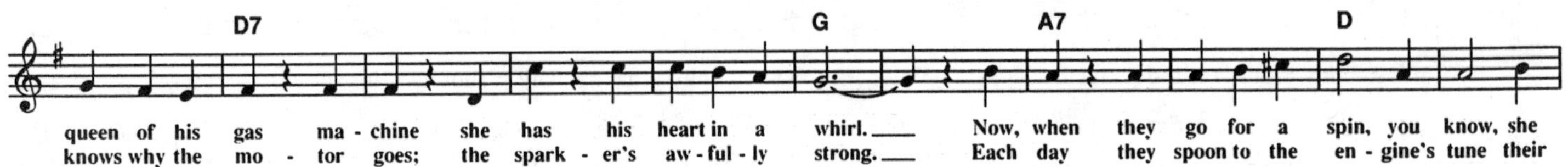
D7 G A7 D
queen of his gas ma - chine she has his heart in a whirl. Now, when they go for a spin, you know, she
knows why the mo - tor goes; the spark - er's aw - ful - ly strong. Each day they spoon to the en - gine's tune their

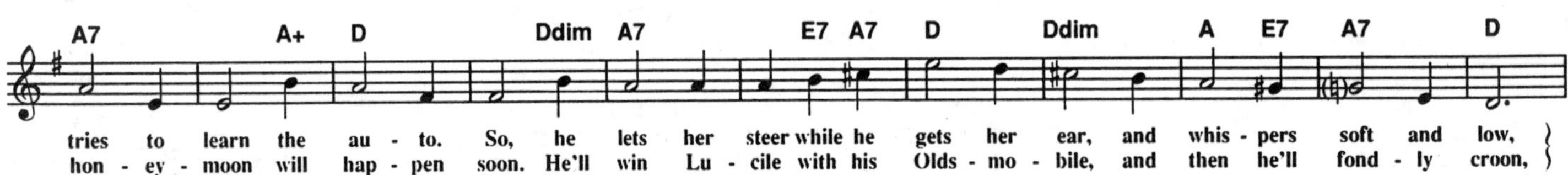
A7 A+ D Ddim A7 E7 A7 D Ddim A E7 A7 D
tries to learn the au - to. So, he lets her steer while he gets her ear, and whis - pers soft and low,
hon - ey - moon will hap - pen soon. He'll win Lu - cile with his Olds - mo - bile, and then he'll fond - ly croon,

Chorus:
D7 G E7 A7 D7
"Come a - way with me, Lu - cile, in my mer - ry Olds - mo - bile. Down the road of life we'll

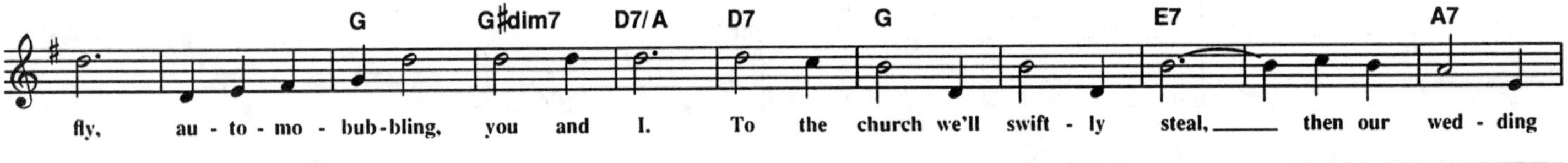
G G♯dim7 D7/A D7 G E7 A7
fly, au - to - mo - bub - bling, you and I. To the church we'll swift - ly steal, then our wed - ding

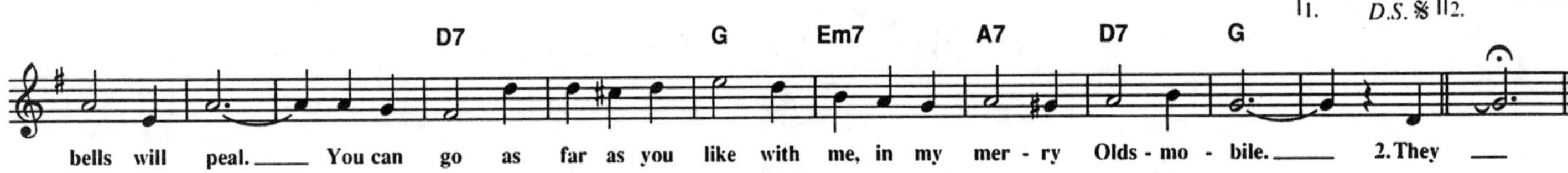
D7 G Em7 A7 D7 G
1. D.S. 2.
bells will peal. You can go as far as you like with me, in my mer - ry Olds - mo - bile. 2. They

IN THE EVENING BY THE MOONLIGHT

Words and Music by
JAMES A. BLAND

Moderately

F A7 Dm F7 B♭ B♭m F
In the eve - ning by the moon - light, you could hear those dark - ies sing - in'. In the
A7 Dm G7 C7 F Fmaj7
eve - nin' by the moon - light, you can hear those ban - joes ring - in'. How the old folks would en -
F7 B♭ B♭m F D7 G7 C7 F
joy it, they would sit all night and lis - ten as we sang in the eve - ning by the moon - light.

I'M GETTING SENTIMENTAL OVER YOU

Lyrics by NED WASHINGTON
Music by GEORGE BASSMAN

Moderately slow
F E7 Cm D7(♯5) D7 G7 1. C7 F D7(♭9) Gm7 C7
Nev - er thought I'd fall, but_ now I hear love call;
Things you say and do, just_ thrill me through and through.
I'm get - in' sen - ti - men-tal o - ver you.

2. C7 C7(♯5) F B♭ F E7 Am Am(♯5) B7 Dm
men - tal o - ver you. I thought I was hap - py; I could live with - out love.

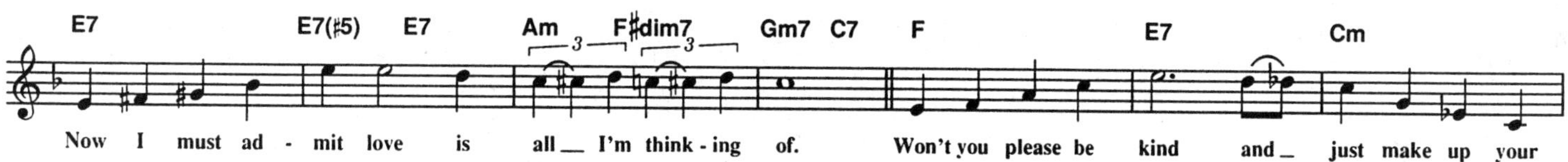
E7 E7(♯5) E7 Am F♯dim7 Gm7 C7 F E7 Cm
Now I must ad - mit love is all_ I'm think - ing of. Won't you please be kind and_ just make up your

D7(♯5) D7 G7 C7 F Cm/E♭ D7(♯5) D7 G7 C7 C7(♯5) F
mind that you'll be sweet and gen - tle, be gen - tle with me, be - cause I'm sen - ti - men - tal o - ver you.

I'M IN THE MOOD FOR LOVE

By JIMMY McHUGH
and DOROTHY FIELDS

Moderately
C F6 G7 C Em7 E♭dim Dm7
I'm in the mood for love, sim - ply be - cause you're near me.
Heav-en is in your eyes, bright as the stars we're un - der.
If there's a cloud a - bove, if it should rain we'll let it.
Fun - ny, but when you're near me,
Oh! Is it an - y won - der?
But for to - night, for - get it!

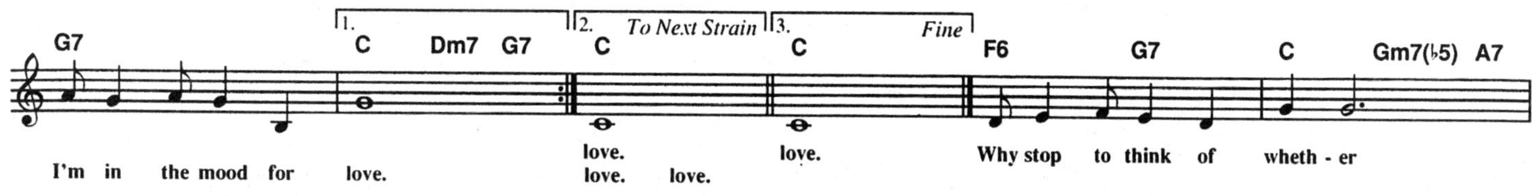
G7 1. C Dm7 G7 2. To Next Strain C 3. C Fine F6 G7 C Gm7(♭5) A7
I'm in the mood for love. love. love. love. love.
Why stop to think of wheth - er

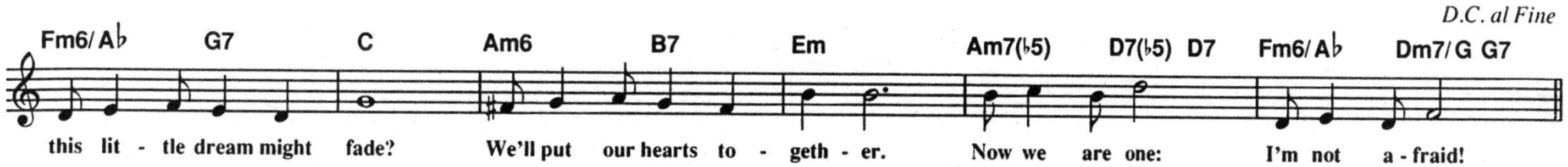
D.C. al Fine
Fm6/A♭ G7 C Am6 B7 Em Am7(♭5) D7(♭5) D7 Fm6/A♭ Dm7/G G7
this lit - tle dream might fade? We'll put our hearts to - geth - er. Now we are one: I'm not a - fraid!

INDIAN SUMMER

Words by AL DUBIN
Music by VICTOR HERBERT

Slowly, with feeling
G
D+
G
D+
Gmaj7
Sum - mer, you old In - dian sum - mer, you're the tear that comes af - ter
o - ver some heart that is bro - ken by a word that some - bod - y

G6
Am7
To Coda
D7
B7
Em
June - time's laugh - ter. You see so man - y dreams that don't come true,
left un - spo - ken.

Em7 (small notes optional)
A9
Bm
D7
D.C. al Coda
dreams we fash - ioned when sum - mer - time was new. You are here to watch

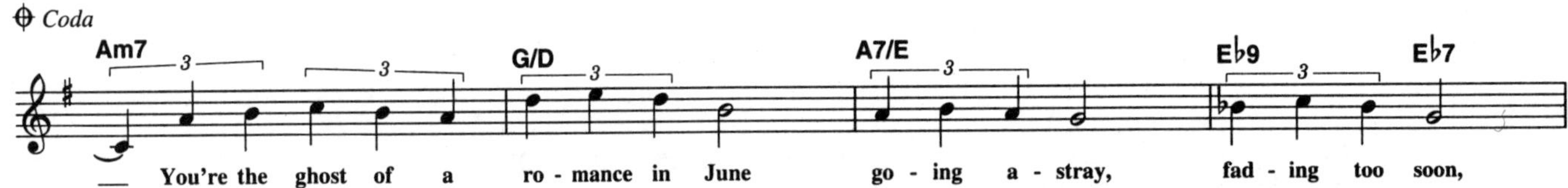
Coda
Am7
G/D
A7/E
E♭9
E♭7
You're the ghost of a ro - mance in June go - ing a - stray, fad - ing too soon,

B♭m7
E♭7
G
D+
G6
That's why I say, "fare - well to you, In - dian sum - mer."

From the Paramount Picture *"HERE COMES THE GROOM"*

IN THE COOL, COOL, COOL OF THE EVENING

Words by JOHNNY MERCER
Music by HOAGY CARMICHAEL

Moderately
F
F♯dim7
Gm
Gm7
C7
In the cool, cool, cool of the eve - nin', tell 'em I'll be there. In the cool, cool, cool of the

C7(♭9)
F6
C7
F
Cm7
F7
eve - nin', bet - ter save a chair. When the par - ty's get - tin' a glow on, 'n' sing - in' fills the air,

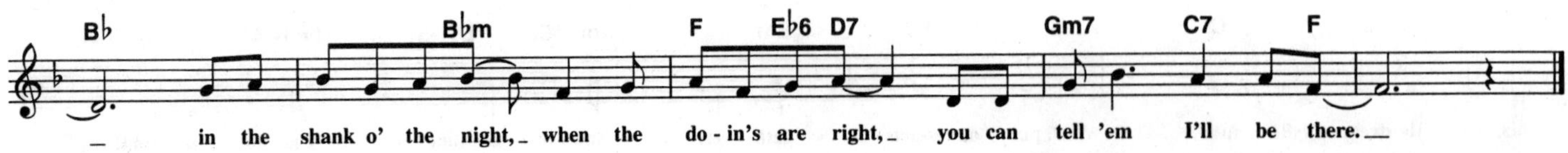
B♭
B♭m
F
E♭6
D7
Gm7
C7
F
in the shank o' the night, when the do - in's are right, you can tell 'em I'll be there.

IN THE GOOD OLD SUMMERTIME

Words by REN SHIELDS
Music by GEORGE EVANS

Moderately
In the good old sum - mer - time, in the good old sum - mer - time, stroll - ing thro' the
shad - y lanes with your ba - by mine; you hold her hand and she holds yours, and that's a ver - y good
sign that she's your toot - sie woot - sie in the good old sum - mer - time. In the time.
From the United Artists Motion Picture "IN THE HEAT OF THE NIGHT"
IN THE HEAT OF THE NIGHT
Copyright © 1967 EMI U CATALOG INC.
All Rights Reserved
Words by MARILYN and ALAN BERGMAN
Music by QUINCY JONES
Slow gospel (12/8) feel)
In the heat of the night, seems like a cold sweat creep-in' 'cross my brow.
In the heat of the night, I'm feel - ing moth - er - less some - how. Stars with e - vil
eyes stare from the skies, all mean and bright. (In the heat of the night.) Ain't a wom - an yet been born,
knows how to make the morn - in' come. So hard to keep con - trol when I'd sell my soul for just a lit - tle
light! (In the heat of the night.) In the heat of the night, when I got trou - ble wall to wall,
I re - peat in the night must be an end - in' to it all!
Hold on it won't be long, just you be strong, and it - 'll be all right! (In the heat of the night.)

IN THE MIDNIGHT HOUR

Words by WILSON PICKETT
Music by STEVE CROPPER

Moderate rock

B♭ G F E♭ C F C F

Bass

I'm gon - na

C F C F C F C F C F

wait 'til the mid - night hour; __ that's when my love comes tum-bl-ing __ down. __ I'm gon-na wait 'til the mid-night hour __
wait 'til __ stars __ come out __ and see that twin - kle in your __ eyes. __ I'm gon-na wait 'til the mid-night hour; __

C F C F C F G F

__ when there's no one else __ a - round. __ I'm gon-na take you girl, __ and hold __ you, and
__ that's when my love be - gins __ to shine. __ You'll be the on - ly girl __ I'll love, ______ and

G F C F C F 1. C F

do all the things I told __ you in the mid-night hour. __ Yes I am, __ oh, yes, I am. __
real - ly love __ you so __ in the mid-night hour. __ Oh __ yeah, __ in the mid-night hour. __

B♭ G 2. C F C F C F C F

Repeat and fade

I'm gon-na __ I'm gon-na wait 'til the mid-night hour. __ I'm gon-na

IN THE MISTY MOONLIGHT

By CINDY WALKER

Moderate rock
C7 F C Dm7
In the mist - y moon-light by the flick-'ring fire - light, an - y - place is all __ right
way land on the trop - ic sea __ sand, if your hand's in my __ hand
1. G7 Dm7 C C7 2. G7 C C7 F
long as I'm with you. In a far a - I won't __ be blue. Way up on the moun-tain or 'way down in the
C D7 G7 C7
val - ley, I know I'll be hap - py __ an - y - place, an - y - where, I don't care. In the mist - y
F C Dm7 G7 C F Cmaj7
moon-light by the flick-'ring fire - light, an - y-place is all __ right long as you are __ there. ______

IN A SIMPLE WAY I LOVE YOU

From the Musical "I'M GETTING MY ACT TOGETHER AND TAKING IT ON THE ROAD"

© 1978 FIDDLEBACK MUSIC PUBLISHING CO., INC.
All Rights Reserved
A TOMMY VALANDO PUBLICATION
Lyrics by
GRETCHEN CRYER
Music by
NANCY FORD
Moderately slow
In a sim-ple way I love you, that's all that I can do.
In a sim-ple way I love you when you're reach-ing out to me.
I'll make mu-sic while you sing your song, I un-der-stand what you're go-ing through.
I will be there when you need a friend, I'll help you be what you want to be.
I hear your voice sing out, just let it go. I'll give you room to breathe and room to grow.
In a sim-ple way I love you, I'm here to see you through.
I'll make mu-sic while you sing your song while you do what you have to do.
I'll be be-side you rain or shine, Love has man-y fac-es, and one of them is mine.
IN VERADERO
© 1952 WB MUSIC CORP. (Renewed)
All Rights Reserved
By NEAL HEFTI
Moderate samba (in 2)
To Coda
D.S. al Coda
Coda

IN THE SHADE OF THE OLD APPLE TREE
Copyright © 1993 by BEAM ME UP MUSIC (ASCAP), c/o CPP/BELWIN, INC., Miami, FL 33014
All Rights Reserved
Words by HARRY H. WILLIAMS
Music by EGBERT VAN ALSTYNE
Brightly
In the shade of the old ap - ple tree, where the love in your eyes I could see, when the voice that I heard, like the song of the bird, seem'd to whis - per sweet mu - sic to me; I could
hear the dull buzz of the bee in the blos - soms as you said to me, with a heart that is true, "I'll be wait - ing for you in the shade of the old ap - ple tree."
INDIAN RESERVATION
(The Lament of the Cherokee Reservation Indian)
Copyright © 1963 (Renewed 1991) by ACUFF-ROSE MUSIC, INC.
All Rights Reserved
Words and Music by
JOHN D. LOUDERMILK
Moderately
They took the whole Cher-o-kee Na-tion; put us on this res - er - va-tion. Took a - way our way of life; tom - a - hawk and the bow and knife. Took a - way our na - tive tongue. Taught their Eng-lish to our young, and all the beads we made by hand are now - a - days made in Ja - pan.
Cher-o-kee peo-ple, Cher-o-kee tribe, so proud you lived, so proud you died. They took the whole In-di-an Na-tion, locked us on this res - er - va-tion. Though I wear a shirt and tie, I'm still a red man deep in - side. But may - be some-day when they've learned, Cher-o-kee Na - tion will re - turn.

From the United Artists Motion Picture "INSPECTOR CLOUSEAU"

INSPECTOR CLOUSEAU THEME

By KEN THORNE

Moderately

Dm Dm(maj7) Dm7 G7 Gm6

Dm E7 A7(♭9) A7 1. Dm6 B♭9 Dm6 B♭9

2. Dm6 B♭9 Dm6 D9 B♭ D7 Gm D+ Gm7

C9 C7 F D7 Gm D+ Gm7 C7 Cm6 Gm

A7 E7 A7 Dm Dm(maj7) Dm7 G7

Gm6 Dm E7 A7 Dm

IN THE SWEET BY AND BY

Words by S.F. BENNETT
Music by J.P. WEBSTER

Moderately
Verse:
G C G D
There's a land that is fair - er than day, and by faith, we can see it a - far. For the
sing on that beau - ti - ful shore the mel - o - di - ous songs of the blest. And our
boun - ti - ful Fa - ther a - bove, we will of - fer our trib - ute of praise for the

G C G C G/D D G
Chorus:
D
Fa - ther waits o - ver the way to pre - pare us a dwell-ing place there.
spir - it shall sor - row no more not a sigh for the bless - ing of rest.
glo - ri - ous gift of His love and the bless-ings that hal - low our days.
In the sweet by and by, we shall
(In the sweet) (by and by,)
D7 G C G/D D7 1.2. G 3. G
meet on that beau - ti - ful shore. In the sweet by and by, we shall rest on that beau - ti - ful shore. 2. We shall shore.
3. To our
(by and by.) (In the sweet) (by and by.)

IN YOUR EYES

Words by DAN HILL
Music by MICHAEL MASSER

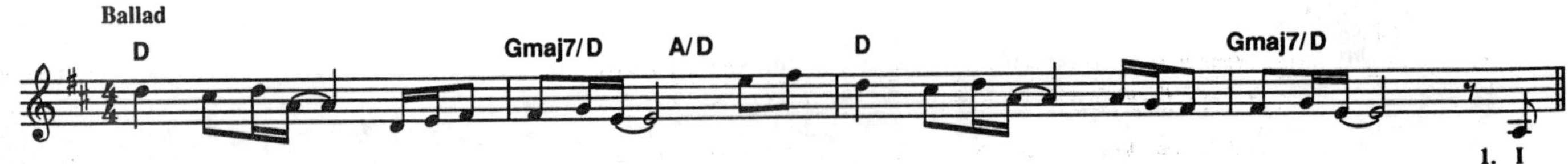
Ballad
D
Gmaj7/D
A/D
D
Gmaj7/D
1. I

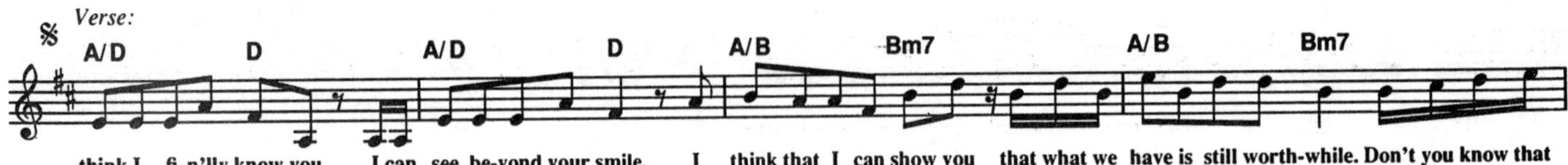
Verse:
A/D
D
A/D
D
A/B
Bm7
A/B
Bm7
think I fi-n'lly know you. I can see be-yond your smile. I think that I can show you that what we have is still worth-while. Don't you know that

Em7
D/F♯
F♯
F♯7/A♯
Bm
Em7
D/F♯
G6/A
A/B
B7
love's just like the thread _ that keeps un - rav - el - ing, but then _ it ties us back to - geth - er in the end? In your

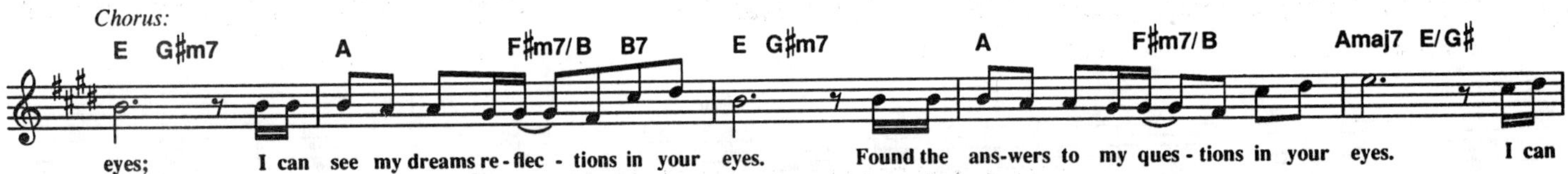
Chorus:
E
G♯m7
A
F♯m7/B
B7
E
G♯m7
A
F♯m7/B
Amaj7
E/G♯
eyes; I can see my dreams re - flec - tions in your eyes. Found the ans-wers to my ques - tions in your eyes. I can

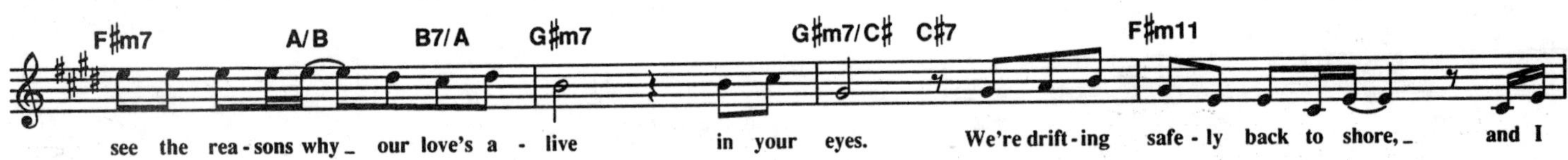
F♯m7
A/B
B7/A
G♯m7
G♯m7/C♯
C♯7
F♯m11
see the rea - sons why _ our love's a - live in your eyes. We're drift - ing safe - ly back to shore, _ and I

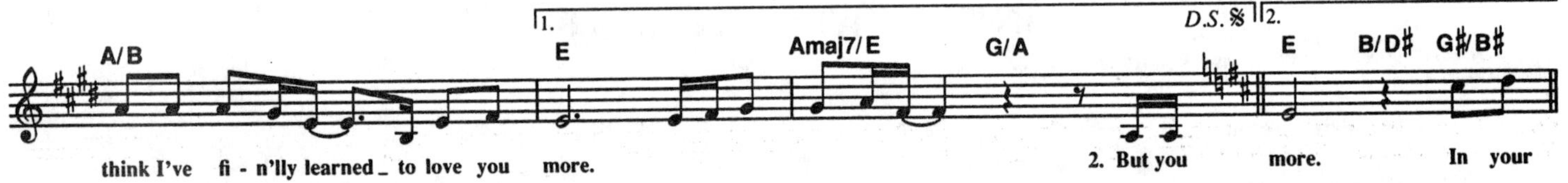
1.
D.S. 𝄋
2.
A/B
E
Amaj7/E
G/A
E
B/D♯
G♯/B♯
think I've fi - n'lly learned _ to love you more. 2. But you more. In your

C♯m
F♯m7
A/B
B7/A
G♯m7
G♯m7/C♯
C♯7
F♯m11
eyes; I can see the rea-sons why our love's a - live, you and I. We're drift-ing safe - ly back to shore, _ and I

F♯m7/B
E
B/E
Amaj7/E
B/E
E
B/E
Amaj7/E
B/E
E
rit.
think I've fi-n'lly learned _ to love you more.

Verse 2:
But you warned me that life changes, and that no one really knows
Whether time would make us strangers, or whether time would make us grow.
Even though the winds of time will change, in a world where nothing stays the same,
Through it all our love will still remain.
(To Chorus:)

IN-A-GADDA-DA-VIDA

Words and Music by
DOUG INGLE

Moderate rock
Dm
In - A - Gad - da - Da - Vi - da, hon - ey, don't you know that I love you?
In - A - Gad - da - Da - Vi - da, ba - by, don't you know that I'll al - ways be true?
G E7 G7 E A
Oh, won't you come with me and take my hand? Oh, won't you
F#7 A F# B Dm
come with me and walk this land? Please take my hand!

IRELAND MUST BE HEAVEN
(For My Mother Came from There)

Words and Music by
JOSEPH McCARTHY, HOWARD JOHNSON
and FRED FISHER

Moderately
B♭ F7 B♭ D7 E♭ Edim7 B♭/F F7 B♭ E♭ B♭ F/C Gm7/C C7 F F7
Ire-land must be Heav-en, for an an - gel came from there. I nev - er knew a liv - ing soul one half as sweet or fair. For her
B♭ F7 B♭ G7 C7 F7 B♭ F7 B♭ Fm6/A♭ G7 C9 E♭m/F F7 B♭
eyes are like the star-light, and the white clouds match her hair. Sure Ire-land must be Heav - en, for my moth-er came from there.

IRISH WASHERWOMAN

TRADITIONAL

Moderately fast
G D7 G
D7 1. G 2. G D7
C G C G D7 1. G 2. G

From the Broadway Musical Production "IRENE"

IRENE

Words by JOSEPH McCARTHY
Music by HARRY TIERNEY

Moderately

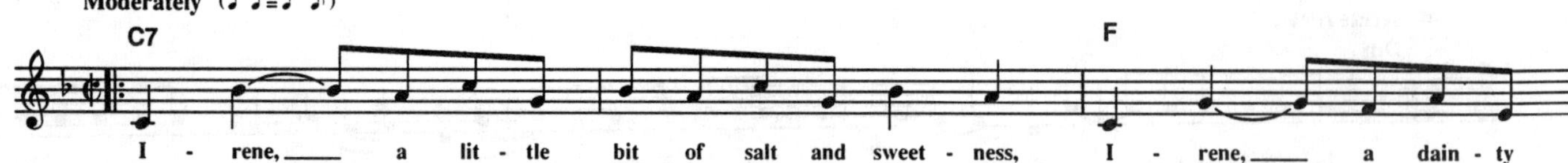
C7
F
I - rene, a lit - tle bit of salt and sweet - ness, I - rene, a dain - ty

Fdim7 Gm7 F D7 Gm7 C7
slip of rare com-plete - ness. Man-ner - i - sm, mag-net - i - sm, eyes of youth in - vit - ing, danc-ing by with glanc-ing eye, the

Bdim7 C7/B♭ F6/A D♭7/A♭ C7 F7 B♭
flush of her ex - cit - ing. Si - ren, the sort who cap-tures hearts to charm them. Care - ful, be - ware!

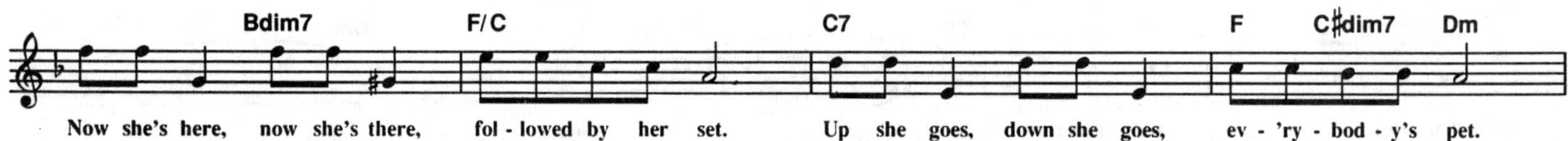
Bdim7 F/C C7 F C♯dim7 Dm
Now she's here, now she's there, fol - lowed by her set. Up she goes, down she goes, ev - 'ry - bod - y's pet.

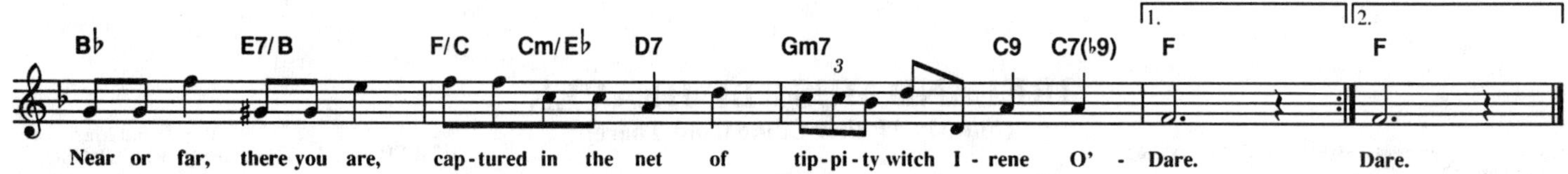
B♭ E7/B F/C Cm/E♭ D7 Gm7 C9 C7(♭9) F F
1. 2.
Near or far, there you are, cap-tured in the net of tip-pi-ty witch I - rene O' - Dare. Dare.

From the Paramount Picture "ISN'T IT ROMANTIC"

ISN'T IT ROMANTIC

Words and Music by
LORENZ HART and
RICHARD RODGERS

Moderately

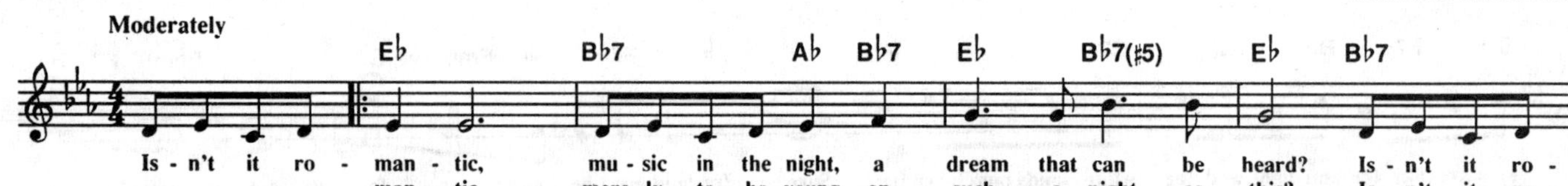
E♭ B♭7 A♭ B♭7 E♭ B♭7(♯5) E♭ B♭7
Is - n't it ro - man - tic, mu - sic in the night, a dream that can be heard? Is - n't it ro -
man - tic, mere - ly to be young on such a night as this? Is - n't it ro -

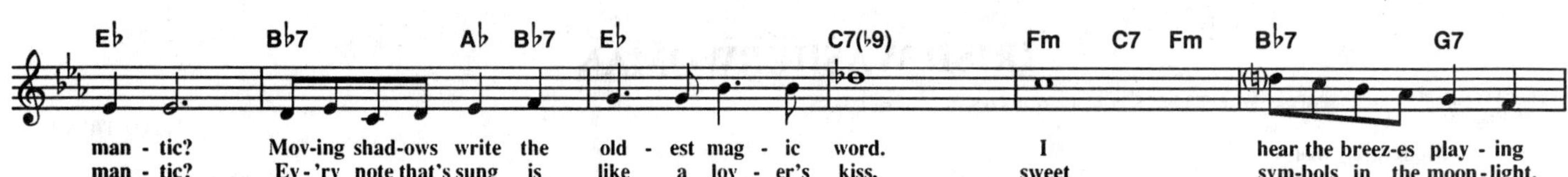
E♭ B♭7 A♭ B♭7 E♭ C7(♭9) Fm C7 Fm B♭7 G7
man - tic? Mov-ing shad-ows write the old - est mag - ic word. I hear the breez-es play - ing
man - tic? Ev - 'ry note that's sung is like a lov - er's kiss, sweet sym-bols in the moon-light.

1.
Cm G7 Cm E♭7 A♭ C7 Fm B♭7 Bdim Cm F7 Edim B♭7
in the trees a - bove, while all the world is say - ing you were meant for love. Is - n't it ro -

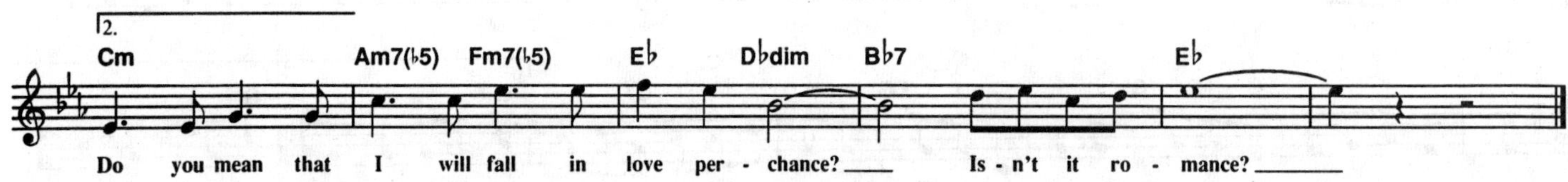
2.
Cm Am7(♭5) Fm7(♭5) E♭ D♭dim B♭7 E♭
Do you mean that I will fall in love per - chance? Is - n't it ro - mance?

ISN'T SHE LOVELY

Words and Music by
STEVIE WONDER

Moderately bright shuffle

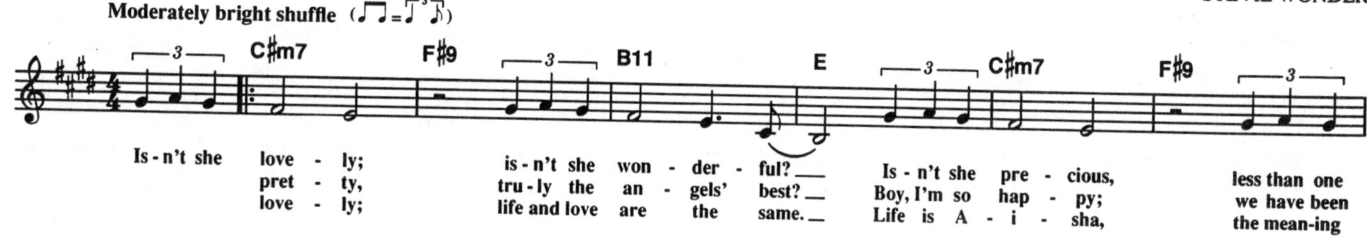
C#m7 F#9 B11 E C#m7 F#9
Is - n't she love - ly; is - n't she won - der - ful? Is - n't she pre - cious, less than one
pret - ty, tru - ly the an - gels' best? Boy, I'm so hap - py; we have been
love - ly; life and love are the same. Life is A - i - sha, the mean-ing

B11 E Amaj7 G#7(♭9) G#7 C#m7
min - ute old? I nev - er thought through love we'd be mak - ing one as love - ly as she.
heav - en blessed. I can't be - lieve what God has done; through us He's giv - en life to one.
of her name. Lon - die, it could have not been done with - out you who con - ceived the one.

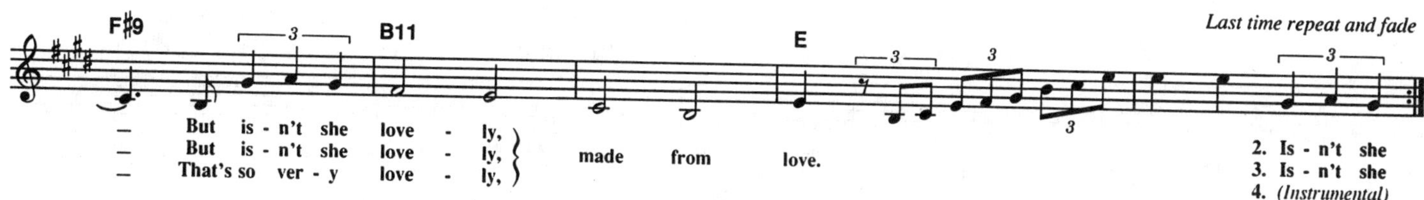
F#9 B11 E
Last time repeat and fade
But is - n't she love - ly,
But is - n't she love - ly,
That's so ver - y love - ly,
made from love.
2. Is - n't she
3. Is - n't she
4. (Instrumental)

From the Paramount Picture "AND THE ANGELS SING"

IT COULD HAPPEN TO YOU

Words by JOHNNY BURKE
Music by JAMES VAN HEUSEN

Moderately slow

G E7 Am F#7 G C B7 Dm E7
Hide your heart from sight. Lock your dreams at night. It could hap - pen to you.

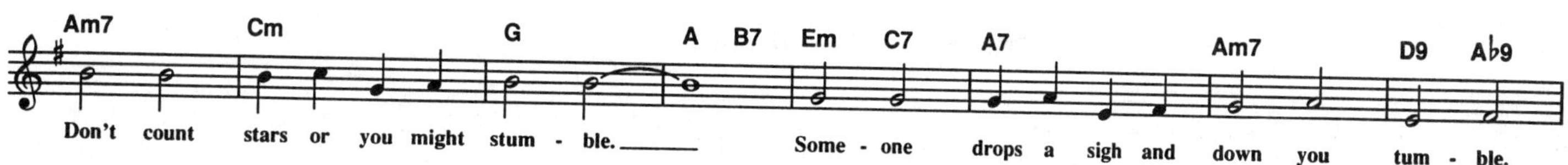
Am7 Cm G A B7 Em C7 A7 Am7 D9 A♭9
Don't count stars or you might stum - ble. Some - one drops a sigh and down you tum - ble.

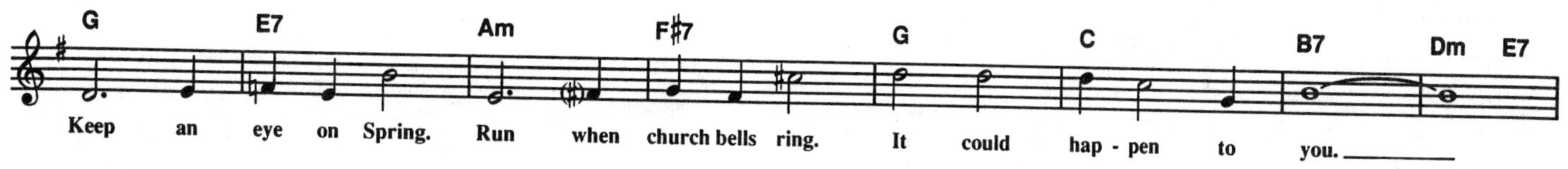
G E7 Am F#7 G C B7 Dm E7
Keep an eye on Spring. Run when church bells ring. It could hap - pen to you.

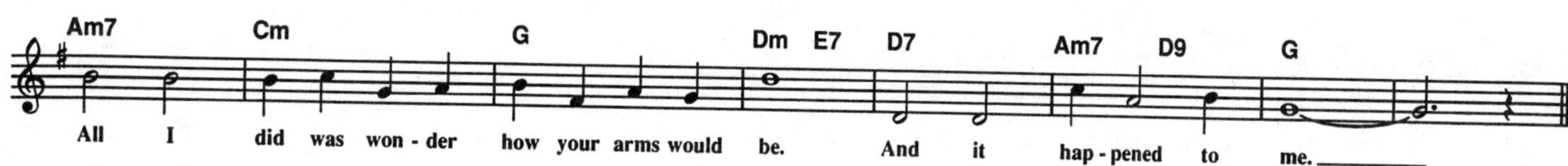
Am7 Cm G Dm E7 D7 Am7 D9 G
All I did was won - der how your arms would be. And it hap - pened to me.

Columbia Pictures Presents a Mirage/Punch Production
a Sidney Pollack Film "TOOTSIE"

IT MIGHT BE YOU

(Theme from "TOOTSIE")

Words by ALAN and MARILYN BERGMAN
Music by DAVE GRUSIN

Slowly
G G/B Bm7 G/B D/C C C/D G
1. Time: I've been pass - ing time _ watch-ing trains go by _ all of my life; _ ly - ing
(2.) _ look-ing back as lov - ers go walk - ing past _ all of my life; _ won-d'ring

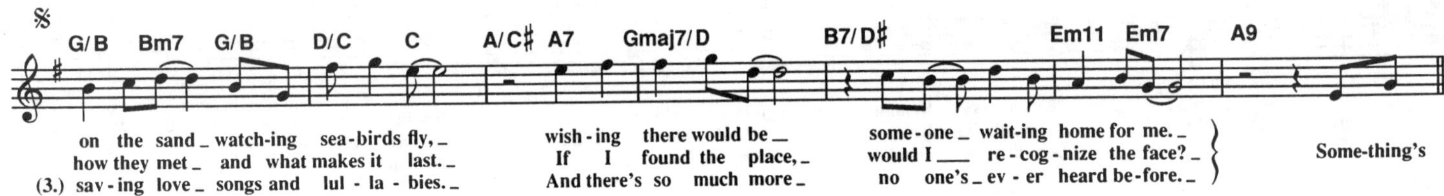
G/B Bm7 G/B D/C C A/C♯ A7 Gmaj7/D B7/D♯ Em11 Em7 A9
on the sand _ watch-ing sea-birds fly, _ wish - ing there would be _ some - one _ wait-ing home for me. _
how they met _ and what makes it last. _ If I found the place, _ would I _ re - cog - nize the face? _
(3.) sav - ing love _ songs and lul - la - bies. _ And there's so much more _ no one's _ ev - er heard be-fore. _
Some-thing's

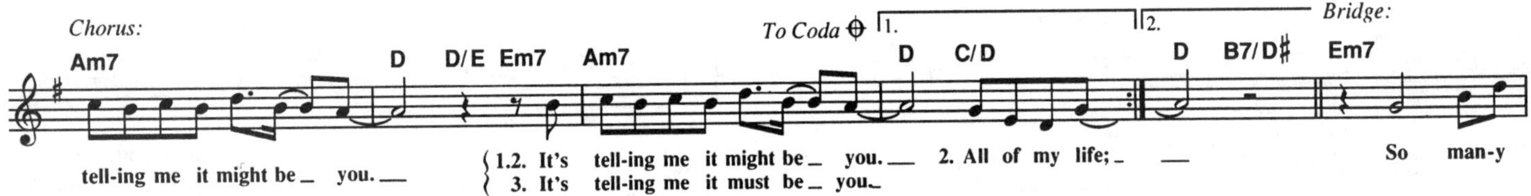
Chorus:
To Coda
1.
2.
Bridge:
Am7 D D/E Em7 Am7 D C/D D B7/D♯ Em7
tell-ing me it might be _ you. _
1.2. It's tell-ing me it might be _ you. _ 2. All of my life; _ _ So man-y
3. It's tell-ing me it must be _ you. _

D/E Bm7 Dm7 Am7 Cm G F♯m7 Bm7 Em7
qui - et walks _ to take. _ So man-y dreams _ to wake. _ And we've so much love _ to make _ I think we're

G/A A Dmaj7 G7sus G Cmaj7 Bm7 Em7 Am7
gon - na need _ some time. _ May-be all we need _ is time. _ And it's tell-ing me it might be _ you _

D.S. al Coda
D C/D G Bm7 D/C G/C D7sus G
_ all of my life. _ 3. I've been

Coda
D/E Em7 Am7 D C/D
_ and I'm feel - ing it - 'll just be _ you _ all of my life. _

Repeat ad lib. and fade
G Bm7 D/C G/C D7sus
_ May - be it's you. _ may - be it's you _ I've been wait - ing for all of my life. _

IT DON'T MEAN A THING
(If It Ain't Got That Swing)

Words by IRVING MILLS
Music by DUKE ELLINGTON

Rubato

Verse:

What good is mel-o-dy? What good is mu-sic if it ain't pos-ses-in' some-thin' sweet.
It ain't the mel-o-dy. It ain't the mu-sic. There's some-thing else that makes the tune com-plete.

Brightly

It don't mean a thing if it ain't got that swing. (Doo wah, doo wah, doo wah, doo wha, doo wah, doo wah, doo wah, doo wah.) It don't mean a thing, all you got to do is sing, (doo wah, doo wah, doo wah, doo wha, doo wah, doo wah, doo wah, doo wah.) It makes no dif-f'rence if it's sweet or hot. Just give that rhy-thm ev-'ry-thing you got. Oh, it don't mean a thing, if it ain't got that swing. (Doo wah, doo wah, doo wah, doo wha, doo wah, doo wah, doo wah, doo wah.)

IT'S A LONG WAY TO TIPPERARY

Words and music by
JACK JUDGE and HARRY WILLIAMS

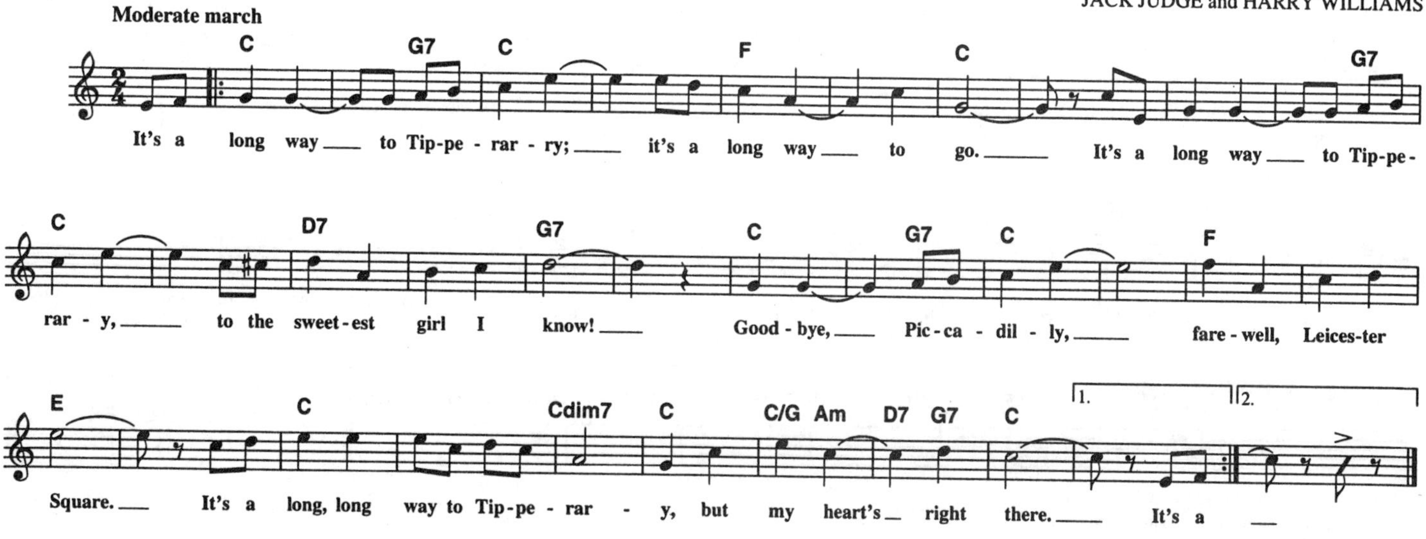

Moderate march

It's a long way to Tip-pe-rar-ry; it's a long way to go. It's a long way to Tip-pe-rar-y, to the sweet-est girl I know! Good-bye, Pic-ca-dil-ly, fare-well, Leices-ter Square. It's a long, long way to Tip-pe-rar-y, but my heart's right there. It's a

IT TAKES A GREAT BIG IRISH HEART TO SING AN IRISH SONG

Words by AL HERMAN
Music by JACK GLOGAU

Moderately

C C7 A7(♭13) Dm A7 Dm A7/E
Sure, it takes a great big I - rish heart to sing an I - rish song, ___

Dm/F G7 F/G G7 C G/B Am A7/C♯ G/D Em A7 D7 G
___ an I - rish tune with all those en - dear - ing charms, and a voice that's sweet and strong. ___

G7 C F C F C
___ Jip, Jip, my lit - tle horse, sure, that's a tune, sir, sung by an I - rish - man,
Sung by an I - rish - man, sure, that's worth hear - in', songs of my na - tive land,

Am7 D7 G7 C G/B Am F
more pow'r to him, sir! Ev - 'ry - bod - y sings of Ire - land, but it takes a great big
good luck to Er - in!

C B♭7(♭5) A7 D7 G7 C C♯dim7 G7/D G7 C
I - rish heart to sing an I - rish song. Sure, it song. ___

From the Metro-Goldwyn-Mayer Motion Picture "LITTLE NELLIE KELLY"

IT'S A GREAT DAY FOR THE IRISH

Words and Music by
ROGER EDENS

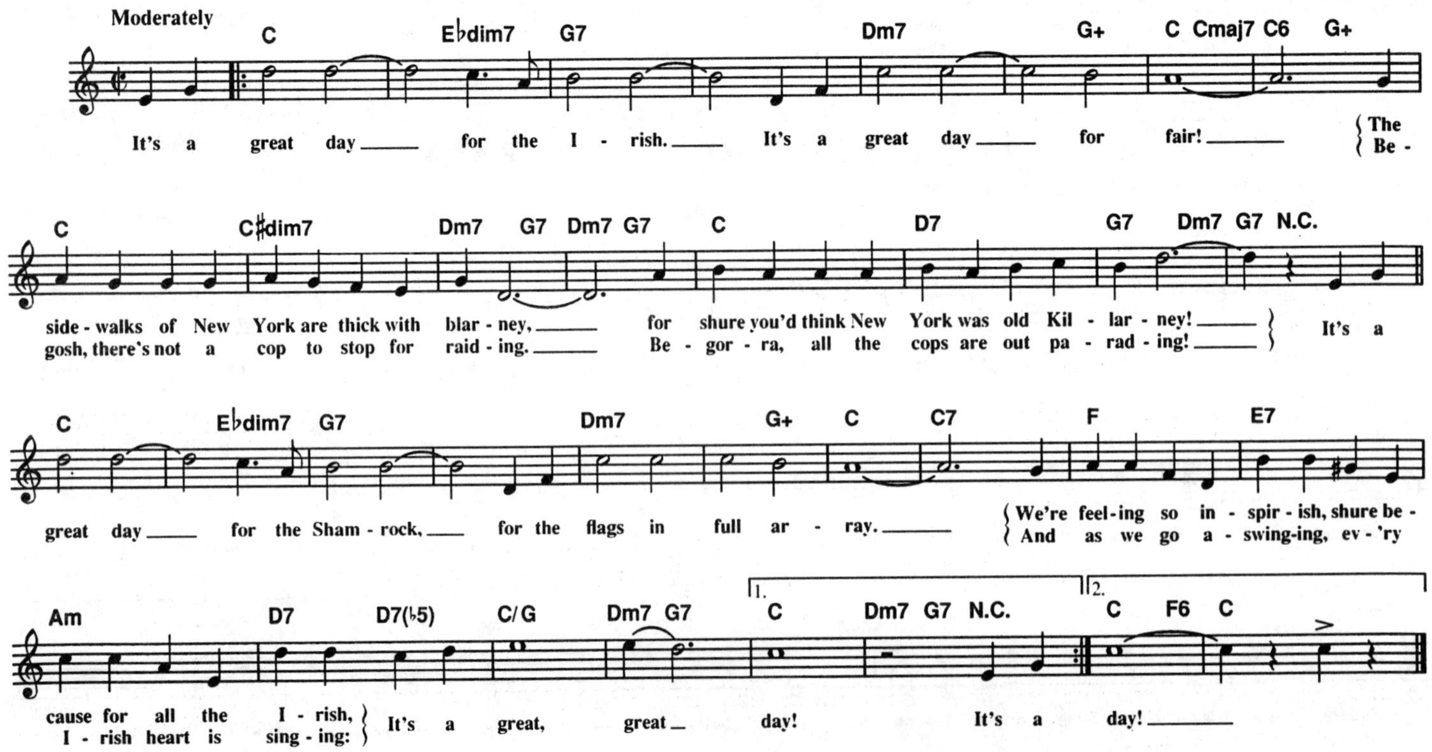

Moderately

C E♭dim7 G7 Dm7 G+ C Cmaj7 C6 G+
It's a great day ___ for the I - rish. ___ It's a great day ___ for fair! ___ The
Be -

C C♯dim7 Dm7 G7 Dm7 G7 C D7 G7 Dm7 G7 N.C.
side - walks of New York are thick with blar - ney, ___ for shure you'd think New York was old Kil - lar - ney! ___ It's a
gosh, there's not a cop to stop for raid - ing. ___ Be - gor - ra, all the cops are out pa - rad - ing! ___

C E♭dim7 G7 Dm7 G+ C C7 F E7
great day ___ for the Sham - rock, ___ for the flags in full ar - ray. ___ We're feel - ing so in - spir - ish, shure be -
And as we go a - swing-ing, ev - 'ry

Am D7 D7(♭5) C/G Dm7 G7 C Dm7 G7 N.C. C F6 C
cause for all the I - rish, It's a great, great ___ day! It's a day! ___
I - rish heart is sing - ing:

IT'S A MOST UNUSUAL DAY

Words by HAROLD ADAMSON
Music by JIMMY McHUGH

Moderately

F♯7/G G Gdim G Am7 D7 F♯7/G G Gdim G Am7 D7

It's a most un - u - su - al day. Feel like throw-ing my wor - ries a - way, as an
most un - u - su - al sky, not a sign of a cloud pass - ing by. And if
most un - u - su - al time. I keep feel - ing my tem - p'ra - ture climb. If my

G C C♯dim G/D D G/D Bm *To Coda* Em7 A7 D7 D7 D9

old na - tive born Cal - i - for - nian would say, it's a most un - u - su - al day. There's a u - su - al
I want to sing, throw my heart in the ring, it's a most un -
heart won't be - have in the u - su - al way, well, there's on - ly

G Em7 E♭dim7 Dm7 G7 Cmaj7 C6 Em7 E♭dim7 Dm7 G7

day. There are peo - ple meet - ing peo - ple. There is sun - shine ev - 'ry -

Cmaj7 C6 Em7 A7 Dmaj7 D6 Am7 D7 Am7 D7 *D.S. al Coda*

where. There are peo - ple greet - ing peo - ple, and a feel - ing of spring in the air. It's a

Coda

Em7 A7 D7 G Am7/G D7/G G Am7 D7 G Am7 D7 G

one thing to say: It's a most un - u - su - al, most un - u - su - al, most un - u - su - al day.

IT'S A RAGGY WALTZ

By DAVE BRUBECK

Swinging waltz tempo
G Am/G Gdim G7 C7
C♯dim G7 G E7 A7 D7 G C/G G G7
More gentle
Cmaj7 Bm7 Em7 B♭m7 E♭7 A♭maj7 A♭6 Gm7 C7 Fm7 B♭7 Em7 E♭7(♯11) D7
G Am/G Gdim G7 C7 C♯dim
G7 G E7 A7 D7 G G7 C/G G

IT'S ALL IN THE GAME

Words by CARL SIGMAN
Music by CHARLES G. DAWES

Moderately slowly
C13 F Gm7 C9 F C13 F Gm7 /C F
Man-y a tear has to fall, but it's all in the game, all in the won-der-ful game that we know as love.
F6 G7 C Fm(maj7) C Cdim7 C Dm7 G7 C7 Cdim7
You have words with him, and your fu-ture's look-ing dim; but these things your heart can rise a-bove.
C7 F Gm7 C9 F C13 F Gm7 /C F
Once in a while, he won't call, but it's all in the game. Soon, he'll be there at your side with a sweet bou-quet,
F6 Am7 Dm7 G7 F/C C9 F
and he'll kiss your lips, and ca-ress your wait-ing fin-ger-tips, and your hearts will fly a-way.

From the Paramount Picture "MISSISSIPPI"

IT'S EASY TO REMEMBER

Words by LORENZ HART
Music by RICHARD RODGERS

Slowly *Verse:*

Fm7 B♭7 E♭ Fm7 B♭7 E♭ E♭7 A♭
With you, I owned the earth. With you, I ruled cre-a-tion. No you, and what's it

Fm7(♭5) E♭/B♭ A♭m/C♭ F7/C Fm7(♭5)/C♭ B♭7 N.C. Fm7 B♭7 E♭
worth? It's just an im-i-ta-tion. Your sweet ex-pres-sion, the smile you gave me, the way you
whis-per, "I'll al-ways love you." I know it's

Fm7 B♭7 E♭ E♭+ A♭ E♭/G Fm7 E♭/B♭ B♭9 1. E♭/G Fm7 B♭7
looked when we met. It's eas-y to re-mem-ber but so hard to for-get. I hear you
o-ver and yet, it's

2. E♭ B♭m7 E♭7 A♭maj7 A♭6 B♭m7 E♭7 A♭maj7 A♭6 A♭m7 D♭9
get. So, I must dream to have your hand ca-ress me, fin-gers press me tight. I'd rath-er dream than have that

G♭maj7 G♭6 B♭/F Cm7/F F7 B♭ B♭7 Fm7 B♭7 E♭
lone-ly feel-ing steal-ing through the night. Each lit-tle mo-ment is clear be-fore me, and though it

Fm7 B♭7 E♭ E♭+ A♭ E♭/G D♭9 E♭/B♭ B♭9 E♭
brings me re-gret, it's eas-y to re-mem-ber and so hard to for-get.

I'VE BEEN WORKING ON THE RAILROAD

TRADITIONAL

Moderately

G C Cm6 G A7 D7 G G7 C Am6 B7 C C♯dim7 G/D D7 G C A7 D7 G D7 G

I've been work-ing on the rail - road, all the live-long day. I've been work-ing on the rail - road, to pass the time a - way. Don't you hear the whis-tle blow - ing, "Rise up so ear - ly in the morn"? Don't you hear the cap-tain shout - ing: "Din - ah, blow your horn"? Di-nah, won't you blow, Di-nah, won't you blow, Di-nah, won't you blow your horn? Di-nah, won't you blow, Di - nah, won't you blow, Di - nah, won't you blow your horn? Some-one's in the kitch-en with Di - nah, some-one's in the kitch-en I know. Some-one's in the kitch-en with Di - nah, strum-min' on the old ban - jo and sing - in', fee, fie, fid-dle-ee-i - o, fee, fie, fid-dle-ee-i - o, fee, fie, fid-dle-ee-i - o, strum-min' on the old ban - jo.

I'VE GOT THE WORLD ON A STRING

Words by TED KOEHLER
Music by HAROLD ARLEN

Moderately
I've got the world on a string, sit - tin' on a rain-bow. Got the string a - round my fin - ger. What a world, what a life. I'm in love!
song that I sing, I can make the rain go, an - y time I move my fin - ger. Luck - y me, can't you see? I'm in love!
I've got a love. Life is a beau - ti - ful thing, as long as I hold the string. I'd be a sil - ly so-and - so, if I should ev - er let go. I've got the world on a string, sit-tin' on a rain-bow. Got the string a-round my fin - ger. What a world, what a life. I'm in love!

IT'S NOT FOR ME TO SAY

Words by AL STILLMAN
Music by ROBERT ALLEN

Moderately, with much expression

Gm Gm7 C9 C7(♭9) Fmaj7 F6 Fmaj7 F6 Gm Gm7 C9 C9/B♭
It's not for me to say ___ you love me, ___ it's not for me to say ___ you'll al - ways

F/A D7/F♯ D7(♭9) Gm Gm7/F Gm6/E A7(♭9) Dm A7 Dm7 A/C♯ F♯7
care. ___ Oh, but here for the mo - ment I can hold you fast, ___ and press your lips to mine, ___

Bm7 E7 Amaj7 A6 Gm7 C7 Gm Gm7 C9 C7(♭9) Fmaj7 F6
_ and dream that love will last. As far as I can see, ___ this is heav - en ___ and

Cm7 F7 F7(♯5) B♭ B♭maj7 B♭6 B♭ B♭6 B♭maj7 B♭m6 Gm7(♭5) F/C Am7(♭5)
speak-ing just for me, ___ it's ours to share; ___ per - haps the glow of love will grow with ev-'ry pass-ing day, ___

1. D7 D7(♭9) G7 G+ C9 C+ F6 Fmaj7 F6 Gm7 C7
_ or we may nev - er meet a - gain, but then it's not for me to say. It's

2. D7 D7(♭9) Gm E♭/G C9/E C9 C+ F6 Fmaj7 F6 Fmaj7
_ or we may nev - er meet a - gain, but then it's not for me to say. ___

From the Broadway Musical Production "ANNIE"

IT'S THE HARD-KNOCK LIFE

Words by MARTIN CHARNIN
Music by CHARLES STROUSE

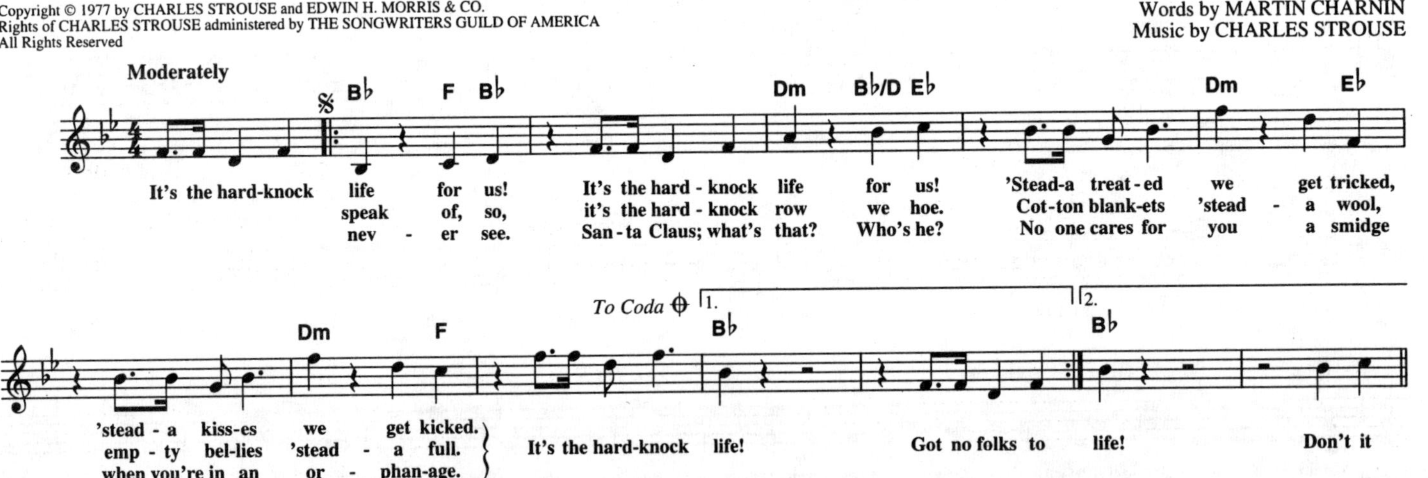
Moderately
B♭ F B♭ Dm B♭/D E♭ Dm E♭
It's the hard-knock life for us! It's the hard - knock life for us! 'Stead-a treat - ed we get tricked,
speak of, so, it's the hard - knock row we hoe. Cot-ton blank-ets 'stead - a wool,
nev - er see. San - ta Claus; what's that? Who's he? No one cares for you a smidge
Dm F
To Coda
1. B♭
2. B♭
'stead - a kiss-es we get kicked.
emp - ty bel-lies 'stead - a full.
when you're in an or - phan-age.
It's the hard-knock life! Got no folks to life! Don't it

E♭m7
feel like the wind is al-ways howl-in'? Don't it
C♯m7
seem like there's nev-er an-y light? Once a
Bm7
day don't you want to throw the towel in? It's
G
eas-i-er than put-tin' up a
C
fight.
Cm7
No one's there when your dreams at night get creep-y.
B♭m7
No one cares if you grow or if you shrink. No one
A♭m7
dries when your eyes get wet and weep-y. From the
E
cry-in' you would think this place would sink.
A
A+
Oh!
N.C.
D.S. 𝄋 al Coda
F
San-ta Claus we
Coda
B♭
life.
N.C.
(Yes, it is.) It's
F
the hard-knock
B♭
life.
N.C.
(Yes, it is.) It's
F
the hard-knock
B♭
life!
From the Musical "LITTLE ME"
I'VE GOT YOUR NUMBER
Copyright © 1962 by CAROLYN LEIGH and CY COLEMAN
All Rights throughout the World Controlled NOTABLE MUSIC CO., INC. and EMI CARWIN CATALOG INC.
All Rights Reserved
Lyric by CAROLYN LEIGH
Music by CY COLEMAN
Moderately fast
G6 Dm7 G6 Dm7 G6 Dm7 G6 Gdim7 G7 C6 Gm7 C6 Cdim7 C7 C6 Gm7 C7 A♭7
I've got your num-ber, I know you in-side out. You ain't no Ea-gle Scout, you're all at sea! Oh, yes, you'll
D♭maj7 A♭6 B♭m7 A♭ E9 E7(♭9) Amaj7 D9 B♭m7 E♭9 G6 Dm7 G6 Dm7
brag a lot, wave your own flag a lot, but you're un-sure a lot, you're a lot like me. Oh, I've got your num-ber
G6 Dm7 G6 Gdim7 G7 C6 Gm7 C6 Cdim7 C7 C6 Gm7 C7 A♭7 D♭maj9 A♭6
and what you're look-ing for. And what you're look-ing for just suits me fine! We'll break the rules a lot,
B♭m7 Bdim7 Cm7 A♭9 D♭maj7 A♭6 Fm7 B♭9 A♭9 G6 Dm7 G6 Dm7
we'll be damn' fools a lot. But then, why should we not? How could we not com-bine, when I've got your num-ber and
G6 Dm7 G6 Dm7 G7 G6 C6 G6 G7 Dm7 G6 Dm7 C6
I've got the glow you've got. I've got your num-ber and ba-by, you know you've got mine!

From the Film "ROMANCE ON THE HIGH SEAS"

IT'S YOU OR NO ONE

Words by SAMMY CAHN
Music by JULE STYNE

Moderato
It's you or no one for me, I'm sure of this, each time we kiss.
Now and for - ev - er, and when for - ev - er's done, you'll find that you are still the one.
Please don't say "No" to my plea, 'cause if you do, then I'm all through.
There's this a - bout you, my world's an emp - ty world with - out you, it's you or no one for me.
1. me.
2. me.
JA-DA
Words and Music by BOB CARELTON
Revised Lyric and Arrangement by
NAN WYNN and KEN LANE
Copyright © 1918, 1939 (Renewed 1946,1967) EMI FEIST CATALOG INC.
All Rights Reserved
Brightly
Ja - da, ja - da, ja - da, ja - da, jing, jing, jing.
Ja - da, ja - da, ja - da, ja - da, jing, jing, jing.
That's a fun - ny lit - tle bit of mel - o - dy.
It's so sooth-ing and ap - peal - ing to me.
It goes ja - da, ja - da, ja - da, ja - da, jing, jing, jing.

JAMAICA FAREWELL

TRADITIONAL

Moderately
C F C G7 C
In Ja - mai - ca, where hearts are light, where the mu - sic has you danc-ing all the night,
F C G7 C
a boy was walk-ing a - long the pier, he sang a lit - tle song that I still can hear. Oh! So
Dm7 G7 C
sad am I to say "good - bye" I'll come back, no more will I cry; I
Dm7 C G7 C
hate to say "Fare-well, Ja - mai - ca" to - day, be - cause the girl I love is here, down King - ston way!
Moderately Verse:
C G7
Good-bye, 1. Joe, me got - ta go, me oh my oh. Me got - ta go pole the pi - rogue down the
(2.) daux, Fon - tain - eaux, the place is buzz - in'. Kin - folk come to see Y - vonne by the
C G7
bay - ou. My Y - vonne, the sweet - est one, me oh my oh.
doz - en. Dress in style and go hog wild, me oh my oh.
Son of a gun, we'll have big
C Chorus: G7
fun on the bay - ou Jam - ba - la - ya and a craw - fish pie and fil - let gum - bo, 'cause to -
C G7
night I'm gon - na see my ma cher a - mi - o. Pick gui - tar, fill fruit jar and be gay - o.
1.2. 3.
C C
Son of a gun, we'll have big fun on the bay - ou. 2. Thi - bo - bay - ou.

JAMBALAYA
(on the Bayou)

Words and Music by
HANK WILLIAMS

Verse 3:
Settle down far from town, get me a pirogue,
And I'll catch all the fish in the bayou.
Swap my mon to buy Yvonne what she need-o.
Son of a gun, we'll have big fun on the bayou.
(To Chorus:)

From the United Artists Motion Picture "DR. NO"

THE JAMES BOND THEME

By MONTY NORMAN

Moderately
To Coda
D.S. al Coda
Coda
JEANIE WITH THE LIGHT BROWN HAIR
Copyright © 1993 by BEAM ME UP MUSIC (ASCAP), c/o CPP/BELWIN, INC., Miami, FL 33014
All Rights Reserved
STEPHEN C. FOSTER
Moderately
I dream of Jean - ie with the light brown hair, borne, like a va - por, on the sum - mer air. I
sigh for Jean - ie, but her light form strayed far from the fond hearts 'round her na - tive glade. Her
see her trip - ping where the bright streams play, hap - py as the dai - sies that dance on her way. Man - y were the wild notes her
smiles have van - ished and her sweet songs flown, flit - ting like the dreams that have cheered us and gone. Now the nod - ding wild flow'rs may
mer - ry voice would pour. Man - y were the blithe birds that war - bled them o'er. I dream of Jean - ie with the
with - er on the shore, while her gen - tle fin - gers will cull them no more. I sigh for Jean - ie with the
light brown hair, float - ing like a va - por on the soft, sum - mer air. I soft sum - mer air.
light brown hair, float - ing like a va - por on the

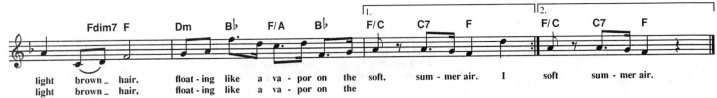

JENIFER JUNIPER
Copyright © 1968 by DONOVAN MUSIC LTD. London
Sole Selling Agent: PEER INTERNATIONAL CORPORATION
All Rights Reserved
Words and Music by
DONOVAN LEITCH
Moderately
Jen-i-fer Jun-i-per, lives up-on the hill, Jen-i-fer Jun-i-per, sit-ting ver-y still.
rides a dap-pled mare, li-lacs in her hair.
Is she sleep-ing? I don't think so. Is she breath-ing? Yes, ve-ry low. What-cha do-in', Jen-i-fer, my love?
Is she dream-ing? Yes, I think so. Is she pret-ty? Yes, ev-er so. What-cha do-in', Jen-i-fer, my love?
I'm think-ing of what it would be like if she loved me.
You know just late-ly this hap-py song, it came a-long and I like to some-how try and tell you:
Jen-i-fer Jun-i-per, hair of gold-en flax, Jen-i-fer Jun-i-per longs for what she lacks.
Do you like her? Yes, I do, sir. Would you love her? Yes, I would, sir. What-cha do-in', Jen-i-fer, my love? Jen-i-fer Jun-i-per, Jen-i-fer Jun-i-per, Jen-i-fer Jun-i-per.
(I Got Spurs That)
JINGLE JANGLE JINGLE
Copyright © 1942 (Renewed 1969) by PARAMOUNT MUSIC CORPORATION
All Rights Reserved
Words by FRANK LOESSER
Music by JOSEPH J. LILLEY
I got spurs that jin-gle jan-gle jin-gle, as I go rid-in' mer-ri-ly a-long. And they
sing, "Oh, ain't you glad you're sin-gle!", and that song ain't so ver-y far from wrong.
Oh, Lil-lie Belle, oh, Lil-lie Belle, though I may have done some fool-in', this is why I nev-er fell. I got spurs that
sing, "Oh,
jin-gle jan-gle jin-gle as I go rid-in' mer-ri-ly a-long. And they
ain't you glad you're sin-gle," and that song ain't so ver-y far from wrong. So I'll jin-gle on a-long.

JESU, JOY OF MAN'S DESIRING

By J.S. BACH

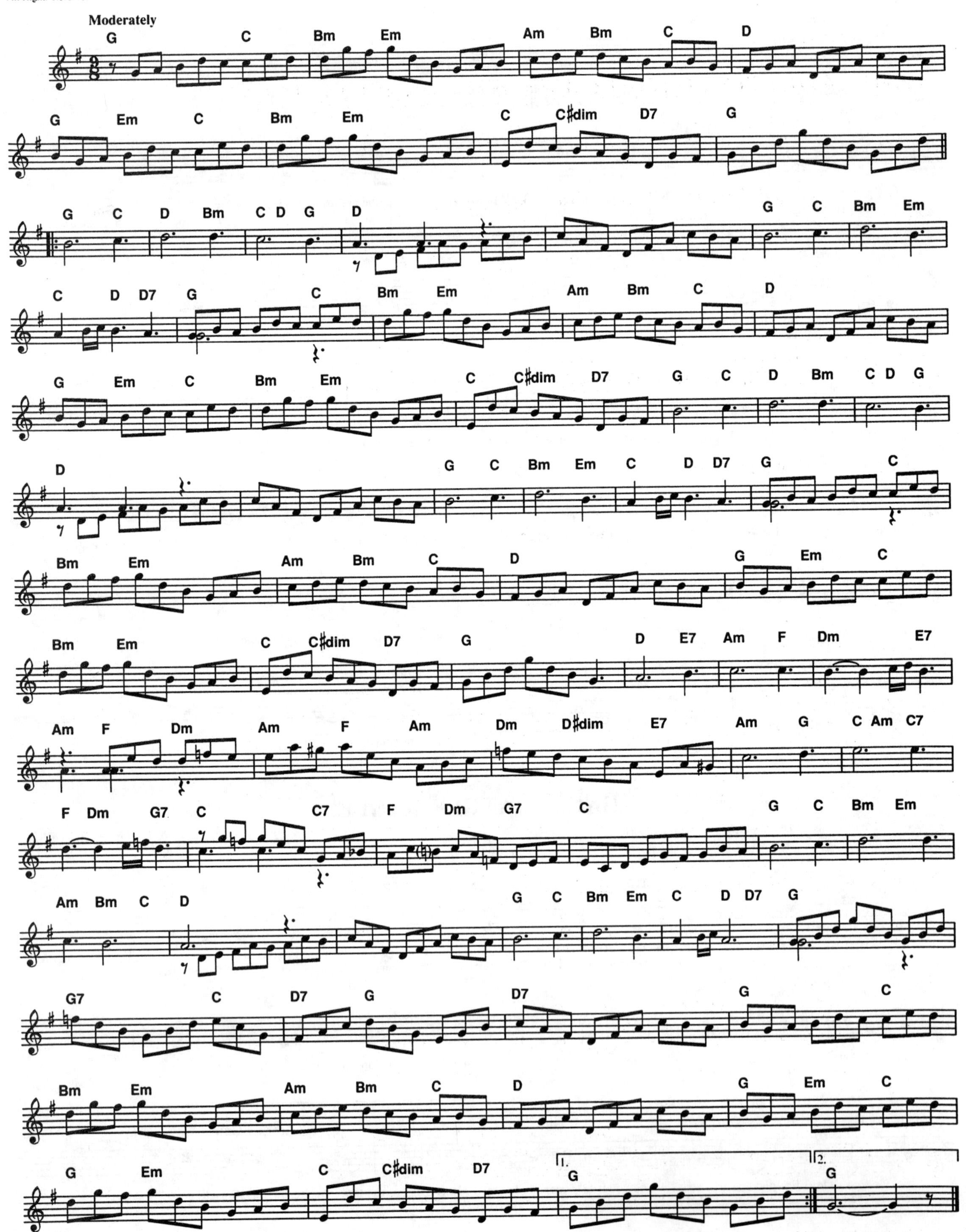
Moderately
G C Bm Em Am Bm C D
G Em C Bm Em C C♯dim D7 G
G C D Bm C D G D G C Bm Em
C D D7 G C Bm Em Am Bm C D
G Em C Bm Em C C♯dim D7 G C D Bm C D G
D G C Bm Em C D D7 G C
Bm Em Am Bm C D G Em C
Bm Em C C♯dim D7 G D E7 Am F Dm E7
Am F Dm Am F Am Dm D♯dim E7 Am G C Am C7
F Dm G7 C C7 F Dm G7 C G C Bm Em
Am Bm C D G C Bm Em C D D7 G
G7 C D7 G D7 G C
Bm Em Am Bm C D G Em C
G Em C C♯dim D7 1. G 2. G

From the Warner Bros. Film "GOING PLACES"

JEEPERS CREEPERS

Words by JOHNNY MERCER
Music by HARRY WARREN

With a swing
F6 F7 B♭maj7 B♭6 F7 F9sus F7 B♭6 B♭ F6 F7 B♭maj7 B♭6
Jeep - ers creep - ers! Where'd ya get those peep - ers? Jeep - ers creep - ers!
Gosh all git up! How'd they get so lit up? Gosh all git up!
F7 F9sus F7 B♭ Fm7 B♭6 E♭maj9 E♭6 Fm7 B♭6 B♭7 E♭maj7 E♭ E♭6 Gm7 C6
Where'd ya get those eyes? Gol - ly gee! When you turn those heat - ers on, woe is
How'd they get that size?
Fmaj7 F6 Gm7 C6 C7 F9sus F7 F6 F7 B♭maj7 B♭6 F7 F9sus F7 B♭6 B♭
me! Got to put my cheat - ers on, jeep - ers creep - ers! Where'd ya get those peep - ers?
F6 F7 Dm7(♭5) G7 Cm7 F9sus F7 B♭ G7 E♭6 F9sus F7 B♭
Oh! those weep - ers! How they hyp - no - tize! Where's ya get those eyes?

JOHNNY ANGEL

Words by LYN DUDDY
Music by LEE POCKRISS

Moderately
F Dm Gm7
John - ny An - gel, how I love him. He's got some-thing that I can't re - sist. But he
An - gel, how I want him. How I tin - gle when he pass - es by. Ev - 'ry
An - gel, 'cause I love him. And I pray that some-day he'll love me. And to -
C7 1. F F♯dim7 C7 2. F B♭ F To Next Strain
does - n't e - ven know that I ex - ist. John - ny fly. I'm in
time he says, "Hel - lo" my heart be - gins to
geth - er we will see how love - ly heav'n can
3. F Gm7 F Fine Cm7 F7 Cm7 F7 B♭ F+ B♭
be. heav - en. I get car - ried a - way. I dream of him and me and how it's gon - na be. Oth - er
Dm7 G7 Dm7 G7 C6 B♭6 Dm6 G7 C7 D.S. 𝄋 al Fine
fel - las call me up for a date but I just sit and wait, I'd rath - er con - cen - trate for John - ny

JINGLE BELLS

Words and Music by
JAMES PIERPONT

Brightly
G C Am D7 G
Dash-ing through the snow, in a one-horse o - pen sleigh; o'er the fields we go, laugh-ing all the way.
Now the ground is white, go it while you're young, take the girls to - night, and sing a sleigh-ing song. Just
C Am G D7 G D7
Bells on bob-tail ring, mak-ing spir-its bright; what fun it is to ride and sing a sleigh - ing song to - night. Oh!
get a bob-tail nag, two for - ty for his speed and hitch him to an o - pen sleigh and crack, you'll take the lead!
G C G A7 D7
Jin - gle bells, jin - gle bells, jin - gle all the way; oh what fun it is to ride in a one-horse o - pen sleigh. Hey!
G C G D7 G
Jin - gle bells, jin - gle bells, jin - gle all the way; oh what fun it is to ride in a one-horse o - pen sleigh!

JOLLY OLD ST. NICHOLAS

TRADITIONAL

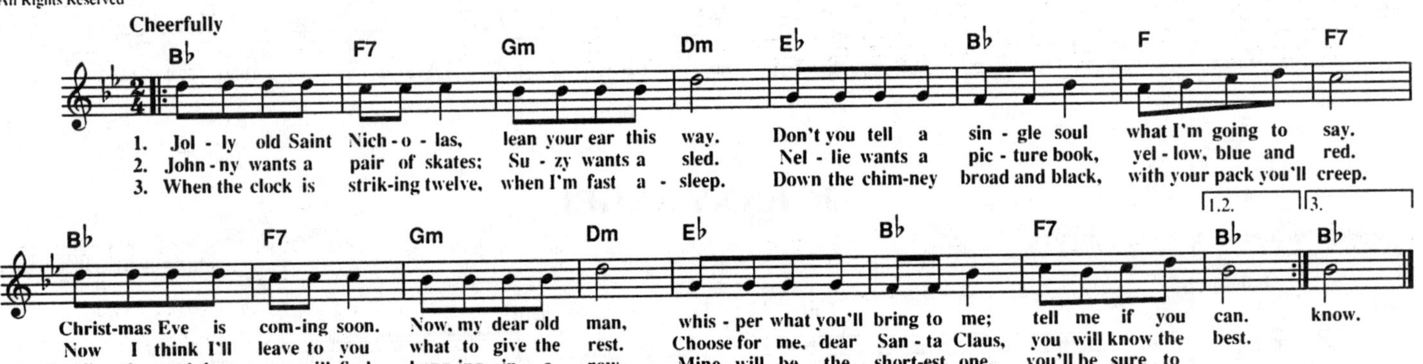
Cheerfully
B♭ F7 Gm Dm E♭ B♭ F F7
1. Jol - ly old Saint Nich - o - las, lean your ear this way. Don't you tell a sin - gle soul what I'm going to say.
2. John - ny wants a pair of skates; Su - zy wants a sled. Nel - lie wants a pic - ture book, yel - low, blue and red.
3. When the clock is strik-ing twelve, when I'm fast a - sleep. Down the chim-ney broad and black, with your pack you'll creep.
B♭ F7 Gm Dm E♭ B♭ F7 1.2. B♭ 3. B♭
Christ-mas Eve is com-ing soon. Now, my dear old man, whis - per what you'll bring to me; tell me if you can. know.
Now I think I'll leave to you what to give the rest. Choose for me, dear San - ta Claus, you will know the best.
All the stock-ings you will find hang-ing in a row. Mine will be the short-est one, you'll be sure to

JOY TO THE WORLD
(Christmas Carol)

Words by ISAAC WATTS
Music by LOWELL MASON

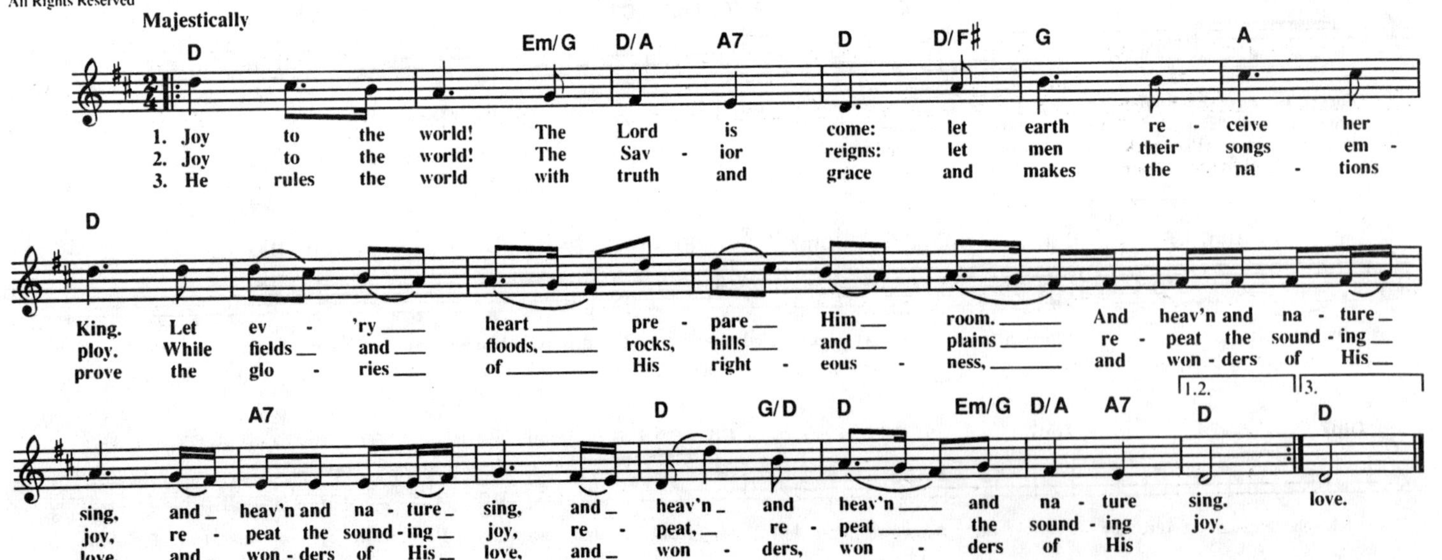
Majestically
D Em/G D/A A7 D D/F♯ G A
1. Joy to the world! The Lord is come: let earth re - ceive her
2. Joy to the world! The Sav - ior reigns: let men their songs em -
3. He rules the world with truth and grace and makes the na - tions
D
King. Let ev - 'ry heart pre - pare Him room. And heav'n and na - ture
ploy. While fields and floods, rocks, hills and plains re - peat the sound - ing
prove the glo - ries of His right - eous - ness, and won - ders of His
A7 D G/D D Em/G D/A A7 1.2. D 3. D
sing, and heav'n and na - ture sing, and heav'n and heav'n and na - ture sing. love.
joy, re - peat the sound - ing joy, re - peat, re - peat the sound - ing joy.
love, and won - ders of His love, and won - ders, won - ders of His

JOHNSON RAG

Words by JACK LAWRENCE
Music by GUY HALL
and HENRY KLEINKAUF

Brightly
Hep, hep, there goes the John-son Rag._ Hoy, hoy, there goes the lat-est shag._ Ho, ho, it real-ly is-n't a gag._ Hep, hep, there goes the John-son Rag._ Jump,
jump, don't let your left foot drag._ Jeep, jeep, it's like a game of tag._ Juke, juke, it's e-ven good for a stag._ Jump, jump, and do the John-son Rag._
zig, then add a zig, zig, zag._ Zoop, zoop, just let your shoul-ders wag._ Zoom, zoom, and now it's right in the bag._ Get hep, and do the John-son Rag._
To Next Strain
Fine
If you're feel-in' in the groove,_it sends you out of the world._ Fun-ny how it makes you move._ I don't wan-na coax,_but don't_ be a "Mokes."_Zig,
D.S. al Fine

THE JOINT IS JUMPIN'

Words by ANDY RAZAF and J.C. JOHNSON
Music by THOMAS "FATS" WALLER

Bright swing

This joint is jump-in', it's real-ly jump-in', come in cats_ an' check_your hats,_ I mean_this joint_ is jump-in'. The pi-an-o's thump-in', the danc-ers bump-in'. This here spot_is more than hot,_ in fact the joint is jump-in'.

This joint is jump-in', it's real-ly jump-in'. Ev-'ry Mose_is on___ his toes,_ I mean_the joint_ is jump-in'. No_time for talk-in', it's time_for walk-in'. *(Yes!)* Grab a jug_and cut the rug,_ I mean this joint is jump-in'.

Check your weap-ons at the door,_ be sure to pay your quar-ter. Burn your leath-er on the floor,_grab an-y-bod-y's daugh-ter.

Get your pig feet, beer and gin,_ there's plen-ty in the kitch-en. Who is that that just came in?_ Just look at the way he's switch-in'.

The roof is rock-in', the neigh-bor's knock-in'. We're all bums_when the wag-on comes._ I mean__ this joint is jump-in'. *(Spoken:) Let it beat!*

Don't mind the hour,___ 'cause I'm in pow-er. I got bail_ if we go to jail_ I mean_ this joint is jump-in'.

This joint is jump-in', it's real-ly jump-in'. We're all bums_when the wag-on comes,_ I mean_ this joint is jump-in'. *(Spoken:) Don't give your right name. No, No, No!*

JOY TO THE WORLD
(Popular Song)
Words and Music by
HOYT AXTON
Copyright © 1970 by LADY JANE MUSIC. c/o ROWPOR MUSIC INTERNATIONAL
All Rights Reserved
Moderately
Verse:
1. Je-re-mi-ah was a bull - frog, was a good friend of mine. Never under-stood a sin-gle word he said, but I helped him a-drink-in' his wine. Yes, he al-ways had some might-y fine wine.
(2.) If I were the king of the world, tell you what I'd do, throw a-way the cars and the bars and the wars, and make sweet love to you. Yes, I'd make sweet love to you.
(3.) know I love the la - dies, love to have my fun. I'm a high night fly-er and a rain-bow ri - der, a straight shoot-in' son-of-a-gun, yes, a straight shoot-in' son-of-a-gun.
Chorus:
Sing-ing joy to the world, all the boys and girls now. Joy to the fish-es in the deep blue sea, joy to you and me.
To Coda
D.S. al Coda
(Inst. solo . . . . end solo) 3. You
Coda
Joy to the world, all the boys and girls. Joy to the world, joy to you and me.
Repeat and fade
Joy to the world, all the boys and girls. Joy to the fish-es in the deep blue sea, joy to you and me.
JUNE NIGHT
(Just Give Me a June Night, The Moonlight and You)
Words by CLIFF FRIEND
Music by ABEL BAER
Copyright © 1924 (Renewed 1952) EMI FEIST CATALOG INC.
All Rights Reserved
Moderately
Just give me a June night, the moon-light and you. In my arms, with all your charms, 'neath stars a-bove, and we'll make love, I'll
hold you, en-fold you, then dreams will come true. So give me a June night, the moon-light and you.

From "HERE IN MY HEART"

JUNE IN JANUARY

Words and Music by
LEO ROBIN and
RALPH RAINGER

Moderately

E♭ Edim Fm Fm7 B♭7 A♭ B♭9 E♭
It's June in Jan - u - ar - y be-cause I'm in love. It al-ways is spring in my heart, with you in my arms.

A♭ B♭7(♯5) E♭ Edim Fm Fm7 B♭7 A♭ B♭7(♭9) E♭maj7 E♭6
The snow is just white blos-soms that fall from a - bove. And here is the rea-son my dear, your mag-i-cal charms.

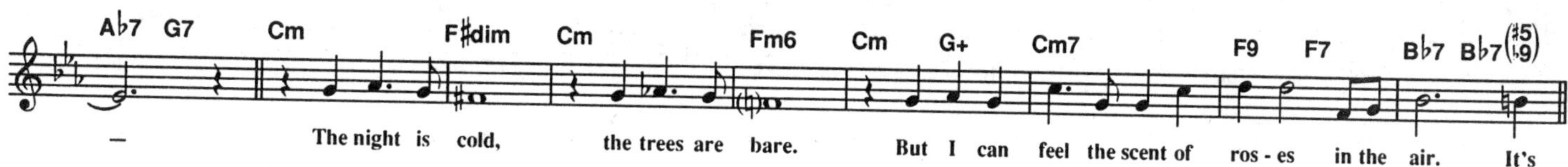
A♭7 G7 Cm F♯dim Cm Fm6 Cm G+ Cm7 F9 F7 B♭7 B♭7(♯5 ♭9)
The night is cold, the trees are bare. But I can feel the scent of ros - es in the air. It's

E♭ Edim Fm7 B♭7 Fm7 B♭9 E♭6
June in Jan - u - ar - y be - cause I'm in love. But on - ly be - cause I'm in love with you.

JUST FRIENDS

Lyric by SAM M. LEWIS
Music by JOHN KLENNER

Moderately

G7 Cmaj7 Cm7 F7 Gmaj7 B♭m7 E♭7
Just friends, lov-ers no more. Just friends, but not like be - fore. To

Am7 D7 Bm7 Em7 A7 Am7 D7 G7(♯5)
think of what we've been, and not to kiss a - gain seems like pre - tend - ing it is-n't the end - ing. Two

Cmaj7 Cm7 F7 Gmaj7 B♭m7 E♭7
friends drift-ing a - part; two friends, but one bro-ken heart. We

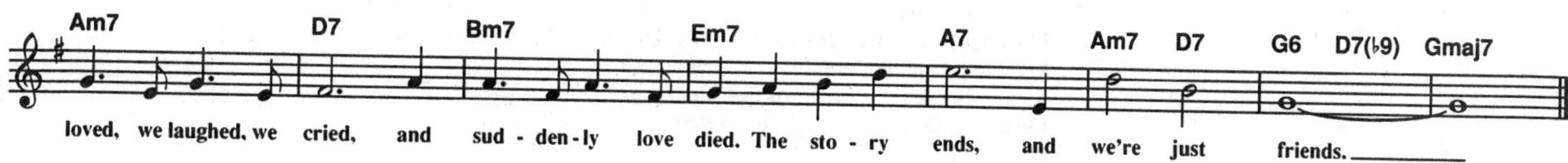
Am7 D7 Bm7 Em7 A7 Am7 D7 G6 D7(♭9) Gmaj7
loved, we laughed, we cried, and sud - den - ly love died. The sto - ry ends, and we're just friends.

JUST A CLOSER WALK WITH THEE

K. MORRIS

Slowly
Verse:
C C/E E♭dim7 Dm7 G7 Dm7 G7 Dm7 C C7
I am weak but thou art strong, Je - sus, keep me from all wrong. I'll be sat - is - fied as
In this world with toil and snare, if I fal - ter, Lord, who cares. Who will all my bur-dens
F F♯dim7 C/G G7 C
Chorus:
C/E E♭dim7 Dm7 G7
long as I walk, let me walk close to Thee.
bear? None but Thee, dear Lord, none but Thee.
Just a clos - er walk with thee,
Dm7 G7 G11 C C7 F E♭dim7 C/E F G7 C C
1. 2.
grant it Je - sus is my plea, Dai - ly walk-ing close to Thee. Let it be, dear Lord, let it be. be.

JUST DROPPED IN (To See What Condition My Condition Was In)

Words and Music by
MICKEY NEWBURY

Moderately
Verse:
Em
1. Jumped up this morn-ing with the sun down shin - ing in. Found my bro-ken mind in a brown pa-per bag, but
B7 Em Am Em
then I tripped on a cloud and fell eight miles high. Tore my mind on the jag-ged sky. I just dropped in to
B7 Em
Chorus:
Em
see what con-di-tion my con - di-tion was in. Pushed my soul in a deep, dark hole and fol-lowed it in; when I
B7 Em Am
met my-self crawl-ing out as I was crawl-ing in. Got up so tight I could-n't un - wind; saw so much it near-ly
Em
1. 2.
broke my mind. I just dropped in to see what con-di-tion my con - di-tion was in. di-tion was in.

Verse 2:
Someone painted, "April-fool" in big black letters on a dead end sign.
I had my foot in the gas when I left the road and blew out my mind.
Eight miles out of Memphis and I got no spare,
Eight miles straight up downtown somewhere.
I just dropped in to see what condition my condition was in.
(To Chorus:)

JUST ONE OF THOSE THINGS

Words and Music by
COLE PORTER

Allegretto
Dm A F7
It was just one of those things, just one of those
Bm7(♭5) B♭dim F/A Fm/A♭ Gm7 C7 F6 F♯dim
cra - zy flings. One of those bells that now and then rings, just one
C7 A7 Dm A
of those things. It was just one of those nights,
F7 Bm7(♭5) B♭dim F/A
Just one of those fab - u - lous flights, a trip to the
G♯dim F/A Gm7 C7 Dm7 F♯dim Fm7 B♭7
moon on gos - sa - mer wings, just one of those things. If we'd
E♭ E♭dim E♭ B♭7 E♭
thought a bit of the end of it when we start - ed paint - ing the
G7 G+ G7 C6 C+ C6 F♯m7(♭5) Fm7 Fm6
town, we'd have been a - ware that our love af - fair was too
Em7 E♭dim C A7 Dm
hot not to cool down. So good - bye, dear and a -
A F7 B♭
men, here's hop - ing we meet now and then, it was
Am D7 Am7(♭5)/G Gm C7 F
great fun, but it was just one of those things.

JUST THE TWO OF US
Words and Music by
RALPH MacDONALD, WILLIAM SALTER
and BILL WITHERS
Copyright © 1981 by ANTISIA MUSIC, INC.
All Rights Reserved
Moderate funk rock
Verse:
I see the cry - stal rain-drops fall and the beau - ty of it all is when the sun comes shin - ing through
We look for love, no time for tears, wast - ed wa - ter's all that is, and it don't make no flow - ers grow.
I hear the crys - tal rain-drops fall on the win - dow down the hall, and it be - comes the morn-ing dew.
to make those rain - bows in my mind when I think of you some - time and I want to spend some time with
Good things might come to those who wait, but not for those who wait too late, we've got to go for all we
And dar - ling when the morn - ing comes and I see the morn - ing sun I want to be the one with
you. know. you.
Chorus:
Just the two of us, we can make it if we try, just the two of us. (Just the two of us.)
Just the two of us, build-ing cas - tles in the sky, just the two of us, you and I.
1. D.S.
2.4. To next strain
3.5.6 Repeat ad lib. and fade
Just the
1.3.
2. D.S.S.
4. D.C.
Just the
JUST YOU, JUST ME
Music by
JESSE GREER
Copyright © 1929 (Renewed 1957) METRO-GOLDWYN-MAYER INC., c/o EMI ROBBINS CATALOG INC.
All Rights Reserved
Moderately
Just you, just me; let's find a co - zy spot, to cud - dle and coo.
Just us, just we; I've missed an aw - ful lot, my trou - ble is
you. Oh, gee! What are your charms for? What are my arms for? Use your i - mag - i - na - tion!
Just you, just me; I'll tie a lov - er's knot 'round won - der - ful you!

KAW-LIGA

Words and Music by
HANK WILLIAMS and
FRED ROSE

Moderately
Verse:
Dm
1. Kaw - li - ga was a wood - en in - di - an stand - ing by the door. He fell in love with an
(2.) al - ways wore his Sun - day feath - ers and held a tom - a - hawk. The maid - en wore her
(3.) li - ga was a lone - ly In - di - an, nev - er went no - where. His heart was set on the
(4.) then one day a wealth - y cus - tom - er bought the In - di - an maid and took her, oh, so
In - di - an maid - en o - ver in the an - tique store. Kaw - li - ga just stood there and
beads and braids and hoped some day he'd talk. Kaw - li - ga, too stub - born to
In - di - an maid - en with the coal black hair. Kaw - li - ga just stood there and
far a - way, but ol' Kaw - li - ga stayed. Kaw - li - ga just stands there as
A7
1.3.
2.4.
Dm
Dm
nev - er let it show, so she could nev - er an - swer "yes" or "no." 2. He pine.
ev - er show a sign be - cause his heart was made of knot - ty "no." 4. And tree.
nev - er let it show, so she could nev - er an - swer "yes" or
lone - ly as can be and wish - es he was still an old pine
Chorus:
D
G
Poor ol' Kaw - li - ga, he nev - er got a kiss. Poor ol' Kaw - li - ga, he don't know what he missed.
D
A7
1.
D.S. 𝄋
2.
D
Dm
Is it an - y won - der that his face is red? Kaw - li - ga, that poor ol' wood - en head. 3. Kaw - head.
JUST WALKING IN THE RAIN
Copyright © 1953 (Renewed) GOLDEN WEST MELODIES
All Rights Reserved
Words and Music by
ROBERT S. RILEY
JOHNNY BRAGG
Moderately
D7(♯5)
G G♯dim D7/A D7
G C G Am D9
To Coda
Just walk - ing in the rain, get - ting soak - ing wet; tor - tur - ing my heart
rain, so a - lone and blue; all be - cause my heart
rain, think - ing how we met; know - ing things have changed,
1.
2.
G G♯dim D7/A D7(♯5)
Am7 D7 G C G G7
by try - ing to for - get. Just walk - ing in the still re - mem - bers you.
C D9 G Am7 D7 G A7 Em7 A7
Peo - ple come to win - dows and they al - ways stare at me; shake their heads in sor - row, say - ing,
D9 Fdim7 D7/F♯ D7(♯5)
D.S. 𝄋 al Coda
Coda
D7 G C G
"Who can that fool be?" Just walk - ing in the
some - how I can't for - get.

KENTUCKY WALTZ

Words and Music by
BILL MONROE

Moderate waltz
C G7 Gdim7 G7
We were waltz-in' that night _ in Ken-tuck-y, ____ be-neath the beau - ti-ful har - vest moon. ___ And I was the boy that was
C C7 F
luck-y, ____ but it all end-ed too soon. ___ As I sit here _ a - lone in the moon-light, ___ I see your smil - ing face; _
A♭7 C/G A7 D7 G7 C F♯dim7 G7 C Fm6 C
_ and I long _ once more for your _ em - brace, and that beau - ti-ful Ken-tuck - y waltz. ____ We were waltz. ____
1. 2.

KIDS!

Words by LEE ADAMS
Music by CHARLES STROUSE

Charleston tempo
C C6 Cmaj7 C6 C C6 G9
Kids! I don't know what's wrong _ with these kids to-day! Kids! 1.2. Who can un-der - stand _ an - y - thing they say?
3. E - ven I don't un - der-stand what they say!
G7 E7 A7 Am7 D7 Am7 D7
Kids! They are dis - o - be - di-ent, dis - re-spect-ful oafs! _ Nois - y cra - zy slop - py la - zy
Kids! They are so ri - dic - u-lous and so im - ma-ture! _ I don't see why an - y-bod - y
Dm7 G7 G7(♯5) Tacet C C6 Cmaj7
loaf - ers! _ While we're on the sub - ject: Kids! You can talk and talk _ till your face is blue!
wants 'em! _ Why are they so dread-ful? Kids! They are just im - pos - si - ble to con - trol!
Why are they so dread-ful? Kids! What the dev - il's wrong _ with these kids to - day?
C6 C7 F E F6 F
Kids! But they still do just _ what they want to do!
Kids! With their aw - ful clothes _ and their rock and roll!
Kids! Who could guess that they _ would turn out that way!
Why can't they be like
B7(♯5) B7 Em7 A7(♯5) A7 F6 D9 G7 C6
we / you were, per-fect in ev - 'ry way? What's the mat - ter with kids to - day? ____

KILLING ME SOFTLY WITH HIS SONG

Words by NORMAN GIMBEL
Music by CHARLES FOX

Moderately

Dm7 G C F Dm7

I heard he sang a good song, I heard he had a style. And so I came
I felt all flushed with fe - ver em - bar - rassed by the crowd, I felt he found
He sang as if he knew me, in all my dark des - pair. And then he looked

G Am Dm7 G

to see him to lis - ten for a - while. And there he was this young boy,
my let - ters and read each one out loud. I prayed that he would fin - ish,
right through me as if I was - n't there. But he was there this stran - ger,

C E7

a stran - ger to my eyes.
but he just kept right on.
sing - ing clear and strong.

Chorus:

Am F G

Strum - ming my pain with his fin - gers, sing - ing my life with his words,

C Am D/F♯ G F

kill - ing me soft - ly with his song, kill - ing me soft - ly with his song; tell - ing my whole

C F B♭ 1.2. A 3. A

life with his words, kill - ing me soft - ly with his song.

From the Metro-Goldwyn-Mayer Motion Picture "THE STRIP"

A KISS TO BUILD A DREAM ON

Words and Music by
BERT KALMAR, HARRY RUBY and
OSCAR HAMMERSTEIN II

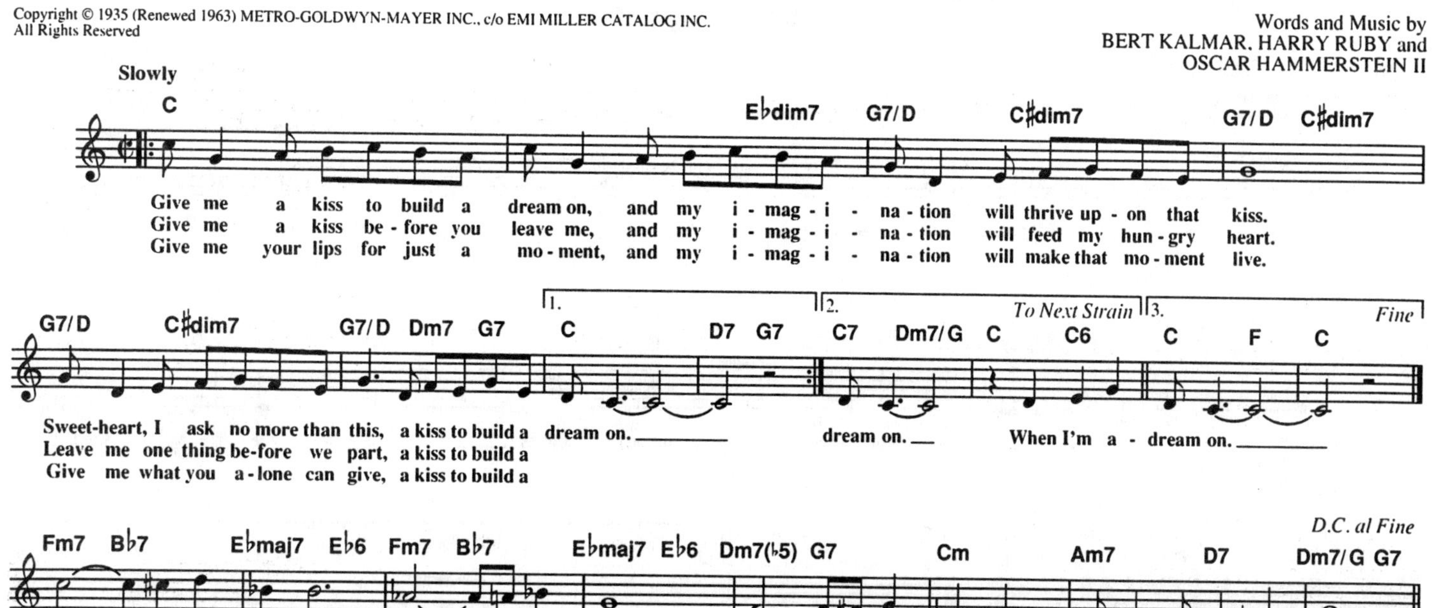
Slowly
C E♭dim7 G7/D C♯dim7 G7/D C♯dim7
Give me a kiss to build a dream on, and my i - mag - i - na - tion will thrive up - on that kiss.
Give me a kiss be - fore you leave me, and my i - mag - i - na - tion will feed my hun - gry heart.
Give me your lips for just a mo - ment, and my i - mag - i - na - tion will make that mo - ment live.
G7/D C♯dim7 G7/D Dm7 G7 1. C D7 G7 2. C7 Dm7/G C C6 To Next Strain 3. C F C Fine
Sweet-heart, I ask no more than this, a kiss to build a dream on. dream on. When I'm a - dream on.
Leave me one thing be-fore we part, a kiss to build a
Give me what you a - lone can give, a kiss to build a
Fm7 B♭7 E♭maj7 E♭6 Fm7 B♭7 E♭maj7 E♭6 Dm7(♭5) G7 Cm Am7 D7 Dm7/G G7 D.C. al Fine
lone with my fan - cies I'll be with you weav - ing ro - manc - es mak-ing be - lieve they're true.

KISS AN ANGEL GOOD MORNIN'
Copyright © 1971 by BEN PETERS MUSIC
All Rights Reserved
By BEN PETERS
Moderately
Verse:
C C7 F G7
1.When - ev - er I chance to meet __ some old friends __ on __ the street, __ they won-der how does a man __
(2) peo-ple may try to guess __ the se-cret of hap-pi - ness, __ but some of them nev - er learn __
C C7 F
get to be this way. I've al-ways got a smil - in' __ face __ an - y-time and an - y - place, __
it's a sim-ple thing. The se-cret I'm __ speak-in' __ of __ is a wom-an and a man in __ love, __
Chorus:
G7 C F C N.C. C G
And ev-'ry time they ask me why, __ I just smile and say. You've got to kiss an an-gel good morn - in' and
And the an-swer is __ in this song __ that I al - ways sing.
F C N.C. C G F
let her know you think a-bout her when you're __ gone. __ Kiss an an-gel good morn - in and love her like the dev-il when you
1. C N.C. G D.S. 2. C N.C. 3. F C F C
get back home. __ 2. Well, get back home. Got to get back home.
K-K-K-KATY
Copyright © 1918 (Renewed 1945) EMI FEIST CATALOG INC.
All Rights Reserved
Words and Music by
GEOFFREY O'HARA
Bright march
C A7 D7 G7
K - K - K - Ka - ty, beau - ti - ful Ka - ty, you're the on - ly g - g - g -
C C♯dim7 G7/D G7 C A7 D7
girl that I a - dore; and when the m - moon shines o - ver the cow - shed,
G7 1. C 2. C
I'll be wait - ing at the k - k - k - kitch - en door. K - K - K - door.

KNOCK ON WOOD

Words and Music by
EDDIE FLOYD and
STEVE CROPPER

Moderate rock

F Ab Bb C Eb C Bb13 F7

1. I don't wan-na lose this good thing that I got. If I do, I will sure-ly, sure-ly lose a lot.
sti-tious a-bout ya; I can't take no chance. Got me spin-nin', ba-by. Ba-by, I'm in a trance.
-cret that wom-an fills my lov-in' cup, 'cause she sees to it, that I get e-nough.

Chorus:

Bb13

(1.2.) 'Cause our love is bet-ter than an-y love I know.
(3.) Just one touch from her, you know it means so much.

It's like thun-der, light-nin'. The way you love me is fright-nin'. I bet-ter knock on wood.

F Bb7 F7 Bb7 F Ab Bb C Eb C

1. D.S. 𝄋 — 2. I'm not su-per-

2. C Bb Ab G7 A7 Bb7 Db7 D.S. 𝄋

3. It's no se-

3. C Bb Ab F Bb7 F7 Bb7 *Repeat and fade*

Oh, yeah. Think I bet-ter knock on wood. Think I bet-ter.

KUM BA YA

TRADITIONAL

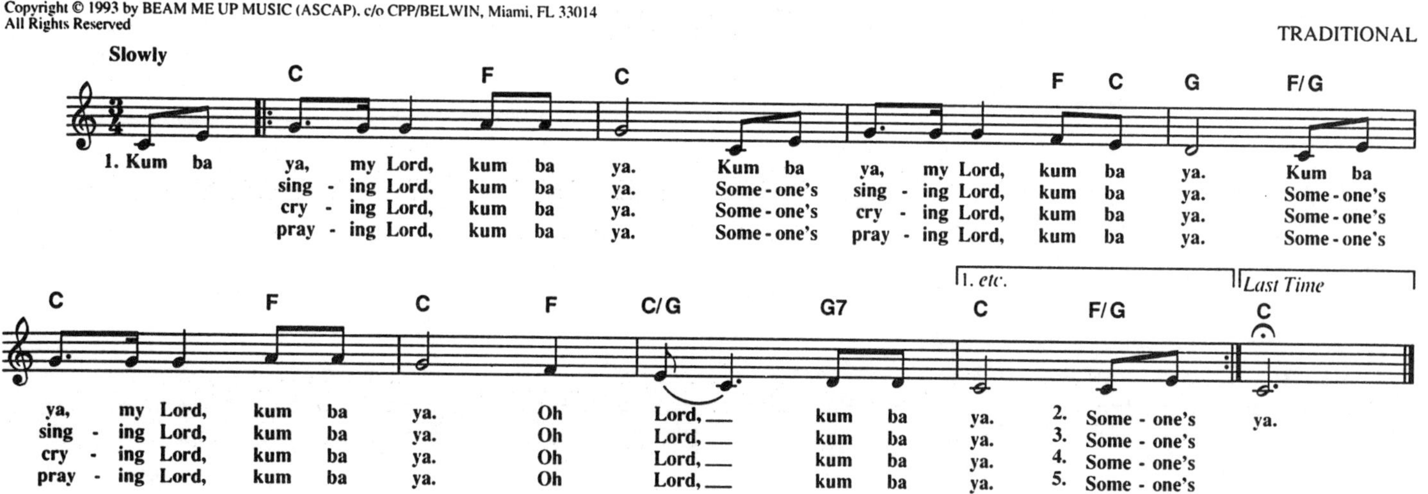
Slowly
C F C F C G F/G
1. Kum ba ya, my Lord, kum ba ya. Kum ba ya, my Lord, kum ba ya. Kum ba
sing - ing Lord, kum ba ya. Some-one's sing - ing Lord, kum ba ya. Some-one's
cry - ing Lord, kum ba ya. Some-one's cry - ing Lord, kum ba ya. Some-one's
pray - ing Lord, kum ba ya. Some-one's pray - ing Lord, kum ba ya. Some-one's
C F C F C/G G7 C F/G C
1. etc.
Last Time
ya, my Lord, kum ba ya. Oh Lord, kum ba ya. 2. Some - one's ya.
sing - ing Lord, kum ba ya. Oh Lord, kum ba ya. 3. Some - one's
cry - ing Lord, kum ba ya. Oh Lord, kum ba ya. 4. Some - one's
pray - ing Lord, kum ba ya. Oh Lord, kum ba ya. 5. Some - one's

Additional verses may be added. Some Examples:

Someone's learning Lord...
Someone's hoping...
Someone's working...
etc.

L.A. WOMAN

Words and Music by
THE DOORS

Brightly
A
Well, I just got in - to town a-bout an hour a - go;
took a look a-round, see which way the wind blow,
where the lit - tle girls in their Hol - ly - wood bun - ga - lows.
Are you a
luck - y lit - tle la - dy in the cit - y of light?
Or just an - oth - er lost an - gel?
G G♯ A G G♯ A
City of night, cit-y of night, cit-y of night, cit-y of night.
To Coda
A
L. A. wom-an, L. A. wom-an.
L. A. wom - an, Sun-day af - ter-noon.
L. A. wom - an, Sun-day af - ter - noon;
drive through your sub-urbs
G G♯ A
in - to your blues, in - to your blues,
G G♯ A
in - to your blue, blue blues, in - to your blues.
A G A G
2nd time only
I
A G A G A G A G A G A G A G
1.2.
A G
see your hair is burn - ing. Hills are filled with fi - re. If they
say I nev - er loved you, you know they are a li - ar.
Driv - ing down the free - way; mid - night al - leys roam.
3.
A G A
Cops in cars, the top-less bars; nev-er saw a wom-an
G G♯ A
so a - lone, so a - lone,
G G♯ A
so a - lone, so a - lone.
Mo - tel mon-ey mur-der mad - ness . . .

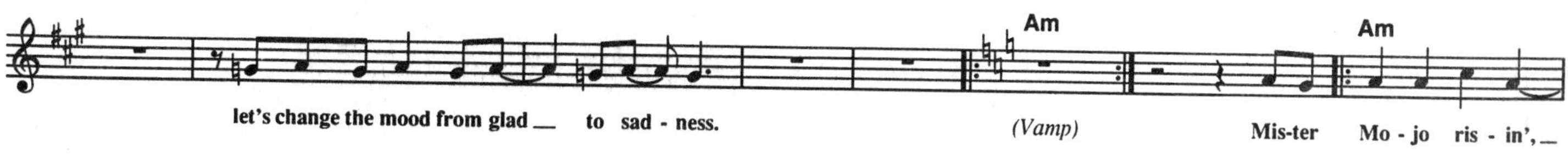
Am
Am
let's change the mood from glad __ to sad - ness.
(Vamp)
Mis-ter Mo - jo ris - in', __

(Getting gradually faster and faster)
1.
2.
— Mis-ter Mo - jo ris - in', ___ Mis-ter — got to keep on ris - in', ___ Mis-ter Mo - jo __ ris - in', ___ Mis-ter

1.
2.
Mo - jo ris - in', ___ Mo - jo ris - in', ___ Mis-ter — got to keep on ris - in', ___

Repeat four times.
Original tempo
D.S. 𝄋 al Coda
A
ris - in', ris - in', ___ ris - in', ris - in'. ___
Well , I

Coda
A
Repeat ad lib. and fade
L. A. ___ wom - an. L. A. ___ wom - an.

LA MARSEILLAISE

FRENCH NATIONAL ANTHEM

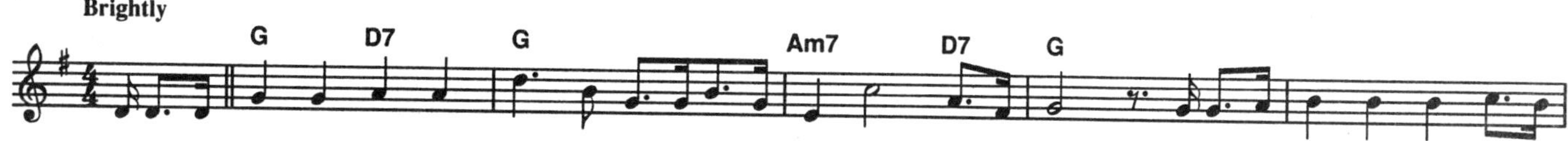
Brightly
G D7 G Am7 D7 G

D7 G D D7 G G7

C A7 D Gm D7 Gm A7 D G

D7 G D7 G D7 G G7 C G C D7 G D7 G

LA CUCARACHA

(La Cu-Ca-Ra-Cha)

English Lyrics by NED WASHINGTON
Transcription by D. SAVINO

Brightly

F
C7
Hear the reb-els' hap-py voic-es as they march in-to the val-ley. Ev-'ry troop-er's heart re-joic-es 'round their tat-tered flag they
U - na co-sa me da ri-sa: Pan-cho Vil - la sin ca - mi-sa Ya se van los car-ran-cis-tas Por - que vie-nen los vil -

F
C7
ral - ly. Can't you hear the bul-lets ring-ing? See the mus-kets in their hand. Can't you hear the song they're sing-ing
lis - tas. Pa - ra su - ra-pes, Sal - til - lo, Chi-hua-hua pa-ra sol - da - dos; Pa - ra mu - je - res, Ja - lis - co;

Chorus:
F
F
C7
as they brave-ly make their stand? La Cu-ca - ra - cha La Cu-ca - ra - cha when the stars are up a - bove. La Cu-ca -
Pa-ra a-mar, to-di - tos la - dos? La Cu-ca - ra - cha, La Cu-ca - ra - cha, Ya no pue-de ca-mi - nar, Por-que no

F
ra - cha La Cu-ca - ra - cha, it can be a song of love. La Cu-ca - ra - cha La Cu-ca - ra - cha
tie - ne, por-que no tie - ne Ma - ri-hua-na que fu - mar La-Cu-ca - ra - cha La-Cu-ca - ra - cha

C7
1.
F C7
2.
F
Se - ño-ri-tas can't re - sist. La Cu-ca - ra - cha La Cu-ca - ra - cha, they'll be cry-ing to be kissed. La-Cu-ca- kissed.
Ya no pue-de ca-mi - nar Por-que le fal - ta por-que le fal - ta Ma - ri-hua-na que fu- mar. La Cu-ca- mar.

LA PALOMA

S. YRADIER

Moderate tango

C
G7
1.
C
2.
C
G7
1.
C
2.
C
N.C.
C
G7
Dm
G7
Dm
G7
C
N.C.
C
G7
Dm
G7
Dm
G7
C
G7
C

LA CUMPARSITA

TRADITIONAL

Moderate tango

D7 Gm D7 Gm

Cm Gm D7

Gm D7 1. Gm D7 Gm 2. *To Next Strain* Gm D7 Gm 3. *Fine* Gm D7 Gm

D7 Gm G7

Cm Am7(♭5) D7 Gm D7 Gm D7 Gm Gm D7 Gm

Cm Gm D7 Gm Cm Gm

D7 Gm D7 *D.C. al Fine* Gm D7 Gm

LARGO FROM "THE NEW WORLD SYMPHONY"

ANTONIN DVOŘÁK

Slowly
C
G7
C
C+
Dm G7 C
F
C F
C F

C F
C F
C
G7
C G Am C F G9 C

LA DONNA È MOBILE
(Woman Is Fickle)

By GIUSEPPE VERDI

Allegretto
legato
Wo - man is fick - le false al - to - geth - er; moves like a feath - er borne on the breez - es.
La don - na è mo - bi - le qual piu - ma al ven - to, mu - ta d'ac - cen - to e di pen - sie - ro.
Wo - man with witch - ing smile, will e'er de - ceive you; oft - en will grieve you, yet as she pleas - es.
Sem - pre un a - ma - bi - le leg - gia - dro vi - so, in pian - to o in ri - so è men - zo - gne - ro.
leggiero
Her heart's un - feel - ing false al - to - geth - er, moves like a feath - er borne on the
La don - na è mo - bil qual piu - ma al ven - to, mu - ta d'ac - cen - to e di pen -
breeze, borne on the breeze. Ah,
sier, e di pen - sier, e,
con forza
borne on the breeze.
e di pen - sier.
Wretch - ed the day is,
È sem - pre mi - se - ro
when she looks kind - ly, trusts to her blind - ly, his life thus wast - ing. Yet he must sure - ly be,
chi a lei s'af - fi - da, chi le con - fi - da, mal - cau - to il co - re! Pur mai non sen - te - si
dull be - yond meas - ure; who of love's hap - pi - ness, ne'er has been tast - ing. Wo - man's un - feel - ing
fe - li - ce ap - pie - no chi su quel se - no non li - ba a mo - re! La don - na è mo - bil
leggiero
false al - to - geth - er; moves like a feath - er borne on the breeze, borne on the
qual piu - ma al ven - to, mu - ta d'ac - cen - to e di pen - sier, e di pen -
con forza
breeze. Ah, borne on the breeze.
sier, e, e di pen - sier!

LA MALAGUENA

Spanish Words by PEDRO GALINDO and
ELPIDIO RAMIREZ
Music by ELPIDIO RAMIREZ

Moderately fast

Dm Gm
Que bo - ni - tos o - jos tie - nes de - ba - jo de e - sas dos ce - jas, de ba - jos de e - sas dos
po - bre me des - pre - cias, yo te con - ce - do ra - zón, yo te con - ce - do rá -
C7 B♭ A A7 Dm
ce - jas, qué bo - ni - tos o - jos tie - nes! E - llos me quie - ren mi - rar, pe -
zón si por po - bre me des - pre - cias. Yo no te o - frez - co ri - que - zas te o -
Gm C7 B♭
ro si tú no los de - jas, pe - ro si tú no los de - jas ni si - quie - ra pàr - pa -
frez - co mi co - ra - zón, te o - frez - co mi co - ra - zón a cam - bio de mi po -
A
dear.
bre - za. Ma - la -
A7 Dm C
gue - ña sa - le - ro - sa, be - sar tus la - bios qui - sie - ra, be -
Dm A7
sar tus la - bios qui - sie - ra, ma - la - gue - ña sa - le - ro - sa y de -
Dm C7 Dm
cir - te, ni - ña her - mo - sa, e - res lin - da y he - chi - ce - ra, e - res lin - da y he - chi - ce - ra, co -
A A7 Dm C
mo el can - dor de u - na ro - sa. Y de - cir - te, ni - ña her - mo - sa, e - res lin - da y he - chi - ce - ra, e -
C7 1. A A7 Dm
res lin - da y he - chi - ce - ra co - mo el can - dor de u - na ro - sa.
D.S. 𝄋 2. Dm N.C. A7 N.C. Dm
Si por ce - ra co mo el can - dor de u - na ro - sa.

THE LADY IN MY LIFE

Words and Music by
ROD TEMPERTON

Slowly
Amaj9 Dm9 Em7 Amaj9 Dm9 Em7 Am7 D6/A
Am7 D6/A Am7 D6/A Am7 Em7 Dm7 G/D Em7 Dm7 Em7
There'll be no dark-ness to - night, la - dy, our love will shine, (light-ing the light.)
Am7 D6/A Am7 Em7 Dm7 G/D Em7 Dm7 C G
Just put your trust in my heart and meet me in par - a - dise, (now is the time.) You're ev-'ry won-der in this
Fmaj7 G D/E Amaj9 Dm7
world to me, a trea-sure time won't steal a - way. So, lis-ten to my heart. Lay your
And I will keep you warm through the
F/G Cmaj7 Fmaj7 Bm7 D/E Amaj7 Dm7
bod - y close to mine. Let me fill you with my dreams. I can make you feel so right.
shad - ows of the night. Let me touch you with my love. I can make you feel so right.
Amaj9 Dm7 F/G Cmaj7 Fmaj9 Bm7
And ba - by, through the years, gon - na love you more each day. So, I prom - ise you to - night that you will
And ba - by through the years, e - ven when we're old and gray, I will love you more each day, 'cause you will
D/E Amaj9 Dm9 To Coda Em7 Dm9 Em7
al - ways be the la - dy in my life.
al - ways be the la - dy in my life.
Lay back in my ten - der-ness.
Dm9 Em7 Am7 G6/9 Em7
Let's make this a night we won't for - get. Girl, I need your sweet ca - ress.
D.S. al Coda
Dm9 Em7 Dm9 Em7 D/E E
Reach out to a fan - ta - sy, two hearts in the beat of ec - sta - sy. come to me.
Coda Em7 Amaj9 Dm9 Em7 Amaj9 Em7 Amaj9 Dm9 Em7
Repeat ad lib. and fade

THE LADY IN RED

Words and Music by
CHRIS DeBURGH

Moderately slow

Bb Ebmaj7 Fsus Bb Ebmaj7 Fsus

Verse:

Bb Ebmaj7
1. I've nev-er seen you look-ing so love - ly as you did _ to-night; _

F(2) D7 /F# Gm F Eb
I've nev-er seen you shine so bright. Mm mm mm. __

Bb Ebmaj7
I've nev-er seen so man-y men ask ___ you if you want-ed to dance _

F(2) D7 /F# Gm Bb7/F Eb
— They're look-ing for a lit-tle ro - mance, giv-en half a chance.

Cm7
I have nev-er seen that dress you're wear-ing, or the

F7 Gm F /Eb
high-lights in your hair that catch your eyes; I have been blind.

Chorus:

Bb /D Eb(2) F
The la - dy in red ___ is danc-ing with me _

Gm F/A Gm Cm7 F(9)
cheek to cheek. __ There's no-bod-y here, ___ it's just you and me. __

Bb Bb7 Eb
It's where I wan-na be. But I hard-ly know ___

D7/F# D7 Gm /F C7/E Cm7 F(9) F
this beau-ty by my side. __ I'll nev - er for - get ___ the way you look to - night.

1. Bb *D.S.* 𝄋 2. Bb
night.

Verse 2:
I've never seen you looking so gorgeous as you did tonight;
I've never seen you shine so bright. You were amazing.
I've never seen so many people want to be there by your side,
And when you turned to me and smiled
It took my breath away. I have never had such a feeling,
Such a feeling of complete and utter love as I do tonight.
(To Chorus:)

LET ME CALL YOU SWEETHEART (I'm in Love with You)

Words by BETH SLATER WHITSON
Music by LEO FRIEDMAN

Slowly (with sentiment)
Chorus:
Bb C#dim7 Bb/D Eb G7/D C7 F7
Let me call you sweet-heart, I'm in love with you. ___ Let me hear you whis-per
Cm7 A7/C# Bb/D Bdim7 F7/C F7 C7/G F7/A Bb C#dim7 Bb/D Eb G7/D
that you love me, too. ___ Keep the love - light glow - ing In your eyes so
C Edim7 Bb/F G+ G7 C7 F7 1. Bb F C7/G F7/A 2. Bb
true. ___ Let me call you sweet-heart, I'm in love with you. you. ___

LAST DATE

(Instrumental)

By FLOYD CRAMER

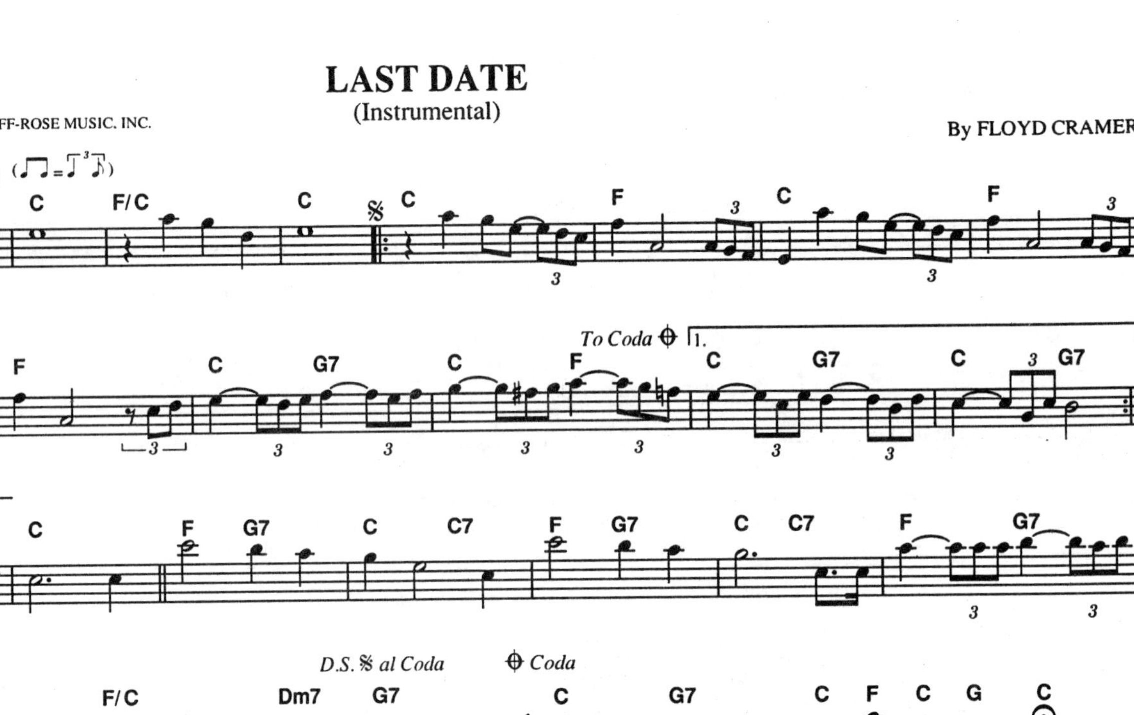
Slow country swing
F/C C F/C C C F C F
C F C G7 C F C G7 C G7
To Coda
1.
2.
C G7 C F G7 C C7 F G7 C C7 F G7
C Am F F/C Dm7 G7
D.S. al Coda
Coda
C G7 C F C G C

From the United Artists Motion Picture "LAST TANGO IN PARIS"

LAST TANGO IN PARIS

Lyric by DORY PREVIN
Music by GATO BARBIERI

Moderately

Am7 Am6 Am7 Am6 Dm7 Dm6 Dm7 Dm6 Am7 Am6
We don't ex - ist, we are noth-ing but shad-ow and mist. In the mir-ror we look as we pass

Am7 Am6 Dm7 Dm6 Dm7 Dm6 Gm7 Gm6 Gm7 Gm6 Cm7 Cm6
no re-flec-tion's re - vealed in the glass. Don't you know that the blood in your vein is as life-less as yes-ter-day's rain?

Cm7 Cm6 Gm7 Gm6 Dm7 Dm6 Cm7 C♯m7
It's a game where we come to con - ceal the con - fu - sion we feel. But as long as we're name-less, our

Bm7/D E7(♭9) Am7 Am6 Am7 Am6 Dm7 Dm6 Dm7 Dm6
bod - ies are blame-less. You cried when we kissed, it was noth-ing but shad-ow and mist. Two il - lu - sions who

Am7 Am6 Am7 Am6 Dm7 Dm6 Dm7 Dm6 Gm7 Gm6
touch in a trance, mak-ing love not by choice but by chance, to a theme that we tore from the past,

Repeat ad lib. and fade

Gm7 Gm6 Cm7 Cm6 Cm7 Cm6 1. Gm7 Dm E7 2. Gm7 Cm7 Cm6 Gm7
to a tan-go we swore was the last, we are shad-ows who dance. dance. We are shad-ows who dance.

LATELY

Words and Music by
STEVIE WONDER

Slowly
Verse:
Db Bbm7 Ebm7
Late - ly I have had the strang - est feel - ing with no viv - id rea - son here to find.
Late - ly I've been star - ing in the mir - ror, ver - y slow - ly pick - ing me a - part
Ab7 Ebm Bb7(b13) Ebm7 Gb/Ab Ab7 Db
Yet, the thought of los - ing you's been hang - ing 'round my mind.
trying to tell my - self I have no rea - son with your heart.
Ebm9 Ab Db Bbm7 Ebm7
Far more fre - quent-ly you're wear - ing per - fume with, you say, no spe - cial place to go.
Just the oth - er night while you were sleep-ing, I vague-ly heard you whis-per some-one's name.
Ab7 Bb7(b13) Ebm Bb7(b13) Ebm7 Gb/Ab Ab7
But when I ask will you be com - ing back soon, you don't
But when I ask you of the thoughts you're keep - ing, you just
Db Ebm7 Abm7 Db13 Chorus: Gbmaj7 Gbm7 To Coda Cb13
know, nev - er know.
say noth-ing's changed.
Well, I'm a man of man-y wish - es, hope my pre - mo-ni-tion miss - es,
Fm7 Bb9sus Bb9 Ebm7 Fm7 Gbm7 Ebm7/Ab Db
but what I real-ly feel, my eyes won't let me hide, 'cause they al - ways start to cry;
Bb7sus Bb7 Ebm9 Fm7 Gbm7 Gb/Ab Ab7 Db Bbm7 G7(#9 b13) Gbmaj9 D7(#9 b13) Ebm7 Gb/Ab Ab7 D.C. al Coda
'cause this time could mean good - bye.
Coda
Bbm7 Db/Eb Eb7 Abm7 Bbm7 Bm7 Db7 Gb Eb7sus Eb7
but what I real-ly feel my eyes won't let me hide, 'cause they al - ways start to cry; 'cause this
Abm7 Bbm7 Bm7 Cb/Db Gb Ebm7 Gb/Db Cbmaj7 Gb/Bb Abm7 Abm7/Db Bbm7 Ebmaj13
time could mean good - bye.

From the 20th Century-Fox Motion Picture "LAURA"

LAURA

Lyric by JOHNNY MERCER
Music by DAVID RAKSIN

Slowly

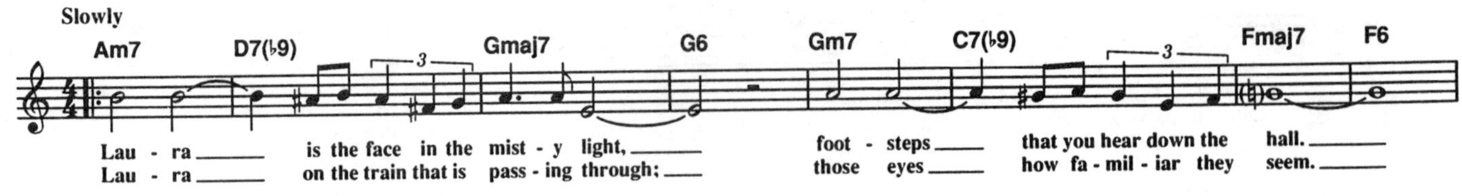
Am7 D7(♭9) Gmaj7 G6 Gm7 C7(♭9) Fmaj7 F6
Lau - ra is the face in the mist - y light, foot - steps that you hear down the hall.
Lau - ra on the train that is pass - ing through; those eyes how fa - mil - iar they seem.

1.
Fm7 B♭7(♭9) E♭maj7 E♭6 Am7(♭5) D7(♭5/♭9) D7 Bm7 E9 E7(♭9)
The laugh that floats on a sum - mer night, that you can nev - er quite re - call. And you see

2.
Fm7 Fdim Cmaj9 D7 D7(♭9) D7(♯5/♭9) G9 C6/9
She gave your ver - y first kiss to you. That was Lau - ra, but she's on - ly a dream.

LAZY RIVER

By HOAGY CARMICHAEL
and SIDNEY ARODIN

Slowly

D7 D♭7/A♭ C7/G F♯dim G7 A♭9 G9
Up a la - zy riv - er by the old mill - run, that la - zy, la - zy riv - er in the noon - day sun.

C7 D♭7 C7 F C7 F F7/C E7/B E♭7/B♭
Lin - ger in the shade of a kind old tree: throw a - way your trou - bles, dream a dream with me.

D7 D♭7/A♭ C7/G F♯dim G7
Up a la - zy riv - er where the rob - in's song a - wakes a bright new morn - ing, we can

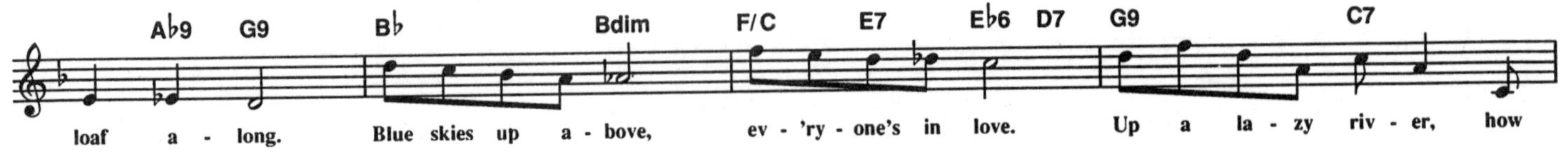
A♭9 G9 B♭ Bdim F/C E7 E♭6 D7 G9 C7
loaf a - long. Blue skies up a - bove, ev - 'ry - one's in love. Up a la - zy riv - er, how

F E7 D7 G9 C7 1. F 2. F
hap - py you can be, up a la - zy riv - er with me. me.

LAZY BONES

Words and Music by
JOHNNY MERCER and
HOAGY CARMICHAEL

Slow blues

C F C F C F G+ C C7 A♭dim7 Gdim7 D7/F♯ Gm/D
La - zy-bones, sleep-in' in the sun, how you 'spec' to get your day's work done? Nev - er get your day's work

Dm D7(♭5) G7 F C G7 C F C F C F G+
done, sleep-in' in the noon - day sun. La - zy-bones, sleep-in' in the shade, How you 'spec' to get your

C C7 A♭dim7 Gdim7 D7/F♯ Gm/D Dm D7(♭5) G7 F C F C
corn meal made? Nev - er get your corn meal made sleep - in' in the eve - nin' shade. When

F F6 Fmaj7 F6 C G7 C F7 E♭7
'tat - ers need spray-in', I bet you keep pray-in' the bugs fall off of the vine, and when you go fish - in' I

D7 G7 D7 Dm7 G7 C F C F C F G+
bet you keep wish-in' the fish won't grab at your line. La - zy-bones, loaf - in' thru the day. How you 'spec' to make a

C C7 A♭dim7 Gdim7 D7/F♯ Gm/D Dm 3 D7(♭5) G7 F C
dime that way? Nev - er make a dime that way, (well look-y here.) He nev - er heared a word I say!

LET A SMILE BE YOUR UMBRELLA

Words by IRVING KAHAL and FRANCIS WHEELER
Music by SAMMY FAIN

Moderately
F B♭/F F B♭/F F C+ F C7 Cdim7 C7
Just let a smile be your um - brel - la on a rain - y, rain - y day. And if your
F6 F C+ F D7
sweet - ie cries just tell her that a smile will al - ways pay. When-ev - er skies are
D7(♭9) G7 C7 F
gray don't wor - ry or fret. A smile will bring the sun-shine and you'll nev - er get wet. So, let a smile be
B♭/F F C7/E F7/E♭ D7 G7 C7 1. F A♭dim7 C7/G N.C. 2. F B♭ F
your um - brel - la on a rain - y, rain - y, day. Just let a day!

LEAD ME ON

Words and Music by
DAVID LASLEY and
ALLEE WILLIS

Moderate ballad

Verse:

C Am7 Em7 Dm7
1. I have of - ten heard you say you love me as a friend. But I love you more than an - y - one, you
know I told you from the start ex - act - ly how I feel. Time goes on, seems noth - ing's changed and

F/G C Am7 Em7
know I can't pre - tend no long - er. I would give you an - y - thing, I'd throw my world a - way. But you don't
I'm in love for real. We have nev - er played the games that real lov - ers do, so may - be

Dm7 F/G *Chorus:* Am7 Em7
want to hear that an - y - more than you want to hear me say: Come on and lead me on, come on and
we are bet - ter off, though, ba - by, I'd still like this from you: (you.)

Am7 Em7 Dm7 F/G
tease me all night long. Lov - ing you, I know it's right, I'll al - ways need you, I'll nev - er leave you. Come on and

Am7 Em7 Am7 Em7 Dm7
lead me on, tease me all night long. I'd rath - er be a fool with a bro - ken heart than

1. F/G C Em7 F F/G D.C. 2. F/G *Repeat ad lib. and fade*
some - one who nev - er had a part of you. 2. You some - one who nev - er had a part of

From the Musical Production "GODSPELL"

LEARN YOUR LESSONS WELL

Words and Music by
STEPHEN SCHWARTZ

Bright tempo
C G C7 F A♭7 G7 C G11
I can see a swath of sin - ners set - tin' yon - der, and they're act - in' like a pack of fools.
Ev - 'ry bright de - scrip - tion of the prom - ised land meant you could reach it if you keep a - lert.
C G C7 Am7 D7 G7
Gaz - in' in - to space, they let their minds all wan - der, 'stead of stud - y - in' the good Lord's rules. You
Learn - in' ev - 'ry line in ev - 'ry last com - mand - ment may not help you, but it could - n't hurt.
Em7 A7 Dm7 B♭7
bet - ter pay at - ten - tion, your com - pre - hen - sion there's gon - na be a quiz at your as - cen - sion,
First you got - ta read 'em then you got - ta heed 'em you nev - er know when you're gon - na need 'em,
C G C7 F A♭7 C 1. G7 C G+ 2. G7 C
not to men - tion an - y threat of hell, but if you're smart you'll learn your les - sons well. les - sons well.
just as old E - li - jah said to Jez - e - bel, you bet - ter start to learn your

LET ME BE THE ONE

Lyrics by PAUL WILLIAMS
Music by ROGER NICHOLS

Slowly

Fmaj7 G7/F Em7 Dm7 Em7 A2 Fmaj7
3
1. Some sleep-less night, if you should find your - self a - lone,
2. To set things right when this old world's turned up - side down,
let me be the one _ you run to,

Em7 A7sus A7(♭9) Dm7 G7sus 1. Cmaj7 2. Cmaj7
let me be the one _ you come to when you need some-one to turn to; ___ let me be the one. one.

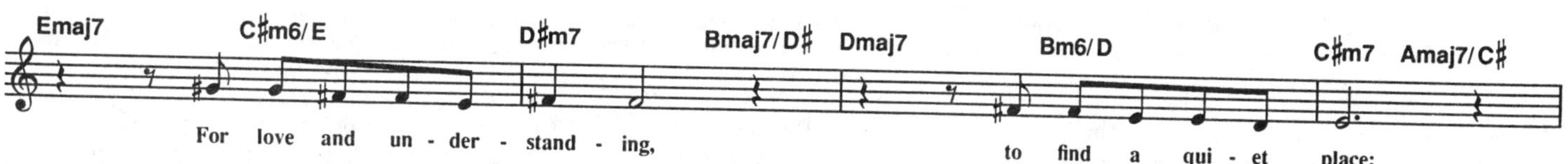
Emaj7 C♯m6/E D♯m7 Bmaj7/D♯ Dmaj7 Bm6/D C♯m7 Amaj7/C♯
For love and un - der - stand - ing, to find a qui - et place;

Cmaj7 D7/C Bm7 Gmaj7/B B♭maj7 Am7 Gm7 C7sus Fmaj7 G/F
for si - lent un - der - stand - ing, a lov - ing ___ touch. ___ Come to me when things go

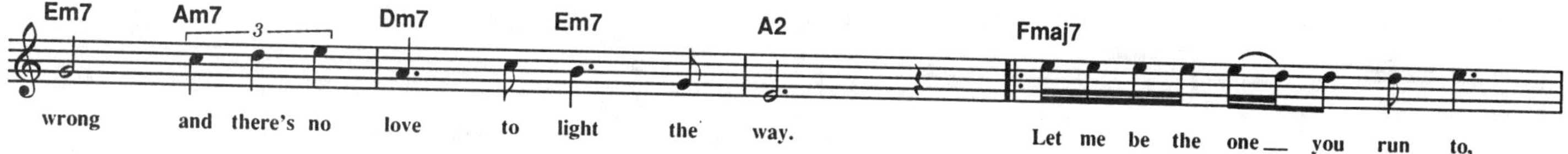
Em7 Am7 Dm7 Em7 A2 Fmaj7
3
wrong and there's no love to light the way. Let me be the one ___ you run to,

Repeat ad lib. and fade
Em7 A7sus A7(♭9) Dm7 G7sus Cmaj7
let me be the one ___ you come to when you need some-one to turn to; ___ let me be the one.

LIEBESTRAUM

FRANZ LISZT

Moderately

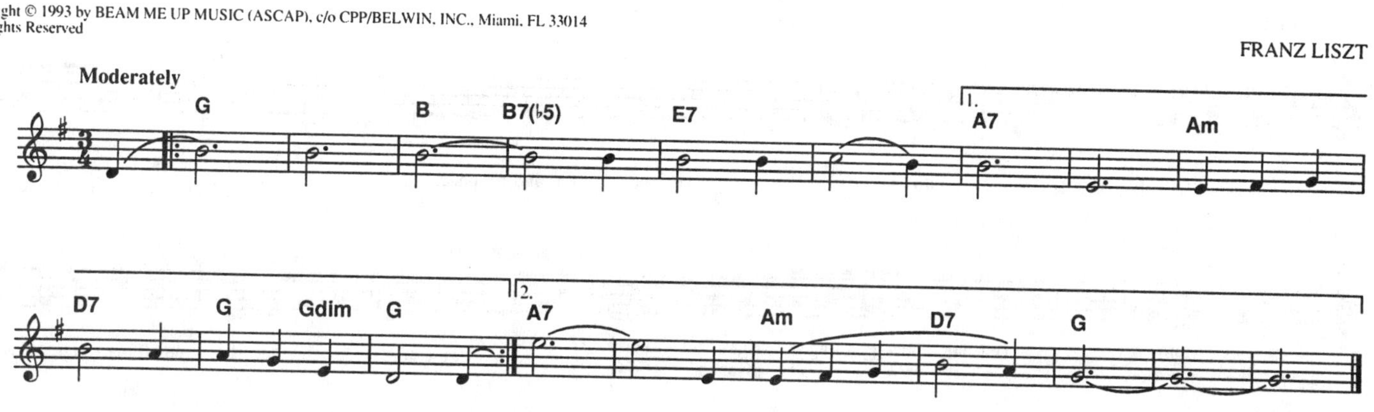
G B B7(♭5) E7 1. A7 Am
D7 G Gdim G 2. A7 Am D7 G

LET ME LOVE YOU ONCE BEFORE YOU GO

Words and Music by
MOLLY ANN LEIKIN and
STEPHEN H. DORFF

Slow country feel
Verse 1:
1. It's like look-ing in the win-dow of a fine bou-tique know-ing there is noth-ing I could ev-er buy. Still I
want to love so much that I could die, but I just can't lead a dou-ble life be-ing one man's love, one man's wife. 2. But you can
a tempo
Verses 2 & 3:
start a fire rag-in' just by touch-ing me, e-ven though I know we're not sup-posed to touch. Oh, I
lock the door and o-pen all my love to you, all the love I've longed to give you since we met. It's the
nev-er want-ed an-y-one so much, how I wish that I had found you first, don't you see my heart's a-bout to burst?
on-ly chance I'm ev-er goin' to get and I just can't let you dis-ap-pear, oh, my dar-ling, please come o-ver here.
Chorus:
Let me love you once be-fore you go. Your eyes keep say-ing "yes" to me so don't keep say-ing "no."
Let me love you once and then you'll see no one's ev-er gon-na love you more than me. 3. Let me me
D.S.
LET THE GOOD TIMES ROLL
Words and Music by
LEONARD LEE
Copyright © 1956, 1959, 1960 by EMI UNART CATALOG INC. and ATLANTIC MUSIC CORP.
All Rights Reserved
Moderate swing rock
Come on, ba-by let the good times roll. Come on, ba-by let me thrill your soul.
Come on, ba-by, gon-na have a ball; put our trou-bles up a-gainst the wall.
Come on, ba-by, let the good times roll, roll on and on.
Come on, ba-by, let me hold you tight. Tell me ev-'ry-thing is right to-night.
Come on, ba-by, let us paint the town. Don't let noth-ing ev-er bring us down.
Come on, ba-by, let the good times roll,

roll on and on. on. Feel so good in my arms.
Sugar baby, you're my good luck charm. Come on, baby, let the good times roll. Come on, baby, let me
thrill your soul. Come on, baby, let the good times roll, roll on and on.
LET THE SUNSHINE IN
Copyright © 1966, 1967, 1968 JAMES RADO, GEROME RAGNI, GALT MacDERMOT, NAT SHAPIRO, EMI U CATALOG INC.
All Rights Reserved
Words by JAMES RADO
and GEROME RAGNI
Music by GALT MacDERMOT
Moderately
We starve, look at one an-oth-er short of breath, walk-ing proud-ly in our win-ter coats, wear-
ing smells from lab-'ra-tor-ies, fac-ing a dy-ing na-tion of mov-ing pa-per fan-ta-sy,
lis-t'ning for the new told lies with su-preme vi-sions of lone-ly tunes. Some-where, in-side some-thing, there is a
rush of great-ness. Who knows what stands in front of our lives; I fash-ion my fu-ture on films in space.
Si-lence tells me se-cret-ly ev-'ry-thing, ev-'ry-thing. Sing-ing my space songs on a spi-der-
web si-tar, "Life is a-round you and in you." An-swer for Tim-oth-y Lear-y, dear-y.
Repeat ad lib. and fade
Let the sun shine, let the sun-shine in, the sun shine in.

LET'S DO IT
(Let's Fall in Love)

Words and Music by
COLE PORTER

Gracefully

B♭6 B♭ F7 B♭ E♭6 E♭m B♭6 B♭
Birds do it, bees do it, e - ven ed - u - cat - ed fleas do it, let's do it,
Spon - ges, they say, do it, oy - sters, down in Oy - ster Bay, do it,

F7 B♭ E♭m B♭ F+ B♭6 B♭ F7
let's fall in love. In Spain, the best up - per sets do it,
Cold Cape Cod clams, 'gainst their wish, do it,

B♭ E♭6 E♭m B♭6 B♭ F7 B♭ E♭6
Lith - u - an - i - ans and Letts do it, Let's do it, let's fall in love.
E - ven la - zy Jel - ly - fish do it,

B♭ Gm Cm7 B♭ B♭7
The Dutch in old Am - ster - dam do it, not to men - tion the Finns,
E - lec - tric eels, I might add, do it, though it shocks 'em I know.

E♭ A♭7 D♭ B♭m7 F7 F+
folks in Si - am do it, think of Si - am - ese twins. Some Ar - gen -
why ask if shad do it, wait - er, bring me shad - roe. In shal - low

B♭6 B♭ F7 B♭ B♭6 E♭7
tines, with - out means, do it, peo - ple say, in Bos - ton, e - ven beans do it,
shoals, Eng - lish soles do it, Gold - fish, in the pri - va - cy of bowls, do it,

B♭/F Gm/F Cm7 F7 B♭ E♭m 1. B♭ F+ 2. B♭
lets do it, let's fall in love. 2. Ro - man - tic.

LITTLE PONY

By NEAL HEFTI

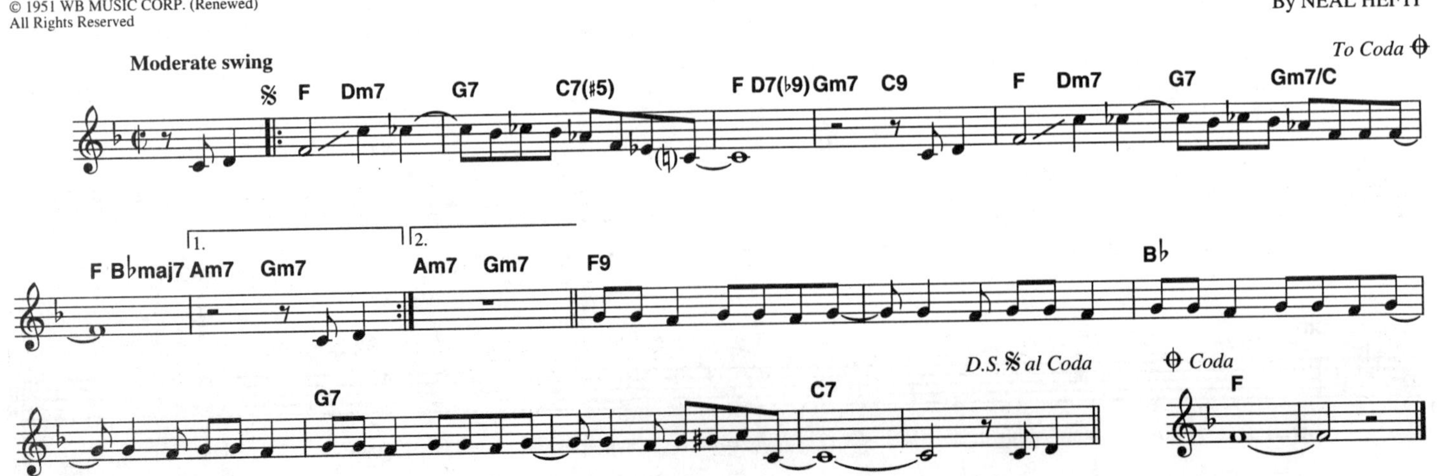
Moderate swing
To Coda
F Dm7 G7 C7(♯5) F D7(♭9) Gm7 C9 F Dm7 G7 Gm7/C
1. 2.
F B♭maj7 Am7 Gm7 Am7 Gm7 F9 B♭
D.S. al Coda
Coda
G7 C7 F

LA BAMBA

Adaptation and Arrangement by
RITCHIE VALENS

Moderate "Latin Rock" beat
Pa - ra bai - lar la Bam - ba. Pa - ra bai - lar la Bam - ba se ne - ce - si -
- ta un po - ca de gra - cia. U - na po - ca de gra - cia pa ra mi pa ra ti y a - rri - ba a - rri -
- ba; a - rri - ba a - rri - ba por ti se - re por ti se - re se - re. You no soy ma - ri -
ne - ro. Yo no soy ma - ri - ne - ro, soy ca - pi - tan; yo no soy ma - ri - ne - ro, soy ca - pi - tan.
To Coda
Bam - ba, bam - ba, bam - ba bam - ba, bam - ba, bam -
- ba, bam - ba bam... Pa - ra bai - lar la Bam-
D.S. al Coda
Coda
Repeat and fade
Bam - ba, bam - ba!
LIMBO ROCK
Copyright © 1961 (Renewed 1989) by ACUFF-ROSE MUSIC, INC.
All Rights Reserved
Music by
WILLIAM E. "BILLY" STRANGE
Lyric by
JON SHELDON
Bright Latin rock
1. Ev - 'ry lim - bo boy and girl all a - round the lim - bo world, gon - na do the lim - bo rock
(2.) spread your lim - bo feet, then you move to lim - bo beat. Lim - bo an - kle, lim - bo knee;
(3.) self a lim - bo girl, give that chick a lim - bo whirl. There's a lim - bo moon a - bove,
all a - round the lim - bo clock.
bend back, like the lim - bo tree.
you will fall in lim - bo love.
Jack be lim - bo, Jack be quick, Jack go un - der lim - bo stick.
All a - round the lim - bo clock, hey, let's do the lim - bo rock. (Spoken:) "Limbo lower now, limbo lower now.
How low can you go?"
2. First you
3. Get your -
(Spoken:) "Don't move that limbo bar. You'll be a limbo star. How low can you go?"

LET'S HEAR IT FOR THE BOY

Music by TOM SNOW
Words by DEAN PITCHFORD

Moderately bright

C F G C | 1. F G | 2. F G

1. My

Verse:

C Am7 F G C Am7 F(2) G C Am7

ba - by, he don't talk sweet; he ain't got much to say. But he loves me, loves me, loves me. I
ba - by may not be rich; he's watch-in' ev - 'ry dime. But he loves me, loves me, loves me. We

F G C Am7 F(2) Dm/G C Am7 F G

know that he loves me an - y - way And may - be he don't dress fine, but I don't real - ly
al - ways have a real good time. And may - be he sings off key, but that's al - right by

C Am7 F(2) G B♭maj9 C(2) G *Chorus:* D G/B

mind. 1.3. 'Cause ev - 'ry time he pulls me near I just wan-na cheer: Let's hear it for the boy,
me, yeah. But what he does, he does so well. Makes me wan-na yell:

C(2) G/A D G/B C(2) G/A D G/B C(2) G/A

let's give the boy a hand. Let's hear it for my ba - by, you know you got - ta un - der-stand.

To Coda

D G/B C G/A Em7 F♯m7 G C G/B

Oh, may-be he's no Ro-me-o, but he's my lov-in' one man show. Oh, wo, wo,

A7sus | 1. D F F/C C G6/A G F G C F G *D.S.* | 2. D F

wo, let's hear it for the boy. 2. My

C F G C | 1.2. F G | 3. *D.S.S. al Coda* F G

Instrumental solo ad lib. 3. 'Cause

Coda

A7sus

wo, let's hear it for the boy.

Repeat ad lib. and fade

D G/B C G/A D G/B C G/A

Let's hear it for my man. Let's hear it for the boy.
(Bkgrd.) Let's hear it for the boy. Let's hear it for my ba - by.

LET'S STAY TOGETHER

Words and Music by
WILLIE MITCHELL, AL GREEN
and AL JACKSON

Moderate rock

Gm9 Am7 Gm7 Am7 Gm9 Am7 Gm7 C7

Verse:

F

1. I'm, I'm so___ in love with you._ Whatev-er you want to do___ is al-right_ with me,___ 'cause you___ make me feel so___ brand new.___ And I___ want to___ spend my life with you.___

(2.) since, since we've been to-geth-er, lov-ing you for-ev-er, is what I___ need.___ Let me be the one you come run-ning to.___ And I'll___ nev-er___ be un-true.___

3. Why, why peo-ple break up, turn a-round and make up; I just can't_ see.___ You'd___ nev-er do that to___ me.___ Be-ing a-round___ you is all I see.___

Dm9 Bb Bbm Am7 Gm7 Fmaj7 Em7 Dm9 Am7 Gm7 Fmaj7 Am7 Dm9

1. 2. Let me say

2.3. Oh,_ ba-by,

Chorus:

Gm9 Am7 Gm9 Bbmaj7 Am7 Dm C Gm7 Abmaj7

let's___ let's stay to-geth-er,___ lov-ing you_ wheth-er,___ wheth-er_ times are good or bad,___ hap-py or sad;___

Gm7 Abmaj7 Bbmaj7 Am7 Dm C

wheth-er times are good or bad,___ hap-py or sad.___

1. *D.S.* 𝄋

2.3. *etc.* *Repeat and fade*

Gm7 C

-py or sad.___

LI'L LIZA JANE

TRADITIONAL FOLK SONG

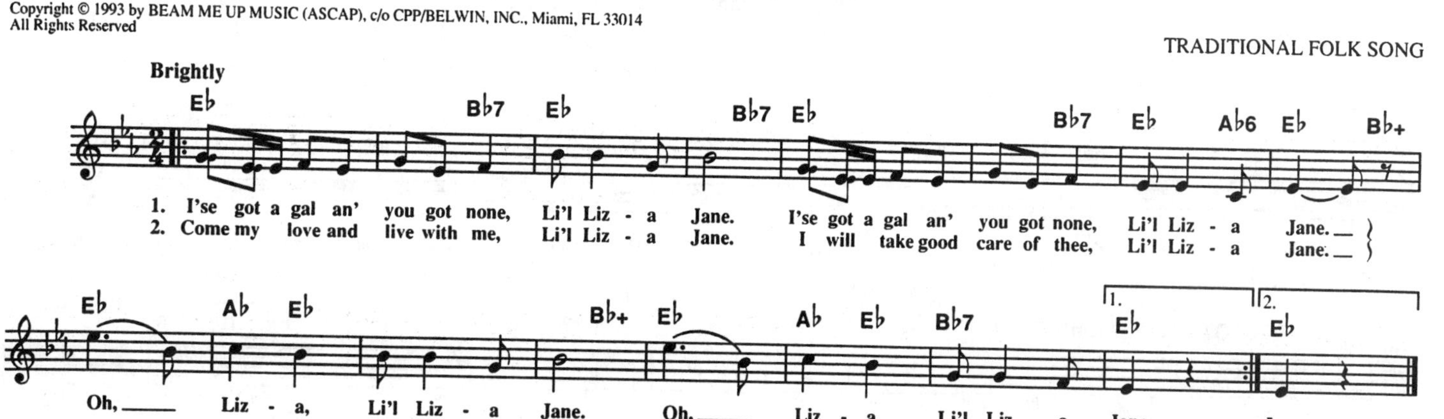
Brightly
Eb Bb7 Eb Bb7 Eb Bb7 Eb Ab6 Eb Bb+
1. I'se got a gal an' you got none, Li'l Liz - a Jane. I'se got a gal an' you got none, Li'l Liz - a Jane.
2. Come my love and live with me, Li'l Liz - a Jane. I will take good care of thee, Li'l Liz - a Jane.
Eb Ab Eb Bb+ Eb Ab Eb Bb7 Eb Eb
1. 2.
Oh, Liz - a, Li'l Liz - a Jane. Oh, Liz - a, Li'l Liz - a Jane. Jane.

LIES
(Are Breakin' My Heart)

Words and Music by
BUDDY RANDELL and
BEAU CHARLES

Moderately bright

C
Lies, lies, you're tell - in' me that you'll be true. Lies, lies, that's

G7 C
all I ev - er get from you. Tears, tears, I shed a mil - lion tears for you.
Lies, lies, I can't be - lieve a word you say.

G7 Am D Am
Tears, tears, and now you're lov - in' some-one new. Some day I'm gon-na be hap - py. I don't know when just
Lies, lies, are gon - na make you sad some day. Some day you're gon-na be lone - ly. You won't find me a -

To Coda
D C F Am D
now. But lies, lies, are break-in' my heart. You think that you're such a smart girl and
round. But lies, lies, are

D.S. al Coda
Am D Am D Am Am7 Dm E
I'll be - lieve what you say. But who do you think you are, girl, to lead me on this way? Hey!

Coda
Repeat and fade
Am
break - in' my heart, are break - in' my heart, are

LINGER AWHILE

Words by HARRY OWENS
Music by VINCENT ROSE

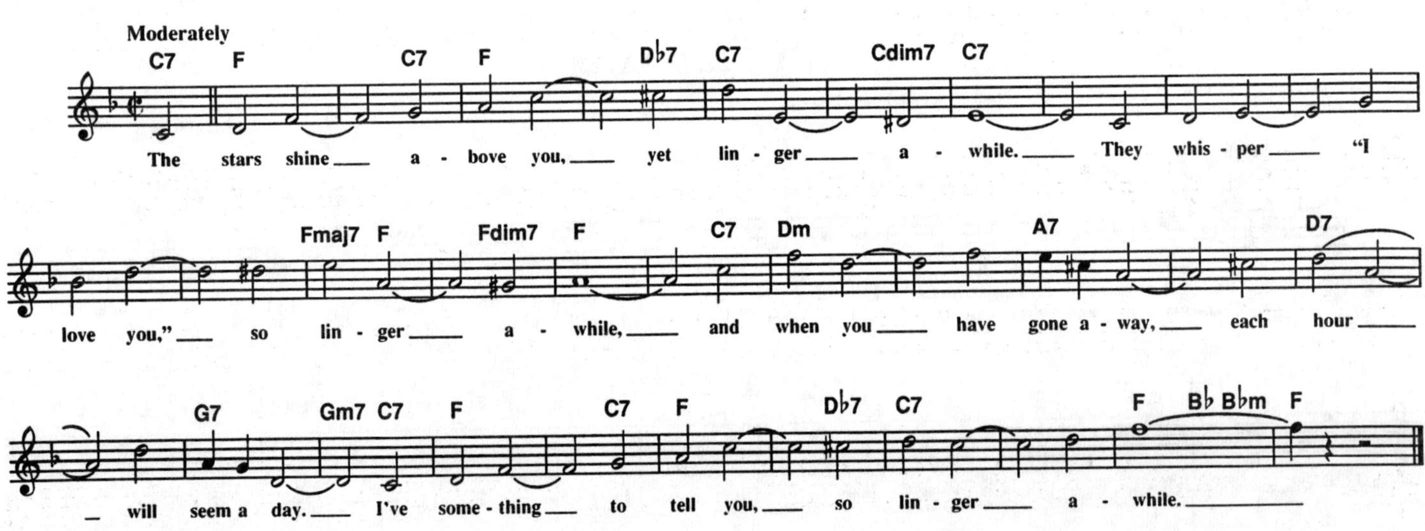
Moderately
C7 F C7 F D♭7 C7 Cdim7 C7
The stars shine a - bove you, yet lin - ger a - while. They whis - per "I
Fmaj7 F Fdim7 F C7 Dm A7 D7
love you," so lin - ger a - while, and when you have gone a - way, each hour
G7 Gm7 C7 F C7 F D♭7 C7 F B♭ B♭m F
will seem a day. I've some - thing to tell you, so lin - ger a - while.

LIGHT MY FIRE
Copyright © 1967 DOORS MUSIC CO.
All Rights Reserved
Words and Music by
THE DOORS
Moderate rock
G D F B♭ E♭ A♭ A
(Fine)
1. You
Verses 1 & 2:
Am7 F♯m7 Am7 F♯m7 Am7 F♯m7
know that it would be un - true;
time to hes - i - tate is through,
you know that I would be a liar;
no time to wal-low in the mire.
if I was to say to you;
Try now we can on - ly lose,
and our
Am7 F♯m7
Chorus:
G A D G A D B G D
girl, we could-n't get much higher.
love be-come a fune-ral pyre.
Come on, ba-by, light my fire,
come on, ba-by, light my fire,
try to set the night on
E
1.
2.
Verse 3:
Am7 F♯m7 Am7 F♯m7
fire.
2. The
3. The time to hes - i - tate is through,
no time to wal-low in the mire.
Am7 F♯m7 Am7 F♯m7
Chorus:
G A D
Try now we can on - ly lose,
and our love be-come a fune-ral pyre.
Come on, ba - by, light my fire,
G A D F C D
Play 3 times
F C D
D.C. al Fine
come on, ba - by, light my fire,
try to set the night on fire,
try to set the night on fire.
LINUS AND LUCY
Copyright © LEE MENDELSON FILM PRODUCTIONS, INC. 1965
All Rights Reserved
By VINCE GUARALDI
Brightly
A♭
(Bass riff)
(continue riff)
C♭
A♭
D♭ E♭
D♭ E♭
D♭ E♭
A♭

LIL' RED RIDING HOOD

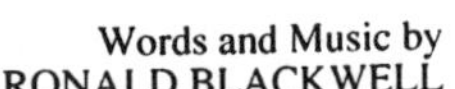
Words and Music by
RONALD BLACKWELL

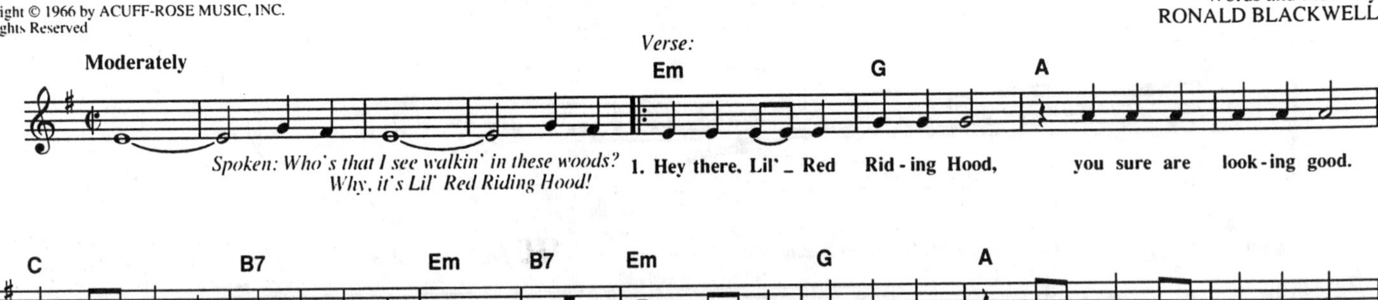
Moderately
Verse:
Em G A
Spoken: Who's that I see walkin' in these woods?
Why, it's Lil' Red Riding Hood!
1. Hey there, Lil' Red Riding Hood, you sure are look-ing good.

C B7 Em B7 Em G A
You're ev-'ry-thing a big bad wolf could want.
Spoken: (Listen to me)
Lil' Red Rid-ing Hood, I don't think lit-tle big girls should

C B7 Em B7
Chorus:
G Em
go walk-ing in these spook-y old woods a - lone.
Ooh! (Wolf call)
What big eyes you have, the kind of eyes that drive wolves mad. So,

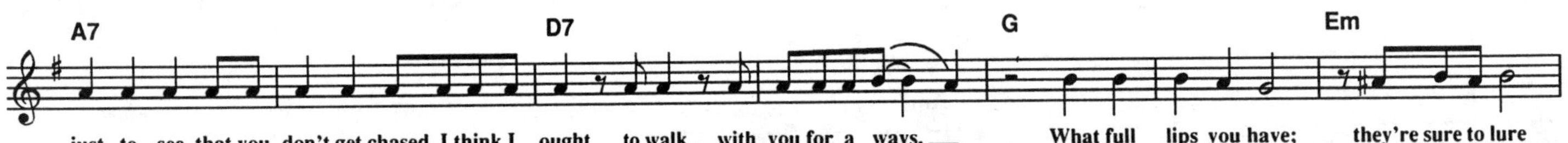
A7 D7 G Em
just to see that you don't get chased, I think I ought to walk with you for a ways.
What full lips you have; they're sure to lure

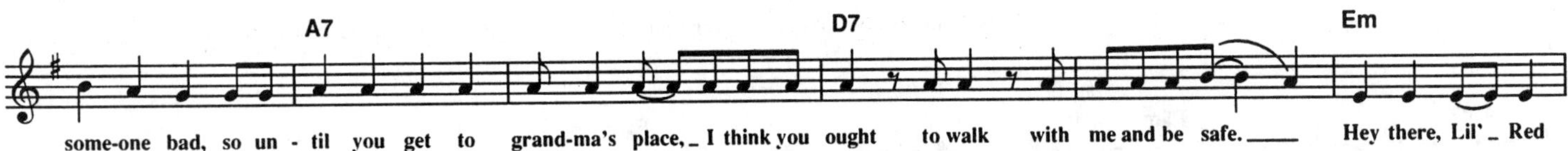
A7 D7 Em
some-one bad, so un - til you get to grand-ma's place, I think you ought to walk with me and be safe.
Hey there, Lil' Red

G A C B7
1. Em B7
2. Em
Rid-ing Hood, you sure are look-ing good. You're ev-'ry-thing a big bad wolf could want.
Spoken: (Listen to me.)
want.

Verse 2:
I'm gonna keep my sheep suit on
Until I'm sure that you've been shown,
That I can be trusted walkin' with you alone.
Spoken: Ooh! Lil' Red Riding Hood,
I'd like to hold you if I could.
But you might think I'm a big bad wolf so I won't.
(To Chorus 2:)

Chorus 2:
Ooh! What a big heart I have,
The better to love you with.
Lil' Red Riding Hood, even bad wolves can be good.
Spoken: Ooh! I'll try to be satisfied,
Just to walk close by your side.
Maybe you'll see things my way,
Before we get to grandma's place.
Spoken: Hey there, Lil' Red Riding Hood.
You sure are looking good.
You're everything that a big bad wolf could want.

THE LONELY BULL
(El Solo Toro)

SOL LAKE

G F G F G F
E♭ D G C G B♭ G C G
A7 D7 B♭ A♭ G♭ A♭ G♭

From the United Artists Motion Picture "PIECES OF DREAMS"

LITTLE BOY LOST

(Pieces of Dreams)

Lyric by MARILYN and ALAN BERGMAN
Music by MICHEL LEGRAND

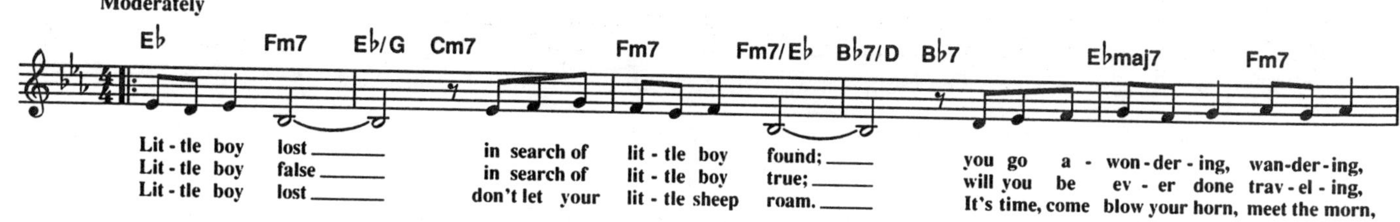
Moderately
E♭ Fm7 E♭/G Cm7 Fm7 Fm7/E♭ B♭7/D B♭7 E♭maj7 Fm7
Lit - tle boy lost in search of lit - tle boy found; you go a - won - der - ing, wan - der - ing,
Lit - tle boy false in search of lit - tle boy true; will you be ev - er done trav - el - ing,
Lit - tle boy lost don't let your lit - tle sheep roam. It's time, come blow your horn, meet the morn,

To Coda
1.
Gm7 Cm7/G B♭m7 B♭7 Bdim7 Cm Cm/B♭ Am7(♭5) D7 Gm Gm7 Gm6
stum - bl - ing, tum - bl - ing, round; round! When will you find what's on the tip of your mind?
al - ways un - rav - el - ing, you, you?
look and see, can you be far from

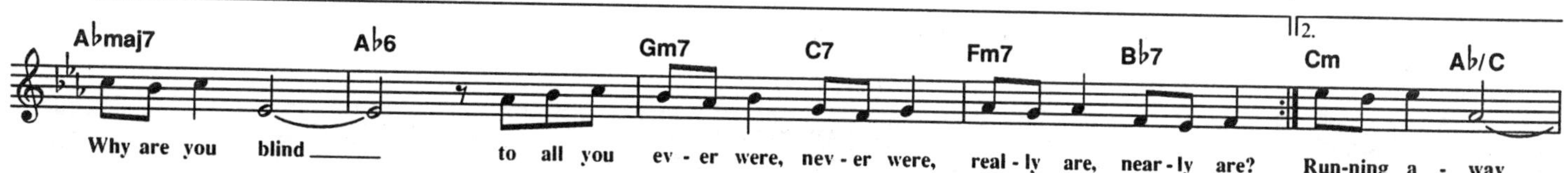
2.
A♭maj7 A♭6 Gm7 C7 Fm7 B♭7 Cm A♭/C
Why are you blind to all you ev - er were, nev - er were, real - ly are, near - ly are? Run - ning a - way

A♭m6/C♭ E♭/B♭ Am7(♭5) E♭/B♭ E♭+/B♭ Fm7/B♭ B♭m7 E♭maj7/B♭ E♭7/B♭
could lead you fur - ther a - stray. And as for fish - ing in streams for piec - es of dreams,

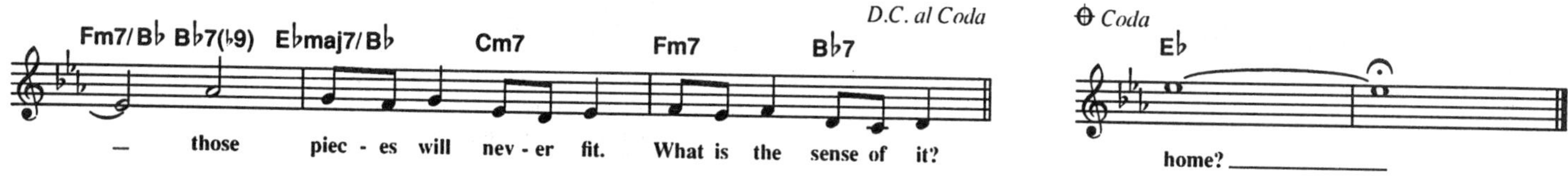
D.C. al Coda
Coda
Fm7/B♭ B♭7(♭9) E♭maj7/B♭ Cm7 Fm7 B♭7 E♭
those piec - es will nev - er fit. What is the sense of it? home?

LITTLE BROWN JUG

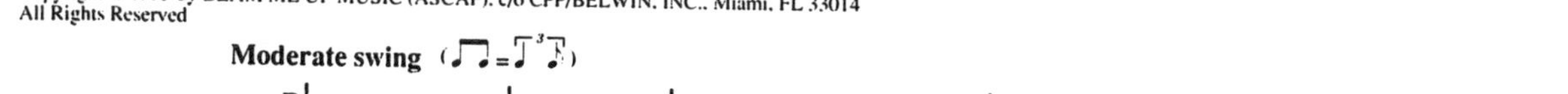

TRADITIONAL

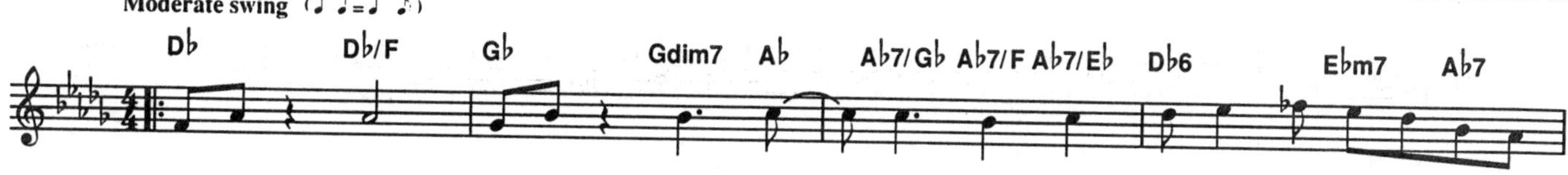
Moderate swing
D♭ D♭/F G♭ Gdim7 A♭ A♭7/G♭ A♭7/F A♭7/E♭ D♭6 E♭m7 A♭7

1.
2.
D♭ D♭/F G♭ Gdim7 A♭ A♭7/G♭ A♭7/F A♭7/E♭ D♭6/9 A♭7 D♭6/9

LITTLE DEUCE COUPE

Music by BRIAN WILSON
Words by ROGER CHRISTIAN

Moderate rock
C
Well, I'm not brag - gin', babe, so don't put me down, but I've got the fast - est set of
lit - tle deuce coupe with a flat - head mill, but she'll walk a Thun - der - bird like it's
F
wheels in town. When some - thing pulls up to me, it don't e - ven try. And if it
stand - in' still. She's port - ed and re - lieved, and she's stroked and she's bored. She'll do a
C G Dm
had a set of wings, man, I know I could fly, she's my lit - tle deuce coupe
hun - dred and for - ty with the top end floored, she's my lit - tle deuce coupe
G7 C 1. G7 2. C7
you don't know what I got. Just a She's got a
you don't know what I got.
F C
com - pe - ti - tion clutch, with four on the floor yeah, she purrs like a kit - ten till the lake pipes roar, and
F D7 G7
if that ain't e - nough to make you flip your wig, there's one more thing, I've got the pink slip, dad - dy! And
C
com - in' off the line, when the lights turn green, she blows 'em out - ta the wa - ter like you've nev - er seen. I get
F C
pushed out of shape, and it's hard to steer, when I get rub - ber in a all four gears. She's my
G Dm G7 1. C C7 2. C C9(♯11)
lit - tle deuce coupe, you don't know what I've got! She's got a

THE LITTLE DRUMMER BOY

Words and Music by
KATHERINE DAVIS, HENRY ONORATI
and HARRY SIMEONE

Moderately slow march
F
Come, they told me pa - rum pum pum pum, our new - born
Lit - tle Ba - by pa - rum pum pum pum, I am a
(Ba - by Ge - su)
C
King to see, pa - rum pum pum pum. Our fin - est gifts we bring pa - rum pum pum pum,
poor boy too, pa - rum pum pum pum. I have no gift to bring pa - rum pum pum pum,
F7 B♭ F C
to lay be - fore the King pa - rum pum pum pum rum pum pum pum, rum pum pum pum,
that's fit to give our King pa - rum pum pum pum rum pum pum pum, rum pum pum pum.
F
so to hon - or Him pa - rum pum pum pum,
Shall I play for you, pa - rum pum pum pum,
1. C7 F
when we come.
2. C7 F
on my drum?
C(no3) F
Ma - ry nod - ded pa - rum pum pum pum.
C
The Ox and Lamb kept time pa - rum pum pum pum. I played my drum for Him pa -
F B♭ F7 B♭ F
rum pum pum pum. I played my best for Him pa - rum pum pum pum rum pum pum pum
a tempo (a little slower)
C F(no3) C(no3)/G C(no3) F
rum pum pum pum. Then He smiled at me pa -
C7 F F(no3)
rum pum pum pum; me and my drum.

LITTLE SAINT NICK

Words and Music by
BRIAN WILSON

Moderate shuffle

D Am7 D7 Am7 D7 G G♯dim Am7 D7

1. Well, way up north where the air gets cold, __ there's a tale a-bout Christ-mas that you've all been told, and a real fa-mous cat all dressed

Chorus: *To Coda*

Am7 D7 G C Am7 D7

up in red, and he spends the whole year work-in' out on his sled. _ It's the lit-tle saint Nick. It's the lit-tle Saint Nick. 2. Just a
(bkgrd.) Oo, lit-tle Saint Nick. Oo, lit-tle Saint Nick.

D.S. al Coda

D7 C F C A

Saint Nick. Run, run rein - deer. _ Run, run rein-deer. _ Run, run rein - deer. _ Run, run rein - deer. *(lead)* 3. He's
(bkgrd.) He don't miss no one.

Coda

G G♯dim Am7 D7 Am7 D7 G G♯dim *Repeat and fade*

lit - tle Saint Nick. Oo, Mer - ry Christ-mas, St. __ Nick. ____
Oo, lit - tle Saint Nick. Christ - mas comes this time each year.

Verse 2:
Just a little bobsled, we call it Old Saint Nick,
But she'll walk the toboggan with a four-speed stick.
She's a candyapple red with a ski for a wheel.
And when Santa gives the gas, man, just watch her peel. *(To Chorus:)*

Verse 3:
He's haulin' through the snow at a fright'nin' speed
With a half dozen deer with a Rudy to lead.
He's got to wear goggles, 'cause the snow really flies,
And he's cruisin' every pad with a little surprise. *(To Chorus:)*

LITTLE THINGS MEAN A LOT

Words and Music by
EDITH LINDEMAN and CARL STUTZ

Slowly

To Coda

E♭ Cm7 Fm7 B♭7 E♭ Fm7 E♭ E♭maj7 Fm7 Gm7 Cm7

Blow me a kiss from a - cross the room. Say I look nice when I'm not. Touch my hair as you
Give me your arm as we cross the street. Call me at six on the dot; a line a day when you're
Send me the warmth of a se - cret smile to show me you have - n't for -

Fm7 A♭m6 F7 Cm7 F9 Fm7 B♭7 F9 Fm7 B♭7 E♭ Fm7 E♭ B♭m7 E♭7 B♭m7 E♭7

pass my chair, lit - tle things mean a lot. lit - tle things mean a lot. Don't have to buy me dia-monds and pearls,
far a - way,

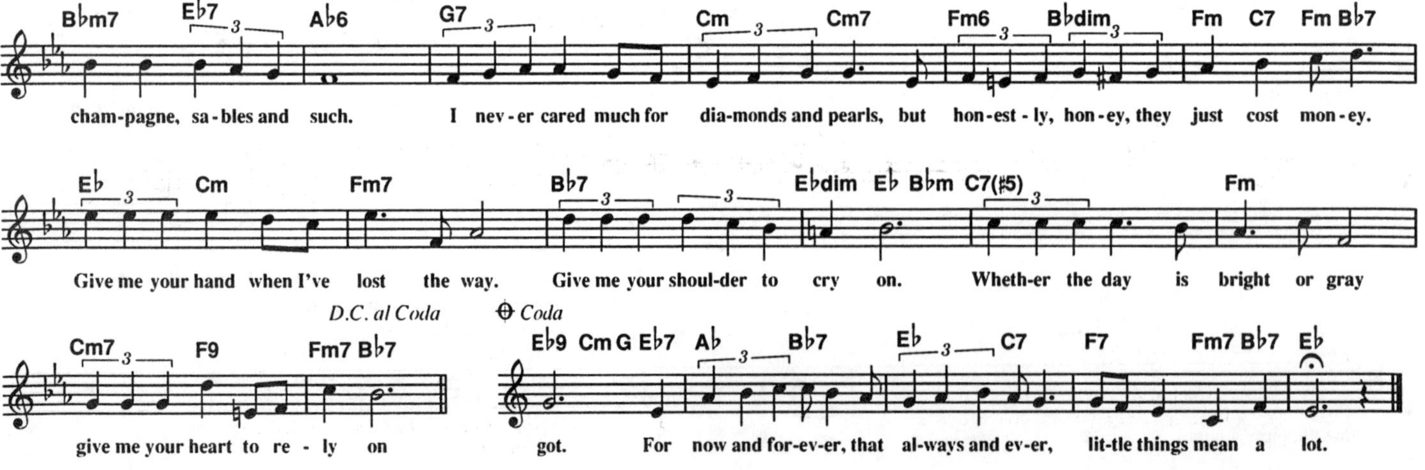
B♭m7 E♭7 A♭6 G7 Cm Cm7 Fm6 B♭dim Fm C7 Fm B♭7
cham-pagne, sa - bles and such. I nev - er cared much for dia-monds and pearls, but hon-est - ly, hon - ey, they just cost mon - ey.
E♭ Cm Fm7 B♭7 E♭dim E♭ B♭m C7(♯5) Fm
Give me your hand when I've lost the way. Give me your shoul-der to cry on. Wheth-er the day is bright or gray
D.C. al Coda
Coda
Cm7 F9 Fm7 B♭7 E♭9 Cm G E♭7 A♭ B♭7 E♭ C7 F7 Fm7 B♭7 E♭
give me your heart to re - ly on got. For now and for-ev-er, that al-ways and ev-er, lit-tle things mean a lot.

LIVE FOR LOVING YOU

Words and Music by
GLORIA ESTEFAN, DIANNE WARREN
and EMILIO ESTEFAN, JR.

Moderately fast

Ooh, la-la - la-la - la-la - la; la-la - la-la - la-la - la;

Verse:

1. Ly-ing a-wake, I turn to you as you are soft-ly sleep-ing. I think of what I'd like to do, while you are some-where dream-ing. I, I feel so hap-py by your side. Oh, I, I won-der, won-der, won-der why.

Bridge:

I need nothing else in life but to hold you. I, oh I am in so deep, I don't need no sleep, I just need you here with me. Ba-by, I

Chorus:

live for lov-ing you. (Ooh, la-la - la-la - la-la - la;) I live for lov-ing you. All I want to do is love you, love you.

D.S. 𝄋

do is live for lov-ing you. (Ooh. la-la - la-la - la-la - la;) I live for lov-ing you. All I want to do is love you. love you. (Ooh, la-la - la-la - la-la - la; la-la - la-la - la-la - la. Ba-by, I live for lov-ing you. (Ooh, la-la - la-la - la-la - la;) I

Repeat ad lib. and fade

Verse 2:
I find it hard to find the words
To say what I am feeling.
I'm so in love, I'm so alive,
And I know you're the reason why,
Why I'm so happy all the time.
Oh, I, I wonder, wonder, wonder why.
(To Bridge:)

Verse 3:
It would never cross my mind,
To find another lover.
'Cause after having been with you,
There could be no other.
I, just touching you I'm satisfied.
Oh, I, I wonder, wonder, wonder why.
(To Bridge:)

From the United Artists Motion Picture "LIVE AND LET DIE"

LIVE AND LET DIE

Words and Music by
PAUL McCARTNEY and LINDA McCARTNEY

Slowly
G Bm C D7 D7(♭9) G Bm
When you were young and your heart was an o - pen book,
(2nd time, instrumental until)
you used to say live and let
C C/D Cm/D G Bm
live. (You know you did, you know you did you know you did.) But if this ev - er - chang - ing
C A D B♭ G7 C/G
world in which we live in makes you give it a cry, say live and let die! Live and let
Gdim G7 C/G Gdim
die, live and let die, live and let die.
Bright rock
Gm
To Coda
C9
What does it mat-ter to ya,
G7 D7 Em F
when you got a job to do you got-ta do it well. You got-ta give the oth-er fel-low hell!
Gm
D.C. al Coda
Coda
Gm
E♭m

LIVING FOR THE CITY

By STEVIE WONDER

Moderate rock
Verse:
G Am/G Gm7 Am/G G Am/G Gm7 Am/G
1. A boy is born in Hard-time, Mis-sis-sip-pi,
2. His fa-ther works some days for four-teen hours,
G Am/G Gm7 Am/G G Am/G Gm7
sur-round-ed by four walls that ain't so pret-ty. His par-ents give him
and you can bet he bare-ly makes a dol-lar. His moth-er goes to
Am/G G Am/G Gm7 Am7/G G
love and af-fec-tion, to keep him strong, mov-in' in the right di-rec-tion. Liv-ing
scrub the floors for man-y, and you'd best be-lieve she hard-ly gets a pen-ny. Liv-ing
1.3.5 2. To Next Strain
C D D7 G Am/G Gm7 Am/G Am/G G
just e-nough, just e-nough for the cit-y. Da da da
just e-nough, just e-nough for the cit-y.
4.6.
Am/G G G/F Em7(♭5) E♭sus E♭ D♭ D♭/C♭
Da da da da da da da da da da da da da da da da da da
B♭ A♭ G
da da da da da da.
1.2. D.S. 3.
G Am/G Gm7 Am/G
(Liv-ing just e-nough for the cit-y. Oh,
1.2.3. 4.
G Am/G Gm7 Am/G Am7/G G G/F Em7(♭5)
liv-ing just e-nough for the cit-y. Oh, for the cit-y.) Da da da da da da da
rit.
E♭sus E♭ D♭ D♭/C♭ B♭ A♭ G
da da da da da da da da da da da da da da da da.

Verse 3:
His sister's black, but she is sho'nuff pretty.
Her skirt is short, but Lord her legs are sturdy.
To walk to school, she's got to get up early.
Her clothes are old, but never are they dirty.
Living just enough, just enough for the city.

Verse 4:
Her brother's smart, he's got more sense than many.
His patience's long, but soon he won't have any.
To find a job is like a haystack needle, 'cause
Where he lives, they don't use colored people.
Living just enough, just enough for the city.

Verse 5:
His hair is long, his feet are hard and gritty.
He spends his life walkin' the streets of New York City.
He's almost dead from breathing in air pollution.
He tried and fought, but to him there's no solution.
Living just enough, just enough for the city.

Verse 6:
I hope you hear inside my voice of sorrow
And that motivates you to think about tomorrow.
This place is cruel, no world could be much colder.
If we don't change, the world will soon be over.
Living just enough, just enough for the city.

LOCH LOMOND

TRADITIONAL

Moderately Verse:
G C D7 G G7 C G /F♯
1. By __ yon bon-nie banks and by yon bon-nie braes where the sun shines bright on Loch Lo - mond, where
then that we part - ed in yon shad-y glen, on the steep, steep side of Ben Lo - mand, where
wee bird-ies sing, and the wild flow-ers spring. And in sun - shine the wa - ters are sleep - ing. But the
Em Bm/D C Am/D D7 G G7 C Bm/D D7 G
me and my true love were ev - er wont to gae, on the bon-nie, bon-nie banks of Loch Lo - mond.
in pur - ple hue the high-land hills we view, and the moon com-ing out in the gloam - ing.
bro - ken heart it kens nae sec - ond spring a - gain, though the wae-ful may cease frae their __ greet - ing.
Oh,
Chorus:
Em Bm/D B/D♯ Em C D7 Em C G7 C Bm
ye'll take the high road, and I'll take the low road. And I'll be in Scot - land a - fore ye. But
Em Bm/D C Am/D D7 G C Bm/D 1.2. D7 G D7 3. D7 G
me and my true love, we'll nev - er meet a - gain on the bon-nie, bon-nie banks of Loch Lo - mond. 2. 'Twas _ Lo - mond.
3. The _

LONELY STREET

By KENNY SOWDER, CARL BELEW
and W.S. STEVENSON

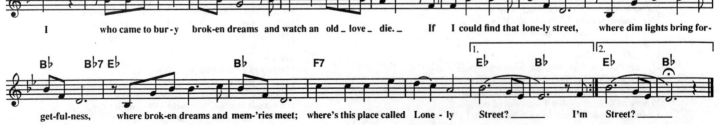

Moderately slow
B♭ B♭7 E♭ B♭ B♭7 E♭ B♭ F7
I'm look-ing for that lone-ly street; I've got a sad, sad tale to tell. I need a place to go and weep. Where's this place called
E♭ B♭ B♭7 E♭ B♭ B♭7 E♭
Lone - ly Street? ______ A place where there's just lone-li-ness, where dim lights bring for - get-ful-ness, where bro-ken dreams
B♭ F7 E♭ B♭ B♭7 E♭ B♭
and mem-'ries meet; where's this place called Lone - ly Street? ______ Per-haps up-on that lone-ly street, there's some-one such as
B♭7 E♭ B♭ F7 B♭ B♭7 E♭
I who came to bur-y brok-en dreams and watch an old _ love _ die. _ If I could find that lone-ly street, where dim lights bring for-
B♭ B♭7 E♭ B♭ F7 1. E♭ B♭ 2. E♭ B♭
get-ful-ness, where brok-en dreams and mem-'ries meet; where's this place called Lone - ly Street? ______ I'm Street? ______

LODI
Copyright © 1969 by JONDORA MUSIC
All Rights Reserved
J.C. FOGERTY
Moderately
Just a-bout a year a-go I set out on the road, seek-in' my fame and for-tune, look-in' for a pot of gold.
Things got bad, and things got worse. I guess you will know the tune.
Oh! Lord, stuck in Lo-di a-gain.
Rode in on the Grey-hound, I'll be walk-in' out if I go.
I was just pass-in' through must be sev-en months or more.
Ran out of time and mon-ey, looks like they took my friends.
Oh Lord! I'm stuck in Lo-di a-gain.
The man from the mag-a-zine said I was on my way.
Some-where I lost con-nec-tions, ran out of songs to play.
I came in-to town, a one night stand. Looks like my plans fell through.
Oh! Lord, stuck in Lo-di a-gain.
If I on-ly had a dol-lar, for ev-'ry song I've sung, and ev-'ry time I've had to play while peo-ple sat there drunk.
You know, I'd catch the next train back to where I live.
Oh Lord! I'm stuck in Lo-di a-gain.
Oh, Lord! I'm stuck in Lo-di a-gain.
LOUISE
Copyright © 1929 (Renewed 1956) by FAMOUS MUSIC CORPORATION
All Rights Reserved
Words by LEO ROBIN
Music by RICHARD A. WHITING
Moderate swing
Ev-'ry lit-tle breeze seems to whis-per "Lou-ise." Birds in the trees seem to twit-ter "Lou-ise."
Each lit-tle rose tells me it knows I love you, love you.
Ev-'ry lit-tle beat that I feel in my heart, seems to re-peat what I felt at the start.
Each lit-tle sigh tells me that I a-dore you, Lou-ise.
Just to see and hear you bring joy I nev-er knew. But to be so near you thrills me through and through.
An-y-one can see why I want-ed your kiss. It had to be, but the won-der is this:
Can it be true, some-one like you could love me, Lou-ise?
To Next Strain
Fine
D.C. al Fine

LONDONDERRY AIR

Copyright © 1993 by BEAM ME UP MUSIC (ASCAP), c/o CPP/BELWIN, INC., Miami, FL 33014
All Rights Reserved
OLD IRISH MELODY
Moderately
Would God I were the ten - der ap - ple - blos - som that floats and falls from off the twist - ed
(Yea, would to) God I were a - mong the ros - es that lean to kiss you as you float be -
bough, to lie and faint with - in your silk - en bo - som, with - in your silk - en bo - som, as that does
tween, while on the low - est branch a bud un - clos - es, a bud un - clos - es, to touch you,
now! Or would I were a lit - tle burn - ish'd ap - ple for you to pluck me, glid - ing by so
queen. Nay, since you will not love, would I were grow - ing, a hap - py dai - sy, in the gar - den
allarg.
a tempo
cold, while sun and shade your robe of lawn will dap - ple, your robe of lawn, and your hair's spun
path; that so your sil - ver foot might press me go - ing, might press me go - ing e - ven un - to
gold.
Yea, would to
death.
LOOKIN' OUT MY BACK DOOR
Copyright © 1970 by JONDORA MUSIC
All Rights Reserved
J.C. FOGERTY
Moderately fast
Verse:
Just got home from Il - li - nois, lock the front door, oh boy!
gi - ant do - ing cart-wheels, a stat - ue wear - in' high heels.
For-ward trou - bles Il - li - nois, lock the front door, oh boy!
Got to sit down, take a rest on the porch. I - mag - i - na - tion sets in, pret - ty soon I'm sing - in':
Look at all the hap - py crea-tures danc-ing on the lawn. A di - no - saur Vic - tro - la list-'ning to Buck O - wens.
Look at all the hap - py crea-tures danc-ing on the lawn. Both - er me to - mor-row, to - day I'll buy no sor - rows.
To Next Strain
Fine
Bridge:
Doo, doo, doo, look - in' out my back door. There's a door. door. Tam - bou - rines and el - e - phants are
play - ing in the band. Won't you take a ride on the fly - in' spoon? Doo, doo, doo.
Won-d'rous ap - pa -
Both - er me to -
D.S. 𝄋 al Fine
ri - tion pro - vid - ed by ma - gi - cian.?
mor - row, to - day I'll buy no sor - rows.
Doo, doo, doo, look - in' out my back door. door.

LOOKS LIKE WE MADE IT
Copyright © 1976 IRVING MUSIC, INC. and RONDOR MUSIC (LONDON) LTD.
All Rights Reserved
Words by WILL JENNINGS
Music by RICHARD KERR
Slowly
Verse:
There you are, looking just the same as you did last time I touched you. And here I am, close to get-tin' tan-gled up in-side the thought of you. Do you love him as much as I love her, and will that love be strong when old feel-ings start to stir?
Love's so strange, play-ing hide and seek with hearts and al-ways hurt-ing. And we're the fools, stand-ing close e-nough to touch those burn-ing mem-o-ries. And if I hold you for the sake of all those times love made us lose our minds, could I ev-er let you go?
Chorus:
Looks like we made it, Oh no we've made it, left each oth-er on the way to an-oth-er love.
Looks like we made it, or I thought so till to-day, un-til you were there, ev-'ry-where and all I could taste was love the way we made it.
D.C.
all I could taste was love the way we made it. Oh. We made it. Looks like we
D.S.
3.4. etc.
Repeat and fade
all I could taste was love the way we
LOVE THEME FROM "THE WINDS OF WAR"
Copyright © 1983 by BRUIN MUSIC COMPANY
All Rights Reserved
By BOB COBERT
Moderately

A LOT OF LIVIN' TO DO

Lyric by LEE ADAMS
Music by CHARLES STROUSE

Moderate swing
Cmaj7 C6 Cmaj7 C7
There are {girls / boys} just ripe_ for some kiss - in'_ and I mean to kiss_ me a
F6 Fmaj7 G7 C Dm7
few! Oh, those {girls / guys} don't know_ what they're miss - in',_ I've got a lot of
G7 C G7 Cmaj7 C6 Cmaj7
liv - in'___ to do! {And there's wine / Siz - zlin' steaks} all read - y for tast - in',_ and there's Cad-il-lacs
C7 F6 Fmaj7 G7 C Dm7
all shin-y and new! Got - ta move, 'cause time_ is a - wast - in',_ there's such a lot of
G7 C C7 F6 Fm7 E♭
liv - in'___ to do! There's mu - sic to play,_ plac - es to go!_ Peo-ple to see!___
B♭ G G7 Cmaj7 C6
Ev - 'ry - thing___ for you and me!___ Life's a ball, if on - ly you know it!_
Cmaj7 C7 F6 Fmaj7 G7
And it's all just wait - in' for you! You're a - live, so come on and
C Dm7 1. G7 C G7 2. G7
show it!_ There's such a lot of liv - in'___ to do! There are liv - in',___
Dm7 G7 Dm7 G7(♭9) C6
such a lot of liv - in',___ what a_ lot of_ liv - in'_ to do!___

From the Paramount Picture "SHE LOVES ME NOT"

LOVE IN BLOOM

Words and Music by
LEO ROBIN and
RALPH RAINGER

Moderately
G B7 Em C Am7 D7 D7(♯5)
Can it be { the trees that fill the breeze with rare and mag-ic per - fume? / the spring that seems to bring the stars right in - to my room? } Oh, no, it is - n't the trees, it's
G Am7 D7 D7/G G Bm F♯7
love in bloom! spring, it's love in bloom. My heart was a des - ert;
Bm F♯7 Bm F♯7 Bm D7 Am7 D7 G
you plant-ed a seed. And this is the flow - er, this hour of sweet ful - fill - ment! Is it all a dream the
B7 Em C C♯dim G/D D7(♯5) D7 G
joy su-preme, that came to us in the gloom? You know it is - n't a dream, it's love in bloom.

From the 20th Century-Fox Motion Picture "LOVE IS A MANY-SPLENDORED THING"

LOVE IS A MANY-SPLENDORED THING

Lyrics by PAUL FRANCIS WEBSTER
Music by SAMMY FAIN

Moderately
To Coda
E♭ Cm Gm B♭m7 E♭7 A♭ A♭6 A♭maj7 Fm6
Love is a man - y splen - dored thing, it's the A - pril rose that on - ly grows in the
Once on a high and wind - y hill, in the morn - ing mist two lov - ers kissed and the
Cm Fm7 Dm7(♭5) G7(♭9) Cm Cm7
ear - ly Spring. Love is na - ture's way of giv - ing a rea - son to be liv - ing; the gold - en crown that
D.C. al Coda
D7 G B♭7
makes a man a king.
Coda
Gm7 C9 Gm7 C7 Fm Fm7
world stood still. Then your fin - gers touched my
Dm7(♭5) G7(♯5) C7(♯5) C7 F7 A♭m6 E♭/B♭ Cm Fm7 B♭7(♭9) E♭
si - lent heart and taught it how to sing. Yes, true love's a man - y splen - dored thing.

LOVE IS JUST AROUND THE CORNER
Words and Music by
LEO ROBIN and
LEWIS E. GENSLER
Copyright © 1934 (Renewed 1961) by FAMOUS MUSIC CORPORATION
All Rights Reserved
Moderate swing
Love is just a-round the cor - ner, an - y coz - y lit - tle cor - ner. Love is just a-round the cor - ner when
I'm a sen - ti - men - tal mourn-er and I could-n't be for - lorn - er when you keep me on a cor - ner just
let's go cud-dle in a cor - ner, an - y coz - y lit - tle cor - ner. Love is just a-round the cor - ner and
I'm a - round you. you. you. Ve - nus de Mi - lo was
wait - ing for
I'm a - round
To Next Strain
Fine
D.C. al Fine
not - ed for her charms. But strict-ly be-tween us, you're cut - er than Ve - nus and what's more you've got arms. So
LOVE LETTERS
Words and Music by
EDWARD HEYMAN and VICTOR YOUNG
Copyright © 1945 (Renewed 1972) by FAMOUS MUSIC CORPORATION
All Rights Reserved
Moderately slow
Love let - ters straight from your heart keep us so near while a - part.
I'm not a - lone in the night when I can have all the love you write.
I mem - o - rize ev - 'ry line, I kiss the name that you sign.
And dar - ling, then I read a - gain right from the start, love let - ters straight from your heart.
LOVE MAKES THE WORLD GO 'ROUND
(Theme from "Carnival")
Words and Music by
BOB MERRILL
Copyright © 1961 EMI ROBBINS CATALOG INC.
All Rights Reserved
Moderately slow waltz
Love makes the world go 'round, love makes the world go 'round. Some-bod - y soon will
High in some si - lent sky, love sings a sil - ver song, mak - ing the earth whirl
love you, if no one loves you now. love makes the world go 'round.
soft - ly;

LOVE ME WITH ALL YOUR HEART
(Cuando Calienta El Sol)

English Lyric by SUNNY SKYLAR
Spanish Lyric by MARIO RIGUAL
Music by CARLOS RIGUAL and
CARLOS ALBERTO MARTINOLI

Moderately

D Bm F♯m G6 A7 D B7
Love me with all your heart, that's all I want love. Love me with all of your heart or not at all.
Em Em7 A7 D Bm F♯m G A A7
Just promise me this: that you'll give me all your kisses, ev'ry winter ev'ry summer, ev'ry fall.
D Bm F♯m G6 A7 D B7 Em Em7 A7
When we are far apart or when you're near me, love me with all of your heart as I love you. Don't give me your love for a
D Bm F♯m G A A7 D Bm Em7 D
moment or an hour. Love me always as you loved me from the start, with ev'ry beat of your heart.

From "LOVE ME TONIGHT"

LOVER

Words by LORENZ HART
Music by RICHARD RODGERS

Moderate slow waltz

C6 B7sus B7 B♭7sus B♭7 Em7 A7 A♭7sus
Lover, when I'm near you and I hear you speak my name, softly
Lover, when we're dancing keep on glancing in my eyes till love's

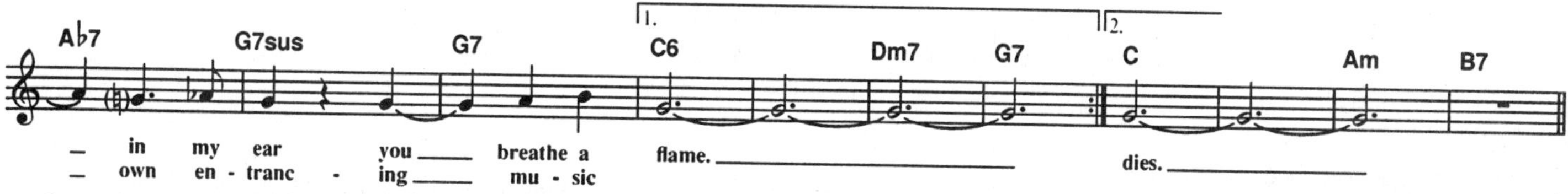
A♭7 G7sus G7 1. C6 Dm7 G7 2. C Am B7
in my ear you breathe a flame. dies.
own entrancing music

Bridge:

Emaj7 C♯m7 F♯m7 B7 Emaj7 C♯m7 F♯m7 B7 G Em7
All of my future is in you. Your ev'ry plan I design. Promise you'll always con-

Am7 D7 Dm7/G C♯dim/G Dm7/G G7 C B7sus B7 B♭7sus
tinue to be mine. Lover, please be tender, when you're tender

B♭7 Em7 A7 A♭7sus A♭7 G7sus G7 C6 Dm7/G C6/9
fears depart. Lover, I surrender to my heart.

From the Motion Picture "LOVE STORY"

(WHERE DO I BEGIN) LOVE STORY

Lyrics by CARL SIGMAN
Music by FRANCIS LAI

Moderately slow

Gm D7 Gm

Where do I be-gin __ to tell the sto - ry of how great a love can be, __ the sweet love sto - ry that is old - er than the sea,
With her first hel-lo __ she gave a mean-ing to this emp-ty world of mine, __ there'd nev - er be an - oth - er love an - oth - er time.
How long does it last? __ Can love be mea-sured by the hours in a day? __ I have no ans-wers now, but this much I can say;

E♭maj7 D7 | 1. D11 D7 D7(♭9) Gm | 2. D11 D7

the sim - ple truth a - bout the love she brings to me? __ Where do I start? __ __ She fills my
She came in - to my life and made the liv - ing fine. __
I know I'll need her till the stars all burn a - way, __

Gmaj7 G7 G11 G7 *To Next Strain* | 3. D11 D7 Gm E♭maj7 Gm *Fine* | Cm F7

heart, __ she fills my __ and she'll be there. __ heart __ with ver - y spe-cial things, _ with an - gel

B♭maj7 E♭maj7 Am7(♭5) D7 Gm Cm

songs, __ with wild im - ag - in - ings. __ She fills my soul __ with so much love that an - y - where I go __ I'm nev - er

F7sus F7 B♭maj7 E♭ A7 Dmaj7 D7 *D.C. al Fine*

lone - ly. __ With her a - long, __ who could be lone - ly? __ I reach for her hand; __ it's al - ways there. __

Columbia Pictures Presents a Channel-Lauren Shuler Production
A Joel Schumacher Film "ST. ELMO'S FIRE"

LOVE THEME FROM ST. ELMO'S FIRE

(Instrumental)

By DAVID FOSTER

Moderately slow
A♭ B♭m7/A♭ A♭ B♭m/A♭ E♭/A♭ A♭
B♭m/A♭ Adim B♭m E♭7/G A♭
1. D.S. 2.3. To Next Strain 4. Fine
Fm Adim B♭m E♭7/G D♭ E♭ D♭ E♭ D♭ E♭ D♭ E♭ A♭
rit.
1. D.C. 2. D.C. al Fine
B♭m E♭/G A♭ B♭m E♭/B♭ Fm E♭/G A♭ A♭/G Fm B♭/D E♭ Cm7 D♭ E♭ E♭
3

LOUISIANA MAN

Words and Music by
DOUG KERSHAW

Moderately bright

Verse 1:

D
A7
D
1. At birth mom and pa - pa called their lit - tle boy, Ned, raised him on the banks of a riv - er bed. A

A7
D
house boat tied to a big tall tree; a home for my pa - pa and my ma - ma and me. The clock strikes three, pa - pa

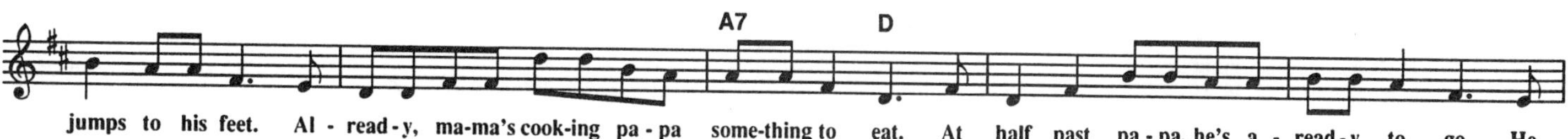
A7
D
jumps to his feet. Al - read - y, ma-ma's cook-ing pa - pa some-thing to eat. At half past pa - pa, he's a - read - y to go. He

A7
D
G
jumps in his pi - rogue, head - ed down the bay - ou. He's got fish - ing lines strung a - cross the Loui - si - an - a riv - ers,

D7
G
got - ta catch a big fish for us to eat. He's set - ting traps in the swamps catch - ing an - y - thing he can.

D7
G
D7
G
Got - ta make a liv - ing, he's a Loui - si - an - a man. Got - ta make a liv - ing, he's a Loui - si - an - a man.

D
A7
D
Mus - crat hides hang-ing by the doz - ens. E - ven got a la - dy mink, a musk - rat's cou - sin. Got 'em out dry - ing in the

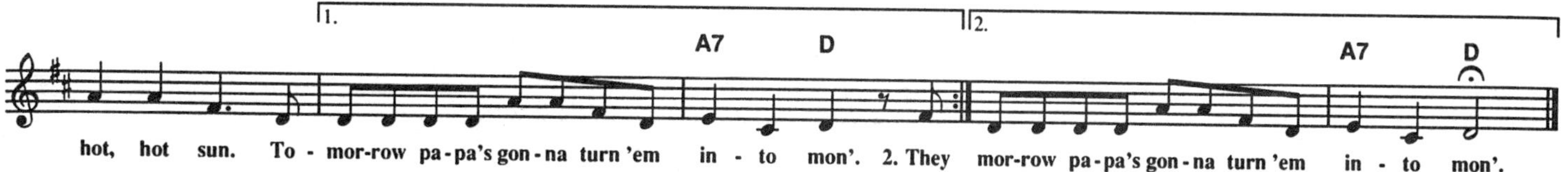
1.
2.
A7
D
A7
D
hot, hot sun. To - mor-row pa - pa's gon - na turn 'em in - to mon'. 2. They mor-row pa - pa's gon - na turn 'em in - to mon'.

Verse 2:

They call mama Rita and my daddy Jack, little baby brother on the floor, that's Mack.
Bren and Lin are the family twins. Big brother Ed's on the bayou, fishing.
On the river, floats papa's great big boat. That's how papa goes into town.
Takes every bit of a night and a day to even reach a place where people stay.
I can hardly wait until tomorrow comes around. That's the day papa takes the furs to town.
Papa promised me, Ned and I could go; even let me see a cowboy show.
I seen cowboys and Indians for the first time then I told my papa, "I gotta go again."
Papa said, "Son, we got lines to run. We'll come back again, first there's work to be done."

Theme Song from the Motion Picture "SIX PACK"

LOVE WILL TURN YOU AROUND

Words and Music by
KENNY ROGERS, EVEN STEVENS
THOM SHUYLER and DAVID MALLOY

Moderate country two-beat
Verse:
1. You can run, you can hide, nev-er let it in-side; keep liv-ing your life in the dark. Soon-er or lat-er, that gen-tle per-suad-er is gon-na catch up with your heart; make you a dream-er, be-liev-er, be-liev-er in love.
Chorus:
Well, it's your mind that tricks you in-to leav-ing ev-'ry time.
heart that talks you in-to stay-ing where you are.
Love will turn you a-round, turn you a-round.
D.S.
Repeat ad lib. and fade
Turn you a-round.

Verse 2:
Right when the man's doing all that he planned,
And he thinks he's got just what he needs.
Life will deliver a shot that will shiver him.
Driving him down to his knees.
Make him start giving, living,
Living again. *(To Chorus:)*

Verse 3:
Out of the blue, she reaches for you,
And you tell her you don't have the time.
So you move away fast, but you know it won't last,
'Cause you can't get her off of your mind.
Thoughts are burning, turning,
Turning around.

Verse 4:
How do you know when to stay or to go,
And how do you know when it's real?
You don't need a sign to make up your mind;
You've got your heart at the wheel.
You want to start sharing, caring,
Caring again. *(To Chorus:)*

LOVE ME OR LEAVE ME

Words by GUS KAHN
Music by WALTER DONALDSON

Slowly
Love me or leave me, and let me be lone-ly; you won't be-lieve me, and I love you on-ly; I'd rath-er be lone-ly, than hap-py with some-bod-y else.
might find the night-time, the right time for kiss-ing; but night-time is my time for just rem-i-nisc-ing, re-gret-ing, in-stead of for-get-ting with some-bod-y else.
I want your love, but I don't want to bor-row, to have it to-day, and to give it back to-mor-row; for my love is your love, no love for no-bod-y else!
You
To Next Strain
Fine
D.C. al Fine
There'll be no-one un-less that some-one is you, I in-tend to be in-de-pen-dent-ly blue.

LUSH LIFE

By BILLY STRAYHORN

Verse: tempo ad lib.
D♭6 B7 D♭maj7 B7 D♭maj7 B7
I used to vis - it all the ver - y gay plac - es; those come-what - may plac - es, where one re -
girls I knew had sad and sul - len gray fac - es with dis - tant gay trac - es that used to
D♭maj7 E♭m Emaj7 F♯m7 Am9 D9 D♭6/9 D9 D♭maj9
lax - es on the ax - is of the wheel of life to get the feel of life, from jazz and cock-tails. The
be there, you could see where they'd been
Am9 D9 D♭6/9 D9 D♭6/9 C7(♯5) Fm Fm6 Fm7 Dm7(♭5)
washed a - way by too man-y thru the day twelve o' - clock tales, then you came a - long with your si - ren song to
Gm7 C7(♭9) Fm Fm6 Fm7 Dm7(♭5) D♭maj7/F C7(♭9)/E
tempt me to mad - ness. I thought for a while that your poig-nant smile was tinged with the sad - ness
E♭m7 A♭9 B9(♭5) B♭7(♭9) E♭m7 A9(♭5) A♭11 A♭7(♭9)
of a great love for me. Ah! yes I was wrong, a - gain I was wrong.
Slowly:
Chorus:
D♭ D9 D♭6 D9 D♭6 C9(♭5) B7(♭9) E E♭9(♯5) D9 D7 D♭ D9
Life is lone-ly a - gain and on - ly last year ev-'ry-thing seemed so sure. Now life is aw-ful a -
D♭ D9 D♭6 D♭9 C13 F E7(♯5) B♭m7 E♭7 A♭ E♭7(♯9) A9 A♭6 Em9 A7(♭9)
gain, a trough-ful of hearts could on-ly be a bore. A week in Pa - ris will ease the bite of it;
D6 Dm7 G9 C6 B7 B♭13 A13(♯9) A♭13 D♭ D9 D♭6 D9 D♭6 C9(♭5) B7(♭9)
all I care is to smile in spite of it. I'll for-get you I will while yet you are still burn-ing in-side my
B♭13 E♭m11 G♭m9 B9 A9(♯5) A♭9 D♭maj7 D♭m7 G♭7(♭9) C♭maj7 C♭6 Fm11 B♭7
brain. Ro - mance is mush, sti-fling those who strive. I'll live a lush life in some small dive, and
E♭m7 G♭m9 B9 A9(♯5) A♭13 D9 E E♭6 Dmaj7 G9 D♭6/9 D♭maj7
there I'll be, while I rot with the rest of those whose lives are lone - ly too.

LOVING ARMS

Words and Music by
TOM JANES

Moderately slow
Verse:
1. If you could see me now, the one who said that she'd rath-er roam, the one who said that she'd rath-er be a-lone. If you could on-ly see me now.
hold you now, just for a mo-ment. If I could real-ly make you mine. Just for an hour turn back the hands of time. If I could on-ly hold you
2. If I could now.
Chorus:
I've been too long in the wind, too long in the rain, tak-in' an-y com-fort that I can. Look-ing back and long-in' for the free-dom of my chains and ly-in' in your lov-in' arms a-gain.
To Coda
If you could hear me now sing-in' some-where through the lone-ly night. And dream-in' of your arms that held me tight. If you could on-ly see me now. I've been
D.S. al Coda
Coda
gain I can al-most feel your lov-in' arms a-gain.

From the M-G-M Musical Production "THE GREAT CARUSO"

THE LOVELIEST NIGHT OF THE YEAR

Music adapted by
IRVING AARONSON

Slowly
When you are in love, it's the love-li-est night of the year. Stars twin-kle a-bove, and you al-most can touch them from here. Words fall in to rhyme an-y-time you are hold-ing me near. When you are in love, it's the love-li-est night of the year.
Waltz-ing a-long in the blue like a breeze drift-ing o-ver the sand, thrilled by the won-der of you, and the won-der-ful touch of your hand. And my heart starts to beat like a child when a birth-day is near. So, kiss me my sweet, it's the love-li-est night of the year. year.

MA

(He's Making Eyes at Me)

Words by SIDNEY CLARE
Music by CON CONRAD

Moderately fast
E♭ F7 B♭7 B♭7(♭5) B♭7 B♭+ E♭
"Ma, he's mak - ing eyes at me! Ma, he's aw - ful nice to me!
Cdim B♭7 E♭ Cdim B♭7
Ma, he's al - most break-ing my heart. I'm be - side him. Mer - cy! Let his con-science guide him!
E♭ F7 B♭7 B♭7(♯5) E♭ Cm7 F9 B♭7 E♭ E♭dim
Ma, he wants to mar - ry me, be my hon - ey - bee. Ev - 'ry min - ute
B♭7 E♭ E♭dim B♭7 F7 Cdim F7 B♭7 E♭ E♭dim Fm7 B♭7 E♭
he gets bold - er, now he's lean - ing on my should-er; Ma, he's kiss - ing me!"

Theme From the 20th Century-Fox Motion Picture "THE RAZOR'S EDGE"

MAM'SELLE

Words by MACK GORDON
Music by EDMUND GOULDING

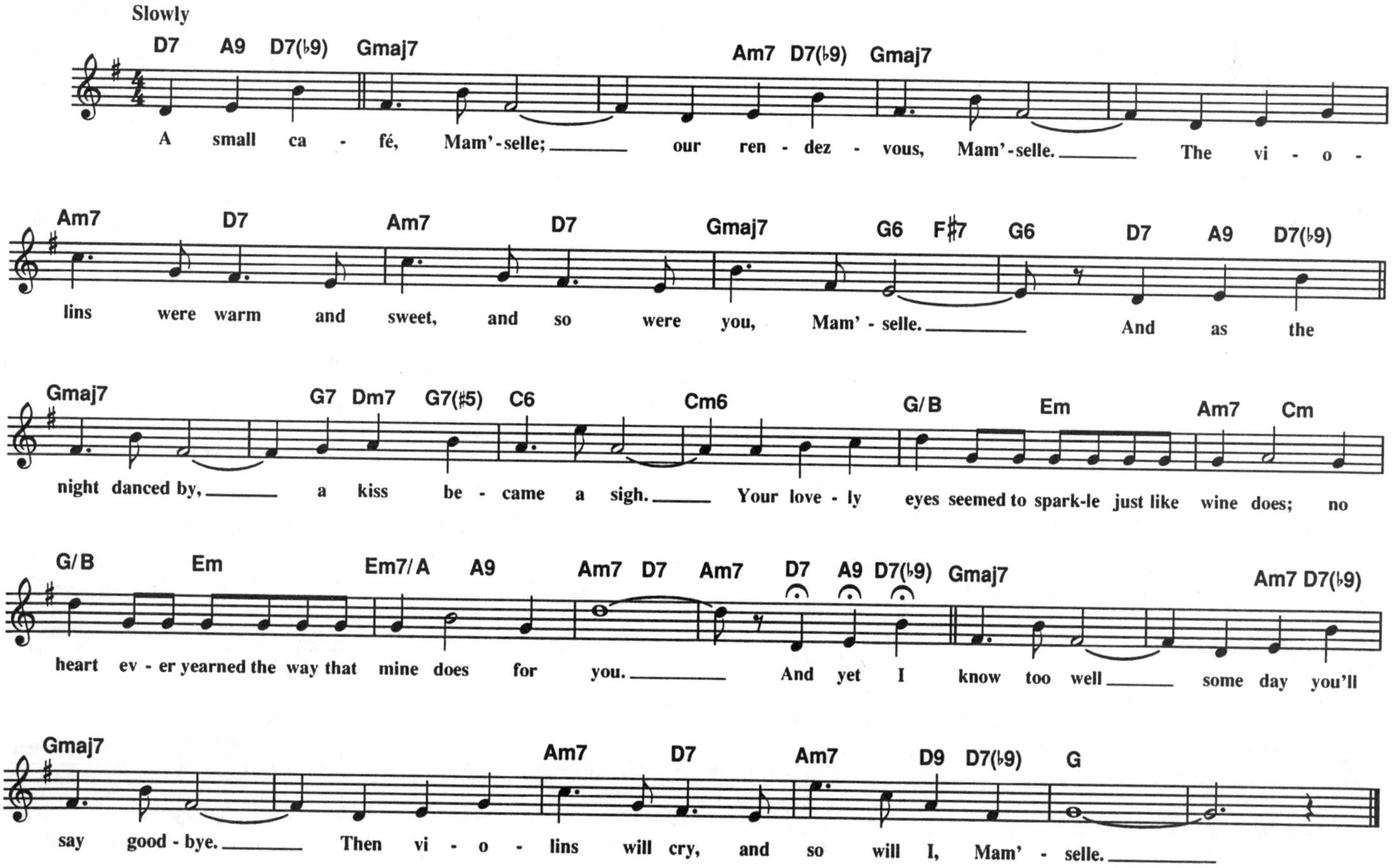

Slowly

D7 A9 D7(♭9) Gmaj7 Am7 D7(♭9) Gmaj7
A small ca - fé, Mam' - selle; our ren - dez - vous, Mam' - selle. The vi - o -

Am7 D7 Am7 D7 Gmaj7 G6 F♯7 G6 D7 A9 D7(♭9)
lins were warm and sweet, and so were you, Mam' - selle. And as the

Gmaj7 G7 Dm7 G7(♯5) C6 Cm6 G/B Em Am7 Cm
night danced by, a kiss be - came a sigh. Your love - ly eyes seemed to spark-le just like wine does; no

G/B Em Em7/A A9 Am7 D7 Am7 D7 A9 D7(♭9) Gmaj7 Am7 D7(♭9)
heart ev - er yearned the way that mine does for you. And yet I know too well some day you'll

Gmaj7 Am7 D7 Am7 D9 D7(♭9) G
say good - bye. Then vi - o - lins will cry, and so will I, Mam' - selle.

MacARTHUR PARK

Words and Music by
JIMMY WEBB

Moderately slow
Dm Dm/C Eb/Bb
Spring was nev - er wait - ing for us, girl, it ran one step a - head as we fol - lowed in the
I re-call the yel-low cot-ton dress foam - ing like a wave on the ground a-round your
Gm Bb/F Ab Bb/Eb Gm Ab/Eb Db/Eb Eb/F Dm
dance.
knees.
Be - tween the part-ed pag - es and were
The birds like ten-der ba - bies in your
Dm/C Eb/Bb Gm Bb/F
pressed in love's hot fe-vered i - ron like a strip-ed pair of pants.
hands and the old men play-ing cheq - uers by the trees.
Chorus:
Ab Bb C Cmaj7 Gm7/C F
Mac - Ar-thur's park is melt-ing in the dark, all the sweet green ic-ing flow-ing down. Some-one left the cake out in the rain;
Fmaj7 C/E Dm7 C/E Fmaj7
I don't think that I can take it 'cause it took so long to bake it, and I'll nev-er have that rec-i - pe a - gain, oh,
Eb 1. Db Abmaj7 Cm/F Db 2. Cm Ab Ebmaj9 Gm7 Dm7
no.
Cmaj7 Am7 Fmaj9 Bm7 Fmaj7 Bbmaj7 Eb Ab Abmaj7 Ab7 Db Eb/Bb F
Bridge:
F Fmaj7 Bbmaj7 Bb6 Bbdim7
There will be an-oth-er song for me, for I will sing it; there will be an-oth-er dream for me some-one will
take my life in to my hands and I will use it; I will win the wor - ship in their eyes and I will
F(9)/A F Fmaj7 Bbmaj7 Em7(b5)
bring it. I will drink the wine while it is warm and nev-er let you catch me
lose it. I will have the things that I de - sire and my pas - sion flow like
Am7 D7sus D7 C D7 Gm7 Gm7/C C7(b9) Fmaj7
look-ing at the sun, and af - ter all the loves of my life, af - ter all the loves of my
riv - ers to the sky, and af - ter all the loves of my life, oh af - ter all the loves of my

1.
2.
B♭maj7 E♭maj7 Gm7/C C7 B♭maj7 E♭maj7 Csus Dm
life, you'll still be the one. I will life, I'll be think-ing of you and won-der-ing why.
Dm/C E♭/B♭ Gm B♭/F A♭ B♭/E♭ Gm A♭/E♭
Double time
D♭/E♭ E♭/F Am/D C/F Gm Am/G Gm7 C/D Gm Am/G Gm7 C/D Gm Am/G Gm7 C/D
Gm Am/G Gm7 Am7 Dm7 G/D Dm7 G/D Dm7 G/D Dm7 G/D E♭maj9
Am7 E♭maj9 B♭maj7 Am7 E♭maj9 F
G A/G Gm7 C/D G A/G Gm7 Am7 E♭/B♭ B♭ E♭sus/B♭ E♭/B♭ G7/B G7(♭9)/B G7 Cm B+ E♭/B♭
Am7(♭5) Fm E A♭/E♭ Dm7(♭5) E♭m7 E♭m7/A♭
Tempo I
G♭
Chorus:
D♭ F Fmaj7 Cm7 Cm7/F
Mac-Ar-thur's Park is melt-ing in the dark, all the sweet green ic-ing flow-ing down.
B♭ B♭maj7 C6 Dm F/C Bm7(♭5)
Some-one left the cake out in the rain; I don't think that I can make it 'cause it took so long to bake it, and I'll nev-er have that rec-i-pe a-
B♭m(maj7) B♭m6 F C9 A♭ Fm G♭ B♭sus B♭ B♭sus Fsus B♭
gain, oh, no. Oh, no. No, no, no, no, no.

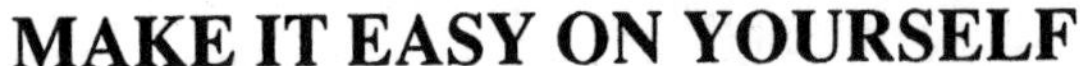

MAKE IT EASY ON YOURSELF

Lyric by HAL DAVID
Music by BURT BACHARACH

Moderately slow

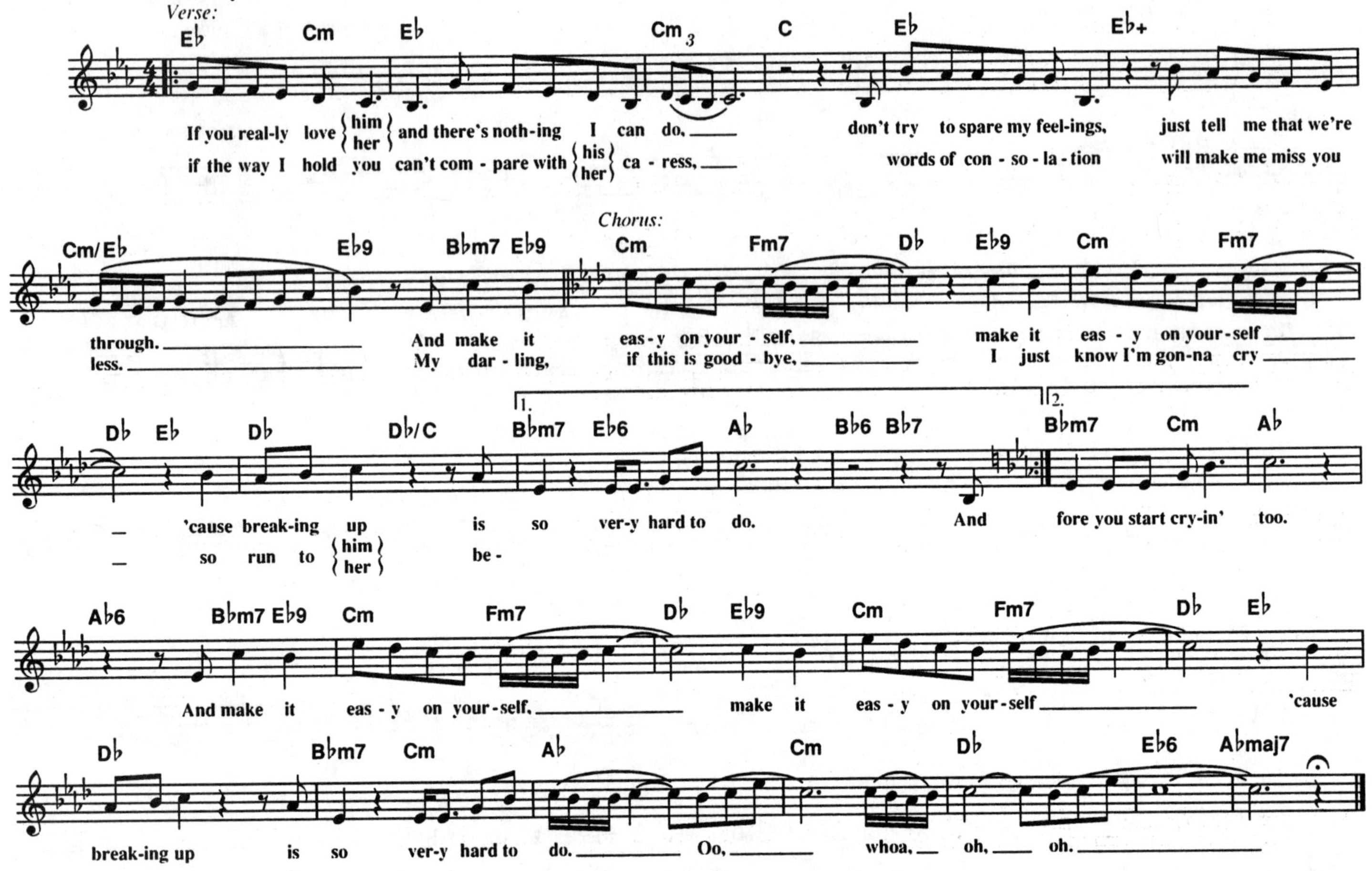

Verse:
Eb Cm Eb Cm Eb C Eb Eb+
If you real-ly love {him / her} and there's noth-ing I can do, don't try to spare my feel-ings, just tell me that we're
if the way I hold you can't com - pare with {his / her} ca - ress, words of con - so - la - tion will make me miss you
Cm/Eb Eb9 Bbm7 Eb9
through. And make it
less. My dar - ling,
Chorus:
Cm Fm7 Db Eb9 Cm Fm7
eas-y on your - self, make it eas - y on your-self
if this is good - bye, I just know I'm gon-na cry
Db Eb Db Db/C Bbm7 Eb6 Ab Bb6 Bb7 Bbm7 Cm Ab
'cause break-ing up is so ver-y hard to do. And fore you start cry-in' too.
so run to {him / her} be -
Ab6 Bbm7 Eb9 Cm Fm7 Db Eb9 Cm Fm7 Db Eb
And make it eas - y on your-self, make it eas - y on your-self 'cause
Db Bbm7 Cm Ab Cm Db Eb6 Abmaj7
break-ing up is so ver-y hard to do. Oo, whoa, oh, oh.

From the Paramount T.V. Series "LAVERNE DeFazio and SHIRLEY Feeney"

MAKING OUR DREAMS COME TRUE

Lyric by NORMAN GIMBEL
Music by CHARLES FOX

Bright four

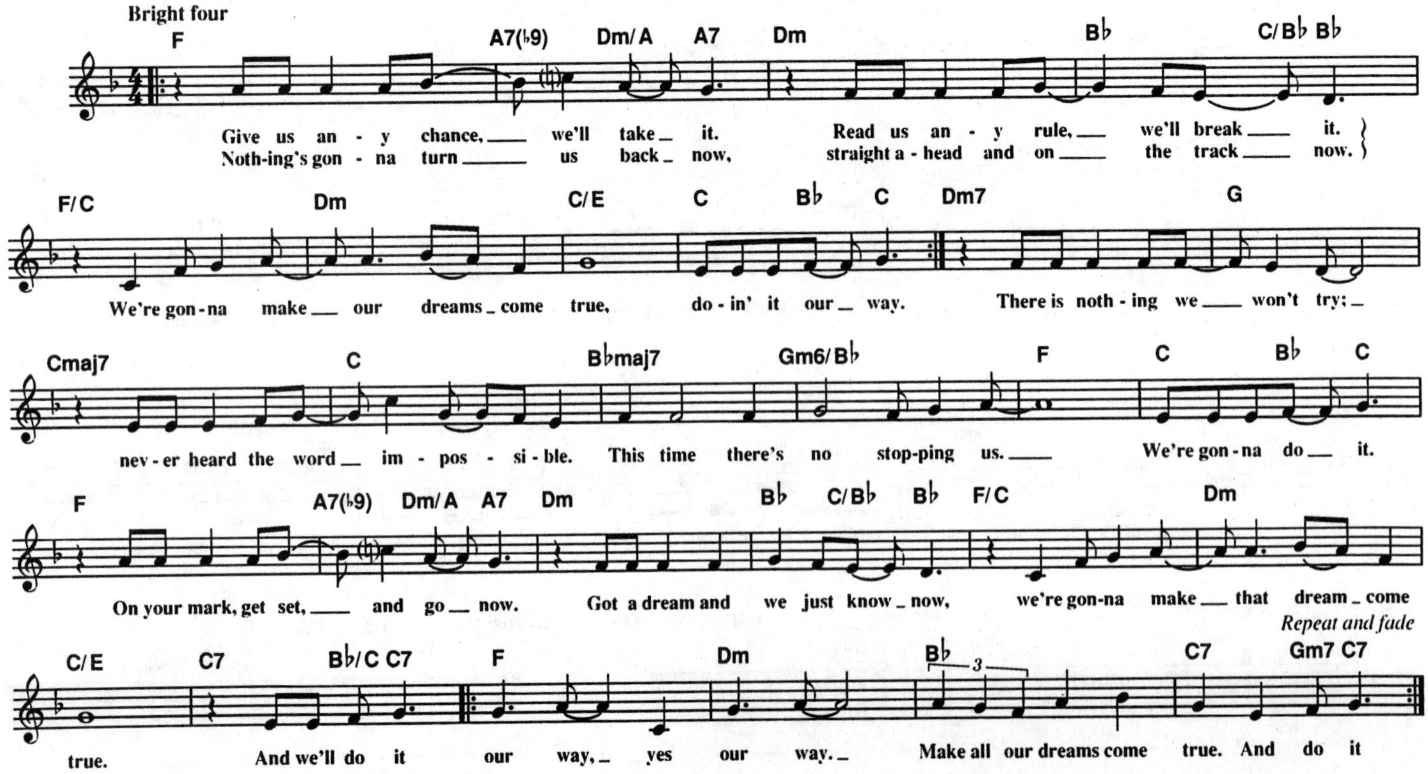

F A7(b9) Dm/A A7 Dm Bb C/Bb Bb
Give us an - y chance, we'll take it. Read us an - y rule, we'll break it.
Noth-ing's gon - na turn us back now, straight a - head and on the track now.
F/C Dm C/E C Bb C Dm7 G
We're gon-na make our dreams come true, do-in' it our way. There is noth - ing we won't try;
Cmaj7 C Bbmaj7 Gm6/Bb F C Bb C
nev - er heard the word im - pos - si - ble. This time there's no stop-ping us. We're gon-na do it.
F A7(b9) Dm/A A7 Dm Bb C/Bb Bb F/C Dm
On your mark, get set, and go now. Got a dream and we just know now, we're gon-na make that dream come
Repeat and fade
C/E C7 Bb/C C7 F Dm Bb C7 Gm7 C7
true. And we'll do it our way, yes our way. Make all our dreams come true. And do it

From the United Artists Motion Picture "THE MAGNIFICENT SEVEN"

THE MAGNIFICENT SEVEN

By ELMER BERNSTEIN

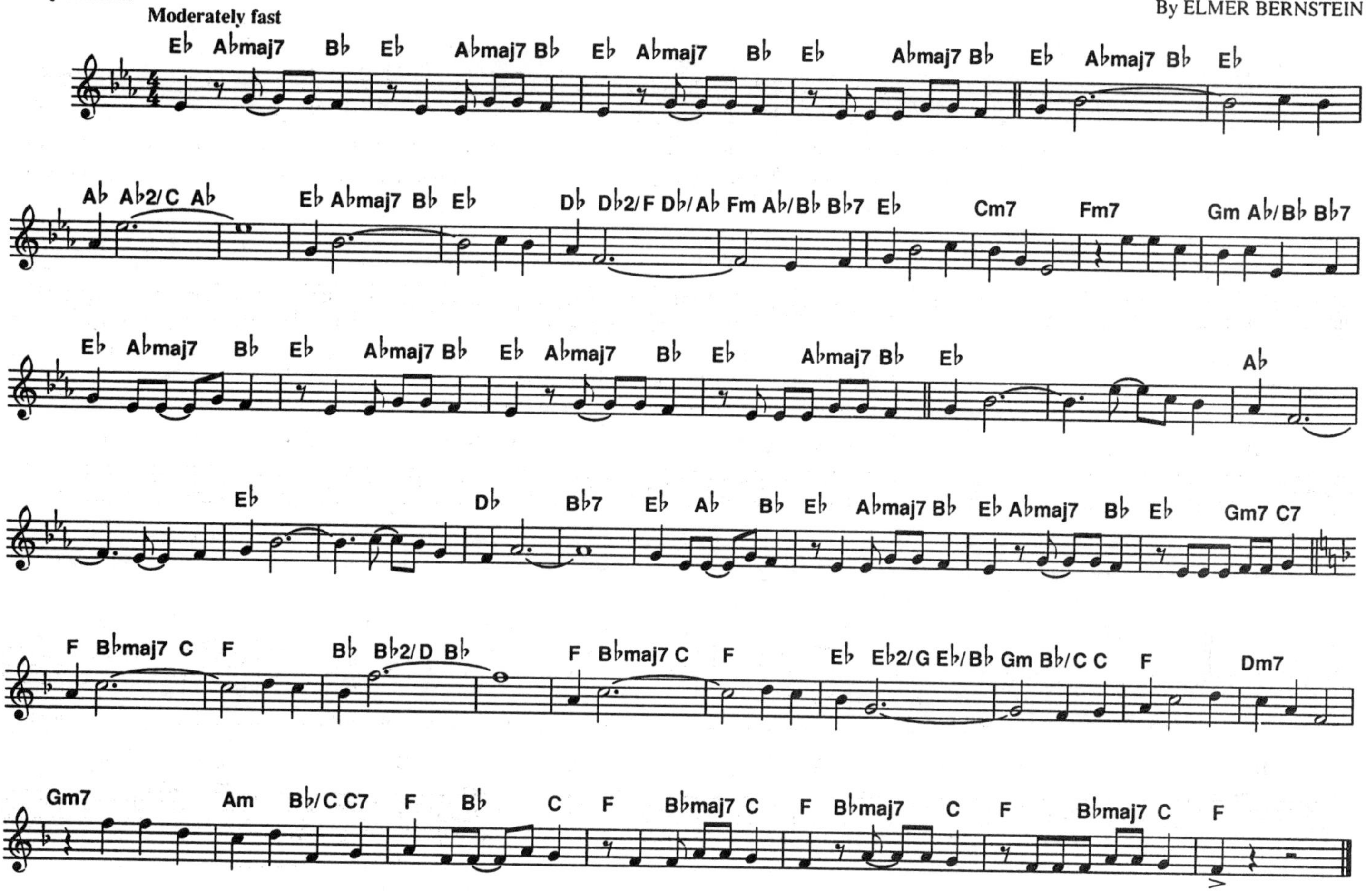

Moderately fast

MANHATTAN SERENADE

Words and Music by
LOUIS ALTER

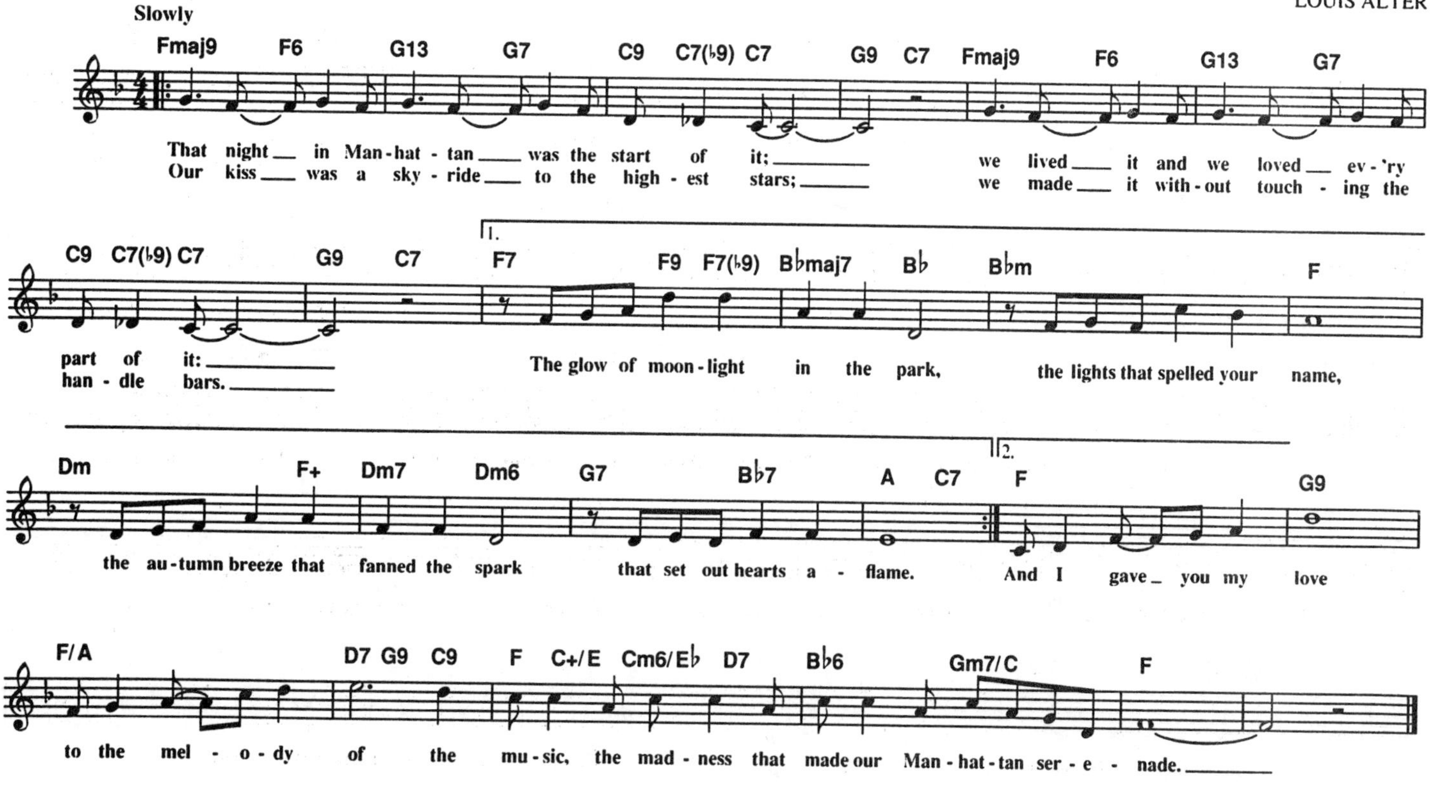

Slowly

That night in Man-hat-tan was the start of it; we lived it and we loved ev-'ry part of it:
Our kiss was a sky-ride to the high-est stars; we made it with-out touch-ing the han-dle bars.

1. The glow of moon-light in the park, the lights that spelled your name, the au-tumn breeze that fanned the spark that set out hearts a-flame.

2. And I gave you my love to the mel-o-dy of the mu-sic, the mad-ness that made our Man-hat-tan ser-e-nade.

MALA FEMMENA

Female Words by TOTO and RAY ALLEN
Words and Music by TOTO

Moderate rhumba

B♭ B♭maj7 B♭6
Fem - me - na, tu si na ma - la fem - me - na, chist 'uo cchie'e fat - to chia - gne - re

G7/B Cm F9
la - creme e'n - fa - mi - tà. Fem - me - na si tu peg-gio'e na vi - pa - ra, m'e 'ntus-se - ca - ta

F7 F+ B♭ Bdim Cm F7 B♭ B♭maj7
l'a - ne - ma, nun poz - zo-cchiù cam - pà. Fem - me - na, si ddo - ce com-me'o zuc - che - ro

B♭6 G7/B Cm E♭m6
pe - ro' sta fac - cia d'an - ge - lo te ser - ve pe 'ngan - na. Fem - me - na,

a tempo
B♭/F Gm7 C7 F7 B♭ E♭m6 B♭
tu si a' cchiu bel - la fem - me - na, te vo-glio be-ne e t'o dio, nun te poz-zo scur - da'.

THE MAN ON THE FLYING TRAPEZE

Words and Music by WALTER O'KEEFE

Brightly

A♭ B♭m E♭7 A♭ A♭dim7 A♭
Once I was hap - py, but now I'm for - lorn, like an old coat that is tat - tered and torn. I'm left in this

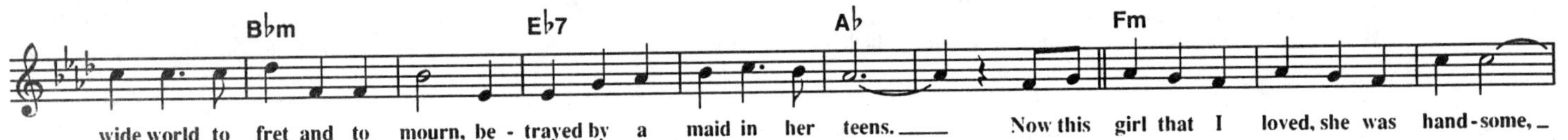
B♭m E♭7 A♭ Fm
wide world to fret and to mourn, be - trayed by a maid in her teens. Now this girl that I loved, she was hand - some,

C7 Fm C
and I tried all I knew, her to please. But I nev - er could please her a quar - ter as well as the man on the

Chorus:
Fm/C C rall. E♭7 A♭ B♭m E♭7
fly - ing tra - peze! Woah! He flies through the air with the great - est of ease, this dar - ing young man on the

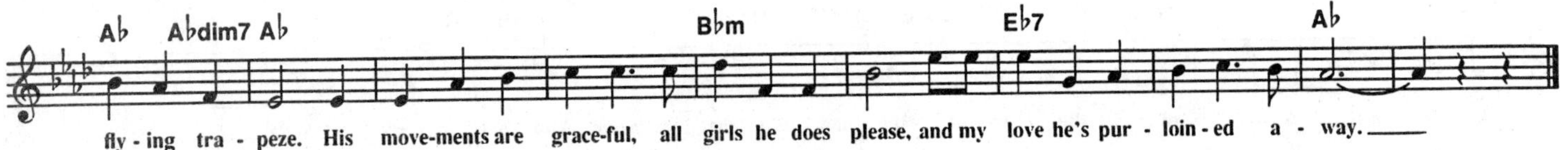
A♭ A♭dim7 A♭ B♭m E♭7 A♭
fly - ing tra - peze. His move-ments are grace-ful, all girls he does please, and my love he's pur - loin - ed a - way.

MAPLE LEAF RAG

Music by SCOTT JOPLIN

Tempo di marcia

Ab Adim7 Eb7/Bb Ab Adim7 Eb7/Bb Fb Eb

Fb Eb N.C. 8va 8va Ddim7 Ab/Eb

Fb Ab/Eb Eb7 Ab Ddim7 Ab/Eb Fb Ab/Gb To Coda ⊕

1. Eb7 Ab 2. Eb7 Ab Adim Eb7/Bb Ab

F/A Eb7/Bb Bdim7 Ab/C

Ab F/A Eb7/Bb Ab N.C.

F Bbm Bb9 Eb7 1. Ab Adim7 2. Ab D.C. al Coda

⊕ Coda Eb7 Ab Ab7 Db

Ab7 Db F7

Bb7 Ebm Gdim7

Db/Ab Bb7 Eb7 Ab7 1. Db Ddim7 2. Db

Db Bbm Bdim7 Ab/C Ab F/A Eb7/Bb

Ab Db Bbm Bdim7 Ab/C

Ab Db Bb7(b5)/D Ab/Eb E7 Bb7/F Eb7/G 1. Ab /Bb /C 2. Ab Eb7 Ab

MARCH

(From "The Nutcracker Suite")

Music by
PETER ILYICH TCHAIKOVSKY

Brightly
G Em Bm Em G Em Bm Em Am D
G C Am B Em Am D G Em
Bm Em G Em Bm Em Am D Bm Em
To Coda
C D Em B Em Am7/C Am7 Am/F♯ B
Em Am F♯m7(♭5) B Em Am7/C Am7 Am/F♯ B
Coda
D.C. al Coda
Em Am D7
G/B Am D G

MARCH OF THE TOYS

Music by
VICTOR HERBERT

Moderate march tempo
Am Am E7 Am E7 Am
E7 Am E7 Am E7 Am C E7
a tempo
Am Am/G Am/F E7 Am N.C. B♭ C7 F Gm
ritard.
C7 F B♭ C7 F B♭7(♭5) A B♭7(♭5) A B♭7(♭5)
A N.C. B♭ C7 F Gm C7 F B♭
A7 Dm G7 F C7 F N.C. C7 F

MARGIE

Words by BENNY DAVIS
Music by CON CONRAD and
J. RUSSELL ROBINSON

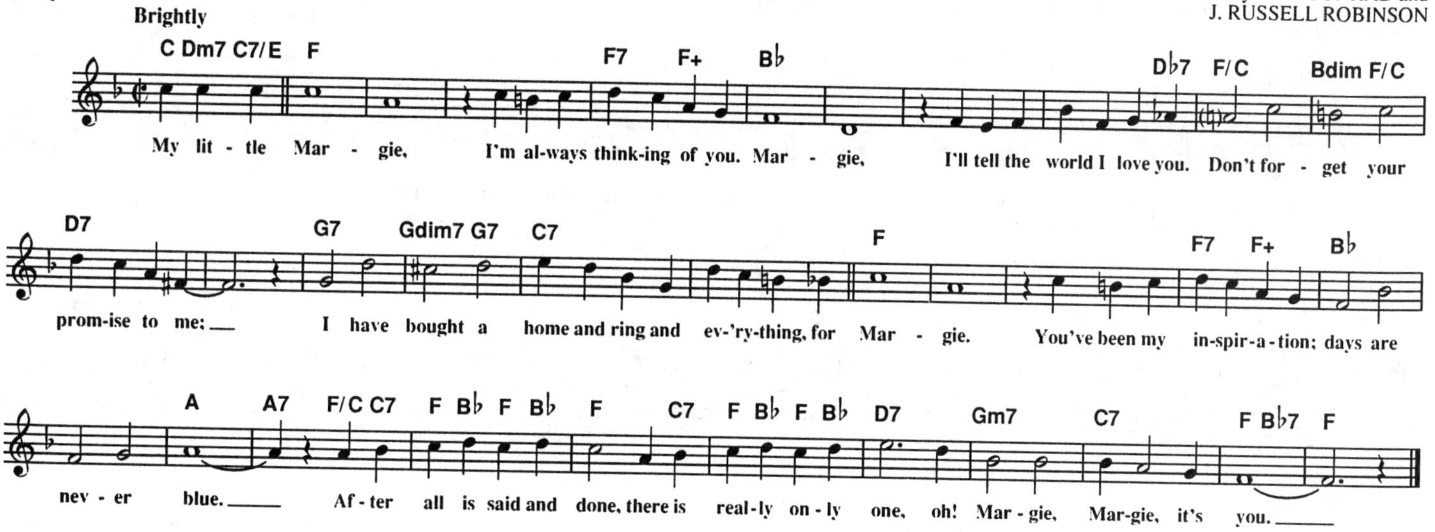

Brightly

C Dm7 C7/E F F7 F+ B♭ D♭7 F/C Bdim F/C

My lit - tle Mar - gie, I'm al-ways think-ing of you. Mar - gie, I'll tell the world I love you. Don't for - get your

D7 G7 Gdim7 G7 C7 F F7 F+ B♭

prom-ise to me; ___ I have bought a home and ring and ev-'ry-thing, for Mar - gie. You've been my in-spir-a-tion; days are

A A7 F/C C7 F B♭ F B♭ F C7 F B♭ F B♭ D7 Gm7 C7 F B♭7 F

nev - er blue. ___ Af - ter all is said and done, there is real-ly on-ly one, oh! Mar-gie, Mar-gie, it's you. ___

MARIA ELENA

English Lyric by
S.K. RUSSELL
Music and Spanish Lyric by
LORENZO BARCELATA

Moderately

C F6 C Dm7 C♯dim7 Dm7 G7 C F7 C F6 C

Like fall-ing rain to a flow'r, ___ or like the shore to the sea; ___ like min-utes are to an hour, ___
Quie-ro can - tar - te, mu - jer, ___ mi más bo - ni - ta can - ción. ___ Por-que‿e-res tú mi que - rer, ___

Dm7 G7 C Am E7 Am Dm Am D7 Ddim D7

— dar-ling, so you are to me. ___ This I can nev - er dis - guise, ___ here in my heart, or my
— rei - na de mi co - ra - zon. ___ No me‿a-ban - do - nes, mi bien, ___ que‿e-res to - do mi que -

Dm7 G7 C Csus C Cmaj7 Dm7 G7 G7(♯5) C

eyes. ___ Ma - ri - a‿E - le - na, you're the an - swer to a pray'r; ___ Ma - ri - a‿E - le - na can't you see how much I care? ___
rer. ___ Tu-yo‿es mi co - ra - zón, oh, sol de mi que - rer, ___ mu-jer de mi‿i-lu - sion, mi‿a - mor te con - sa - gre! ___

G7(♯5) C F♯dim7 Dm7 G7 Cmaj7 F♯dim7 C

— To me your voice is like the ech - o of a sigh, and when you're near, my heart can't speak a - bove a sigh. Ma - ri - a‿E - le - na,
— Mi vi - da la‿em-be - lle-ce‿u-na‿es-pe - ran - za‿a - zul, mi vi - da tie - ne‿un cie - lo que le dis - te tu. Tu-yo‿es mi co-ra -

Csus C Cmaj7 Dm7 G7 E7 E7(♭9) E7 Am F Fm6 D7(♭5)

say that we will nev - er part; ___ Ma - ri - a‿E - le - na, take me to your heart. ___ A love like mine is great e - nough for
zón. oh, sol de mi que - rer, ___ tu-yo‿es to-do mi ser, tu - yo‿es, mu - jer! ___ Ya to - do‿el co - ra - zón te lo‿en - tre -

C C6 D7 G7 1. C G7 2. C Fm6 C

two; ___ to share this love is real-ly all I ask of you. Ma - ri - a‿E - le - na, you, my love. ___
gue. ___ E - res mi fe, e - res mi Dios, e - res mi‿a - mor! Tu-yo‿es mi co - ra - mor, mi‿a - mor! ___

MARINES' HYMN
(Song of the U.S. Marine Corps)

Brightly
C G7 C G7 C
From the halls of Mon - te - zu - ma to the shores of Trip - o - li; we
fight our coun - try's bat - tles, on the land as on the
C F C F C C♯dim7 G7/D G7
sea. First to fight for right and free - dom, and to keep our hon - or clean. We are
C G7 C G7 C
proud to claim the ti - tle of U - nit - ed States Ma - rines.

THE MAN I LOVE

Music and Lyrics by
GEORGE GERSHWIN and
IRA GERSHWIN

Andantino semplice
C Cm7 Gm/B♭ A7
Some day he'll come a - long, the man I love; and he'll be big and strong, the man I love
He'll look at me and smile, I'll un - der - stand; and in a lit - tle while he'll take my hand;
He'll build a lit - tle home, just meant for two, from which I'll nev - er roam, who would, would you?
Dm7(♭5) G7 C Fmaj7 Em G7
and when he comes my way, I'll do my best to make him stay.
and though it seems ab - surd, I know we both won't
And so all else a - bove, I'm wait - ing for the
C F C F♯dim F7 E7 Am Am7 B7/A G7/A G♯dim Am Am6
Fine
say a word. May - be I shall meet him Sun - day, may - be Mon - day, may - be
man I love.
E7 Am Am7 B7/A G7/A G♯dim Am Edim F G7
D.C. al Fine
not; still I'm sure to meet him one day, may - be Tues - day will be my good news day.

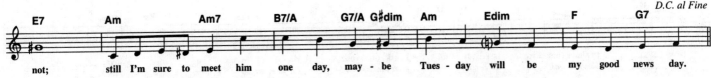

MARY ANN

TRADITIONAL

Moderately
Verse:
F Gm7 C7 Gm7 F C7
1. Mar - y Ann, oh Mar - y Ann, oh you're the girl for me, e - ven though your dear old ma - ma will not say "si
F F7 B♭ Gm7 C7 F Cdim
si." Mar - y Ann, oh Mar - y Ann, oh won't you please a - gree? You and I should mar - ry,
Chorus:
Gm7 C7 F C7 Gm7 C9 F
raise a fam - i - ly. All day, all night, Mar - y Ann, down by the sea - side sift - in' sand,
C7 Gm7 C7 F 1. D.C. 2.
all the lit - tle chil - dren love Mar - y Ann, down by the sea - side sift - in' sand.

Verse 2:
When I met sweet Mary Ann, her mother said to me:
"Would you care to tell me where you stand financially?"
She does not approve of me, 'cause I'm no millionaire,
But I love her daughter, more than I can bear.
(To Chorus:)

ME AND YOU AND A DOG NAMED BOO

Words and Music by KENT LAVOIE

Moderately
Verse:
F F7 B♭ Csus C F
1. I re - mem-ber to this day the bright red Geor-gia clay, how it stuck to the tires
2. I can still re - call the wheat - fields of Saint Paul and the morn-in' we got caught
nev - er for-get that day we mo-tored state-ly in-to big L. A. The lights of the cit - y put set -
C Csus F F9 B♭ Csus C
af - ter the sum - mer rain. Will - pow-er made that old car go; a wom-an's mind told me that it's so.
rob-bin' from an old hen. Old Mac-Don-ald he made us work, but then he paid us for what it was worth.
lin' down in my brain. Though it's on - ly been a month or so, that old car's bug - gin' us to go.
F E♭ B♭ C
Oh, how I wish we were back on the road a - gain.
An - oth - er tank of gas, and back on the road a - gain.
You got - ta get a - way and get back on the road a - gain.
Chorus:
B♭ C Fsus F B♭ C F B♭ C
Me and you and a dog named Boo, trav - el - in' and liv - in' off the land. Me and you and a dog
Fsus F E♭ B♭ F Fsus F 1.2. D.S. Fsus F 3.4. etc. Repeat ad lib. and fade Fsus F
named Boo; how I love be - in' a free man.
2.
3. I'll

MARY'S A GRAND OLD NAME

GEORGE M. COHAN

MASTERPIECE

Words and Music by
KENNY NOLAN

Moderately
G E7 A7 D7 G G/B B♭dim D7/A D7 D7(♯5)
For it is Ma - ry, Ma - ry, plain as an - y name can be; but with pro - pri - e - ty, so - ci - e - ty will say "Ma -
G E7 A7 D7 G F7 E7 /G♯ Am A7 D7 G
rie." But it was Ma - ry, Ma - ry, long be-fore the fash-ions came. And there is some-thing there that sounds so fair; it's a grand old name!
Verse:
F Gm7(♭5)/F
1. The sim - ple touch _ of your hand, _ and ev - 'ry - thing _ is right. _ The
count - less ways _ you've touched my heart _ is more than I _ can say. _ The
F Gm7(♭5)/F F Am7
gen - tle way _ you look at me _ when we kiss _ good-night. _ You've giv - en me _ the free - dom no
beau - ty that _ you've shown to me _ takes my breath _ a - way. _ A pic - ture per - fect paint - ing,
B♭(2) B♭m6 F 1.3. B♭/C 2.4. B♭/C D♭/E♭ E♭/F
oth - er love _ has known, _ and now I thank you, girl. _ Thank you, girl. _ 2. The now I know, _ ooh, _
that's what our _ love is. _ And, yes, I need you so, _ and
Chorus:
D♭maj7 Cm7 E♭/F B♭m7 D♭maj7/E♭ D♭/E♭ E♭/F
I've found a mas-ter-piece _ in _ you; _ a work of art, _ it's true, _ and I trea-sure you, my love. _ Ooh, _
1. D.S. 2. To Next Strain 3.4. etc. Repeat ad lib. and fade
D♭maj7 Cm7 B♭m7 B♭/C B♭/C B♭/C
I've found a mas-ter-piece _ in _ you; _ a work of art, _ it's true, _ and I trea-sure you. 3. Some - you. you.
Bridge: D.S.S.
F B♭m F D♭/E♭ E♭/F
When I'm lost _ and in - se-cure, _ you build me up _ and make _ me sure. _ Ev-'ry-thing will turn out right, _ my love. Oh, _

Verse 3:
Sometimes I wonder what I'd be had I not found you.
A lost and lonely soul,
This world could show me nothing new.
But now my life's a canvas, painted with your love.
And it will always be, and now I see . . .

Verse 4:
The two of us together, thru time will never part.
This fairy tale we're sharing is real inside our hearts.
Let it be forever, never let it end.
This promise I do make:
Heaven is ours to take.
(To Chorus:)

THE MASTERPIECE

By J.J. MOURET
and PAUL PARNES

Moderately
(Bass)
To Coda
To Next Strain
Fine
D.S. al Coda
Coda
D.S. al Fine
From the New Broadway Musical "Meet Me In St. Louis"
MEET ME IN ST. LOUIS, LOUIS
Copyright © 1944 (Renewed 1972) LEO FEIST, INC.
All Rights of LEO FEIST, INC. Assigned to EMI CATALOGUE PARTNERSHIP
All Rights Controlled and Administered by EMI FEIST CATALOG, INC.
All Rights Reserved
Music and Lyric adaptation by
HUGH MARTIN & RALPH BLAINE
Original Words and Music by
ANDREW B. STERLING & KERRY MILLS
Moderately
"Meet me in St. Lou - is, Lou - is, meet me at the fair. Don't tell me the lights are
shin - ing an - y - place but there. We will dance the Hooch - ee Kooch - ee, I will be your toot - sie
woot - sie. Meet me in St. Lou - is, Lou - is, meet me at the fair." fair."

MAMBO NO. 5

By PEREZ PRADO

Moderately
Fm7 Bb7 Fm7 Bb7 Eb Fm7 Bb7 Fm7 Bb7
Eb Fm7 Bb7 Fm7 Bb7 Fm7 Bb7 Fm7 Bb7
Fm7 Bb7 Fm7 Bb7 Fm7 Bb7 Fm7 Bb7 Eb

MAMBO NO. 8

By PEREZ PRADO

Brightly

Gm7 C7 F Gm7 C7 F Gm7

F Gm7 C7 F C7 C7-9 C9 C7+9

C7 C7-9 C9 C7+9

C7-9 Fm Fm/Eb C7-9

Fm Fm/Eb C7-9 Fm C7/G

Fm/Ab C7/G Fm C7/E F C7-9

Fm C7-9 Fm

No Chord Fm6 N.C.

Uno Dos

Tres Quatro Cinco Seis Siete Ocho Mam - bo!

MEET ME TONIGHT IN DREAMLAND
Copyright © 1993 by BEAM ME UP MUSIC (ASCAP), c/o CPP/BELWIN, INC., Miami, FL 33014
All Rights Reserved
Words by BETH SLATER WHITSON
Music by LEO FRIEDMAN
Moderately
Meet me to - night in Dream - land, un - der the sil - very moon. Meet me to - night in Dream - land, where love's sweet ro - ses bloom. Come with the love - light gleam - ing in your dear eyes of blue. Meet me in Dream-land, sweet dream-y Dream-land; there let my dreams come true. true.
MELLOW YELLOW
Copyright © 1968 DONOVAN MUSIC LTD., London
Sole Selling Agent: PEER INTERNATIONAL CORPORATION All Rights Reserved
Words and Music by
DONOVAN LEITCH
Moderately slow rock
Verse:
I'm just mad a-bout Saf - fron; a - Saf - fron's mad a - bout me. I'm-a just mad a-bout Saf - fron; she's just mad a - bout me. They call me Mel - low
Chorus:
Yel - low, they call me Mel-low Yel - low, they call me Mel-low Yel - low.
He's so mel - low, he's so mel - low.
Repeat ad lib. and fade
Yel - low. They call me Mel - low

Verse 2:
I'm just mad about Fourteen;
A-Fourteen's mad about me.
I'm-a just mad about Fourteen;
She's just mad about me.
(To Chorus:)

Verse 3:
Born high forever to fly;
A-wind-a velocity nil.
Born high forever to fly;
If you want, your cup I will fill.
(To Chorus:)

Verse 4:
Elec-a-trical banana
Is gonna be a sudden craze.
Electrical banana
Is bound to be the very next phase.
(To Chorus:)

Verse 5:
I'm just mad about Saffron;
A-Saffron's a-mad about me.
All the boys are mad about a-Saffron;
A-Saffron's a-mad about me.
(To Chorus:)

MELODY IN F

A. RUBENSTEIN

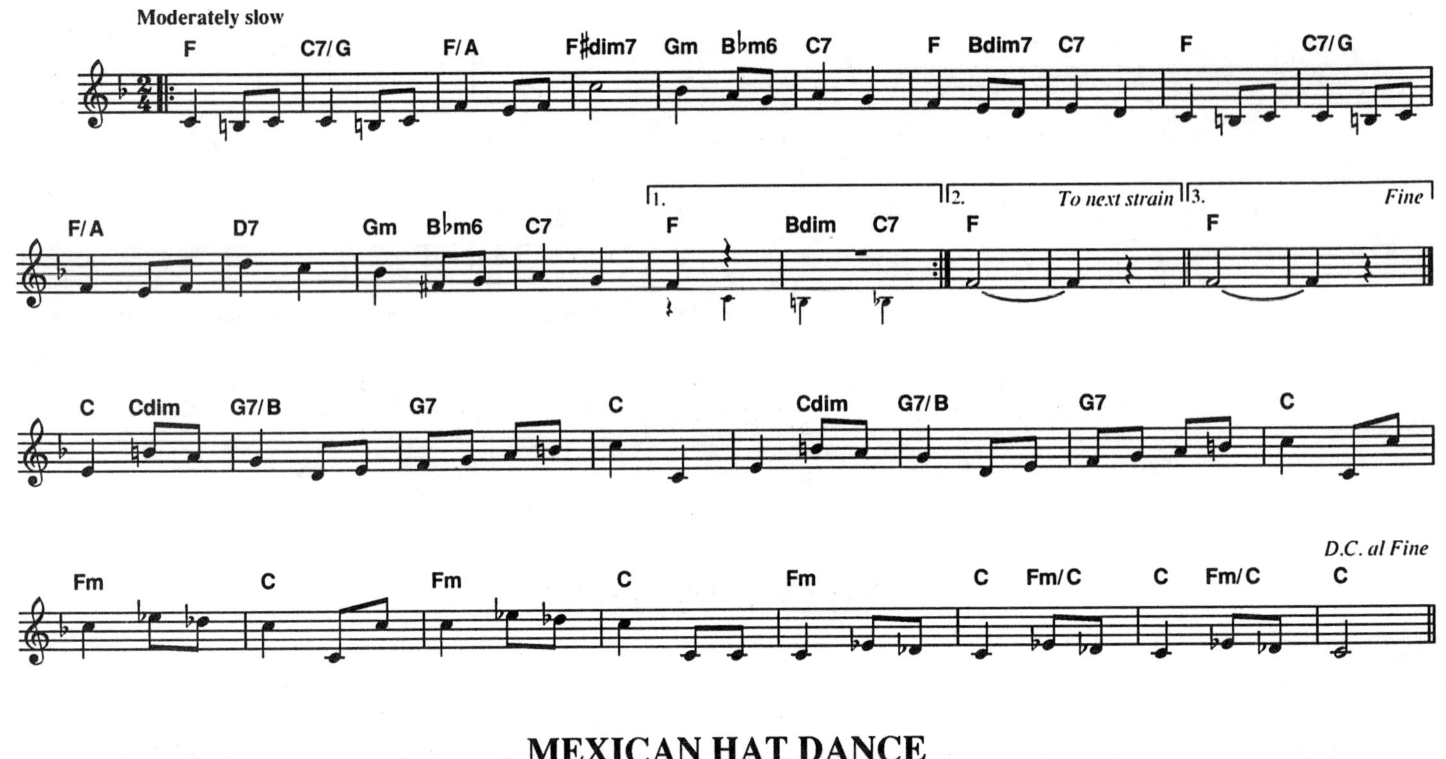
Moderately slow
F C7/G F/A F♯dim7 Gm B♭m6 C7 F Bdim7 C7 F C7/G
F/A D7 Gm B♭m6 C7 1. F Bdim C7 2. To next strain F 3. Fine F
C Cdim G7/B G7 C Cdim G7/B G7 C
D.C. al Fine
Fm C Fm C Fm C Fm/C C Fm/C C

MEXICAN HAT DANCE

FELICE PARTICHALA

Brightly
F C7
1. F 2. F F C7
1. F 2. F G7 C G7 C G7
C G7 1. C 2. C F
C7 1. F 2. F F
C7 1. F 2. F

MEMORIES

Words by
GUS KAHN
Music by
EGBERT VAN ALSTYNE

Slowly
F G7 C7 F7 B♭
Mem - o - ries, mem - o - ries, dreams of love so true, o'er the sea of
F C7 F C G7 C7 F G7 C7
mem - o - ry I'm drift - ing back to you. Child - hood days, wild - wood days, a - mong the birds and
F B♭ Bdim7 F D7 G7 C7 F
bees, you left me a - lone but still, you're my own in my beau - ti - ful mem - o - ries.

MERRY WIDOW WALTZ

FRANZ LEHAR

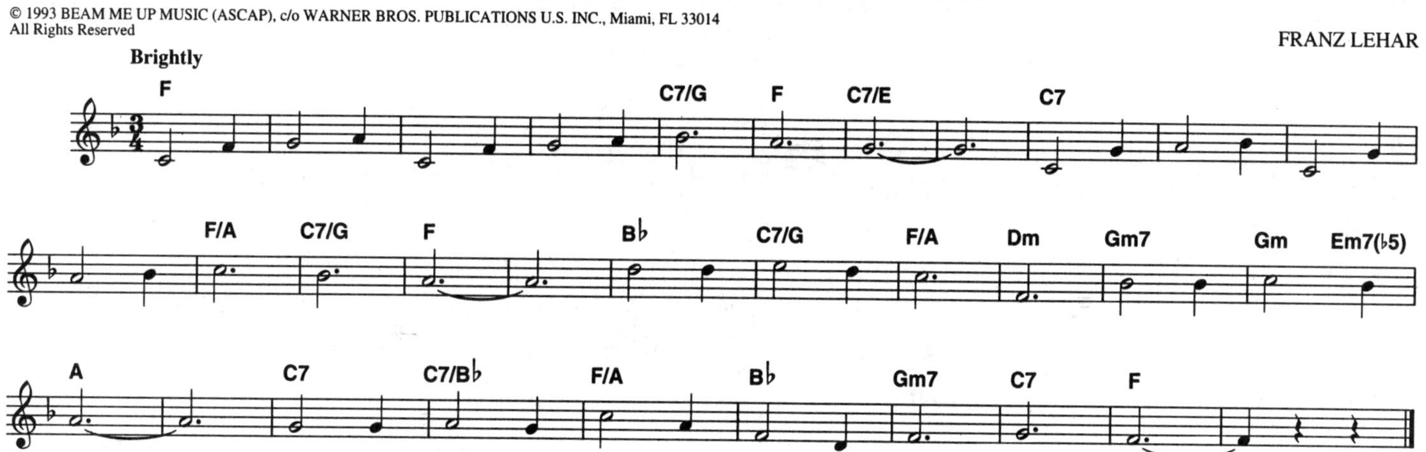
Brightly
F C7/G F C7/E C7
F/A C7/G F B♭ C7/G F/A Dm Gm7 Gm Em7(♭5)
A C7 C7/B♭ F/A B♭ Gm7 C7 F

MICHAEL, ROW THE BOAT ASHORE

TRADITIONAL

Moderately
Verse:
C F C
1. Mi - chael, row the boat a - shore, hal - le - lu - jah; Mi - chael,
Em Dm G7
1.-6.
C
7.
C
row the boat a - shore, hal - le - lu - jah. 2. Sis - ter, jah.

Verse 2:
**Sister, help to trim the sail, hallelujah;
Sister, help to trim the sail, hallelujah.**

Verse 3:
**Michael's boat's a gospel boat, hallelujah;
Michael's boat's a gospel boat, hallelujah.**

Verse 4:
**Jordan's river is chilly and cold, hallelujah;
Kills the body, but not the soul, hallelujah.**

Verse 5:
**Gabriel, blow the trumpet horn, hallelujah;
Blow the trumpet loud and long, hallelujah.**

Verse 6:
**If you get there before I do, hallelujah;
Tell my people I'm coming too, hallelujah.**

Verse 7:
**Michael, row the boat ashore, hallelujah;
Michael, row the boat ashore, hallelujah.**

MENUET A L'ANTIQUE

(Theme)
By IGNACE JAN PADEREWSKI
OP. 14, No. 1
Allegretto
G/B D7/A G D7/A G/B D7/A G D7/A G/B C
mp non legato
G/B C G/B D7 G
p
D7 G D7 G Am7 D7 G
MERRYILY WE ROLL ALONG
© 1935 WARNER BROS. INC. (Renewed)
All Rights Reserved
By EDDIE CANTOR, CHARLIE TOBIAS and MURRAY MENCHER
Moderato
C D7
Mer - ri - ly We Roll A - long, My hon - ey and me,
G7 C Am A♭+
Ver - i - ly there's no one half as hap - py as we.
Why we get a - long is ver - y eas - y to see.
C C6 C C6 C+ G7 Dm/A B♭7
Though we're twice as poor as mice, Say what do we care?
She and I won't buy un - less We pay for in cash.
G7 G7(-9 +5) C Am G7/B
For we've been so wealth - y in the love that we share.
And we still en - joy the thrill of corn - beef and hash,
C D7
Mer - ri - ly we dance a - long, while fac - ing the sun,
Though we're bound to quar - rel, for it's hu - man, I'm sure.
G7 G♯dim Am C7/G
Ver - i - ly our slo - gan is, "Say don't we have fun?"
Still we found there's noth - ing that a kiss can - not cure.
F Fm C Em A7
We live in style with a smile and a song
We're for each oth - er, how can we go wrong
As we
D7 D7♭5/A♭ G7 1. C C7 C♯dim G7 Dm/A G7 2. C Fm6 C
mer - ri - ly roll a - long.
long?

LOVE'S OLD SWEET SONG

Words by G. CLIFTON BINGHAM
Music by JAMES LYMAN MOLLOY

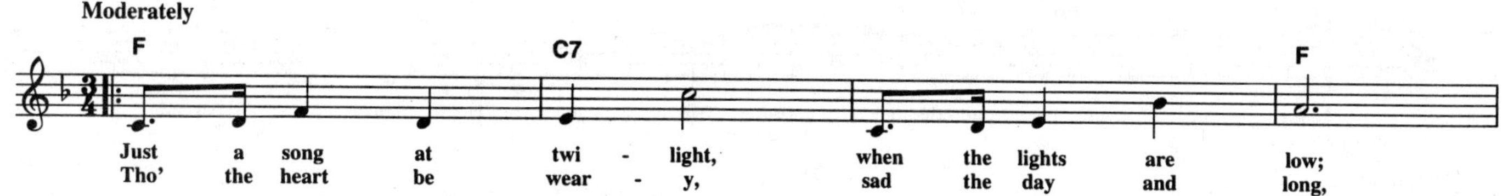
Moderately
F
C7
F
Just a song at twi - light, when the lights are low;
Tho' the heart be wear - y, sad the day and long,

1.
A7
Dm
G7
C7
2.
F7
and the flick - 'ring shad - ows, soft - ly come and go.
Still to us at

B♭
Gm7
C7
F
B♭
F
C7
F
twi - light comes love's old song. Comes love's old sweet song.

(THEME FROM) "MIDNIGHT COWBOY"

by JOHN BARRY

Moderately slow
C
B♭
C
1.
B♭
2.
B♭
C

B♭
A♭
D♭maj7
G7
C
B♭
A♭

To Coda
D♭maj7
G7
C
B♭
A♭
D♭maj7
G7
C
B♭

D.S. al Coda
Coda
Repeat ad lib. and fade
C
B♭
C
B♭
D♭maj7
G7
C
B♭

MIMI

Words by LORENZ HART
Music by RICHARD RODGERS

Moderately
G Am7/D D7 G D7 G
Mi-mi, you fun-ny lit-tle good for noth-ing Mi-mi, am I the guy? Mi-mi, you
Am7/D D7 G G7 C Cdim Em7
sun-ny lit-tle hon-ey of a Mi-mi, I'm aim-ing high! Mi-mi, you've got me sad and dream-y; you could free

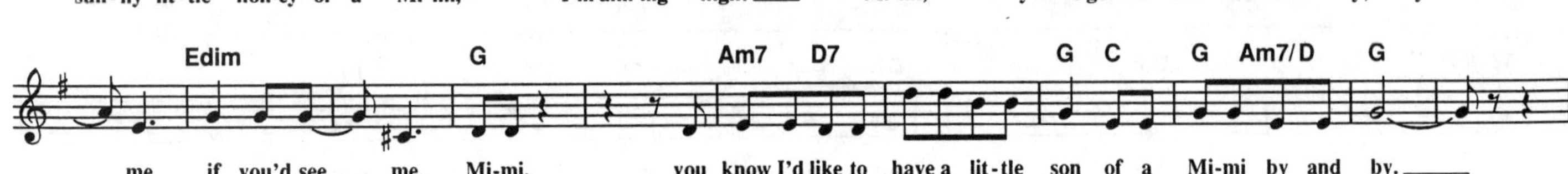
Edim G Am7 D7 G C G Am7/D G
me if you'd see me. Mi-mi, you know I'd like to have a lit-tle son of a Mi-mi by and by.

MINNIE THE MOOCHER
(The Ho-De-Ho Song)

By CAB CALLOWAY
and IRVING MILLS

Moderately
Verse:
Em Am Em B7 Em B7
1. Now here's a sto-ry 'bout Min-nie the Mooch-er. She was a low-down hooch-y cooch-er.
messed a-round wid a bloke named Smoke-y. She loved him though he was a "coke-y."

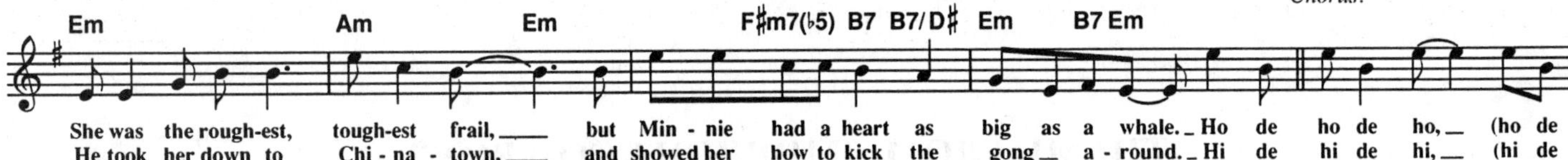
Em Am Em F♯m7(♭5) B7 B7/D♯ Em B7 Em
Chorus:
She was the rough-est, tough-est frail, but Min-nie had a heart as big as a whale. Ho de ho de ho, (ho de
He took her down to Chi-na-town, and showed her how to kick the gong a-round. Hi de hi de hi, (hi de

ho de ho.) Rah de dah de dah, (rah de dah de dah.) Tee-dle dee de dee, (tee-dle dee de dee.) Ho de
hi de hi.) Ree de dah de doo, (ree de dah de doo.) Bo de dah do dah, (bo de dah do dah.)

1.-6. D.S. 7.
B7 Em F♯m7(♭5) Em B7 Em B7 Em B7 Em F♯m7(♭5) B7 Em
ho de ho, (ho de ho de ho.) 2. She ho de ho. Poor Min', poor Min', poor Min'.

Verse 3:
She had a dream 'bout the King of Sweden.
He gave her things that she was needin'.
Gave her a home built of gold and steel;
A platinum car with diamond-studded wheels.
(To Chorus:)

Verse 4:
He gave her his town house and racing horses.
Each meal she ate was a dozen courses.
She had, a million dollars in nickels and dimes.
And ev-'ry day she counted 'em a million times.
(To Chorus:)

Verse 5:
Now Min' and Smokey they started jaggin'.
They got a free ride in a wagon.
She gave him the money to pay her bail,
But he left her flat in the County Jail.
(To Chorus:)

Verse 6:
Poor Minnie met Old Deacon Low-down.
He preached to her she ought to slow down.
But Minnie wiggled her jelly roll.
Deacon Low-down hollered, "Oh, save my soul."
(To Chorus:)

Verse 7:
They took her where they put the crazies.
Now poor old Min' is kickin' up daisies.
You've heard my story, this ends the song.
She was just a good gal but they done her wrong.
(To Chorus:)

MINUET IN G
Copyright © 1993 by BEAM ME UP MUSIC (ASCAP), c/o CPP/BELWIN, Miami, FL 33014
All Rights Reserved
By LUDWIG VAN BEETHOVEN
Allegretto grazioso
To next strain
Fine
D.S. 𝄋 al Fine
MISTY
Copyright © 1954, 1955 VERNON MUSIC CORPORATION
Copyright Renewed © 1982, 1983 MARKE MUSIC PUBLISHING CO. INC., LIMERICK MUSIC CORP., REGANESQUE MUSIC CO. and TIMOCO MUSIC
All Rights Administered by THE SONGWRITERS GUILD OF AMERICA, New York, N.Y.
All Rights Reserved Used by Permission
Lyrics by JOHNNY BURKE
Music by ERROLL GARNER
Slowly
Verse:
Look at me, I'm as help - less as a kit - ten up a tree, and I feel like I'm
way and a thou - sand vi - o - lins be - gin to play, or it might be the
own, would I wan - der through this won - der - land a - lone, nev - er know-ing my
cling-ing to a cloud; I can't un - der - stand, I get mis - ty just hold - ing your hand. Walk my
sound of your hel - lo. That mu - sic I hear, I get mis - ty, the mo - ment you're
right foot from my left, my hat from my glove, I'm too mis - ty and too much in
To Coda
near.
Bridge:
You can say that you're lead-ing me on, but it's just what I want you to do. Don't you no-tice how
hope-less - ly I'm lost, that's why I'm fol - low-ing you. On my
D.S. 𝄋 al Coda
Coda
love.

MISS YOU LIKE CRAZY

Lyrics and Music by
PRESTON GLASS, MICHAEL MASSER
and GERRY GOFFIN

Slowly
Verse 1:
E♭ B♭/D Gsus(♭9) G/B
E - ven though it's been so long, my love for you keeps
Cm7 A♭maj7 Gm7 Cm7
go - ing strong. I re - mem - ber the things that we used to do, a
A♭maj7 Gm7 Cm7 Fm7 A♭/B♭
kiss in the rain till the sun shined through. I tried to de - ny it, but I'm still in love with you.
E♭ Dm7 G
Chorus 1:
C G/B C/B♭ F/A
I miss you like cra - zy, I miss you like cra - zy,
Fm/A♭ Csus/G C/G Dm7 /G G/F
ev - er since you went a - way, ev - 'ry hour of ev - 'ry day. I
E♭ B♭/D E♭/D♭ A♭/C
miss you like cra - zy, I miss you like cra - zy. No
A♭m/C♭ E♭sus/B♭ E♭/B♭ A♭/B♭ B♭ A♭/B♭ B♭
mat - ter what I say or do, there's just no get - ting o - ver you.
Verse 2:
E♭ B♭/D Gsus(♭9) G/B
I can see the love shin - ing in your eyes, and it comes as such a
Cm7 A♭maj7 Gm7 Cm7
sweet sur - prise. It seems be - liev - ing is worth the wait, so
A♭maj7 Gm7 Cm7 Fm7 A♭/B♭
hold me and tell me it's not too late. We're so good to - geth - er, we're start-ing for - ev - er now.
E♭
Chorus 2:
B♭/D
And I miss you like cra - zy, I

E♭/D♭ A♭/C A♭m/C♭ E♭sus/B♭ E♭/B♭
miss you like cra - zy, ev - er since you went a - way,
A♭/B♭ B♭ A♭/B♭ B♭/A♭ G♭ D♭/F
ev - 'ry hour of ev - 'ry day. I miss you like cra - zy,
G♭/F♭ C♭/E♭ C♭m/D G♭sus/D♭ G♭/D♭
I miss you, ba - by. Love like ours will nev - er end, just
C♭/D♭ D♭ C♭/D♭ D♭/C♭ A E/G♯
touch me and we're there a - gain.
Instrumental solo...
A/G D/F♯ Dm/F Asus/E A/E D/E E D/E E
Bridge:
C B Em Am7 /D G
Just one night, and we'll have to find the feel - ings like we used to do.
C B Em Am7 /D
Hold on tight, and what - ev - er comes our way, we're gon - na make it through.
D Cmaj7 Bm7 Em7
It seems be - liev - ing is worth the wait, so
Cmaj7 Bm7 Em7 Am7 /D
hold me and tell me it's not too late. We're so good to - geth - er, we're start - ing for - ev - er now.
Chorus 3:
G G D/F♯ G/F C/E
And I miss you like cra - zy, I miss you like cra - zy. No
Repeat ad lib and fade
Cm/E♭ Gsus/D G/D C/D D C/D D
mat - ter what I say or do, there's just no get - ting o - ver you. And I

MINE

Words by IRA GERSHWIN
Music by GEORGE GERSHWIN

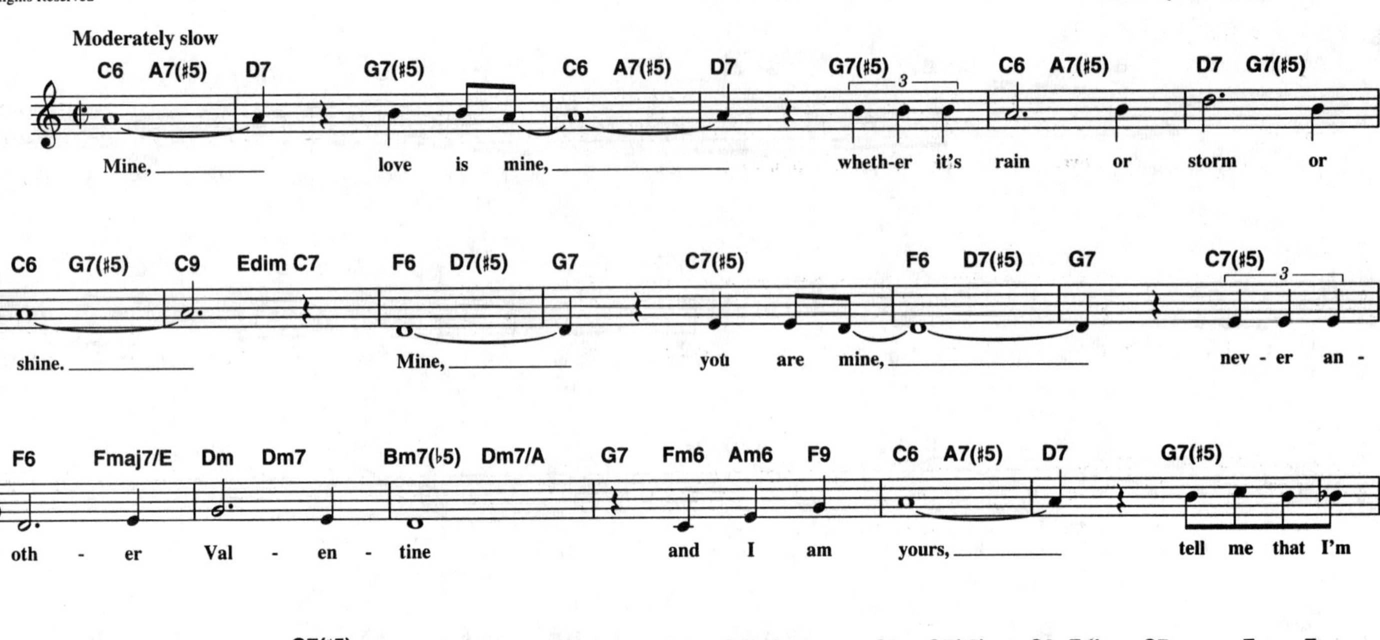
Moderately slow
C6 A7(♯5) D7 G7(♯5) C6 A7(♯5) D7 G7(♯5) C6 A7(♯5) D7 G7(♯5)
Mine, love is mine, wheth-er it's rain or storm or
C6 G7(♯5) C9 Edim C7 F6 D7(♯5) G7 C7(♯5) F6 D7(♯5) G7 C7(♯5)
shine. Mine, you are mine, nev - er an -
F6 Fmaj7/E Dm Dm7 Bm7(♭5) Dm7/A G7 Fm6 Am6 F9 C6 A7(♯5) D7 G7(♯5)
oth - er Val - en - tine and I am yours, tell me that I'm
C6 A7(♯5) D7 G7(♯5) C6 A7(♯5) D7 G7(♯5) C6 G7(♯5) C9 Edim C7 F E
yours, show me that smile my heart a - dores. Mine,

E♭ D9 Cmaj7/G B7 E7 A7 Dm9 G11 C
more than di - vine to know that love like yours is mine.

MOLLY MALONE
(Cockles and Mussels)

TRADITIONAL

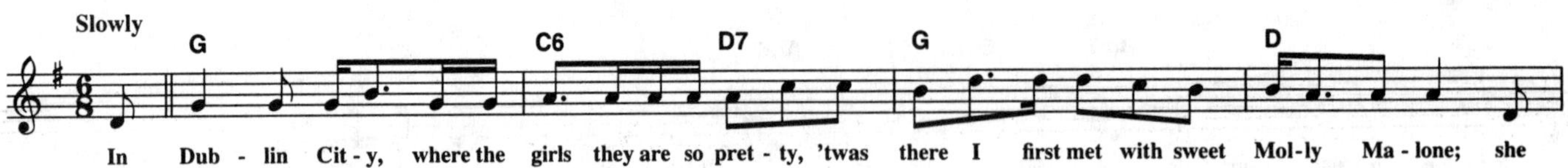
Slowly
G C6 D7 G D
In Dub - lin Cit - y, where the girls they are so pret - ty, 'twas there I first met with sweet Mol-ly Ma - lone; she

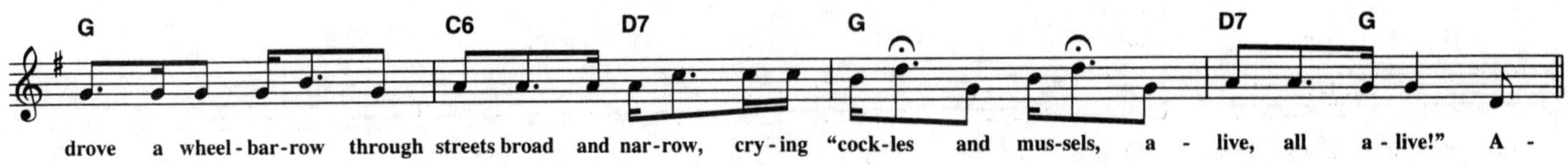
G C6 D7 G D7 G
drove a wheel - bar - row through streets broad and nar - row, cry - ing "cock - les and mus - sels, a - live, all a - live!" A -

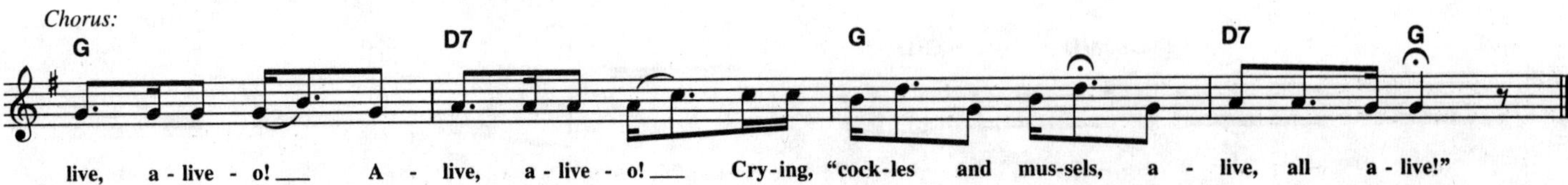
Chorus:
G D7 G D7 G
live, a - live - o! A - live, a - live - o! Cry - ing, "cock - les and mus - sels, a - live, all a - live!"

THE MISSOURI WALTZ

Words by JAMES R. SHANNON
Music by JOHN VALENTINE EPPEL

Dreamily
F C7 F
Hush - a - bye, my ba - by, slum - ber - time is com - ing soon; rest your head up -
C7 F B♭
on my breast while Mom - my hums a tune. The sand - man is call - ing where
F G7 C C7
shad - ows are fall - ing, while the soft breez - es sigh as in days long gone by.
F C7 F
'Way down in Mis - sou - ri, where I heard this mel - o - dy,
C7 F B♭
when I was a hap - py young - ster on my Mom - my's knee, the young folks were
Bdim7 F/C /A G7 C7 F
Fine
hum - ming, their ban - jos were strum - ming so sweet and low.
Dm Gm A7 Dm
Strum, strum, strum, strum, strum; seems I hear those ban - jos play - ing once a - gain.
A7 Dm
Hum, hum, hum, hum, hum, that same old plain - tive strain.
A7 Dm A7 Dm A7 Dm
Hear that mourn - ful mel - o - dy, it just haunts you the whole day long, and you
B♭ F/C G7 C7 F
D.C. al Fine
wan - der in dreams back to Dix - ie, it seems, when you hear that old - time song.

MOCKINGBIRD

Words and Music by INEZ FOXX and CHARLIE FOXX
Additional Lyrics by JAMES TAYLOR

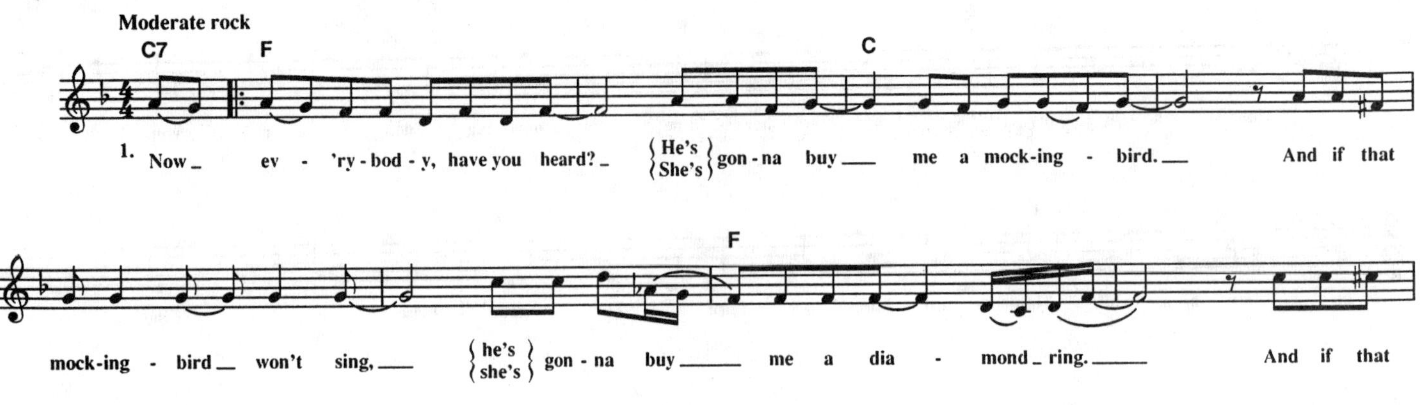
Moderate rock
C7 F C
1. Now ev - 'ry - bod - y, have you heard? He's / She's gon - na buy me a mock-ing - bird. And if that
F
mock-ing - bird won't sing, he's / she's gon - na buy me a dia - mond ring. And if that
B♭ F
dia - mond ring won't shine, he's / she's gon - na sure - ly break this heart of mine. And that's

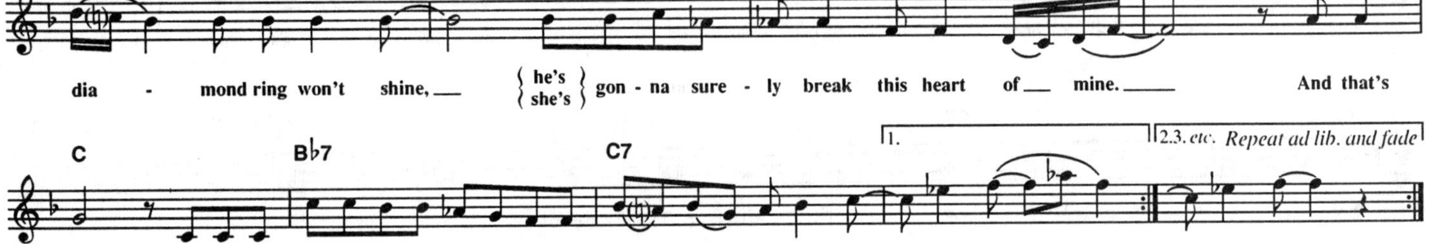
C B♭7 C7
1. 2.3. *etc. Repeat ad lib. and fade*
why I keep on tell - in' ev - 'ry - bod - y, say - in' yeah, yeah, wo, wo, wo, wo, wo. wo, wo.

Verse 2:
**Hear me now and understand, he's (she's) gonna find me some peace of mind.
And if that peace of mind won't stay, I'm gonna find myself a better way.
And if that better way ain't so, I-I-I'll ride with the tide and go with the flow.
And that's why I keep shoutin' in your ear, sayin' yeah, yeah, wo, wo, wo, wo, wo.**

MONA LISA

Words and Music by
JAY LIVINGSTON
and RAY EVANS

Slowly

E♭
Mo - na Li - sa, Mo - na Li - sa, men have named you. You're so like the la - dy with the mys - tic

Fm7 B♭7 Fm B♭7
smile. Is it on - ly 'cause you're lone - ly they have blamed you for that Mo - na Li - sa strang - ness in your

E♭
smile? Do you smile to tempt a lov - er, Mo - na Li - sa, or is this your way to hide a bro - ken

A♭ A♭m E♭ B♭7 E♭ E♭7
heart? Man - y dreams have been brought to your door - step. They just lie there, and they die there. Are you

A♭ E♭/B♭ Fm7 B♭7 E♭
warm, are you real, Mo - na Li - sa, or just a cold and lone - ly, love - ly work of art?

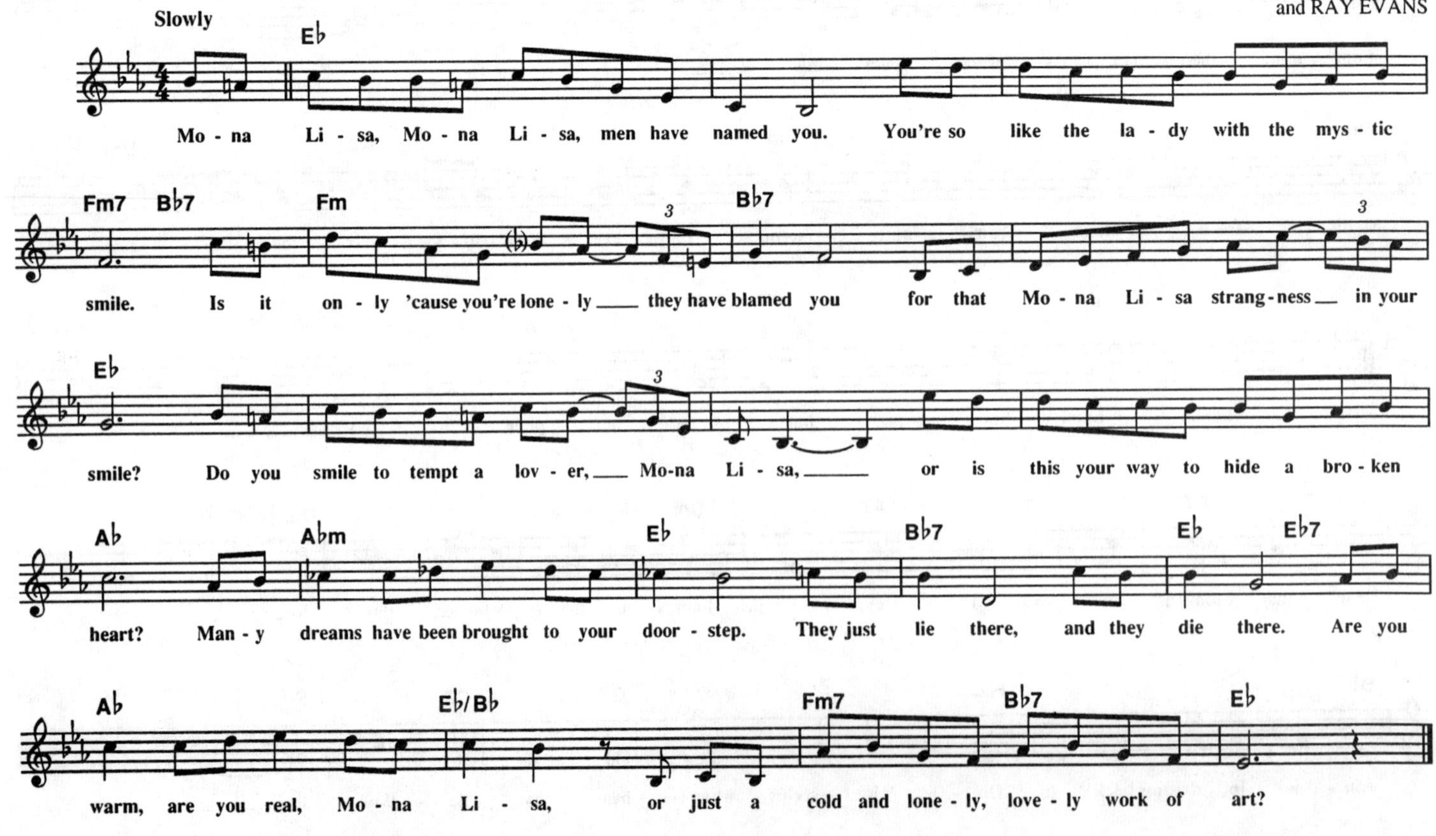

MISS OTIS REGRETS
(She's Unable to Lunch Today)

Words and Music by
COLE PORTER

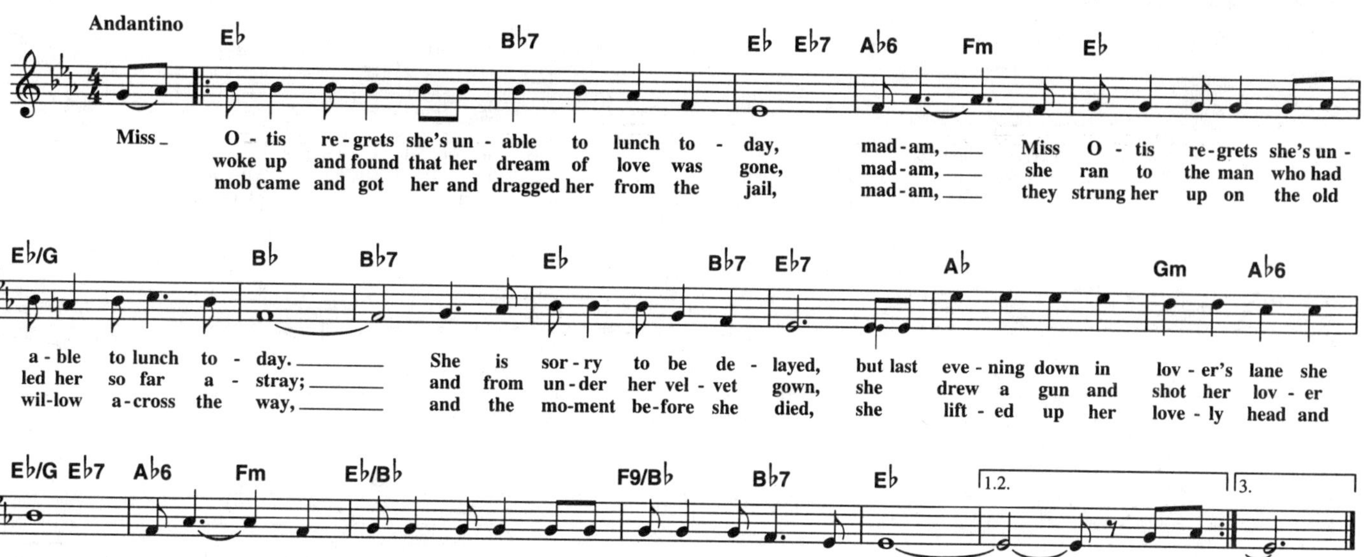
Andantino
Eb Bb7 Eb Eb7 Ab6 Fm Eb
Miss_ O - tis re - grets she's un - able to lunch to - day, mad - am,___ Miss O - tis re - grets she's un -
woke up and found that her dream of love was gone, mad - am,___ she ran to the man who had
mob came and got her and dragged her from the jail, mad - am,___ they strung her up on the old
Eb/G Bb Bb7 Eb Bb7 Eb7 Ab Gm Ab6
a - ble to lunch to - day.___ She is sor - ry to be de - layed, but last eve - ning down in lov - er's lane she
led her so far a - stray;___ and from un - der her vel - vet gown, she drew a gun and shot her lov - er
wil - low a - cross the way,___ and the mo - ment be - fore she died, she lift - ed up her love - ly head and
Eb/G Eb7 Ab6 Fm Eb/Bb F9/Bb Bb7 Eb
1.2. 3.
strayed, mad - am,___ Miss O - tis re - grets she's un - a - ble to lunch to - day.___ When she ___
down. When the
cried

MONEY FOR NOTHING

Words and Music by
MARK KNOPFLER

Medium rock
Verse:
G5 Bb5/G G5 Bb5 C5 G5 Bb5/G
1. Now look at them _ yo-yos, that's _ the way you do it; you play the gui-tar on the M - T - V. That ain't _ work-in'; that's _
To Coda 1.5. 2.3.4.6. Bridge:
G5 F5 G5 F5 G5 Eb Bb
_ the way you do it. Mon-ey for noth-in' and chicks for free. _ blis-ter on your thumb. We got-ta in - stall mi-cro-wave ov-ens,
Eb F G5 C5 D5 E5 1.2.3. D.S.
cus-tom kitch-en de - liv-er-ies.___ We got-ta move these re-frig-er-a-tors; we got-ta move these col-or T - V's.___
4. D.S. al Coda
Coda
Repeat ad lib. and fade
F5 G5 G5 Bb5 C5 G5 F5 G5
chicks for free. _ Mon-ey for noth-in' and chicks for free. _ Mon-ey for noth-in' and chicks for free. _

Verse 2:
Now, that ain't workin', that's the way you do it.
Lemme tell ya, them guys ain't dumb;
Maybe get a blister on your little finger,
Maybe get a blister on your thumb.
(To Bridge:)

Verse 3:
See the little faggot with the earring and the makeup?
Yeah, buddy, that's his own hair.
That little faggot got his own jet airplane;
That little faggot, he's a millionaire.
(To Bridge:)

Verse 4: Instrumental
(To Bridge:)

Verse 5:
I shoulda learned to play the guitar;
I shoulda learned to play them drums.
Look at that mama,
She's got it stickin' in the camera;
Man, we could have some fun.

Verse 6:
And he's up there, what's that? Hawaiian noises?
Bangin' on the bongos like a chimpanzee.
That ain't workin', that's the way you do it,
Get your money for nothin', get your chicks for free.
(To Bridge:)

Verse 7:
Now that ain't workin'; that's the way you do it,
You play the guitar on the MTV.
That ain't workin'; that's the way you do it.
Money for nothin' and chicks for free.
(To Coda:)

MONTEGO BAY

Words and Music by
JEFF BARRY and
BOBBY BLOOM

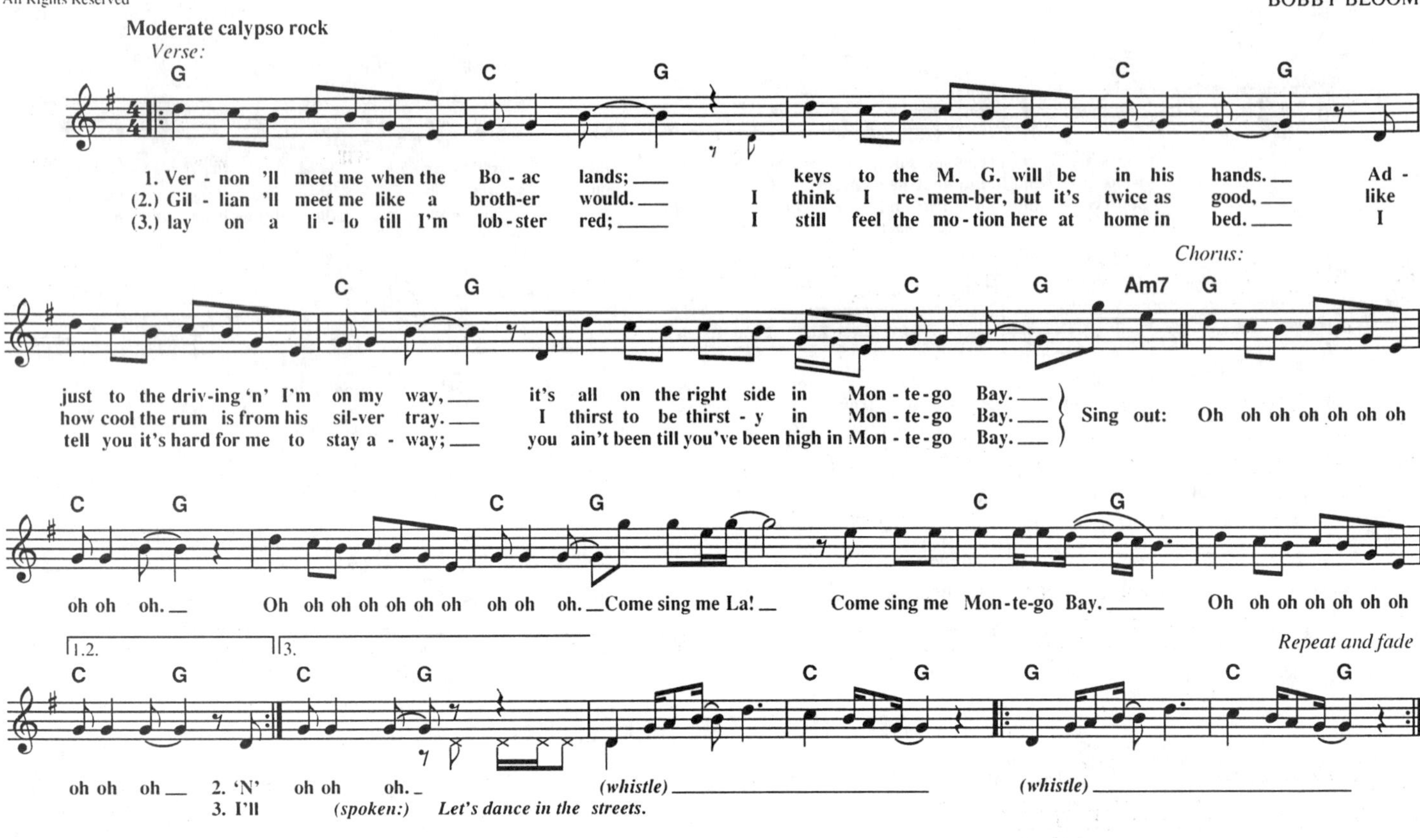
Moderate calypso rock
Verse:
1. Ver - non 'll meet me when the Bo - ac lands; keys to the M. G. will be in his hands. Ad -
(2.) Gil - lian 'll meet me like a broth-er would. I think I re - mem-ber, but it's twice as good, like
(3.) lay on a li - lo till I'm lob - ster red; I still feel the mo - tion here at home in bed. I
just to the driv-ing 'n' I'm on my way, it's all on the right side in Mon - te - go Bay.
how cool the rum is from his sil-ver tray. I thirst to be thirst - y in Mon - te - go Bay.
tell you it's hard for me to stay a - way; you ain't been till you've been high in Mon - te - go Bay.
Chorus:
Sing out: Oh oh oh oh oh oh oh
oh oh oh. Oh oh oh oh oh oh oh oh oh oh. Come sing me La! Come sing me Mon-te-go Bay. Oh oh oh oh oh oh oh
1.2.
3.
oh oh oh 2. 'N' oh oh oh.
3. I'll (spoken:) Let's dance in the streets.
(whistle)
Repeat and fade
(whistle)

MOOD INDIGO

By DUKE ELLINGTON, IRVING MILLS
and ALBANY BIGARD

Moderately slow
You ain't been blue, no, no, no. You ain't been blue, till you've had that mood in - di - go.
Fine
That feel - in' goes steal-in' down to my shoes, while I sit and sigh: "Go 'long blues."
Al-ways get that mood in - di - go, since my ba - by said good - bye. In the eve - nin' when lights are low,
I'm so lone-some I could cry, 'cause there's no - bod - y who cares a - bout me. I'm just a soul who's
D.C. al Fine
blu - er than blue can be. When I get that mood in - di - go, I could lay me down and die.

MOON LOVE

Words and Music by
MACK DAVID, MACK DAVIS
& ANDRE KOSTELANETZ

Moderately
B♭7 B♭7/A♭ E♭/G E♭ Fm7
Will this be moon love nothing but moon love? Will you be gone when the
B♭7 E♭ E♭/G B♭7 B♭7/A♭ E♭/G E♭
dawn comes steal - ing through? Are these just moon dreams, grand while the moon beams? But when the
Am7(♭5)/C /E♭ D7 Gm Gm7(♭5)/F C7/E Fm7 B♭7/D
moon fades a - way will my dreams come true? Much as I love you don't let me love you,
E♭ F9/C E♭/B♭ F9/A B♭7/A♭ E♭/G Cm7 B♭7 B♭7/A♭
if I must pay for your kiss with lone - ly tears. Say it's not moon love, tell me it's
E♭/G E♭ Cm7 F7 Fm9/B♭ B♭7 1. E♭ B♭7 2. E♭ A♭maj7 E♭
true love. Say you'll be mine when the moon dis - ap - pears. Will this be pears.

MOMENTS TO REMEMBER

Words by AL STILLMAN
Music by ROBERT ALLEN

Moderately
Gmaj7 G6 Gmaj7 G6 G G+ C Am D7
The New Year's Eve we did the town, the day we tore the goal - post down,
qui - et walks, the nois - y fun, the ball room prize we al - most won,
oth - er nights and oth - er days may find us gone our sep' - rate ways,
We will have these
1. Gdim7 G 2. Cm G To Next Strain
mo - ments to re - mem - ber. The mo - ments to re - mem - ber.
3. Cm G Fine Dm7 G9 G7 C G
mo - ments to re - mem - ber. Tho' sum - mer turns to win - ter and the
D7 G G7 C G Em Em7 A7 Am7 D7 D.S. al Fine
pre - sent dis - ap - pears. The laugh - ter we were glad to share will e - cho thru the years. When

As Sung in the Paramount Picture "BREAKFAST AT TIFFANY'S"

MOON RIVER

Words by JOHNNY MERCER
Music by HENRY MANCINI

Moderate waltz
C Am F Cmaj7 F Cmaj7 Bm7(♭5) E7 Am C7
Moon Riv - er, wid - er than a mile: I'm cross - in' you in style some - day. Old dream - mak - er you

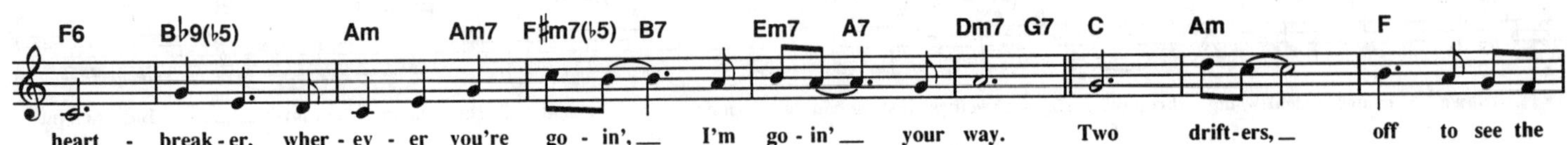
F6 B♭9(♭5) Am Am7 F♯m7(♭5) B7 Em7 A7 Dm7 G7 C Am F
heart - break - er, wher - ev - er you're go - in', I'm go - in' your way. Two drift - ers, off to see the

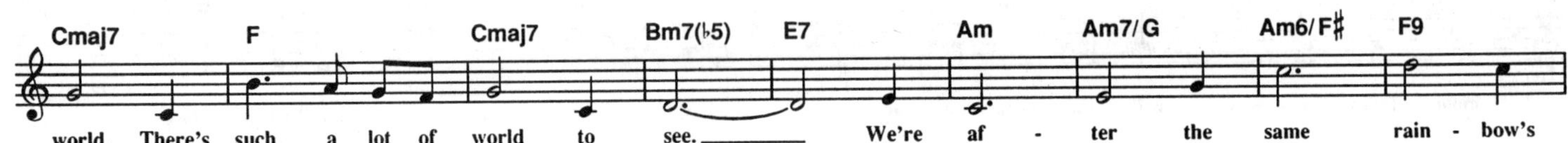
Cmaj7 F Cmaj7 Bm7(♭5) E7 Am Am7/G Am6/F♯ F9
world. There's such a lot of world to see. We're af - ter the same rain - bow's

C F C F C Am Dm G7(♭9) C
end wait - in' 'round the bend, my huck - le - ber - ry friend. Moon Riv - er and me.

MOTHER MACHREE

Words by RIDA JOHNSON YOUNG
Music by CHAUNCEY OLCOTT
and ERNEST R. BALL

Moderately, with expression
D Bm G D G D/F♯ A7/E
1. There's a spot in my heart which no col - leen may own. There's a depth in my soul nev - er
sor - row or care in the dear days gone by was made bright by the light of the

D E7/B Em7(♭5)/B♭ A7 D Bm C G G♯dim7
sound - ed or known. There's a place in my mem - 'ry, my life, that you fill. No
smile in your eye. Like a can - dle that's set in a win - dow at night, your

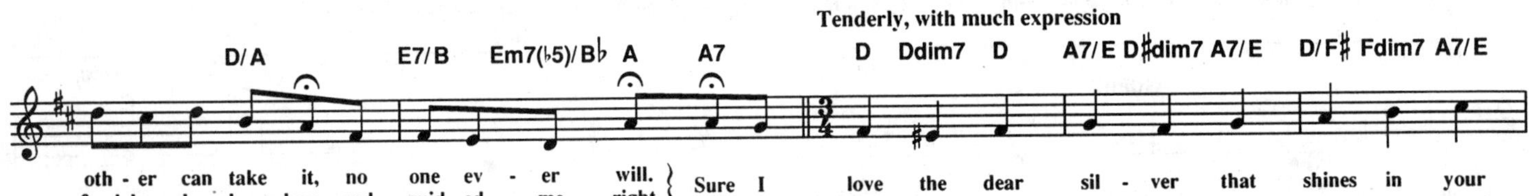
Tenderly, with much expression
D/A E7/B Em7(♭5)/B♭ A A7 D Ddim7 D A7/E D♯dim7 A7/E D/F♯ Fdim7 A7/E
oth - er can take it, no one ev - er will.
fond love has cheered me, and guid - ed me right.
Sure I love the dear sil - ver that shines in your

D G B♭dim7 G/B D E9 E6 E7 A7 D Ddim7 D A7/E D♯dim7 A7/E
hair, and the brow that's all fur - rowed and wrin - kled with care. I kiss the dear fin - gers so

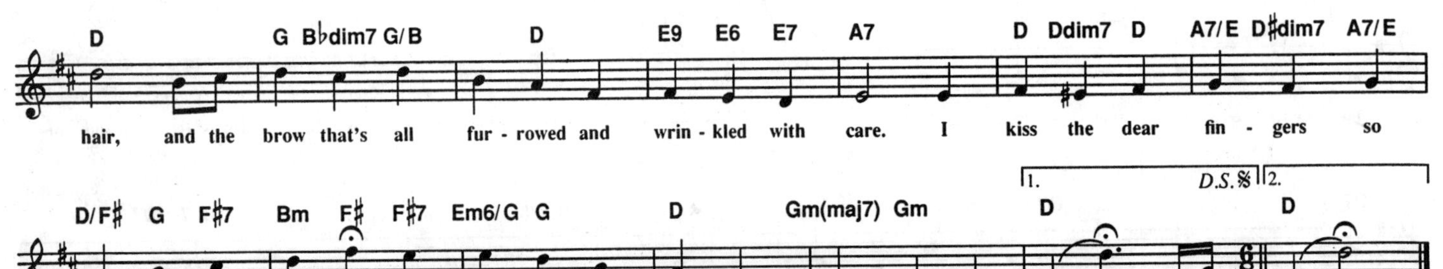
1. D.S. 𝄋 2.
D/F♯ G F♯7 Bm F♯ F♯7 Em6/G G D Gm(maj7) Gm D D
toil - worn for me; oh, God bless you and keep you, Moth - er Ma - chree! 2. Ev - 'ry chree!

MOONGLOW

Words and Music by WILL HUDSON, EDDIE DE LANGE and IRVING MILLS

Slowly
Am7 Cm(♯7) G/B A7 Am7 D7 G6 E♭7/G
It must have been moon-glow, way up in the blue. It must have been moon-glow that led me
Am7(♭5)/G E♭7/G G6 Am7 Cm(♯7) G/B A7 Am7 D7
straight to you. I still hear you say-ing, "Dear one, hold me fast." And I start in pray-ing,
G E♭7/G Am7(♭5)/G E♭7/G G6 G7 F♯7 F7 E7
oh Lord, please let this last. We seemed to float right through the air,
A7 D7 E♭7 D7 Am7 Cm(♯7) G/B
heav-en-ly songs seemed to come from ev-'ry-where. And now when there's moon-glow way up in the
A7 Am7 D7 G6 E♭7/G Am7(♭5)/G E♭7/G G6 D7 Am7(♭5)/G E♭7/G G6
1. 2.
blue, I al-ways re-mem-ber that moon-glow gave me you. gave me you.

From the Paramount Picture "ROAD TO MOROCCO"

MOONLIGHT BECOMES YOU

Words by JOHNNY BURKE
Music by JIMMY VAN HEUSEN

Moderately slow
F F♯dim7 Gm7 C7 F A♭dim Gm7 C7(♭9) Am7 D7(♭9) Gm7 C7 Fmaj7 Gm7 C9
Moon-light be-comes you, it goes with your hair. You cer-tain-ly know the right thing to wear.
F F♯dim7 Gm7 C7 F A♭dim Gm7 C7(♭9) Am7 D7(♭9) Gm7 C7 C7(♭9) F E♭6 F6 F7(♯5)
Moon-light be-comes you; I'm thrilled at the sight. And I could get so ro-man-tic to-night. You're
B♭ B♭+ E♭ E♭6 F7 B♭ Em7(♭5) A7(♭9) Dm
all dressed up to go dream-ing, now don't tell me I'm wrong, and what a night to go dream-ing.
G7 Gm7 C7 F F♯dim Gm7 C9 Am7 A♭dim Gm7 C7(♭9)
Mind if I tag a-long? If I say I love you, I want you to know it's
Am7 D7(♭9) Gm7 C9 A7 D7(♭9) G7 Gm7/C F6
not just be-cause there's moon-light, al-though moon-light be-comes you so.

MOONLIGHT BAY

Words by EDWARD MADDEN
Music by PERCY WENRICH

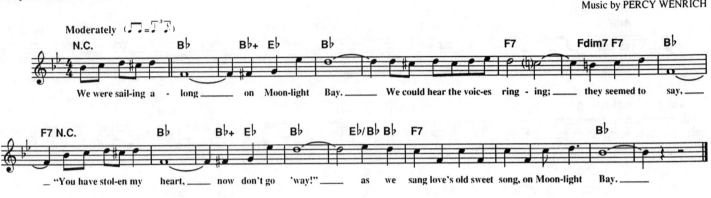

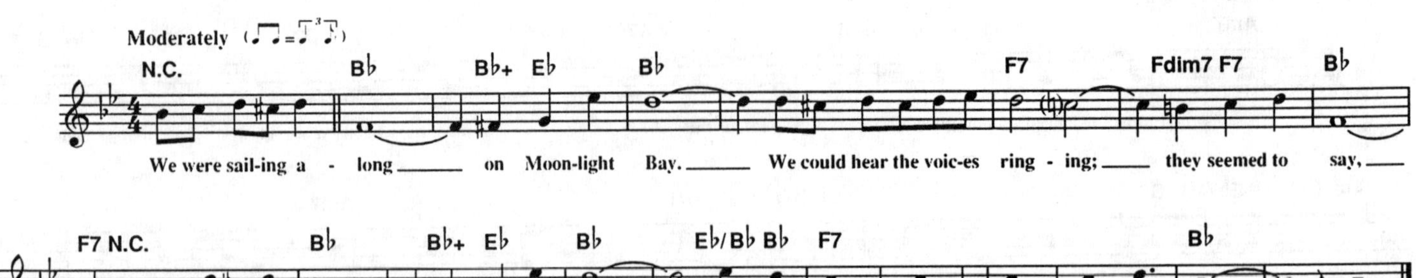
Moderately
N.C. B♭ B♭+ E♭ B♭ F7 Fdim7 F7 B♭
We were sail-ing a - long ___ on Moon-light Bay. ___ We could hear the voic-es ring - ing; ___ they seemed to say, ___
F7 N.C. B♭ B♭+ E♭ B♭ E♭/B♭ B♭ F7 B♭
_ "You have stol-en my heart, ___ now don't go 'way!" ___ as we sang love's old sweet song, on Moon-light Bay. ___

MOTHER-IN-LAW

By ALLEN TOUSSAINT

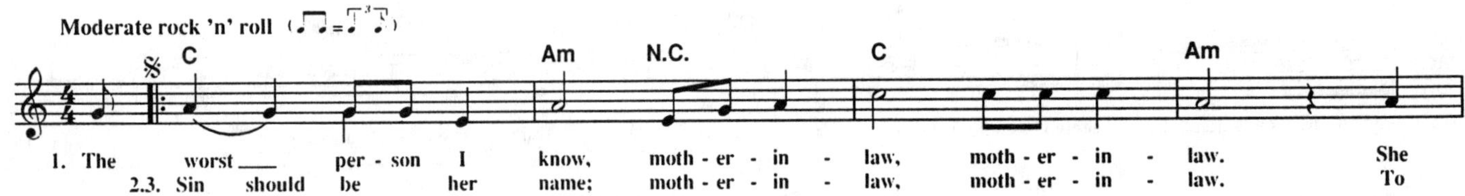
Moderate rock 'n' roll
C Am N.C. C Am
1. The worst ___ per - son I know, moth - er - in - law, moth - er - in - law. She
2.3. Sin should be her name; moth - er - in - law, moth - er - in - law. To

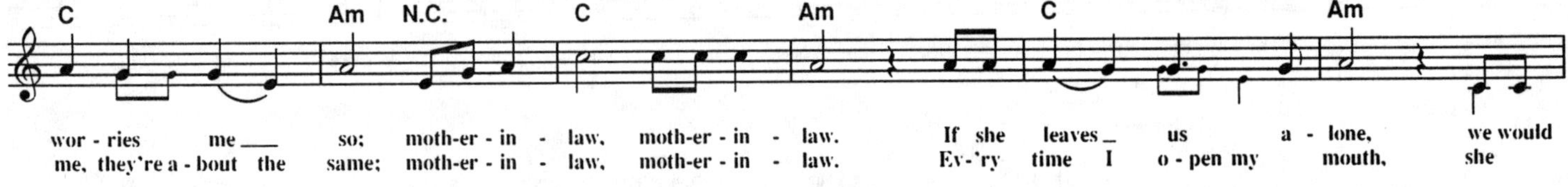
C Am N.C. C Am C Am
wor - ries me ___ so; moth-er - in - law, moth-er - in - law. If she leaves _ us a - lone, we would
me, they're a - bout the same; moth-er - in - law, moth-er - in - law. Ev-'ry time I o - pen my mouth, she

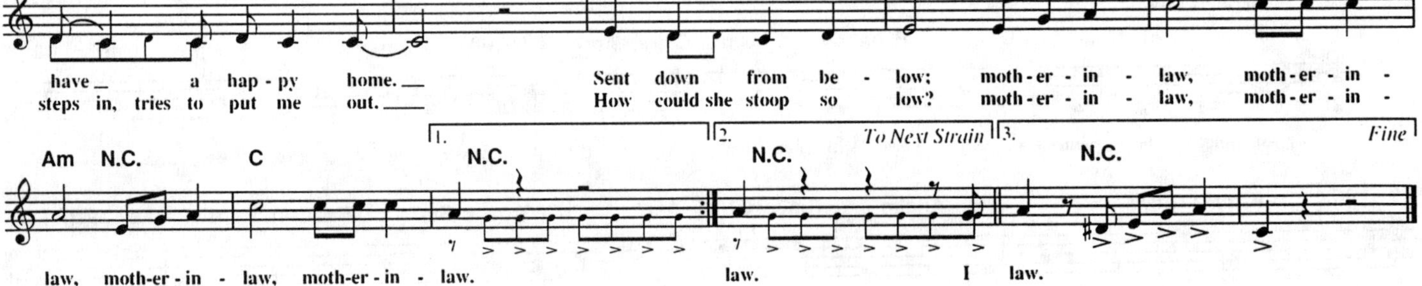
F6 D7 D9 G13 N.C. C
have _ a hap - py home. ___ Sent down from be - low; moth - er - in - law, moth - er - in -
steps in, tries to put me out. ___ How could she stoop so low? moth - er - in - law, moth - er - in -
Am N.C. C 1. N.C. 2. N.C. To Next Strain 3. N.C. Fine
law, moth-er - in - law, moth-er - in - law. law. I law.
law, moth-er - in - law, moth-er - in -

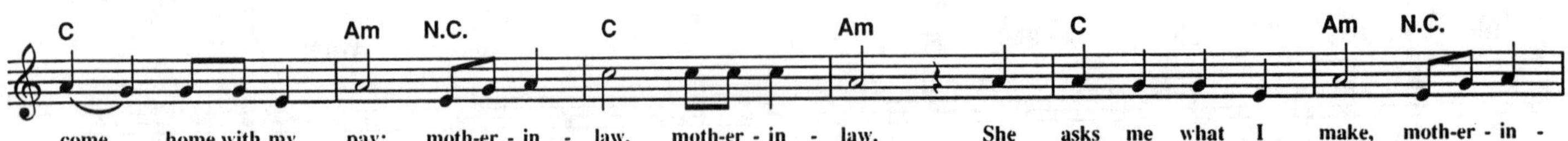
C Am N.C. C Am C Am N.C.
come _ home with my pay; moth-er - in - law, moth-er - in - law. She asks me what I make, moth-er - in -

C Am C Am7 F6 D7
law, moth-er - in - law. She thinks her ad-vice is a con - tri - bu-tion, but if she will leave, that will be a so - lu-tion; and

D9 G13 N.C. C Am N.C. C N.C. D.S. al Fine
don't come back no more, moth-er - in - law, moth-er - in - law, moth-er - in - law, moth-er - in - law.

MOONLIGHT SERENADE

Copyright © 1939 (Renewed 1967) EMI ROBBINS CATALOG INC.
All Rights Reserved
Lyric by MITCHELL PARISH
Music by GLENN MILLER
Moderately
I stand at your gate and the song that I sing is of moon-light. I stand and I wait for the touch of your hand in the June night. The ros-es are sigh-ing a moon-light ser-e-nade.
stars are a-glow and to-night how their light sets me dream-ing. My love, do you know that your eyes are like stars bright-ly beam-ing? I bring you and sing you a moon-light ser-e-
don't let me wait; come to me ten-der-ly in the June night. I stand at your gate and I sing you a song in the moon-light, a love song, my dar-ling, a moon-light ser-e-
The nade. nade.
To Next Strain
Fine
Let us stray till break of day in love's val-ley of dreams, just you and I, a sum-mer sky, a heav-en-ly breeze kiss-ing the trees. So
D.S. al Fine
MORE THAN YOU KNOW
Copyright © 1929 (Renewed 1957) by EMI MILLER CATALOG INC. and VINCENT YOUMANS, INC.
All Rights Reserved
Lyrics by WILLIAM ROSE
and EDWARD ELISCU
Music by VICTOR YOUMANS
Slowly
More than you know, more than you know, girl of my heart, I love you so. Late-ly I find you're on my mind, more than you know.
right, wheth-er you're wrong, girl of my heart, I'll string a-long. You need me
cry, oh, how I'd cry, if you got tired and said "good-bye," more than I'd
To Coda
Wheth-er you're so more than you'll ev-er know.
Lov-ing you the way that I do there's noth-ing I can do a-bout it.
Lov-ing may be all you can give, but hon-ey, I can't live with-out it.
Oh, how I'd
D.S. al Coda
Coda
show more than you'd ev-er know.

MORE THAN WORDS

Lyrics and Music by
BETTENCOURT, CHERONE

Moderate rock
Verse:
1. Say-in', "I love you" is not the words I want to hear from you. It's not that I want you not to say. But if you on-ly knew how eas-y it would be to show me how you feel, more than words is all you have to do to make it real. Then, you would-n't have to say that you love me, 'cause I'd al-read-y know.
Chorus:
What would you do if my heart was torn in two? More than words to show you feel that your love for me is real.
if I took those words a-way? Then, you could-n't make things new just by say-
What would you say- in', "I love you." in', "I love you."
1.3.
2. To Next Strain
4.
La di da da di da di dai dai da. More than words.
1.
D.S.
2.3.4.
5.
La di da da di da. More than words. More than words.
(Ooh, ooh.) (Guitar cadenza) More than words.

Verse 2:
**Now that I have tried to talk to you
And make you understand.
All you have to do is close your eyes
And just reach out your hands.
And touch me, hold me close, don't ever let me go.
More than words is all I ever needed you to show.
Then you wouldn't have to say
That you love me 'cause I'd already know.**
(To Chorus:)

MOVE IT ON OVER

By HANK WILLIAMS

Moderately fast

Verse:

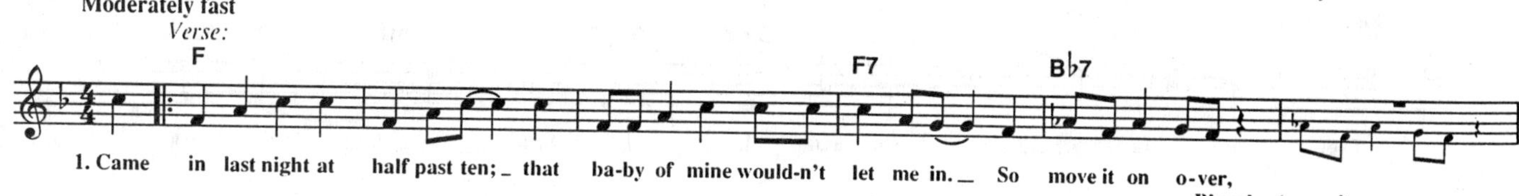
F F7 B♭7
1. Came in last night at half past ten; _ that ba-by of mine would-n't let me in. _ So move it on o-ver,
Bkgrd.: (move it on o-ver,

F C7 F/C C7 1.2.3. F 4. F C7 F
move it on o-ver, move o-ver li'l dog, 'cause the big dog's mov-in' _ in. 2. She in.
move it on o-ver,)

Verse 2:
She changed the lock on our front door;
Now my door key don't fit no more.
So get it on over, (move it on over,)
Scoot it on over, (move it on over,)
Move over skinny dog, 'cause the fat dog's movin' in.

Verse 3:
This doghouse here is mighty small,
But it's better than no house at all.
So ease it on over, (move it on over,)
Drag it on over, (move it on over,)
Move over old dog, 'cause a new dog's movin' in.

Verse 4:
She told me not to play around,
But I done let the deal go down.
So pack it on over, (move it on over,)
Tote it on over, (move it on over,)
Move over nice dog, 'cause a bad dog's movin' in.

MR. BLUE

Words and Music by
DEWAYNE BLACKWELL

Moderately slow

F Am7 B♭ C7 Dm7 C6 B♭ C7
I'm Mis - ter Blue when you say you love me, then prove it by
I'm Mis - ter Blue when you say you're sor - ry, then turn a - round,

Am7 Dm7 Gm7 /B♭ Am7 Gm7 Gm7/C 1. F /A Gm7 C7 2. F
go - in' out on the sly, prov-in' your love _ is - n't true; call me Mis - ter Blue. Blue.
head-in' for the lights of town, hurt-in' me through _ and _ through, call me Mis - ter

C7/G Gm7 C7 F C7/G Gm7 C7 F Am7 Dm7 G7
I stay at home at night, right by the phone at night, but you won't call and I _ won't hurt _ my

B♭/C Cm7(♭5) C7 Gm7 C7(♭9) F Am7 B♭ C7 Dm7 C6 B♭ C7
pride; call me Mis-ter... I won't tell you, while you paint the town _ a bright red _ to turn it

Repeat ad lib. and fade

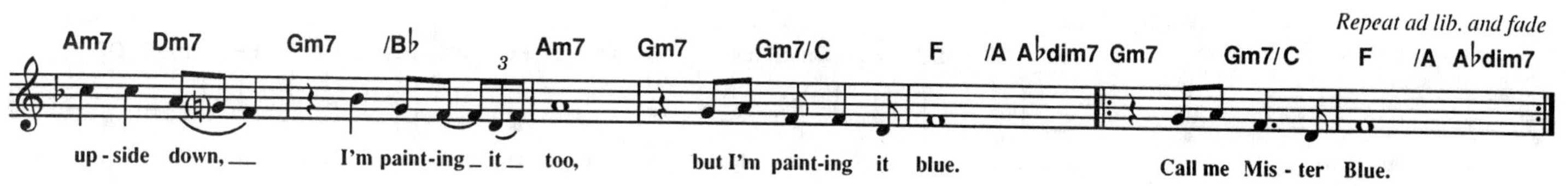
Am7 Dm7 Gm7 /B♭ Am7 Gm7 Gm7/C F /A A♭dim7 Gm7 Gm7/C F /A A♭dim7
up - side down, _ I'm paint-ing _ it _ too, but I'm paint-ing it blue. Call me Mis - ter Blue.

Theme from the Television Production "MR. LUCKY"

MR. LUCKY

Words by JAY LIVINGSTON and RAY EVANS
Music by HENRY MANCINI

Moderately
D13 Dm7 G9(♯5) Cm7 F7 F7(♯5) B♭maj9
They call us luck - y, you and I, luck - y girl, luck - y guy.
Am7 D9(♭5) D9 Bm7 Em7 Cm7 Am7 D7 Dm7 G7 N.C.
When you take my hand or touch my cheek I know I'm on a life-time luck - y streak. A luck - y
D13 Dm7 G9(♯5) F7 F7(♯5) B♭maj9 E7(♯5) B♭7/D
rain - bow lights the sky when we kiss, when we sigh. He: They She: They
E♭ Cm7/G D9 Bm7 B♭9 Am9 Am7/D G6/9 N.C. G6/9
say I'm luck - y, mis - ter luck - y guy, and you're the rea - son why. They call us I.
say you're luck - y, mis - ter luck - y guy, but dar - ling, so am
MY CHERIE AMOUR
Words and Music by STEVIE WONDER, HENRY COSBY and SYLVIA MOY
Copyright © 1968, 1969, 1970, 1971, 1973, by JOBETE MUSIC CO., INC.
All Rights Reserved
Moderately
D7 Cmaj7 C6 Fmaj7 F6 Fmaj7 F7(♭5) F7 Gmaj7 D7 Gmaj7
La la la la la la, la la la la la la. My Che - rie A - mour
ca - fé or
some - day you'll
C11 Fmaj7 Gmaj7 C11 Fmaj7
love - ly as a sum - mer day. My Che - rie A - mour dis - tant as the Milk - y Way.
some - times on a crowd - ed street. I've been near you but you nev - er no - ticed me.
see my face a - mong the crowd. May - be some - day I'll share your lit - tle dis - tant cloud.
D11 Cmaj7 D11 F9 Bm7 E7 A7
My Che - rie A - mour, pret - ty lit - tle one that I a - dore, you're the on - ly girl my heart beats for.
My Che - rie A - mour, won't you tell me how could you ig - nore, that be - hind that lit - tle smile I wore.
Oh, Che - rie A - mour, pret - ty lit - tle one that I a - dore, you're the on - ly girl my heart beats for.
To Coda
D7 G6 D11 D7 G6 D11 D7 Cmaj7 C6 C Fmaj7 F6 Fmaj7 D7(♭9) D11
How I wish that you were mine. In a La la la la la la, la la la la la
How I wish that you were mine.
How I wish that you were mine.
D.S. al Coda
Coda
Repeat and fade
Gmaj7 D7 G6 F9 G6 D7 Cmaj7 C6 C Fmaj7 F6 Fmaj7 F7(♭5) F7 F9 Gmaj7 D7
la. May - be La la la la la la, la la la la la la la la

From "LA BOHEME"

MUSETTA'S WALTZ

G. PUCCINI

Slow waltz
(Piano:)
When through the street above I wander dimlessly, the people turn to look at me.
Quando me'n vo'... quando me'n vo' soletta per la via la gente sosta e mira...
Yes, how they look around, because they know I'm charming, a very charming, charming girl.
e la bellezza mia tutta ricerca in me... ricerca in me da capo a piè;
And when 'tis mine to mark their hidden longing, and all the passion in their eyes, and then the joy of conquest overcomes me; ev'ry man is my prize!
ed assaporo allor la bramosia sottil, che da gl'occhi traspira e dai palesi vezzi intender sa alle occulte beltà.
And thus their hearts, their hearts I capture, as if by magic all my own, ah! rapture! ah! rapture! 'tis mine, alone!
Così l'effluvio del desio tutta m'aggira felice mi fa, felice mi fa!
Now, you that once your passion once betrayed, why should you be dismayed? Yet though deep in your heart, deep in your heart rankles the smart you'd never never confess but rather die!
E tu che sai che memori e ti strugi, da me tanto rifuggi? So ben le angoscie tue non le vuoi dir, non le vuoi dir, so ben ma ti senti morir!

MY BONNIE

TRADITIONAL SCOTTISH SONG

Moderately
My Bonnie lies over the ocean, my Bonnie lies over the sea. My Bonnie lies over the ocean; oh bring back my Bonnie to me.
Bring back, bring back, bring back my Bonnie to me, to me. Bring back, bring back, oh, bring back my Bonnie to me.

MY EYES ADORED YOU
Words and Music by
BOB CREWE and KENNY NOLAN
Copyright © 1974 by STONE DIAMOND MUSIC CORP., TANNYBOY MUSIC CO. and KENNY NOLAN PUBLISHING
All Rights Reserved
Slowly
Chorus:
My eyes a - dored you though I nev - er laid a hand on you. My eyes a - dored you like a mil - lion miles a - way from me, you couldn't see how I a - dored you.
So close, so close and yet so far.
1.2. To Next Strain
3. Fine
far.
Verse:
1. Car - ried your books from school play - in' make be - lieve you're mar - ried to me. You were fifth - grade, I was sixth when we came to be. Walk - in' home ev - 'ry day o - ver Bon - ni - cut Bridge and Bay till we grew in - to the me and you who went our sep - 'rate ways.
2. Head - ed for cit - y lights; climbed the lad - der up to for - tune and fame. I worked my fin - gers to the bone; made my - self a name. Fun - ny I seemed to find that no mat - ter how the years un - wind, still I rem - i - nisce 'bout the girl I miss, and the love I left be - hind.
1st time D.S.
2nd time D.S. al Fine
My eyes a -
MY GAL SAL
Words and Music by
PAUL DRESSER
Copyright © 1993 by BEAM ME UP MUSIC (ASCAP), c/o CPP/BELWIN, INC., Miami, FL 33014
All Rights Reserved
Moderately
They called her fri - vo - lous Sal, a pe - cu - liar sort of a gal, with a heart that was mel - low, an all 'round good fel - low was my old pal. Your trou - bles, sor - rows and care she was al - ways will - ing to share. A wild sort of dev - il, but dead on the lev - el, was my gal Sal.

THE MORE I SEE YOU
© 1945 WB MUSIC CORP. (Renewed)
All Rights Reserved
Words by
MACK GORDON
Music by
HARRY WARREN
Slowly, with feeling
The More I See You, the more I want you. Somehow this feeling just grows and grows. With ev-'ry sigh I become more mad about you; More lost without you, and so it goes. Can you imagine how much I'll love you, The More I See You, as years go by? I know the only one for me can only be you. My arms won't free you, my heart won't try. The More I try.
MORE THAN I CAN SAY
© 1960 WARNER-TAMERLANE PUBLISHING CORP. (Renewed)
All Rights Reserved
Words and Music by
SONNY CURTIS and
JERRY ALLISON
Moderately
Oh, oh! Yea, yea!
I love you More Than I Can Say. I'll love you twice as much tomorrow.
I miss you ev-'ry single day. Why must my life be filled with sorrow?
Oh, love you More Than I Can Say.
To Coda
Oh, oh! Yea,
Don't you know I need you so? Tell me, please; I gotta know. Do you mean to make me cry? Am I just another guy?
D.S. al Coda (1st lyric)
Oh, oh! Yea,
Coda
I Love You More Than I Can Say. I Love You More Than I Can Say.

MR. WONDERFUL

Words and Music by
JERRY BOCK, LARRY HOLOFCENER
and GEORGE DAVID WEISS

Slowly and Expressively
C Dm7 G7
Why this feel - ing? Why this glow? Why the
Trem - bling when you speak why this
much more I could say, but the
C D7 G7 Dm E7 Am Am7
thrill when you say, "Hel - lo!"? It's a strange and ten - der
joy when you touch my cheek? I must tell you what my
words keep slip - ping a - way; and I'm left with on - ly
D#° C Em7-5 A7 Dm7 D9
mag - ic you do. Mis - ter won - der - ful, that's
heart knows is true:
one point of view:
1. Dm B♭7 G7
you! Why this
2. C F6 C
you! And why this
Gm7 C7 F
long - ing to know your charms; to spend for -
Am7 D7 G7 B7 G7 D.C. al Coda
ev - er here in your arms! Oh! there's
CODA G7 C Dm7 Em7 D#m7 Dm7 G7 C
that's you! One more thing,
Em7 B♭7 A7 Dm7 D#° C6
then I'm through; mis - ter won - der - ful, mis - ter won - der - ful,
A7 Dm9 F6 F#7 G7 C Fm C
mis - ter won - der - ful, I love you!

MY HERO
Copyright © 1993 by BEAM ME UP MUSIC (ASCAP), c/o CPP/BELWIN, INC., Miami, FL 33014
All Rights Reserved
By OSCAR STRAUS
Slow waltz tempo
Come! come! I love you on - ly, my heart is true.
Come! come! my life is lone - ly,
I long for you;
Come! come! naught can ef - face you; my arms are ach - ing now to em - brace you.
Thou are di - vine!
Come! come! I love you on - ly; come, he - ro mine!
MY LITTLE GRASS SHACK IN KEALAKEKUA, HAWAII
Copyright © 1933 (Renewed 1961) EMI MILLER CATALOG INC.
All Rights Reserved
Words and Music by
BILL COGSWELL, TOMMY HARRISON and JOHNNY NOBLE
Moderately
I want to go back to my lit - tle grass shack in Ke - a - la - ke - kua, Ha - wai - i.
I want to be with all the ka - nes and wa - hi - nes that I knew long a - go.
I can hear old gui - tars a - play - ing on the beach at Ho - o - nau - nau;
I can hear the Ha - wai - ians say - ing, "Ko - mo - mai no ka - u - a i - ka ha - le we - la - ka - hao."
It won't be long till my ship will be sail - ing back to Ko - na,
a grand old place that's al - ways fair to see.
I'm just a lit - tle Ha - wai - ian and a home - sick Is - land boy;
I want to go back to my fish and poi.
I want to go back to my lit - tle grass shack in Ke - a - la - ke - kua, Ha - wai - i,
where the Hu - mu - hu - mu, Nu - ku - nu - ku a pu - a - a goes swim - ming by,
where the Hu - mu - hu - mu, Nu - ku - mu - ku a pu - a - a goes swim - ming by.

From the Columbia Motion Picture "FUNNY GIRL"

MY MAN

Words by ALBERT WILLEMETZ
and JACQUES CHARLES
English lyric by
CHANNING POLLOCK
Music by
MAURICE YVAIN

Moderately
Oh, my man I love him so, he'll nev - er know. All my life is just de - spair, but I don't care. When he takes me in his
arms the world is bright all right. What's the dif-f'rence if I say I'll go a - way, when I know I'll come back
on my knees some day? For what-ev - er my man is I am his for - ev - er - more!
NOW AND FOREVER
Music and Lyrics by
RICHARD MARX
Copyright © 1993 by CHI-BOY MUSIC (ASCAP) Used by Permission
All Rights Reserved
Slowly
Verse:
1.When - ev - er I'm wear - y from the bat - tles that rage in my head, you make sense of
2.Some-times I just hold you, too caught up in me to see I'm hold - ing a
(3rd time Instrumental solo ad lib....
mad - ness when my san - i - ty hangs by a thread. I lose my way, but still you seem to un - der - stand.
for - tune that heav-en has giv - en to me. I'll try to show you each and ev - 'ry way I can,
... end solo) Un - til the day the o - cean does - n't touch the sand,
To Coda
Now and for - ev - er, I will be your man.
now and for - ev - er, I will be your man.
now and for - ev - er, I will be your man.
Bridge:
Now I can rest my wor - ries and al-ways be sure that I won't be a - lone an - y - more. If I'd on - ly known
you were there all the time, all this time.
D.C. al Coda
Coda
Now and for - ev - er, I will be your man.

MY MELANCHOLY BABY

Words by GEORGE A. NORTON
Music by ERNIE BURNETT

Moderately
Come to me my mel - an - cho - ly ba - by. Cud - dle up and don't be blue. All your fears are fool - ish fan - cy may - be. You know, dear, that I'm in love with you.
Ev - 'ry cloud must have a sil - ver lin - ing. Wait un - til the sun shines through. Smile, my hon - ey dear while I kiss a - way each tear or else I shall be mel - an - cho - ly too.
MY MELODY OF LOVE
Copyright © 1973, 1974 by EDITION RHYTHMUS ROLF BUDDE KG GERMANY and RADIO MUSIC INTERNATIONAL LUXEMBOURG.
English and Polish Lyrics by BOBBY VINTON
German Lyrics by GEORGE BUSCHOR
Music by HENRY MAYER
Moderately
Verse:
1. I'm look-ing for a place to go, so I can be all a - lone from thoughts and mem-o - ries, so that when the mu-sic plays I don't go back to the days when love was you and me.
wish I had a place to hide all my sor-row, all my pride. I just can't get a - long, 'cause the love, once so fine, keeps on hurt-in' all the time. Where did I go wrong? Oh,
Chorus:
1.2. Mo - ja dro-ga ja-cie ko-cham means that I love you so. Mo - ja dro-ga ja-cie ko-cham more than you'll ev - er know, ko-cham cie-bie ca-lem ser - ce, love you with all my heart.
3. la la la la la la la la, my mel-o-dy of love. La la la la la la la la, my mel - o - dy of love. La la la la la la la la, my mel - o - dy of love.
Re-turn to me and al-ways be my mel - o - dy of love.
D.S. 𝄋
2. I
Repeat ad lib. and fade
love. Oh,

MY MOTHER'S EYES

Words by WOLFE GILBERT
Music by ABEL BAER

Moderately

C Cmaj7 C7 F Fm Fm6 C/G Am7 D7 Dm7/G G7 1. C Am7 Dm7 G7

One bright and guid-ing light that taught me wrong from right, I found in my moth-er's eyes.
Those ba - by tales she told, that road all paved with gold, I found in my moth-er's

2. C F/C C F6 E7 Am Adim7 B7 E7 Em7 A7 D7 Am7 D7 G7 C♯dim7

eyes. Just like a wan-d'ring spar-row, one lone-ly soul, I walked the straight and nar-row to reach my

Dm7 G7 C Cmaj7 C7 F Fm Fm6 C/E Am7 D7 Dm7/G G7 C

goal. God's gift sent from a - bove. a real un - self - ish love I found in my moth-er's eyes.

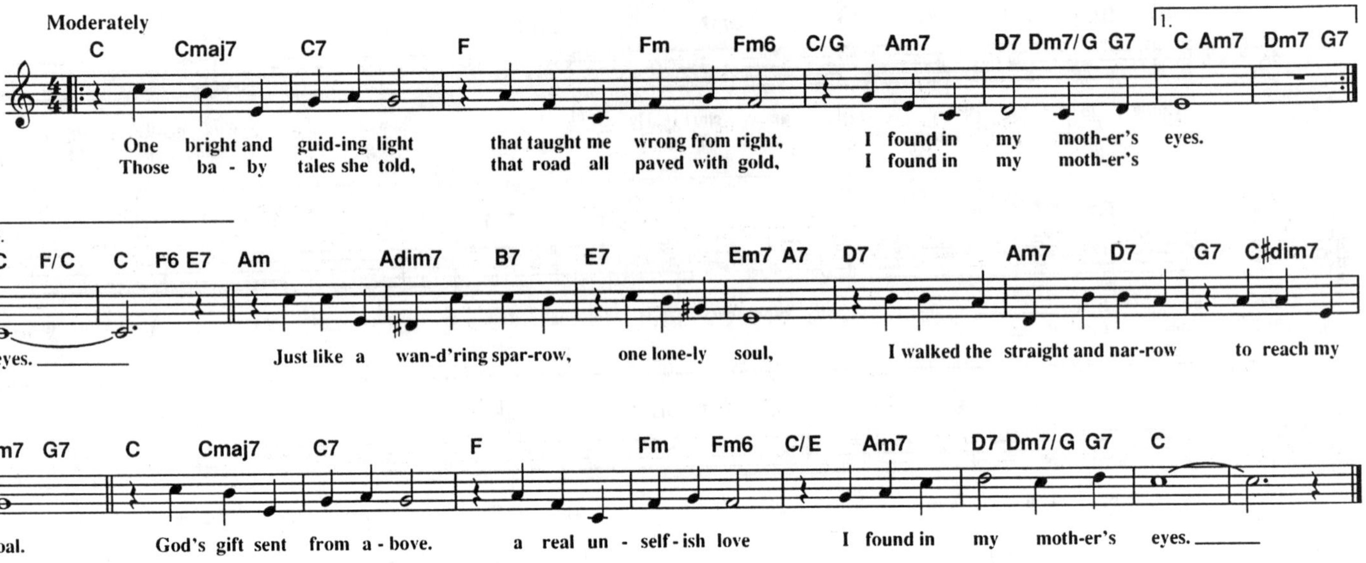

MY OLD FLAME

Words and Music by
ARTHUR JOHNSTON
and SAM COSLOW

Moderately slow

G Bm Bm7(♭5) E7 Am7 A7(♭5) D7(♭5) G6 C7 F7

My old flame, I can't e - ven think of his name. But it's fun - ny now and then, how my

B♭ E♭7 D7 E♭7 Am7 D7(♭9) D7(♯5) G Bm Bm7(♭5) E7 Am7

thoughts go flash-ing back a - gain, to my old flame. My old flame; my new lov-ers all seem so

A7(♭5) D7(♭5) G6 C7 F7 B♭ E♭7 D7 E♭7 F7 B♭6

tame, for I have-n't met a gent so mag - ni - fi - cent or el - e - gant as my old flame. I've met so man-y who had

Cm6 A♭7 G7 C9 F9 D7

fas - ci - na-tin' ways, a fas - ci - na-tin' gaze in their eyes; some who took me up to the skies. But

A7 D9 D7(♯5 ♭9) G Bm Bm7(♭5) E7 Am7

their at-tempts at love were on - ly im - i - ta-tions of my old flame, I can't e - ven think of his

A7(♭5) D7(♭9) G6 C7 F7 B♭ E♭7 D7sus D7(♯5 ♭9) G6

name. But I'll nev - er be the same un - til I dis - cov - er what be-came of my old flame.

MY OLD KENTUCKY HOME
© 1993 BEAM ME UP MUSIC (ASCAP), c/o WARNER BROS. PUBLICATIONS U.S. INC., Miami, FL 33014
All Rights Reserved
Words and Music by
STEPHEN C. FOSTER
Slowly
Verse:
1. The sun shines bright in my old Ken - tuck - y home; 'tis sum - mer, the folks there are gay. The corn top's ripe, and the mead - ow's in the bloom, while the birds make mu - sic all the day. 2. The
young folks roll on the lit - tle cab - in floor, all mer - ry, all hap - py and bright. By'n by, hard times come a - knock - in' at the door; then, my old Ken - tuck - y home, good- night.
Chorus:
Weep no more, my la - dy; oh, weep no more to - day. We will sing one song for the old Ken-tuck-y home, for the old Ken-tuck-y home far a - way. 3. They way.
D.S. 𝄋
Verse 3:
They hunt no more for the 'possum and the 'coon
On the meadow, the hill and the shore;
They sing no more by the glimmer of the moon
On the bench by that old cabin door.
Verse 4:
The day goes by like a shadow o'er the heart,
With sorrow where all was delight;
The time has come when the old friends have to part,
Then, my old Kentucky home, good night.
(To Chorus:)
Verse 5:
The head must bow and the back will have to bend
Wherever the poor folks may go;
A few more days, and the trouble all will end
In the field where the sugar canes grow.
Verse 6:
A few more days for to tote the weary load;
No matter, 'twill never be light.
A few more days till we totter on the road,
Then, my old Kentucky home, good night.
(To Chorus:)
MY HEART STOOD STILL
(From "A Connecticut Yankee")
© 1927 WARNER BROS. INC. (Renewed)
Rights for the Extended Renewal Term in the United States Controlled by THE ESTATE OF LORENZ HART and WILLIAMSON MUSIC
All Rights behalf of THE ESTATE OF LORENZ HART Administered by WB MUSIC CORP.
All Rights Reserved
Words by LORENZ HART
Music by RICHARD RODGERS
Slow but liltingly (Molto tranquillo)
dolciccimo
I took one look at you, that's all I meant to do; and then My heart stood still! still!
My feet could step and walk, my lips could move and talk, and yet
Though not a sin - gle word was spo - ken, I could tell you knew, that un - felt clasp of hands told me so well you knew.
rall. a tempo
I nev - er lived at all, un - till the thrill of that mo - ment when my heart stood still.

From the Broadway Musical Production "SWEET CHARITY"

MY PERSONAL PROPERTY

Words by DOROTHY FIELDS
Music by CY COLEMAN

Brightly

B♭ F/A Gm B♭7 E♭ Gm7 Cm7 F7 B♭ D7

To-day I feel New York is real-ly my per-son-al prop-er-ty, right down Broad-way to Cit-y Hall.
The Zoo in Cen-tral Park is mere-ly my pri-vate me-nag-er-ie; I've carved my name on ev-'ry tree.

Fm6 G7 C/E E♭dim7 B♭/D Em7(♭5) A7 Dm7 D♭7(♯5)

Ev-'ry su-per-mar-ket, ev-'ry five-and-ten, all of Lin-coln Cen-ter and the great U. N., they're all
From Yon-kers Race-way to Bowl-ing Green, I own ev-'ry-thing a-round and in be-tween. It's all

C7 1. F7 B♭ F7 2. F7 B♭ F7 Fm D♭ Fm7 B♭7

my per-son-al prop-er-ty. prop-er-ty. The Plan-e-tar-i-um is mine a-lone, the
my per-son-al

E♭m C♭ Cm7(♭5) F7 Gm F7 B♭ F/A Gm Gm/F Cm/E♭ Gm7 B♭m6 Cm7

old A-quar-i-um I al-so own. And since I feel to-day New York is real-ly my per-son-al prop-er-ty, I'll tell you

F7 Dm G7 G7(♭9) G Cm Cm7 F7 Dm7 G7 Cm7 E♭/F F7 B♭

what I'm gon-na do: since I like you ver-y much, so ver-y, ver-y much, I'm gon-na split it with you.

Melody based on Claude Debussy's "REVERIE"

MY REVERIE

By LARRY CLINTON

Slowly

Dm7 G7 Cmaj7 C6 Dm7 G7 C *To Coda* Dm7 G7 C

Our love is a dream, but in my rev-er-ie I can see that this love was meant for me.
love me as I love you in my rev-er-ie. Make my dream a re-al-i-ty.

Am Em Dm Am Em Dm Dm7 G7 C

On-ly a poor fool nev-er schooled in the whirl-pool of ro-mance could be so cruel as you are to me.

C9 Fmaj7 F6 Fmaj7 F6 B♭9 B♭9(♭5) A7(♭5) *D.C. al Coda*

My dreams are as worth-less as tin to me. With-out you, life will nev-er be-gin to be. So

Coda

Am F♯m7(♭5) B7 B7(♭9)/D♯ Dm7 G7 G7(♯5) C

Let's dis-pense with for-mal-i-ty. Come to me in my rev-er-ie.

MY WAY

Original French Words by GILES THIBAULT
English Words by PAUL ANKA
Music by JACQUES REVAUX and CLAUDE FRANCOIS

Slowly

Verse:

𝄋 C | Em/B | Gm6/B♭ | A7 | Dm

1. And now the end is near, and so I face the fi - nal cur - tain. My friend, I'll say it
grets, I had a few, but then a - gain, too few to men - tion. I did what I had to
loved, I've laughed and cried. I've had my fill, my share of los - ing. And now, as tears sub -

Dm7 | G7 | C | C7 | F

clear, I'll state my case, of which I'm cer - tain. I've lived a life that's full, I trav-eled each and ev - 'ry
do, and saw it through with-out ex - cemp-tion. I planned each chart-ered course, each care-ful step a - long the
side, I find it all so a - mus - ing. To think I did all that, and may I say, "Not in a

Fm | C | G7 | 1. F6 | C | 2.3. F6 | C

high - way. And more, much more than this, I did it my way. 2. Re - my way. Yes there were
by - way. And more, much more than this, I did it
shy way." Oh no, oh no, not me. I did it
For what is a

Chorus:

C7 | F | Dm7 | G7

times, I'm sure you knew when I bit off more than I could chew. But through it all, when there was doubt, I ate it
man, what has he got, if not him - self, then he has not to say the things he tru - ly feels, and no the

Em7 | Am | Dm7 | G7 | 1. Dm G7 | C *D.S.* 𝄋 | 2. Dm G7 | C

up, and spit it out. I faced it all, and I stood tall and did it my way. 3. I've my way.
words of one who kneels. The rec-ord shows I took the blows, and did it

MY WILD IRISH ROSE

Words and Music by CHAUNCEY OLCOTT

Moderately
B♭ E♭m/B♭ B♭ E♭ B♭ Bdim F7/C F7 B♭ Bdim
My wild I - rish rose, the sweet-est flow'r that grows. You may search ev - 'ry - where, but
wild I - rish rose, the dear-est flow'r that grows. And some day for my sake, she
F7/C F7 B♭ C7 F7 Cm7/F F7 B♭ E♭ B♭/D C7 F7 B♭
1.
2.
none can com - pare with my wild I - rish rose. My take the bloom from my wild I - rish rose.
may let me

MYSTERY

Words and Music by
ROD TEMPERTON

Moderately slow
Dmaj7 C♯m7 Bm7 F♯m7 C♯m7 Bm7
Verse:
F♯m9 B/F♯ F♯m9
1. Turn-in' back the hands of time, hold-in' on to mis-ty mem-'ries; chas-in' sha-dows through
2. Dia-monds shin-in' in the night; ly-in' soft and warm to-geth-er; on-ly im-ag-es
B/F♯ Bm7 C♯m7
the night; try'n' to find that hap-py end-ing. Reach-ing out for an-oth-er chance at heav-en, we can
sur-vive. Can't this dream go on for-ev-er? There is still time to lock a-way the sad-ness. Let the
Dmaj7 D/E
Chorus:
F♯m9 C♯m7
still find the way if we try. You got-ta be-lieve in the (1.4.) mys-ter-y how it used to be. We were
se-crets of love start to smile. It's on-ly be-liev-in' the (2.3.) mys-ter-y, like it used to be. Ba-by,
Bm7 G♯m7 C♯7 F♯m9 C♯m7
more than lone-ly drift-ers in the dark. Oh, I can re-mem-ber the sun in-side when love held us tight. Can't you
bring back all the pas-sion to my life. Oh, don't you re-mem-ber the ten-der days, all the love we made? Can't we
1.
D.S. 𝄋
2. To Next Strain
Bm7 G♯m7 Gmaj7 F♯m9 B/F♯ G♯m7 Gmaj7
see I need that mag-ic in my heart, in-stead of it tear-ing a-part? night?
feel that warm sen-sa-tion here to-
3.4. etc.
Repeat ad lib. and fade
Bridge:
G♯m7 Gmaj7 Dmaj7 C♯m7 Bm7
night? You got-ta be-lieve in the Lone-ly spir-its seem to whis-per in the wind. It's a
heart. It's on-ly be-liev-in' the
F♯m9 E6 Dmaj7 C♯m7 Bm7
si-lent song that's nev-er meant to be. Since the dawn of time the mys-t'ry nev-er ends; we can
D.S.S. 𝄋𝄋
Gmaj7 E7sus Fm7 F♯m9 B/F♯
find for-ev-er if we let love rise a-gain. 3. Won't you

Verse 3: (D.S.S.)
Won't you reach for another chance at heaven?
We can still find the way if we try.
It's only believin' in the . . .
(To Chorus:)

M-I-S-S-I-S-S-I-P-P-I

Lyrics by BERT HANLON and BENNY RYAN
Music by HARRY TIERNEY

M-O-T-H-E-R

Lyrics by HOWARD JOHNSON
Music by THEODORE MORSE

Moderately
Verse:
When I was sev - en years of age, I used to go to school, And when it came to spell - ing, I was aw - ful as a rule. I could - n't spell a sin - gle word when "S' s" were con - cerned. I've tried to o - ver - come my lisp, and suc - cess came in re - turn. Now that word Mis - sis - sip - pi was aw - ful hard to spell. But now I will con - vince you that I can spell it well.
lot of words would puz - zle me; ba - na - nas was no cinch. Sas - a - pa - ril - la, that was hard, though I'd spell it in a pinch. But words like Cin - cin - nat - i, Psy - cho - lo - gi - cal and such, gee, when it came to spell - ing those I sure - ly was in Dutch. I can't spell Cin - der - el - la and sau - sa - ges, that's tough. But I can spell Mis - sis - sip - pi, and be - lieve me that's e - nough.
Chorus:
M - I - S - S - I - S - S - I - P - P - I, that used to be so hard to spell, it used to make me cry. But since I've stud - ied spell - ing, it's just like pump - kin pie; M - I - S - S - I - S - S - I - P - P - I. A I.
Moderately
"M" is for the mil - lion things she gave me; "O" means on - ly that she's grow - ing old. "T" is for the tears were shed to save me; "H" is for her heart of pur - est gold. "E" is for her eyes, with love - light shin - ing; "R" means right, and right she'll al - ways be. Put them all to - geth - er, they spell "MOTH - ER," a word that means the world to me.

THE NEARNESS OF YOU

Words by NED WASHINGTON
Music by HOAGY CARMICHAEL

Slowly

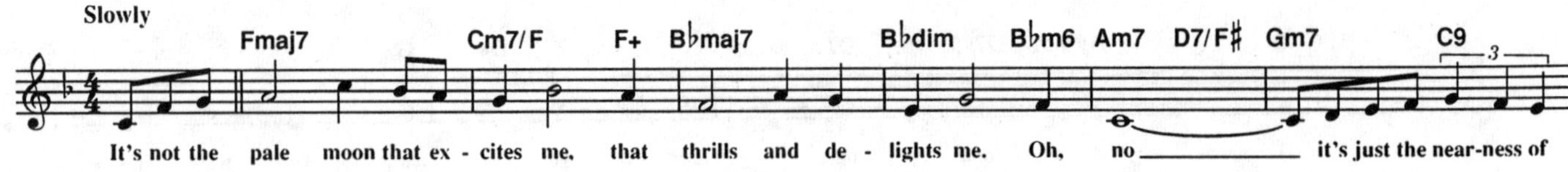
Fmaj7 Cm7/F F+ B♭maj7 B♭dim B♭m6 Am7 D7/F♯ Gm7 C9
It's not the pale moon that ex - cites me, that thrills and de - lights me. Oh, no ___ it's just the near-ness of

F6 Dm7 Gm7 C9 Fmaj7 Cm7/F F+ B♭maj7 B♭dim B♭m6 Am7 D7/F♯
you. ___ It is - n't your sweet con - ver - sa - tion that brings this sen - sa - tion. Oh, no ___

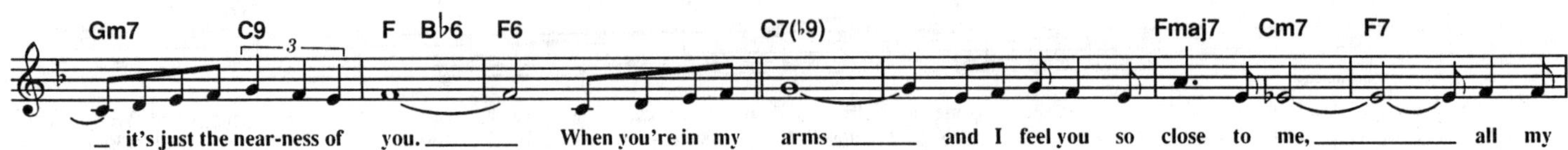
Gm7 C9 F B♭6 F6 C7(♭9) Fmaj7 Cm7 F7
___ it's just the near-ness of you. ___ When you're in my arms ___ and I feel you so close to me, ___ all my

B♭ D9 D7(♭9) Gm7 E♭7 C9 Fmaj7 Cm7/F F+ B♭maj7 B♭dim B♭m6
wild - est dreams come true. ___ I need no soft lights to en - chant me if you'll on - ly grant me the

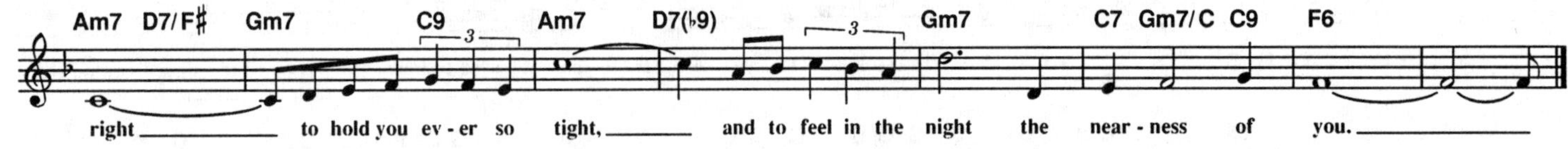
Am7 D7/F♯ Gm7 C9 Am7 D7(♭9) Gm7 C7 Gm7/C C9 F6
right ___ to hold you ev - er so tight, ___ and to feel in the night the near - ness of you. ___

NEVER BEEN TO SPAIN

Words and Music by HOYT AXTON

Rock blues feel

C G
1. Well, I nev - er been to Spain, ___ but I kind - a like the mus - ic. I hear the la - dies are in -
Eng - land, but I kind - a like the Beat - les. Oh, I head - ed for Las
Heav - en, but I've been to O - kla - ho - ma. Oh, they tell me I was

C G D
sane ___ there, and they sure know how to use it. They don't a - buse it; they'll nev - er
Ve - gas; on - ly made it out to Need - les. Can you feel it? It must be
born ___ there, but I real - ly don't re - mem - ber. In O - kla - ho - ma, not Ar - i -

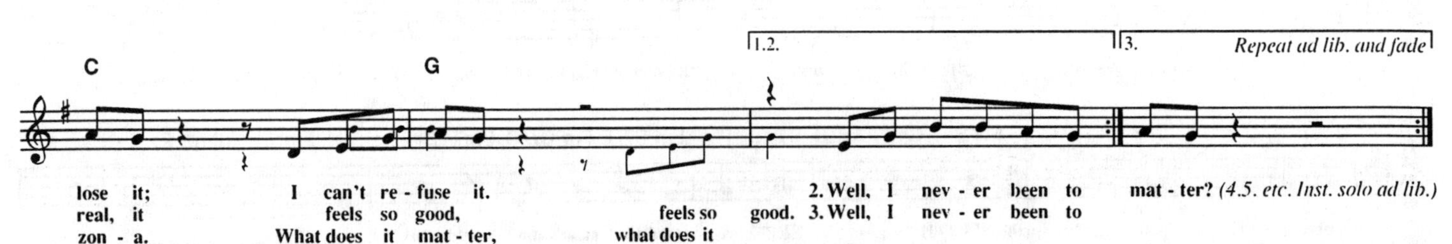
C G
1.2. 3. Repeat ad lib. and fade
lose it; I can't re - fuse it. 2. Well, I nev - er been to mat - ter? (4.5. etc. Inst. solo ad lib.)
real, it feels so good, feels so good. 3. Well, I nev - er been to
zon - a. What does it mat - ter, what does it

NEEDLES AND PINS

Words and Music by
SONNY BONO and JACK NITZSCHE

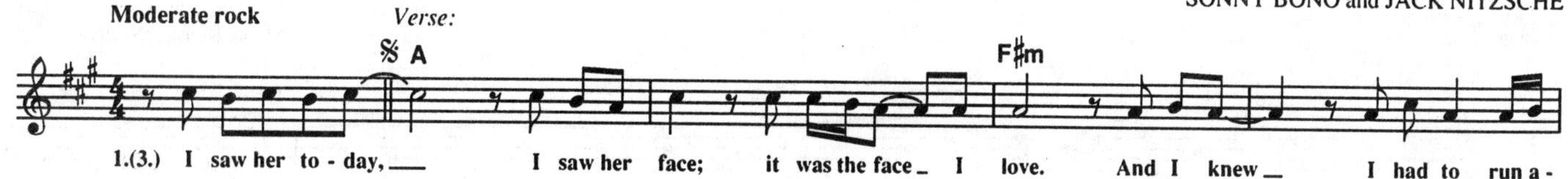
Moderate rock
Verse:
A
F♯m
1.(3.) I saw her to - day, I saw her face; it was the face I love. And I knew I had to run a -

A
F♯m
Chorus:
A
F♯m
way and get down on my knees and pray that there'd come a day. (1.3.) But still it be-gins a; nee-dles and pins a;

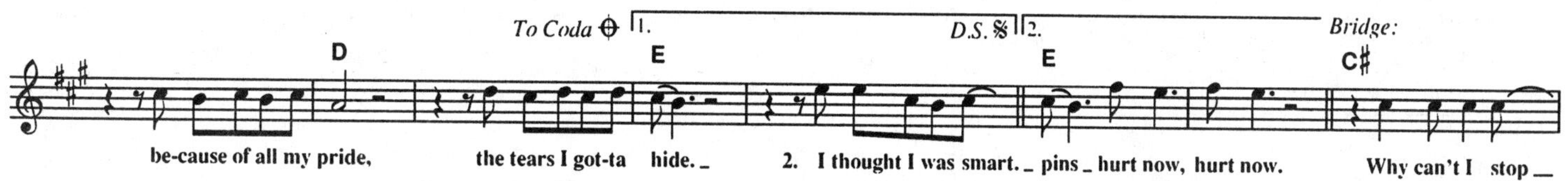
D
To Coda
1.
E
D.S.
2.
E
Bridge:
C♯
be-cause of all my pride, the tears I got-ta hide. 2. I thought I was smart. pins hurt now, hurt now. Why can't I stop

B
A
G♯
N.C.
D.S. al Coda
and tell my-self I'm wrong, I'm wrong, so wrong? Why can't I stand up and tell my-self I'm strong? 3. Be-cause I saw her to-day,

Coda
E
A
hide. Nee-dles and pins, nee-dles and pins, nee-dles and pins.

Verse 2:
I thought I was smart,
I broke her heart;
She didn't think I'd do.
But now I see she's lost her care for me.
Let her go ahead, chase his love instead.
And one day she will see . . .
(To Chorus 2:)

Chorus 2:
. . . Just how to say please-a,
And get down on her knees-a.
Yeah, that's how it begins-a.
She'll feel those needles and pins
Hurt now, hurt now.
(To Bridge:)

NOBODY KNOWS THE TROUBLE I'VE SEEN

TRADITIONAL SPIRITUAL

Slowly
F B♭ F B♭ F B♭ F C7
No-bod - y knows the trou-ble I've seen; no-bod - y knows but Je - sus. No-bod - y knows the trou-ble I've seen; glo - ry hal - le -
1. To Next Strain
2. Fine
F F F C F G9 C7 F
D.C. al Fine
lu - jah! Some - lu - jah! times I'm up, some - times I'm down; oh, yes, Lord! Some-times I'm al-most to the ground; Oh, yes, Lord!

From the Broadway Show "ON THE TOWN"

NEW YORK, NEW YORK

Words by BETTY COMDEN and ADOLPH GREEN
Music by LEONARD BERNSTEIN

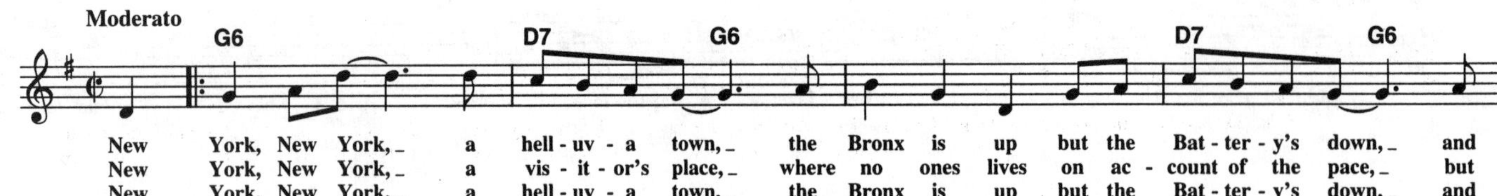
Moderato
G6
D7
G6
D7
G6
New York, New York, a hell-uv-a town, the Bronx is up but the Bat-ter-y's down, and
New York, New York, a vis-it-or's place, where no ones lives on ac-count of the pace, but
New York, New York, a hell-uv-a town, the Bronx is up but the Bat-ter-y's down, and

1.2.
D7
G6
F7
B♭
D7
G
D7
peo-ple ride in a hole in the ground; New York, New York, it's a hell-uv-a town! New
sev-en mil-lion are scream-ing for space; New York, New York, is a vis-it-or's place! New
peo-ple ride in a hole in the ground; New

3.
B♭
D7
G
C7
G6
E♭
D9
G
York, New York, it's a hell-uv-a-town!

NEVER ENDING SONG OF LOVE

Words and Music by
DELANEY BRAMLETT

Moderately
C
G7
C
1.2. I've got a nev-er end-ing
3.4. nev-er end-ing
love for you; from now on, that's all I want to do. From the first

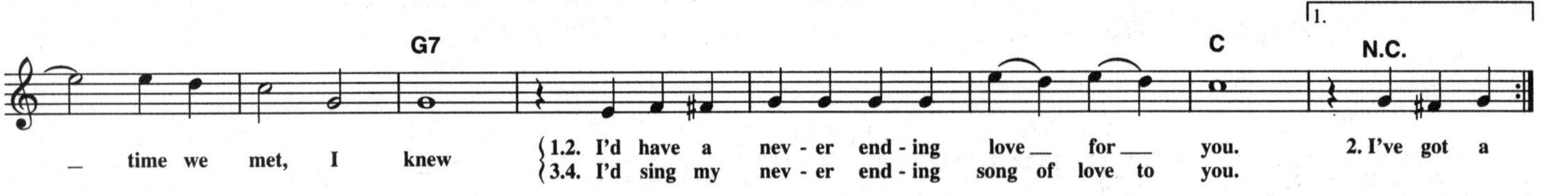
G7
C
1.
N.C.
time we met, I knew
1.2. I'd have a nev-er end-ing love for you.
3.4. I'd sing my nev-er end-ing song of love to you.
2. I've got a

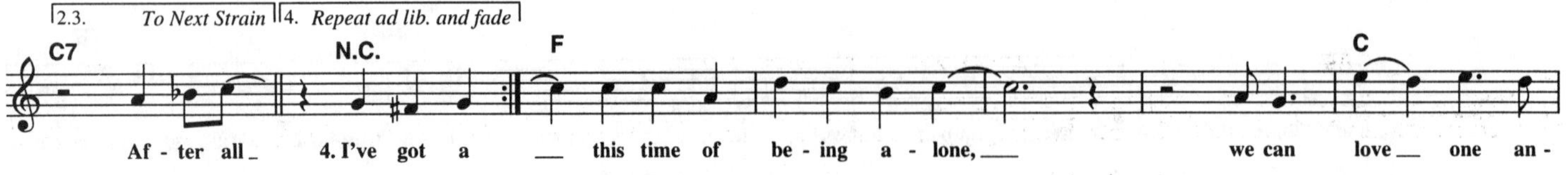
2.3. To Next Strain
4. Repeat ad lib. and fade
C7
N.C.
F
C
Af-ter all 4. I've got a this time of be-ing a-lone, we can love one an-

D.S. 𝄋
F
G
oth-er, feel for each oth-er from now on. Feels so good I can hard-ly stand it.

From the United Artists Motion Picture "NEVER ON SUNDAY"

NEVER ON SUNDAY

Words by BILLY TOWNE
Music by MANOS HADJIDAKIS

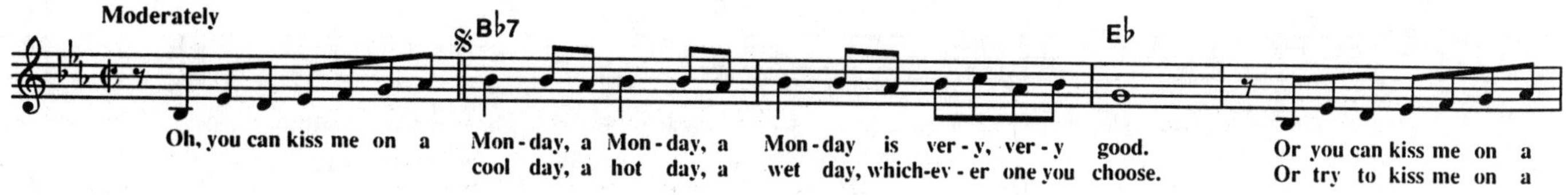
Moderately
B♭7
E♭
Oh, you can kiss me on a Mon-day, a Mon-day, a Mon-day is ver-y, ver-y good. Or you can kiss me on a
cool day, a hot day, a wet day, which-ev-er one you choose. Or try to kiss me on a

B♭7 E♭ B♭7
Tues-day, a Tues-day, a Tues-day, in fact I wish you would. Or you can kiss me on a Wednes-day, a Thurs-day, a Fri-day and Sat-ur-day is
gray day, a May day, a pay day, and see if I re-fuse. And if you make it on a bleak day, a freak day, a week-day, why you can be my

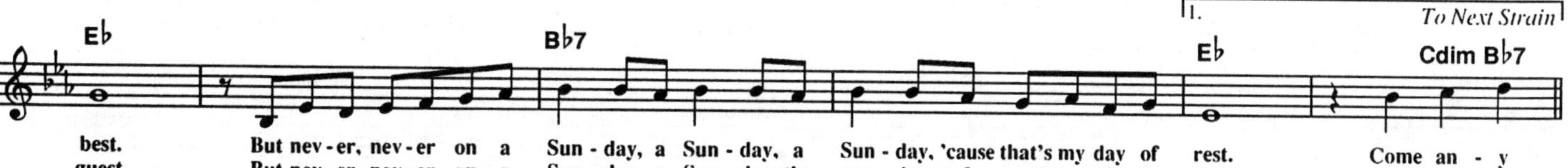
E♭ B♭7 1. To Next Strain E♭ Cdim B♭7
best. But nev-er, nev-er on a Sun-day, a Sun-day, a Sun-day, 'cause that's my day of rest. Come an-y
guest. But nev-er, nev-er on a Sun-day, a Sun-day, the one day I need a lit-tle

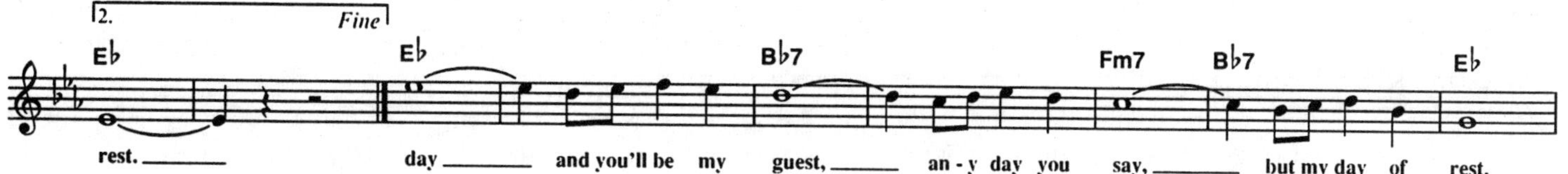
2. Fine
E♭ E♭ B♭7 Fm7 B♭7 E♭
rest. day and you'll be my guest, an-y day you say, but my day of rest.

Cdim B♭7 E♭ B♭7 Fm7 B♭7 E♭
D.S. 𝄋 al Fine
(Tacet)
Just name the day that you like the best, on-ly stay a-way on my day of rest. Oh, you can kiss me on a

NOBODY'S SWEETHEART

Words and Music by GUS KAHN, ERNIE ERDMAN,
BILLY MEYERS and ELMER SCHOEBEL

Moderately
D7 G Dm/F E7 Bm7 E7 A9 A7(♭9) A7 D7 Ddim D7
You're no-bod-y's sweet-heart now; they don't ba-by you, some-how. Fan-cy hose,

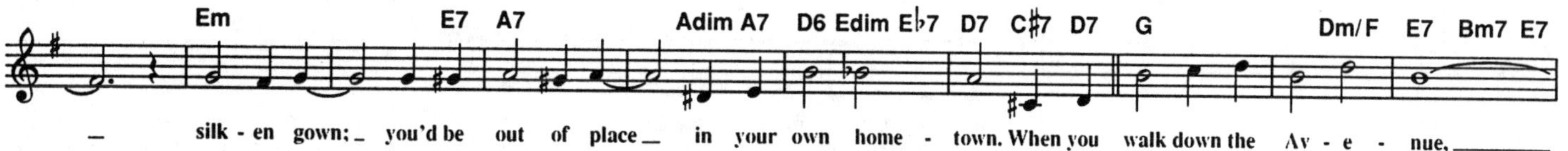
Em E7 A7 Adim A7 D6 Edim E♭7 D7 C♯7 D7 G Dm/F E7 Bm7 E7
silk-en gown; you'd be out of place in your own home-town. When you walk down the Av-e-nue,

A9 A7(♭9) A7 E♭dim G7/D C Cm G G7 E7
I just can't be-lieve that it's you; paint-ed lips, paint-ed eyes, wear-ing a bird of

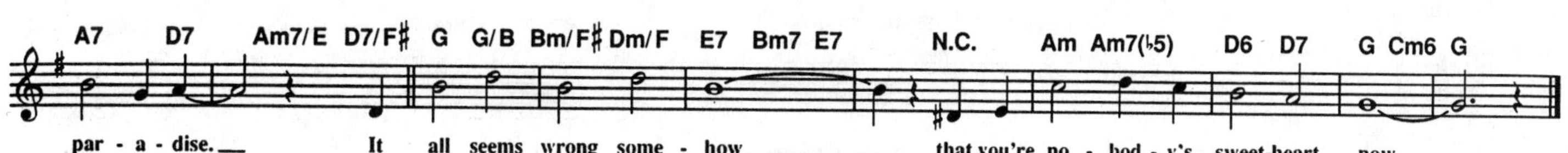
A7 D7 Am7/E D7/F♯ G G/B Bm/F♯ Dm/F E7 Bm7 E7 N.C. Am Am7(♭5) D6 D7 G Cm6 G
par-a-dise. It all seems wrong some-how that you're no-bod-y's sweet-heart now.

THE NIGHT HAS A THOUSAND EYES

Words by BUDDY BERNIER
Music by JERRY BRAININ

Moderate beguine tempo
Don't whis-per things to me you don't mean, for words deep down in - side can be seen by the night. The night
has a thou-sand eyes, and it knows a truth-ful heart from one that lies. Though ro-mance may have called in the past, my
love for you will be ev-er - last-ing and bright, as bright as the star-lit skies. And this won - d'rous night that has a thou-sand
eyes. I've lived my life walk-ing through a dream, for I knew that I would find this mo-ment su - preme, a
night of bliss and ten-der sighs, and the smil-ing down of a thou-sand eyes. The night has a thou-sand eyes.
From the United Artists Motion Picture "THE SPY WHO LOVED ME"
NOBODY DOES IT BETTER
Copyright © 1977 DANJAQ S.A.
All Rights Controlled and Administered by EMI U CATALOG INC., and EMI UNART CATALOG INC.
All Rights Reserved
Lyrics by CAROLE BAYER SAGER
Music by MARVIN HAMLISCH
Slowly
Chorus:
No-bod-y does it bet - ter
makes me feel sad for the rest.
some-times I wish some-one would.
No-bod-y does it
half as good as you. Ba - by, you're the best.
quite the way you do. Did you have to be so good.
To Coda
Verse:
1. I was - n't look - in but some-how you found me. I tried to hide from your love light.
2. The way that you hold me when-ev - er you hold me. There's some kind of mag - ic in - side you
But like heav-en a - bove me the spy who loved me is keep - in' all my se-crets safe to - night.
that keeps me from run - nin' but just kept it com - in.' How'd you learn to do the things you do?
And
1st time D.C.
2nd time D.C. al Coda
Coda
Ba - by, ba - by, ba - by, you're the best.

NOW AND FOREVER (YOU AND ME)

a/k/a You and Me (Now and Forever)

Words and Music by
JIM VALLANCE, DAVID FOSTER
and RANDY GOODRUM

Moderately slow rock

G C(9) Dsus

D *Verse:* G C(9) Dsus D G

1. Up un - til now I've learned to live _ with-out love; like a ship with-out _ a sail, _

C(9) Dsus D 𝄋 Am7 D/F♯

wan - der-ing aim - less - ly lost. I nev-er knew how _ it felt _ to lose my _ con-trol, but now that I've

Am7 C/D D *Chorus:* G Em7 Bm7

found you, ___ this is all so new. You and _ me, _ we've got a des - ti - ny ___ start-ing to - night; ___

C G/D D G Em7 1. Bm7 C/D *D.C.*

we'll be _ to-geth - er. You and _ me; _ this is what love _ should be, _ and it's gon-na be right; ___ now and _ for - ev - er.

2. *To Next Strain* Bm7 3.4. *etc.* Bm7 C/D *Repeat and fade* Am

___ if you ___ now and _ for - ev - er. tell ___ me there's a heav-en up _ a - bove, _ then

Am7(♭5)/E♭ G C(9) Dsus 1. D 2. D *D.S.* 𝄋

that's what I'll be-lieve, _ 'cause you're the one thing that I'm _ so sure _ of.

Verse 2:
**Darlin', inside your eyes, I can see mysteries there.
And you're melting the ice surrounding me. I'm no longer scared.
I feel you inside my soul, and I'm captured tonight.
But don't let go; this is paradise.** ***(To Chorus:)***

Verse 3:
**I feel you inside my soul, and I'm captured tonight.
But don't let go; this is paradise.** ***(To Chorus:)***

O PERFECT LOVE

Words and Music by
JOSEPH BARNBY

Slowly

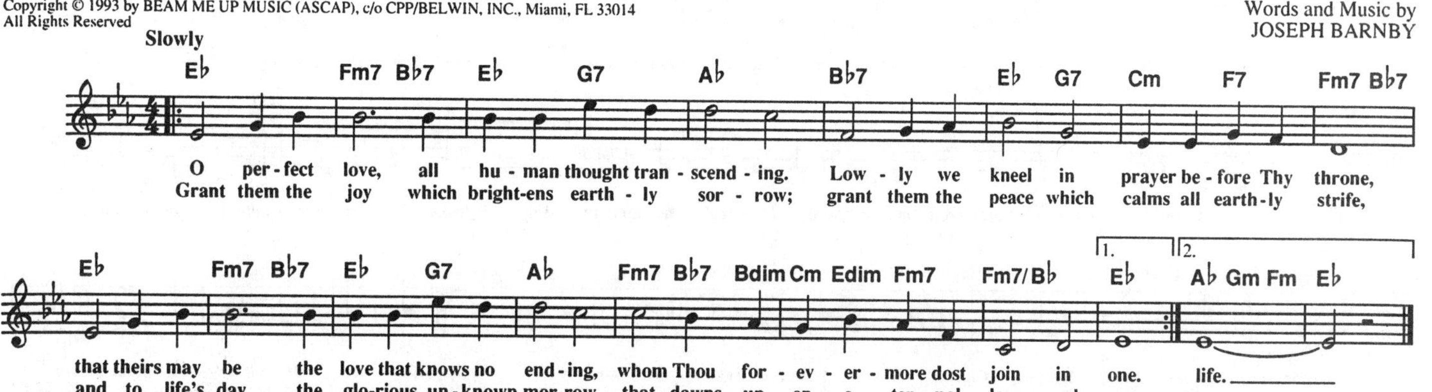
E♭ Fm7 B♭7 E♭ G7 A♭ B♭7 E♭ G7 Cm F7 Fm7 B♭7
O per - fect love, all hu - man thought tran - scend - ing. Low - ly we kneel in prayer be - fore Thy throne,
Grant them the joy which bright-ens earth - ly sor - row; grant them the peace which calms all earth-ly strife,
E♭ Fm7 B♭7 E♭ G7 A♭ Fm7 B♭7 Bdim Cm Edim Fm7 Fm7/B♭ 1. E♭ 2. A♭ Gm Fm E♭
that theirs may be the love that knows no end-ing, whom Thou for - ev - er - more dost join in one. life.
and to life's day the glo-rious un-known mor-row that dawns up - on e - ter - nal love and

NIGHT AND DAY

Words and Music by
COLE PORTER

Moderato
Edim Bb7 Eb Ebm Bb7 B7
Like the beat, beat beat, of the tom - tom; when the jun - gle shad - ows fall, like the drip, drip, drip, of the
tick, tick, tock of the state - ly clock, as it stands a - gains the wall, like the
E C7 F Fm Ddim Eb Ebm Bb Dbm6 Eb Bb7 Eb Eb6
rain-drops, when the sum - mer show'r is through; so a voice with - in me keeps re - peat - ing, you, you, you. Night and day _
Bmaj7 Bb7 Bb+ Ebmaj7 Eb6 Bmaj7 Bb7 Bb+ Ebmaj7
you are the one, _ on - ly you _ be - neath the moon and un - der the sun. _
why is it so, _ that this long - ing for you fol - lows where - ev - er I go? _
Eb6 Am7(b5) Abm7 Gm7 Gbdim
_ wheth - er near to me or far, _ it's no mat - ter, dar - ling, where you are _
_ in the roar - ing traf - fic's boom _ in the si - lence of my lone - ly room, _
I
Fm7 Fm7(b5) Bb7sus Bb7 Eb 1. 2. Gb
think of you _ night and day. _ Day and night _ _ Night and day _ un - der the
Eb Gb Abm Gb Abm Gb Abm Gb Eb
hide of me, _ there's an oh, such a hun - gry yearn - ing, burn - ing in - side of me. _ And it's
Am7(b5) Abm7 Gm7 Gbdim Fm7 Bb7 Bb7sus Eb
tor - ment won't be through _ 'til you let me spend my life mak - ing love _ to you, day and night, _ night and day. _

NINE TO FIVE

Words and Music by
DOLLY PARTON

Lively

Verse:

G C G D

1. Tum-ble out of bed and stum-ble to the kitch-en; pour my-self a cup _ of am-bi-tion, and yawn, and stretch, and try to come _ to life. _

G C G D G

Jump in the show-er, and the blood starts pump-ing; out on the street, the traf - fic starts jump-ing, with folks _ like me on the job from nine to five.

Chorus:

C G

1. Work-ing (1.3.) nine to _ five, _ what a way to make _ a liv - ing; bare - ly get - ting by, _ it's all tak-ing and _ no

2. Nine to _ five, _ for ser-vice and _ de - vo - tion; you would think _ that I _ would de - serve a fair _ pro -

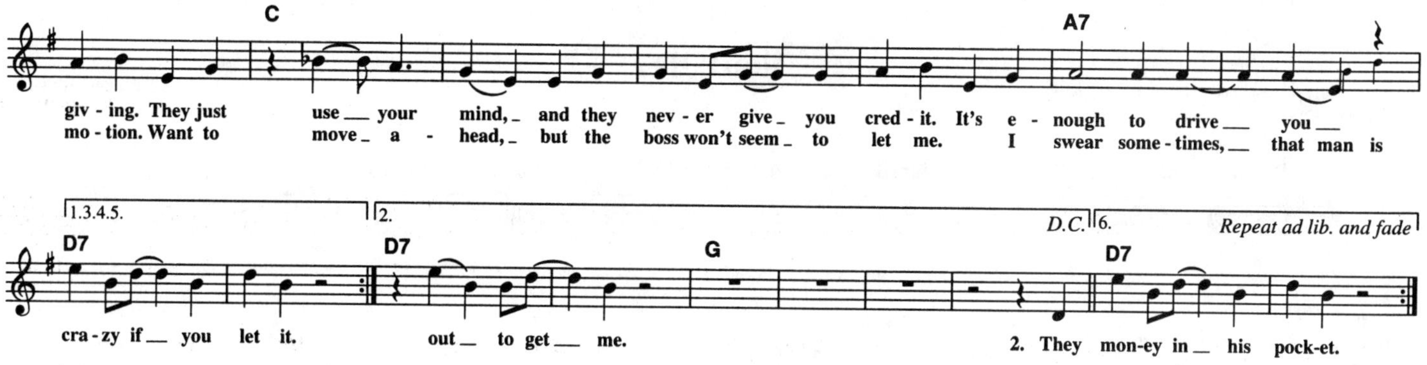

C A7

giv - ing. They just use __ your mind, _ and they nev - er give _ you cred - it. It's e - nough to drive __ you __
mo - tion. Want to move _ a - head, _ but the boss won't seem _ to let me. I swear some - times, __ that man is

1.3.4.5. D7 | 2. D7 G D.C. | 6. D7 *Repeat ad lib. and fade*

cra - zy if __ you let it. out __ to get __ me. 2. They mon - ey in __ his pock - et.

Verse 2:
They let you dream just to watch them shatter;
You're just a step on the boss man's ladder,
But you've got dreams he'll never take away.
In the same boat with a lot of your friends;
Waitin' for the day your ship'll come in,
And the tide's gonna turn, and it's all gonna roll your way.
(To Chorus)

Chorus 3: Repeat Chorus 1

Chorus 4:
Nine to five, they've got you where they want you;
There's a better life, and you dream about it, don't you?
It's a rich man's game, no matter what they call it;
And you spend your life putting money in his pocket.

Chorus 5 & 6: Repeat Chorus 1 & 4.

NO NIGHT SO LONG

Words and Music by
RICHARD KERR and
WILL JENNINGS

Slowly
Verse:

G * Bm7 C(9) G Bm7 Em7 Am7 /D D/C Bm7 Am7/D

1. An old friend told me that you just ran out of chanc-es, one _ too man-y danc-es down the nar-row street of time. ___
2. That day the long and dust - y road had us both cry - ing, we _ used up our last joke just to try to smile _ a - gain. ___

G Bm7 C(9) G Em7 Bm7/D A/C♯ A Bm

Re-mem-ber how we faced the world, like two tramps shin - ing. Please, _ don't let that mag - ic ev - er end. ___
And on - ly now I find I know what we were learn-ing, though _ it's dark and you have trav-eled far. ___

Em7 Bm7/D Am7 /D *Chorus:* G(9) Em7 C Am7/D D/C G/B Em7

Don't for-get what we learned liv - ing on _ the wind. ___
Ev - 'ry long night gives you one bright shin-ing star. ___
No night so long that you _can't find the day; no day so wrong

C Am7/D D/C Bm7 Am7 D7sus *To Coda* | 1. Am7 /D G Am7/G G Am7/G D.C.

that you _can't find _ your way; _ call on me like you used to do, _ I still can show you who _ you are. _

2. Am7 /D G Em7 C D G Em7 C D *D.S. al Coda*

I can still show _ you who _ you are. (Bkgr.) Deep in the night, you know that you'll find, deep in the night, you know that you'll _find _ the way.

Coda Am7 /D G Em7 C Am7/D D/C G/B Em7 C Am7/D *Repeat ad lib. and fade*

I can still show you who _ you are. No night so long that you can't find the day; no day so wrong that you can't find your way.

*Vocal sung one octave lower

NOBODY

Words and Music by
KYE FLEMING and
DENNIS W. MORGAN

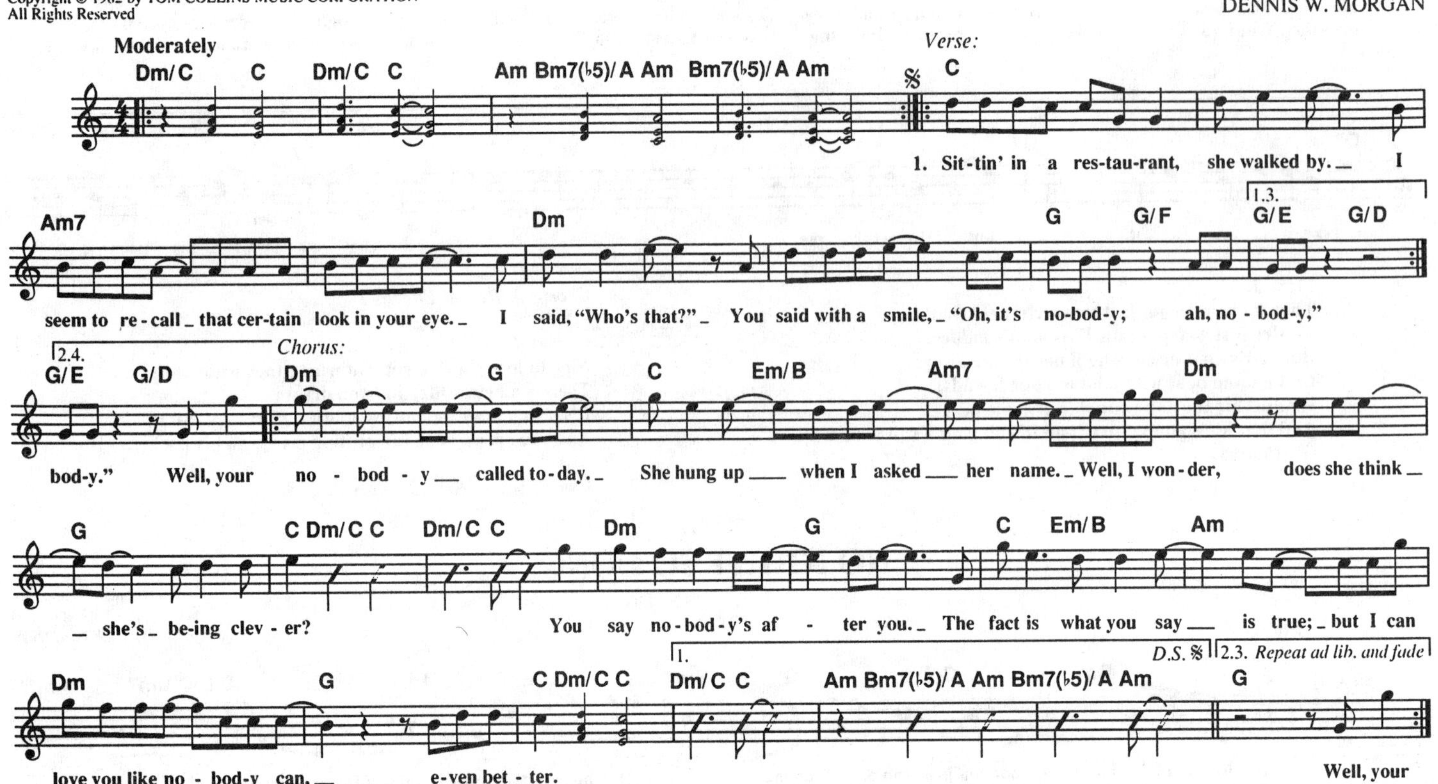
Moderately
Verse:
Dm/C C Dm/C C Am Bm7(♭5)/A Am Bm7(♭5)/A Am C
1. Sit-tin' in a res-tau-rant, she walked by. __ I
Am7 Dm G G/F 1.3. G/E G/D
seem to re-call _ that cer-tain look in your eye. _ I said, "Who's that?" _ You said with a smile, _ "Oh, it's no-bod-y; ah, no-bod-y,"
2.4. G/E G/D Chorus: Dm G C Em/B Am7 Dm
bod-y." Well, your no - bod - y __ called to-day. _ She hung up __ when I asked __ her name. _ Well, I won-der, does she think __
G C Dm/C C Dm/C C Dm G C Em/B Am
_ she's _ be-ing clev - er? You say no-bod-y's af - ter you. _ The fact is what you say __ is true; _ but I can
1. D.S. 𝄋 2.3. Repeat ad lib. and fade
Dm G C Dm/C C Dm/C C Am Bm7(♭5)/A Am Bm7(♭5)/A Am G
love you like no - bod-y can, __ e-ven bet - ter. Well, your

Verse 2:
**Maybe that explains the last two weeks.
You called me up, dead on your feet.
Workin' late again; I asked, "Who with?"
You said, "Nobody; ah nobody."**

Verse 3:
**Late last night we went for a drive.
You were miles away; I asked, "Who's on your mind?"
You said, "Nobody. Why do you ask?"
Oh, her again, I could've told you that.**

Verse 4:
**We came back home, got ready for bed.
I said to myself, "I got one shot left."
You're still mine, I won't stand in line behind
Nobody, nobody.**

NOTHING FROM NOTHING

Words and Music by
BILLY PRESTON and BRUCE FISHER

Moderately bright
C Bm7 E7 Am7 Gm7 C7 F E7 Dm7 G7
Noth-ing from noth-ing leaves noth - ing. You got-ta have some-thing if you wan-na be with me. __
C Gm7/C C7 F E7 A7 D7 G7 C
Noth-ing from noth-ing leaves noth - ing. __ You got-ta have some-thing if you wan-na be with me. __
Bm7 E7 Am7 Gm7 C7 F E7 Dm7 G7 C Gm7/C C7
I'm not try'n to be your he - ro, 'cause that ze - ro is too cold for me. __ I'm not try'n to be your high -
F E7 A7 D7 G7 C Bm7 E7 Am7 Gm7 C7
ness, 'cause that mi - nus is too low to see. __ Noth-ing from noth-ing leaves noth - ing, and I'm not
D.C. and fade out
F E7 Dm7 G7 C Gm7/C C7 F E7 A7 D7 G7 C
stuff-in' be-lieve you me. __ Don't you re-mem-ber I told ya, I'm a sol - dier in the war on pov-er-ty. __

NOBODY LOVES ME LIKE YOU DO
Copyright © 1983, 1984 by ENSIGN MUSIC CORPORATION
All Rights Reserved
Words by PAMELA PHILLIPS
Music by JAMES P. DUNNE
Slowly, with expression
1. Like a can - dle burn-ing bright love is glow-ing in your eyes. A flame to light our way; that glows bright-er ev-'ry day: now I have you: no-bod-y loves me like you do.
2. Like a leaf up - on the wind, I could find no place to land. I dreamed the hours a - way, and won-dered ev-'ry day, do dreams come true? No-bod-y loves me like you do.
3. I was words with - out a tune, I was a song with-out a tune. A po - em with no rhyme, a danc - er out of time; but now there's you. No-bod-y loves me like you do.
Chorus:
What if I nev-er met you? Where would I be right now? Fun-ny how life just falls in place some-how. You touched my heart in plac-es that I nev-er e-ven knew. No-bod-y loves me like you do.
D.C.
No-bod-y loves me, no-bod-y loves me, no-bod-y loves me like you do. No-bod-y loves me like you do.
rit.
NOCTURNE, OP. 9, NO. 2
Copyright © 1993 by BEAM ME UP MUSIC (ASCAP), c/o CPP/BELWIN, INC., Miami, FL 33014
All Rights Reserved
CHOPIN
Andante
poco rall.
a tempo
tr
poco a poco rit.

NOBODY DOES IT LIKE ME
Copyright © 1973 by CY COLEMAN and DOROTHY FIELDS
All Rights throughout the world controlled by NOTABLE MUSIC COMPANY, INC.
In Co-Publication with ALDI MUSIC COMPANY Used By Permission
All Rights Reserved
Music by CY COLEMAN
Lyric by DOROTHY FIELDS
Slow swing
1. If there's a wrong way to say it, a wrong way to play it, no - bod - y does it like me.
wrong bell, I ring it; a wrong note, I sing it; no - bod - y does it like me.
If there's a wrong way to do it, a right way to screw it up, no - bod - y does it like me.
If there's a prob - lem, I duck it; I don't solve it, I just muck it up; no - bod - y does it like me.
I've got a big loud mouth, I'm al - ways talk - ing much too free. If you
And so I try to be a la - dy; I'm no la - dy, I'm a fraud. And when I
go for tact and man - ners, bet - ter stay a - way from me. If there's a wrong way to keep it cool, a
talk like I'm a la - dy, what I sound like is a broad. If there's a wrong way to get a guy, the
right way to be a fool, no - bod - y does it like me. 2. If there's a
right way to lose a guy,
no - bod - y does it like me.
no - bod - y does it, no, no - bod - y does it, no - bod - y does it, like me.
O CHRISTMAS TREE
(O Tannenbaum)
Copyright © 1993 by BEAM ME UP MUSIC (ASCAP), c/o CPP/BELWIN, INC., Miami, FL 33014
All Rights Reserved
TRADITIONAL
Moderately
1. O Christ - mas tree, O Christ - mas tree, thy leaves are so un - chang - ing. O Christ - mas tree, O
(2. O) Christ - mas tree, O Christ - mas tree, you fill all hearts with gai - ety. O Christ - mas tree, O
(3. O) Tan - nen - baum, O Tan - nen - baum, wie treu sind dei - ne Blät - ter. O Tan - nen - baum, O
Christ - mas tree, thy leaves are so un - chang - ing. Not on - ly green when sum - mer's here, but al - so when 'tis
Christ - mas tree, you fill all hearts with gai - ety. On Christ - mas Day you stand so tall, af - ford - ing joy to
Tan - nen - baum, wie treu sind dei - ne Blät - ter. Du grünst nicht nur zur Som - mer - zeit, nein auch im Win - ter
cold and drear. O Christ - mas tree, O Christ - mas tree, thy leaves are so un - chang - ing. 2. O Blät - ter.
one and all. O Christ - mas tree, O Christ - mas tree, you fill all hearts with gai - ety. (3. O)
wenn es schneit. O Tan - nen - baum, O Tan - nen - baum, wie treu sind dei - ne

NUTBUSH CITY LIMITS

Words and Music by
TINA TURNER

Fast rock
A
Verse 1:
A
1. A church house, gin house, a school-house, out-house on High-
- way Num-ber Nine - teen, the peo-ple keep the cit - y clean.
C
They call it Nut - bush, oh
G
Nut - bush.
They call it
A
Nut - bush cit - y lim - its, Nut - bush cit - y.
2. Twen-ty
Verses 2-5:
A
five was the speed lim - it, mo-tor - cy-cle not al-lowed in it. You go to store on Fri - day, you go to
church on Sun-days.
C
They call it Nut-bush,
G
oh Nut-bush.
Said they call it
A
Nut-bush cit - y lim-its,
Nut - bush cit - y.
1.-4.
3. Yo go t'the
5.
A li'l old town on the Ten - nes-see,
quiet lit-tle old com - mu-ni-ty, one-horse town, you got to watch what you're put-tin' down
old Nut - bush. They call it Nut - bush. They call it
Nut - bush. Oh, Nut - bush.
C
G
A
They call it Nut-bush. They call it Nut-bush. Nut-bush cit - y lim-its!

Verse 3:
**You go t'the fields on week days,
And have a picnic on Labor Day.
You go to town on Saturday,
But go to church every Sunday.
They call it Nutbush, Nutbush,
They call it Nutbush city limits,
Nutbush city.**

Verse 4:
(Inst. solo ad lib.)

Verse 5:
**No Whiskey for sale,
You get drunk, no bail.
Salt pork and molasses,
Is all you get in jail.
They call it Nutbush,
Oh, Nutbush,
They call it Nutbush city limits,
Nutbush city.**

NON DIMENTICAR

(T'ho Voluto Bene)

English Words by SHELLY DOBBINS
Italian Text by MICHELE GALDIERI
Music by P.G. REDI

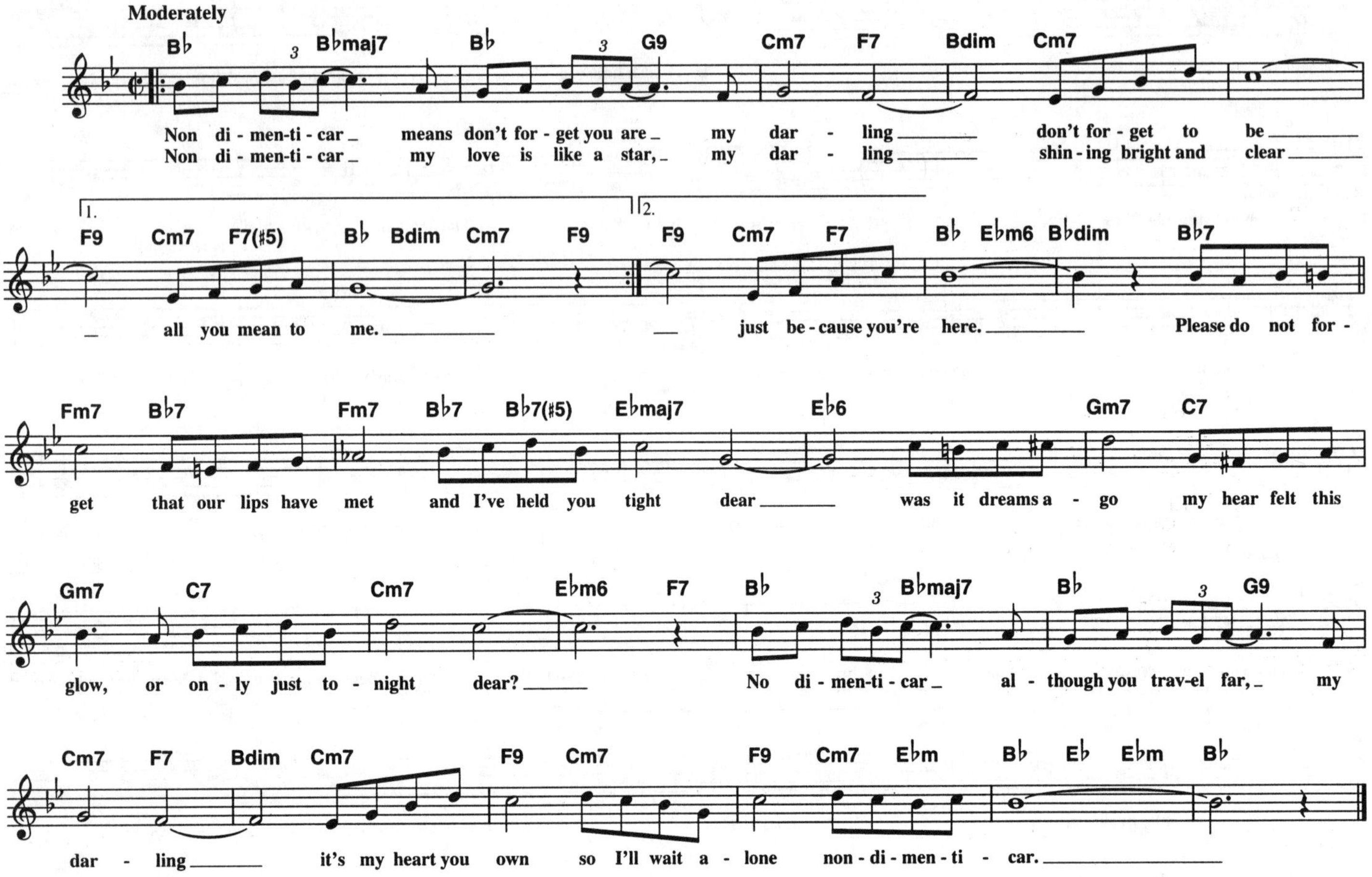

Moderately

B♭ B♭maj7 B♭ G9 Cm7 F7 Bdim Cm7

Non di - men-ti - car _ means don't for - get you are _ my dar - ling ___ don't for - get to be ___
Non di - men-ti - car _ my love is like a star, _ my dar - ling ___ shin - ing bright and clear ___

1. F9 Cm7 F7(♯5) B♭ Bdim Cm7 F9 | 2. F9 Cm7 F7 B♭ E♭m6 B♭dim B♭7

_ all you mean to me. ___ | _ just be - cause you're here. ___ Please do not for -

Fm7 B♭7 Fm7 B♭7 B♭7(♯5) E♭maj7 E♭6 Gm7 C7

get that our lips have met and I've held you tight dear ___ was it dreams a - go my hear felt this

Gm7 C7 Cm7 E♭m6 F7 B♭ B♭maj7 B♭ G9

glow, or on - ly just to - night dear? ___ No di - men-ti - car _ al - though you trav-el far, _ my

Cm7 F7 Bdim Cm7 F9 Cm7 F9 Cm7 E♭m B♭ E♭ E♭m B♭

dar - ling ___ it's my heart you own so I'll wait a - lone non - di - men - ti - car. ___

O SOLE MIO

E. DI CAPUA

Moderately
B♭7 E♭ B♭7 E♭
Che bel - la co - sa 'na iur-na - ta'e so - le, n'a - ria se - re - na dop - po 'na tem - pe - sta!
B♭7 E♭ B♭7 E♭ B♭7 E♭
Pe' - ll'a - ria fre - sca pa - re già 'na fe - sta. Che bel - la co - sa 'na iur - na ta'e so - le.
Fm B♭7 E♭ B♭7 Fm7 B♭7 E♭
Ma n'a - tu so - le ___ cchiù bel - lo ohi ne'. _ 'O so - le mi - o ___ sta - nfron - te a te. ___
A♭m E♭ B♭7 Fm7 E♭
_ 'O so - le'o so - le mi o sta - nfron - te a te, ___ sta - nfron - te a te. ___

O COME, ALL YE FAITHFUL

(Adeste Fideles)

English Words by FREDERICK OAKELEY
Latin Words Attributed to JOHN FRANCIS WADE
Music by JOHN READING

Broadly
G D G D/F♯ G C G/D D Em A7/E D A7
1. O come, all ye faith - ful, joy - ful and tri - um - phant, O come ye, O
(2. O) sing, choirs of an - gels, sing in ex - ul - ta - tion; O sing all ye
3. Yea, Lord we greet Thee born this hap - py morn - ing; Je - sus, to
D G/B D/F♯ Em7/G D/A A7 D G/B Am G Am7 D7/A G
come ye to Beth - le - hem. Come and be - hold Him,
cit - i - zens of heav'n a - bove. Glo - ry to God
Thee be glo - ry giv'n. Word of the Fa - ther,
D/F♯ G Em A/C♯ D G/B D/A G/B D7/C G/B G D/F♯ G D7/A
born the King of an - gels,
in the high - est.
now in flesh ap - pear - ing.
O come, let us a - dore Him, O come let us a -
G D/F♯ G D7/A G D7/F♯ A7/E D G/B C G/D D7 G G
1.2. 3.
dore Him, O come let us a - dore Him, Christ, the Lord. 2. O Lord.

O LITTLE TOWN OF BETHLEHEM

Words by PHILLIPS BROOKS
Music by LEWIS H. REDNER

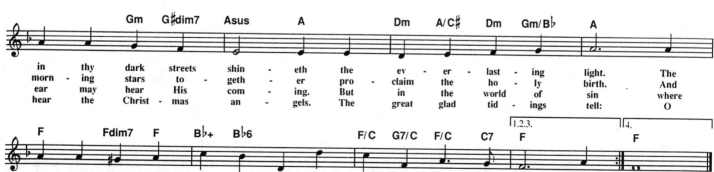

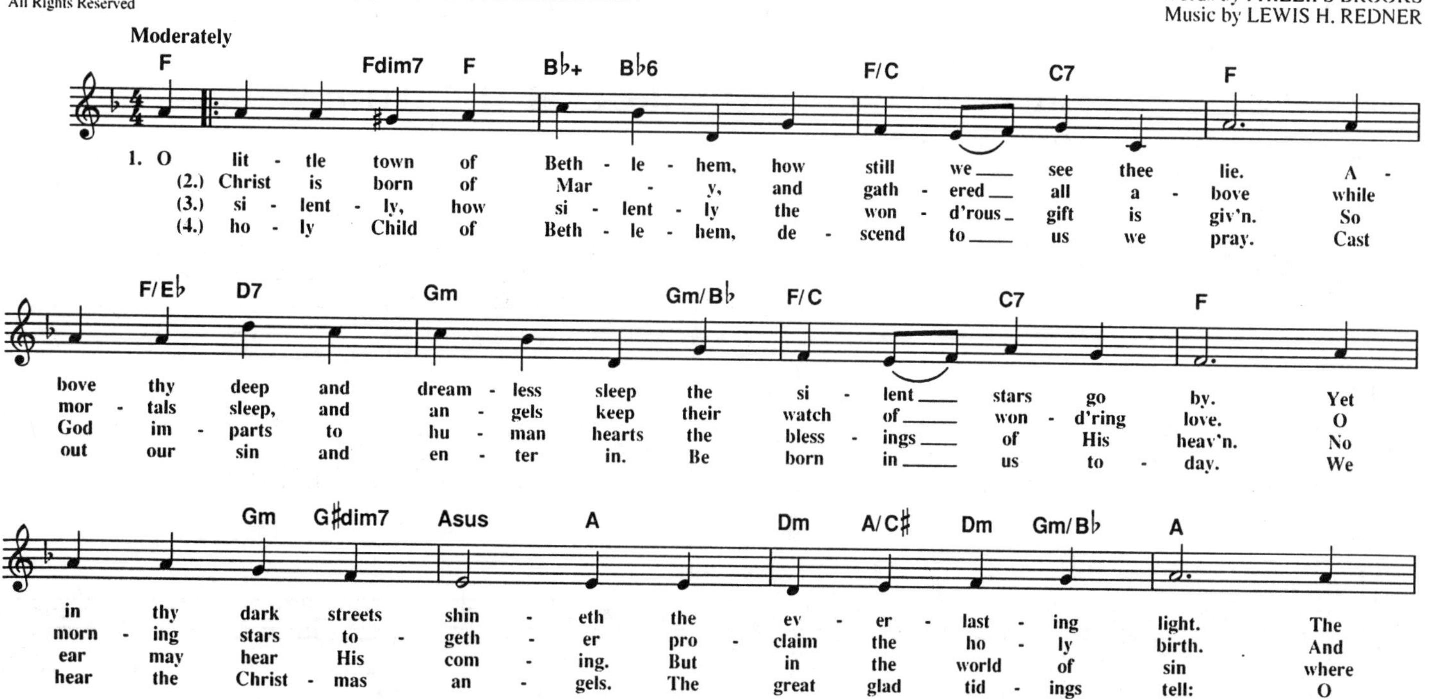
Moderately
F Fdim7 F B♭+ B♭6 F/C C7 F
1. O lit - tle town of Beth - le - hem, how still we see thee lie. A -
(2.) Christ is born of Mar - y, and gath - ered all a - bove While
(3.) si - lent - ly, how si - lent - ly the won - d'rous gift is giv'n. So
(4.) ho - ly Child of Beth - le - hem, de - scend to us we pray. Cast
F/E♭ D7 Gm Gm/B♭ F/C C7 F
bove thy deep and dream - less sleep the si - lent stars go by. Yet
mor - tals sleep, and an - gels keep their watch of won - d'ring love. O
God im - parts to hu - man hearts the bless - ings of His heav'n. No
out our sin and en - ter in. Be born in us to - day. We
Gm G♯dim7 Asus A Dm A/C♯ Dm Gm/B♭ A
in thy dark streets shin - eth the ev - er - last - ing light. The
morn - ing stars to - geth - er pro - claim the ho - ly birth. And
ear may hear His com - ing. But in the world of sin where
hear the Christ - mas an - gels. The great glad tid - ings tell: O
F Fdim7 F B♭+ B♭6 F/C G7/C F/C C7 F F
1.2.3. 4.
hopes and fears of all the years are met in thee to - night. 2. For el.
prais - es sing to God the King, and peace to men on earth. 3. How
meek souls will re - ceive Him still, the dear Christ en - ters in. 4. O
come to us, a - bide with us, our Lord Em - man - u -

O HOLY NIGHT

Words by JOHN SULLIVAN DWIGHT
Music by ADOLPHE CHARLES ADAM

Slowly

C F C G C

1. O ho - ly night, the stars are bright - ly shin - ing; it is the night of the dear Sav - ior's birth.
2. Led by the light of faith se - rene - ly beam - ing, with glow - ing hearts by His cra - dle we stand.
3. Tru - ly He taught us to love one an - oth - er; His law is love and His gos - pel is peace.

F C C7 Em B7 Em

Long lay the world in sin and er - ror pin - ing, till He ap - peared and the soul felt its worth. A
So led by light of a star sweet - ly gleam - ing, here came the wise men from the Or - ient land. The
Chains shall He break, for the slave is our broth - er, and in His name all op - pres - sion shall cease. Sweet

G7 C G7 C Am

thrill of hope, the wea - ry soul re - joic - es, for yon - der breaks a new and glo - rious morn. Fall on your
King of Kings lay in low - ly man - ger, in all our tri - als born to be our friend. He knows our
hymns of joy in grate - ful cho - rus rise we, let all with - in us praise His ho - ly name. Christ is the

Em Dm Am C G7 C F C G7

knees, oh hear the an - gel voic - es! O night di - vine, O night when Christ was
need, to our weak - ness no strang - er. Be - hold your King! Be - fore the low - ly
Lord, then ev - er, ev - er, praise we; His pow'r and glo - ry ev - er more pro -

C G G7/F C/E Dm/F C/G G7 | 1.2. C | 3. C

born! O night, O ho - ly night, O night di - vine! claim!
bend! Be - hold your King, your King be - fore Him bend!
claim, His pow'r and glo - ry ev - er more pro -

OVER THE RIVER AND THROUGH THE WOODS

TRADITIONAL

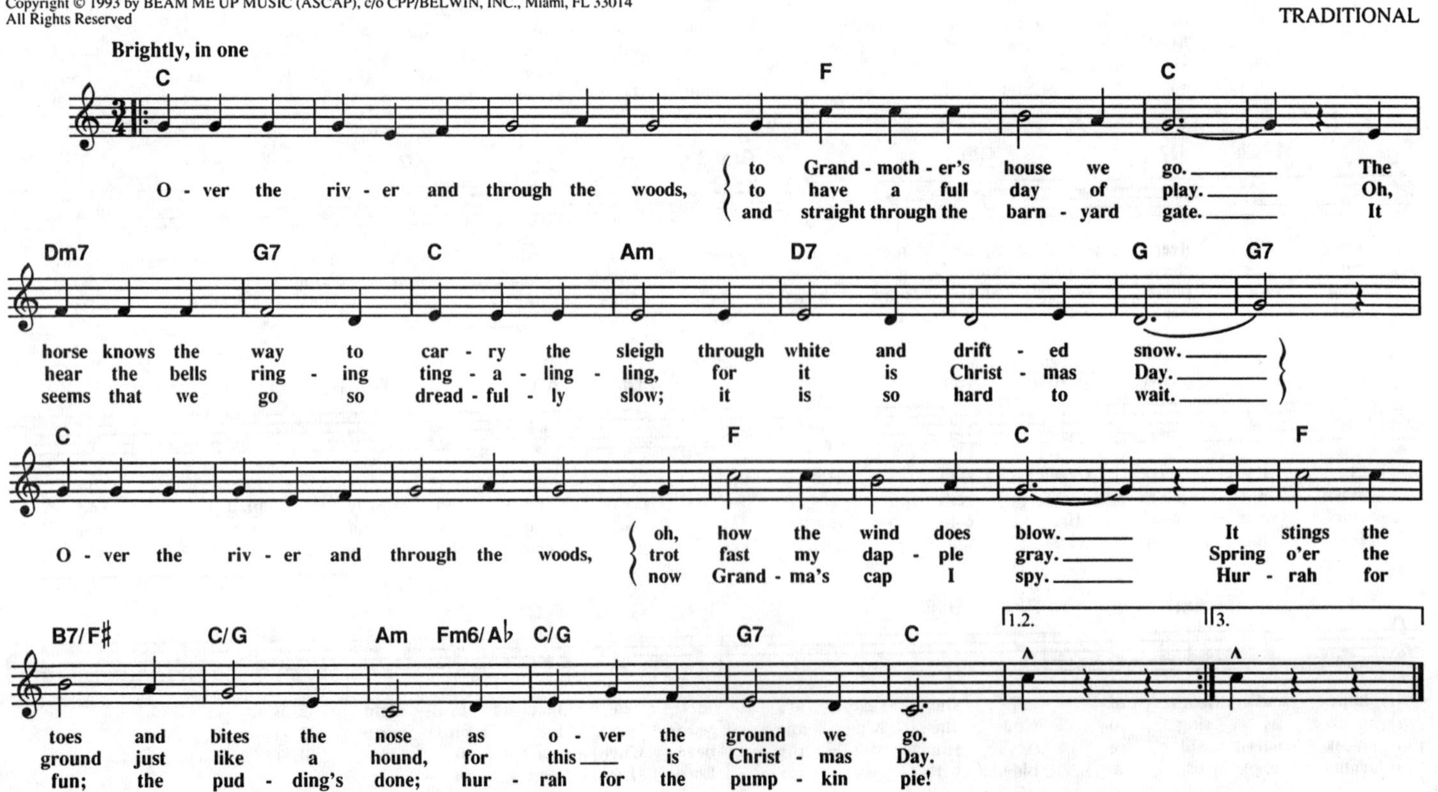
Brightly, in one
C F C
O - ver the riv - er and through the woods,
to Grand - moth - er's house we go. The
to have a full day of play. Oh,
and straight through the barn - yard gate. It
Dm7 G7 C Am D7 G G7
horse knows the way to car - ry the sleigh through white and drift - ed snow.
hear the bells ring - ing ting - a - ling - ling, for it is Christ - mas Day.
seems that we go so dread - ful - ly slow; it is so hard to wait.
C F C F
O - ver the riv - er and through the woods,
oh, how the wind does blow. It stings the
trot fast my dap - ple gray. Spring o'er the
now Grand - ma's cap I spy. Hur - rah for
B7/F♯ C/G Am Fm6/A♭ C/G G7 C
1.2.
3.
toes and bites the nose as o - ver the ground we go.
ground just like a hound, for this is Christ - mas Day.
fun; the pud - ding's done; hur - rah for the pump - kin pie!

From the Motion Picture "THE ODD COUPLE"
THE ODD COUPLE
Copyright © 1968 by FAMOUS MUSIC CORPORATION
All Rights Reserved
Words by SAMMY CAHN
Music by NEAL HEFTI
Moderate shuffle
Dm7 G9 Dm7 G7 Dm G Dm7 G Dm7 G Dm Gm7 C9
No mat-ter where they go they are known as the cou - ple. They're nev - er seen a - lone,
hab - its, I con - fess, none can guess with the cou - ple. If one says no it's yes,
Gm7 C7 Gm C Gm7 C Gm7 C Gm F7 B♭maj7
so they're known as the cou - ple. As I've in - di - cat - ed
more or less, with the cou - ple. But they're laugh pro - vok - ing,
1. Em7 A7 Dm7 G7 B♭maj7 A7(♭9) Dm7 F7 Em7(♭5) A7
they are nev-er quite sep - a - rat - ed, they are peas in a pod. Don't you think that it's odd? Their
2. Em7 A7(♭9) Dm7 F7 B♭ Gm7 Gm7/C F
yet they real-ly don't know they're jok - ing. Don't you find when love is blind it's kind of odd?
ODE TO BILLY JOE
Copyright © 1967 by NORTHRIDGE MUSIC CO., c/o ALL NATIONS MUSIC
All Rights Reserved
Words and Music by
BOBBIE GENTRY
Moderately
A7 Em7 A7
1. It was the third of June, an - oth - er sleep - y, dust - y, del - ta day. I was
Em7 A7 D7
out chop-pin' cot-ton and my broth-er was bail-in' hay. And at din-ner time we stopped and walked back to the house to
A7 Em7 A7
eat. And Ma-ma hol-lered at the back door, "Y'all re - mem-ber to wipe your feet." Then she
D7 A7
said "I got some news this morn - in' from Choc-taw Ridge. To - day Bil - ly Joe Mc Al - lis - ter jumped
G7 1.2.3.4. A7 5. A7
off the Tal-la-hat-chee Bridge."

Verse 2:
Papa said to Mama, as he passed around the black-eyed peas,
"Well, Billy Joe never had a lick o' sense, pass the biscuits please.
There's five more acres in the lower forty I've got to plow."
And Mama said it was a shame about Billy Joe anyhow.
Seems like nothin' ever comes to no good up on Choctaw Ridge.
And now Billy Joe McAllister's jumped off the Tallahatchee Bridge.

Verse 3:
Brother said he recollected when he and Tom and Billy Joe,
Put a frog down my back at the Carroll County picture show.
And wasn't I talkin' to him after church last Sunday night.
I'll have another piece of apple pie, you know it don't seem right.
I saw him at the sawmill yesterday on Choctaw Ridge,
And now you tell me Billy Joe's jumped off the Tallahatchee Bridge.

Verse 4:
Mama said to me, "Child what's happened to your appetite?
I been cookin' all mornin' and you haven't touched a single bite.
That nice young preacher Brother Taylor dropped by today,
Said he'd be pleased to have dinner on Sunday. Oh, by the way,
He said he saw a girl that looked a lot like you up on Choctaw Ridge,
And she an' Billy Joe was throwin' somethin' off the Tallahatchee Bridge."

Verse 5:
A year has come and gone since we heard the news 'bout Billy Joe.
Brother married Becky Thompson, they bought a store in Tupelo.
There was a virus goin' 'round, Papa caught it and he died last spring,
And now Mama doesn't seem to want to do much of anything.
And me I spend a lot of time pickin' flowers up on Choctaw Ridge,
And drop them into the muddy water off the Tallahatchee Bridge.

ODE TO JOY

LUDWIG VAN BEETHOVEN

Slowly
A
E/G♯
A
E7
A
E7
A
E7 A

E
A/E
E
A/E
Bm/E
C♯m C♯7
F♯m
Bm E A
A7
D
A/E
E7 A

With more movement
D
A
D
1.
A
2.
A D
A
D
A
D

A
F♯7/A♯
Bm E A D
A
D
A D
poco rit.

G
D
G
D
G
D
G
D G
a tempo

D G
D G
D
B/D♯
Em Am D G
D
G
D G

OH HAPPY DAY

Words and Music by EDWIN R. HAWKINS

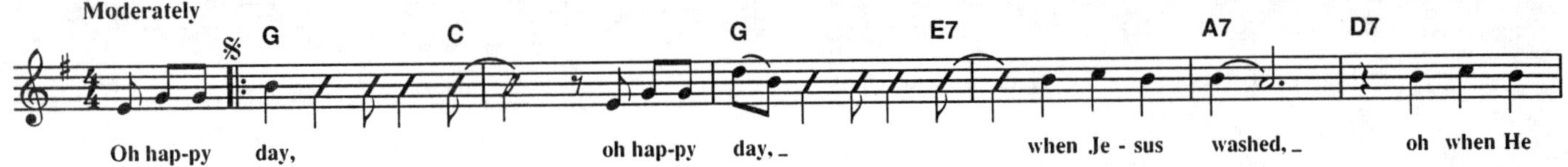
Moderately
G
C
G
E7
A7
D7
Oh hap-py day,
oh hap-py day, _
when Je - sus washed, _
oh when He

A7
D7
A7
D7
G
C
G
1.
C
washed, _
when Je - sus washed, _
He washed my sins _ a - way. _
Aw hap-py day.
Oh hap-py

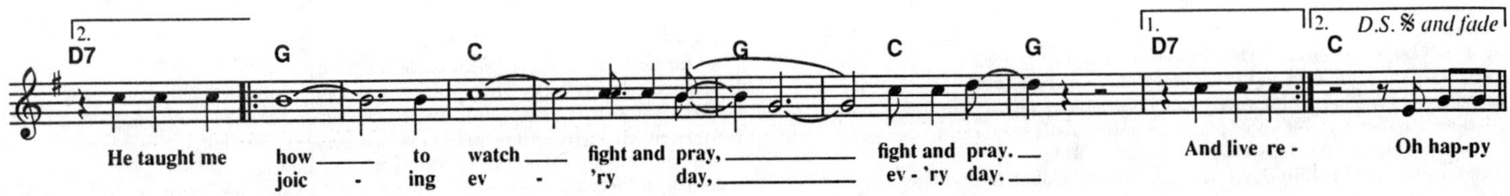
2.
D7
G
C
G
C
G
1.
D7
2. D.S. 𝄋 and fade
C
He taught me
how _ to watch _ fight and pray, _ fight and pray. _
joic - ing ev - 'ry day, _ ev - 'ry day. _
And live re -
Oh hap-py

OH, LONESOME ME

Words and Music by
DON GIBSON

Brightly

C G7 C
Ev - 'ry - bod - y's go - in' out and hav - in' fun. I'm just a fool for stay - in' home and hav - in' none.
bad mis - take I'm mak - in' by just hang - in' 'round. I know that I should have some fun and paint the town.

C7 F G7 1. C
I can't get o - ver how she set me free. Oh, lone - some me. A
A love - sick fool that's blind and just can't see, oh, lone - some

2. C G D7 G
me. I'll bet she's not like me, she's out and fan - cy free, flirt - ing with the boys with all her charms.

D7 G G7
But I still love her so and, broth - er, don't you know, I'd wel - come her right back here in my arms. Well, there

C G7 C
must be some way I can lose these lone - some blues, for - get a - bout the past and find some - bod - y new. I've

C7 F G7 C G7 C
thought of ev - 'ry - thing from A to Z. Oh, lone - some me.

OH MARIE

E. DI CAPUA

Moderately
C
G7
Oh, Ma - rie, oh, Ma - rie, there is no one by you, dear for me. My heart's re -
a tempo
C
peat - ing each word you can hear in it's beat - ing. Oh, Ma - rie, oh, Ma - rie, fair - est
A7
Dm
Fm/A♭
C/G
F♯dim7
C/G
G7
C
flow - er in all It - al - y, I beg of thee, hear my plea, oh, Ma - rie.

OH, PRETTY WOMAN

Words and Music by
ROY ORBISON and
BILL DEES

Moderate rock
E7
riff
1. Pret-ty
A F♯m A F♯m D
wom-an, walk-ing down the street; pret-ty wom-an, the kind I like to meet; pret-ty wom-an,
wom-an, won't you par-don me? Pret-ty wom-an, I could-n't help but see; pret-ty wom-an,
E7
I don't be - lieve you, you're not the truth. No one could look as good as you. (Riff)
that you look love - ly as can be. Are you lone - ly just like me? (Spoken:) Mercy.
1. 2.
Dm G7 C Am
2. Pret-ty
Pret-ty wom - an, stop a - while, pret-ty wom - an, talk a - while;
Pret-ty wom - an, yeah, yeah, yeah; pret-ty wom - an, look my way;
Dm G7 1. C 2. C A F♯m Dm
pret-ty wom-an, give your smile to me. me. 'Cause I need you, I'll treat you
pret-ty wom-an, say you'll stay with
E7 A F♯m Dm E7 (Riff)
right. Come to me ba - by, be mine to - night. Pret-ty
A F♯m A F♯m D
wom-an, don't walk on by; pret-ty wom-an, don't make me cry; pret-ty wom-an, don't
E7
walk a - way, hey. O. K. If that's the way it must be, O. K. I guess I'll
go on home, it's late. There'll be to - mor-row night, but wait! What do I see? Is she
(Riff)
A
walk-ing back to me? Yeah, she's walk-ing back to me! Oh, pret-ty wom-an.

OH, LADY BE GOOD!

Music and Lyrics by
GEORGE GERSHWIN and
IRA GERSHWIN

Slow & Gracefully

G D7 G C7 G G♯dim D7
Oh, sweet and love - ly la - dy, be good! Oh, La - dy, Be Good to
G D7 G C7 G G♯dim
me! I am so aw - f'ly mis - un - der - stood, So
D7 G G7 C D7
la - dy be good to me.
Oh, please have some
This is tu - lip
C G D7 Em B+ Em A7 Am7/D D7
pit - y, I'm all a - lone in this big cit - y.
weath - er, So let's put two and two to - geth - er.
D6 Am7 A7-5 G D7 G C7 G G♯dim
I tell you I'm just a lone - some babe in the wood, So
D7 G C7 G
la - dy, be good to me!
ONLY LOVE CAN BREAK A HEART
© 1962 (Renewed 1990) NEW HIDDEN VALLEY MUSIC and CASA DAVID
All Rights Reserved
Words by
HAL DAVID
Music by
BURT BACHARACH
Moderately slow
B♭ B♭7 E♭ F7 B♭ A♭ G7 E♭6 F
Last night I hurt you, but dar - lin', re - mem - ber this, on - ly love can break a heart,
sor - ry, I'll prove it with just one kiss, on - ly love can break a heart,
E♭6 F 1. B♭ B♭7 2. B♭ F7 B♭ B♭7
on - ly love can mend it a - gain. You know I'm gain. Give me a
E♭ Cm B♭ B♭7 E♭ C7
chance to make up for the harm I've done, try to for - give me and let's keep the
F7 E♭ F7 Tacet E♭ F7 B♭ G7
two of us one! Please let me hold you and love you for al - ways and al - ways,
E♭6 F E♭6 F F7 B♭ E♭ B♭
on - ly love can break a heart, on - ly love can mend it a - gain.

OH! SUSANNA

Words and Music by STEPHEN C. FOSTER

Brightly
F G7 C7 F B♭ F C7
I ___ come from Al - a - bam - a wid my ban - jo on my knee. I'm _ go'n to Lou - si - an - a, my ___ true love for to

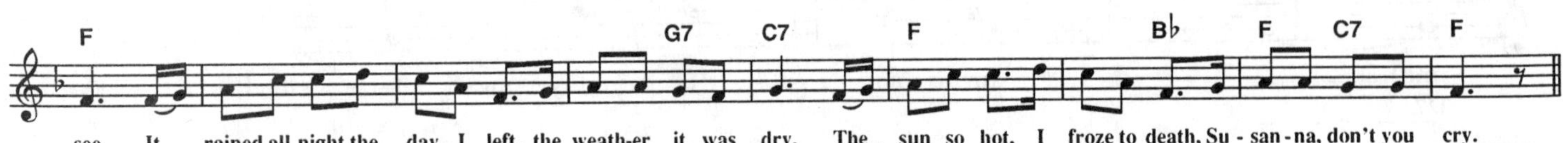
F G7 C7 F B♭ F C7 F
see. It _ rained all night the day I left, the weath-er it was dry. The _ sun so hot, I froze to death, Su - san - na, don't you cry.

B♭ F C7 F B♭ F C7 F
Oh! Su - san - na, oh don't you cry for me, I've _ come from Al - a - bam - a with my ban - jo on my knee.

OH, THEM GOLDEN SLIPPERS

Words and Music by JAMES A. BLAND

Brightly
G D7
1. Oh, my gol - den slip-pers am ___ laid a - way 'cause I don't 'spect to wear 'em till my wed - ding day. And my
old ban - jo ___ hangs _ on the wall 'cause it ain't been _ tuned ___ since ___ way last fall. But the

G
long - tailed coat, that I loved so well, I will wear up in the char - iot in the morn. And my
folks all say we will have a good time, when we ride in the char - iot in the morn. There's old

D7
long, white robe, _ that I bought last June, I'm ___ go - ing to get changed 'cause it fits too soon. And the
broth - er Ben ___ and ___ sis - ter Luce, they will tel - e - graph the news to Un - cle To - bac - co Juice. What a

G
old gray horse that I used to drive, I will hitch him to the char - iot in the morn.
great camp meet - in' there will be that day, when we ride up in the char - iot in the morn.
Oh, them

C D7 G
gol - den slip-pers! Oh, them gol - den slip-pers! Gol - den slip-pers I'm going to wear, be - cause they look so neat. Oh, them

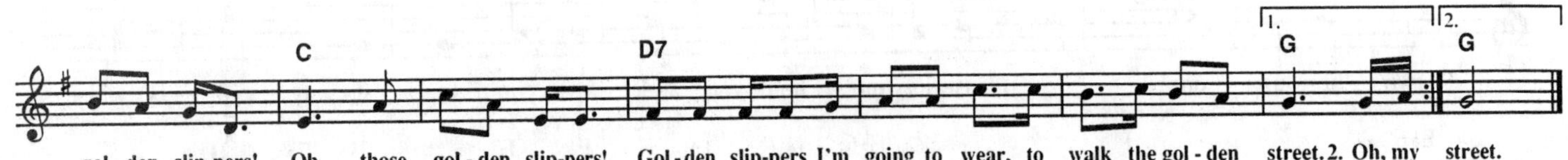
C D7 1. G 2. G
gol - den slip-pers! Oh, those gol - den slip-pers! Gol - den slip-pers I'm going to wear, to walk the gol - den street. 2. Oh, my street.

OH WHERE HAS MY LITTLE DOG GONE?
Copyright © 1993 by BEAM ME UP MUSIC (ASCAP), c/o CPP/BELWIN, INC., Miami, FL 33014
All Rights Reserved
TRADITIONAL
Moderately
F C7 F
Oh where, oh where has my lit - tle dog gone? Oh where, oh where can he be?
C7 F C7 F
With his hair so short and his tail so long, oh where, oh where can he be?
AN OLD FASHIONED LOVE SONG
Copyright © 1970 ALMO MUSIC CORP. (ASCAP)
All Rights Reserved
Word and Music by
PAUL WILLIAMS
Moderately
Verse 1:
Gm Bb/F Eb D Gm Bb/F Eb D
Just an old fa - shioned love song play-ing on the ra - di - o. And
Gm Bb/F Eb D Gm Bb/F Eb D G
wrapped a-round the mus - ic is the sound of some-one prom-is - ing they'll nev-er go.
You'll swear you've heard
G/F Eb D Gm Bb/F Eb D
it be-fore as it slow - ly ram - bles on and on. No need in bring-ing 'em back 'cause they've ne-ver real-ly gone.
Chorus:
Bb C Eb F Bb Bbdim Eb6/Bb Bb
Just an old fa - shioned love song, com-ing down in three part har - mo-ny.
1. To Next Strain
2.3. etc.
Repeat ad lib. and fade
C Eb F F Bb
Just an old fa - shioned love song, one I'm sure they wrote for you and for you and me.
Verse 2:
Gm Bb/F Eb D Gm Bb/F Eb D
me to weave our dreams up-on and lis-ten to each eve-ning when the lights are low, to un-
D.S. 𝄋
Gm Bb/F Eb D Gm Bb/F Eb D Am Gm D7
- der - score our love af - fair with ten-der-ness and feel-ings that we've come to know.

OH, YOU BEAUTIFUL DOLL
Copyright © 1993 by BEAM ME UP MUSIC (ASCAP), c/o CPP/BELWIN, INC., Miami, FL 33014
All Rights Reserved
Words by A. SEYMOUR BROWN
Music by NAT D. AYER
Moderate swing
Ab Ab7/Gb F7 Bb7 Eb7
Oh, you beau - ti - ful doll, you great big beau - ti - ful doll! Let me put my
Ab Ab/C Db6 Eb7(b9) Ab Ab7/Gb F7
arms a - bout you, I could nev - er live with - out you. Oh, you beau - ti - ful doll, you
Bb7 Eb7 Ab E
great big beau - ti - ful doll! If you ev - er leave me, how my heart will ache. I want to hug you but I
Ab C7/G Fm Fm7/Eb Bb7/D Eb7 1. Ab 2. Ab
fear you'd break. Oh, oh, oh, oh, oh, you beau - ti - ful doll! doll!
OLD CAPE COD
Copyright © 1956 (Renewed) by GEORGE PINCUS & SONS MUSIC CORP.
All Rights Reserved
Words and Music by CLAIRE ROTHROCK, MILT YAKUS and ALLEN JEFFREY
Slowly, with expression
Eb Bbm7 Eb9 Ab Db9
1. If you're fond of sand dunes and salt - y air, quaint lit - tle vil - lag - es here and there,
2. If you like the taste of a lob - ster stew, served by a win - dow with an o - cean view,
Eb C7 1. F7 Bb7 2. F7 Bb7 Eb Eb7
you're sure to fall in love with Old Cape Cod. Old Cape Cod.
Ab Bb7 Eb Edim7 Fm7 Bb7(b9) Ebmaj7 Eb7 Ab Adim7
Wind - ing roads that seem to beck - on you; miles of green be - neath the skies of blue; church bells chim - ing on a
Eb Bbm C7 Fm7 F7 Bb7 Bb7(#5) Eb Bbm7 Eb9
Sun - day morn', re - mind you of the town where you were born. If you spend an eve - ning, you'll want to stay,
Ab Db9 Eb C7 F7 Bb7 Eb
watch - ing the moon - light on Cape Cod Bay. You're sure to fall in love with Old Cape Cod.

OLD BLACK JOE

Words and Music by
STEPHEN C. FOSTER

Moderately

D G D Em A7
Gone are the days when my heart was young and gay. Gone are my friends from the cot - ton fields a - way,

D G D A7 D A7 D
gone from the earth to a bet - ter land I know. I hear their gen - tle voic - es call - ing "Old Black Joe." I'm

G D A7 D A7 D
com - ing, I'm com - ing, for my head is bend - ing low. I hear those gen - tle voic - es call - ing "Old Black Joe."

OLD FOLKS AT HOME

Words and Music by
STEPHEN C. FOSTER

Moderately
Verse:

C F C D7 Dm7/G G7
Way down up - on the Swa - nee Riv - er, far, far a - way,
All 'round the lit - tle farm I wan - dered when I was young.
One lit - tle hut a - mong the bush - es, one that I love,

C F C D7 Dm7/G G7 C
there's where my heart is turn - ing ev - er, there's where the old folks stay. All up and down the
Then man - y hap - py days I squand-ered, man - y the songs I sung. When I was play - ing
still sad - ly to my mem - 'ry rush - es no mat - ter where I rove. When will I see the

F C D7 Dm7/G G7 C F
whole cre - a - tion, sad - ly I roam, still long - ing for the old plan - ta - tion,
with my broth - er, hap - py was I. Oh, take me to my kind old moth - er;
bees a - hum-ming all 'round the comb? When will I hear the ban - jo strum-ming

C D7 Dm7/G G7 C
and for the old folks at home.
there let me live and die
in my good old home?

Chorus:

G7 C C7 F C G7
All the world is sad and drear - y ev - 'ry - where I roam.

C F C D7 Dm7/G G7 | 1.2. C F C G7 | 3. C F C
Oh, broth-ers, how my heart grows wear - y far from the old folks at home. home.

THE OLD GRAY MARE
Copyright © 1993 by BEAM ME UP MUSIC (ASCAP), c/o CPP/BELWIN, INC., Miami, FL 33014
All Rights Reserved
FOLK SONG
With spirit
Oh, the old gray mare, she ain't what she used to be, ain't what she used to be, ain't what she used to be. The
old gray mare, she ain't what she used to be many long years ago. Many long years ago;
many long years ago. Oh, the old gray mare, she ain't what she used to be, many long years ago.
OLD TIME ROCK & ROLL
Copyright © 1977 by MUSCLE SHOALS SOUND PUBLISHING CO., INC.(BMI)
All Rights Reserved
Words and Music by
GEORGE JACKSON and
THOMAS E. JONES III
Moderate rock
N.C.
Verse:
1. Just take those old records off the shelf, I sit and listen to them by myself. Today's music ain't got the same soul. I like that old time rock and roll. Don't try to take me to a disco, you'll never even get me out on the floor. In ten minutes I'll be late for the door. I like that old time rock and roll.
tango, I'd rather hear some blues and funky old soul. There's only one sure way to get me to go. Start playin' old time rock and roll. Call me a relic, call me what you will. Say I'm old fashioned, say I'm over the hill. Today's music ain't got the same soul. I like that old time rock and roll.
Still like that old time
Chorus:
rock and roll, that kind of music just soothes the soul. I reminisce about the days of old, with that old time rock and roll.
1. D.S. 𝄋
2.Won't go to hear 'em play a
2. Still like that old time
3.

ON GREEN DOLPHIN STREET

Lyric by NED WASHINGTON
Music by BRONISLAU KAPER

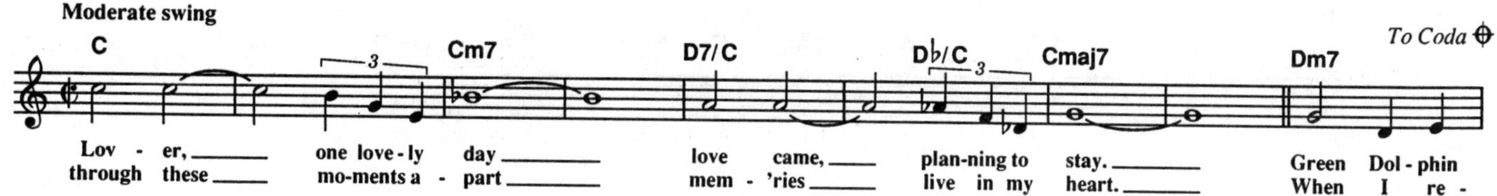
Moderate swing
C
Cm7
D7/C
D♭/C
Cmaj7
Dm7
To Coda
Lov - er, one love-ly day love came, plan-ning to stay. Green Dol-phin
through these mo-ments a - part mem - 'ries live in my heart. When I re -

G7
G7(♭9 ♯5)
Cmaj7
Fm7
B♭7
B♭7(♭9 ♯5)
E♭maj7
G7
D.C. al Coda
Street sup-plied the set - ting; the set-ting for nights be-yond for-get - ting. And

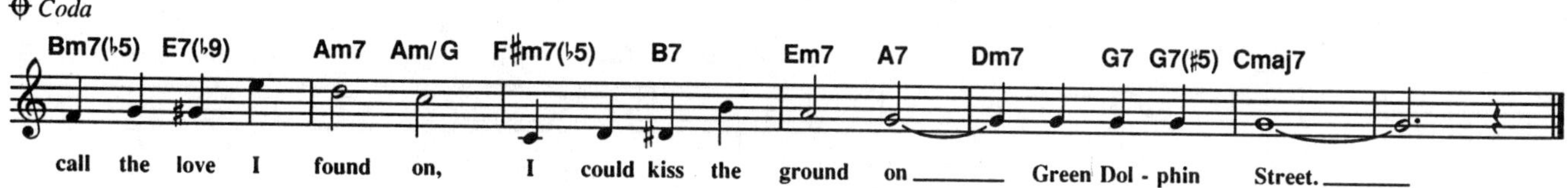
Coda
Bm7(♭5) E7(♭9) Am7 Am/G F♯m7(♭5) B7 Em7 A7 Dm7 G7 G7(♯5) Cmaj7
call the love I found on, I could kiss the ground on Green Dol-phin Street.

From the M-G-M Picture "THE HARVEY GIRLS"

ON THE ATCHISON, TOPEKA AND THE SANTA FE

Lyric by JOHNNY MERCER
Music by HARRY WARREN

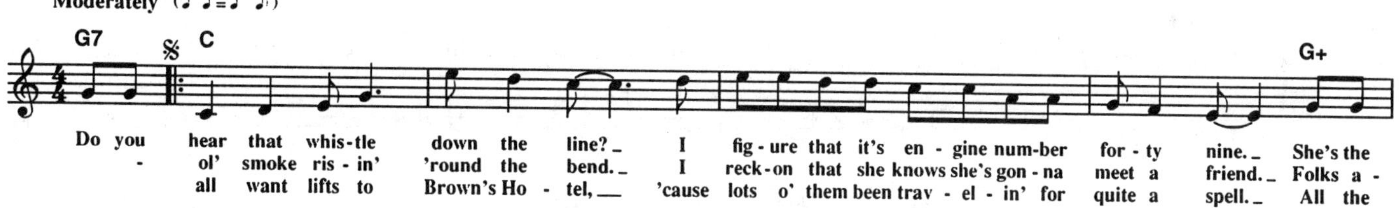
Moderately
G7
C
G+
Do you hear that whis-tle down the line? I fig-ure that it's en-gine num-ber for-ty nine. She's the
- ol' smoke ris-in' 'round the bend. I reck-on that she knows she's gon-na meet a friend. Folks a -
all want lifts to Brown's Ho - tel, 'cause lots o' them been trav - el - in' for quite a spell. All the

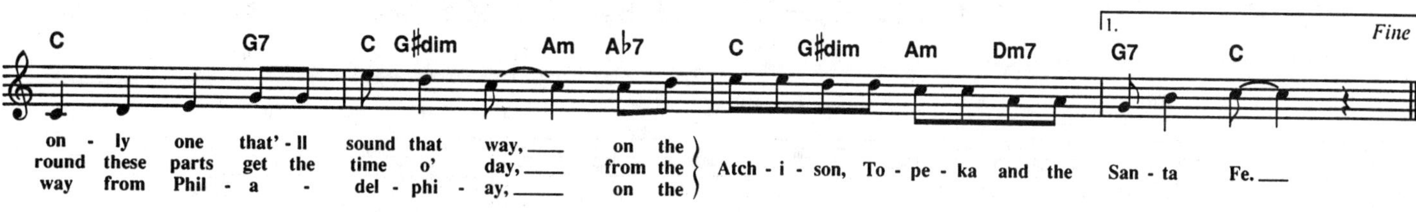
C G7 C G♯dim Am A♭7 C G♯dim Am Dm7 G7 C
Fine
on - ly one that'-ll sound that way, on the
round these parts get the time o' day, from the
way from Phil - a - del - phi - ay, on the
Atch-i-son, To-pe-ka and the San-ta Fe.

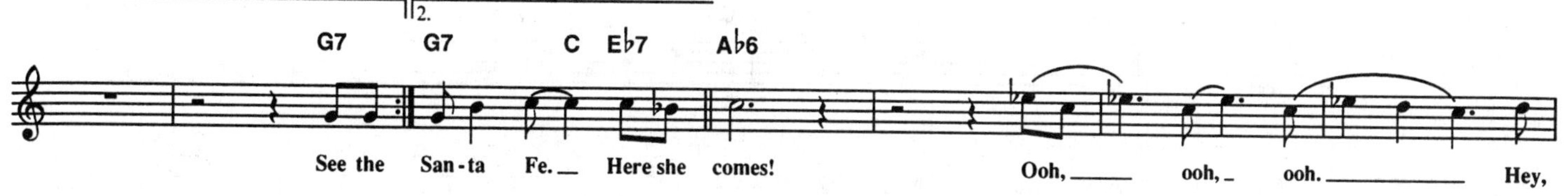
G7 G7 C E♭7 A♭6
See the San-ta Fe. Here she comes! Ooh, ooh, ooh. Hey,

D.S. al Fine
Cm E♭maj7 Fm6 Cm7 Fm7 Dm7(♭5) G7
Jim! Yuh bet-ter git the rig! Ooh, ooh, ooh. She's got a list o' pas-sen-gers that's pret-ty big. And they'll

From the United Artist Motion Picture "ON HER MAJESTY'S SECRET SERVICE"

ON HER MAJESTY'S SECRET SERVICE

By JOHN BARRY

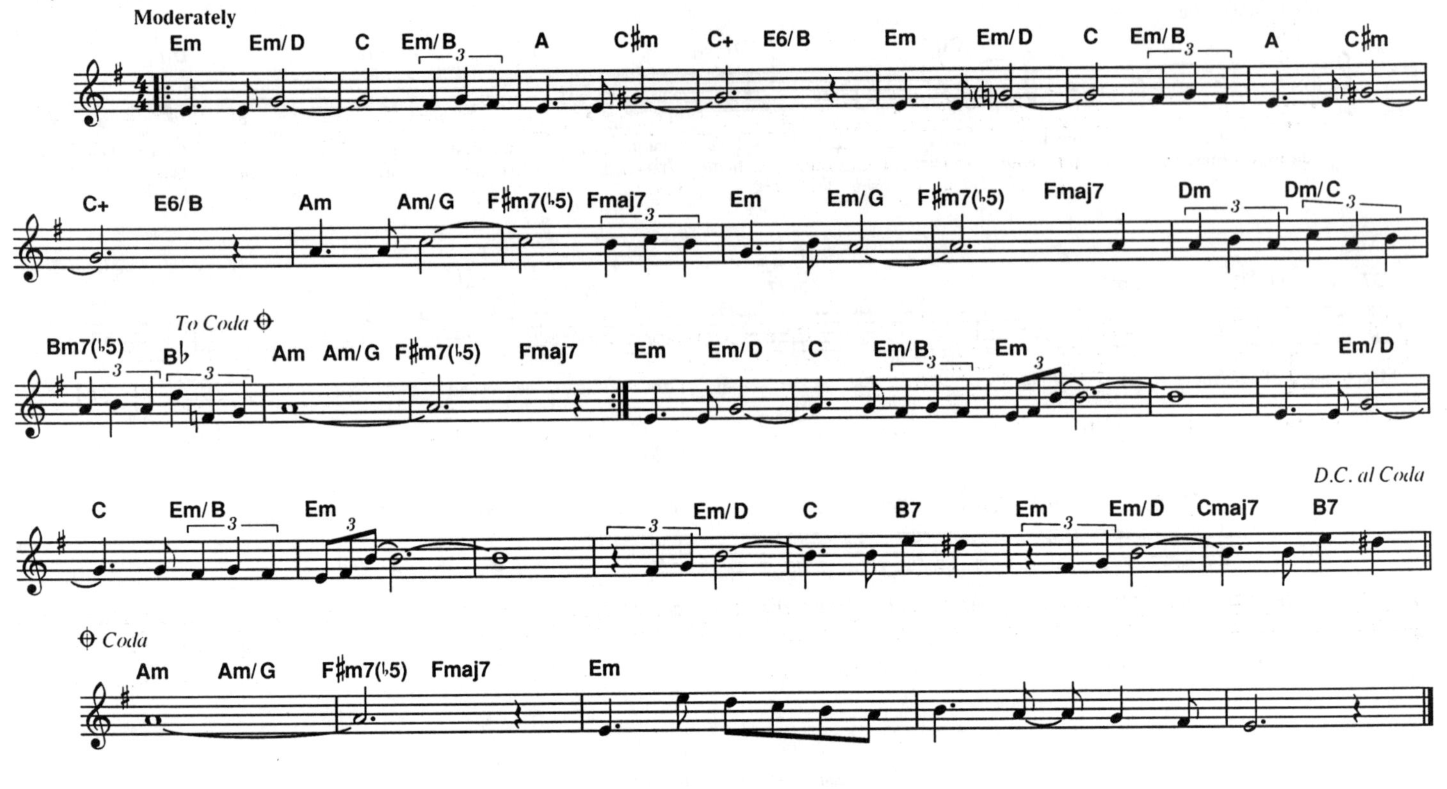
Moderately
Em Em/D C Em/B A C♯m C+ E6/B Em Em/D C Em/B A C♯m
C+ E6/B Am Am/G F♯m7(♭5) Fmaj7 Em Em/G F♯m7(♭5) Fmaj7 Dm Dm/C
Bm7(♭5) B♭ To Coda Am Am/G F♯m7(♭5) Fmaj7 Em Em/D C Em/B Em Em/D
D.C. al Coda
C Em/B Em Em/D C B7 Em Em/D Cmaj7 B7
Coda
Am Am/G F♯m7(♭5) Fmaj7 Em

ON THE TRAIL

By FERDE GROFÉ

Moderately

G G6 G Em G G6 G Em G Em G Em

G Em G Em Am7 Am6 Am D Am7 Am6 Am D

Am D Am D Am D Am D G Em G Em G Em

G Em G Em G Em G Em G Em Am7 D Am7 D6 Am7 D7

Am7 D6 Am7 D Am7 D6 Am7 D7 Am7 D11 G Em G Em G Em

G Em G Em G Em G Em G D11 G Em7 G

ON THE SUNNY SIDE OF THE STREET

Lyrics by DOROTHY FIELDS
Music by JIMMY McHUGH

Bright swing

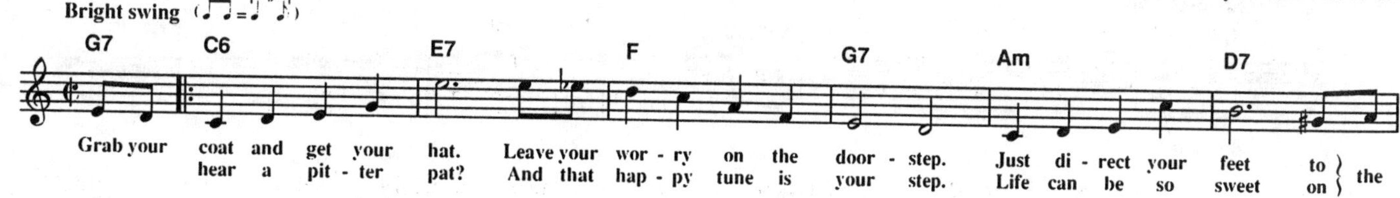
G7 C6 E7 F G7 Am D7
Grab your coat and get your hat. Leave your wor - ry on the door - step. Just di - rect your feet to the
hear a pit - ter pat? And that hap - py tune is your step. Life can be so sweet on

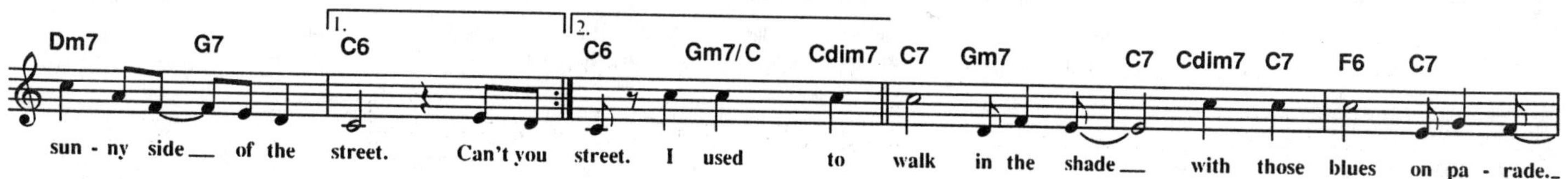
Dm7 G7 1. C6 2. C6 Gm7/C Cdim7 C7 Gm7 C7 Cdim7 C7 F6 C7
sun - ny side of the street. Can't you street. I used to walk in the shade with those blues on pa - rade.

F6 D7 Am7 D7 G7 Gdim7 G7 C6
But I'm not a - fraid. This ro - ver crossed o - ver. If I nev - er have a

E7 F G7 Am D7 Dm7 G7 C6
cent, I'll be rich as Rock - e - fel - ler; gold dust at my feet on the sun - ny side of the street.

ONCE IN A WHILE

Words by BUD GREEN
Music by MICHAEL EDWARDS

Slowly

E♭ Gm7 C7(♯5) C7 Gm7 C7 Fm
Once in a while will you try to give one lit - tle thought to me, though some-one else may
Once in a while will you dream of the mo - ments I shared with you, mo - ments be - fore we
I know that I'll be con - tent - ed with yes - ter - day's mem - o - ry, know - ing you think of
Fm7 B♭7 1. E♭6 Edim7 Fm7 B♭7(♭9) 2. E♭ A♭6 E♭ D7 To Next Strain 3. E♭ Fm7 E♭6 Fine G Em
be near-er your heart? part? In while. love's smol-der-ing
two drif-ted a -
me once in a

D.C. al Fine
Am7 D9 G Em Am7 D7 G Em Am7 D7(♭9) G Edim Fm7 B♭7
em - ber, one spark may re - main. If love still can re - mem - ber, the spark may burn a - gain.

ON THE WINGS OF LOVE

Words by JEFFREY OSBORNE
Music by PETER SCHLESS

Moderately slow
C G/B Am C/D G C G/B
Keyboard:
Am C/D G
Verse:
Em Em(♯7)/D♯ G/D C♯m7(♭5) Am7 G/B
1. Just smile for me and let the day be-gin. You are the sun-shine that
2. You look at me and I be-gin to melt just like the snow when a
Am7/D D B7(♯5) Em Em(♯7)/D♯ G/D C♯m7(♭5) Am7 G/B
lights my heart with-in. And I'm sure that you're an an-gel in dis-guise. Come take my hand and to-
ray of sun is felt. And I'm cra-zy 'bout you, ba-by, can't you see? I'd be so de-light-ed if
Am7/D D(9)
geth-er we will ride.
you would come with me.
Chorus:
G G/B Cmaj7 C/D D
On the wings of love, up and a-bove the clouds; the on-ly way to fly
Em Em(♯7) Em7/B Em7/A Am7/D G G/B Cmaj7 C/D D
is on the wings of love. On the wings of love, on-ly the two of us to-geth-er fly-ing high;
Em Em(♯7) G/D G/A A7 Am7/D
To Coda 1. D.S. 2.
G(9) G(9)
fly-ing high up-on the wings of love
Bridge:
C G/B Am Am/D
Yes, you be-long to me and I'm yours ex-clu-sive-ly. And right now we live and
Am/G G F/G G C G/B
breathe to-geth-er. In-sep-'ra-ble it seems, we're flow-ing like a
D.S.S. al Coda
C G/B Am7 Am7/D
stream run-ning free trav-'ling on the wings of love.
Coda
C G/B Am C/D G

ON TOP OF OLD SMOKY
Copyright © 1993 by BEAM ME UP MUSIC (ASCAP), c/o CPP/BELWIN, INC., Miami, FL 33014
All Rights Reserved
FOLK SONG
Moderate waltz
On top of old Smo - ky, all cov - ered with snow, I lost my true lov - er for court - in' too slow. For court-in's a plea - sure and part - ing is grief. And a false heart - ed lov - er is worse than a thief. A thief will just rob you, and take what you have. But a false heart - ed lov - er will lead you to the grave. And the grave will de -
cay you, and turn you to dust. There ain't one in a mil - lion a poor girl can trust. They'll hug you and kiss you, and tell you more lies, than the cross - ties on rail - roads, or stars in the sky. They'll tell you they love you to give your heart ease. But as soon as your back's turned, they'll court whom they please. So come you young
maid - ens and lis - ten to me. Never place your af - fec - tion on a green wil - low tree. For the leaves they will with - er, and the roots they will die. And your true love will leave you, and you'll nev - er know why. On top of old Smo - ky, all cov - ered with snow, I lost my true lov - er from a - court - in' too slow.
1.2.
3.
ON WISCONSIN!
Copyright © 1993 by BEAM ME UP MUSIC (ASCAP), c/o CPP/BELWIN, INC., Miami, FL 33014
All Rights Reserved
Words by CARL BECK
Music by W.T PURDY
March
On, Wis - con - sin! On, Wis - con - sin! Plunge right thru that line!
Run that ball { clear 'round Chi - ca - go, / 'round Min - ne - so - ta, } a touch - down sure this time.
On, Wis - con - sin! On, Wis - con - sin! Fight on for her fame!
Fight! fel - lows, fight! And we will win this game. game.
1.
2.

From the Broadway Musical Production "ALL AMERICAN"

ONCE UPON A TIME

Words by CHARLES STROUSE
Music by LEE ADAMS

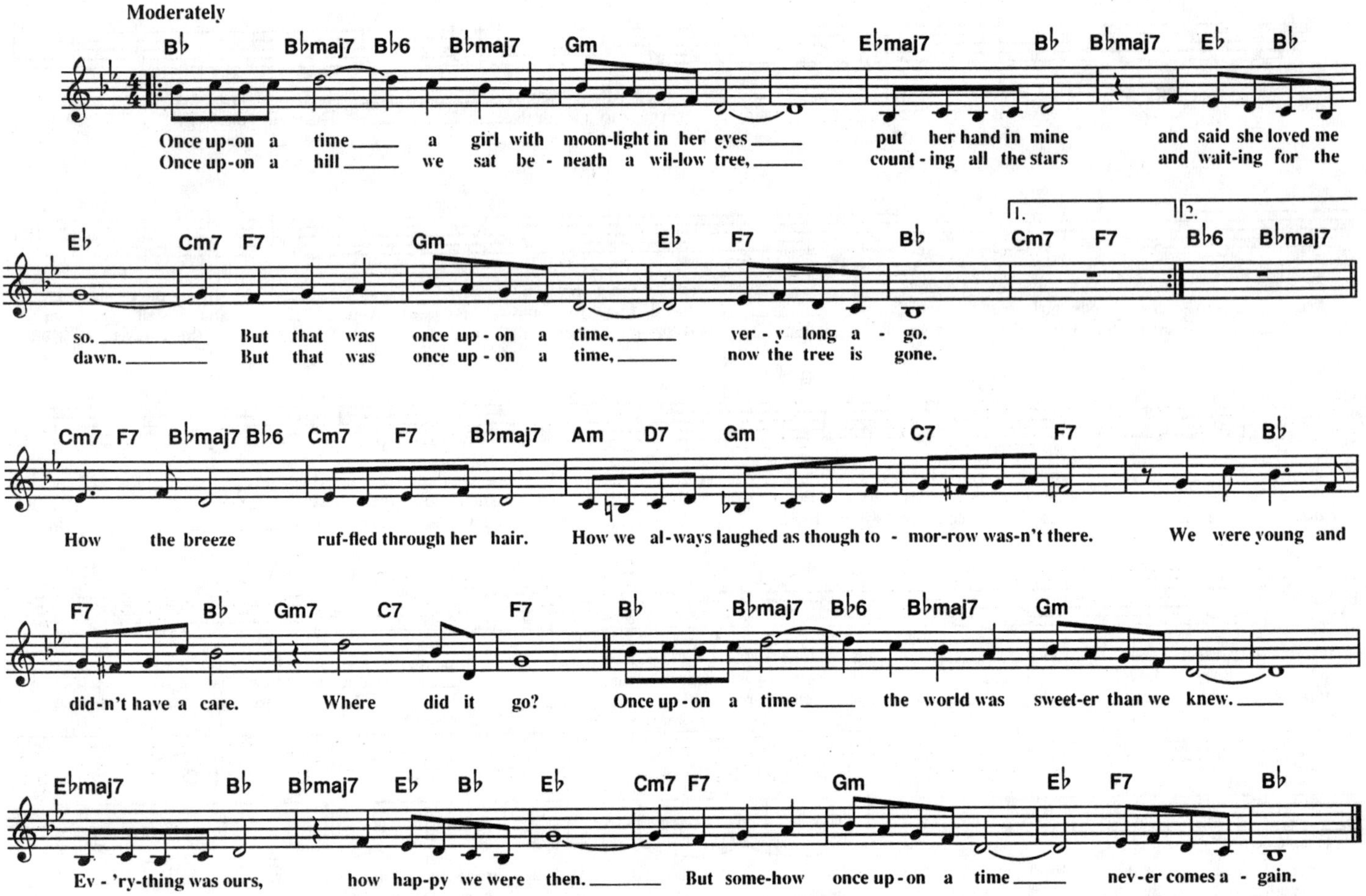

Moderately

B♭ B♭maj7 B♭6 B♭maj7 Gm E♭maj7 B♭ B♭maj7 E♭ B♭
Once up-on a time a girl with moon-light in her eyes put her hand in mine and said she loved me
Once up-on a hill we sat be - neath a wil-low tree, count - ing all the stars and wait-ing for the

E♭ Cm7 F7 Gm E♭ F7 B♭ 1. Cm7 F7 2. B♭6 B♭maj7
so. But that was once up - on a time, ver - y long a - go.
dawn. But that was once up - on a time, now the tree is gone.

Cm7 F7 B♭maj7 B♭6 Cm7 F7 B♭maj7 Am D7 Gm C7 F7 B♭
How the breeze ruf-fled through her hair. How we al-ways laughed as though to - mor-row was-n't there. We were young and

F7 B♭ Gm7 C7 F7 B♭ B♭maj7 B♭6 B♭maj7 Gm
did-n't have a care. Where did it go? Once up-on a time the world was sweet-er than we knew.

E♭maj7 B♭ B♭maj7 E♭ B♭ E♭ Cm7 F7 Gm E♭ F7 B♭
Ev - 'ry-thing was ours, how hap-py we were then. But some-how once up-on a time nev-er comes a - gain.

ONE DOZEN ROSES

Words by ROGER LEWIS and
COUNTRY WASHBURN
Music by DICK JURGEN and
WALTER DONOVAN

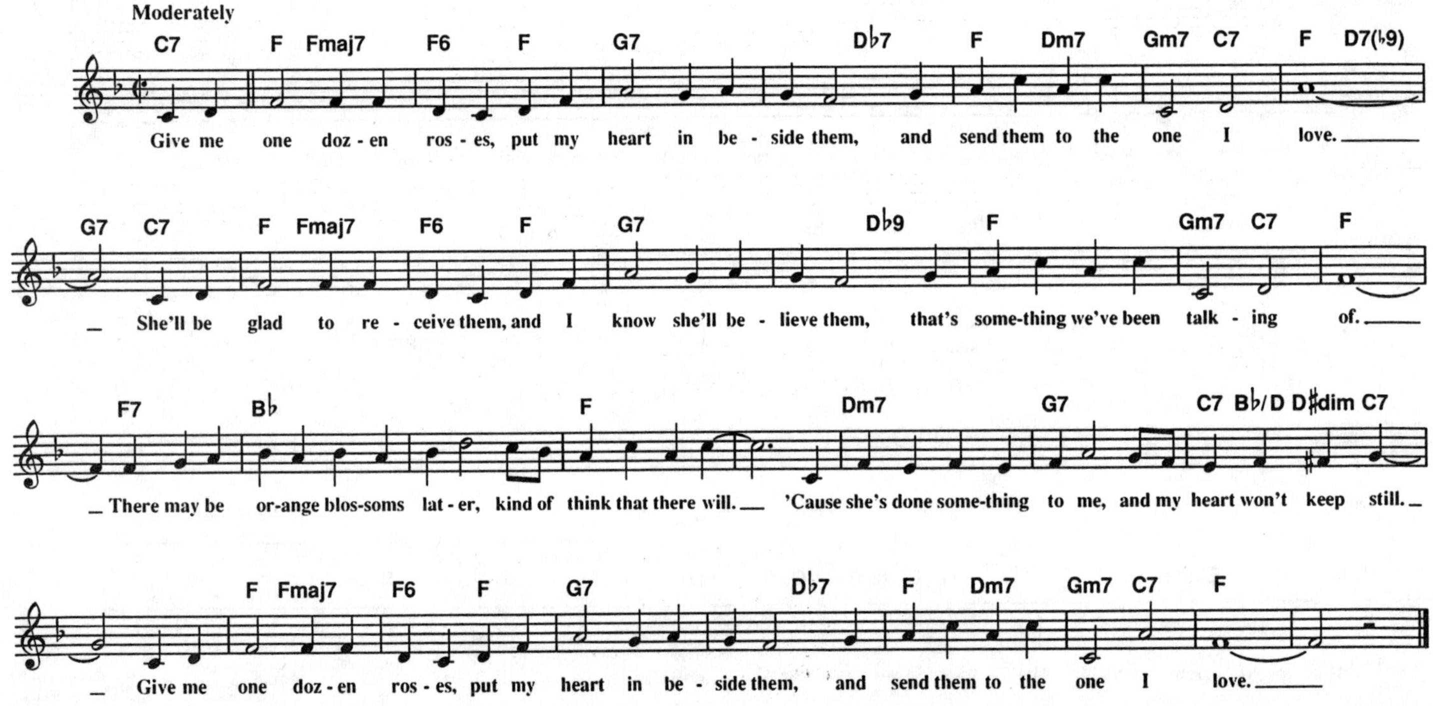

Moderately

C7 F Fmaj7 F6 F G7 D♭7 F Dm7 Gm7 C7 F D7(♭9)
Give me one doz - en ros - es, put my heart in be - side them, and send them to the one I love.

G7 C7 F Fmaj7 F6 F G7 D♭9 F Gm7 C7 F
She'll be glad to re - ceive them, and I know she'll be - lieve them, that's some-thing we've been talk - ing of.

F7 B♭ F Dm7 G7 C7 B♭/D D♯dim C7
There may be or-ange blos-soms lat - er, kind of think that there will. 'Cause she's done some-thing to me, and my heart won't keep still.

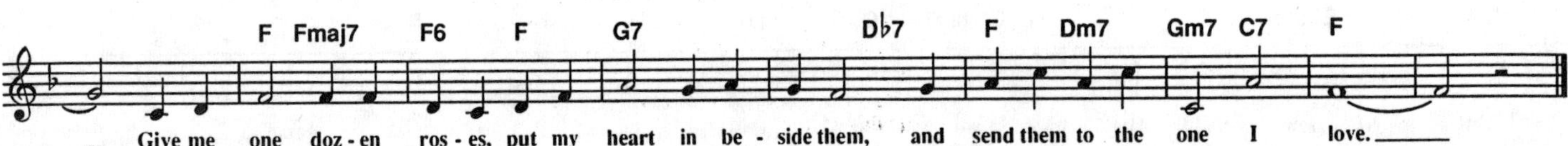
F Fmaj7 F6 F G7 D♭7 F Dm7 Gm7 C7 F
Give me one doz - en ros - es, put my heart in be - side them, and send them to the one I love.

ONE DAY AT A TIME

Words and Music by
MARIJOHN WILKIN and
KRIS KRISTOFFERSON

Moderate waltz
Verse:
G D
1. I'm on - ly hu - man, I'm just a wom - an.
G
Help me be - lieve in what I could be and all that I am. Show me the
G7 C G
stair - way I have to climb. Lord, for my sake,
Chorus:
D G C G/B Am7 G Am7 G/B C
teach me to take one day at a time. One day at a time sweet
G
Je - sus, that's all I'm ask - ing from you. Just give me the
D Am D G G7 G Am7 G/B C
strength to do ev - 'ry day what I have to do. Yes - ter - day's gone
G
sweet Je - sus, and to - mor - row may nev - er be mine. Lord, help me to -
1.
D Am D G C G/B Am7 G
day, show me the way one day at a time. 2. Do you re -
D.S.
2.
D Freely
a tempo
G C G C/D D6 G
way one day at a time.
rit.

Verse 2:
Do you remember when you walked among men?
Well, Jesus, you know, if you're looking below,
It's worse now than then.
Cheating and stealing, violence and crime,
So for my sake, teach me to take one day at a time.
One day at a . . .
(To Chorus:)

ONE IN A MILLION YOU

Words and Music by
SAM DEES

Slowly

Verse:

Bb Bbmaj9 Fm9/Bb Ab/C Bb7/D

1. Love had played _ its games _ on me _ so long. ____ I start - ed to ____ be - lieve _ I'd nev - er find ____

Ebmaj7 Ab13 Ab7 1. Bb/F Cm7 F11 2.3. Bb/F F#dim

an - y - one. Doubt had tried ____ to con - vince me to give in, said you can't win. ________ 2. But one la - tion to

Chorus:

Gm7 Cm7 Eb/F Bb Bbmaj9 Bb7 Ab/C Bb7/D

see some - one was say - ing, "I love you" to me. ____ A one in a mil - lion, _ chance of a

Ebmaj7 Ab13 Bb/F Cm7 Dm7 Ebmaj7 F11 Bb

life - time, _ and life ______ showed com - pas - sion _ and sent to me a stroke of love called you, ______

Bb7/Ab Eb 1. Ab13 Ab7 *D.C.* 2. Eb/F 3. Ab13 Ab7 Bb(2)

_ a one in a mil-lion you. ________ 3. I was a __ A __ A one in a mil-lion you.

Verse 2:
But one day the sun came a-shinin' through
The rain had stopped and the skies were blue.
And oh, what a revelation to see;
Someone was saying, "I love you" to me.
(To Chorus:)

Verse 3:
I was a lonely man with empty arms to fill,
Then I found a piece of happiness to call my own.
Now life is worth livin' again.
For to love you, to me, is to live.
(To Chorus:)

ONE O'CLOCK JUMP

By COUNT BASIE

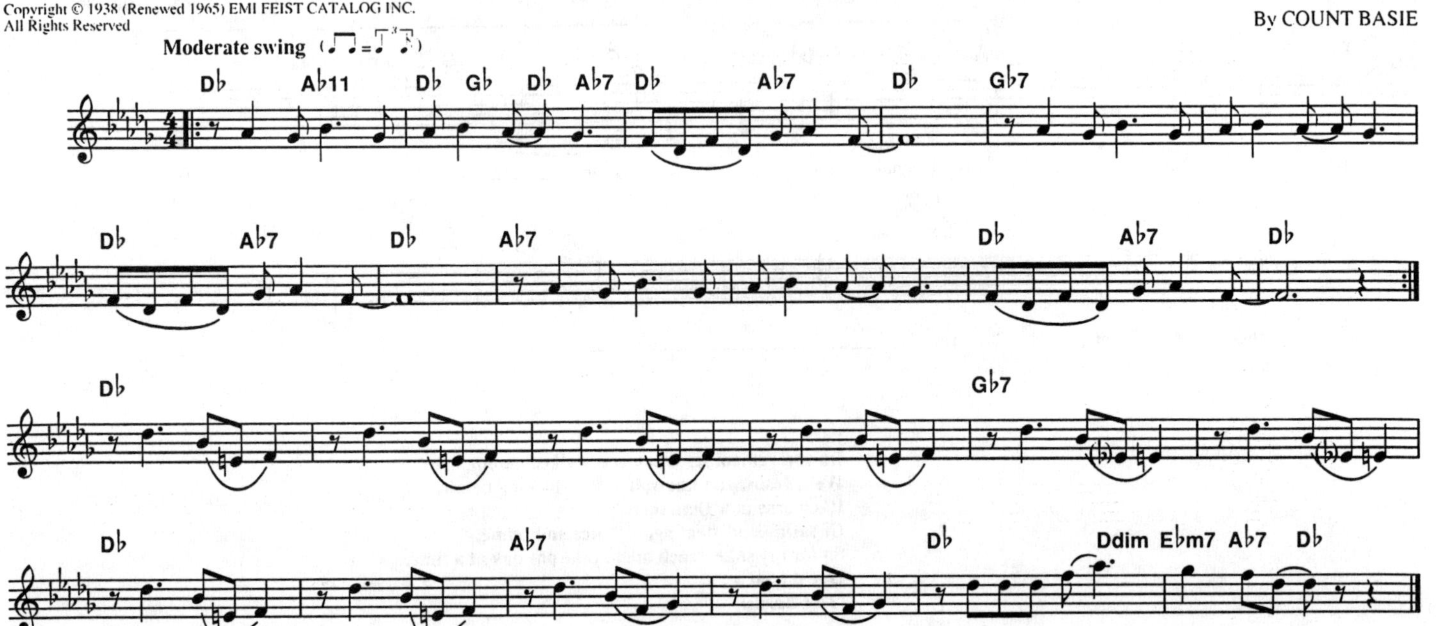
Moderate swing
Db Ab11 Db Gb Db Ab7 Db Ab7 Db Gb7
Db Ab7 Db Ab7 Db Ab7 Db
Db Gb7
Db Ab7 Db Ddim Ebm7 Ab7 Db

ONLY A ROSE

Word and Music by
BRIAN HOOKER and
RUDOLPH FRIML

Moderately
Ab Eb7 Ab Ab7 Db Dbm Ab
On-ly a rose I give you, on-ly a song dy-ing a - way.
Eb7 Ab C G7 C F7
On-ly a smile to keep in mem-o - ry, un-til we meet an-oth-er day;
Bb7 Eb7 Ab Eb7 Ab Ab7 Db F7
on-ly a rose to whis - per blush-ing as ros - es do;
Bbm Dbm Ab Eb7 Ab
I'll bring a-long a smile or a song for an - y - one, on-ly a rose for you.

ONLY THE LONELY
(Know the Way I Feel)

Words and Music by
ROY ORBISON and
JOE MELSON

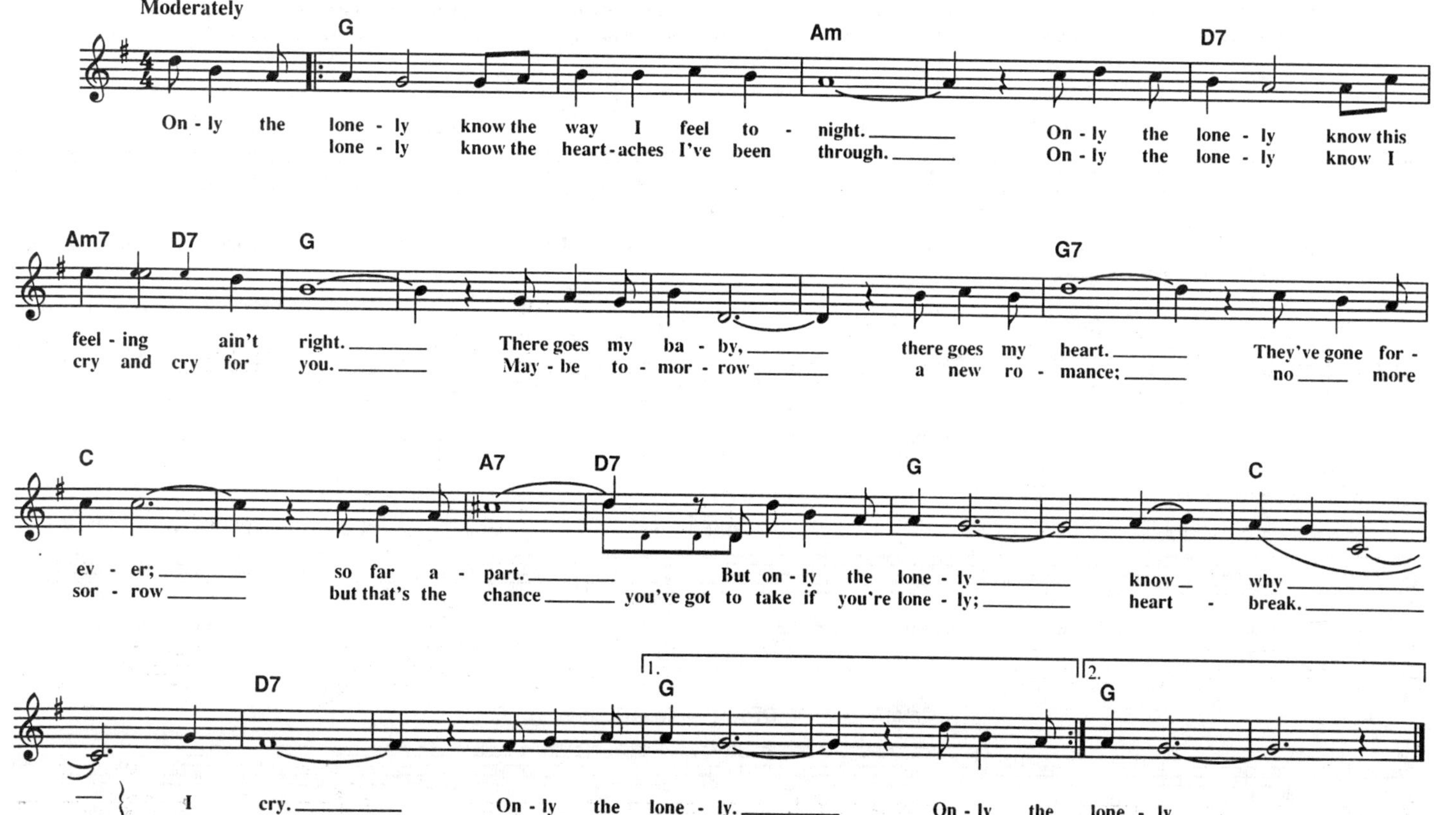
Moderately
G Am D7
On - ly the lone - ly know the way I feel to - night. On - ly the lone - ly know this
lone - ly know the heart-aches I've been through. On - ly the lone - ly know I
Am7 D7 G G7
feel - ing ain't right. There goes my ba - by, there goes my heart. They've gone for -
cry and cry for you. May - be to - mor - row a new ro - mance; no more
C A7 D7 G C
ev - er; so far a - part. But on - ly the lone - ly know why
sor - row but that's the chance you've got to take if you're lone - ly; heart - break.
D7 1. G 2. G
I cry. On - ly the lone - ly. On - ly the lone - ly.

ONWARD, CHRISTIAN SOLDIERS

SIR ARTHUR SEYMOUR SULLIVAN

Moderately

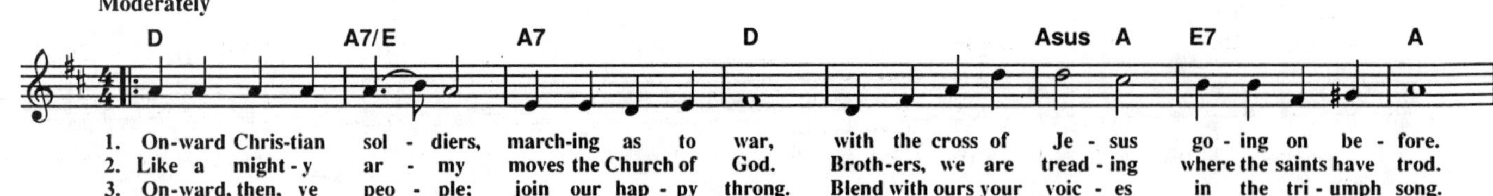
D A7/E A7 D Asus A E7 A
1. On-ward Chris-tian sol - diers, march-ing as to war, with the cross of Je - sus go - ing on be - fore.
2. Like a might - y ar - my moves the Church of God. Broth-ers, we are tread - ing where the saints have trod.
3. On-ward, then, ye peo - ple; join our hap - py throng. Blend with ours your voic - es in the tri - umph song.

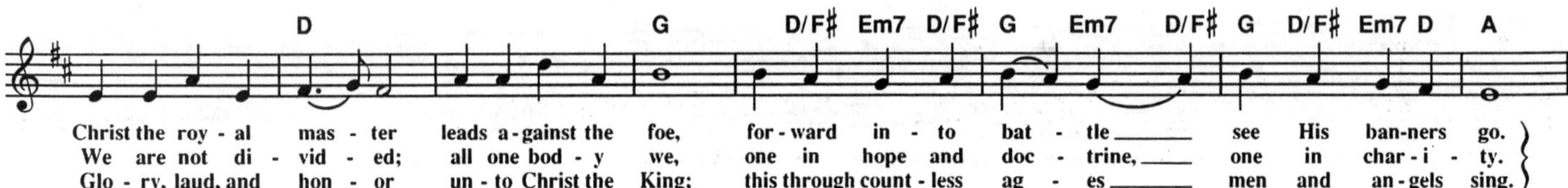
D G D/F♯ Em7 D/F♯ G Em7 D/F♯ G D/F♯ Em7 D A
Christ the roy - al mas - ter leads a - gainst the foe, for - ward in - to bat - tle see His ban-ners go.
We are not di - vid - ed; all one bod - y we, one in hope and doc - trine, one in char - i - ty.
Glo - ry, laud, and hon - or un - to Christ the King; this through count - less ag - es men and an - gels sing.

Chorus:
D A7sus A7 D /F♯ G A7 Bm F♯m G D A D D
1.2. 3.
On-ward Chris-tian Sol - diers march-ing as to war. With the cross of Je - sus, go - ing on be - fore. fore.

From the M-G-M Motion Picture "FAME"

OUT HERE ON MY OWN

Lyrics by LESLIE GORE
Music by MICHAEL GORE

Moderate ballad

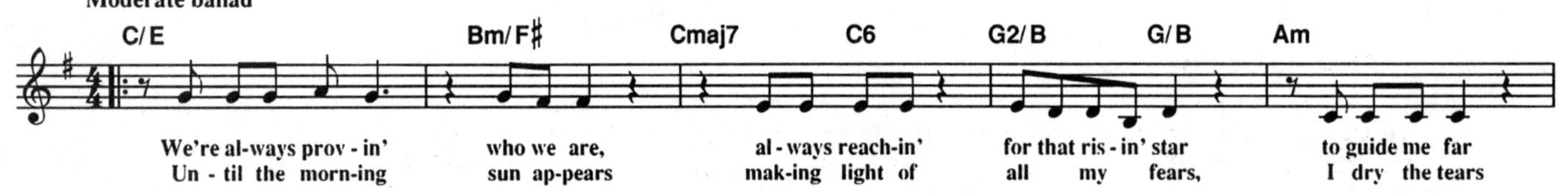
C/E Bm/F♯ Cmaj7 C6 G2/B G/B Am
We're al-ways prov - in' who we are, al - ways reach-in' for that ris - in' star to guide me far
Un - til the morn-ing sun ap-pears mak-ing light of all my fears, I dry the tears

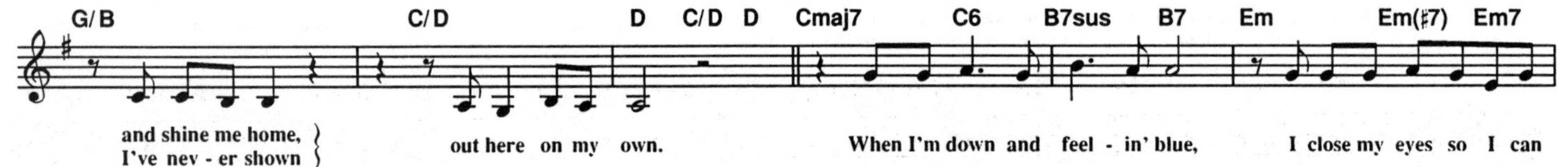
G/B C/D D C/D D Cmaj7 C6 B7sus B7 Em Em(♯7) Em7
and shine me home,
I've nev - er shown
out here on my own. When I'm down and feel - in' blue, I close my eyes so I can

G/A A F♯m7 Bm7 F♯m7 Bm7 C C(9) C
be with you. Oh, ba - by, be strong for me; ba - by, be - long to me. Help me through. Help

1. 2.
F♯sus F♯ F♯sus F♯ C/E Bm/F♯ Cmaj7 C6 G2/B G/B
me need you. me need you. Some-times I won-der where I've been, who I am, do I fit in.

Am7 G/B Cmaj7 D7sus D7 G D/G C/G G
I may not win, but I can't be thrown, out here on my own, on my own.

OOBY DOOBY

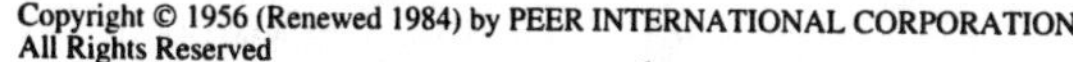

Words and Music by
WADE MOORE and
DICK PENNER

Bright shuffle

Verse:

C Gm6 C Gm6 C Gm6 C Gm6 C Gm6
Hey, ba - by come o - ver here. _ When you do the Oo - by Doo - by, I want to be near. _ You wig - gle and you shake like a

Chorus:
C Gm6 C F7 G7 C F C9 F Fm6 C
big rat - tle snake. _ You do the Oo - by Doo - by till you think you're gon - na break. Oo - by Doo - by, Oo - by Doo - by, Oo - by Doo - by, Oo - by

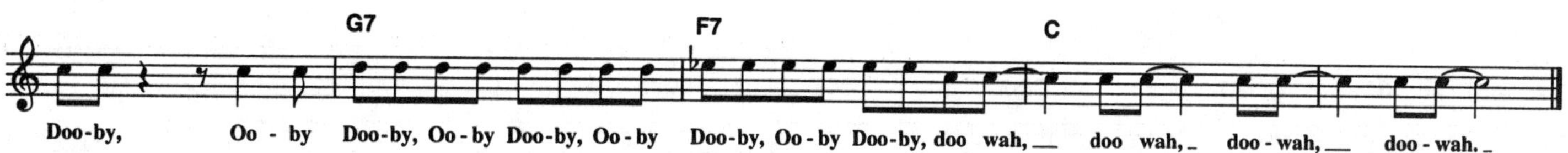
G7 F7 C
Doo - by, Oo - by Doo - by, Oo - by Doo - by, Oo - by Doo - by, Oo - by Doo - by, doo wah, _ doo wah, _ doo - wah, _ doo - wah. _

OUR DELIGHT

By TADD DAMERON

Medium swing tempo

E♭9(♭5) B♭9 A9 Em7 A9 A♭maj7 Cm7 F13 B9(♭5) B♭9)
To Coda

1.
F9 E9 E♭9 D9 D♭9 C7(♯9) B9(♭5)
2.
F9 E9 E♭9 D9 D♭9 C7(♯9) B♭m7 A9 A♭maj7 E♭m7

Em7 A9 Am7 D7(♭9) D♭maj7 D♭6/9 E♭m7 Fm7 D♭maj7 Dm7 D♭maj7 D♭maj7 G♭9

D.S. al Coda
Cm7 F9 Bm7 E9 Bm7 B♭m7 B9(♭5)
Coda
F9 E9 E♭9 D9 D♭9 C7(♯9) B♭m7 A9 A♭maj7

OUR DAY WILL COME

Words by BOB HILLIARD
Music by MORT GARSON

Moderately

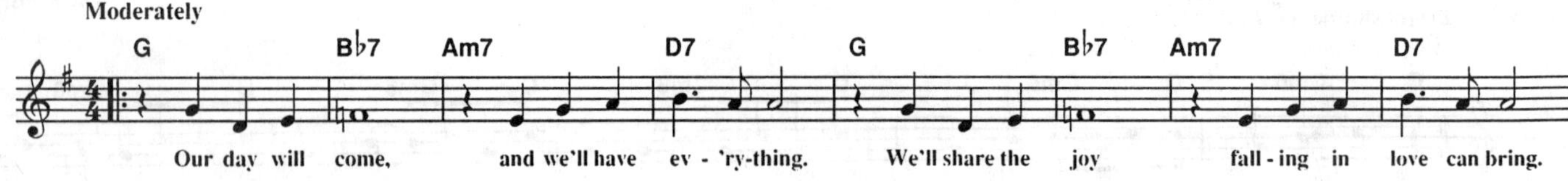
G
B♭7
Am7
D7
G
B♭7
Am7
D7
Our day will come, and we'll have ev - 'ry-thing. We'll share the joy fall - ing in love can bring.

Dm7
Dm7/G
Dm7
G7
Cmaj7
Cm7
Bm7
B♭7
Am7
D7
3
3
No one can tell me that I'm too young to know I love you so, and you love me.

G
B♭7
Am7
D7
G
B♭7
Am7
D7
Dm7
Dm7/G
Our day will come if we just wait a while. No tears for us; think love and wear a smile. Our dreams have

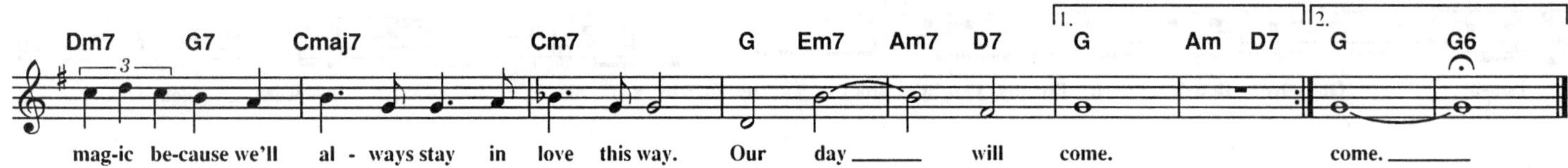
Dm7
G7
Cmaj7
Cm7
G
Em7
Am7
D7
1.
G
Am
D7
2.
G
G6
3
mag-ic be-cause we'll al - ways stay in love this way. Our day will come. come.

OVER THE WAVES

J. ROSAS

Moderately

G
D7

G

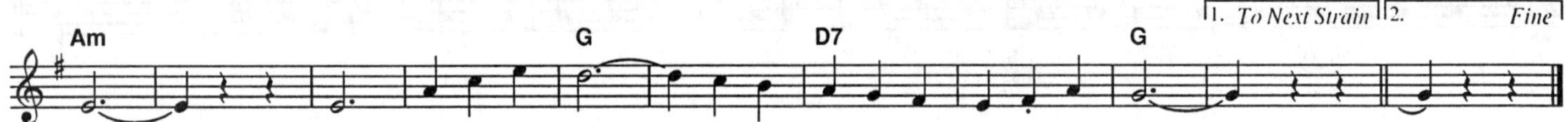
Am
G
D7
G
1. To Next Strain
2. Fine

G
D7

G
E7

Am
G
D7
G
1.
2. D.C. al Fine

OUT OF NOWHERE

Words and Music by
EDWARD HEYMAN and
JOHNNY GREEN

Moderately
Gmaj7 B♭m7 E♭7 B♭m7 E♭7 Gmaj7
You came to me from out of no - where. You took my heart and found it
Bm7 E7 Bm7 E7 Am Bm7(♭5) E7 Am7 E♭9
free. Won-der - ful dreams, won - der - ful schemes from no - where made ev - 'ry hour
D7 B♭7 Am7 A♭9 D9 Gmaj7 B♭m7 E♭7
sweet as a flow - er for me. If you should go back to your no - where,
B♭m7 E♭7 Gmaj7 Bm7 E7 Bm7 E7 Am7
leav - ing me with a mem - o - ry, I'll al - ways wait
Bm7(♭5) E7 Am7 Cm(maj7) Bm7 B♭dim Am7 D7 G (Am7 D7)
for your re - turn out of no - where, hop - ing you'll bring your love to me.

Featured in the M-G-M Picture "THE WIZARD OF OZ"

OVER THE RAINBOW

Lyric by E.Y. HARBURG
Music by HAROLD ARLEN

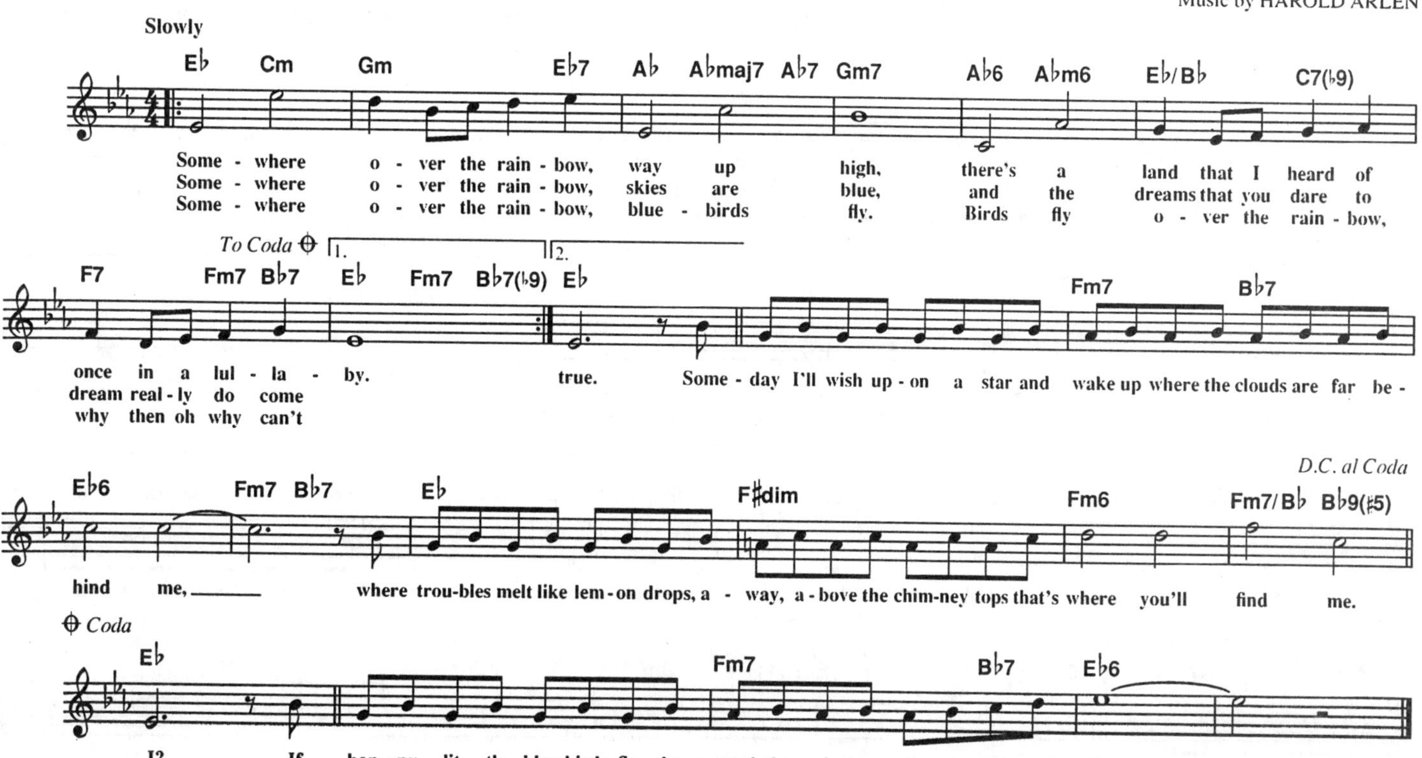
Slowly
E♭ Cm Gm E♭7 A♭ A♭maj7 A♭7 Gm7 A♭6 A♭m6 E♭/B♭ C7(♭9)
Some - where o - ver the rain - bow, way up high, there's a land that I heard of
Some - where o - ver the rain - bow, skies are blue, and the dreams that you dare to
Some - where o - ver the rain - bow, blue - birds fly. Birds fly o - ver the rain - bow,
To Coda 1. 2.
F7 Fm7 B♭7 E♭ Fm7 B♭7(♭9) E♭ Fm7 B♭7
once in a lul - la - by. true. Some - day I'll wish up - on a star and wake up where the clouds are far be -
dream real - ly do come
why then oh why can't
D.C. al Coda
E♭6 Fm7 B♭7 E♭ F♯dim Fm6 Fm7/B♭ B♭9(♭5)
hind me, where trou-bles melt like lem - on drops, a - way, a - bove the chim-ney tops that's where you'll find me.
Coda
E♭ Fm7 B♭7 E♭6
I? If hap - py lit - tle blue birds fly be - yond the rain - bow, why oh why can't I?

OVER THERE

Words and Music by GEORGE M. COHAN

Moderately, march-like

Bb F7 Bb
O - ver there; o - ver there; send the word, send the word o - ver there; that the
Eb Ebm F7 Bb Cdim Gm Bbm6 F Cdim C7 Cm Ab7 F7
Yanks are com - in', the Yanks are com - in', the drums rum - tum-ming ev - 'ry - where. So pre -
Bb F7
pare, say a prayer. Send the word, send the word to be - ware. We'll be
Bb F7 Bb Bb7 Eb Gb7 F7 Bb
o - ver, we're com - ing o - ver, and we won't be back till it's o - ver o - ver there.

From the "PATTY DUKE" T.V. Show

PATTY DUKE THEME

Lyric by BOB WELLES
Music by SID RAMIN

Moderately

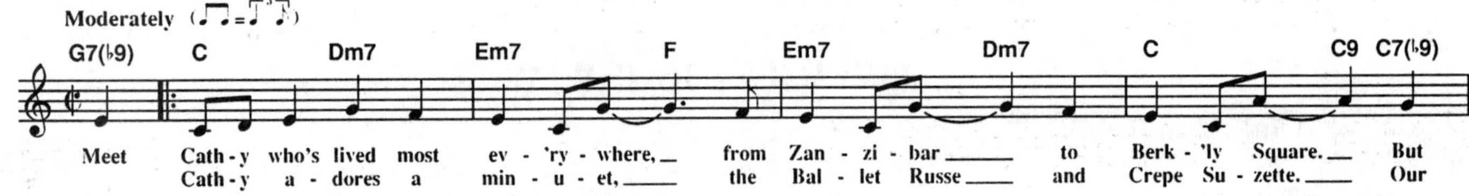
G7(b9) C Dm7 Em7 F Em7 Dm7 C C9 C7(b9)
Meet Cath - y who's lived most ev - 'ry - where, from Zan - zi - bar to Berk - 'ly Square. But
Cath - y a - dores a min - u - et, the Bal - let Russe and Crepe Su - zette. Our

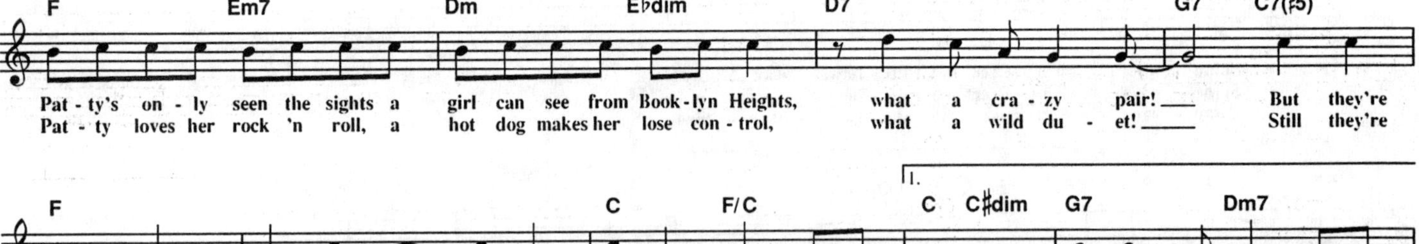
F Em7 Dm Ebdim D7 G7 C7(#5)
Pat - ty's on - ly seen the sights a girl can see from Book - lyn Heights, what a cra - zy pair! But they're
Pat - ty loves her rock 'n roll, a hot dog makes her lose con - trol, what a wild du - et! Still they're
1.
F C F/C C C#dim G7 Dm7
cous - ins, i - den - ti - cal cous - ins, all the way. One pair of match - ing book -
cous - ins, i - den - ti - cal cous - ins, and you'll find,

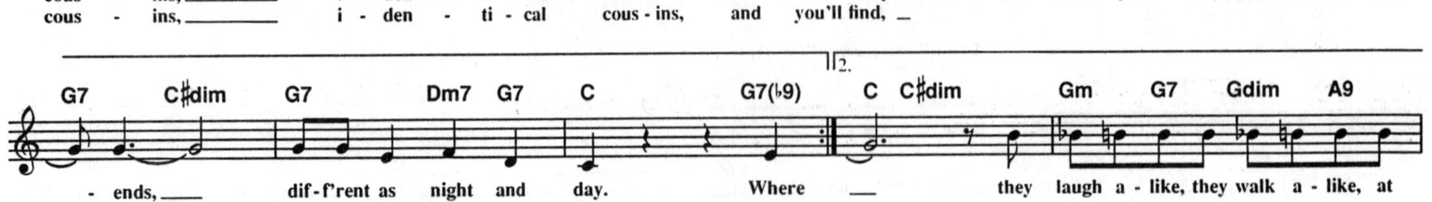
2.
G7 C#dim G7 Dm7 G7 C G7(b9) C C#dim Gm G7 Gdim A9
- ends, dif - f'rent as night and day. Where they laugh a - like, they walk a - like, at

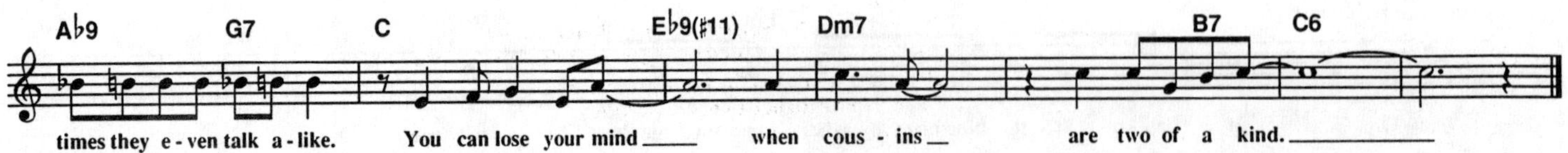
Ab9 G7 C Eb9(#11) Dm7 B7 C6
times they e - ven talk a - like. You can lose your mind when cous - ins are two of a kind.

OVERJOYED

Words and Music by
STEVIE WONDER

Moderately slow ballad
Bb(2) Eb(2) Cm7 Fm7
1. O - ver time, I've been build - ing my cas - tle of love
I have picked out a per - fect come true,
Bb(2) Eb(2) Cm7 F/A G/B
just for two, though you nev - er knew you were my rea - son. I've
though you nev - er knew it was of you I'd been dream - ing. The
C(2) G(2)/B Gm/C F(2)
gone much too far for you now to say that I've got to throw my
sand - man has come from too far a - way for you to say, "Come back
1. Bb(2) 2.3. Bb(2) Chorus: Abmaj7
cas - tle a - way. 2. O - ver dreams some oth - er day." 1.2. And though you don't be - lieve that they do,
im - prob - a - ble,
Eb(2)/G Fm7 Bb Db C
they do come true. For did my dreams come true when I looked at you; can make it true if
what do they know? For in ro - mance all true love needs is a chance. And may-be with a
Bbmaj7 F(2)/A Fm/Ab Fm7 Bb7/F
you would be - lieve, you too might be o - ver - joyed o - ver love.
chance you will find you too like I
1. Bbsus Bb Db6 C7 Cbmaj7 C7 Db6 C7 Cbmaj7 Bb D.S.
o - ver me. 3. O - ver hearts
2. Fm7/Bb Bb Fm7/Bb Bb 3. Fm7/Bb
o - ver me. 3. And though the odds say o - ver you.
Eb Abmaj7 Emaj7 Ebmaj7 Dmaj7 Ab/Eb Ab Db
O - ver you.

Verse 3:
Over hearts I have painfully turned every stone
Just to find I have found what I've searched to discover.
I've come much too far for me now to find
Love that I sought can never be mine.
(To Chorus:)

PAGAN LOVE SONG

By ARTHUR FREED and
NACIO HERB BROWN

Moderately
C F9 C G7 C
Come with me where moon-beams light Ta - hi - tian skies, and the star - lit wa - ters
G7 C G7 C A♭7
lin - ger in your eyes. Na - tive hills are call - ing, to them we be -

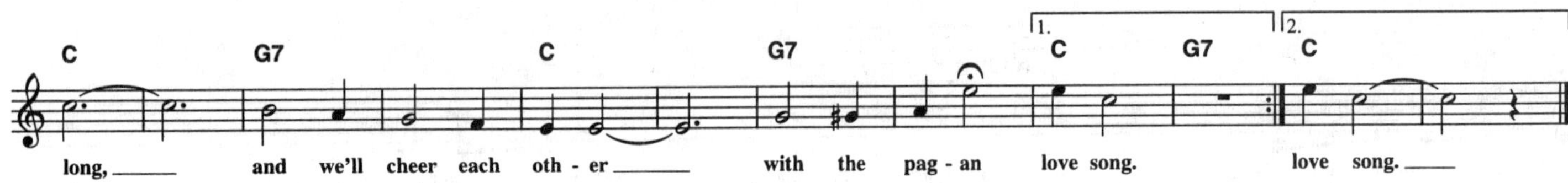
1. 2.
C G7 C G7 C G7 C
long, and we'll cheer each oth - er with the pag - an love song. love song.

PEPPERMINT TWIST

Words and Music by
JOEY DEE and HENRY GLOVER

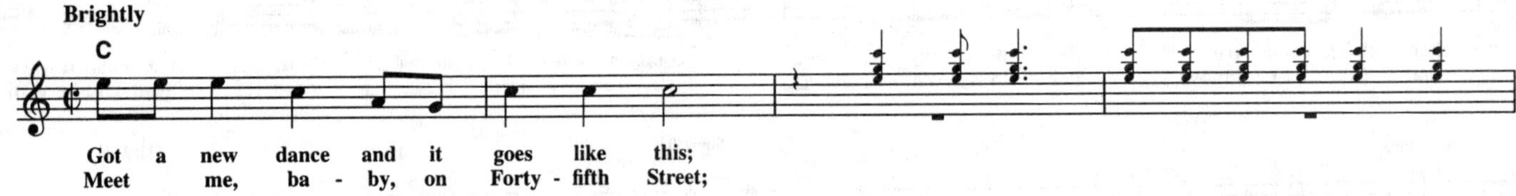
Brightly
C
Got a new dance and it goes like this;
Meet me, ba - by, on Forty - fifth Street;

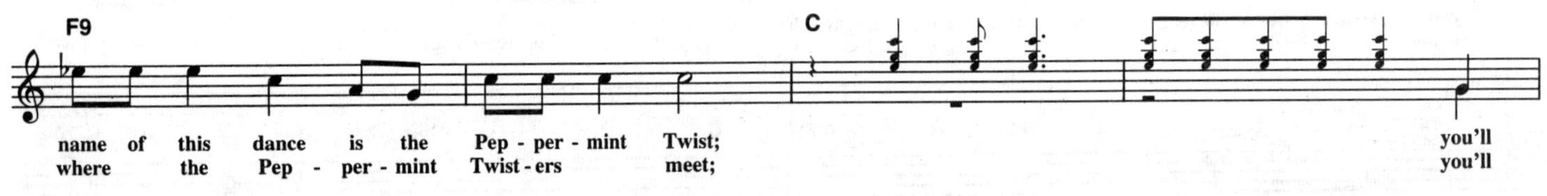
F9 C
name of this dance is the Pep - per - mint Twist; you'll
where the Pep - per - mint Twist - ers meet; you'll

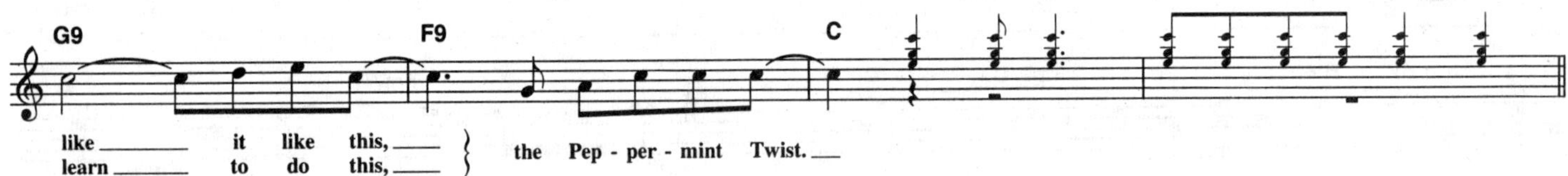
G9 F9 C
like it like this,
learn to do this,
the Pep - per - mint Twist.

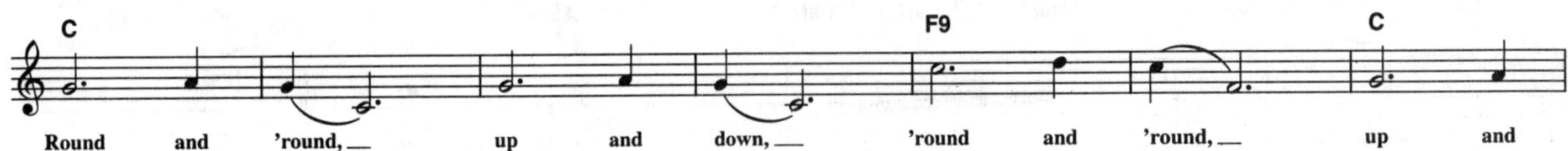
C F9 C
Round and 'round, up and down, 'round and 'round, up and

D.C.
G7 F9 C
down, it's 'round and 'round and up and down, one - two - three kick! One - two - three jump!

PAINTING THE CLOUDS WITH SUNSHINE

Words by AL DUBIN
Music by JOE BURKE

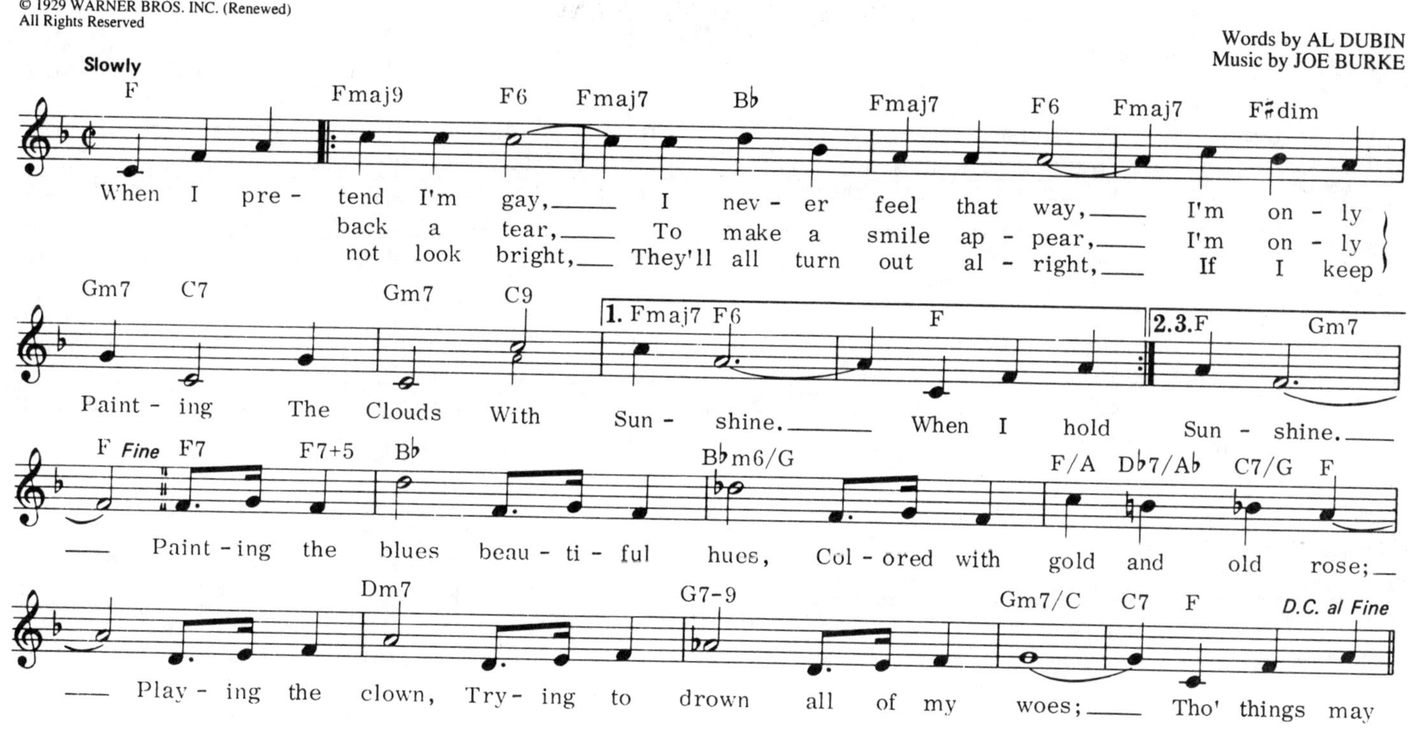
Slowly
F Fmaj9 F6 Fmaj7 B♭ Fmaj7 F6 Fmaj7 F♯dim
When I pre - tend I'm gay, I nev - er feel that way, I'm on - ly
back a tear, To make a smile ap - pear, I'm on - ly
not look bright, They'll all turn out al - right, If I keep
Gm7 C7 Gm7 C9 1. Fmaj7 F6 F 2.3. F Gm7
Paint - ing The Clouds With Sun - shine. When I hold Sun - shine.
F Fine F7 F7+5 B♭ B♭m6/G F/A D♭7/A♭ C7/G F
Paint - ing the blues beau - ti - ful hues, Col - ored with gold and old rose;
Dm7 G7-9 Gm7/C C7 F D.C. al Fine
Play - ing the clown, Try - ing to drown all of my woes; Tho' things may

PARA LOS RUMBEROS

Words and Music by
TITO PUENTE

Moderately (double time feeling)

Gm C F Gm

Gm C Gm C Gm C
Va - mos rum - be - ros que la rum - ba ya va em - pe - zar Va - mos rum - be - ros que la

Gm C Repeat 4 times Gm C 3 Gm C
rum - ba ya va em - pe - zar.

Gm C Gm C Gm C
Va - mos {tim - be - ro / con - gue - ro} que la rum - ba ya va em - pe - zar, Va - mos {tim - be - ro / con - gue - ro} que la

Gm C Gm C Gm C Gm C Gm C
rum - ba ya va em - pe - zar.

Gm C Gm C Gm
Va - mos San - ta - na que la rum - ba ya va em - pe - zar.

C F Gm C F Gm

From the United Artists Motion Picture "PARIS BLUES"

PARIS BLUES

Words by BILLY STRAYHORN
and HAROLD FLENDER
Music by DUKE ELLINGTON

Moderately
Dmaj7 G7(♭5) Dmaj7 D7 G Gm6 D E9(♭5) D6 D7(♭9)
Left bank ca - fés, stroll-ing the quays, watch-ing the boats on the Seine, come back a - gain. Where is that
Sip-ping cham - pagne a - long the main bou - le-vards, she was so fine, just like that wine. Now ev - 'ry

1. To next strain
2. Fine
E7(♭9) A7 D6 D7(♭9) E7(♭9) A7 D6 D7(♭9) E7(♭9) A13(♯9) E7(♭9) A13(♯9) D G7(♭5) Dmaj7
girl I met? The girl that made me get those Par - is blues, and won - der: lose those Par - is blues.
day is black. Please, some - one send her back so I can

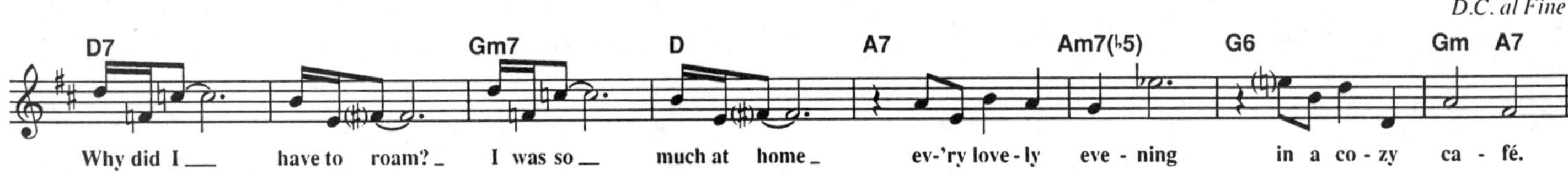
D.C. al Fine
D7 Gm7 D A7 Am7(♭5) G6 Gm A7
Why did I have to roam? I was so much at home ev-'ry love - ly eve - ning in a co - zy ca - fé.

PEG O' MY HEART

Words by ALFRED BRYAN
Music by FRED FISHER

Slowly
B♭ C9 Cm7 F9
Peg o' my heart, I love you. Don't let us part, I love you. I al - ways knew
Peg o' my heart, your glan - ces make my heart say, "How's chan - ces?" Come, be my own,
1. 2.
Cm7 F9 B♭ B♭maj7 D♭dim F7/C F7 Cm7 F9 B♭
it would be you. Since I heard your lilt - ing laugh-ter, it's your I-rish heart I'm af-ter. come, make your home in my heart.

PEGGY O'NEIL

Words and Music by
HARRY PEASE, ED G. NELSON, GILBERT DODGE

Moderately
C Cdim G7 F G7
If her eyes are blue as skies, that's Peg - gy O' - Neil. If she's smil - ing all the

C Cdim G7 C Cdim G7
while, that's Peg - gy O' - Neil. If she walks like a sly lit - tle rogue, if she talks with a cute lit - tle

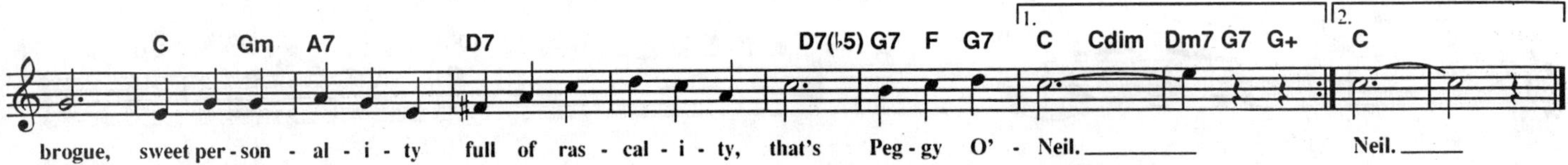
1. 2.
C Gm A7 D7 D7(♭5) G7 F G7 C Cdim Dm7 G7 G+ C
brogue, sweet per - son - al - i - ty full of ras - cal - i - ty, that's Peg - gy O' - Neil. Neil.

PENNSYLVANIA 6-5000

Words by CARL SIGMAN
Music by JERRY GRAY

Moderate swing

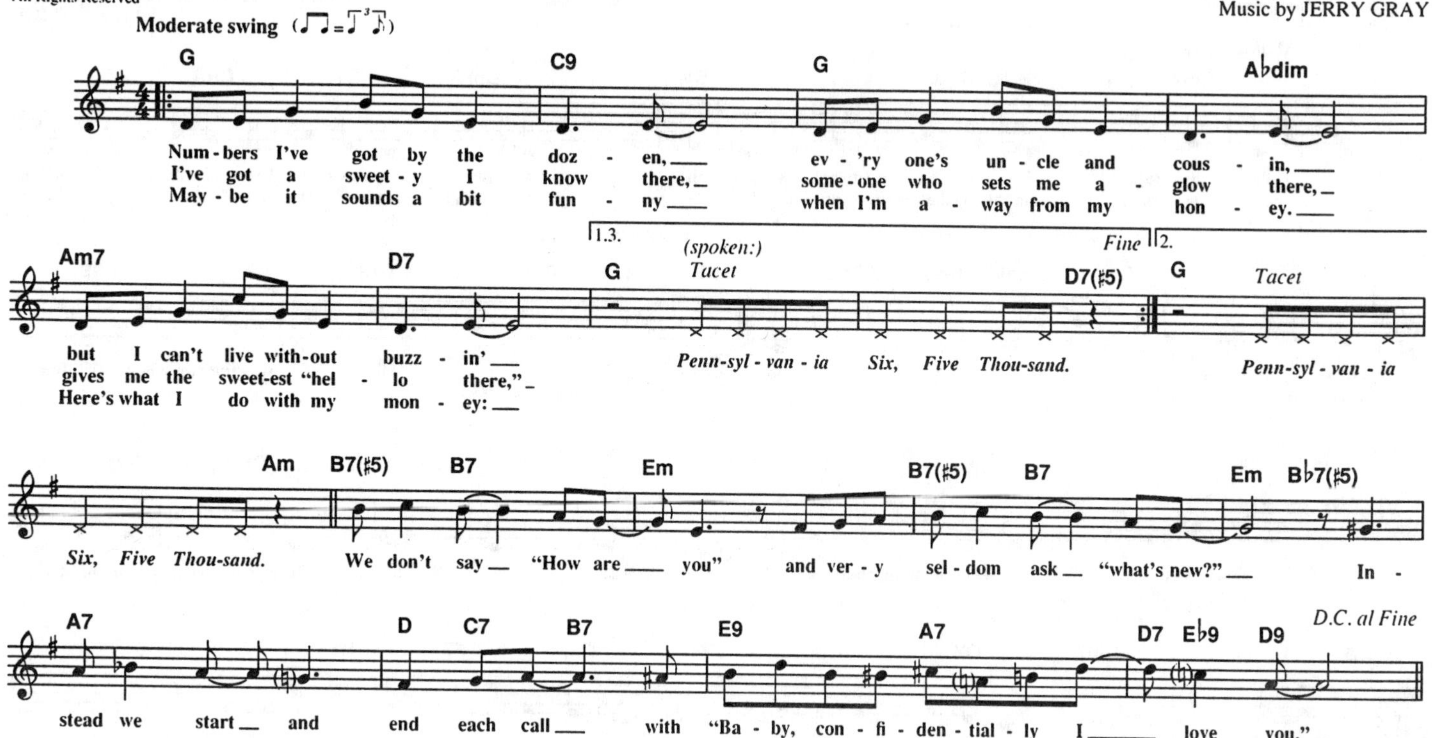
G C9 G A♭dim
Num-bers I've got by the doz - en, ev - 'ry one's un - cle and cous - in,
I've got a sweet - y I know there, some-one who sets me a - glow there,
May - be it sounds a bit fun - ny when I'm a - way from my hon - ey.
Am7 D7
but I can't live with-out buzz - in'
gives me the sweet-est "hel - lo there,"
Here's what I do with my mon - ey:
1.3. G (spoken:) Tacet D7(♯5) Fine
Penn-syl - van - ia Six, Five Thou-sand.
2. G Tacet
Penn-syl - van - ia Six, Five Thou-sand.
Am B7(♯5) B7 Em B7(♯5) B7 Em B♭7(♯5)
We don't say "How are you" and ver - y sel - dom ask "what's new?" In -
A7 D C7 B7 E9 A7 D7 E♭9 D9 D.C. al Fine
stead we start and end each call with "Ba - by, con - fi - den - tial - ly I love you."

PENTHOUSE SERENADE

Words and Music by
WILL JASON and
VAL BURTON

Moderately

Just picture a pent-house 'way up in the sky, with hing-es on chim-neys for stars to go by; a sweet slice of heav-en for just you and I when we're a - lone. From all of so-ci-e-ty we'll stay a-loof, and live in pro-pri-e-ty there on the roof, two heav-en-ly her-mits we will be in truth when we're a - lone.

We'll see life's mad pat-tern as we view old Man-hat-tan then we can thank our luck-y stars, that we're liv-ing as we are.

In our lit-tle pent-house, we'll al-ways con-trive to keep love and ro-mance for-ev-er a-live, in view of the Hud-son just o-ver the drive, when we're a - lone.

PERDIDO

By
H.J. LENGSFELDER, ERVIN DRAKE
and JUAN TIZOL

Medium swing
Cm7 F7 Cm7 F7 B♭ Dm7 G7 Cm7 F7
Per - di - do, I look for my heart, it's Per - di - do. I lost it way down in Tor - ri - do, while
le - ro, she glanced as she danced a bo - le - ro. I said, tak - ing off my som - bre - ro, "Let's
Cm7 F7 1. B♭6 E♭9 Dm7 G7(♭9) 2. B♭6 E♭9 B♭6 D13 D9 A♭9
chanc-ing a dance fi - es - ta. Bo - es - ta." High was the sun when we first
meet for a sweet si -
G13 C13 C9 G♭9 F13 Cm7 F7 Cm7 F7
came close; low was the moon when we said, "A - dios!" Per - di - do, since then has my heart been Per -
B♭ Dm7 G7 Cm7 F7 Cm7 F7 B♭6 E♭9 B♭6
di - do, I know I must go to Tor - ri - do, that yearn-ing to lose Per - di - do.

PLEASE BE KIND

Words and Music by
SAMMY CAHN and SAUL CHAPLIN

Moderato

C Cmaj7/E E♭dim Dm7 G11 Fm6/A♭ G7 C Cmaj7/E E♭dim
This is my first af - fair, so, please be kind. Han-dle my heart with care, oh,

Dm7 G11 Fm6/A♭ G7 C7 Gm7(♭5) C7 F E♭7 D7 Am7(♭5)
please be kind. This is all so grand, my dreams are on pa - rade, if you'll just un - der -

D7 Dm7/A Fm6/A♭ G7 C Cmaj7/E E♭dim Dm7 G11
stand, they'll nev - er, nev - er fade. So tell me your love's sin - cere, oh, please be kind.

Fm6/A♭ G7 C7 Cm6 C7 F Fm C7 Fm
Tell me I need - n't fear, oh, please be kind, 'cause if you leave me,

C7 Fm C/G Gm6/B♭ A7 A♭7 A7 D7 Fm6/A♭ G9 Fm6/G C
dear, I know my heart will lose its mind. If you love me, please be kind.

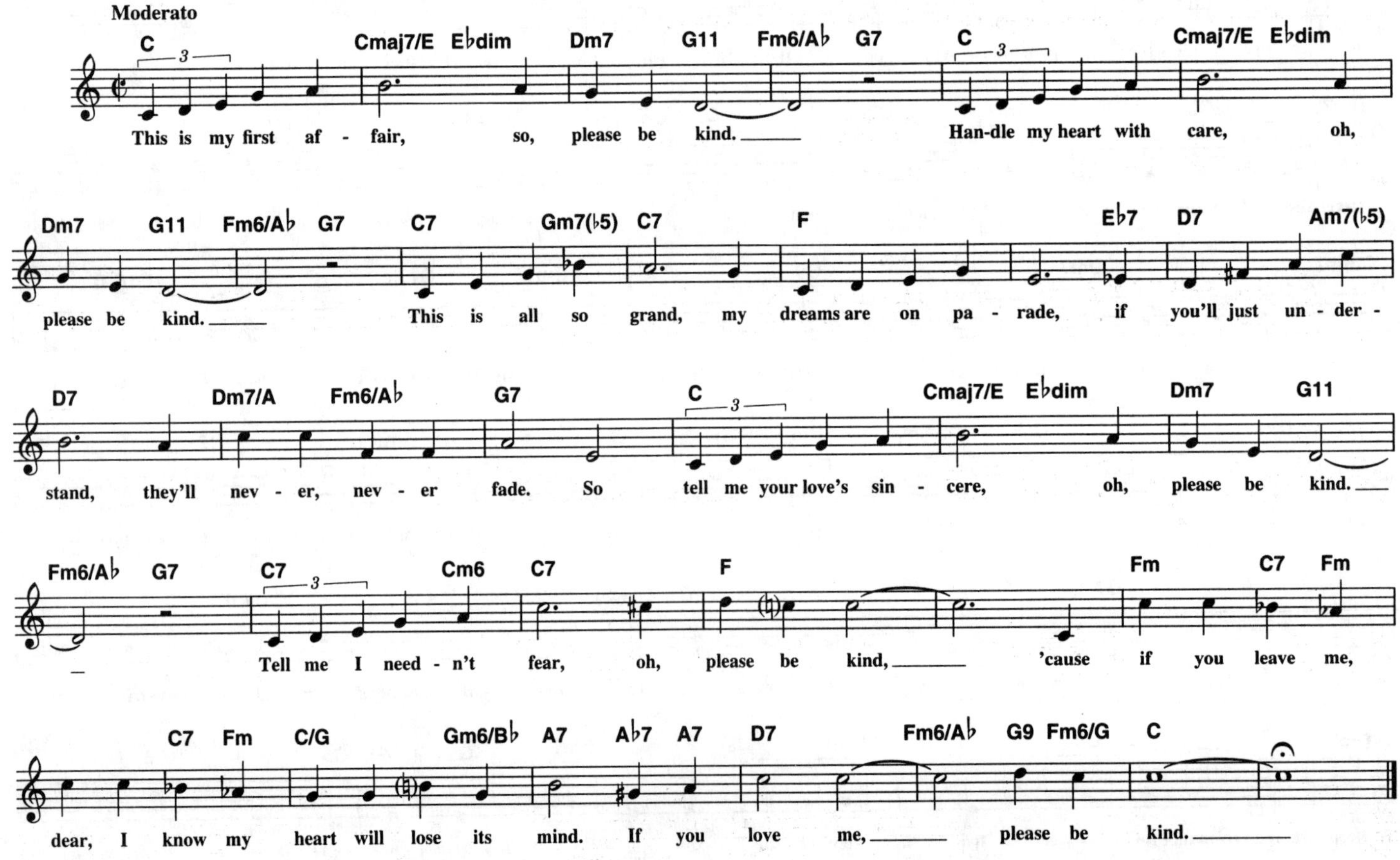

PERHAPS, PERHAPS, PERHAPS
(Quizas, Quizas, Quizas)

English Lyrics by JOE DAVIS

Moderate Latin beat

Em Am B7 Em A Em B7

You won't ad-mit you love me,_ and so how am I ev - er_ to know? You al-ways tell me,_ "Per -

Em B7 Em Am6 Em Am B7 Em Am B7

haps, per-haps, per - haps."___ A mil-lion times I've asked you,_ and then I ask you o - ver_ a - gain. You on-ly

Em B7 Em B7 Em Am6 Em F♯m7 B7 F♯m7 B7 E

an - swer,_ "Per - haps, per-haps, per - haps."___ If you can't make your mind up,_ we'll ne - ver_ get start - ed.___

F♯m7 B7 F♯m7 B7 E Em Am B7

_ And I don't want to wind up_ be-ing part - ed,_ brok-en heart-ed.___ So, if you real-ly love me,_ say, "yes." But if you

Em Am B7 Em B7 Em B7 1. Em 2. Em

don't, dear,_ con - fess. And please don't tell me,_ "Per - haps, per-haps, per - haps." You won't ad-mit you haps."___

A PARISIAN THOROUGHFARE

By EARL "BUD" POWELL

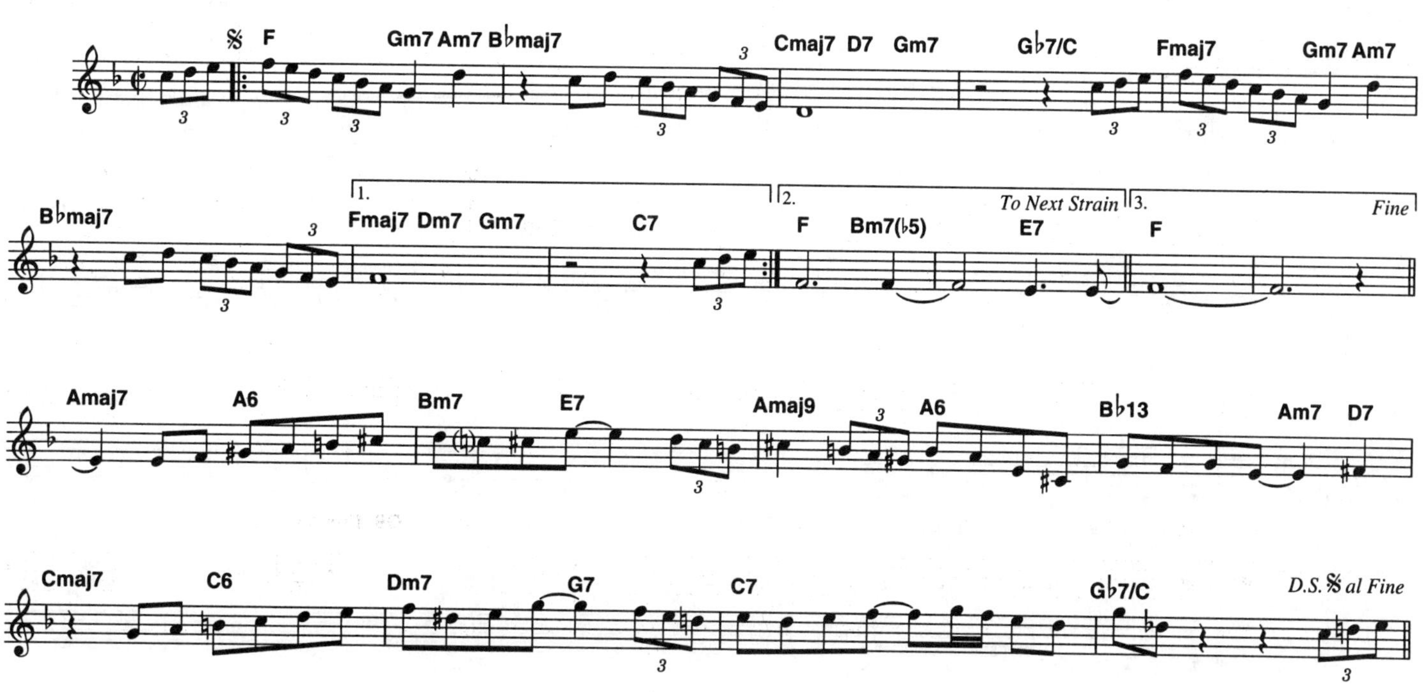
F Gm7 Am7 B♭maj7 Cmaj7 D7 Gm7 G♭7/C Fmaj7 Gm7 Am7
B♭maj7
1. Fmaj7 Dm7 Gm7 C7
2. F Bm7(♭5) E7
To Next Strain
3. F
Fine
Amaj7 A6 Bm7 E7 Amaj9 A6 B♭13 Am7 D7
Cmaj7 C6 Dm7 G7 C7 G♭7/C
D.S. al Fine

PETER GUNN THEME

By HENRY MANCINI

Moderate rock
F9
1.
2.
3
E9/F F9
Gbmaj13
Fmaj7

Theme Song from the Mirisch - G & E Production, "THE PINK PANTHER," a United Artists Release

THE PINK PANTHER

Music by
HENRY MANCINI

Moderately slow
Em
C7
simile
F7
Em N.C.
To Coda
C
D.S. al Coda
Coda
Em(maj9)

Inspired by the Columbia Pictures' Feature Film "THE PRINCE OF TIDES"

PLACES THAT BELONG TO YOU

Lyrics by
ALAN and MARILYN BERGMAN
Music by
JAMES NEWTON HOWARD

Moderate ballad

A Amaj7 Dmaj7 Bm9 Bm9/E Esus E A Amaj7 Dmaj7
Morn - ings, eve - nings, days that hur - ried past, dreams that should have last - ed. Mo - ments, ho - urs,
Bm9 B7sus Bm7 Em9 A7sus A Dmaj7 F♯maj7 Em7(4) A A/G F♯m7 Bm7
slip - ping by as we told each oth - er se - crets. Some - how I'll nev - er let go of the mem - 'ries.
Em7 Asus Bm7(2) A(2) G D(9)/F♯ Em7 G/A F♯/A♯ Bm(2)
Some-thing al - ways seems to re - mind me of how it was, of what it was, when it was all there
Esus 4 2 E A Amaj7 Dmaj7 Bm9 Bm9/E Esus E A Amaj7
was. Laugh - ter, love songs, foot - steps that I hear make me think you're near me. Po - ems,
Dmaj7 Bm9 Em9 A7sus A Dmaj7 F♯m7 Cmaj9 Am9
pic - tures, let - ters nev - er mailed, boats that nev - er sailed. Re - mem - ber that e - ven though we can't be to -
F♯m7 Bm Em7 Asus Bm(2) A(2) G D(9)/F♯ Cmaj9 Dsus 4 2 D♯dim
geth - er, we're more for hav - ing loved one an - oth - er. We shared the sky, we learned to fly.
Emaj7 G♯m7 Dmaj9 Bm9 G♯m7 C♯m7 F♯m7 B5 B7sus C♯m(2) B(2)
Some - day when some-one else - 's arms are a - round us, when time has put some dis - tance be - tween us, the
A E(sus2)/G♯ F♯m7 E(sus2)/G♯ Amaj7 A/B G♯5/B♯ C♯(2) E/F♯ F♯
years will kind - ly show how mem - 'ries come and go. They ebb and flow like the tides.
B Bmaj7 Emaj7 C♯m9 C♯m9/F♯ E/F♯ F♯ B Bmaj7 Emaj7 C♯m9
There are qui - et plac - es in my heart ev - er since we part - ed. Gen - tle, ten - der, trac - es of a song,
C♯m9/F♯ E/F♯ F♯ B(2) B Bmaj7 Emaj7 C♯m9 E/F♯ F♯7sus F♯ B(2)
plac - es that be - long to you.

POP! GOES THE WEASEL

TRADITIONAL

Rather quickly
F C F C F
All a - round the cob - bler's bench, the mon - key chased the wea - sel; the

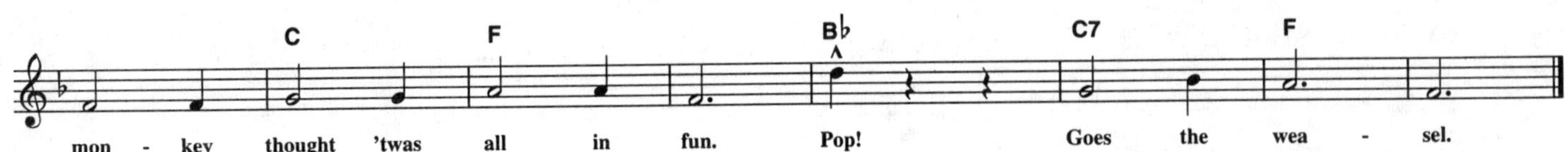
C F B♭ C7 F
mon - key thought 'twas all in fun. Pop! Goes the wea - sel.

PLYMOUTH ROCK

By NEAL HEFTI

Slow blues
A♭9 D9 D♭9 E♭m7 A♭9 E♭m7 A♭9

D♭9 D9 D♭9 E♭m7 A♭9 G♭9 F9 B♭9 E9 E♭9
1.
A♭9 F9 B♭m7 E♭9
2.
A♭11 G7(♯9) G♭9 F7(♭9) B♭m7 A7(♯5) A♭9

POLLY WOLLY DOODLE

TRADITIONAL

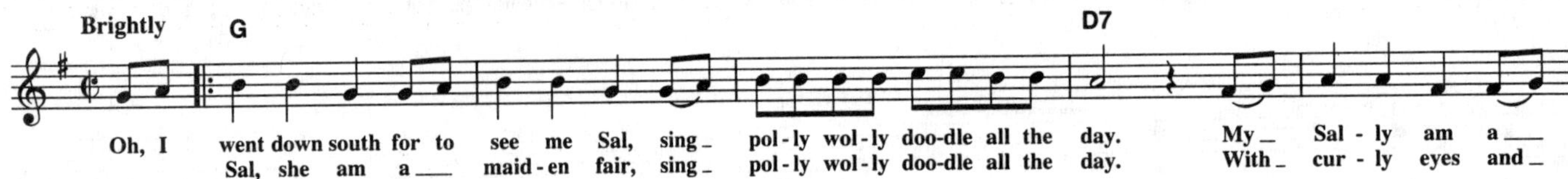
Brightly
G D7
Oh, I went down south for to see me Sal, sing pol - ly wol - ly doo - dle all the day. My Sal - ly am a
Sal, she am a maid - en fair, sing pol - ly wol - ly doo - dle all the day. With cur - ly eyes and

G
spunk - y girl, sing pol - ly wol - ly doo - dle all the day.
laugh - ing hair, sing pol - ly wol - ly doo - dle all the day.
Fare thee well, fare thee well, fare thee well, my fair - y

D7
1. G
2. G
fay. For I'm going to Lou'-is - an - a, for to see my Su - sy - an - na, sing pol - ly wol - ly doo - dle all the day. Oh, my day.

POLOVETZIAN DANCE (1st Theme)

BORODIN

Moderately

Gm7 C7 F Gm Dm

B♭m6 F B♭m F Gm7

Gm6 Dm Gm Gm6 A Gm7 C7 F

Gm F Cdim Gm7 C7 F

POMP AND CIRCUMSTANCE

E. ELGAR

Slowly

B♭ F7 B♭ E♭ B♭ Cm F B♭ C7 F Dm Gm7

C7 F F7 B♭ F7 B♭ E♭ B♭ C7 F B♭ C7 F

E♭ F7 B♭ B♭7 E♭ F7 B♭ Gm Cm F7 B♭

PUT ON YOUR OLD GREY BONNET

Words by STANLEY MURPHY
Music by PERCY WENRICH

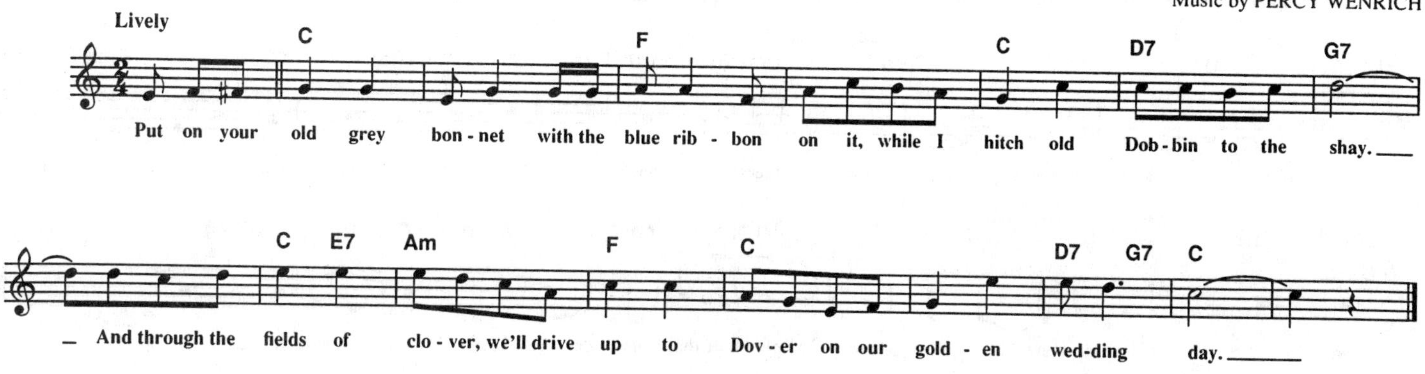

Lively

C F C D7 G7

Put on your old grey bon - net with the blue rib - bon on it, while I hitch old Dob - bin to the shay.

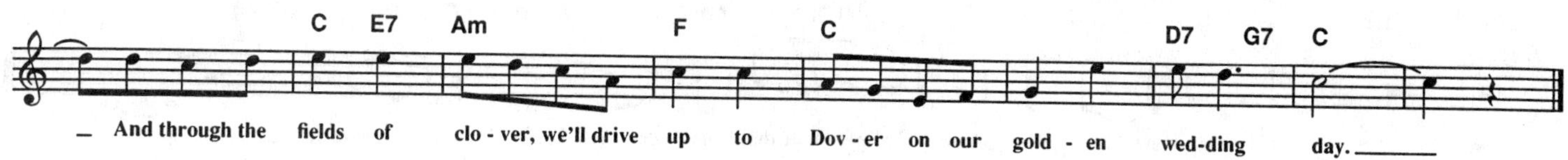
C E7 Am F C D7 G7 C
— And through the fields of clo - ver, we'll drive up to Dov - er on our gold - en wed-ding day.

PRAISE THE LORD AND PASS THE AMMUNITION

FRANK LOESSER

Moderately
Praise the Lord and pass the am - mu-ni - tion! Praise the Lord and pass the am - mu-ni - tion. Praise the Lord and pass the am - mu-ni - tion and we'll all stay free.
Praise the Lord and swing in-to po-si - tion. Can't af - ford to sit a-round a-wish - in'. Praise the Lord we're all be-tween per-di - tion and the deep blue sea.
Yes, the sky pi - lot said it you've got to give him cred - it for a son-of-a-gun of a gun - ner was he.
Shout-ing: "Praise the Lord, we're go - ing on a mis-sion! All a-board! We're not a-go - in' fish - in'. Praise the Lord and pass the am - mu-ni - tion and we'll all stay free."
PRELUDE TO A KISS
Copyright © 1938 (Renewed 1966) MILLS MUSIC, INC., c/o EMI MUSIC PUBLISHING
World-wide Print Rights administered by CPP/BELWIN, INC., Miami, FL 33014
All Rights Reserved
By DUKE ELLINGTON, IRVING MILLS
and IRVING GORDON
Slowly
If you hear a song in blue, like a flow - er cry - ing for the dew, that was my heart ser - e - nad - ing you; my prelude to a kiss.
If you hear a song that grows from my ten - der sen - ti - men - tal woes, that was my heart try-ing to com - pose a pre-lude to a kiss.
Though it's just a sim-ple mel - o - dy with noth-ing fan - cy, noth-ing much, you could turn it to a sym - pho - ny, a Schu-bert tune with a Gersh-win touch. Oh, how my love song gent - ly cries for the ten - der - ness with - in your eyes. My love is a pre - lude that nev - er dies, a pre-lude to a kiss.

PRECIOUS AND FEW

Words and Music by
WALTER D. NIMS

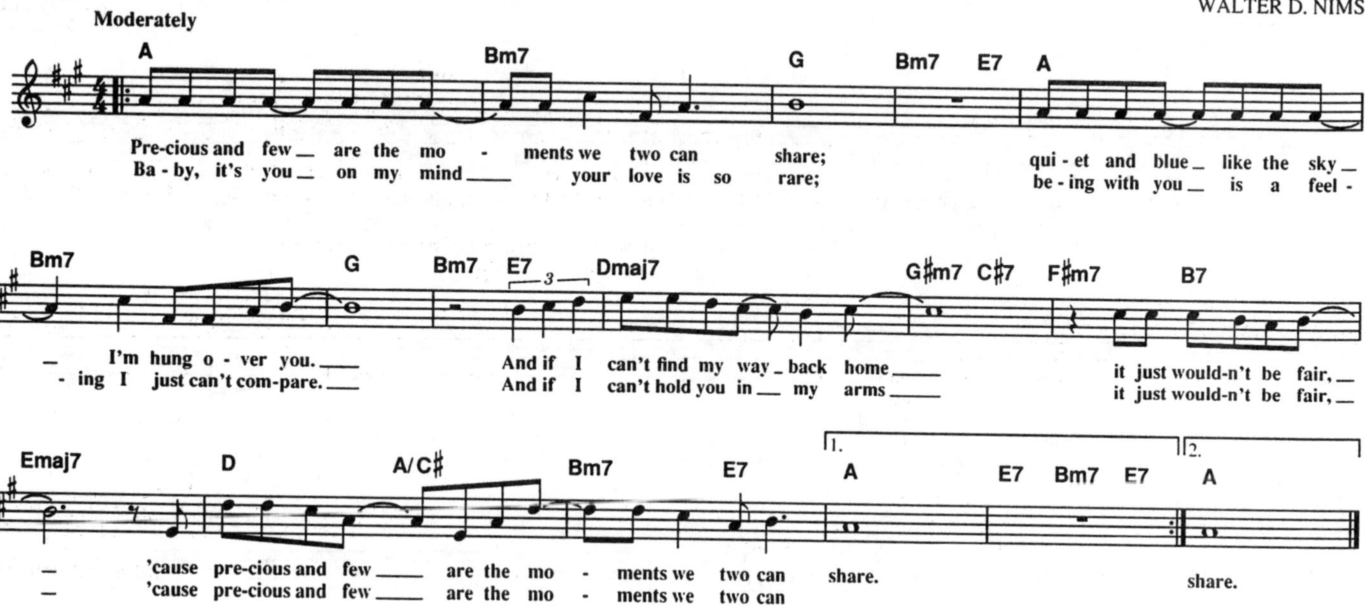

Moderately

Pre-cious and few are the mo - ments we two can share; qui - et and blue like the sky I'm hung o - ver you. And if I can't find my way back home it just would-n't be fair, 'cause pre-cious and few are the mo - ments we two can share.

Ba - by, it's you on my mind your love is so rare; be - ing with you is a feel - ing I just can't com-pare. And if I can't hold you in my arms it just would-n't be fair, 'cause pre-cious and few are the mo - ments we two can share.

PROUD MARY

Words and Music by
J.C. FOGERTY

Moderately

Fine

Verse:

Left a good job in the cit - y, work-in' for the man ev - 'ry night and day; and I nev - er lost one min - ute of sleep - in' wor-ry-ing 'bout the way things might have been.

Chorus:

Big wheel keep on turn - in', Proud Mar - y keep on burn - in'. Roll - in', roll - in', roll - in' on the riv - er.

1.2. *D.C.* | 3.

Roll - in', roll - in', roll - in' on the riv - er.

D.C. al Fine

Verse 2:
Cleaned a lot of plates in Memphis,
Pumped a lot of pain in New Orleans,
But I never saw the good side of the city,
Until I hitched a ride on a river boat queen.
(To Chorus:)

Verse 3:
If you come down to the river,
Bet you gonna find some people who live.
You don't have to worry 'cause you have no money,
People on the river are happy to give.
(To Chorus:)

PUT A LITTLE LOVE IN YOUR HEART

Words and Music by
JIMMY HOLIDAY, RANDY MEYERS
and JACKIE DE SHANNON

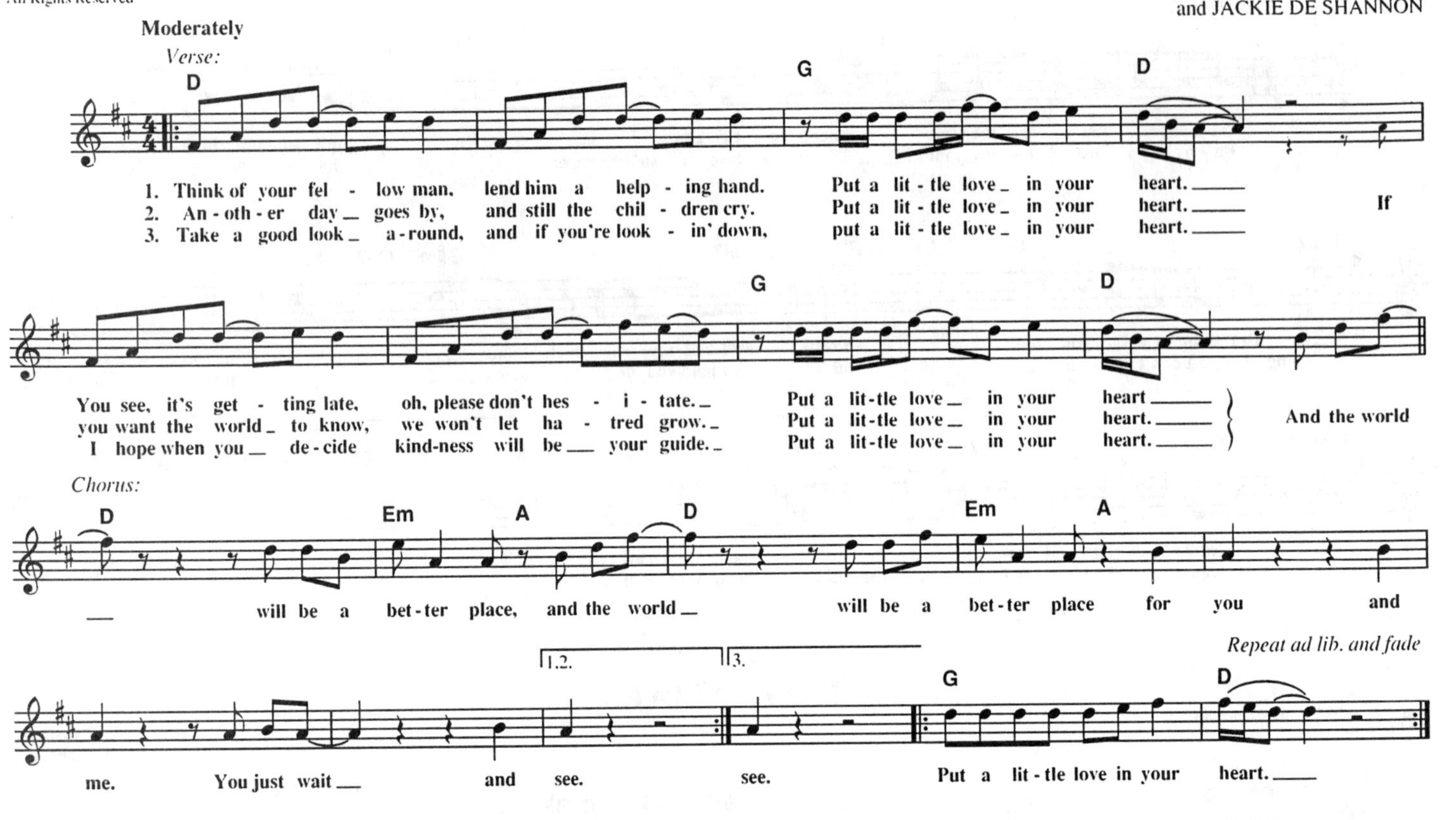
Moderately
Verse:
D G D
1. Think of your fel - low man, lend him a help - ing hand. Put a lit - tle love in your heart.
2. An - oth - er day goes by, and still the chil - dren cry. Put a lit - tle love in your heart.
3. Take a good look a - round, and if you're look - in' down, put a lit - tle love in your heart.
If
G D
You see, it's get - ting late, oh, please don't hes - i - tate. Put a lit-tle love in your heart
you want the world to know, we won't let ha - tred grow. Put a lit-tle love in your heart.
I hope when you de - cide kind-ness will be your guide. Put a lit-tle love in your heart.
And the world
Chorus:
D Em A D Em A
will be a bet - ter place, and the world will be a bet - ter place for you and
1.2. 3. G D
Repeat ad lib. and fade
me. You just wait and see. see. Put a lit - tle love in your heart.

From the Broadway Musical "BYE BYE BIRDIE"

PUT ON A HAPPY FACE

Lyric by LEE ADAMS
Music by CHARLES STROUSE

Moderate swing
Refrain:
Eb Eb6 Gm7 C7 Fm7 Bb9 Fm7 Bb9 Eb Eb6 Gm7 C7
Gray skies are gon - na clear up, put on a hap - py face. Brush off the clouds and cheer up,
Fm7 Bb9 Bbm7 Eb7 Abmaj7 D7 G7 C7 F7 Bb7 Ebmaj7 Eb7 Eb6
put on a hap - py face. Take off that gloom - y mask of trag - e - dy, it's not your style.
Abmaj7 D7 G7 C7 F7 Fm7/Bb Bb9 Eb Eb6 Gm7 C7 Fm7 Bb9
You'll look so good that you'll be glad ya' de - cid - ed to smile! Pick out a pleas-ant out-look, stick out that no - ble
Fm7 Bb9 Eb Eb6 Gm7 C7 Fm7 Bb9 Bbm7 Eb7 Abmaj7 Bb9/Ab Eb/G Eb
chin. Wipe off that "full of doubt" look, slap on a hap - py grin! And spread sun - shine all
Fm7 Bb7 G7(#5) G7 C9 F9 Fm7/Bb Bb9 1. Eb Eb6 Fm7 Bb7 2. Eb Eb6 Fm7 Eb
o - ver the place, just put on a hap - py face! face!

PUT YOUR ARMS AROUND ME, HONEY
Copyright © 1994 by BEAM ME UP MUSIC (ASCAP), c/o CPP/BELWIN, INC., Miami, FL 33014
All Rights Reserved
Words by JUNIE McCREE
Music by ALBERT VON TILZER
Moderately bright
Put your arms a-round me, hon-ey, hold _ me tight. Hud-dle up and cud - dle up with all _ your might. Oh! Oh!
Won't you roll those eyes, _ eyes that I just i-dol-ize. _ When they look at me, _ my heart be - gins _ to float.
Then it starts a-rock - in' like a mo - tor boat. Oh! Oh! I nev-er know _ an-y { girl _ / boy _ } like you. _
QUIEN SERA
(Sway)
Copyright © 1953 by EDITORIAL MEXICANA DE MUSICAL INTERNACIONAL, S.A.
Copyright © 1954 (Renewed) by PEER INTERNATIONAL CORPORATION All Rights Reserved
English Lyric by NORMAN GIMBEL
Spanish Words and Music by
PABLO BELTRAN RUIZ
Moderately
When ma-rim-ba rhy-thms start to play, dance with me, make me sway, _ like the la-zy o-cean hugs the shore,
hold me close, sway me more. _ Like a flow-er bend-ing in the breeze, bend with me, sway with ease. _
When we dance you have a way with me, stay with me, sway with me. _ Oth-er danc-ers may be on the floor,
dear, but my eyes will see on-ly you. _ On-ly you have that mag-ic tech - nique, _ when we sway I grow weak.
I can hear the sound of vi - o-lins, long be-fore it be-gins. _ Make me thrill as on-ly you know how, sway me smooth,
sway me now. _ When ma-rim-ba rhy-thms sway me now. _ Sway me smooth, sway me now. _

RACING WITH THE MOON

Words by VAUGHN MONROE and PAULINE POPE
Music by JOHNNY WATSON

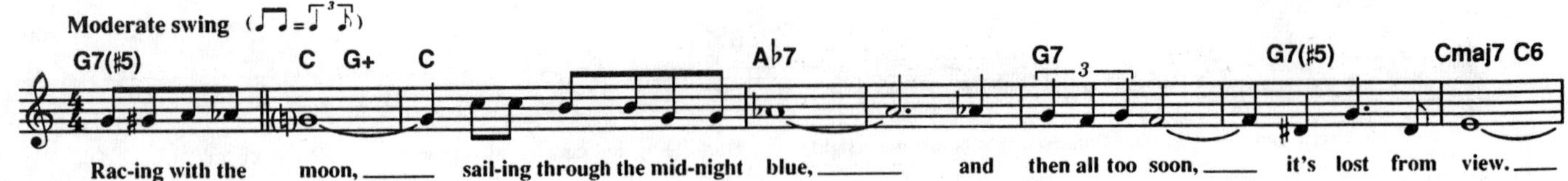
Moderate swing
G7(♯5) C G+ C A♭7 G7 G7(♯5) Cmaj7 C6
Rac-ing with the moon, sail-ing through the mid-night blue, and then all too soon, it's lost from view.

Dm7 G7(♯5) C G+ C A♭7 G7 G7(♯5) C A♭7 C
Gaz-ing at the stars shin-ing in the sum-mer night, but just like the moon, they fade from view. In the

Am B7 Gm6 A7(♯5) A7 Dm7 Ddim Am A♭7 G7 G7(♯5)
blue heav-ens I see your face smil-ing at me. My heart will nev-er be free un - til we're back to - geth-er. Rac-ing with the

C G+ C A♭7 G7 G7(♯5) C
moon, that is what I'll al-ways do, till I o-ver-take the moon and you.

RAGTIME COWBOY JOE

Words By GRANT CLARKE
Music by LEWIS F. MUIR and MAURICE ABRAHAMS

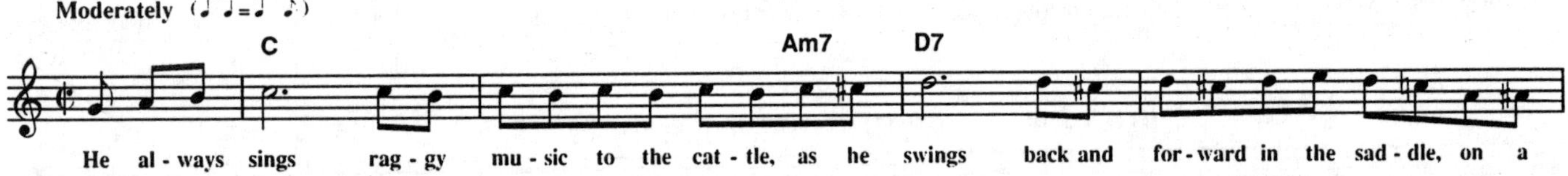
Moderately
C Am7 D7
He al-ways sings rag-gy mu-sic to the cat-tle, as he swings back and for-ward in the sad-dle, on a

G7 C C+ C6 D7 G7
horse that is syn-co-pat-ed, gait-ed, and there's such a fun-ny me-ter to the sound of his re-peat-er. How they

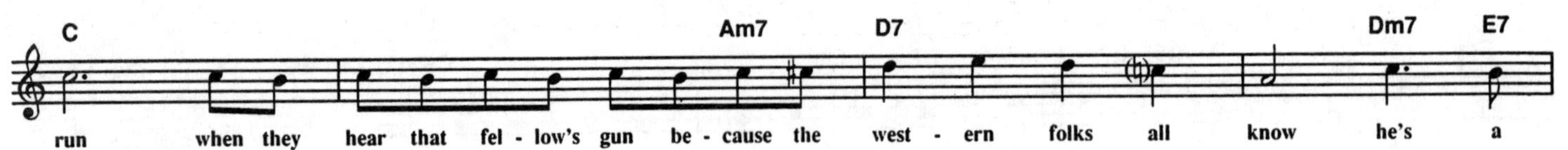
C Am7 D7 Dm7 E7
run when they hear that fel-low's gun be-cause the west-ern folks all know he's a

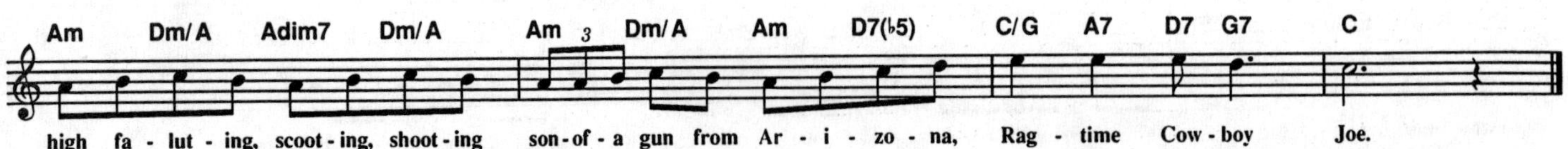
Am Dm/A Adim7 Dm/A Am Dm/A Am D7(♭5) C/G A7 D7 G7 C
high fa-lut-ing, scoot-ing, shoot-ing son-of-a gun from Ar-i-zo-na, Rag-time Cow-boy Joe.

Paramount Pictures Presents a Lucasfilm Ltd. Production a Steven Spielberg Film "RAIDERS OF THE LOST ARK"

RAIDERS MARCH

Music by JOHN WILLIAMS

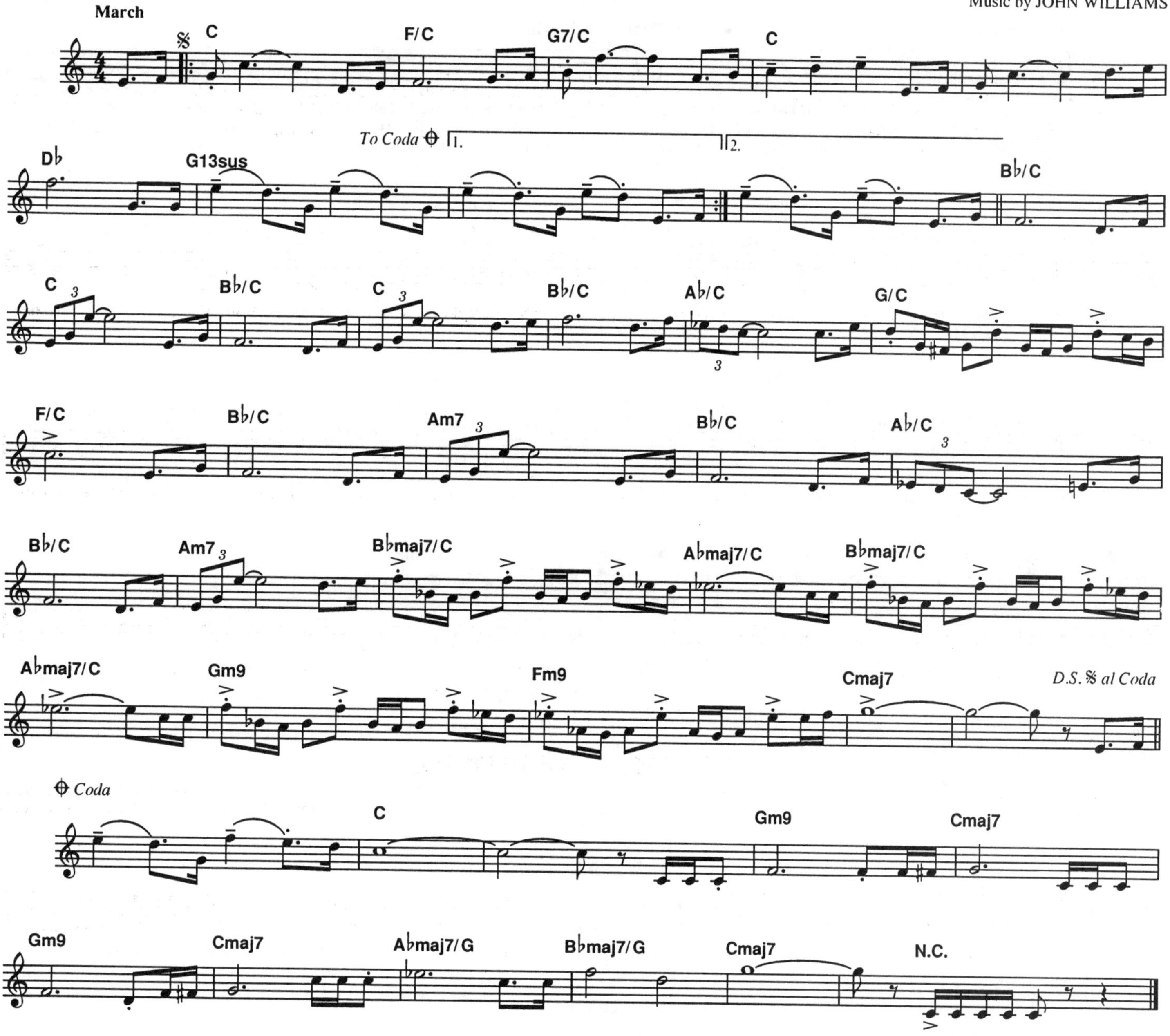

March

To Coda ⊕

D.S. 𝄋 al Coda

⊕ *Coda*

N.C.

RAMBLIN' ROSE

Words and Music by NOEL SHERMAN
and JOE SHERMAN

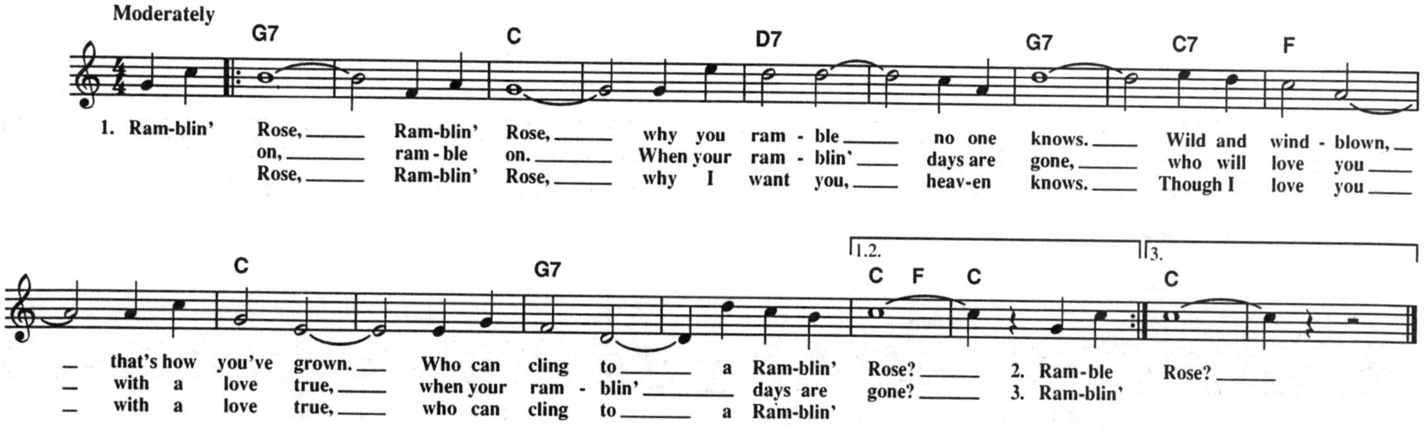

Moderately

1. Ram-blin' Rose, Ram-blin' Rose, why you ram-ble no one knows. Wild and wind-blown, that's how you've grown. Who can cling to a Ram-blin' Rose?
2. Ram-ble on, ram-ble on. When your ram-blin' days are gone, who will love you with a love true, when your ram-blin' days are gone?
3. Ram-blin' Rose, Ram-blin' Rose, why I want you, heav-en knows. Though I love you with a love true, who can cling to a Ram-blin' Rose?

RAINY DAYS AND MONDAYS

Words and Music by
PAUL WILLIAMS and
ROGER NICHOLS

Moderately

F Am Am7(♭5) D7sus D7 Gm Am7 Gm

1. Talk - in' to my - self ___ and feel - in' old, ___ some - times I'd like to quit, ___ noth - in' ev - er seems to fit. ___
2. What I've got they used ___ to call the blues, ___ noth - in' is real - ly wrong, ___ feel - in' like I don't be - long. ___
3. What I feel has come ___ and gone be - fore, ___ no need to talk it out, ___ we know what it's all a - bout. ___

Am Dm7 B♭maj7 Gm7 *To Coda* ⊕ F B♭ B♭/C

___ Hang - in' a - round, ___ noth - ing to do but frown. ___
___ Walk - in' a - round, ___ some kind of lone - ly clown. ___
___ Hang - in' a - round, ___ noth - ing to do but frown. ___
Rain - y days and Mon - days al - ways get me ___

F C7sus [1. F C7sus] [2. F] A7 Dm7 B♭maj7 Gm7 C7 Fmaj7

___ down. ___ ___ Fun - ny but it seems ___ I al - ways wind up here with you, ___

Am7 B♭maj7 C7 A7 Dm7 B♭maj7 Gm7 C7 Am7

nice to know some - bod - y ___ loves ___ me. ___ Fun - ny but it seems ___ that it's the on - ly thing to do, ___

B♭maj7 C7sus C7 *D.C. al Coda*

run and find ___ the one who ___ loves ___ me.

⊕ *Coda*

B♭ Gm7 Am B♭/C F

Rain - y days and Mon - days al - ways ___ get me down.

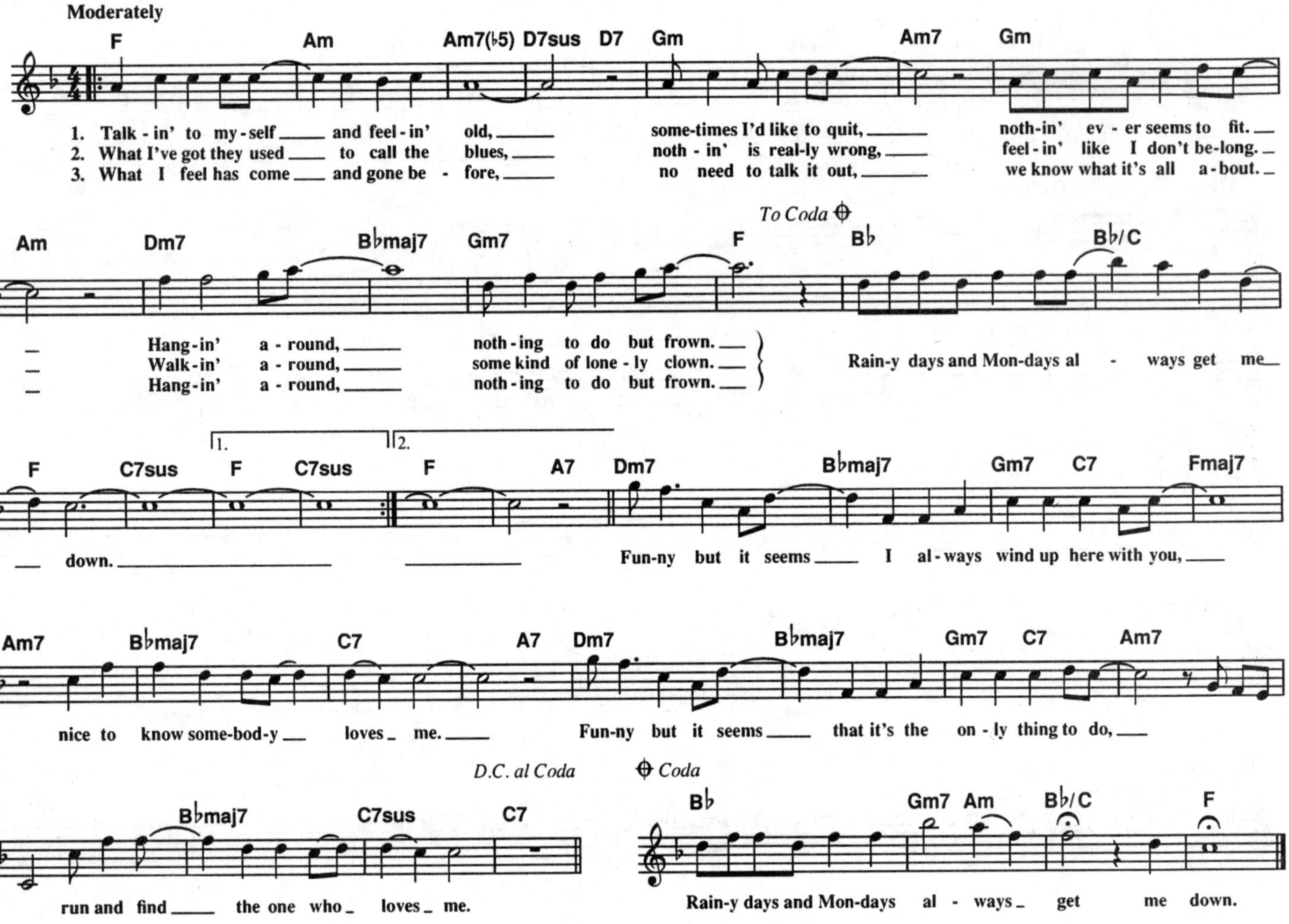

RAMONA

Words by L. WOLFE GILBERT
Music by MABEL WAYNE

Moderately

E♭ B♭7 E♭

Ra - mon - a, I hear the mis - sion bells a - bove. ___ Ra - mon - a, they're ring - ing out our song of love. ___ I

B♭7 E♭

press you, ca - ress you, and bless the day you taught me to care, to al - ways re - mem - ber the ram - bling rose you wear in your

B♭7 C7

hair. Ra - mon - a, when day is done you'll hear my call. ___ Ra - mon - a, we'll meet be - side the wat - er fall. ___ I

Fm A♭m6 Gm E♭dim D♭ C7 Fm B♭7 E♭

dread the dawn when I a - wake to find you gone. Ra - mon - a, I need you my own. ___

RHAPSODY IN BLUE

By GEORGE GERSHWIN

Moderately slow, with expression

play one octave higher 2nd time

F
C7
F
F/A
F6
Fmaj7
F
G7
C7(♯5)

F
C7
F
F/A
F6
Fmaj7
F7/E♭
B♭/D

D7/A
Gm7
C
Gm7
B♭m
B♭m6
B♭m(maj7)
B♭m
F/A
F6
Fmaj7
Dm7

1.
G7
G♭7
rit.
2.
G9(♭5)

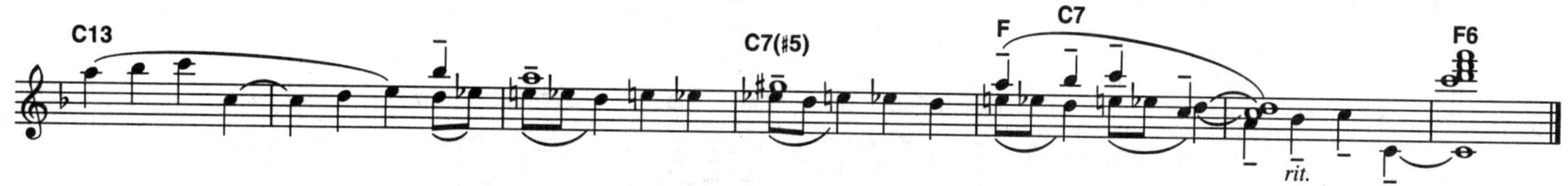
C13
C7(♯5)
F
C7
rit.
F6

From the Broadway Musical "LITTLE ME"

REAL LIVE GIRL

Lyric by CAROLYN LEIGH
Music by CY COLEMAN

Moderate waltz

G
Gmaj7
G6
Gmaj7
Am
Am(♯7)
Am7
D9
Am7
D9
Par-don me, miss, but I've nev-er done this with a real live girl.
Strayed off the farm with an

Am7
D9
G6
G13
G7(♯5)
ac-tu-al arm-ful of real live girl.
Par-don me if your af-fec-tion-ate squeeze.

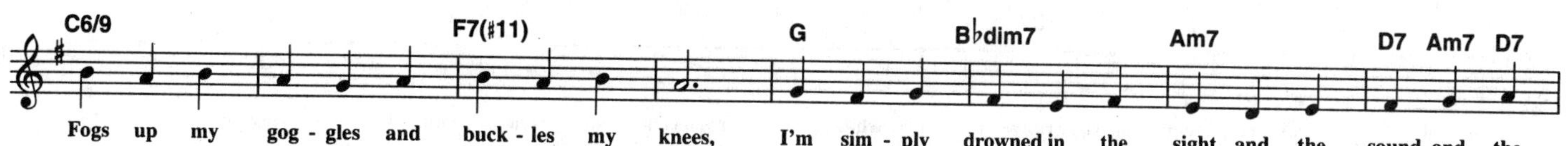
C6/9
F7(♯11)
G
B♭dim7
Am7
D7
Am7
D7
Fogs up my gog-gles and buck-les my knees, I'm sim-ply drowned in the sight and the sound and the

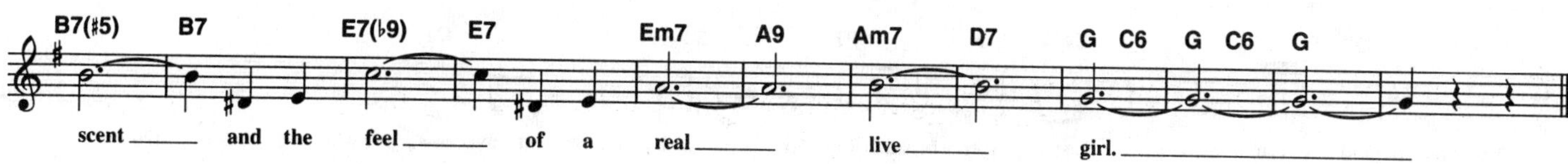
B7(♯5)
B7
E7(♭9)
E7
Em7
A9
Am7
D7
G
C6
G
C6
G
scent and the feel of a real live girl.

REMEMBER ME?

Words by AL DUBIN
Music by HARRY WARREN

Moderato

D Eb D Eb D Eb D Eb D Eb D Eb F#dim

Do you re-mem-ber one Sep-tem-ber af-ter-noon, I stood with you and lis-tened to a wed-ding tune, and
you re-call a cot-tage small up-on a hill, where ev-'ry day I had to pay an-oth-er bill? And

Fm7 Bb7 Fm Gm Db7 G7(b5) C7 | 1. F7 F9 Fm7/Bb Bb7 | 2. F7 Bb7 Eb

did-n't I go with you on your hon-ey-moon? Re-mem-ber me? Do mem-ber me?
if I'm not mis-tak-en, dear, I pay them still, re-

Ab Fm7 Bbm7 Eb7 Ab Bdim Bbm7 Eb7 B Abm6 Ebm Ebm7

I can see that lit-tle an-gel on your knee, can't you see, he

F7/C F7(b5)/Cb Fm7/Bb Bb7 D Eb D Eb D Eb

kind-a sort-a looks like me, for I'm the boy whose on-ly joy is lov-ing you, who

D Eb D Eb D Eb F#dim Fm7 Bb7 Fm Gm Db7 G7(b5) C7 F9 Fm7 Bb7 Eb

wor-ries till he hur-ries home when day is through, and I'm the guy you give your good-night kiss-es to, re-mem-ber me?

RED RIVER VALLEY

TRADITIONAL

Slow
F F7 Bb F C7 F F7
From this val-ley, they say, you are go-ing. I shall miss your sweet face and your smile. Just be-cause you are wea-ry and
Bb F C7 F C7 F
tir-ed, you are chang-ing your range for a while. Then come sit here a-while ere you leave us. Do not
D7 Gm7 C7 F F7 Bb C7 F
has-ten to bid us a-dieu. Just re-mem-ber the Red Riv-er Val-ley and the cow-boy who loves you so true.

From the Paramount Picture "FOUL PLAY"
READY TO TAKE A CHANCE AGAIN
Copyright © 1977 & 1978 by ENSIGN MUSIC CORPORATION and KAMAKAZI MUSIC CORPORATION
All Rights Reserved
Words by NORMAN GIMBEL
Music by CHARLES FOX
Moderato
Verse 1:
Am E/G♯ A/G A7 Dm Dm/C
1. You re - mind me I live in a shell, safe from the past, and do - in' o - kay, but not ver - y well.
F/G G9 F/G G9 C G/B Gm/B♭ A7sus A7 Dm
No jolts, no sur - pris - es, no cri - sis a - ris - es; my life goes a - long as it should, it's
Dm7/C Bm7(♭5) Bm7(♭5)/E E7(♭9) Am7 Dm7 F/G G/F
Chorus:
all ver - y nice, but not ver - y good. And I'm read - y to take a chance a - gain. Read - y to put my love
C/E Am/E E7/G♯ Am Am/G C7(♭5)/G♭ Fmaj7 Em7 Dm7 Em7 Dm7 F/G
on the line with you. Been liv - ing with noth - ing to show for it: you get what you get when you go
To Coda
G/F C/E Fmaj7 E/G♯ Am
Verse 2:
for it, and I'm read - y to take a chance a - gain with you. 2. When she left
D.S. al Coda
E/G♯ A/G A7 Dm Dm7/C Bm7(♭5) Bm7(♭5)/E E7(♭9)
me in all my des - pair, I just held on; my hopes were all gone, then I found you there. And I'm
Coda
Fmaj7 F♯m7(♭5) C/G E/G♯ Am7
a - gain, read - y to take a chance a - gain with you, with you.
RELEASE ME
Copyright © 1954 (Renewed 1982) by ACUFF-ROSE MUSIC, INC. & ROSCHELLE PUBLISHING, for U.S.A.
World Outside U.S.A. controlled by ACUFF-ROSE MUSIC, INC.
All Rights Reserved
Words and Music by
EDDIE MILLER, DUB WILLIAMS
and ROBERT YOUNT
Moderately slow
F Fdim B♭6 F F7 B♭ C7 Gm C7 F C7 F Fdim
1. Please re - lease me, let me go, for I don't love you an - y - more. To waste our
2. I have found a new love dear, and I will al - ways want her near. Her lips are
3. Please re - lease me, can't you see, you'd be a fool to cling to me. To live a
B♭6 F F7 B♭ F C7 1.2. F C7 3. F B♭ F
lives would be a sin. Re - lease me and let me love a - gain.
warm while yours are cold. Re - lease me my dar - ling, let me go.
lie would bring us pain. So re - lease me and let me love a - gain.

THE RIFF SONG

Words by OTTO HARBACH and OSCAR HAMMERSTEIN II
Music by SIGMUND ROMBERG

Moderately bright

D D♯dim A7 D D♯dim A7 Bm F♯7 Bm

Ho! So we sing as we are rid - ing Ho! It's a time you
Ho! That's the sound that comes to warn you So! In the night or

F♯7 G Em6/G Gm6/B♭ D/A 1. E7 E6 E7

best be hid - ing low, it means the riffs are a - broad, Go, be - fore you've
ear - ly morn, you know, if you're the "Red Shad - ow's" foe,

A7 2. E E7 D/A A7 D Bm Em7 A7 D

bit - ten the sword. The riffs will strike with a blow that brings you woe.

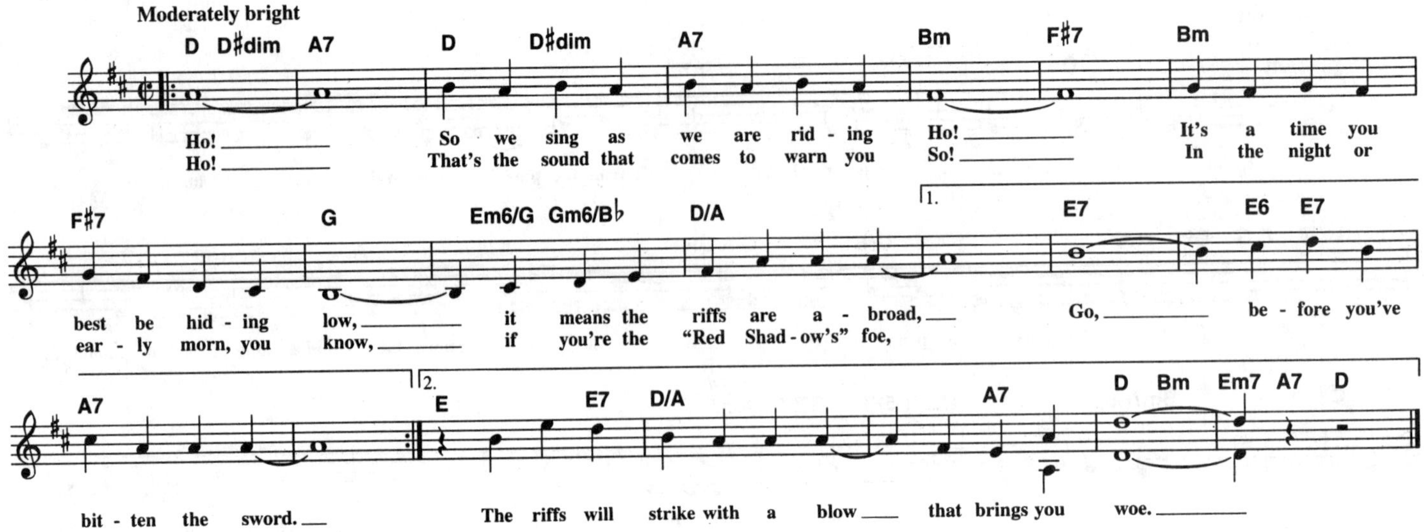

RESPECT

Words and Music by
OTIS REDDING, JR.

Moderate rock

C F C F

Verse:

G F G F G F

1. What you want, ba - by, I got. What you need, do you know I got it? All I'm ask - in' is for a lit - tle re -

Chorus:

C7 F7 C7 *To Coda*

spect when you come home, hey, ba - by when you come home, mis -
(Just a lit - tle bit, just a lit - tle bit. Just a lit - tle bit,

1.2. F7 *D.S.* 3. F7 F♯m7 B F♯m7

ter. ter.
just a lit - tle bit.) just a lit - tle bit.)

(Inst. solo ad lib.)

G7 *D.S. al Coda*

Coda

F7 C7 F7

ter. R - e - s - p - e - c - t; find out what it means to me.
just a lit - tle bit.)

C7 F7 C7 F7 *Repeat and fade*

R - e - s - p - e - c - t; take out t - c - p. A lit - tle re - spect,
(Just a lit - tle bit, just a lit - tle bit.)

Verse 2:
I ain't gonna do you wrong
While you gone.
I ain't gonna do you wrong
'Cause I don't wanna.
All I'm askin' is for a little respect.
(To Chorus:)

Verse 3:
I'm out to give you
All my money.
But all I'm askin' in return, honey,
Is to give me my proper respect
When you get home.
(To Chorus:)

Verse 4:
Ooh, your kisses, sweeter than honey.
But guess what; so here's my money.
All I want you to do for me
Is give you some here
When you get home.
(To Chorus:)

From "ALL IN THE FAMILY"

REMEMBERING YOU

Words by CARROLL O'CONNOR
Music by ROGER KELLAWAY

Moderately
Got a feel-in' it's all o - ver now, all o - ver now we're through. And to - mor - row I'll be lone-some re - mem - ber-ing you.
Got a feel-in' the sun will be gone, the day will be long and blue. And to - mor - row I'll be cry - in' re - mem - ber-ing you.
There's a far-a-way look in your eye when you try to pre-tend to me that ev - 'ry - thing is the same as it used to be. I see it's all o - ver now, all o - ver now we're through.
And to - mor-row I'll be start - in' re - mem-ber-ing you. Got a feel-in' it's
sad be-cause we're part - in', re - mem-ber-ing, con - so-late my heart in, re - mem-ber-ing you.

ROMANCE

A. RUBENSTEIN

Moderately

RESPECT YOURSELF

Words and Music by
MACK RICE and
LUTHER INGRAM

Moderate rock
Cm7
1.3.
2.4.
1. Now if you
Verse:
Cm7
dis - re - spect ev - 'ry - bod - y that you run in - to,
how in the world do you think an - y -
bod - y 'sposed to re - spect you?
If you don't give a heck a - bout the man with the Bi - ble in his
hand, just get out the way, and let the gen-tle-man do his thing.
You the kind of gen-tle-man that
wants ev-'ry-thing their way;
take the sheet off your face boy, it's a brand new day.
Re-spect your - self,
Chorus:
Eb6 Cm7 Eb6 G7
(nah, nah, nah, nah, nah;) re-spect your - self, (re, re, re, re.)
If you don't re - spect your - self ain't no - bod - y
1. D.C.
F7 Eb6 Cm7 Eb6 Cm7 Eb6 Cm
gon-na give a good, good hoot, nah, nah, nah. Oh, oh, re - spect your - self,
re - spect your - self.
2.
Cm
2. 3.
Re -
1.2.3. 4.
Cm7 Eb6 Cm7 Eb6 Cm7 Eb6 Cm
spect your - self,
re - spect your - self.
Re - spect your - self.

Verse 2:
If you're walking around thinking that the world owes you something 'cause you're here,
You're going out the world backward like you did when you first came here.
You keep talkin' 'bout the president, you wanna stop air pollution.
Put your hand on your mouth when you cough; that'll help the solution.
You cuss around women, you don't even know their name,
Then you're dumb enough to think that it makes you a big ol' man.
(To Chorus:)

RISE 'N' SHINE

Words by B.G. DeSYLVA
Music by VINCENT YOUMANS

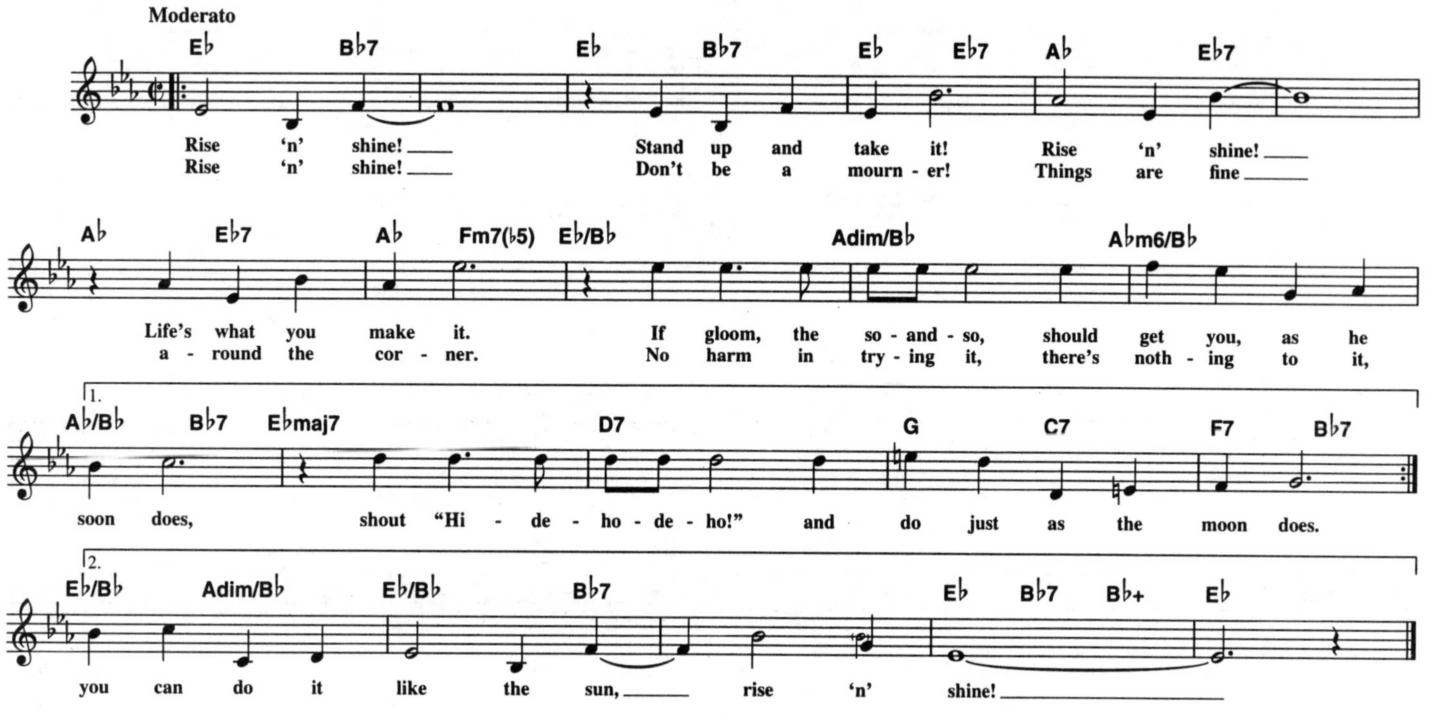
Moderato
E♭ B♭7 E♭ B♭7 E♭ E♭7 A♭ E♭7
Rise 'n' shine! Stand up and take it! Rise 'n' shine!
Rise 'n' shine! Don't be a mourn - er! Things are fine
A♭ E♭7 A♭ Fm7(♭5) E♭/B♭ Adim/B♭ A♭m6/B♭
Life's what you make it. If gloom, the so - and - so, should get you, as he
a - round the cor - ner. No harm in try - ing it, there's noth - ing to it,
1.
A♭/B♭ B♭7 E♭maj7 D7 G C7 F7 B♭7
soon does, shout "Hi - de - ho - de - ho!" and do just as the moon does.
2.
E♭/B♭ Adim/B♭ E♭/B♭ B♭7 E♭ B♭7 B♭+ E♭
you can do it like the sun, rise 'n' shine!

RING OF FIRE

By MERLE KILGORE and JUNE CARTER

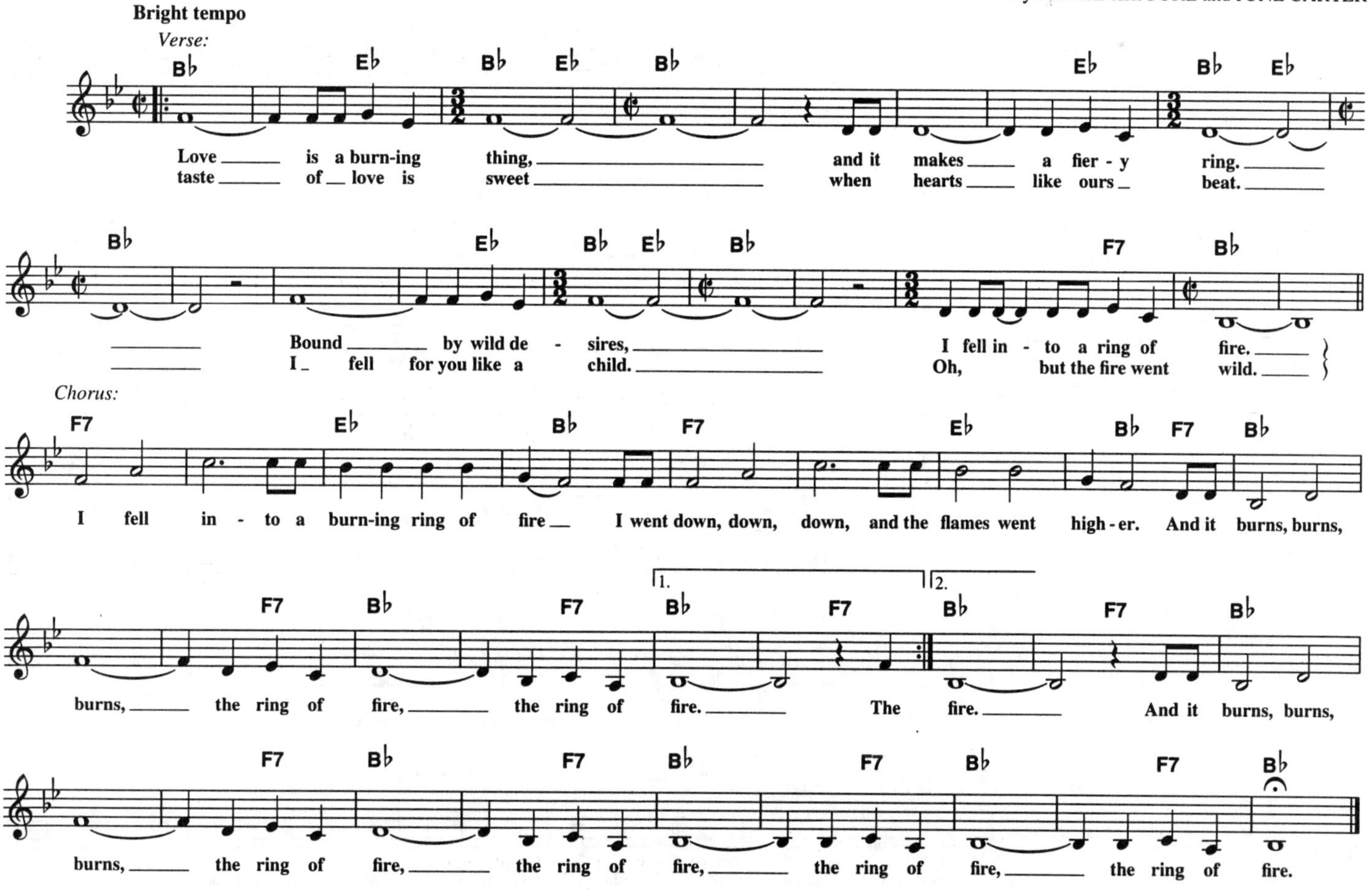

Bright tempo

Verse:

B♭ E♭ B♭ E♭ B♭ E♭ B♭ E♭

Love is a burn-ing thing, and it makes a fier - y ring.

taste of love is sweet when hearts like ours beat.

B♭ E♭ B♭ E♭ B♭ F7 B♭

Bound by wild de - sires, I fell in - to a ring of fire.

I fell for you like a child. Oh, but the fire went wild.

Chorus:

F7 E♭ B♭ F7 E♭ B♭ F7 B♭

I fell in - to a burn-ing ring of fire I went down, down, down, and the flames went high - er. And it burns, burns,

F7 B♭ F7 1. B♭ F7 2. B♭ F7 B♭

burns, the ring of fire, the ring of fire. The fire. And it burns, burns,

F7 B♭ F7 B♭ F7 B♭ F7 B♭

burns, the ring of fire, the ring of fire, the ring of fire, the ring of fire.

RIDERS ON THE STORM

Words and Music by
THE DOORS

Moderate rock
Rid-ers on the storm, rid-ers on the storm, in - to this house we're born. In - to this world we're thrown
like a dog with-out a bone, an act-or out on loan, rid-ers on the storm.
To Coda
There's a kil-ler on the road, his brain is squirm-ing like a toad. Take a long hol-i-day, let your chil-dren play. If you give this man a ride, sweet fam-i-ly will die, kil-ler on the road.
got-ta love your man, girl, you got-ta love your man. Take him by the hand, make him un-der-stand. The world on you de-pends, our life will nev-er end. You got-ta love your man.
Girl, you
D.C. al Coda
Coda
Repeat ad lib. and fade
Rid-ers on the storm; rid-ers on the storm.
THE ROCK 'N' ROLL WALTZ
Copyright © 1955 (Renewed) EMI UNART CATALOG INC.
All Rights Reserved
By ROY ALFRED
and SHORTY ALLEN
Moderate waltz
Verse:
One night I was late, came home from a date, slipped out of my shoes at the door. Then from the front room I heard a jump tune. I looked in and here's what I saw.
There in the night was a won-der-ful scene. Mom was danc-ing with Dad to my rec-ord ma-chine.
And while they danced on-ly one thing was wrong. They were try-ing to waltz to a rock and roll song.
Chorus:
One, two and then rock, one, two and then roll, they did the rock and roll waltz.
Rock, two, three, roll, two, three, it looked so cute to me. I love the rock and roll waltz.

RISE

By ANDY ARMER
and RANDY BADAZZ

Moderately
Fm7 Bbm7 Gbmaj7
1. We've all got to rise and reach up for the sky, not let life pass us by not let life
(2.) shine and do the best we can, reach out to un - der - stand, reach out a
(3.) rise and fly to oth - er lands, a - way from all our plans, and find what
Cbmaj7 Bbm7 Abm7 Gb E Eb Fine
seem so shy. If you just be - lieve, you will re - al - ize, you will sense it's time we've all got to rise.
help - ing hand. If you just be - lieve, we are what we seem, hid-ing from our - selves, hid - ing from our dreams.
peace we can. If you just be - lieve, you will re - al - ize, you will sense it's time we've all got to rise.
Gm7 C7(#5) Eb9 Eb7 Abmaj7 G11 C7(#9) C7 Abmaj7 Dm7/G
2. We all need to Rise and shine, reach up for the sky, let your life live in-side your mind.
D.S. al Fine
Ab Ebm7 D7/Ab Dbmaj9 Cm7 F9 F#m9 B9 Emaj9 A7(b5) C7 Gb7
Fly a - way and find who you are, and just find your own star and shine. 3. We've all got to
(We're Gonna)
ROCK AROUND THE CLOCK
Copyright © 1953 by MYERS MUSIC
U.S.A. Copyright Renewed and Assigned to CAPANO MUSIC
All Rights Reserved
Words and Music by
MAX C. FREEDMAN and
JIMMY DE KNIGHT
Moderate swing rock
F N.C. E7 F N.C. E7 F N.C.
One, two, three o'-clock, four o'-clock rock. Five, six, sev-en o-'clock, eight o'-clock rock. Nine, ten, e - lev-en o'-clock,
C7 F
twelve o'-clock rock. We're gon-na rock a-round the clock to-night. 1. Put your glad rags on and join me hon. We'll
clock strikes two and three and four, if the
chimes ring five and six and sev - en, we'll be
F7 Bb7 F
have some fun when the clock strikes one.
band slows down we'll yell for more.
rock - in' up in sev - enth heav - en.
We're gon-na rock a-round the clock to - night. We're gon-na rock, rock, rock till broad day-light. We're gon-na
Bb C7 F N.C. F
rock, we're gon-na rock a-round the clock to-night. 2. When the
3. When the

Verse 4:
When it's eight, nine, ten, eleven too,
I'll be going strong and so will you.
We're gonna rock around the clock tonight.
We're gonna rock, rock, rock till broad daylight.
We're gonna rock, we're gonna rock around the clock tonight.

Verse 5:
When the clock strikes twelve, we'll cool off,
Then start a-rockin' 'round the clock again.
We're gonna rock around the clock tonight.
We're gonna rock, rock, rock till broad daylight.
We're gonna rock, we're gonna rock around the clock tonight.

ROCK-A-BYE YOUR BABY WITH A DIXIE MELODY

Words by SAM M. LEWIS
and JOE YOUNG
Music by JEAN SCHWARTZ

Moderately

Rock - a - bye your ba - by with a Dix - ie mel - o - dy. When you croon,

croon a tune from the heart of Dix - ie. Just hang my cra - dle, Mam-my mine

right on that Ma-son - Dix-on Line, and swing it from Vir - gin - ia to Ten-nes-see with all the love that's in ya.

"Weep no more my la - dy;" sing that song a - gain for me, and "Old Black Joe," just as though you

had me on your knee. A mil-lion ba - by kiss - es I'll de - liv - er the min-ute that you sing the

"Swan-ee Riv - er;" Rock - a - bye your rock - a - bye ba - by with a Dix - ie mel - o - dy.

ROSES ARE RED
(My Love)

By AL BYRON
and PAUL EVANS

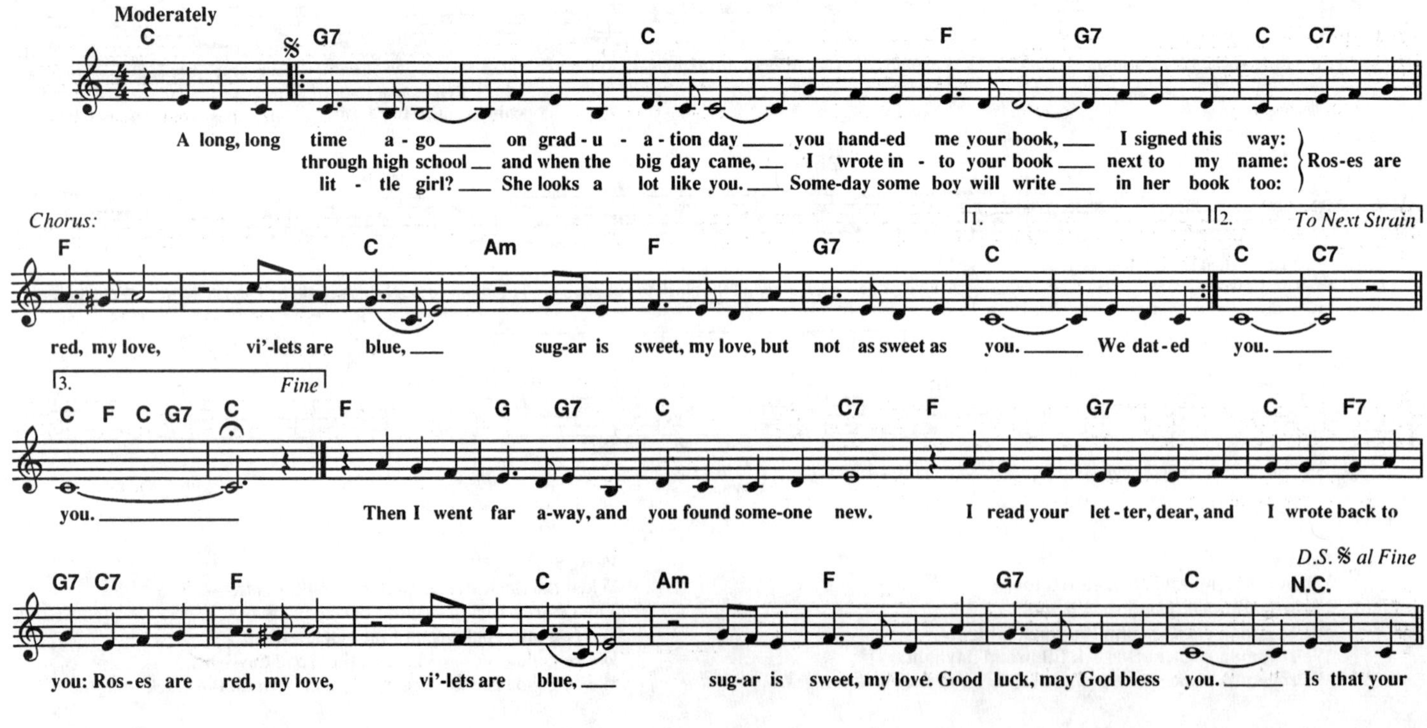

Moderately

A long, long time a - go on grad - u - a - tion day you hand-ed me your book, I signed this way:
through high school and when the big day came, I wrote in - to your book next to my name: Ros-es are
lit - tle girl? She looks a lot like you. Some-day some boy will write in her book too:

Chorus:

red, my love, vi'-lets are blue, sug-ar is sweet, my love, but not as sweet as
1. you. We dat-ed
2. you. *To Next Strain*
3. you. *Fine*

Then I went far a-way, and you found some-one new. I read your let - ter, dear, and I wrote back to

you: Ros-es are red, my love, vi'-lets are blue, sug-ar is sweet, my love. Good luck, may God bless you. Is that your

D.S. 𝄋 al Fine
N.C.

From "RUBY GENTRY"

RUBY

Words by MITCHELL PARISH
Music by HEINZ ROEMHELD

Slowly
They say, Ru-by, you're like a dream, not al-ways what you seem, and though my heart may break when I a-wake, let it be so. I on-ly know, Ru-by, it's you. They
say, Ru-by, you're like a song; you don't know right from wrong. And in your eyes I see heart-aches for me, but from the start, who stole my heart? Ru-by, it's you.
say, Ru-by, you're like a flame, in-to my life you came. And though I should be-ware, still I don't care, you thrill me so. I on-ly
To Coda
I hear your voice and I must come to you, I have no choice, what else can I do? They
D.S. al Coda
Coda
know, Ru-by, it's you.
(I Never Promised You a) ROSE GARDEN
Copyright © 1967, 1970 by LOWERY MUSIC CO., INC.
All Rights Reserved
Words and Music by
JOE SOUTH
Moderately bright country
Chorus:
I beg your par-don, I nev-er prom-ised you a rose garden. A-long with the sun-shine, there's got to be a lit-tle rain some-time. When you take you got to give so live and let live or let go, oh, oh, oh, I beg your par-don, I nev-er prom-ised you a rose gar-den.
To Next Strain
2.3.etc. Repeat ad lib. and fade
I could I beg your
Verse:
prom-ise you things like big dia-mond rings but you don't find ros-es grow-ing on stalks of clo-ver, so you bet-ter think it o-ver. 2. When it's
sweet talk-ing you could make it come true I would give you the world right now on a sil-ver plat-ter, but what would it mat-ter.
So smile for a-while and let's be jol-ly, love should-n't be so mel-an-chol-y, come a-long and share the good times while we can. I beg your
D.S.

ROCK WITH YOU
Copyright © 1979 RONDOR MUSIC (LONDON) LTD.
All Rights Administered in the U.S. and Canada by ALMO MUSIC CORP.
All Rights Reserved
Words and Music by
ROD TEMPERTON
Moderate rock
Verse:
Girl, close your eyes, let that rhy-thm get in - to you. Don't try to fight _ it, there ain't noth - in' that you can do. Re - lax _ your mind, _ lay back _ and groove _ with mine. _ You got - ta feel that heat. And we can ride the boog - ie, share that beat of love. _
Out on the floor, _ there ain't no - bod - y there but us. Girl, _ when you dance there's a mag - ic that must be love. _ Just take _ it slow, _ 'cause we got _ so far _ to go. _ When you feel that heat. And we're gon-na ride the boog - ie, share that beat of love. _
Chorus:
I wan-na rock with you, _ (all night. _) Dance you in - to day, _ (sun - light. _) I wan-na rock with you, _ (all night. _) We're gon-na rock the night _ a - way. _
1. D.C.
2. To Next Strain
3.4. etc. Repeat ad lib. and fade
Bridge:
And when the groove is dead and gone, _ (yeah, _) you know that love sur - vives, _ so we can rock for - ev - er _ on. I wan-na
D.S.
ROMEO AND JULIET
(Love Theme)
Copyright © 1994 by BEAM ME UP MUSIC (ASCAP), c/o CPP BELWIN, INC., Miami, FL 33014
All Rights Reserved
TSCHAIKOWSKY
Slowly

ROCKABYE BASIE

By COUNT BASIE, SHAD COLLINS
and LESTER YOUNG

Medium jump tempo
F Dm7 Gm7 C7 F Dm7 Gm7 C7 F Dm7
To Coda
1.
2.
Gm7 C7 F Dm7 B♭ F B♭ F Cm7 F7 Cm7 F7
B♭6 F7(♯5) B♭6 Dm7 G9 G7 Am7 B♭9 Bdim7
C7 B7 F♯dim7 Gm Dm C7
D.C. al Coda
Coda
F

'ROUND HER NECK SHE WEARS A YELLOW RIBBON

TRADITIONAL

Moderate two-beat

E♭ F7 B♭7

'Round her neck she wears a yel - low rib - bon, she wears it in the win - ter and the sum - mer, so they say.

E♭ B♭7 E♭ A♭dim7 E♭
If you ask her, "Why the dec - o - ra - tion?", she'll say, "It's fur my lov - er who is fur, fur a - way." Fur a -

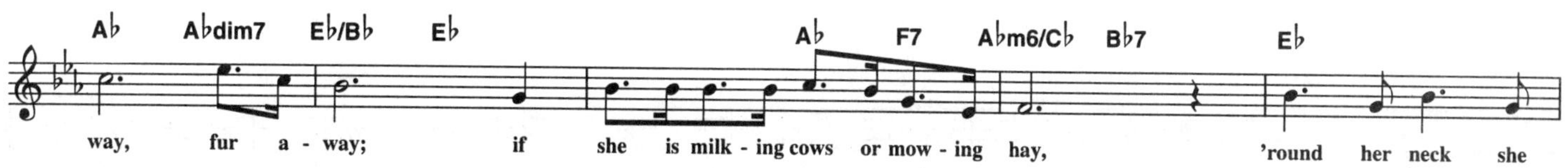
A♭ A♭dim7 E♭/B♭ E♭ A♭ F7 A♭m6/C♭ B♭7 E♭
way, fur a - way; if she is milk - ing cows or mow - ing hay, 'round her neck she

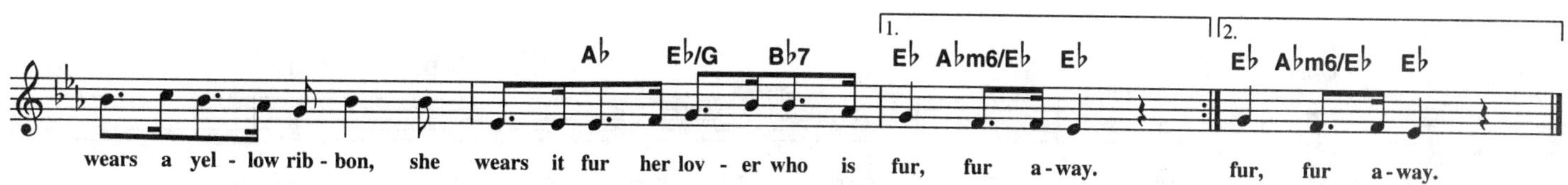
1.
2.
A♭ E♭/G B♭7 E♭ A♭m6/E♭ E♭ E♭ A♭m6/E♭ E♭
wears a yel - low rib - bon, she wears it fur her lov - er who is fur, fur a - way. fur, fur a - way.

ROUTE 101

Music by JUAN CARLOS CALDERON

Moderately bright

Dm7 Em7 Dm7 Em7 Dm7

Em7 Dm7 Fm7(♭5) B7(♯5) Em7 A9 Em7

E/F♯ B7(♯5) Em7 A9 A7(♯5) Dm7 1. G7 2. G7

Dm7 Em7 Fm7 Gm7 G♯m7 B♭m7 Bm7 C♯m7 Dm7 Em7

Dm7 Em7 Dm7 Em7 Dm7 Em7 Dm7 Em7 Dm7

Fm7 B♭13 Fm7 B♭13 Dm7 Em7 Dm7 Em7

Repeat and fade

ROW ROW ROW

Words by WILLIAM JEROME
Music by JIMMIE V. MONACO

Brightly

G D7 G C E7 Am A7
And then he'd row, row, row, way up the riv - er he would row, row, row. A hug he'd give her, then he'd

D7 G6 F♯7 G6 G♯dim7 D7 N.C.
kiss her now and then. She would tell him when. He'd fool a - round and fool a - round and then they'd kiss a - gain. And then he'd

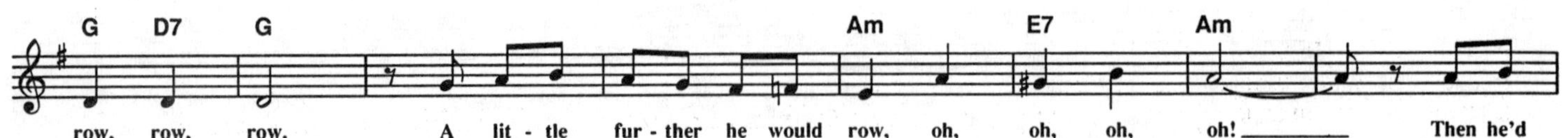
G D7 G Am E7 Am
row, row, row. A lit - tle fur - ther he would row, oh, oh, oh, oh! Then he'd

C Cm6 G A7 Am7 D7 G
drop both his oars, take a few more en - cores, and then he'd row, row, row.

From the Videocraft Musical Spectacular "RUDOLPH, THE RED-NOSED REINDEER"

RUDOLPH, THE RED-NOSED REINDEER

Words and Music by
JOHNNY MARKS

Rubato

Dm7 Em7 G7 C Dm7 Em7 G7 C Bm7 E7

You know Dash-er and Danc-er and Pranc-er and Vix-en, Com-et and Cu-pid and Don-ner and Blitz-en; but do you re-

Am7 D7 G7 Brightly C Cdim G7

call the most fa-mous rein-deer of all? Ru-dolph The Red-Nosed Rein-deer had a ver-y shin-y nose,

G7(♯5) C Cdim

and if you ev-er saw it, you would e-ven say it glows. All of the oth-er rein-deer used to laugh and call him

G7 C C7 F C

names. They nev-er let poor Ru-dolph join in an-y rein-deer games. Then one fog-gy Christ-mas Eve,

Dm7 G7 C C♯dim G/D E7 Am D7 G7 C

San-ta came to say: "Ru-dolph, with your nose so bright, won't you guide my sleigh to-night?" Then all the rein-deer

Cdim G7 C

loved him, as they shout-ed out with glee: "Ru-dolph The Red-Nosed Rein-deer, you'll go down in his-to-ry."

RUM AND COCA COLA

Words by MOREY AMSTERDAM
Additional Lyrics by AL STILLMAN
Music by JERI SULLAVAN and PAUL BARON

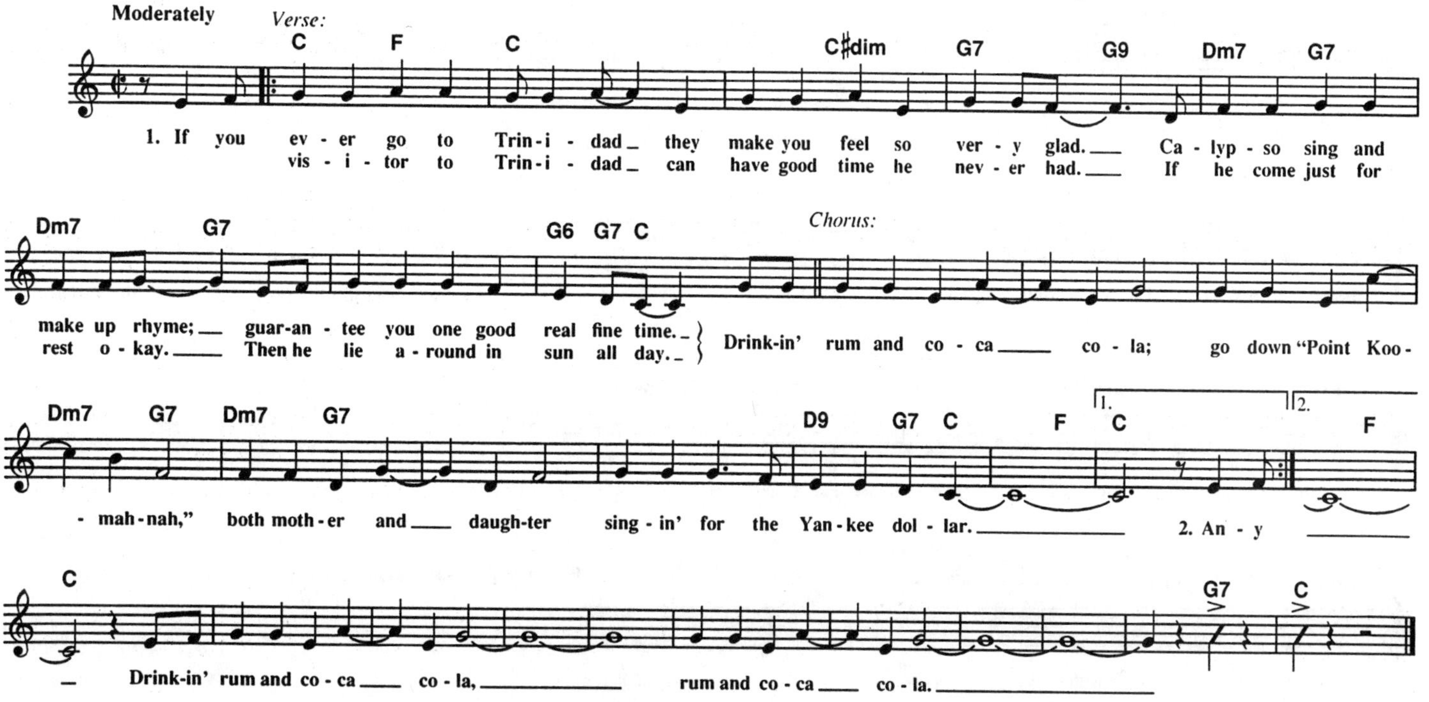

Moderately *Verse:*

C F C C♯dim G7 G9 Dm7 G7

1. If you ev-er go to Trin-i-dad_ they make you feel so ver-y glad.__ Ca-lyp-so sing and
vis-i-tor to Trin-i-dad_ can have good time he nev-er had.__ If he come just for

Dm7 G7 G6 G7 C *Chorus:*

make up rhyme;__ guar-an-tee you one good real fine time._
rest o-kay.__ Then he lie a-round in sun all day._
Drink-in' rum and co-ca__ co-la; go down "Point Koo-

Dm7 G7 Dm7 G7 D9 G7 C F 1. C 2. F

-mah-nah," both moth-er and__ daugh-ter sing-in' for the Yan-kee dol-lar.__ 2. An-y__

C G7 C

_ Drink-in' rum and co-ca__ co-la,__ rum and co-ca__ co-la.__

SANTA CLAUS IS COMIN' TO TOWN

Words by HAVEN GILLESPIE
Music by J. FRED COOTS

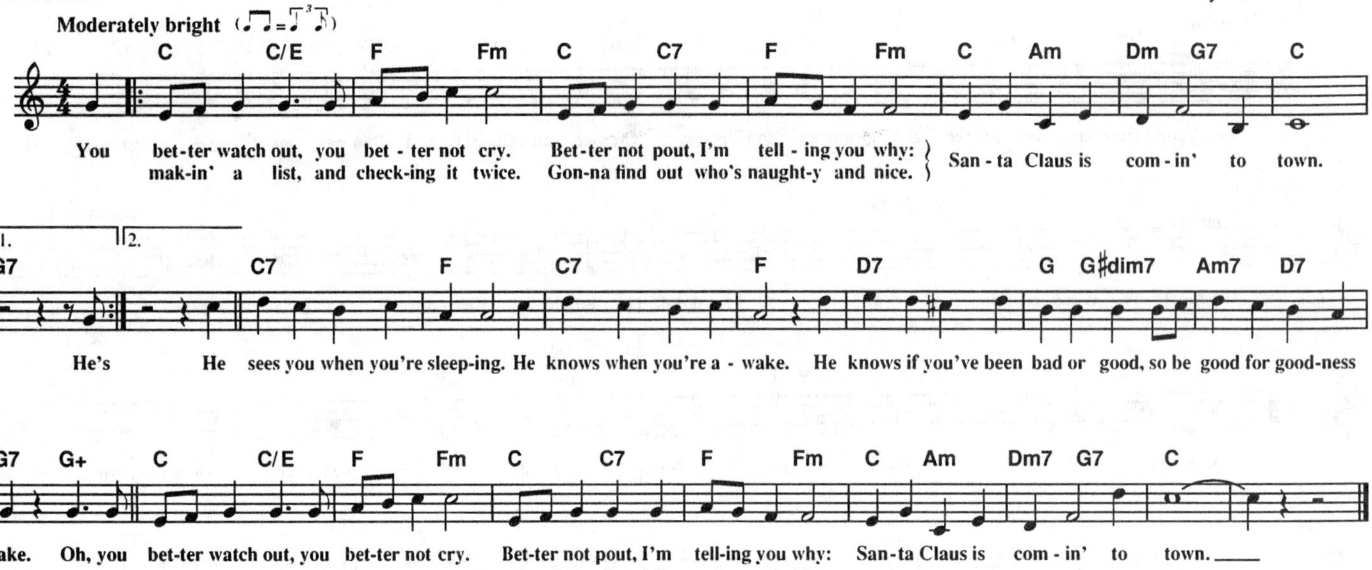

Moderately bright

C C/E F Fm C C7 F Fm C Am Dm G7 C

You bet-ter watch out, you bet - ter not cry. Bet-ter not pout, I'm tell - ing you why:
mak-in' a list, and check-ing it twice. Gon-na find out who's naught-y and nice.
San - ta Claus is com - in' to town.

1. G7 2. C7 F C7 F D7 G G♯dim7 Am7 D7

He's He sees you when you're sleep-ing. He knows when you're a - wake. He knows if you've been bad or good, so be good for good-ness

G7 G+ C C/E F Fm C C7 F Fm C Am Dm7 G7 C

sake. Oh, you bet-ter watch out, you bet-ter not cry. Bet-ter not pout, I'm tell-ing you why: San-ta Claus is com - in' to town.

MERRY CHRISTMAS, DARLING

Lyric by FRANK POOLER
Music by RICHARD CARPENTER

Rubato

Cm7 Dm7 Gm7 Cm7 F7 B♭ Gm G♭+ B♭/F C/E Cm7 F

Greet-ing cards have all been sent, the Christ-mas rush is through, but I still have one wish to make, a spe-cial one for you;

Moderately slow

B♭maj9 Cm/B♭ B♭maj9 Fm7 B♭7sus E♭ F/E♭ Dm7 Gm7 Cm7 Dm Cm F

Mer-ry Christ-mas dar - ling. We're a-part that's true, but I can dream and in my dreams, I'm Christ-mas-ing with you.

B♭maj9 Cm/B♭ B♭maj9 Fm7 B♭7sus E♭ F/E♭ Dm7 Gm7 Cm/E♭ E♭m6 A♭7

Hol-i-days are joy - ful. There's al-ways some-thing new. But ev-'ry-day's a hol-i-day, when I'm near to you. The

𝄋 D♭ E♭/D♭ Cm7 Fm B♭m7 E♭7 A♭ Fm Fm/E Fm7/E♭ F9

lights on my tree, I wish you could see, I wish it ev - 'ry day. The logs on the fire fill me with de - sire,

To Coda ⊕

B♭ Cm Dm Cm7 F B♭maj9 Cm/B♭ B♭maj9 Fm7 E7(♭5) E♭ F/E♭ Dm7 Gm7

to see you and to say; that I wish you Mer-ry Christ-mas, Hap-py New Year too; I've just one wish on this Christ-mas Eve;

D.S. 𝄋 al Coda

Cm7 F7 B♭ A♭7

I wish I were with you. The

⊕ *Coda*

Cm F E♭ Dm7(♭5) G7 Cm7 F7 B♭

I wish I were with you, I wish I were with you.

SATURDAY NIGHT

(Is The Loneliest Night In The Week)

Words by SAMMY CAHN
Music by JULE STYNE

Not too fast (rhythmically)

Eb Bb7/F Eb/G Bb7/F Eb Bbm6/Db
Sat - ur - day Night — is the lone - li - est night — in the week, —

C7 C7-9 C+ C7 Fm Db7/F Fm Db7/F
'Cause that's the night that my sweet - ie and I — used to dance — cheek to cheek. —
I sing the song that I sang for the mem - 'ries I u - sual - ly seek. —

Fm Abm6/Cb Bb7 Eb G7/D Cm
I don't mind Sun - day night at all, — 'cause that's the
Un - til I hear you at the door, — and hold you

1. Am7-5 D7-9 Gm Gbdim Bb/F Gm7
night friends come to call — And Mon - day to Fri - day go fast —

Cm9 F9 Bb7 Fm7/Bb Bb6 Fm7/Bb Bb7
— and an - oth - er week is past, —

2. Am7-5 Fm7/Ab G7
But in my arms once more; —

Cm Abm Eb/Bb C7 Fm9 Bb11 Eb6 Fm7 Eb/G Bb7-9 Eb6 Eb
— Sat - ur - day Night — is the lone — li - est night — in the week. —

SECRET LOVE

Words by PAUL FRANCIS WEBSTER
Music by SAMMY FAIN

Moderately

Eb6 Fm7 Eb6 Fm7 Bb7-9 Eb Eb6 Fm7 Bb7 Eb6 Bb7-9
Once I had a Se - cret Love — That lived with -
So I told a friend - ly star, — The way that

Eb6 Bbdim Fm7/Bb Bb7 Fm7/Bb Bb7 Fm7 Bb9 Bb7 Fm7
in the heart of me, — All too soon my Se - cret
dream - ers of - ten do, — Just how won - der - ful you

Bb7 Fm7 Bb7 Fm7 Bb6 Fm7 Bb7-9 Eb Eb6
Love — Be - came im - pa - tient to be free. —
are, — And why I'm so in love with you. —

1. Fm7 Bb7 2. Cm Cm7 F7 Cm7/G F7/A Bb Dm Bb/D
— Now I shout it from the high - est hills,

Eb11 Eb7 Abmaj7 Ab6 Abm7 Abm6 Eb/G Eb
E - ven told the gold - en daf - fo - dils; At last my heart's an o - pen

Gm7-5 C7-9 C7 Fm7 Bb7sus4 Bb9 Bb7-9 Eb6 Abmaj7 Fm7 Eb6
door, — And my se - cret love's no se - cret an - y more. —

SCATTER-BRAIN

Words by JOHNNY BURKE
Music by KEENE-BEAN and FRANKIE MASTERS

Moderate schottishe tempo

B♭7(♯5) E♭ E♭/G A♭ Fm E♭/B♭ B♭7 E♭/G B♭7/F
1. You're as pleas-ant as the morn-ing and re - fresh-ing as the rain, is - n't it a pit - y that you're such a scat-ter-brain. When you
gay as New Year par - ties, you're as sweet as sug-ar cane, but when you get ser - i - ous, you're such a scat-ter-brain. When we

E♭ E♭/G A♭ Fm E♭/B♭ B♭7 E♭ B♭7
smile it's so de-light-ful, when you talk it's so in-sane, still it's charm-ing chat-ter, scat-ter-brain. I know I'll end up ap - o-plec-tic, but there's
dance I think it's heav-en, till a - bout the third re-frain, then you start your pat - ter, scat-ter-brain. Per-haps I'm much too an - a - lyt - ic, but I'm

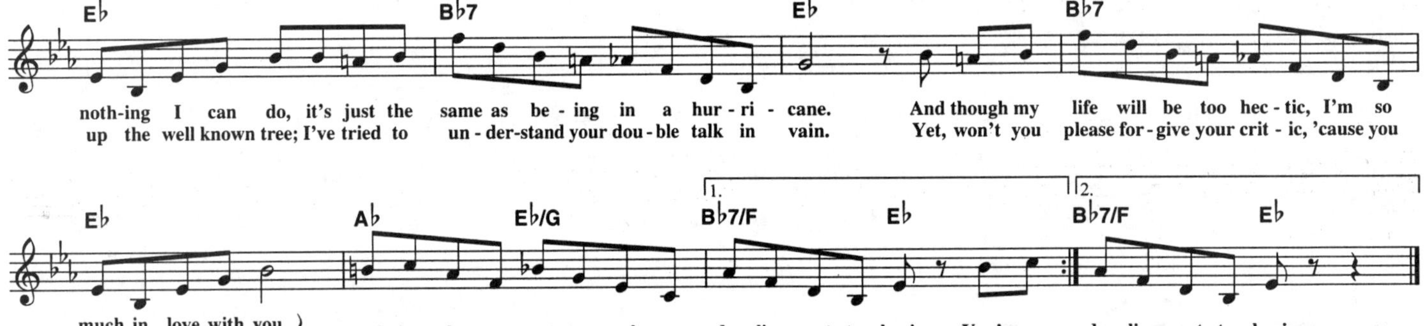
E♭ B♭7 E♭ B♭7
noth-ing I can do, it's just the same as be - ing in a hur - ri - cane. And though my life will be too hec - tic, I'm so
up the well known tree; I've tried to un - der-stand your dou - ble talk in vain. Yet, won't you please for - give your crit - ic, 'cause you
E♭ A♭ E♭/G B♭7/F E♭ B♭7/F E♭
much in love with you, mean so much to me, noth-ing else can mat - ter, you're my dar - ling scat - ter - brain. You're as dar - ling scat - ter - brain.

From the M-G-M Motion Picture "SAN FRANCISCO"

SAN FRANCISCO

Lyric by GUS KAHN
Music by BRONISLAU KAPER
and WALTER JURMANN

Moderately bright

To Coda
C Cmaj7 C7 F F7 C Am Em
San Fran - cis - co, o - pen your gold - en gate. You let no strang - er wait
San Fran - cis - co, here is your wan - der - ing one
San Fran - cis - co, wel - come me home a - gain.

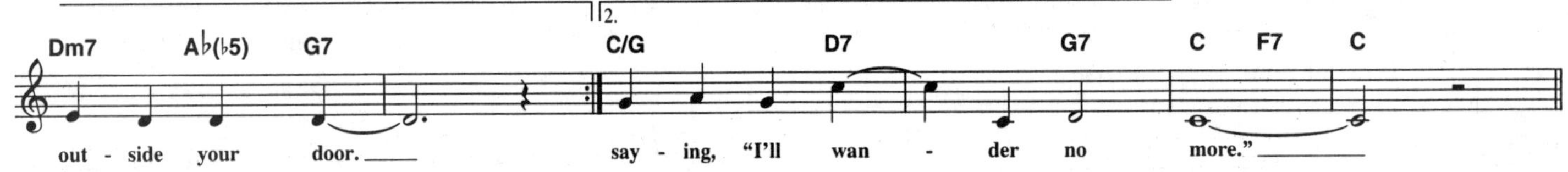
Dm7 A♭(♭5) G7 C/G D7 G7 C F7 C
out - side your door. say - ing, "I'll wan - der no more."

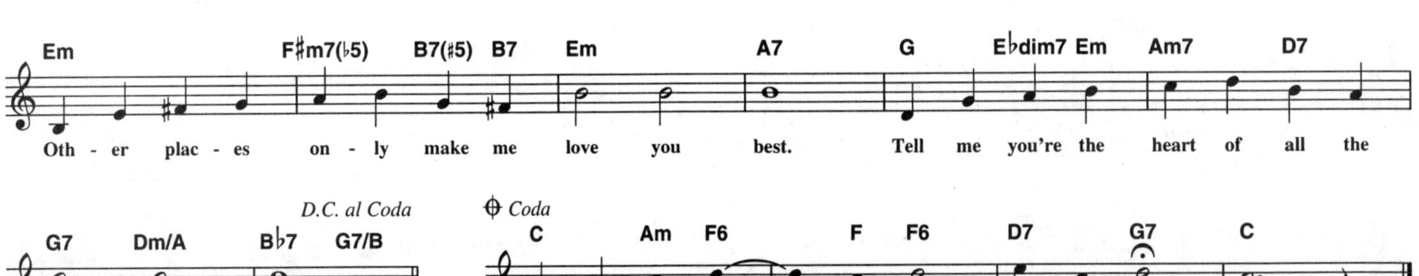
Em F♯m7(♭5) B7(♯5) B7 Em A7 G E♭dim7 Em Am7 D7
Oth - er plac - es on - ly make me love you best. Tell me you're the heart of all the
D.C. al Coda
Coda
G7 Dm/A B♭7 G7/B C Am F6 F F6 D7 G7 C
gold - en west I'm com - ing home to go roam - ing no more.

SANTA LUCIA

(Here In The Twilight)

English Lyrics by
HOWARD JOHNSON

Allegretto poco mosso

C G7 C G7

Twi - light is draw-ing near, bright stars will soon ap - pear. Come out and meet me dear, I want you
Sul ma - re luc - ci - ca L'a - stro d'ar - gen - to, Pla - ci - da è l'on - da, Pro - spe - ro è il

C G7 C G7

bad - ly. Each star that's in the sky, twink - les for you and I. Don't leave me here to sigh,
ven - to; Sul ma - re luc - ci - ca L'a - stro d'ar - gen - to, Pla - ci - da è l'on - da,

C Dm F C

I love you mad - ly. San - ta Lu - ci - a, San - ta Lu - ci - a I can see your lov - ing
Pro - spe - ro è il ven - to; Ve - ni - te al - l'a - gi - le Bar - chet - ta mi - a San - ta Lu -

G7 C Dm F C

eyes so bright just like the star - light. San - ta Lu - ci - a, San - ta Lu - ci - a, whis-per that you will be
ci - a! San - ta Lu - ci - a! Ve - ni - te al - l'a - gi - le Bar - chet - ta mi - a San - ta Lu -

G7 C F C/G G7 C

mine to - night! Here in the twi - light!
ci - a! San - ta Lu - ci - a!

SATIN DOLL

Words and Music by
DUKE ELLINGTON, JOHNNY MERCER
and BILLY STRAYHORN

Moderately
Dm7 G7 Dm7 G7 Em7 A7 Em7 A7 Am7(♭5)/E♭ D7 A♭m7 D♭9
Cig - a - rette hold - er, which wigs me. O - ver her shoul - der, she digs me. Out cat-tin' that Sat-in
Ba - by, shall we go out skip-pin'? Care-ful, a - mi - go, you're flip-pin. Speaks Lat-in, that Sat-in Doll.
1. 2.
C6/9 B♭13 A7(♭9) C6/9 Gm7 C7 Gm7 C7(♭9) F6/9
Doll. She's no - bod - y's fool, so I'm play - ing it cool as can be.
Am7 D7 Am7 D7(♭9) Dm7/G G7 Dm7 G7
I'll give it a whirl, but I ain't for no girl catch-ing me. (Switch-a - roo-ney.) Tel - e-phone num - bers;
Dm7 G7 Em7 A7 Em7 A7 Am7(♭5)/E♭ D7 A♭m7 D♭9 C6/9
well, you know, do'-ing my rhum - bas with u - no. And that 'n' my Sat - in doll.

SAVED

© 1961 (Renewed) JERRY LEIBER MUSIC and MIKE STOLLER MUSIC
All Rights Reserved
Words and Music by
JERRY LEIBER and MIKE STOLLER
Fast Gospel feel
I used to smoke, I used to drink, I used to smoke... drink and
cuss, I used to fuss, I used to cuss... fuss and
lie, I used to cheat, I used to lie... cheat and
dance the hoo-chy-koo. I used to smoke and drink,– smoke and drink and dance the hoo-chy-koo.
boo-gie all night long. I used to cuss and fuss,— cuss and fuss and boo-gie all night long.
step on peo-ple's feet. I used to lie and cheat,– lie and cheat and step on peo-ple's feet.
But now I'm stand-in' on this cor-ner, pray in' for— me and you
But now I'm stand-in' on this cor-ner, I— know– right from wrong
But now I'm step-pin' on to glo-ry, sal-va-tion— is my beat
be-cause I'm saved... saved. Peo-ple let me tell you 'bout-a king-dom come. You know I'm
saved... I'm saved.— I can preach– un-til you're deaf and dumb.– I'm in that
soul-sav-in' ar-my, beat-in' on that big bass drum. I used to
I'm in that soul-sav-in' ar-my, beat-ing on that big bass drum.
© 1958 WB MUSIC CORP. (Renewed)
All Rights Reserved
SCOOT
By NEAL HEFTI
Medium bright
To Coda
D.S. al Coda
Coda

SCARBOROUGH FAIR

Adaptation by ALBERT GAMSE

Moderately slow
Dm Em A7 Dm F Dm G Dm
1. Are you go - ing to Scar - bor-ough Fair? Pars - ley, sage, rose - mar - y and thyme. Re -
2. Have him make me a cam - bric shirt, pars - ley, sage, rose - mar - y and thyme, with -
3. Have him wash it in yon - der dry well, pars - ley, sage, rose - mar - y and thyme, where
B♭ Dm B♭ Gm Dm G C 1.2. Dm 3. Dm
mem - ber me to one who lives there for once he was a true love of mine. mine.
out a seam or fine nee - dle work, and then he'll be a true love of mine.
ne'er a drop of wa - ter e'er fell, and then he'll be a true love of

From the Broadway Musical Production "A LITTLE NIGHT MUSIC"

SEND IN THE CLOWNS
(From "A Little Night Music")

Music and Lyrics by
STEPHEN SONDHEIM

Lento

E♭ E♭sus E♭ E♭maj9 E♭
Is - n't it rich? Are we a pair? Me here at last on the ground, you in mid -
bliss? Don't you ap - prove? One who keeps tear - ing a - round, one who can't

A♭maj9 A♭6 1. B♭/E♭ A♭/E♭ B♭/E♭ A♭/E♭ 2. B♭/E♭ Fm/E♭ E♭
air.. Send in the clowns. Is - n't it clows? Send in the clowns. Just when I'd
move... Where are the

Gm Dm7 Gm Dm7 Gm Cm7 G
stopped o - pen - ing doors, fi - nal - ly know-ing the one that I want-ed was yours, mak-ing my

E♭6/B♭ F7/A A♭6 Gsus Fm7(♭5) Gm/B♭ A♭6/B♭ B♭/E♭ A♭ B♭/E♭ A♭
en-trance a - gain with my u - su - al flair, sure of my lines, no one is there. Don't you love

E♭ E♭sus E♭ E♭maj9 E♭ A♭maj9 A♭6 B♭13/E♭
farce? My fault, I fear. I thought that you'd want what I want. Sor-ry, my dear. But where are the clowns? Quick, send in the
rich, is - n't it queer, los-ing my tim - ing this late in my ca - reer? And where are the clowns? There ought to be

1. B♭9/E♭ E♭ E♭sus E♭ E♭sus 2. B♭9/E♭ E♭ E♭sus E♭
clowns. Don't both-er, they're here. Is - n't it clowns. Well, may-be next year...

SCARLET RIBBONS
(For Her Hair)

Words by JACK SEGAL
Music by EVELYN DANZIG

Moderately

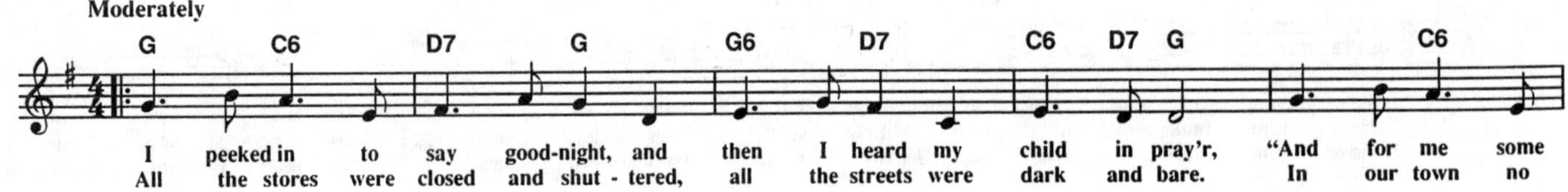
G C6 D7 G G6 D7 C6 D7 G C6
I peeked in to say good-night, and then I heard my child in pray'r, "And for me some
All the stores were closed and shut - tered, all the streets were dark and bare. In our town no

D7 G G6 D7 C6 D7 G G D6/F♯ G7/D C Em Gmaj7/D
scar - let rib - bons, scar - let rib - bons for my hair." Thru the night my heart was ach - ing. Just be - fore the
scar - let rib - bons, not one rib - bon for her hair. If I live to be two hun - dred, I will nev - er

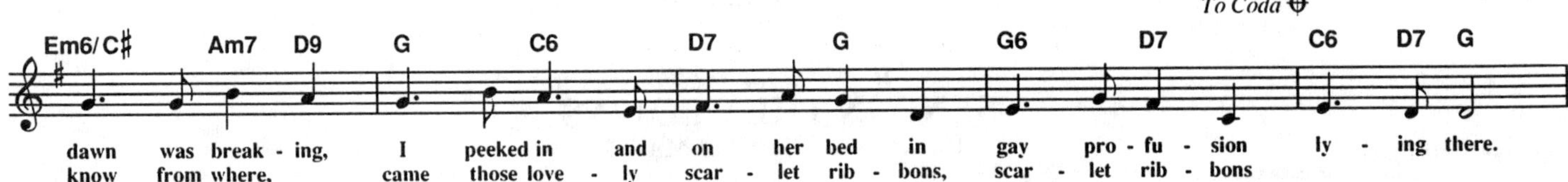
To Coda
Em6/C♯ Am7 D9 G C6 D7 G G6 D7 C6 D7 G
dawn was break - ing, I peeked in and on her bed in gay pro - fu - sion ly - ing there.
know from where, came those love - ly scar - let rib - bons, scar - let rib - bons

D.S. al Coda
Coda
C6 D7 G G6 D7 C6 D7 G
Love - ly rib - bons, scar - let rib - bons, scar - let rib - bons for her hair.
C6 D7 G6
for_ her_ hair.

SCHOOL DAYS
(When We Were a Couple of Kids)

TRADITIONAL

Brightly

B♭ F7 Gm Edim F7
School days, school days, dear old gold - en rule days; read - in' and

B♭
writ - in' and 'rith - me - tic, taught to the tune of a hick - 'ry stick.

G7 C7 F7 B♭
You were my queen in cal - i - co. I was your bash - ful bare - foot beau. And you

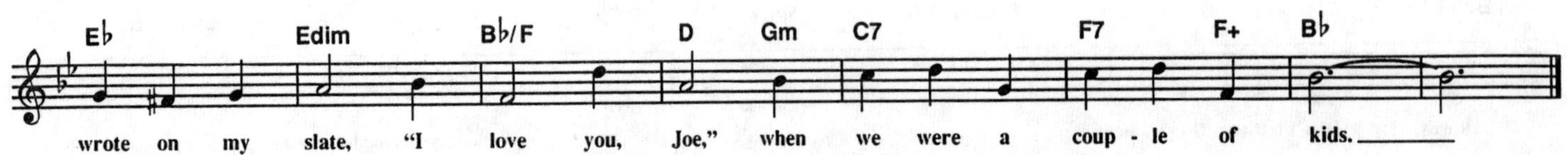
E♭ Edim B♭/F D Gm C7 F7 F+ B♭
wrote on my slate, "I love you, Joe," when we were a coup - le of kids.

SEALED WITH A KISS

Words by PETER UDELL
Music by GARY GELD

Moderately slow
G Gm Dm Gm C F D+
Though we got-ta say good-bye for the sum-mer, dar-ling, I prom-ise you this: I'll send you all my
cold lone-ly sum-mer, but I'll fill the emp-ti-ness. I'll send you all my
Gm7 C7 A7 Dm Gm6 A7 Dm N.C. Dm Gm Dm
love ev-'ry day in a let-ter, sealed with a kiss. Guess it's gon-na be a kiss. I'll
dreams ev-'ry day in a let-ter, sealed with a
G Dm G Dm G Dm
see you in the sun-light. I'll hear your voice ev-'ry-where. I'll run to ten-der-ly hold you, but
E7 A7 N.C. G Gm Dm Gm C
dar-ling, you won't be there. I don't wan-na say good-bye for the sum-mer, know-ing the love we'll
F D+ Gm C Dm Gm6 C Dm Gm Dm
miss. Oh, let us make a pledge to meet in Sep-tem-ber, and seal it with a kiss.

From the 20th Century-Fox Cinemascope Production "THE SECOND TIME AROUND"

THE SECOND TIME AROUND

Words by SAMMY CAHN
Music by JAMES VAN HEUSEN

Slowly
G7(♭9) C C/E E♭dim Dm G9 Cmaj7 C6 C
Love is love-li-er the sec-ond time a-round, just as won-der-ful with both feet on the
comf'-ta-ble the sec-ond time you fall, like a friend-ly home the sec-ond time you
Bm7(♭5) E9 Am C7 F Am7
ground. It's that sec-ond time you hear your love song sung; makes you think per-haps, that
call. Who can
D7 G7 G7(♭9) Am C7 F A7(♭5)/E♭ D7 E♭dim
love like youth is wast-ed on the young. Love's more say what led us to this mir-a-cle we found? There are
Dm7 G7 Fdim E7sus E7 A7 Am7/D D7 Dm7/G Fm/G C
those who'll bet love comes but once, and yet, I'm oh, so glad we met the sec-ond time a-round.

SEESAW

Words by DOROTHY FIELDS
Music by CY COLEMAN

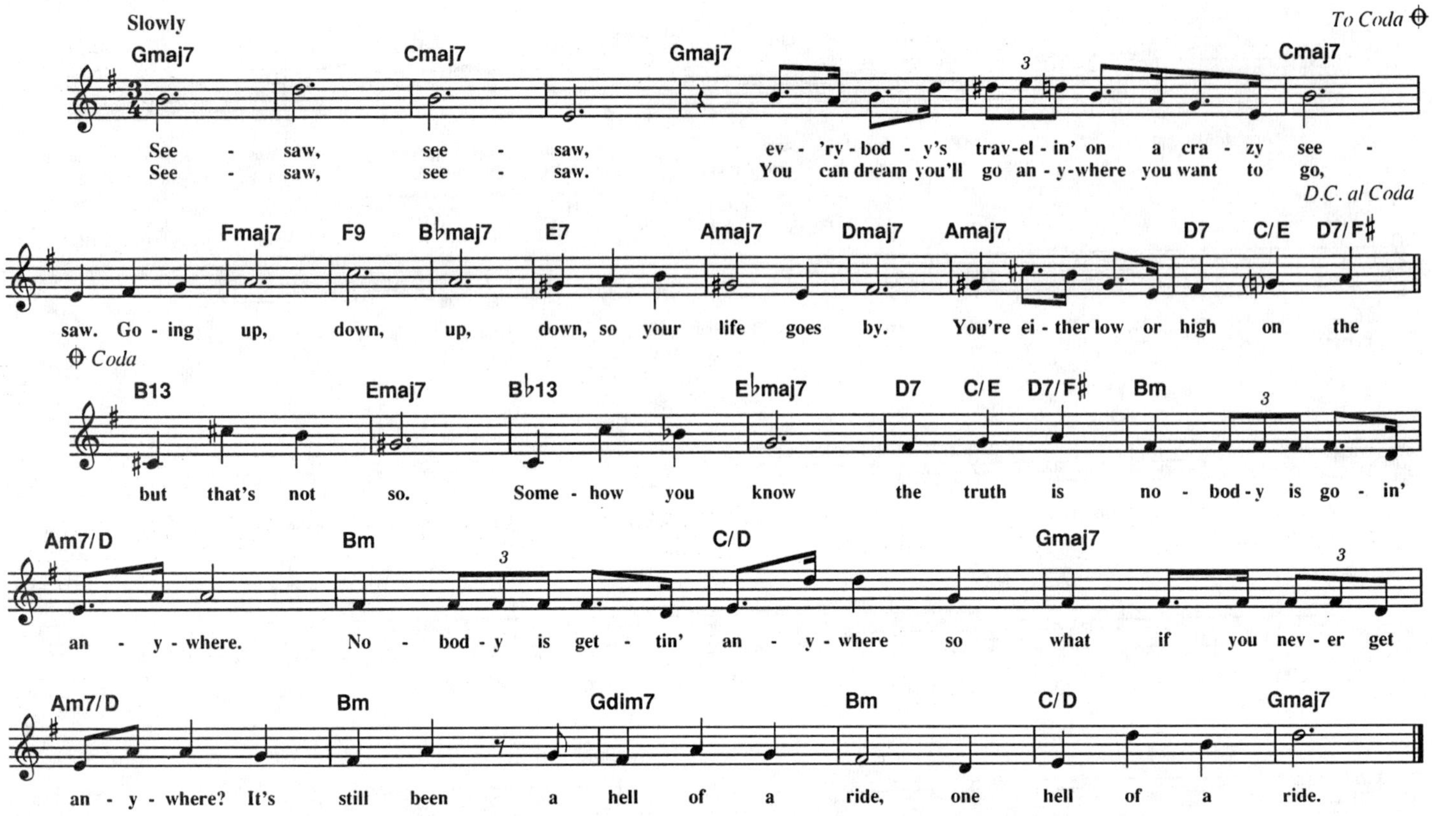

Slowly

To Coda ⊕

See - saw, see - saw, ev - 'ry - bod - y's trav - el - in' on a cra - zy see -
See - saw, see - saw. You can dream you'll go an - y - where you want to go,

D.C. al Coda

saw. Go - ing up, down, up, down, so your life goes by. You're ei - ther low or high on the

⊕ *Coda*

but that's not so. Some - how you know the truth is no - bod - y is go - in'
an - y - where. No - bod - y is get - tin' an - y - where so what if you nev - er get
an - y - where? It's still been a hell of a ride, one hell of a ride.

SEND ME THE PILLOW THAT YOU DREAM ON

Words and Music by
HANK LOCKLIN

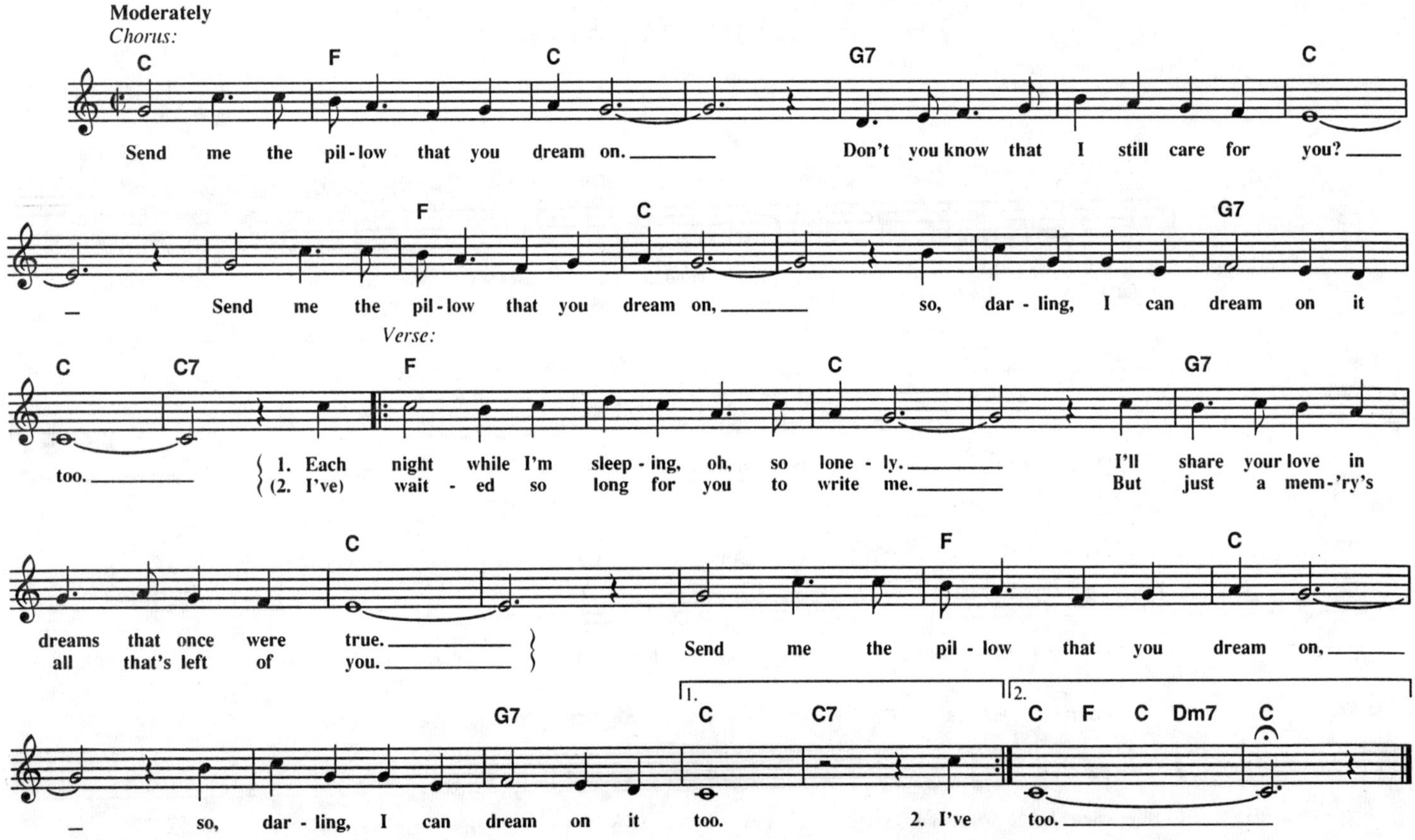

Moderately

Chorus:

Send me the pil - low that you dream on. Don't you know that I still care for you?
Send me the pil - low that you dream on, so, dar - ling, I can dream on it too.

Verse:

1. Each night while I'm sleep - ing, oh, so lone - ly. I'll share your love in dreams that once were true.
(2. I've) wait - ed so long for you to write me. But just a mem - 'ry's all that's left of you.

Send me the pil - low that you dream on, so, dar - ling, I can dream on it

1. too. 2. I've

2. too.

SEMPER FIDELES

JOHN PHILIP SOUSA

Brightly
THE SHADOW OF YOUR SMILE
(Love Theme from "The Sandpiper")
Copyright © 1965 METRO-GOLDWYN-MAYER INC., c/o EMI FEIST CATALOG INC.
World-wide Print Rights Controlled by CPP/BELWIN, INC.
All Rights Reserved
Lyrics by PAUL FRANCIS WEBSTER
Music by JOHNNY MANDEL
Moderately
The sha-dow of your smile when you are gone will col - or all my dreams and light the
star was far too high. A tear drop kissed your lips and so did
dawn. Look in - to my eyes my love and see all the love - ly things you are to
me. Our wist-ful lit - tle I. Now when I re - mem - ber spring all the joy that love can bring,
I will be re - mem - ber - ing the sha-dow of your smile. The sha-dow of your smile.
D.S. 𝄋

SEND ONE YOUR LOVE

Music and Lyrics by
STEVIE WONDER

Moderately slow
(Triangle)
Gb(2) Dbmaj7/Eb Ab(2) Ebmaj7/F Bb(2) Fmaj7/G C(2) B(2) E(2) F(2)
Oh, oh, oh.
(Vocal 2nd time only)
B(2) A6 G#7/D# Gmaj7 F#7 Dm Gmaj9
Send her your love with a doz-en ros-es; make sure that she knows it with a flow-er from your
Amaj7 Amaj7(b5) A6 G#7/D# Gmaj7 F#7
heart. Show him your love, don't hold back your feel - ings. You don't need a
Dm Gmaj9 Amaj7 Eb9(#11) D6 C#7/G#
rea - son when it's straight from the heart.
I've heard so man - y say that the days of ro -
I know that peo - ple say two hearts beat-ing as
C#m7(b5) F#7(b13) Dm7 G9 Amaj7 Eb9(#11)
mance are no more and peo - ple fall-ing in love is so old - fash - ioned. But
one is un - real and can on - ly hap-pen in make-be - lieve sto - ries. But
D6 C#7/G# C#m7(b5) F#7(b13) Dm7 G9
wait-ing are they the day they once let slip a - way, hid - ing need to ful - fill their heart's de - si - re for love's pas -
so blind they all must be that they can-not be - lieve what they see, for a - round us are mir - a-cles of love's glo -
C6/9 B6/9 C6/9 B6/9 N.C. Bb6 A7/E Abmaj7 G7
- sion. Send her your love - ry. (Instrumental)
Eb9 Abmaj7 Bbmaj7 Bbmaj7(#11) Bb6 A7/E
Show him your love, don't hold back your
(Send one your love.)
Abmaj7 G7 Ebm Abmaj9 Bbmaj7 E6 Eb6 Ab6/9 Abmaj7
feel - ings. You don't need a rea - son when it's com-ing from your heart. Huh,

huh, huh, huh. Oh,
oh, oh. (Instrumental)
(Send one your love.)
rit.
SHINE ON HARVEST MOON
Copyright © 1994 by BEAM ME UP MUSIC (ASCAP), c/o CPP/BELWIN, INC., Miami, FL 33014
All Rights Reserved
By NORA BAYES
and JACK NORWORTH
Moderately
The night was might-y dark so you could hard-ly see, for the moon re-fused to shine. Cou-ple sit-ting un-der-neath a wil-low tree, for love they pine. Lit-tle maid was kind-a 'fraid of dark-ness so she said, "I guess I'll go." Boy be-gan to sigh, looked up at the sky, told the moon his lit-tle tale of woe.
can't see why a boy should sigh, when by his side is the girl he loves so true. All he has to say is, "Won't you be my bride, for I love you." Why should I be tell-ing you this se-cret when I know that you can guess har-vest moon will smile, shine on all the while, if the lit-tle girl should an-swer, "Yes."
Oh, shine on, shine on har-vest moon up in the sky. I ain't had no lov-in' since Jan-u-ar-y, Feb-ru-ar-y, June or Ju-ly. Snow time ain't no time to stay out-doors and spoon. So shine on, shine on har-vest
1. moon, for me and my gal. I
D.S.
2. moon, for me and my gal. Oh,
3. moon, for me and my gal.

Columbia Pictures Presents a New Vision Production "WHITE NIGHTS"

SEPARATE LIVES

(Love Theme from "WHITE NIGHTS")

By STEPHEN BISHOP

Freely with expression
You called me from the room _ in your ho - tel all full of ro - mance from some-one you had
met, and tell - ing me how sor-ry you were leav-ing so soon, and that you miss me some-times when you're a -
Slowly with expression
Verse:
lone in your room. _ Do I ___ feel lone - ly too? 1. You have _ no right ___ to ask me how I
To Coda
feel. You have no right _ to speak to me so kind. ___ I can't go on ___ hold - ing on _ to ties _
_ now that we're liv - ing ___ sep - 'rate lives.
(Keyboard:)
2. Well, I held on _ lives.
Bridge:
Oh, it's so typ - i - cal; _ love leads to i - so - la - tion. _
D.S. al Coda
_ So you build that wall, _ as you build that wall, _ and make it stron-ger. ___ 3. You have _ no right _
Coda
Freely
_ find my - self look - ing in _ your eyes. But for now, we'll go on liv-ing sep - 'rate _ lives. Yes, for
now we'll go on liv-ing sep-'rate lives. (Keyboard:)
a tempo

Verse 2:
Well, I held on to let you go.
And if you lost your love for me
You never let it show.
There was no way to compromise.
So now we're living separate lives.

Verse 3:
You have no right to ask me how I feel.
You have no right to speak to me so kind.
Someday I might find myself looking in your eyes.
But for now, we'll go on living separate lives.
Yes, for now we'll go on living separate lives.

SHAKIN' ALL OVER

By JOHNNY KIDD

Moderate rock

Em
1. When you move in right up close _ to me, ___ that's when I get the shakes all o - ver me, ___
2. Just the way you say good-night _ to me ___ brings that feel - ing __ on in - side _ of me, ___

Am
Em
Am
Em
quiv-ers down my back-bone. _ I've got the shakes down the knee-bone. ___ Yeh, the trem-ors in the thigh-bone, _ shak-in' all _
1.
2.
o - ver.
o - ver. Well, you make me shake __ and I like it, ba - by. Well, you
Repeat ad lib. and fade
make me shake ___ and I like it, ba - by. Well, you make me shake ___ and I like it, ba - by. Well, you

SHE'S NOT THERE

Words and Music by
ROD ARGENT

Moderate rock

Verse:

Fm Bb Fm Bb Fm Db Fm Bb

Well, no one told me a - bout ___ her, ___ the way she lied.
Well, no one told me a - bout ___ her. ___ What could I do?

Fm Bb Fm Bb Fm Db F Bb Bbm

Well, no one told me a - bout ___ her, ___ how man-y peo-ple cried.
Well, no one told me a - bout ___ her, ___ though they all knew.
But it's too late to say you're

Fm Cm7 Fm Bb Bbm Ab

sor - ry. How would I know, _ why should I care? ___ Please don't both - er tryin' to find ___ her, she's not there. _

C7

Chorus:

Fm Bb Fm Db

Well, let me tell you 'bout the way she looked, the way she act - ed, the col - or of her

Fm Bb Fm Db Fm Bb F

1. 2.

hair. Her voice was soft and cool, her eyes were clear and bright, but she's not there. ___

Featured on the Jackie Gleason TV Show

SHANGRI-LA

Lyrics by CARL SIGMAN
Music by MATT MALNECK
and ROBERT MAXWELL

SHE LOVES YOU

Words and Music by
JOHN LENNON and PAUL McCARTNEY

Slowly
F Dm7 Gm Gm7/C C7(♭9) F Dm7 Gm7
Your kiss - es take me to Shan - gri - la. Each kiss is mag - ic that makes my lit - tle
And when you hold me, how warm you are. Be mine, my dar - ling, and spend your life with
G♭7 C7(♭9) Fmaj7 F6 N.C. A♭7 D♭maj7 G♭7 Fmaj7 F6 B♭maj7
world a Shan - gri - la; a land of blue-birds and foun-tains and noth - ing to do, but cling to an
me in Shan - gri -
E♭7 Gm7 C7(♭9) Am7(♭5) D7(♭9) D7 Gm7 G♭7 C7(♭9) Fmaj7 G♭9(♭5) Fmaj7
an - gel that looks like you. la. For an - y - where you are is Shan-gri - la.
Moderate rock
Cm F7 A♭ E♭
She loves you, yeah, yeah, yeah. She loves you, yeah, yeah, yeah. She loves you, yeah yeah yeah yeah! You
Cm Gm B♭7 E♭ Cm Gm
think you've lost your love. Well, I saw her yes - ter - day - yi-yay. It's you she's think-ing of, and she told me what to
said you hurt her so. She al - most lost her mind, and now she says she knows you're not the hurt - ing
know it's up to you. I think it's on - ly fair. Pride can hurt you too; a - pol - o - gize to
B♭7 E♭ Cm A♭m B♭7
sa - yi-yay. She says she
kind. She says she
her. Be-cause she
loves you, and you know that can't be bad. Yeah, she loves you, and you know you should be glad. She
Cm F7 A♭m6 B♭7(♯5) E♭
Ooo. She loves you, yeah, yeah, yeah. She loves you, yeah, yeah, yeah. And with a love like that you know you should be glad. You
B♭7 Cm F7 A♭m6 B♭7(♯5) B♭7
Ooo. She loves you, yeah, yeah, yeah. She loves you yeah, yeah, yeah. And with a love like that you know you should be glad.
E♭ Cm A♭m6 B♭7(♯5) B♭7 E♭ Cm A♭m6
With a love like that you know you should be glad. With a love like that you
B♭7(♯5) B♭7 E♭ Cm A♭ E♭6
a tempo
know you should be glad. Yeah, yeah, yeah. Yeah, yeah, yeah. Yeah, yeah, yeah, yeah,

SHE WORE A YELLOW RIBBON

FOLK SONG

Moderately bright
C D7 G7
'Round her neck she wore a yel - low rib - bon. She wore it in the spring-time and in the month of May. And
C G7 C
if you asked her why the heck she wore it. She says, "It's for my lov - er who is far, far a - way." Far a -
F C G7
way, far a - way. She wore it for her lov - er far a - way.
C G7 C
'Round her neck she wore a yel - low rib - bon. She wore it for her lov - er who is far, far a - way.

SHE'LL BE COMIN' 'ROUND THE MOUNTAIN

AMERICAN

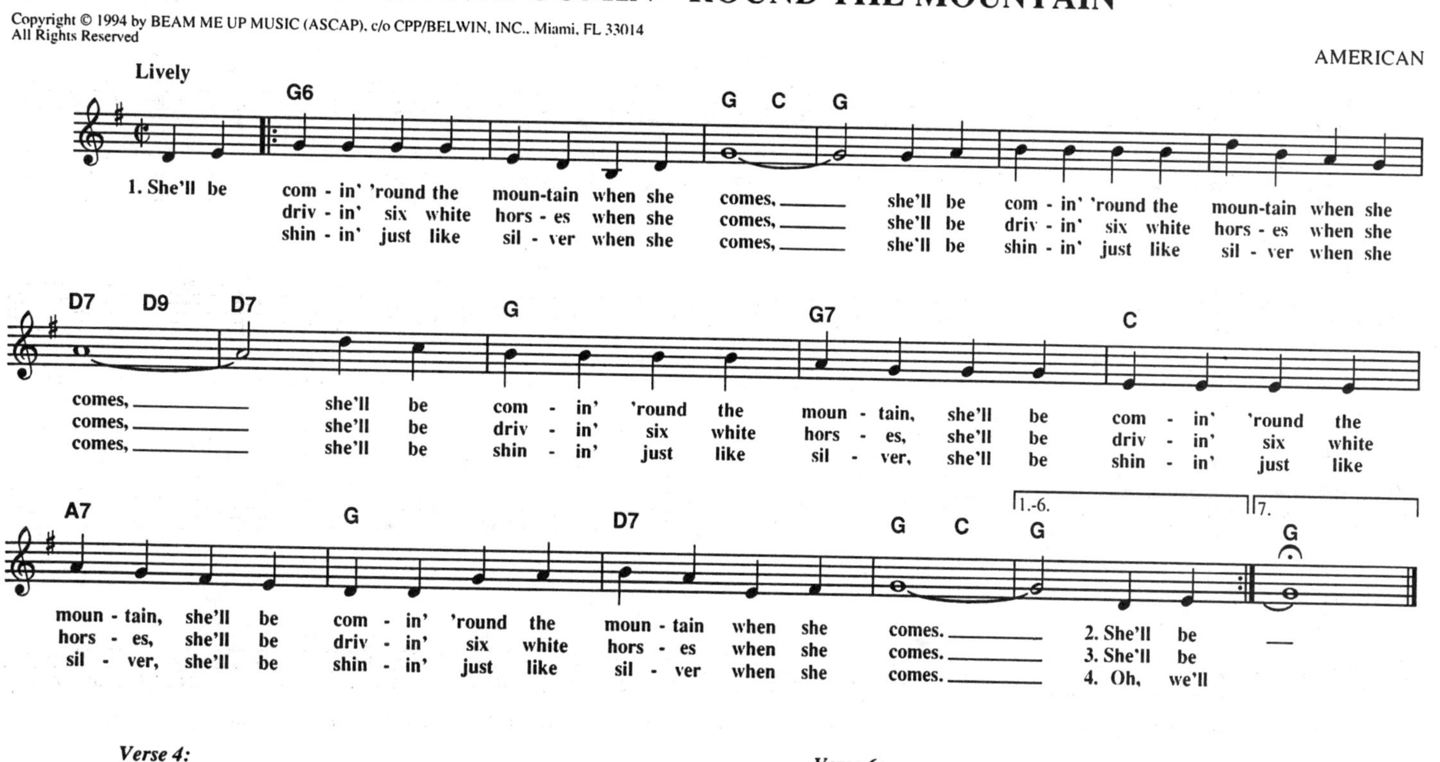
Lively
G6 G C G
1. She'll be com - in' 'round the mountain when she comes, she'll be com - in' 'round the moun-tain when she
driv - in' six white hors - es when she comes, she'll be driv - in' six white hors - es when she
shin - in' just like sil - ver when she comes, she'll be shin - in' just like sil - ver when she
D7 D9 D7 G G7 C
comes, she'll be com - in' 'round the moun - tain, she'll be com - in' 'round the
comes, she'll be driv - in' six white hors - es, she'll be driv - in' six white
comes, she'll be shin - in' just like sil - ver, she'll be shin - in' just like
A7 G D7 G C G G
1.-6. 7.
moun - tain, she'll be com - in' 'round the moun - tain when she comes. 2. She'll be
hors - es, she'll be driv - in' six white hors - es when she comes. 3. She'll be
sil - ver, she'll be shin - in' just like sil - ver when she comes. 4. Oh, we'll

Verse 4:
Oh, we'll all go out to meet her when she comes,
Oh, we'll all go out to meet her when she comes,
Oh, we'll all go out to meet her,
Oh, we'll all go out to meet her,
Oh, we'll all go out to meet her when she comes.

Verse 5:
She'll be breathin' smoke and fire when she comes,
She'll be breathin' smoke and fire when she comes,
She'll be breathin' smoke and fire,
She'll be breathin' smoke and fire,
She'll be breathin' smoke and fire when she comes.

Verse 6:
We'll all have chicken an' dumplin's when she comes,
We'll all have chicken an' dumplin's when she comes,
We'll all have chicken an' dumplin's,
We'll all have chicken an' dumplin's,
We'll all have chicken an' dumplin's when she comes.

Verse 7:
She'll be wearin' red pajamas when she comes,
She'll be wearin' red pajamas when she comes,
She'll be wearin' red pajamas,
She'll be wearin' red pajamas,
She'll be wearin' red pajamas, when she comes.

SHEIK OF ARABY

Words by HARRY B. SMITH
and FRANCIS WHEELER
Music by TED SNYDER

Brightly
F7 B♭ Bdim F7 B♭ B♭maj7/D
I'm the Sheik of Ar - a - by, your love be - longs to me. At night when
D♭dim F7/C F7 Cm7 F7 F+ B♭ C7 F7 B♭ Bdim F7
you're a - sleep, in - to your tent I'll creep. The stars that shine a - bove, will
A7(♭5)/E♭ D G7 C7 F7 B♭
light our way to love. You'll rule this land with me, the Sheik of Ar - a - by.

SHOUT

Words and Music by
O'KELLY ISLEY, RONALD ISLEY
and RUDOLPH ISLEY

Very fast (Brightly)

C Am
You know you make me wan - na come on now, come on now,

C Am C
oh, let's shout now, hey, let's shout now, say you

Am C Am
will, say it right now, ba - by. Say you will, come on, come on.

Am C Am
Say you will, say it a - gain. Say you will, come on

C Am C
now, say that you love me. Say, say that you need me. Say, say that you want me.

Repeat and fade

Am C Am
Say you want to please me. Come on now, come on now,

SHENANDOAH

Copyright © 1994 by BEAM ME UP MUSIC (ASCAP), c/o CPP/BELWIN, INC., Miami, FL 33014
All Rights Reserved
FOLK SONG
Moderately
D G D Bm G D Bm A7 D
O, Shen-an-doah. I long to hear you, a - way, you roll-ing riv - er. Oh
Shen-an - doah I long to hear you, a - way, we're bound a - way, 'cross the wide Mis - sou - ri.
SHOO-BE-DOO-BE DOO-DA-DAY
Copyright © 1968 by JOBETE MUSIC CO., INC.
All Rights Reserved
Words and Music by
STEVIE WONDER, HENRY COSBY
and SYLVIA MOY
Moderate rock
Verse:
E7 A7 E7
1. Your pre-cious sweet - heart, she's so faith-ful, she's so true. Oh, yeah. Her dreams are tum-
A7 E7
- blin', her world is crum - blin' be-cause of you. Uh - huh. One day you'll hurt
A7 F♯7 A/B E7 G A B7(♭13)
her just once too much and when you fi - n'lly lose your ten - der touch. Hey, hey.
Chorus:
E D/E E D/E A/E D/E E
Shoo-be - doo - be - doo - be doo - da - day, her feet may wan-der, her heart may stray. Oh yeah.
D/E E D/E A/E
Shoo - be - doo - be - doo - be doo - da - dee, you're / love's gon-na send your ba - by straight
1. D/E E D.S. 𝄋 2. D/E E E7
to me. 2. I'm gon-na give to me.
D.S. 𝄋 3. D/E E Repeat ad lib. and fade
3. Heart-aches are call - to me. Hey, hey.

Verse 2:
I'm gonna give her all the lovin' within my heart. Oh yeah.
I'm gonna patch up every single little dream you tore apart.
Understand me?
And when she tells you she's cried her last tear, heaven knows
I'm gonna be somewhere near. Oh yeah.
(To Chorus:)

Verse 3:
Heartaches are callin', tears are fallin' because of you. Hey, yeah.
And when you're gone, she'll know I'm the one to go to her rescue.
Baby, you didn't know that thing.
You're gonna leave her once too many times and when you come back,
That girl's gonna be mine, all mine. Hey, hey.
(To Chorus:)

SHOW ME THE WAY

(Peter Frampton)

Words and Music by
PETER FRAMPTON

Moderately
Verse:
D
Dmaj7
Bm
1. I won-der how you're feel-ing. There's ring-ing in my ears, and no one to re-late to 'cept the sea.
(2.) I can see no rea-son you living on your nerves when some-one drops a cup and I sub-merge.
(3.) (Inst. solo ad lib. . . . end solo)
B♭6
D
Dmaj7
Bm
Who can I be-lieve in? I'm kneel-ing on the floor. There has to be a force; who do I phone?
I'm swim-ming in a cir-cle I feel I'm go-ing down there has to be a fool to play my part.
I won-der if I'm dream-ing I feel so un-a-shamed. I can't be-lieve this is happening to me.
B♭
A11
G
The stars are out and shin-ing but all I real-ly want to know . . . .
Some-one thought of heal-ing but all I real-ly want to know . . . .
I watch you when you're sleep-ing but all I real-ly want to know . . . .
Oh won't
Chorus:
Bm
G
To Coda
Bm
1.
G
A11
D
you show me the way, ev-'ry day. Oh won't you show me the way.
Dmaj7
Bm
B♭6
C
2.
G
Bm
G
A11
D.S. al Coda
2. Well, way. I want you day af-ter day. Yeah.
Coda
Bm
G
Bm
G
you to show me the way, ev-'ry day. I want you to show me the way, night and day. I want
Bm
G
A11
D
Dmaj7
Bm
B♭
C
D
you day af-ter day. Hey, whoa.
rit.
SIBONEY
Copyright © 1929 (Renewed 1957) EMI FEIST CATALOG INC.
All Rights Reserved
American Lyric by DOLLY MORSE
Spanish Lyric and Music by ERNESTO LECUONA
Moderately
C
C♯dim7 G7
F G7
Si-bo-ney, that's the tune that they croon at you down Ha-van-a way. Si-bo-ney, that's the
tune brings you dreams so it seems un-der-neath the sil-ver moon. As they play Si-bo-
Dm7 G7
1.
C
2.
C
Fm
Cm
Fm Cm
G7 C
dance that they dance at the Ca-fe. And that way. Fas-ci-nat-ing, cap-ti-vat-ing, Si-bo-ney.
ney, ev-'ry care will fade a-

SHOW ME THE WAY

(Styx)

Lyrics and Music by
DENNIS DE YOUNG

Slowly
Verse:
Ev - 'ry night I say a pray'r in the hopes that there's a heav-en. But ev - 'ry day I'm more con-fused as the
saints turn in - to sin - ners. All the he-roes and leg-ends I knew as a child have fal-len to i - dols of clay. And I
feel this emp - ty place in-side; so a - fraid that I've lost my faith. Show me the
Chorus:
way, show me the way. Take me to- / Bring me to-
night to the riv - er and wash my il - lu-sions a - / night to the moun-tain and take my con - fu-sion a - way.
To Coda
Please show me the way.
1.
D.C.
2. And
2.
Bridge:
And if I see a light, should I be - lieve? Tell me, how will I know?
D.S. al Coda
Show me the
Coda
way, show me the way. Take me to-night to the riv-er and wash my il - lu-sions a - way. Show me the
way, show me the way. Give me the strength and the cour-age to be-lieve that I'll get there some day. And please show me the
slower
way. Ev-'ry night I say a pray'r in the hopes that there's a heav-en.

Verse 2:
And as I slowly drift to sleep
For a moment dreams are sacred.
I close my eyes and know there's peace
In a world so filled with hatred.
Then I wake up each morning and turn on the news
to find we've so far to go.
And I keep on hoping for a sign
So afraid I just won't know.
(To Chorus:)

SINCE I FELL FOR YOU

Words and Music by
BUDDY JOHNSON

Slow drag
Eb Eb6 Ab6 Bbm7 Eb Eb6 Ab/Eb Ebm Ab Abm6 Gb6 F7 Bb7
You made me leave my hap - py home, you took my love and now you're gone,
Love brings such mis - er - y and pain, I know I'll nev - er be the same,
I guess I'll nev - er see the light, I get the blues most ev - 'ry night,
since I fell for
Eb Cm7 1. Fm7 Bb7 2.3. Eb Fine Ebm7 Ab7 Ebm7 Ab7 Ebm7 Ab7 Ebm7 Ab9
you;
It's too bad, it's too sad, but I'm in love with you,
D.C. al Fine
Eb Ebm7 Ab7 Ebm7 Ab7 Eb/Bb Bb6 Eb6 Fm9 F9 Bb7
you love me, then snub me, oh, what can I do, I'm still in love with you;

SKYLARK

Words by JOHNNY MERCER
Music by HOAGY CARMICHAEL

Moderato

Eb6 Bb7/F Eb/G Ab Eb/Bb Gm/Bb Ab Eb/G

Sky - lark,
Have you an - y - thing to say to me? Won't you tell me where my
have you seen a val - ley green with Spring, where my heart can go a
I don't know if you can find these things, but my heart is rid - ing

Ab Eb/G F7 Bb7 To Coda 1. Eb Cm Cm7/Bb Ab Fm7/Bb Bb7

love can be? Is there a mea-dow in the mist, where some-one's wait - ing to be kissed?
jour - ney - ing, o - ver the sha-dows and the
on your wings, so, if you see them an - y

2. Eb Bb7 Eb Ab Eb6 Fm7 E7 Eb7

rain, to a blos - som cov - ered lane? And in your lone - ly flight, Have-n't you heard the mu - sic

Abmaj7 Ebdim Ab6 Db7 C7 Ddim C7/E Fm Fm7 Fdim Db Fm Eb7(#5) Ab

in the night, won-der-ful mu - sic, faint as a "will o' the wisp," cra - zy as a loon,

G A7 D7 G Bb7 D.C. al Coda

sad as a gyp - sy ser - e - nad - ing the moon. (Oh,)

Coda Eb Bb7 Eb E6 Eb6

where won't you lead me there?

THE SIDEWALKS OF NEW YORK

(East Side, West Side)

Words by CHARLES B. LAWLOR
Music by JAMES W. BLAKE

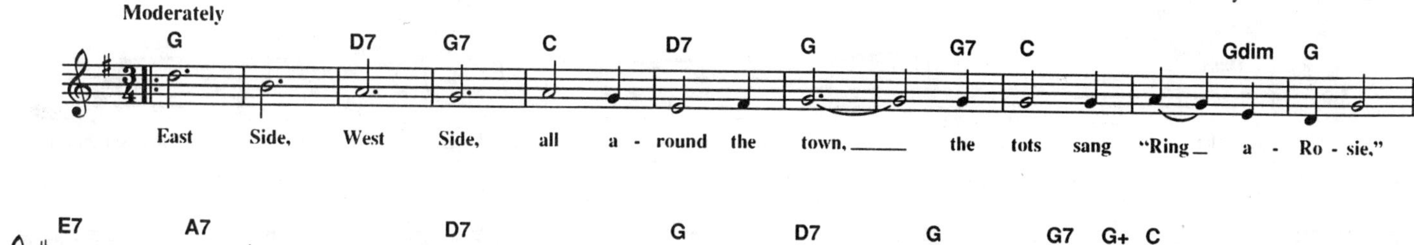
Moderately
G D7 G7 C D7 G G7 C Gdim G
East Side, West Side, all a - round the town, the tots sang "Ring a - Ro - sie,"

E7 A7 D7 G D7 G G7 G+ C
"Lon - don Bridge is Fall - ing Down!" Boys and girls to - geth - er, me and Ma - mie O' -

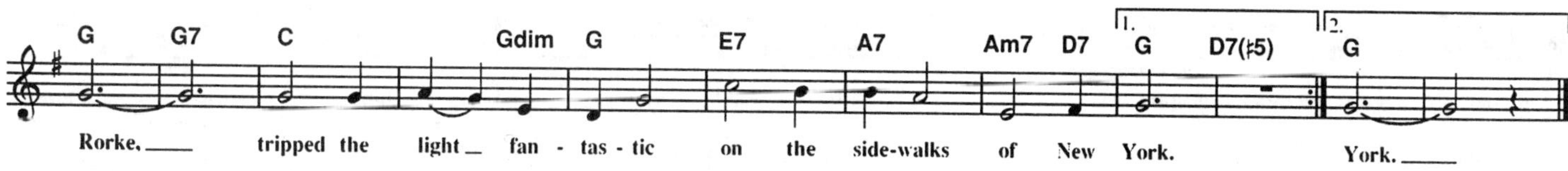
G G7 C Gdim G E7 A7 Am7 D7 G D7(♯5) G
1. 2.
Rorke, tripped the light fan - tas - tic on the side-walks of New York. York.

SINCERELY

Words and Music by
ALAN FREED and HARVEY FUQUA

Slowly

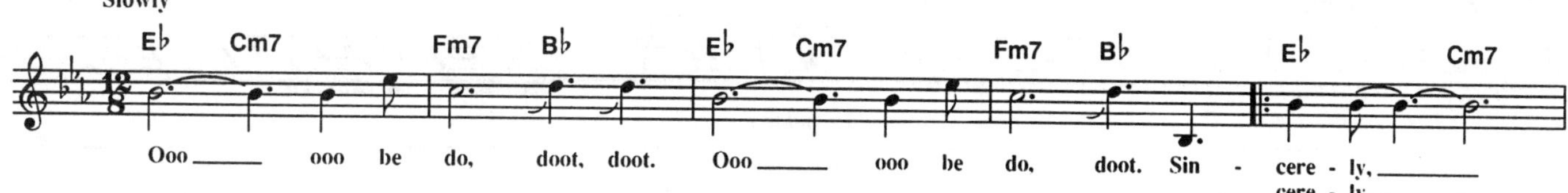
E♭ Cm7 Fm7 B♭ E♭ Cm7 Fm7 B♭ E♭ Cm7
Ooo ooo be do, doot, doot. Ooo ooo be do, doot. Sin - cere - ly,
cere - ly,

Fm7 B♭ E♭ Cm7 Fm7 B♭ E♭ Cm7 Fm7 B♭
oh yes, sin - cere - ly, 'cause I love you so dear - ly, please say you'll be
oh, you know how I love you. I'll do an - y - thing for you. Please say you'll be

1. 2.
E♭ Cm7 Fm7 B♭ E♭ A♭ E♭ E♭7 A♭ A♭m7
mine. Sin - mine. Oh Lord, won't you tell me why I

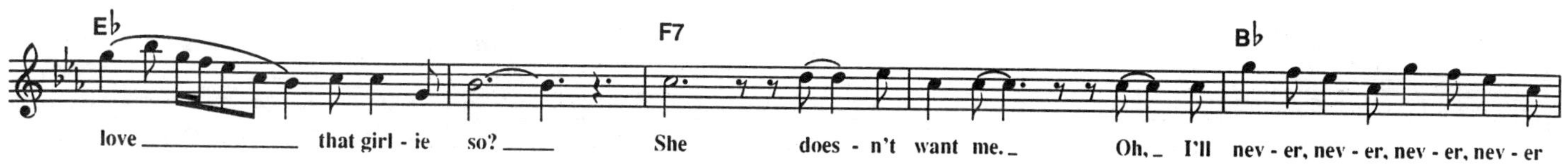
E♭ F7 B♭
love that girl - ie so? She does - n't want me. Oh, I'll nev - er, nev - er, nev - er, nev - er

B♭6 E♭ Cm7 Fm7 B♭ E♭ Cm7 Fm7 B♭ E♭ Cm7
let you go. Sin - cere - ly, oh, you know how I love you. I'll do an - y - thing for you.

Fm7 B♭ E♭ Cm7 Fm7 B♭ E♭ Cm7 Fm7 B♭ E♭6
Please say you'll be mine. Oh, say you'll be mine. Doot, doot, ooo.

SIGNS

Words and Music by
LES EMMERSON

Moderate rock
Verse:
C G/B D/A G D A
1. And the sign says, "Long-haired freak-y peo-ple need not ap-ply." So, I tucked my hair up un-der my hat and I
G A Bm G
went in to ask him why. He said, "You look like a fine up-stand-ing young man, I think you'll do." So, I
Chorus:
D A G A D C G
took off my hat and said, "I-mag-ine that, me work-ing for you." Oh, sign, sign, ev-'ry-where a sign, block-
1.
D G D A C(2) C
-ing out the scen-er-y, break-ing my mind. Do this, don't do that. Can't you read the sign.?
D.S. 𝄋
2.
To Next Strain
D Dsus D Dsus D Csus C D
2. And the
3.
4.
Fine
Csus C Csus C D
Bridge:
A G D A
Hey now, mis-ter, can't you read? You got to have a shirt and tie to get a seat. You can't watch no you can't eat.
G D N.C.
You ain't sup-posed to be here. And the sign says, "You got to have a mem-ber-ship card to get in-side."
D.S. 𝄋
D C G D G D A C(2) D Dsus D Dsus D
(Instrumental solo . . . . . . end solo)
3. And the

Verse 2:
And the sign says, "Anybody caught trespassing will be shot on sight."
So, I jumped the fence and I yelled at a house, "Hey! What gives you the right
To put up a fence and keep me out, or to keep Mother Nature in?
If God was here, He'd tell you to your face, 'Man, you're some kind of sinner.'"
(To Chorus:)

Verse 3:
And the sign says, "Everybody welcome! Come in and kneel down and pray."
But when they passed around the plate at the end of it all, I didn't have a penny to pay.
So, I got me a pen and a paper, and I made up my own little sign.
I said, "Thank you, Lord, for thinkin' 'bout me. I'm alive and doin' fine."
(To Chorus:)

SILENT NIGHT

Words and Music by
JOSEPH MOHR and
FRANZ GRUBER

Slowly
C G7 C
1. Si - lent night, ho - ly night, all is calm, all is bright.
2. Si - lent night, ho - ly night, shep - herds quake at the sight.
3. Si - lent night, ho - ly night, Son of God, love's pure light;
F C F C
Round yon Vir - gin Moth - er and Child, Ho - ly In - fant so ten - der and mild;
Glo - ries stream from heav - en a - far, heav'n - ly hosts sing Al - le - lu - ia;
ra - diant beams from Thy ho - ly face, with the dawn of re - deem - ing grace;
G C G7 1.2. C 3. C
sleep in heav - en - ly peace; sleep in heav - en - ly peace.
Christ the Sav - ior is born; Christ the Sav - ior is born.
Je - sus, Lord, at thy birth; Je - sus, Lord, at Thy birth.

From the Paramount Picture "THE LEMON DROP KID"

SILVER BELLS

Words and Music by
JAY LIVINGSTON and RAY EVANS

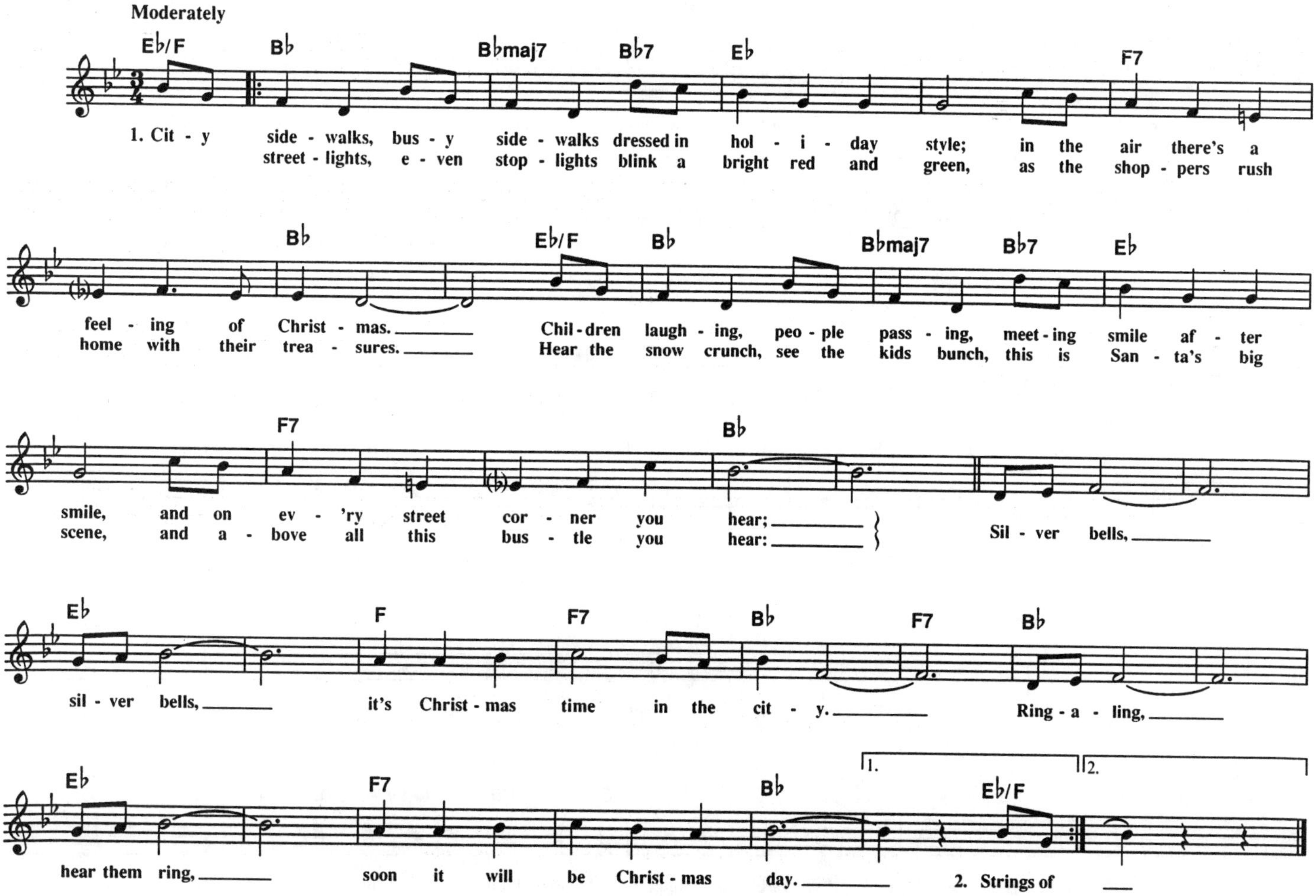

Moderately

E♭/F B♭ B♭maj7 B♭7 E♭ F7

1. Cit - y side - walks, bus - y side - walks dressed in hol - i - day style; in the air there's a
street - lights, e - ven stop - lights blink a bright red and green, as the shop - pers rush

B♭ E♭/F B♭ B♭maj7 B♭7 E♭

feel - ing of Christ - mas. Chil - dren laugh - ing, peo - ple pass - ing, meet - ing smile af - ter
home with their trea - sures. Hear the snow crunch, see the kids bunch, this is San - ta's big

F7 B♭

smile, and on ev - 'ry street cor - ner you hear;
scene, and a - bove all this bus - tle you hear:

Sil - ver bells,

E♭ F F7 B♭ F7 B♭

sil - ver bells, it's Christ - mas time in the cit - y. Ring - a - ling,

E♭ F7 B♭ 1. E♭/F 2.

hear them ring, soon it will be Christ - mas day. 2. Strings of

SINCE I DON'T HAVE YOU

Lyrics by JAMES BEAUMONT, JANET VOGEL, JOSEPH VERSCHAREN, WALTER LESTER and JOHN TAYLOR
Music by JOSEPH ROCK and LENNIE MARTIN

Slowly
I don't have plans and schemes. And I don't have hopes and dreams. I don't have
any-thing since I don't have you.
since I don't have you.
I don't have hap-pi-ness, and I guess I never will ever again.
When you walked out on me, in walked the mis-er-y, and he's been here since then. Now
I don't have much to share. And I don't have one to care. I don't have
any-thing since I don't have you, you, you, you,
you, you, you, you, you, you, you, you, you.
SING, SING, SING
Copyright © 1936 (Renewed 1964) EMI ROBBINS CATALOG INC.
All Rights Reserved
Words and Music by
LOUIS PRIMA
Bright swing
Sing, sing, sing, sing, ev-'ry-bod-y start to sing.
Swing, swing, swing, swing, ev-'ry-bod-y start to swing.
La-dle-la, whoa-ho-ho.
Now you're sing-ing with a swing.
Now you're swing-ing while you sing.
Fine
When the mu-sic goes a-round ev-'ry-bod-y goes to town. But here's some-thing you should know: ho-ho ba-by ho-ho-ho.
D.C. al Fine

From the Metro-Golwyn-Mayer Musical Production "SINGIN' IN THE RAIN"

SINGIN' IN THE RAIN

Words by ARTHUR FREED
Music by NACIO HERB BROWN

Moderately
G6/9
G♯dim7 D7/A
Sing - in' in the rain, just sing - in' in the rain. What a glo - ri - ous feel - ing; I'm hap - py a -
one from the place. Come on with the rain, I've a smile on my

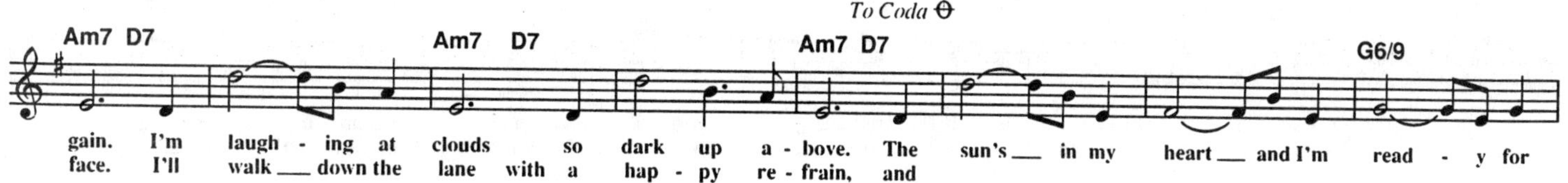
To Coda
Am7 D7
Am7 D7
Am7 D7
G6/9
gain. I'm laugh - ing at clouds so dark up a - bove. The sun's in my heart and I'm read - y for
face. I'll walk down the lane with a hap - py re - frain, and

D.S. al Coda
Coda
D7
G6/9
love. Let the storm - y clouds chase ev - 'ry
sing - in' just sing - in' in the rain.

SINGING THE BLUES

Words and Music by
MELVIN ENDSLEY

Moderate swing
F
B♭
F
Gm
C7
B♭
Well, I never felt more like singing the blues 'cause I never thought that I'd ever lose your love, dear.
C7
F B♭ F C7
F
B♭
F
Why'd you do me this way? Well, I never felt more like crying all night, 'cause ev-'ry-thing's wrong, and
Gm
C7
B♭
C7
F
F7
B♭
nothing ain't right with - out you. You got me singing the blues. The moon and stars no

F
B♭
F
B♭
F
lon - ger shine, the dream is gone I thought was mine. There's noth - ing left for me to do but cry

C7
F
B♭
F
Gm
C7
B♭
o - ver you. Well, I never felt more like running a - way, but why should I go 'cause I could-n't stay with - out you.

C7
1.
F F7/E♭ B♭/D B♭m/D♭ F/C C7
2.
F F7/E♭ B♭/D B♭m/D♭ F/C C7 F
You got me sing - ing the blues. Well, I blues.

SIR DUKE

Words and Music by
STEVIE WONDER

Moderately
N.C.
B G♯m G F♯7
Mu - sic is a world with - in it - self with a lan - guage we all un - der - stand,
Mu - sic knows it is and al - ways will be one of the things that life just won't quit.
B G♯m G F♯7 F7
with an e - qual op - por - tu - ni - ty for all to sing dance and clap their hands. But just be-
But here are some of mu - sic's pi - o - neers, that time will not al - low us to for - get. For there's
E9 E♭9 D9 D♭9 D9 E♭9 E9 E♭9 D9 D♭9
cause a re - cord has a groove don't make it in the groove but you can tell right a - way at let - ter A when the
Ba - sie, Mil - ler, Sach - mo, and the king of all, Sir Duke, and with a voice like El - la's ring - in' out there's no
D9 E♭9 E9 F9 F♯9 B Fm Emaj7
peo - ple start to move. They / You can feel it all o - ver. They / You can feel it all
way the band can lose.
C♯m7 F♯11 B Fm Emaj7
o - ver, peo - ple. They / You can feel it all o - ver. They / You can feel it all
C♯m7 F♯11 N.C.
o - ver, peo - ple, go!
2nd time Fine

THE SKATER'S WALTZ

EMILE WALDTEUFEL

Moderate waltz
C G7 C Am Dm7 G7
1. 2.
C C G7 C
Em B7 Em G7 C
G7 C Am Dm7 G7 C
SKATING
Copyright © LEE MENDELSON FILM PRODUCTIONS, INC., 1969
All Rights Reserved
By VINCE GUARALDI
Bright jazz waltz
C6/9 F6/9 G6/9 F6/9 C F G
F C6 E♭ G♭ A C F G
1. 2.
F C E♭ A♭ D♭ C Dm7 Em7 G♭9
Fm7 B♭13 E♭maj13 E♭m7 A♭13 D7(♯5) D♭maj7 G7(♭9)
C F G F C6 E♭ G♭ A
Repeat ad lib. and fade
C F G F C6/9 F6/9 G6/9 F6/9

SLEEPY TIME GAL

Words by JOSEPH R. ALDEN and RAYMOND B. EGAN
Music by ANGE LORENZO and RICHARD A. WHITING

Moderately

G6/9 E♭7 D7 Gmaj7 F♯7 F7
Sleep-y time gal, you're turn-ing night in-to day. Sleep-y time gal, you've danced the ev-'ning a-way. Be-fore each

E7 A7 D7 D+
sil-ver-y star fades out of sight, please give me one lit-tle kiss, then let us whis-per good-night. It's get-tin' late and dear, your pil-low's wait-in'.

G6/9 E♭7 D7 B7 Em
Sleep-y time gal, when all your danc-in' is through, sleep-y time gal, I'll find a cot-tage for you. You'll learn to

A7 Cm G Dm Bm7(♭5) E7 Am Cm D7 G6/9
cook and to sew. What's more you'll love it, I know, when you're a stay-at-home, play-at-home, eight-o-clock, sleep-y time gal.

SO RARE

Words by JACK SHARPE
Music by JERRY HERST

Moderately

G7(♯5) C6 E♭dim7 G9/D G7(♭9) C6 E♭9 A♭6
So rare, you're like the fra-grance of blos - soms fair, sweet as a breath of air
you're like the spar-kle of old cham-pagne. Or-chids in cel - lo - phane

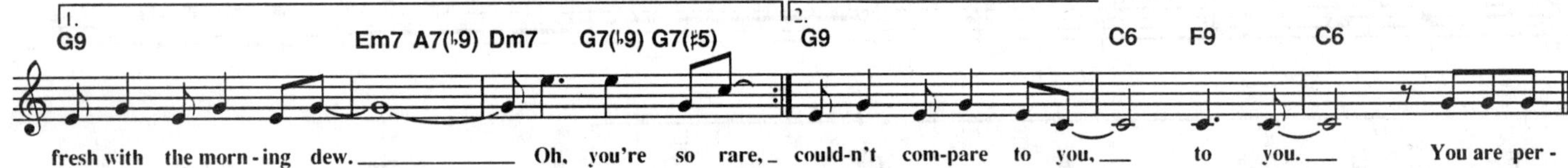
1. 2.
G9 Em7 A7(♭9) Dm7 G7(♭9) G7(♯5) G9 C6 F9 C6
fresh with the morn-ing dew. Oh, you're so rare, could-n't com-pare to you, to you. You are per -

Dm7 G7 Cmaj7 C6 Dm7 G7 Cmaj7 C6 Bm7 E7 Amaj7 A6
fec-tion, you're my i - de - a of an-gels sing-ing the A - ve Ma-ri - a. For you're an an-gel; I breathe and live you, with ev-'ry

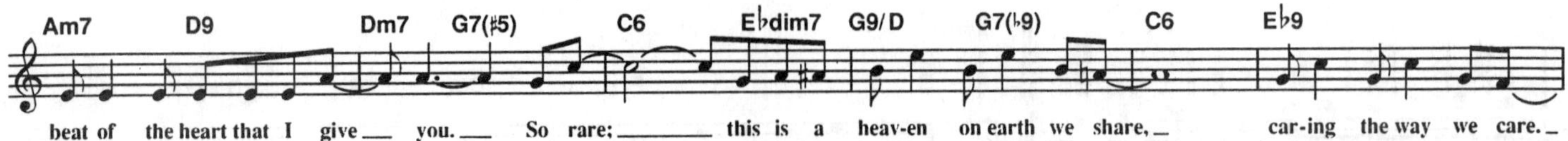
Am7 D9 Dm7 G7(♯5) C6 E♭dim7 G9/D G7(♭9) C6 E♭9
beat of the heart that I give you. So rare; this is a heav-en on earth we share, car-ing the way we care.

A♭6 G9 G9(♯5) C6 G9 G9(♯5) C6 G9 G9(♯5) C6 G7 C
Ours is a love so rare, ours is a love so rare, ours is a love so rare.

SLEIGH RIDE

Lyric by MITCHELL PARISH
Music by LEROY ANDERSON

Moderately bright
G Am7 D7 G
Just hear those sleigh bells jin - gle - ing, ring - ting - tin - gle - ing, too;
Am7 D7 G Am7 D7 G B♭ D7
— come on, it's love - ly weath-er for a sleigh ride to - geth - er with you. Out - side the
G Am7 D7 G Am7 D7 G
snow is fall - ing and friends are call - ing "Yoo - hoo." Come on, it's love - ly weath-er for a
Am7 D7 G C♯m7 F♯7
sleigh ride to - geth - er with you. Gid - dy - yap, gid - dy - yap, gid - dy - yap, let's go;
B C♯m7 F♯7 B
let's look at the show. We're rid - ing in a won - der - land of snow.
Bm Bm7 E7 A
— Gid - dy - yap, gid - dy - yap, gid - dy - yap, it's grand, just hold - ing your hand.
Am7 D7 Am D7
We're glid - ing a - long with a song of a win - ter - y fair - y - land. Our cheeks are
G Am7 D7 G Am7 D7 G
nice and ros - y, and com - fy co - zy are we. We're snug - gled up to - geth - er like two
Am7 D7 G B♭ D7 G Am7 D7
birds of a feath - er would be. Let's take that road be - fore us and sing a chor - us or
G Am7 D7 G Am7 D7 G
two. Come on, it's love - ly weath-er for a sleigh ride to-geth-er with you.

SO INTO YOU
Words and Music by
BUDDY BLUE, ROBERT NIX
and DEAN DAUGHTRY
Copyright © 1977 by LOW-SAL INC.
All Rights Reserved
Moderate rock
When you walked in-to the room _ there was voo-doo in the vibes. _ I was cap-tured by your style; _
but I _ could not catch your eyes. _ Now I stand here _ help-less-ly hop-ing you'll be in - to me. _ I am
so in-to you. _ I can't { think of / get to } noth-ing else. _ I am so _ in-to you. _ I can't _ { think of / get to } noth-ing else. _
To Coda
Think-ing how it's going _ to be _ when-ev-er I get you next to me. _ It's gon-na be good. _
Instrumental 2nd time
Don't you know, _ I'm so in - to you. _ from your head to your toe, _ gon-na love you all ov - er. Ov-er and ov - er. I'm so in-to you. _
Me in - to you, you in - to me, me in - to you. _ Oo. _ When you
D.S. al Coda
Coda
Come on _ ba - by, ba-by, driv-ing me cra - zy. _ I'm so in - to you. _ Love the things you do. _ Lis - ten Come on
Repeat and fade
SOMETIMES I FEEL LIKE A MOTHERLESS CHILD
Copyright © 1973, 1994 by BEAM ME UP MUSIC, c/o CPP/BELWIN, INC., Miami, FL 33014
All Rights Reserved
SPIRITUAL
Slowly
Some-times I feel like a moth-er-less child. Some-times I feel like a moth-er-less child. Some-times I feel like a
moth - er - less child a might-ty long way _ from home, _ yes, a long, long way _ from home!
True be - liev - er, I'm a long, long way _ from home, _ yes, a long, long way _ from home! _

SOFTLY, AS I LEAVE YOU

English Lyric by HAL SHAPER
Music by A. SE VITA

Moderately
C Dm7 G7 C Dm7 G7 C F C
Soft - ly, I will leave you soft - ly, for my heart would break if you should wake and see me go.
Dm7 G7 E♭ Fm7 B♭7 E♭ Fm7 B♭7 E♭ A♭
So I leave you soft - ly long be-fore you miss me, long be-fore your arms can beg me stay for one more
Gm7 Cm7 Fm7 B♭7 Cmaj7 Dm7 G7 C Dm G7 Am Am7/G F A♭
hour or one more day. Af-ter all the years I can't bear the tears to fall so soft - ly,
1. 2.
Fm7 C Dm7 G7 Fm7 C Dm7 G7 C Dm7 G7 C Fm6 C
as I leave you there. as I leave you there, as I leave you there, as I leave you there.

SOLITUDE

Words and Music by
DUKE ELLINGTON, IRVING MILLS
and EDDIE DeLANGE

Slowly, with expression

G7(♯5) Cmaj7 Am7 Dm7 G7 C C♯dim
In my sol - i - tude you haunt me, with rev - er - ies of days gone by.

Dm7 G7(♯5) Cmaj7 Am7 D7 G7 C
In my sol - i - tude you taunt me, with mem - o - ries that nev - er die.

Gm7 C9 F F♯dim C/G C9 F
I sit in my chair, I'm filled with des - pair. There's no one could be so sad. With gloom ev - 'ry - where, I

F♯dim7 C/G C♯dim7 Dm7 G7(♯5) Cmaj7 Am7 Dm7
sit and I stare. I know that I'll soon go mad. In my sol - i - tude I'm pray -

1. 2.
G7 C C♯dim7 Dm7 G7(♯5) C F Fm C6
ing, dear Lord a - bove send back my love. In my love.

SOMEBODY LOVES ME

Words by B.G. DeSYLVA and BALLARD MACDONALD
Music by GEORGE GERSHWIN

Allegro moderato
Some - bod - y loves me I won - der who, I won - der who she can be; ___
some - bod - y loves me I wish I knew, who can she be wor - ries me, ___ for ev - 'ry
girl who pass - es me I shout, hey! May - be, you were meant to be my lov - ing ba - by;
some - bod - y loves me I won - der who, may - be it's you. ___

From The Broadway Musical Production "I MARRIED AN ANGEL"

SOPHISTICATED LADY

Words by
IRVING MILLS and MITCHELL PARISH
Music by
DUKE ELLINGTON

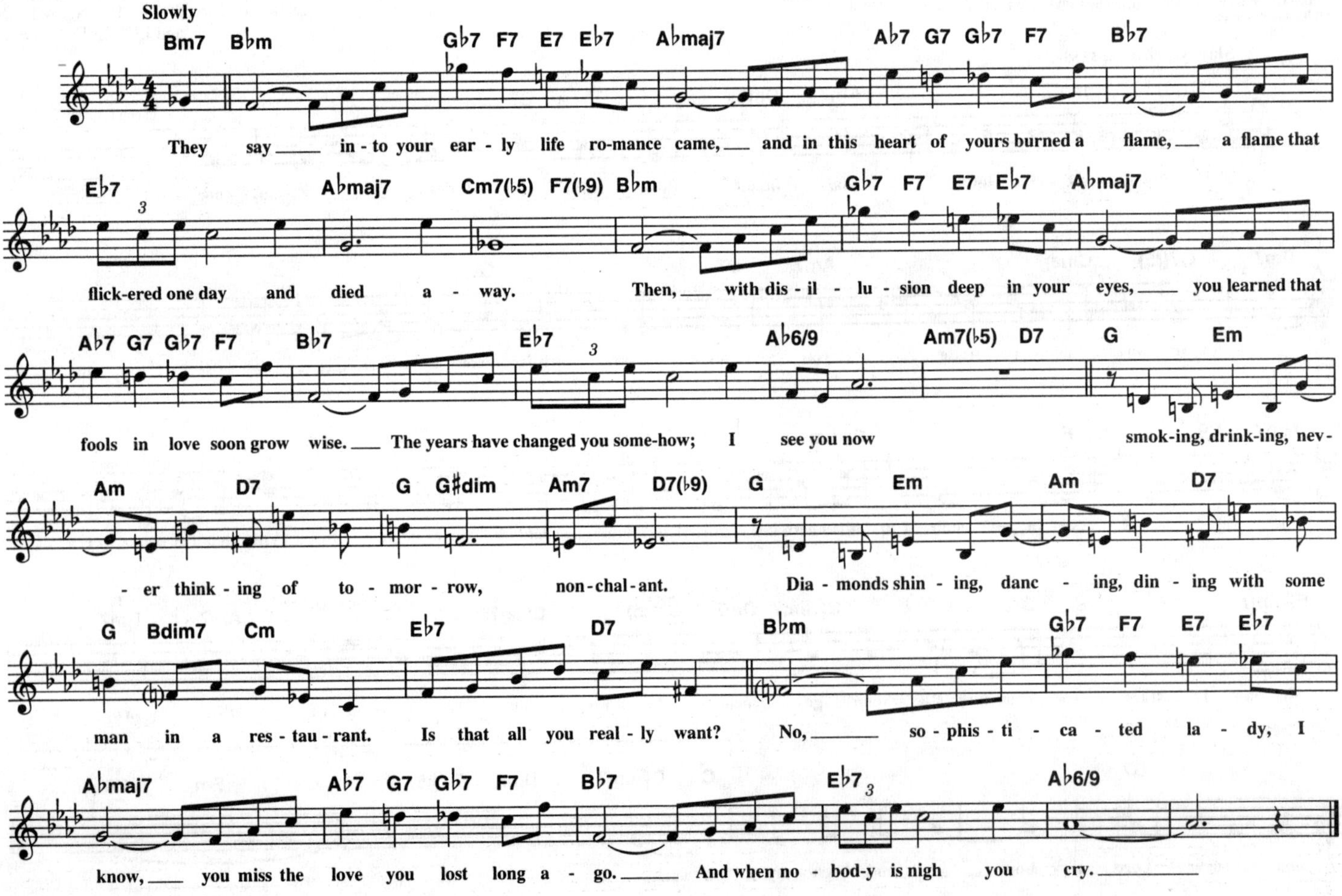

Slowly

They say ___ in - to your ear - ly life ro-mance came, ___ and in this heart of yours burned a flame, ___ a flame that

flick-ered one day and died a - way. Then, ___ with dis - il - lu - sion deep in your eyes, ___ you learned that

fools in love soon grow wise. ___ The years have changed you some-how; I see you now smok-ing, drink-ing, nev-

- er think - ing of to - mor - row, non-chal - ant. Dia - monds shin - ing, danc - ing, din - ing with some

man in a res - tau - rant. Is that all you real - ly want? No, ___ so - phis - ti - ca - ted la - dy, I

know, ___ you miss the love you lost long a - go. ___ And when no - bod-y is nigh you cry. ___

SOMEWHERE, MY LOVE
(Lara's Theme from "Doctor Zhivago")

Lyrics by PAUL FRANCIS WEBSTER
Music by MAURICE JARRE

Moderately
Verse:
To Coda
Some - where, my love, there will be songs to sing, al - though the snow
Some - where a hill blos-soms in green and gold, and there are dreams
You'll come to me out of the long a - go; warm as the sun,
Till then my sweet think of me now and then. God - speed my love,
cov - ers the hope of spring.
all that your heart can hold.
soft as the kiss of snow.
Bridge:
Some - day we'll meet a - gain my love.
Some - day when - ev - er the spring breaks through.
D.C. al 3rd ending to Coda
Coda
till you are mine a - gain. Till you are mine a - gain.

SONG WITHOUT WORDS

PETER TSCHAIKOVSKY

Brightly
To Coda
D.C. al Coda
Coda

SOMEDAY WE'LL MEET AGAIN

By AL HOFFMAN, AL GOODHART and MILTON AGER

Moderato
Eb6 D+ Eb Cm Fm Fm7
Some - day, I know we'll meet a - gain, We'll meet a - gain, my
Bb6 Cm6/Bb Bb7 Eb6 D+ Eb Cm G/D
Dar - ling. Tho', I don't know just where, or when, We'll meet a - gain,
D11 D7 G Edim C7/F Fm C7 C+ Fm
my Dar - ling. I leave my heart to re - mind you,
D7 3 Gm/Bb Fm7 Bb7 Eb6 D+ Eb
Tho' now we part, some- day my love will find you! Some - day when spring is
Cm Fm Bb7 Eb Ab6 Eb
sweet a - gain, We'll meet a - gain, Sweet - heart.

SOMEONE TO WATCH OVER ME

Music and Lyrics by
GEORGE GERSHWIN and
IRA GERSHWIN

Moderato

Eb Eb7 Ab6 Abdim Eb/G Gbdim

There's a some - bod - y I'm long - ing to see. I hope that he
I'm a lit - tle lamb who's lost in the wood. I know I could

Bb7/F Edim Fm C7/G Fm/Ab Am7-5 Fm7/Bb Bb7 1. Eb G7+5 Abmaj7 Bb7

Turns out to be Some - one who'll watch o - ver me.
Al - ways be good To one who'll watch o - ver

2. Eb Eb7 Ab Bb7 Eb Ab

me. Al - though he may not be the man some girls think of as

Eb Adim D7+5 D7 G7-9 G7 G7/F C/E C7 F7 Bb7

hand - some. To my heart he car - ries the key.

Eb Eb7 Ab6 Abdim Eb/G Gbdim

Won't you tell him, please, to put on some speed, Fol - low my lead,

Bb7/F Edim Fm C7/G Fm/Ab Am7-5 Fm7/Bb Bb7 Eb Eb7 Ab Abm Eb

Oh, how I need Some - one To Watch O - ver Me.

SOME PEOPLE'S LIVES

Words and Music by
JANIS IAN and
RHONDA FLEMING

Slowly

C Gm7 Am Gsus G Am/G G C
Some peo-ple's lives _ run down like clocks. _ One day they stop _ and that's all they've got. _ Some lives _ wear out like

Gm7 Am Gsus G Am/G G F Gsus G F G
old ten-nis shoes no one ___ can use. Well, it's sad but it's true. Did-n't an-y-bod-y tell _ them? Did-n't an-y-bod-y see?

F Am/G G Dm7 G C Gm7 Am
Did-n't an-y-bod-y love _ them like you love me? Some peo-ple's eyes fade like their dreams, too tired _ to rise, too _

Gsus G Am/G G C/G G7 C Gm7 Am Gsus G
tired _ to ___ sleep. Some peo-ple laugh when they need to ___ cry, and they nev-er know _ why.

F G F G F Am/G G Dm7 G Dm6/F
Did-n't an-y-bod-y tell _ them that's not how it has to be? Did-n't an-y-bod-y love _ them like you love me?

E E7/G♯ Asus Am E/A Am Asus Am7 D Em7 D7/F♯ Gsus G Am/G
Some peo-ple ask ___ if the tears have to fall. ___ Then why take your chanc-es? Why both-er at ___
rit.

G C/G G7 *a tempo* C Gm7 Am Gsus G *a tempo* F Am/G G
all? And some peo-ple's lives are as cold as their _ lips, they just need to be _ kissed. Does-n't an-y-bod-y tell _ them?
rit.

F G F Am/G G Dm/F E E7(♯9) G♯dim7 Am Em/G F C/E
Does-n't an-y-bod-y see? Does-n't an-y-bod-y love ___ them like you love me? 'Cuz

Dm7 F/G G7 *a tempo* C Dm/C C Dm/C F/C C F C/E D7/A C/G G7 C
rit.
that's all they need. _____________
rit.

SOMETHING TO REMEMBER YOU BY

Words by HOWARD DIETZ
Music by ARTHUR SCHWARTZ

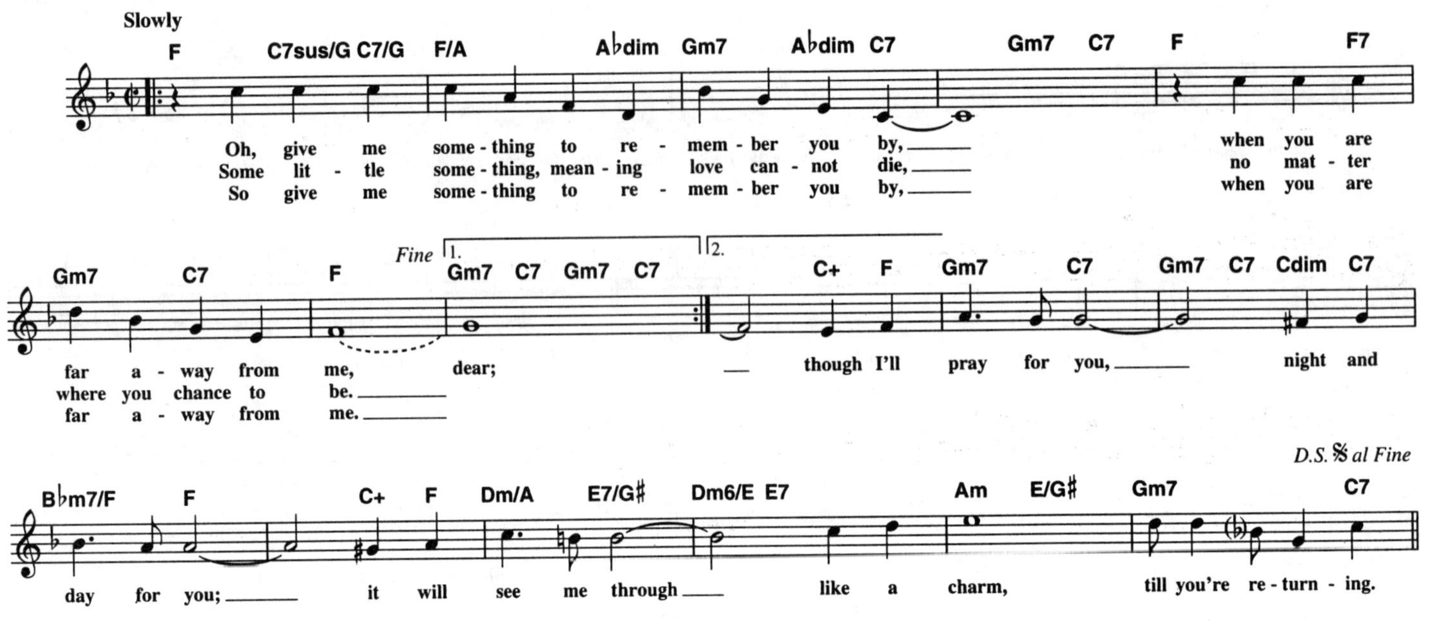
Slowly
F C7sus/G C7/G F/A A♭dim Gm7 A♭dim C7 Gm7 C7 F F7
Oh, give me some - thing to re - mem - ber you by, when you are
Some lit - tle some - thing, mean - ing love can - not die, no mat - ter
So give me some - thing to re - mem - ber you by, when you are
Gm7 C7 F Fine 1. Gm7 C7 Gm7 C7 2. C+ F Gm7 C7 Gm7 C7 Cdim C7
far a - way from me, dear; though I'll pray for you, night and
where you chance to be.
far a - way from me.
D.S. 𝄋 al Fine
B♭m7/F F C+ F Dm/A E7/G♯ Dm6/E E7 Am E/G♯ Gm7 C7
day for you; it will see me through like a charm, till you're re - turn - ing.

From the Paramount Picture "THE GODFATHER"

SPEAK SOFTLY LOVE
(Love Theme from "THE GODFATHER")

Words by LARRY KUSIK
Music by NINO ROTA

Slowly

Cm Fm Cm

Speak soft - ly love and hold me warm a - gainst your heart. I feel your words, the ten - der trem-bling mo-ments

Fm Cm Dm7(♭5) G7sus G7

start. We're in a world our ver - y own shar - ing a love that on - ly few have ev - er

Cm B♭7 E♭ D♭ Fm G N.C.

known. Wine col - ored days warmed by the sun, deep vel - vet nights when we are one. Speak soft - ly

Cm Fm Cm Fm

love so no one hears us but the sky. The vows of love we make will live un - til we die. My life is

Cm Dm7(♭5) G7sus G7 Cm

yours and all be - cause you came in - to my world with love so soft - ly love.

SOUL MAN

Lyrics and Music by
DAVID PORTER and
ISAAC HAYES

Moderate rock
G F B♭
C D G Am/G G Am/G G Am/G G Am/G G
1. Com-in'
Verse:
G Am/G G Am/G G Am/G G Am/G G
to ya on a dust-y road; good lov-in', I got a trunk-load. And
what I got the hard way. And I'll make it bet-ter each and ev-'ry-day.
Am/G G Am/G G Am/G G Am/G G
when you give it, you got soul. So don't wor-ry, 'cause I'm com-in'
So, hon-ey, don't you fret now, 'cause you ain't seen noth-in' yet.
I'm a
Chorus:
G F G
soul man. I'm a soul man. I'm a
F G C D
soul man. I'm a soul man.
1.2.
D.S. 𝄋
2. That's
3.
C D
Bridge:
E♭ B♭ C
Grab a rope and I'll pull you in, give you hope, and
C/D G F
be your on-ly boy-friend, yeah,
B♭ C D G Am/G G Am/G G
Repeat and fade
I'm a soul man, soul man, I'm a

Verse 3:
I was brought up on the southstreet.
I learned how to love before I could eat.
I was educated at Woodstock
When I start lovin', oh, I can't stop.
(To Chorus:)

SPANISH FLEA

Music by JULIUS WECHTER

Moderately
Bb Am7 D7 G7 C7 C9 F7
There was a lit - tle Span-ish Flea, a rec-ord star he thought he'd be. He'd heard of
Flea? And so he hid in-side a dog - gie from Ma - drid, ar - riv - ing
Bb Eb Ab Db Gb B F Bb
sing-ers like Bea - tles, The Chip-munks he'd seen on T. V. Why not a lit - tle Span-ish be.
here in the ci - ty still sing - ing his sweet har - mo - ny, as broke as an - y flea could
Eb Eb7 Ab Eb7 G Ab Eb7 Ab7
He walked a - round as if he owned the town, hum-ming his pint - size mel - o - dy. With his gui -
rage. I'll put you on the stage in cos-tumes like you've nev - er worn." Well, at a
Db Db7 Gb F Bb F7 Bb Am7 D7
tar he knew he'd be a star, and in his old home town how proud they'd be! Then all at once he met a man
glance he knew this was his chance. Yes, all at once a Span-ish star was born. For when the peo - ple heard him play
G7 C7 C9 F7 Bb Eb Ab Db Gb B
who said, "I'll help you if I can." He list-ened first to his song, then he sang right a - long for you
they all be - gan to shout, "O - le!" He was the pride of the na - tion, a sing - ing sen - sa - tion was
F 1. Bb 2. Gb7 F7 Bb
see, he loved the lit - tle Span-ish Flea. "You'll be the though he was just a Span-ish Flea.
he,
SPOOKY
Copyright © 1965,1967 by LOWERY MUSIC CO. INC.
This Arrangement Copyright © 1993 by LOWERY MUSIC CO.,INC.
All Rights Reserved
Words and Music by
HARRY MIDDLEBROOKS and MIKE SHAPIRO
Moderately
Dm7 G7 Dm7 G9
1. In the cool of the ev-'ning as ev - 'ry-thing is get - tin' kind of groo - vy, I
(2.) al - ways keep me guess-ing, I nev - er seem to know what you are think - ing. And if a
3. If you de - cide you'd bet - ter stop this lit - tle game that you are play - ing, I'm
Dm G7 Dm7 G9 Dm7
call you up and ask you if you'd like to go with me and see a mov - ie. And first you say no you've got some
fel - ler looks at you, it's for sure your lit - tle eye will be a - wink - ing. I get con - fused 'cause I don't
gon-na tell you all the things my heart's been a - dy-ing to be say - ing. A - just like a ghost, you've been
G7 Abdim Dm7 G7 Dm7
plans for to - night, and then you stop and say all right.
know where I stand and then you smile, and hold my hand.
haunt-ing my dreams, so I'll pro - pose on Hal - low - ween.
Love is kind a craz-y with a spook-y lit-tle girl like you.
Repeat ad lib. and fade
1.2. G9 3. G7 Dm7 G7 Dm7 G7
2. You Spoo - ky! Love is kind-a craz - y with a spook-y lit - tle girl like you, Spook - y.

SPLISH SPLASH

Words and Music by
BOBBY DARIN and
JEAN MURRAY

Moderately bright rock 'n' roll

B♭

Splish, splash, I was tak-in' a bath _ 'long a-bout a Sat-ur-day night. _ A rub dub, just re-
Ding, dong, I saw the whole gang _ danc-in' on my liv-ing room rug. _ Flip flop, they were

C7 F7 B♭

lax-in' in the tub, think-in' ev-'ry-thing was al-right. _ Well, I stepped out the tub, put my feet on the floor. I
do-in' the bop; all the teens had the danc-in' bug. _ There was Lol-li-pop with Peg-gy Sue. _ Good

E♭ Edim7 F F7 B♭ F

wrapped the towel a-round me and I o-pened the door. And then a-splish splash, I jumped back in the bath. _ Well,
gol-ly Miss _ Mol-ly was-a e-ven there too. A well-a splish splash, I for-got a-bout the bath. _ I

B♭ 1. 2. *Chorus:* B♭

how was I to know there was a par-ty go-ing on. on. I was a-splish-in' and a-splash-in', I was a-
went and put my danc-in' shoes

E♭ B♭ *Repeat and fade*

roll-in' and a-stroll-in'. I was a-mov-in' and a-groov-in', I was a-reel-in' and a-feel-in' I was a-

SPREADIN' RHYTHM AROUND

Words by TED KOEHLER
Additional Lyric by RICHARD MALTBY, JR.
Music by JIMMY McHUGH

Moderate swing

F B♭ F C7 F B♭ F C7 F B♭

- Mu-sic ev-'ry-where, feet are pat-tin', put-tin' tem-po in old Man-hat-tan. Ev-'ry-bod-y is

F Dm G7 C7 F F7

out high-hat-tin', spread-in' rhy-thm a-round. _ Up in Har-lem flats, all _ of the cats give _ it that

F♯7
G7
C9
F
B♭
F
C7
thing.
Which, when you're in
step,
all _
of the
hep
peo-ple call
swing.
Those who can't af-ford
silk and sat-in,

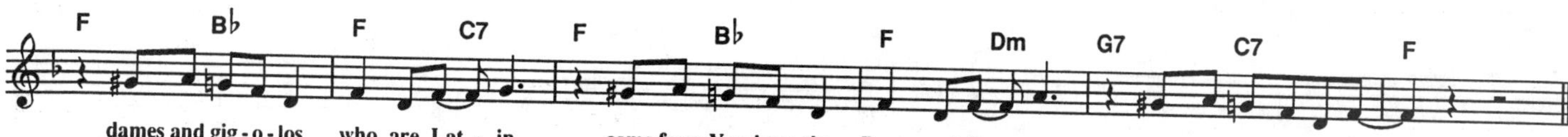
F
B♭
F
C7
F
B♭
F
Dm
G7
C7
F
dames and gig-o-los
who are Lat-in
come from Yon-kers, the
Bronx and Strat-en
spread-in' rhy-thm a-round. _

SPRING IS HERE

Words by LORENZ HART
Music by RICHARD RODGERS

Moderately

Gdim G6 Gdim G6 Ddim D9 Ddim
3
3
Spring is here! Why does-n't my heart go danc - ing? Spring is here! Why is - n't the waltz en -
Spring is here! Why does-n't the breeze de - light me? Stars ap - pear. Why does-n't the night in -

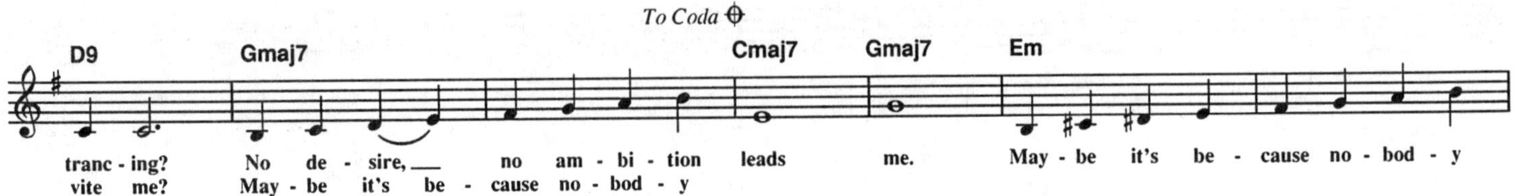
To Coda
D9 Gmaj7 Cmaj7 Gmaj7 Em
tranc - ing? No de - sire, no am - bi - tion leads me. May - be it's be - cause no - bod - y
vite me? May - be it's be - cause no - bod - y

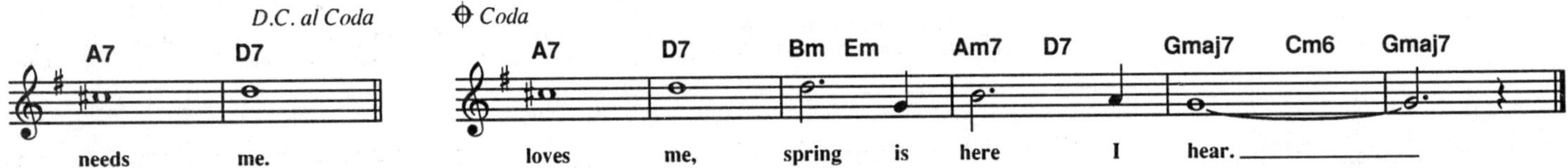
D.C. al Coda
Coda
A7 D7
needs me.
A7 D7 Bm Em Am7 D7 Gmaj7 Cm6 Gmaj7
loves me, spring is here I hear.

STAIRWAY TO THE STARS

Melody based on a Theme from "PARK AVENUE FANTASY"

Words by MITCHELL PARISH
Music by MATT MALNECK
and FRANK SIGNORELLI

Slowly

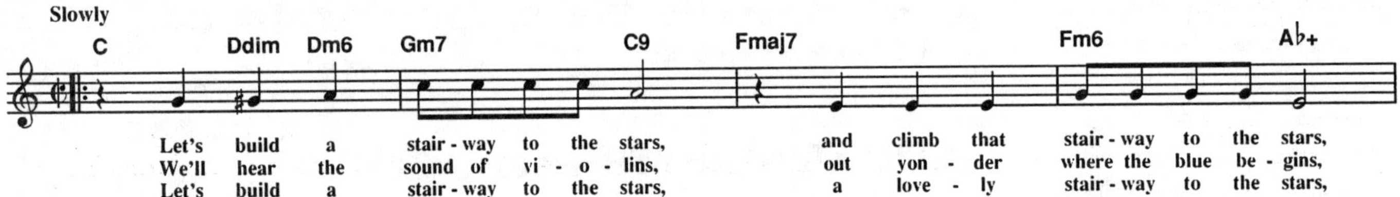
C Ddim Dm6 Gm7 C9 Fmaj7 Fm6 A♭+
Let's build a stair - way to the stars, and climb that stair - way to the stars,
We'll hear the sound of vi - o - lins, out yon - der where the blue be - gins,
Let's build a stair - way to the stars, a love - ly stair - way to the stars,

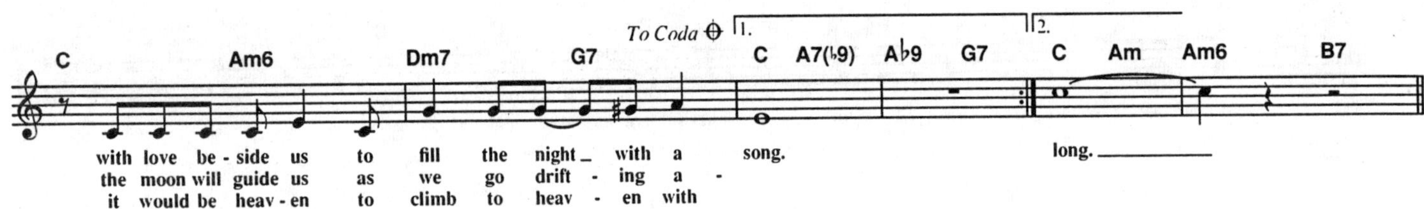
To Coda
1.
2.
C Am6 Dm7 G7 C A7(♭9) A♭9 G7 C Am Am6 B7
with love be - side us to fill the night with a song. long.
the moon will guide us as we go drift - ing a -
it would be heav - en to climb to heav - en with

Em Em7 A7 Am Em Em(♯7) Em7 A9 Dm Dm7
3
3
Can't we sail a - way on a la - zy dai - sy pet - al, o - ver the rim of the hill? Can't we sail a - way

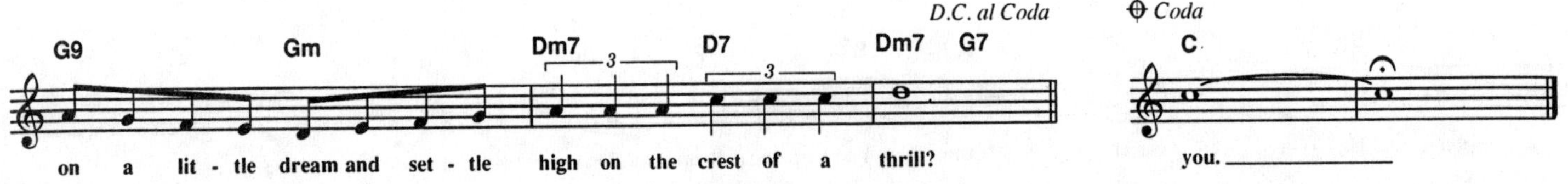
D.C. al Coda
Coda
G9 Gm Dm7 D7 Dm7 G7 C
3
3
on a lit - tle dream and set - tle high on the crest of a thrill? you.

ST. LOUIS BLUES

Words and Music by
W.C. HANDY

Slow blues
I hate to see de ev'-nin' sun go down, hate to see de ev'-nin' sun go down,
Been to de Gyp-sy to get ma' for - tune tole, to de Gyp-sy done got my for - tune tole.
'cause my ba - by, he done lef' dis town. Feel-in' to - mor - row lak I feel to - day,
'cause I'm most wile 'bout ma Jel - ly roll. Gyp-sy done tole me, "Don't you wear no black,"
feel to - mor - row lak I feel to - day. I'll pass my trunk, make me get a - way.
yes, she done tole me, "Don't you wear no black." Go to St. Lou - is, you can win him back.
St Lou - is wom-an wid her di - a - mon' rings pulls dat man roun' by her a - pron strings.
Help me to Cai - ro, make St. Louis by ma - self, git to Cai - ro, finds ma ole friend Jeff.
'Twant for pow - der an' for store bought hair de man I love would not gone no where.
Gwine to pin ma - self close to his side, if ah flag his train, I sho' can ride.
Chorus:
Got de St. Lou - is Blues jes' as blue as ah can be, dat man get a heart lak a rock cast in the sea. Or else he wouldn't have gone so far from me.
I loves dat man lak a school-boy loves his pie, lak a Ken - tuck - y Col - 'nel loves his mint an' rye. I'll love ma ba - by till the day ah die.
1.2.
D.C.
3.

Verse 3:
You ought to see dat stove pipe brown of mine,
Lak he owns de Dimon' Joseph line.
He'd make a cross-eyed o' man go stone blind,
Blacker than midnight, teeth lak flags of truce,
Blackest man in de whole St. Louis.
Blacker de berry, sweeter is the juice.
About a crap game he knows a pow'ful lot,
But when work-time comes he's on de dot.
Gwine to ask him for a cold ten-spot.
What it takes to git it, he's certainly got.

Chorus 3:
A black-headed gal make a freight train jump the track.
Said a black-headed gal make a freight train jump the track,
But a long tall gal makes a preacher ball the jack.

STAGGER LEE

Words and Music by
HAROLD LOGAN and
LLOYD PRICE

Freely
Moderate rock shuffle
D
Bm
Em7
A7
The night was clad, and the moon was yel - low. And the leaves came tum - bling down. 1. I was stand-

D
D7
G7
- ing on the cor - ner when I heard my bull - dog bark. He was bark-

To Coda
D
A7
D
A7
D
- ing at the two men who were gam - bling in the dark. It was Stag - ger Lee and Bil-

D7
G7
D
- ly, two men who gam - ble late. Stag - ger Lee threw sev - en; Bil - ly swore

1.2.
D.S.
3.
D.S. al Coda
A7
D
A7
A7
that he threw eight. 2. Stag - ger Lee 4. Stag - ger Lee

Coda
A7
D
G7
Go Stag - ger Lee, go Stag - ger Lee, go Stag - ger Lee,

Repeat and fade
D
A7
D
A7
go Stag-ger Lee, go Stag-ger Lee, go Stag-ger Lee, go Stag-ger Lee, go Stag-ger Lee.

Verse 2:
Stagger Lee told Billy,
"I can't let you go with that.
You have won all my money,
And my brand new Stetson hat."
Stagger Lee went home
And he pulled his forty four.
Said, "I'm going to the barroom
Just to pay the debt I owe."

Verse 3:
Stagger Lee went to the barroom
And he stood across the barroom door.
Said, "Now nobody move."
And he pulled his forty four.
"Stagger Lee," cried Billy,
"Oh, please don't take my life.
I got three little children,
And a very sickly wife."

Verse 3:
Stagger Lee shot Billy.
Oh, he shot that poor boy so bad.
Till the bullet came through Billy,
And it broke the bartender's glass.
(To Coda:)

STAND BY YOUR MAN

By TAMMY WYNETTE and BILLY SHERRILL

Moderately
Verse:
A E Bm E7 A
Some-times_ it's hard_ to be a wom-an,_ giv-ing all your love to just one man._
But if_ you love him_you'll for-give him,_ e-ven though he's hard to under-stand._
D A B E A
You'll have_ bad times, and he'll have good times,_ do-in' things that you don't_ un-der-stand._ oh_ be proud of
And if you_ love him
D A E7 A D A E F♯m7 E/G♯
him. 'Cause af-ter all_ he's just a man._
Chorus:
A C♯ D
Stand by your man. Give him two
C♯m Bm A F♯7 B E7 A C♯ D
arms to cling to, and_ some-thing warm to come to when nights are cold and lone-ly. Stand by your man and tell the
C♯m Bm A E7 C♯7 F♯ D E A D A E F♯m7 E/G♯
world you love him. Keep giv-ing all the love you can._ Stand by_ your_ man.
A E7 C♯7 F♯ D E A D A E A
Keep giv-ing all the love you can._ Stand by your man._
From "THE BENNY GOODMAN STORY"
STOMPIN' AT THE SAVOY
Copyright © 1936 (Renewed 1964) EMI ROBBINS CATALOG INC.
All Rights Reserved
Lyrics by ANDY RAZAF
Music by BENNY GOODMAN, CHICK WEBB and EDGAR SAMPSON
Moderately bright swing
C9 F6/9 C9 F6/9 To Coda F♯dim7
Sa - voy,_ the home of sweet ro-mance._ Sa - voy,_ it wins you at a glance._ Sa - voy,_
_ just like a cling-in' vine,_ your lips,_ so warm and sweet like wine,_ your cheek_
_ a per-fect hol-i-day!_ Sa - voy,_ where we can glide and sway._
Gm7 C9 F6/9 C9 B♭7 B7 B♭7
_ gives hap-py feet a chance_ to dance._ Your form,_ How my heart is sing-in'_
_ so soft and close to mine_ di-vine._
E♭9 A♭7 A7 A♭7 D♭7 C7 C9
while the band is swing-in'!_ Nev-er tired of romp-in'_ and stomp-in' with you_ at the Sa-voy. What joy!_
D.S. al Coda
Coda
F♯dim7 Gm7 C9 F
_ Sa - voy,_ there let me stomp a-way_ with you._

THE STAR-SPANGLED BANNER

Words by FRANCIS SCOTT KEY
Music by JOHN STAFFORD SMITH

Moderately
Oh! _ say can you see by the dawn's ear - ly light, what so proud - ly we hailed at the twi - light's last gleam - ing; whose broad
stripes and bright stars thro' the per - i - lous fight, o'er the ram - parts we watched were so gal - lant - ly stream - ing. And the
rock - et's red glare, the bombs burst - ing in air, gave proof thro' the night that our flag was still there. Oh,
say does that _ star - span - gled ban - ner _ yet _ wave _ o'er the land _ of the free, and the home of the brave.

THE STARS AND STRIPES FOREVER

JOHN PHILIP SOUSA

Bright march

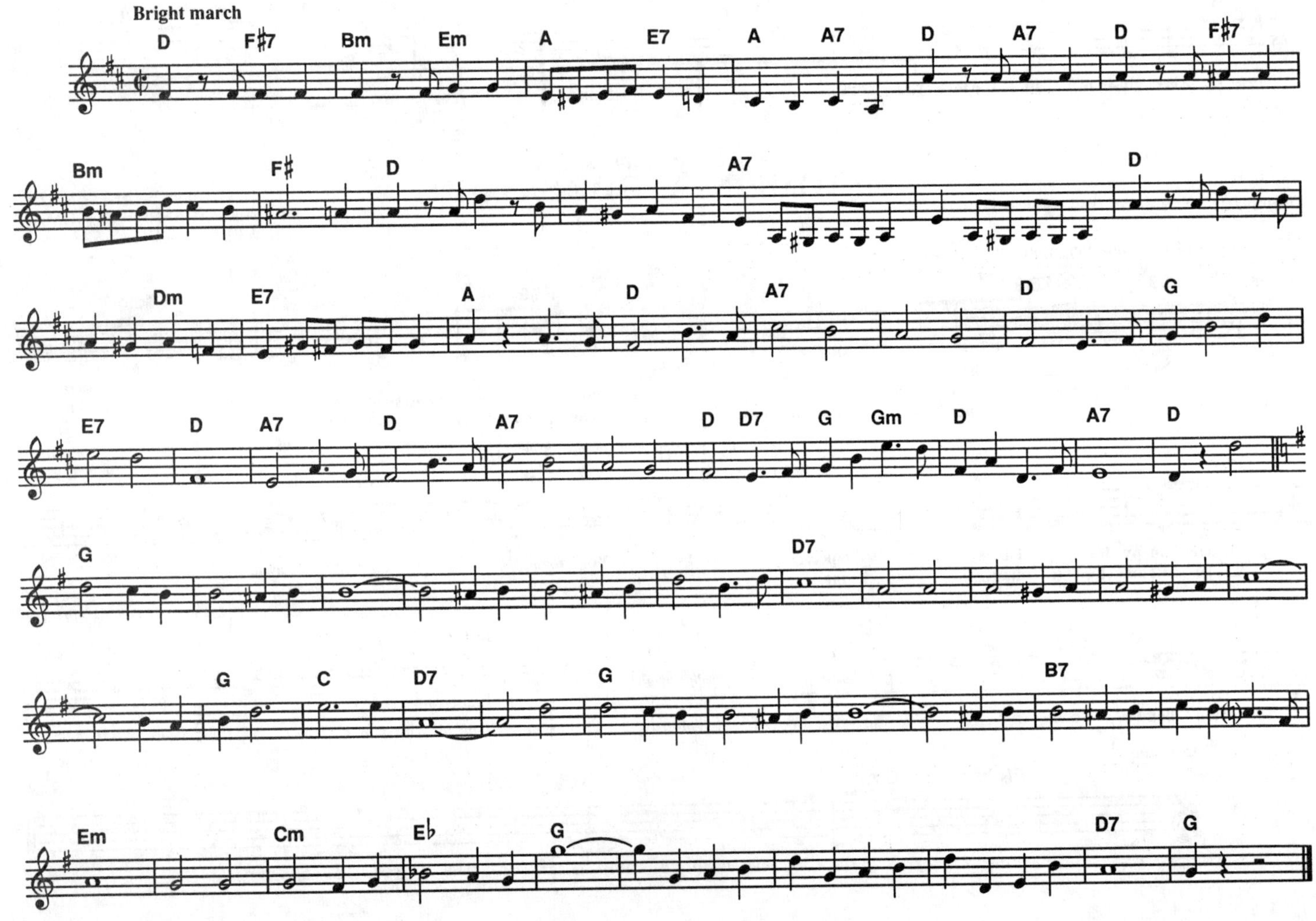

From the Musical Production "WOMAN OF THE YEAR"

SOMETIMES A DAY GOES BY

© 1981 FIDDLEBACK MUSIC PUBLISHING CO., INC. and KANDER & EBB, INC. (BMI)
All Rights Reserved

Words by FRED EBB
Music by JOHN KANDER

Flowingly, with expression

Cmaj7 Dm7/C Am Am7 D9
Some-times a day goes by, one whole en - tire day when I don't
G11 G7 Cmaj7 Dm7/C G7
think of her. Twen - ty - four hours pass, I look a - round and find that
Am C/G Em7/A A9 Dm7 Dm7/G G7 Cmaj7
I have - n't thought of her not e - ven when I'm some-where we used to go.
Am7 C/D D9 Dm7/G G7 Cmaj7
Not e - ven if that's some - one we used to know. It's hard - ly
Dmaj7/C G7 Am Em/G Em7/A
ev - 'ry - day, it's most un - u - su - al, in fact, I can't re - mem - ber when,
A9 A7 Dm7 Dm7/G Cmaj7 Am7 Dm7
But... Some-times a day goes by, when I don't think of her 'til morn - ing
Dm7/G G9 Em7 A7 Dm7 Dm7/G C
comes, and then there she is a - gain.

STREETS OF LAREDO

Copyright © 1994 by BEAM ME UP MUSIC (ASCAP). c/o CPP/BELWIN, INC., Miami, FL 33014
All Rights Reserved

TRADITIONAL

Slowly

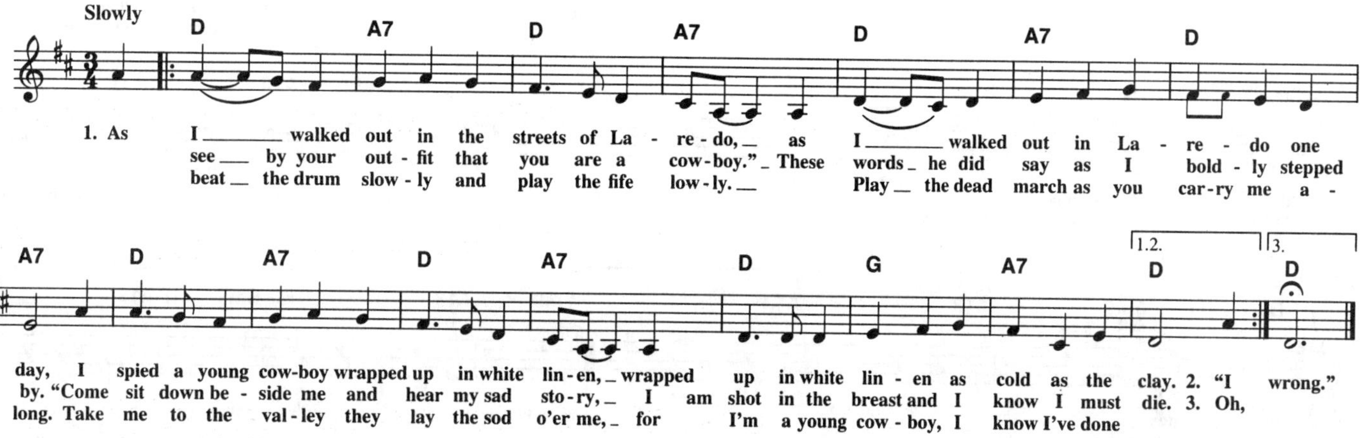
D A7 D A7 D A7 D
1. As I walked out in the streets of La - re - do, as I walked out in La - re - do one
see by your out - fit that you are a cow-boy." These words he did say as I bold - ly stepped
beat the drum slow - ly and play the fife low - ly. Play the dead march as you car-ry me a -
A7 D A7 D A7 D G A7 1.2. D 3. D
day, I spied a young cow-boy wrapped up in white lin - en, wrapped up in white lin - en as cold as the clay. 2. "I wrong."
by. "Come sit down be - side me and hear my sad sto - ry, I am shot in the breast and I know I must die. 3. Oh,
long. Take me to the val - ley they lay the sod o'er me, for I'm a young cow - boy, I know I've done

STAR DUST

Copyright © 1928 (Renewed 1957) MILLS MUSIC, INC. and HOAGY PUBLISHING CO. in the U.S.A.; elsewhere throughout the world by MILLS MUSIC, INC., c/o EMI MUSIC PUBLISHING
All Rights Reserved
Words by MITCHELL PARISH
Music by HOAGY CARMICHAEL
Slowly
And now the pur-ple dusk of twi-light time steals a-cross the mead-ows of my heart. High up in the sky the lit-tle stars climb,
al - ways re-mind-ing me that we're a - part. You wan-dered down the lane and far a-way, leav-ing me a song that will not die.
Love is now the star dust of yes-ter-day, the mu-sic of the years gone by. Some-times I won-der why I spend the lone-ly night
side a gar-den wall, when stars are bright,
To Coda
dream-ing of a song. The mel - o - dy haunts my rev - er - ie, and I am once a - gain with you, when our love was new,
you are in my arms. The night - in - gale tells his fair - y tale of par - a - dise, where ros - es
D.S. al Coda
and each kiss an in-spir - a - tion, but that was long a - go; now my con-so - la - tion is in the star dust of a song. Be -
Coda
grew. Though I dream in vain. In my heart it will re - main; my star dust mel-o - dy, the mem-o-ry of love's re - frain.
STORMY
Copyright © 1968 by LOW-SAL INC.
All Rights Reserved
Words and Music by
BUDDY BUIE and J.R. COBB
Moderately
Verse:
1. You are the sun - shine ba - by when-ev - er you smile But I call you storm-y to - day.
2. Yes-ter-day's love was like a warm sum-mer breeze. But like the weath-er, it changed.
All of a sud - den that old rain's fall-ing down. And my world is cloud - y and
Now things are drear - y, ba - by, and it's wind - y and cold. And I stand a - lone in the
Chorus:
gray. You've gone a - way. Oh storm - y, oh storm - y, bring back that
rain call - in' your name.
Repeat ad lib. and fade
sun - ny day. Oh storm - y, oh storm - y. Oh

STARS FELL ON ALABAMA

Words by MITCHELL PARISH
Music by FRANK PERKINS

Moderately slow

C A7 D7 G7(♯5) C Em7 E♭dim7 Dm7 G7 C A7

We lived our lit - tle dra - ma; we kissed in a field of white, and stars fell on Al - a - ba - ma last night.

Dm7 G7 C A7 D7 G7(♯5) C Em7 E♭dim7 Dm7 G7 C Dm7 G7

I can't for-get the glam-our; your eyes held a ten-der light, and stars fell on Al - a - ba - ma last night. ___

C Dm7 G7 Em7 E♭dim7 Dm7 G7 C

— I nev - er planned in my im - ag - i - na - tion ___ a sit - u - a - tion ___ so heav-en - ly; ___ a fair - y

Dm7 G7 Am Am7/G F♯m7(♭5) B7 E G C A7

land where no one else could en - ter, ___ and in the cen - ter ___ just you and me, dear. My heart beat like a

D7 G7(♯5) C Em7 E♭dim7 Dm7 G7 C Dm7 G7 C

ham - mer; my arms wound a-round you tight, and stars fell on Al - a - ba - ma last night. ___

From "THE UNINVITED"

STELLA BY STARLIGHT

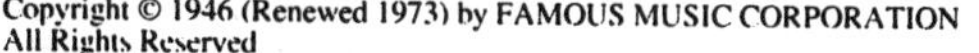

By NED WASHINGTON
and VICTOR YOUNG

Moderately slow

Em7(♭5) A7(♭9) Cm7 F7 Fm7 B♭7 E♭maj7 A♭7 B♭maj7
The song ___ a rob - in sings ___ through years ___ of end - less springs, ___ the mur-mur of a

Em7(♭5) A7(♭9) Dm7 B♭m7 E♭7 Fmaj7 Em7(♭5) A7 Am7(♭5) D7(♭9)
brook at e - ven - tide ___ that rip - ples by a nook where two lov - ers hide; ___ a

G7(♯5) Cm7 A♭7 B♭maj7
3
great ___ sym - phon - ic theme, ___ that's Stel - la by star - light, ___ and not a dream. ___ My

Em7(♭5) A7(♭9) Dm7(♭5) G7(♭9) Cm7(♭5) F7(♭9) B♭maj7
heart ___ and I a - gree, ___ { he's / she's } ev - 'ry - thing ___ on earth to me. ___

From the Warner Bros. Picture "THE PAJAMA GAME"

STEAM HEAT

Words and Music by
RICHARD ADLER and
JERRY ROSS

Moderately

I got *(clang) (clang)* s-s-s - steam heat. _ I got *(clang) (clang)* s-s-s - steam heat. _ I got *(clang) (clang)* s-s-s -

steam heat, _ but I need your love _ to keep a - way the cold. I got *(clang) (clang)* s-s-s - steam heat. _ I got

(clang) clang) s-s-s - steam heat. _ I got *(clang) (clang)* s-s-s - steam heat, _ but I can't get warm _ with -

out your hand to hold. The ra - di - a - tor's hiss - in', still I need your kiss - in' to keep me from freez - in' each night! I got a

hot wat - er bot - tle but noth - ing I got - 'll take the place of you, _ hold - ing me tight. I got *(clang) (clang)* s-s-s -

steam heat. _ I got *(clang) (clang)* s-s-s - steam heat. _ I got *(clang) (clang)* s-s-s - steam heat, _ but I need your love _ to

1. keep a - way the cold. *To Next Strain* 2. They told me to keep a - way the cold, I need your love ___ to keep a - way _

_ the cold. ___ *Fine* *Interlude:* shov - el more coal in the boil - er. ___ They told me to shov - el more coal in the

boil - er. ___ They told me to shov - el more coal in the boil - er, ___ but that don't do no good.

They told me to pour some more oil in the burn - er. ___ They told me to pour some more oil in the burn - er. ___ They told me to

pour some more oil in the burn - er, ___ but that don't do _ no good _ The

D.S. al Fine

STEP TO THE REAR

Words by CAROLYN LEIGH
Music by ELMER BERNSTEIN

Brightly
Will ev - 'ry - one here kind - ly step to the rear, and let a win - ner lead the way?
(1. 3.) Here's where we sep - a - rate the notes from the noise, the men from the boys, the rose from the poi - son i - vy.
(2.) Here's where we sep - a - rate the duck from the quack, the ace from the pack, the pip from the mack - in - tosh - es.
Back in the bunch I came up with a hunch this was an up and at 'em day. It's one of those spells when you hear the right bells and your hor - o - scope tells you to say:
Back in the group, I came up with the scoop; this was the time to rise and say; "I've got in my eye such a ju - bi - lant sky that the Fourth of Ju - ly will seem gray.
Will ev - 'ry - one here kind - ly step to the rear and let a win - ner lead the way.
1.2. To Next Strain
3. Fine
I hear those
As our in -
way.
trum - pets be - gin to blare. And now I'm Wash - ing - ton up - on the Del - a - ware.
vest - ments be - gin to grow, to quote from Dav - ey Crock - ett at the Al - a - mo.
Will
D.S. al Fine
SUNNY
Copyright © 1965, 1966, 1971 by PORTABLE MUSIC COMPANY, INC.
All Rights Reserved
Words and Music by
BOBBY HEBB
Moderate rock
1. Sun - ny, yes - ter - day my life was filled with rain. Sun - ny, you smiled at me and real - ly eased the pain.
2. Sun - ny, thank you for the sun - shine bou - quet. Sun - ny, thank you for the love you've brought my way.
Oh, the dark days are done, and the bright days are here. My sun - ny one shines so sin - cere, oh.
You gave to me your all and all. Now I feel ten feet tall.
Sun - ny, one so true, I love you.
1.2.3.
4.
I love you.
Repeat and fade
I love you.

Verse 3:
Sunny, thank you for the truth you've let me see.
Sunny, thank you for the facts from A to Z.
My life was torn like wind blown sand.
Then a rock was formed when we held hands.
Sunny, one so true, I love you.

Verse 4:
Sunny, thank you for that smile upon your face.
Sunny, thank you for that gleam that flows with grace.
You're my spark of nature's fire.
You're my sweet complete desire.
Sunny, one so true, I love you.

STORMY MONDAY BLUES

Words and Music by
EARL HINES, BILLY ECKSTINE
and BOB CROWDER

Slow blues
C7 F7 C7
It stormed and start-ed rain - in', I'm as lone-some as a man can be. Lawd,
F7 C7 B7 B♭ A7
it stormed and start-ed rain - in', I'm as lone-some as a man can be. Oh,
Dm7 G G7 C7 E♭7 A♭7 D♭7
the way you been treat-in' me well, I've real-ized it's not the same.
C7 F7 C7
It's a down-right rot - ten, low - down, dirt - y shame.
F7 C7 B7 B♭7 A7
Lawd, it's a down-right rot - ten, low - down, dirt - y shame the
Dm7 G G7 C E♭7 A♭7 D♭7
way you treat me, lawd, I know I'm not to blame.

SWEET DREAMS

Words and Music by
DON GIBSON

Moderately slow
C D7 G7 C D7 G7 C
Sweet dreams of you ev - 'ry night I go through. Why can't I for -
Sweet dreams of you, things I know can't come true. Why can't I for -
F C Am C F G7 C F C G7
get you and start my life a - new, in - stead of hav - ing sweet dreams a - bout you?
get the past, start lov - ing some - one new, in - stead of hav - ing sweet dreams a - bout you?
C D7 G7 C D7 G7 C
You don't love me, it's plain. I should know you'll nev - er wear my name. I should
F C Am C F G7 1. C F/G C G7 2. C F/G C
hate you the whole night through, in - stead of hav - ing sweet dreams a-bout you. you.

Theme from "SUPERMAN"

By JOHN WILLIAMS

Medium march tempo
C
C
F6
C
Cmaj7/F
Cmaj7
Cmaj7/F
Cmaj7
Em7
Dm7
G11
1. C
2. C
F6/C
Cmaj7
F6/C
Cmaj7
F6/C
1. G/C
Fm7
D♭maj7/C
Cmaj7
2. G/C
Fm7
F/G
G7
D♭maj7
Cmaj7
F/C
G7/C
D♭maj7/C
Cmaj7
Fmaj7/C
G7/C
Cmaj7
D♭/G♭
G7sus4
C
C(add F)
G/C
C
A♭
B♭
Fm6
G(sus4)
1. C
2. C
f
mp
cresc.
mf
cresc.
f
ff

SUMMER WIND

English Words by JOHNNY MERCER
Original German Words by HANS BRADTKE
Music by HENRY MAYER

Slowly

E♭ B♭7 E♭ E♭7 A♭ A♭m6 E♭ Gm Fm B♭11 B♭7 E♭7 *Fine*

The sum-mer wind came blow-ing in a - cross the sea, it lin - gered there to touch your hair and walk with me. All sum-mer long we sang a song and strolled the gold - en sand, two sweet-hearts and the sum-mer wind. Like

paint-ed kites, the days and nights went fly - ing by, the world was new be - neath a blue um - brel - la sky. Then soft - er than a pip - er man one day it called to you, I lost you to the sum-mer wind. The

au-tumn wind, the win-ter winds have come and gone, and still the days, the lone - ly days go on and on. And guess who sighs his lull - a - bies through nights that nev - er end, my fick - le - friend, the sum-mer wind.

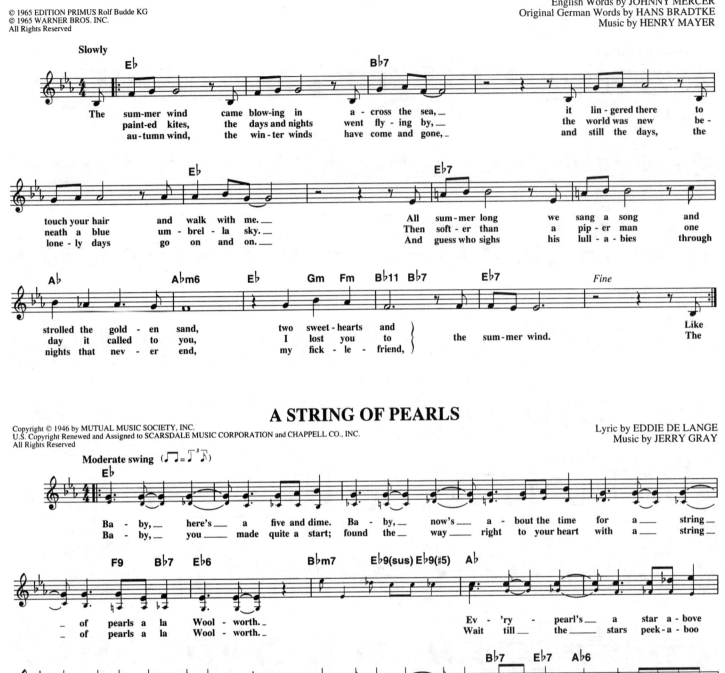

A STRING OF PEARLS

Lyric by EDDIE DE LANGE
Music by JERRY GRAY

Moderate swing

E♭ F9 B♭7 E♭6 B♭m7 E♭9(sus) E♭9(♯5) A♭
Ba - by, here's a five and dime. Ba - by, now's a - bout the time for a string of pearls a la Wool - worth.
Ba - by, you made quite a start; found the way right to your heart with a string of pearls a la Wool - worth.
Ev - 'ry - pearl's a star a - bove wrapped in dreams and filled with love, that old string of pearls a la Wool - worth.
Wait till the stars peek - a - boo I've got some - thing for you. It's a string of kiss - es for ba - by.
B♭7 E♭6 A♭6 B♭7 E♭
Till that hap - py day in spring when you buy the wed-ding ring, please a string of pearls a la Wool - worth.
I found a love so sub - lime right in that old five and dime with a string
1. Cm7 F9 B♭7 E♭6 Adim7 Fm7 B♭7
2. Cm7 F9 B♭7 E♭6/9
of pearls a la Wool - worth.

ST. ELMO'S FIRE (Man in Motion)

Words by JOHN PARR
Music by DAVID FOSTER

Moderate rock, with a steady pulse

Verse:

A A/C♯ D A A/C♯ Esus/D A
1. Grow-in' up ___ you don't see the writ - ing on the wall. Pass-in' by, ___

A/C♯ D A F♯m7 D
mov - in' straight a - head _ you knew it all. But may - be some - time _ if you feel the pain, _ you'll find you're

1. F♯m7 D E — 2.3. F♯m7 D E — *Chorus:* F♯
all a - lone; _ ev - 'ry - thing has changed. _ pris - on - er, ___ and you're tryin' to break _ free. _ 1.2.4. *etc.* I can see a new ho - ri - zon

B(9) C♯sus C♯ F♯ B C♯sus C♯ F♯
un-der-neath the blaz-ing sky. I'll be where the ea - gle's fly - ing high-er and high - er. Gon-na be your man in mo-tion.

B(9) C♯sus C♯ F♯ — 1. B C♯sus C♯ D C♯7/D C♯7 A *D.C.*
All I need is a pair of wheels. Take me where the fu-ture's ly-ing; St. El-mo's fire. ___

2. *To Next Strain* B C♯sus C♯ — 3.4. *etc.* *Repeat and fade* B C♯sus C♯ — F♯ B(9) C♯sus C♯
St. El - mo's fire. ___ St. El - mo's fire. ___ I can climb the high - est moun-tain, cross the wid - est sea.

F♯ B C♯sus C♯ D C♯7/D A
I can feel St. El - mo's fire burn-ing in me, ___ burn-ing in me. ______ Just once in his

D(9)/F♯ E A D(9)/F♯ E *D.S.* 𝄋
life a man has his time. And my time is now; I'm com-in' a - live.

Verse 2:
Play the game; you know you can't quit until it's won.
Soldier of only you can do what must be done.
You know, in some ways you're a lot like me.
You're just a prisoner, and you're tryin' to break free.
(To Chorus:)

Verse 3:
Burning up; don't know just how far that I can go.
Soon be home; only just a few miles down the road.
And I can make it, I know I can.
You broke the boy in me, but you won't break the man.
(To Chorus:)

Chorus 3:
I can hear the music playin'; I can see the banners fly.
Feel like a vet again. I hope I ain't high!
Gonna be your man in motion; all I need is a pair of wheels.
Take me where the future's lying; St. Elmo's fire.

ST. JAMES INFIRMARY

Words and Music by
JOE PRIMOSE

Moderate swing

B7 Em B7 Em Am B7 Em B7
I went down to Saint James In - fir - mary; heard my ba - by groan. I felt so bro - ken

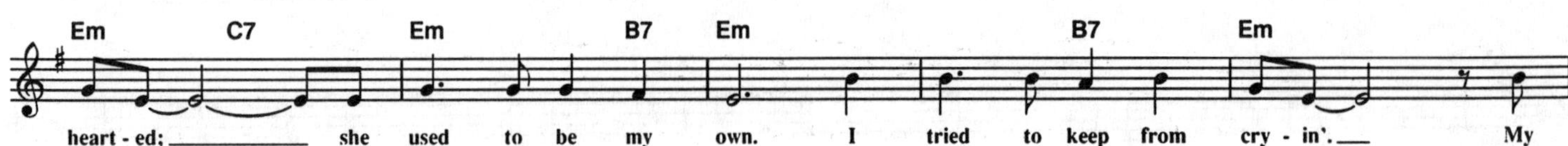
Em C7 Em B7 Em B7 Em
heart - ed; she used to be my own. I tried to keep from cry - in'. My

Am B7 Em B7 Em C7 Em B7 Em
heart felt just like lead. She was all I had to live for; I wished that it was me in - stead.

From the Metro-Goldwyn-Mayer Musical Production "TWO GIRLS AND A SAILOR"

SWEET AND LOVELY

Words and Music by
GUS ARNHEIM, HARRY TOBIAS
and JULES LEMARE

Moderately

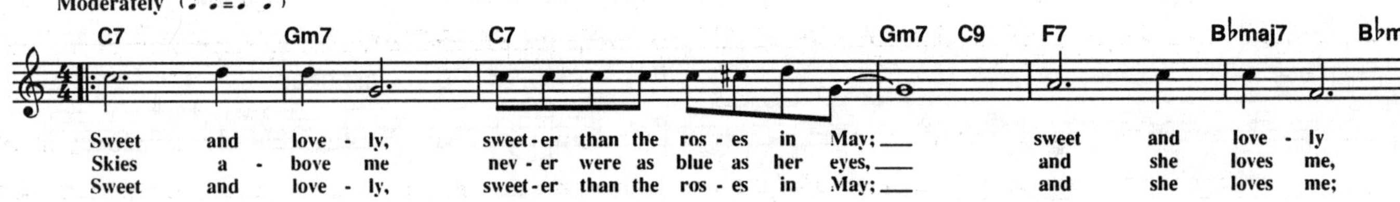
C7 Gm7 C7 Gm7 C9 F7 B♭maj7 B♭m
Sweet and love - ly, sweet - er than the ros - es in May; sweet and love - ly
Skies a - bove me nev - er were as blue as her eyes, and she loves me,
Sweet and love - ly, sweet - er than the ros - es in May; and she loves me;

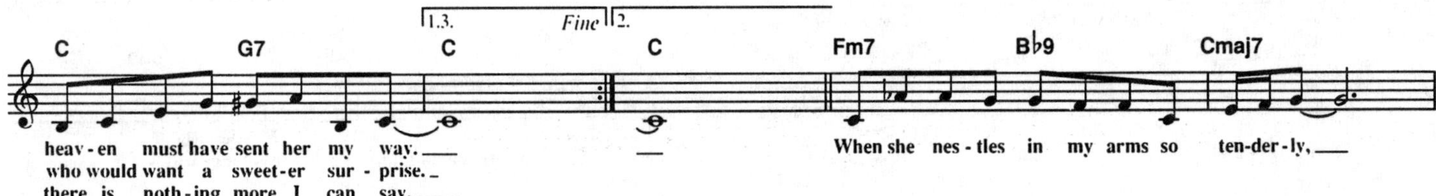
1.3. Fine 2.
C G7 C C Fm7 B♭9 Cmaj7
heav - en must have sent her my way.
who would want a sweet - er sur - prise.
there is noth - ing more I can say.
When she nes - tles in my arms so ten - der - ly,

D.C. al Fine
Fm7 B♭9 Cmaj7 A♭m7 D♭9 E♭maj7 A♭7 G7
there's a thrill that words can - not ex - press. In my heart a song of love is taunt - ing me, mel - o - dy haunt - ing me.

SWEET ADELINE

Words by RICARD H. GERARD
Music by HARRY ARMSTRONG

Slowly

B♭ F7 B♭ D7 E♭ G7 C7 F7 B♭ F7
Sweet A - del - ine, my A - del - ine, at night, dear heart, for you I pine. In all my

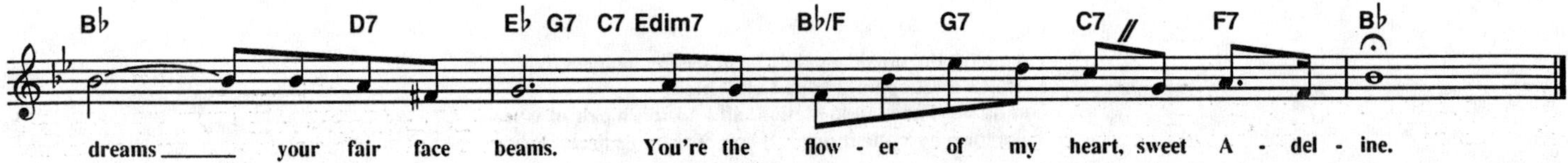
B♭ D7 E♭ G7 C7 Edim7 B♭/F G7 C7 F7 B♭
dreams your fair face beams. You're the flow - er of my heart, sweet A - del - ine.

STAR TREK — THE NEXT GENERATION
(Main Title)

By ALEXANDER COURAGE, GENE RODDENBERRY
and JERRY GOLDSMITH

Maestoso misterioso
N.C. (B♭ Bass)
Spoken: Space . . . the final frontier. These are the voyages of the Starship

Enterprise; its continuing mission: to explore strange new worlds, to seek out new life and new civilizations, to boldly go where no one has gone before.

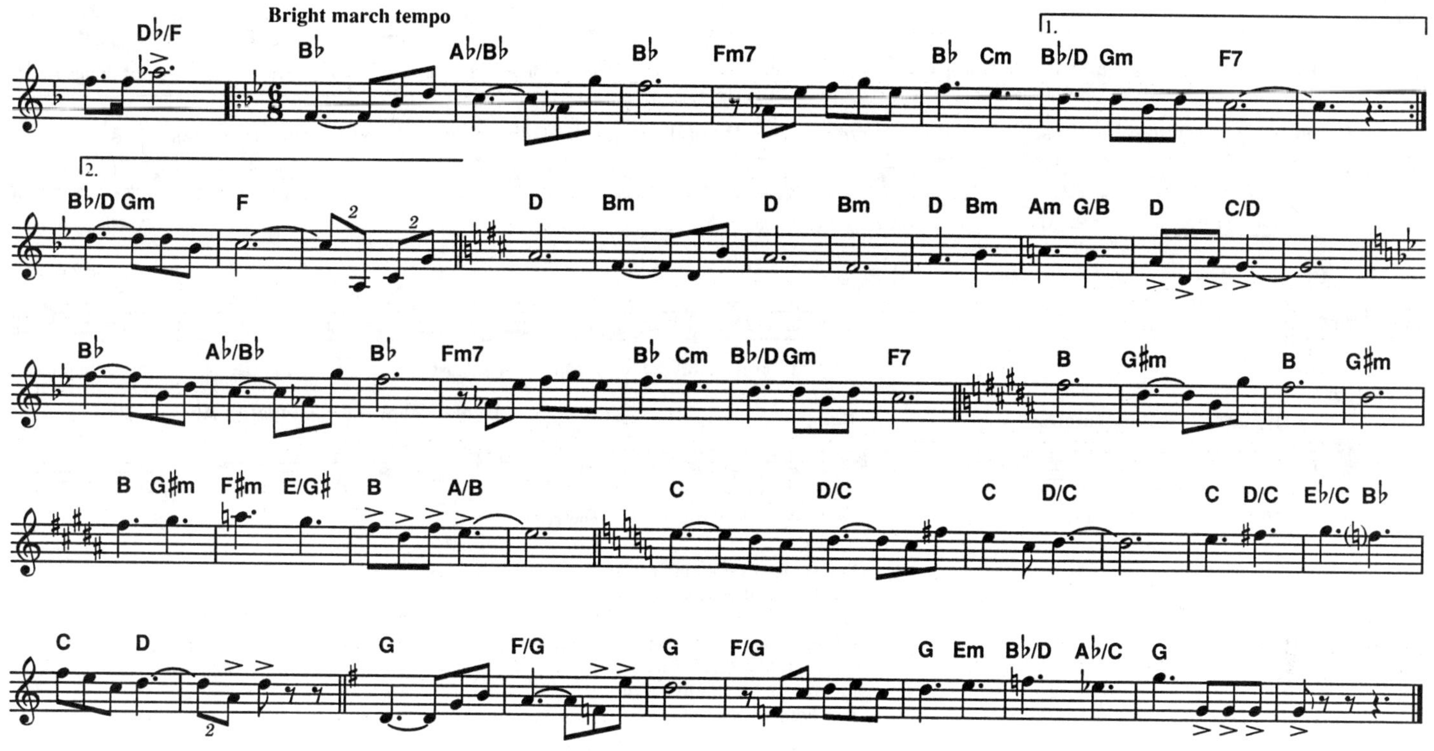
D♭/F
Bright march tempo
B♭ A♭/B♭ B♭ Fm7 B♭ Cm B♭/D Gm F7
B♭/D Gm F D Bm D Bm D Bm Am G/B D C/D
B♭ A♭/B♭ B♭ Fm7 B♭ Cm B♭/D Gm F7 B G♯m B G♯m
B G♯m F♯m E/G♯ B A/B C D/C C D/C C D/C E♭/C B♭
C D G F/G G F/G G Em B♭/D A♭/C G

SWAN LAKE THEME

TSCHAIKOVSKY

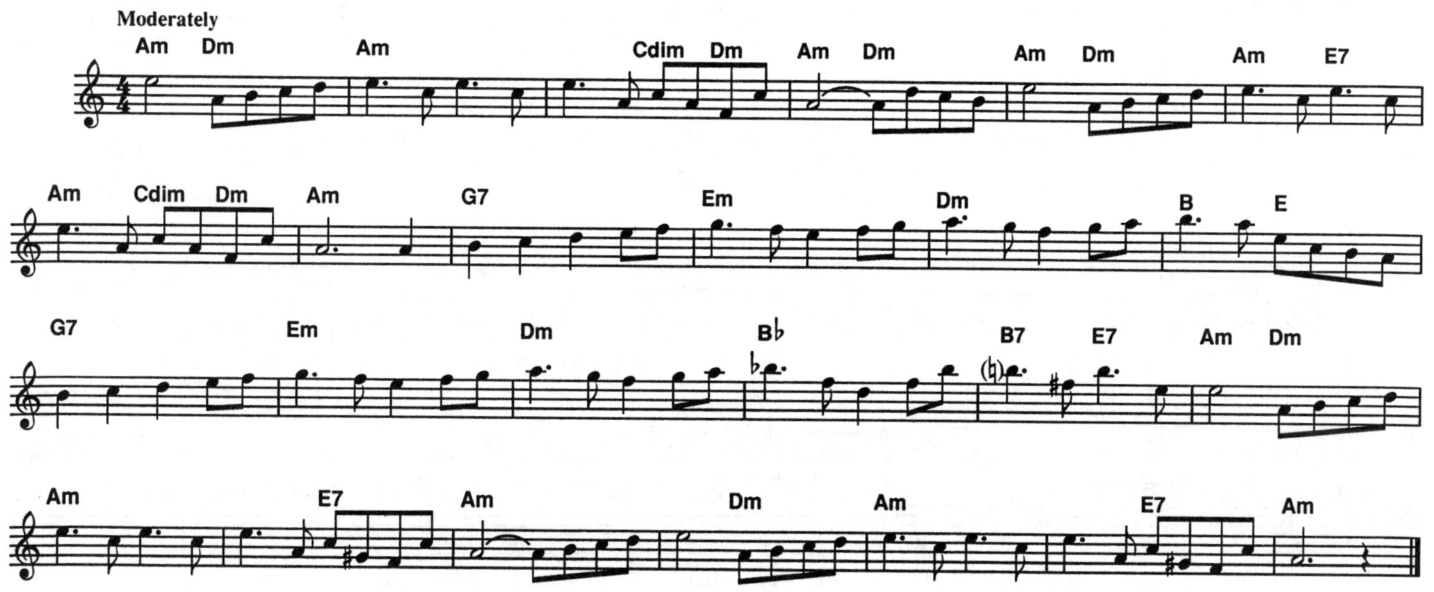
Moderately
Am Dm Am Cdim Dm Am Dm Am Dm Am E7
Am Cdim Dm Am G7 Em Dm B E
G7 Em Dm B♭ B7 E7 Am Dm
Am E7 Am Dm Am E7 Am

SUDDENLY

Copyright © 1984 WILLESDEN MUSIC INC./AQUA MUSIC LTD./KEITH DIAMOND MUSIC
All Rights for KEITH DIAMOND MUSIC Controlled by WILLESDEN MUSIC INC. for the World.
All Rights for AQUA MUSIC LTD. Controlled by ZOMBA ENTERPRISES INC. for U.S.A. and Canada.
All Rights Reserved
By KEITH DIAMOND and BILLY OCEAN
Moderately slow
Verse:
1. I used to think that love was just a fair-y tale, until that first hel-lo, un-til that first smile.
But if I had to do it all a-gain, I would-n't change a thing, 'cause this love is ev-er-last-ing. Sud-den-
Chorus:
ly, life has new mean-ing to me. There's beau-ty up a-bove; and things we
nev-er take no-tice of; you wake up and sud-den-ly you're in love.
To Coda
D.C.
2. Girl, you're
Bridge:
love. Each day I pray this love af-fair would last for-ev-er. Sud-den-
D.S. al Coda
Coda
nev-er take no-tice of; you wake up and sud-den-ly you're in love.
freely
rit.
Verse 2:
Girl, you're everything a man could want and more.
One thousand words are not enough
To say what I feel inside.
Holding hands as we walk along the shore
Never felt like this before.
Now you're all I'm living for.
(To Chorus:)
SWEET LORRAINE
Copyright © 1928 (Renewed 1956) by MILLS MUSIC, INC., c/o EMI MUSIC PUBLISHING
All Rights Reserved
Words by MITCHELL PARISH
Music by CLIFF BURWELL
Moderately
I've just found joy; I'm as hap-py as a ba-by boy with an-oth-er brand new choo-choo toy, when I'm with my sweet Lor-
raine. A pair of eyes that are blu-er than the sum-mer skies when you see them you will re-a-lize
why I love my Sweet Lor-raine. (I'm so hap-py.) When it's rain-ing I don't miss the sun, for it's in my sweet-ie's smile.
Just to think that I'm the luck-y one who will lead her down the aisle. Each night I pray that no-bod-y steals her
heart a-way. Just can't wait un-til that hap-py day, when I mar-ry Sweet Lor-raine.

SUNNY SIDE UP

Words and Music by
B.G. DeSYLVA, LEW BROWN
and RAY HENDERSON

Moderato
C Fm6 G7 C C7(♯5) F Cdim
Keep your sun - ny side up, up! Hide the side that gets
C Cmaj7 C6 Cmaj7 C G7 Gdim G7 Cdim C Cmaj7 G+ Cmaj7 D7 C6 Bdim D
blue. If you have nine sons in a row, base - ball teams make
G7 Fm6 G7 Fdim G7 C Fm6 G7 C C7(♯5)
mon - ey, you know! Keep your fun - ny side up, up!
F E7 D E7 Am A7 F6 F Fm C+ Fm6
Let your laugh - ter come thru, do! Stand up - on your legs,
C A7 F+ A7 D7 G7 F G7 C F7 G7 C
be like two fried eggs. Keep your sun - ny side up!

'S WONDERFUL

Words by IRA GERSHWIN
Music by GEORGE GERSHWIN

Moderately
E♭ E♭6 E♭ E♭6 C7 C♯dim C7 C♯dim B♭13 B♭7
'S Won - der - ful! 'S mar - ve - lous! You should care for
E♭6 E♭ E♭6 E♭ E♭ E♭6 E♭ E♭6 C7 C♯dim C7 C♯dim B♭6
me! 'S aw - ful nice, 'S par - a - dise! 'S what I love
B♭7 E♭6 Am7(♭5) G/D D7/C G/B D7/A D7
to see! You've made my life so glam - o - rous,
My dear, it's four - leaf clo - ver time,
Dm6 C9 F7 B♭9 B♭7(♭9) E♭ E♭6 E♭ E♭6 Cm F9
You can't blame me for feel - ing am - o - rous.
From now on my heart's work - ing o - ver - time.
Oh! 'S Won - der - ful! 'S mar - vel - ous!
Cm F9 Fm7 Edim Fm7 B♭7
1. E♭ Gm Fm A♭ Gm Cm Fm7 B♭
2. E♭ A♭ E♭
That you should care for me! me!

THE SUMMER KNOWS
(Theme from "Summer of '42")

Words by MARILYN and ALAN BERGMAN
Music by MICHEL LEGRAND

Slowly
Fm Fm/E Fm/E♭ Dm7(♭5) B♭m
The sum-mer smiles, the sum-mer knows, and un - a - shamed, she sheds her clothes. The sum-mer smoothes the
B♭m/A B♭m/A♭ Gm7(♭5) Csus C7(♭9) F B♭m6/F
rest-less sky, and lov-ing-ly she warms the sand on which you lie. The sum-mer knows, the sum-mer's wise, she
F Cm7/F B♭maj7 B♭6 Dm6 E7(♭9) Amaj7 E7(♭9) Amaj7 E♭7(♭9)
sees the doubts with - in your eyes, and so she takes her sum-mer time, tells the moon to wait and the sun to lin - ger,
A♭maj7 E♭7(♭9) A♭maj7 D7(♭9) G Gm7(♭5) F/C Gm7(♭5)/C
twists the world 'round her sum-mer fin - ger, lets you see the won-der of it all. And if you've learned your les-son well, there's
F/C B♭m6/C Fm/C Fdim/C Gm7(♭5) Fm
lit - tle more for her to tell, one last ca - ress, it's time to dress for fall.

From the Broadway Musical Production "SWEET CHARITY"

SWEET CHARITY

Words by DOROTHY FIELDS
Music by CY COLEMAN

Slowly
B♭ E♭ F7 B♭ E♭ F7 B♭ F/A Gm7 C7 F E♭ Dm/F F♯dim7 Gm A♭maj7 D7 Gm
Here was a man with no dream and no plan. And one lone - ly night I found Sweet Char - i - ty. You make life fun for me,
A♭maj7 D7 Gm A♭ G Csus Cmaj7 C7 Fmaj7 Bm7(♭5) Em7
oh, what it's done for me, hav - ing you a - round, Sweet Char - i - ty. Warm words I've nev - er said late - ly,
Fmaj7 F7 Gm7 C7 F Fmaj7 F7 B♭ E♭ F7 B♭ E♭ F7
pop off the top of my head, it's in - cred - i - ble. Sud-den - ly I'm the guy I nev - er dared to be.
B♭ F/A Gm7 C7 F E♭ Dm/F F♯dim7 Gm Fm/A♭ G7 Cm7 F9 B♭ E♭ F
Watch me touch the sky quite eas - i - ly. So if you are free, Sweet Char - i - ty. Please be - long to me,
B♭ E♭ F B♭ E♭ F B♭ E♭ F B♭ E♭6 F B♭ E♭6 F7 B♭ E♭ F7 B♭
Sweet Char - i - ty, please be - long to me, Sweet Char - i - ty. Sweet Char - i - ty, be - long to me.

SWEET AND GENTLE

English Lyric by GEORGE THORN
Spanish Lyric and Music by
OTILIO PORTAL

Moderately

Am7 C+ Am7 D7 G Gmaj7 G6 G Am7 C+

I was sweet and gen-tle, kind-a sen-ti-men-tal; no one will de-ny it.

Am7 D7 G D7 Am7 D7 G

I was once so qui-et! And then one mag-ic night I learned to do the cha-cha! And now I'll nev-er be the same! For I have

D7 Am7 D7 G D7 Am7 C+

turned in-to a danc-ing cu-ca-ra-cha! And my { mu-cha-cha / mu-cha-cha } is to blame. How can I be gen-tle,

Am7 D7 G Gmaj7 G6 G Am7 C+ Am7 D7 G

sweet and sen-ti-men-tal, while the cha-cha's play-ing, and my heart is sway-ing? I find that

D7 Am7 D7 G D7 Am7

I am e-ven danc-ing when I'm walk-ing! I'm haunt-ed by that cha-cha beat! I hear the rhy-thm start when-ev-er we are talk-ing,

D7 1. G D7 2. G D7 Am7 C+

I do the cha-cha in my sleep. I was sweet and sleep. Please be sweet and gen-tle,

Am7 D7 G Gmaj7 G6 Am7 D7 Am7 D7 G6 F♯6 G6

treat me sen-ti-men-tal, for I'm tem-p'ra-men-tal, when I'm do-ing the cha-cha with you!

SWEET ROSIE O'GRADY

By MAUD NUGENT

Moderate waltz
B♭ F7 B♭ F7 B♭ F7 B♭ B♭7 Gm Gm/B♭ D7/A Gm
Sweet Ro-sie O' Gra-dy, my dear lit-tle Rose. She's my stead-y
C7 F7 B♭ F7 B♭ F7 B♭ E♭
la-dy, most ev-'ry-one knows. And when we are mar-ried, how hap-py we'll
D7 E♭ C7/E Edim7 B♭/F Gm C7 F7 1. B♭ F7 2. B♭
be. I love sweet Ro-sie O' Gra-dy, and Ro-sie O' Gra-dy loves me. me.

SWEET GEORGIA BROWN

Words and Music by
BEN BERNIE, MACEO PINKARD
and KENNETH CASEY

Brightly

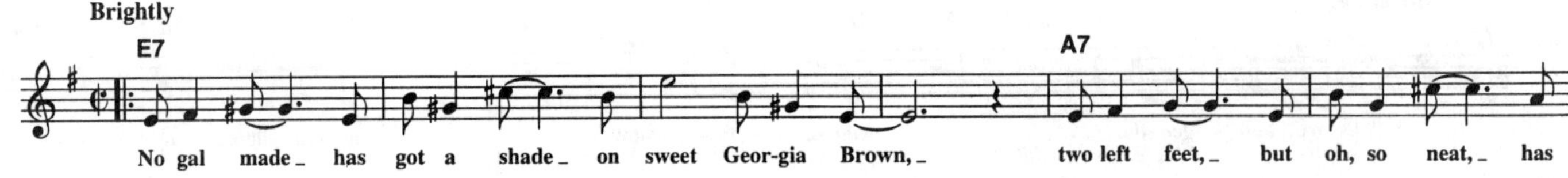
E7
A7
No gal made _ has got a shade _ on sweet Geor-gia Brown, _ two left feet, _ but oh, so neat, _ has

D7
D7(♯5)
sweet Geor-gia Brown, _ they all sigh _ and wan-na die __ for sweet Geor-gia Brown, _ I'll tell __ you just

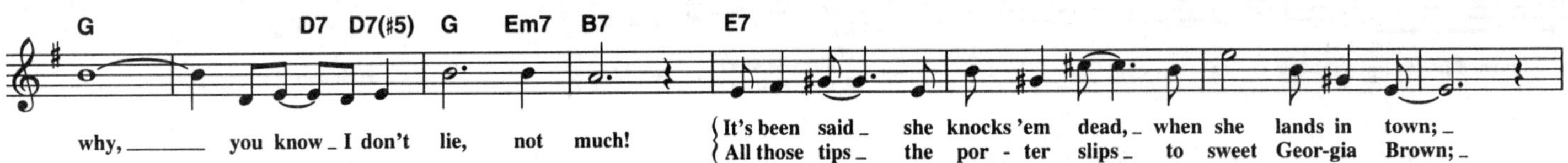
G D7 D7(♯5) G Em7 B7 E7
why, ______ you know _ I don't lie, not much!
It's been said _ she knocks 'em dead, _ when she lands in town; _
All those tips _ the por - ter slips _ to sweet Geor-gia Brown; _

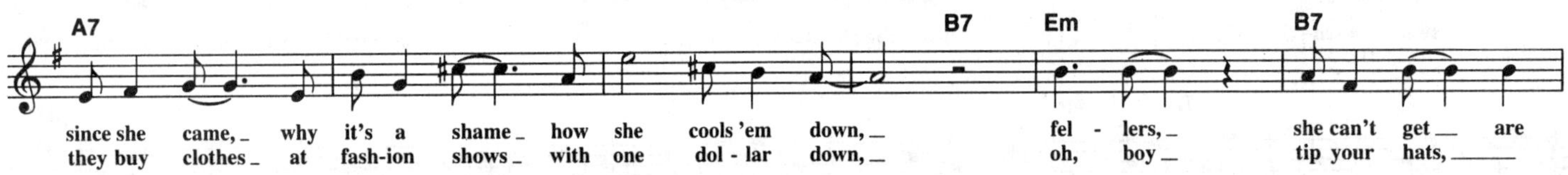
A7 B7 Em B7
since she came, _ why it's a shame _ how she cools 'em down, _ fel - lers, _ she can't get __ are
they buy clothes _ at fash-ion shows _ with one dol - lar down, _ oh, boy _ tip your hats, ______

Em B7 G F7(♭5) E7 A7 D7 G B7 G
1. 2.
fel - lers, _ she ain't met, _ Geor-gia claimed _ her, Geor-gia named _ her, sweet Geor-gia Brown. _ ______
oh, joy, _ she's the "cat's," _ who's that, mis - ter? 'Tain't her sis - ter, sweet Geor-gia Brown. _

SWEETHEART OF SIGMA CHI

Words by BYRON D. STOKES
Music By F. DUDLEIGH VERNOR

Moderately

F A7 A7(♭5) D7 Adim7 D7 Gm D7 Gm B♭m6 C+
The girl of my dreams is the sweet - est girl of all the girls I know. _____ Each sweet co - ed, like a
F6 F D7(♭9) G7 C7 Gm7 C7 F A7 A7(♭5) D7 Adim7 D Gm
rain - bow trail, fades in the af - ter glow. _______ The blue of her eyes and the gold of her hair, are a blend of the
D+ D7 Gm D7 Gm A♭dim7 E7 F F7 D7 G7 G7(♯5) C7 F B♭m6 F6
west - ern sky. _______ And the moon-light beams on the girl of my dreams; she's the Sweet-heart of Sig - ma Chi. _______

SWEET MEMORIES

By MICKEY NEWBURY

Moderately

Verse:

G G7 C C♯ D7 Am7 D7 G G7 C G D7 G C C♯

1. My world is like a riv - er, as dark as it is deep. Night af - ter night, the past slips in, and gath - ers all my sleep. My days are just an end - less stream of emp - ti - ness to me filled on - ly by the fleet - ing mo - ments of her mem - o - ry.

Chorus:

D7 G Am Gdim/B♭ B7 Em A7 G/D D7 1. G C G D7 2. G

Sweet mem - o - ries, sweet mem - o - ries, mmm. 2. She

Verse 2:
She slipped into the silence
Of my dreams last night.
Wandering from room to room,
She's turning on each light.
Her laughter spills like water
From the river to the sea.
I'm swept away from sadness,
Clinging to her memory.
(To Chorus:)

From the Warner Brothers Production "THE GREAT RACE"

THE SWEETHEART TREE

Copyright © 1965 by NORTHRIDGE MUSIC COMPANY (c/o ALL NATIONS MUSIC) and WARNER BROS. MUSIC
All Rights Reserved
Words by JOHNNY MERCER
Music by HENRY MANCINI
Moderately slow
F Am B♭ Gm7/C F Am B♭ C7 C♯dim7
They say there's a tree in the for - est, a tree that will give you a sign. Come a -
Dm Am B♭ F Dm G7 Gm7/C C9
long with me, to the sweet - heart tree, come and carve your name next to mine. They
F Am B♭ Gm7/C F F7/A B♭ Bdim7
say if you kiss the right sweet - heart, the one you've been wait - ing for, big
F/C Cm7 F7 B♭ Bdim7 F/C Gm7/C C7 F B♭/F F
blos - soms of white will burst in - to sight, and your love will be true ev - er - more.

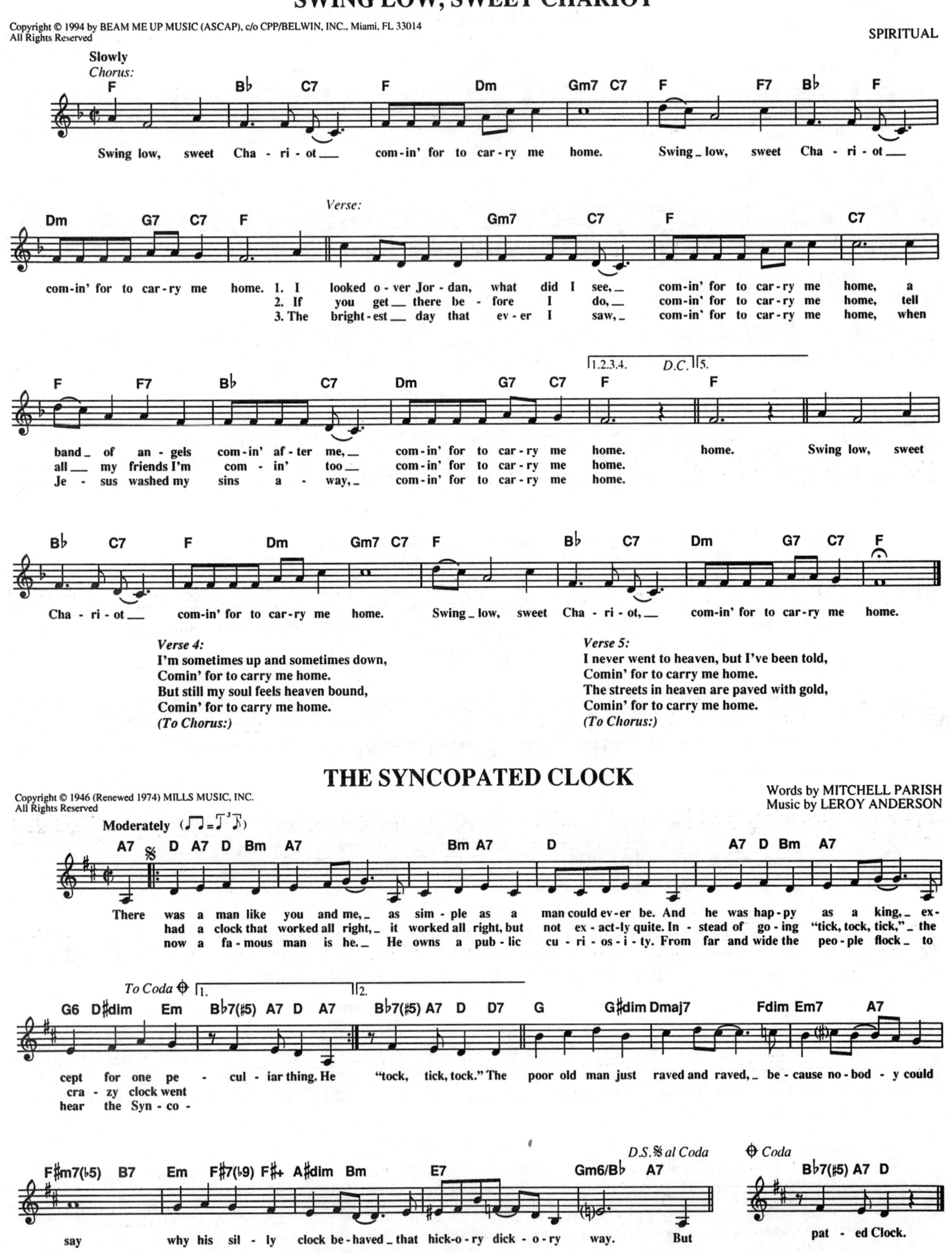
SWING LOW, SWEET CHARIOT
Copyright © 1994 by BEAM ME UP MUSIC (ASCAP), c/o CPP/BELWIN, INC., Miami, FL 33014
All Rights Reserved
SPIRITUAL
Slowly
Chorus:
F Bb C7 F Dm Gm7 C7 F F7 Bb F
Swing low, sweet Cha - ri - ot ___ com - in' for to car - ry me home. Swing _ low, sweet Cha - ri - ot ___
Verse:
Dm G7 C7 F Gm7 C7 F C7
com - in' for to car - ry me home. 1. I looked o - ver Jor - dan, what did I see, _ com - in' for to car - ry me home, a
2. If you get ___ there be - fore I do, ___ com - in' for to car - ry me home, tell
3. The bright - est ___ day that ev - er I saw, _ com - in' for to car - ry me home, when
1.2.3.4. D.C. 5.
F F7 Bb C7 Dm G7 C7 F F
band _ of an - gels com - in' af - ter me, ___ com - in' for to car - ry me home. home. Swing low, sweet
all ___ my friends I'm com - in' too ___ com - in' for to car - ry me home.
Je - sus washed my sins a - way, _ com - in' for to car - ry me home.
Bb C7 F Dm Gm7 C7 F Bb C7 Dm G7 C7 F
Cha - ri - ot ___ com - in' for to car - ry me home. Swing _ low, sweet Cha - ri - ot, ___ com - in' for to car - ry me home.
Verse 4:
I'm sometimes up and sometimes down,
Comin' for to carry me home.
But still my soul feels heaven bound,
Comin' for to carry me home.
(To Chorus:)
Verse 5:
I never went to heaven, but I've been told,
Comin' for to carry me home.
The streets in heaven are paved with gold,
Comin' for to carry me home.
(To Chorus:)
THE SYNCOPATED CLOCK
Copyright © 1946 (Renewed 1974) MILLS MUSIC, INC.
All Rights Reserved
Words by MITCHELL PARISH
Music by LEROY ANDERSON
Moderately
A7 D A7 D Bm A7 Bm A7 D A7 D Bm A7
There was a man like you and me, _ as sim - ple as a man could ev - er be. And he was hap - py as a king, _ ex -
had a clock that worked all right, _ it worked all right, but not ex - act - ly quite. In - stead of go - ing "tick, tock, tick," _ the
now a fa - mous man is he. _ He owns a pub - lic cu - ri - os - i - ty. From far and wide the peo - ple flock _ to
To Coda 1. 2.
G6 D#dim Em Bb7(#5) A7 D A7 Bb7(#5) A7 D D7 G G#dim Dmaj7 Fdim Em7 A7
cept for one pe - cul - iar thing. He "tock, tick, tock." The poor old man just raved and raved, _ be - cause no - bod - y could
cra - zy clock went
hear the Syn - co -
D.S. al Coda
Coda
F#m7(b5) B7 Em F#7(b9) F#+ A#dim Bm E7 Gm6/Bb A7 Bb7(#5) A7 D
say why his sil - ly clock be - haved _ that hick - o - ry dick - o - ry way. But pat - ed Clock.

From the Motion Picture "TOP GUN"

TAKE MY BREATH AWAY
(Love Theme from "TOP GUN")

Words and Music by
GIORGIO MORODER and
TOM WHITLOCK

Moderately slow
Ab Cm/G Fm Cm/G Ab
1. Watch-ing ev-ery mo-tion in my fool-ish lov-er's game; on this end-less o-cean, fi-
Cm/G Fm Cm/G Bbm Db/Ab Eb
-n'lly lov-ers know no shame. Turn-ing and re-turn-ing to some se-cret place in-side;
Ab Cm/G Db Eb
watch-ing in slow mo-tion as you turn a-round and say, "Take my breath a-
To Coda
1.
Ab Cm/G Db Eb Ab Cm/G
way." "Take my breath a-way."
Db Eb
D.C.
2.
Fm Cm/G Ab
Bridge:
Bb Eb/G
Through the hour-glass I saw you. In time,
Db Ab Bb Eb/G Db
you slipped a-way. When the mir-ror crashed, I called you and turned to hear you say,
Ab Bb Eb
"If on-ly for to-day I am un-a-fraid. Take my breath a-
1.
2.
D.C. al Coda
Ab Cm/G Fm Cm/G Cm/G
way." "Take my breath a-
Coda
Repeat and fade
Db Eb Ab Cm/G Db Eb
My love, take my breath a-way. My love, take my breath a-

Verse 2:
Watching, I keep waiting, still anticipating love,
Never hesitating to become the fated ones.
Turning and returning to some secret place to hide;
Watching in slow motion as you turn my way and say,
"Take my breath away."
(To Bridge:)

Verse 3:
Watching every motion in this foolish lover's game;
Haunted by the notion somewhere there's a love in flames.
Turning and returning to some secret place inside;
Watching in slow motion as you turn to me and say,
"Take my breath away."
(To Coda:)

TAKE FIVE

By PAUL DESMOND

Moderately bright swing
Ebm Bbm7 Ebm Bbm7 Ebm Bbm7
Ebm Bbm7 Ebm Bbm7 Ebm Bbm7 Ebm Bbm7 Ebm
Cb Fm7(b5) Bbm7 Ebm7 Abm7 Db7 Gbmaj7
Cb Fm7(b5) Bbm7 Ebm7 Abm7 Db7 Fm7 Bb7
Ebm Bbm7 Ebm Bbm7 Ebm Bbm7 Ebm Bbm7
To Coda
D.S. al Coda
Ebm Bbm7 Ebm Bbm7 Ebm Bbm7 Ebm Bbm7
Coda
Ebm Bbm7 Ebm Bbm7 Ebm Bbm7 Ebm Bbm7 Ebm Bbm7
Ebm Bbm7 Ebm Bbm7 Ebm Bbm7 Ebm Bbm7 Ebm Bbm7 Ebm Bbm7 Ebm
TAKE ME OUT TO THE BALL GAME
Copyright © 1994 by BEAM ME UP MUSIC (ASCAP), c/o CPP/BELWIN, INC., Miami, FL 33014
All Rights Reserved
Lyrics by JACK NORWORTH
Music by ALBERT VON TILZER
Moderately
D Bm A D Bm A7 B7 Em
Take me out to the ball game, take me out to the crowd. Buy me some pea-nuts and crack - er - jack.
E A7 F#m A7 D Bm A7 D7 G
I don't care if I nev - er get back. Let me root, root, root for the home - team. If they don't win it's a shame,
Em/B Bb7 D/A D/F# Fdim7 D/F# E7 A7 D D A7 D
1. 2.
for it's one, two, three strikes, you're out at the old ball game. game.

TAKE THE "A" TRAIN

By BILLY STRAYHORN and
THE DELTA RHYTHM BOYS

Easy swing

C6 D7(♭5) Dm7 G7 C
1. 2.
You ___ must take the "A" train ___ to go to Sug - ar Hill way up in Har-lem. ___
If ___ you miss the "A" train, ___ you'll find you've missed the quick-est way to Har-lem. ___

Fmaj7 D7 Dm9 G9 D♭9
Hur-ry, __ get on now, it's com-ing. ___ Lis - ten __ to those rails a - thrum-ming. ___ All

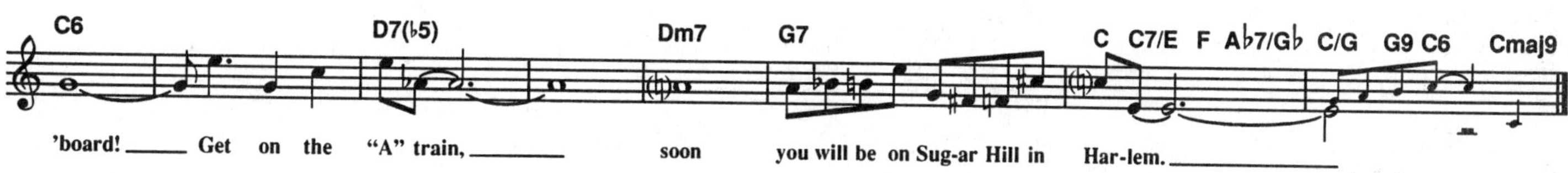
C6 D7(♭5) Dm7 G7 C C7/E F A♭7/G♭ C/G G9 C6 Cmaj9
'board! ___ Get on the "A" train, ___ soon you will be on Sug-ar Hill in Har-lem. ___

From the M-G-M Musical Production "CABIN IN THE SKY"

TAKING A CHANCE ON LOVE

Words by JOHN LATOUCHE and TED FETTER
Music by VERNON DUKE

Moderately

C Edim7 Dm7 G7 Dm7 G7 C
To Coda
Am Am7 D7
Here I go a - gain; _ I hear the trum-pets blow a - gain. _ All a - glow a - gain, _
Here I slide a - gain, _ a-bout to take that ride a - gain. _ Star - ry eyed a - gain, _
Things are mend-ing now; _ I see a rain-bow blend-ing now. _

1. 2.
Dm7 G7 Em7 A7 Dm7 G7 Dm7 G7 C Gm7 C7 F F♯dim
tak-in' a chance _ on love. tak-in' a chance _ on love. I thought the cards _ were a frame-up; I

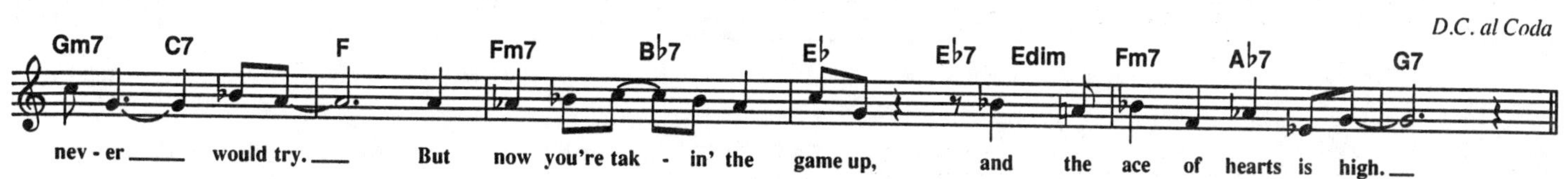
D.C. al Coda
Gm7 C7 F Fm7 B♭7 E♭ E♭7 Edim Fm7 A♭7 G7
nev - er ___ would try. ___ But now you're tak - in' the game up, and the ace of hearts is high. ___

Coda
Am D7 Dm7 G7 C Dm7 Cmaj7 F Dm9 D♭7(♭5) Cmaj9
We'll have a hap - py end-ing now, _ tak-in' a chance _ on love, love, love, love, tak-in' a chance _ on love.

TALK BACK TREMBLING LIPS
Copyright © 1963 (Renewed 1991) by ACUFF-ROSE MUSIC, INC.
All Rights Reserved
By JOHN D. LOUDERMILK
Moderately
Verse:
1. Ev - 'ry day our love's a bat - tle roy - al. Dear, it seems that fight-ing is all we do. But if I let you know how much I love you, you'll do things to me you should - n't do.
Chorus:
So talk back trem - bling lips. Shak - y legs, don't just stand there! Don't let her know she's get - ting through to you. Talk back trem - bling lips. Burn - ing eyes, don't start cry - ing. Heart, don't let her know that you're break - ing in two. break - ing in two.
Verse 2:
Every time you up and hurt my feelings
I pretend it couldn't matter less.
I'm just hiding all of my emotions
Behind my broken heart, I guess.
(To Chorus:)
From "THE FLEETS IN"
TANGERINE
Copyright © 1942 (Renewed 1959) by FAMOUS MUSIC CORPORATION
All Rights Reserved
Words by JOHNNY MERCER
Music by VICTOR SCHERTZINGER
Moderately
Tan - ge - rine, she is all they claim with her eyes of night and lips as bright as flame. Tan - ge - rine, when she danc - es by, se - ño - ri - tas stare and ca - ba - lle - ros sigh. And I've seen toasts to Tan - ge - rine raised in ev - 'ry bar a - cross the Ar - gen - tine. Yes, she has them all on the run. But her heart be - longs to just one, her heart be - longs to Tan - ge - rine.

From the 20th Century-Fox Musical Production "DOCTOR DOLITTLE"
TALK TO THE ANIMALS
Copyright © 1967 TWENTIETH CENTURY MUSIC CORPORATION c/o EMI HASTINGS CATALOG INC.
All Rights Reserved
Words and Music by LESLIE BRICUSSE
Moderately
If we could talk to the an - i - mals, just im - a - gine it, chat-ting to a chimp in chim-pan - zee.
talk to the an - i - mals, learn their lan-guag - es, may - be take an an - i - mal de - gree.
ferred with our fur - ry friends, man to an - i - mal, think of all the things we could dis - cuss.
To Coda
Im - a - gine talk - ing to a tig - er, chat-ting to a chee-tah; what a neat a - chieve-ment it would be.
We'd stud - y el - e - phant and ea - gle, buf - fa - lo and bea - gle, al - li - ga - tor, guin - ea pig and flea.
If we could
If we could
We would con - verse in po - lar bear and py - thon, and we would curse in flu - ent kan - ga - roo.
If peo-ple asked us, "Can you speak rhi - no-cer-os?" We'd say, "Of cours-er-os! Can't you?"
D.S. al Coda
If we con -
Coda
walk with the an - i - mals, talk with the an - i - mals, grunt and squeak and squawk with the an - i - mals,
and they could squeak and squawk and speak and talk to us.
A TASTE OF HONEY
Copyright © 1960 & 1962 (Renewed) by SONGFEST MUSIC CORP.
Sole Selling Agent GEORGE PINCUS & SONS MUSIC CORP.
All Rights Reserved
Words by RIC MARLOW
Music by BOBBY SCOTT
Moderately
Winds may blow o'ver the ic - y sea. I'll take with me the warmth of thee, a taste of hon-ey, a
leave be - hind my heart to wear and may it e'er re - mind you of a taste of hon-ey, a
ne'er came back to his love so fair and so she died dream-ing of his kiss. His kiss was hon-ey, a
taste much sweet-er than wine.
taste much sweet-er than wine.
taste much bit - ter than wine.
I will re - turn I'll re - turn. I'll come back for the hon-ey and
you. 2. I'll 3. He
you. I'll come back for the hon-ey and you. I'll come back for the hon-ey, hon-ey and you.

TARANTELLA
Copyright © 1994 by BEAM ME UP MUSIC (ASCAP), c/o CPP/BELWIN, INC., Miami, FL 33014
All Rights Reserved
ITALIAN DANCE
Brightly
TEARS ON MY PILLOW
Copyright © 1941 (Renewed 1968, 1971) by WESTERN MUSIC PUBLISHING CO.
All Rights Reserved
Words and Music by
GENE AUTRY and
FRED ROSE
Moderately
Chorus:
Tears on my pil - low each morn - ing, I cry when I dream a - bout you. When
I should be sleep-ing, I just lay there weep-ing, won-d'ring if you're weep-ing too. I'm try - ing so
hard to for - get you, but that's not so eas - y to do, with tears on my pil - low each
morn - ing tears that I've shed o - ver you. you.
To Next Strain
Fine
Verse:
We were so hap - py when love lin - gered on, back in the sweet used to be. But
now I'm so lone - ly be - cause you are gone, leav - ing a sad mem - o - ry. I'm
D.S. % al Fine

TA-RA-RA BOOM DE-AY

TRADITIONAL

Brightly
C G7 C
Ta-ra-ra boom-de-ay, ta-ra-ra boom-de-ay, ta-ra-ra boom-de-ay, ta-ra-ra boom-de-ay.
G7 C
Ta-ra-ra boom-de-ay, ta-ra-ra boom-de-ay, ta-ra-ra boom-de-ay, ta-ra-ra boom-de-ay.
THANK GOD FOR KIDS
Copyright © 1974 by MILENE MUSIC, INC.
All Rights Reserved
Words and Music by
EDDY RAVEN
Moderately
Verse:
D G D A7
1. If it weren't for kids have you ev-er thought there would-n't be no San-ta Claus, or
G A7 D A7 D G
"Look what the stork just brought." Thank God for kids. And we'd all live in a qui-et house with-
D A7 G A7 D
out Big Bird or Mick-ey Mouse, and Kool Aid on the couch. Thank God for kids. Thank
Chorus:
G A7 D G A7 D
God for kids, there's mag-ic for a while, a spe-cial kind of sun-shine in a smile.
G A7 Bm G D Em Em7
Do you ev-er stop to think or won-der why the near-est thing to Heav-en is a
1. 2.
Cmaj7 A7 Cmaj7 A7 D G D
child? child? When you get down on your knees to-night to thank the Lord for His
A7 G A7 D G D A7 G D
guid-ing light, and pray they turn out right, thank God for kids.

Verse 2:
"Daddy, how does this thing fly?"
And a hundred other wheres and whys.
You really don't know but you try.
Thank God for kids.
When you look down in those trusting eyes.
That look to you, you realize
There's a love that you can't buy.
Thank God for kids.
(To Chorus:)

THE TEARS OF A CLOWN

Words and Music by
HENRY COSBY, WILLIAM "SMOKEY" ROBINSON
and STEVIE WONDER

Moderately
(B♭ F) C F B♭ F C F B♭ F
(1. Now if there's a smile) up-on my face it's on-ly there try'n' to fool the pub - lic, but when it comes
C F B♭ F C F B♭ F C F
down to fool - in' you, now hon - ey that's quite a dif-f'rent sub - ject. Don't let my glad ex - pres-
B♭ F C F B♭ F C F B♭ F
- sion give you the wrong im - pres - sion. Real - ly I'm sad, oh, sad - der than sad;
C F B♭ F C F B♭ F C F
you're gone and I'm hurt - ing so bad; like a clown, I pre - tend to be glad.
B♭ F G E/G♯ Am F
Now there's some sad things known to man, but ain't too much sad - der than the tears of a
*
C C F
(1.)2.
clown, when there's no one a - round.
D.S. 𝄋 3.
B♭ F C F B♭ F C F B♭ F C F
Oh, yeah ba - by. (1. Now if there's a smile) Just like Pag - li - ac - ci did, I try to keep my sad-
2. Now if I ap - pear
B♭ F C F B♭ F C F B♭ F
- ness hid; smil - ing in the pub - lic eye, but in my lone - ly room I cry the tears of a
C F B♭ F C F B♭ F
D.S. 𝄋 and fade
clown. Oh, yeah ba - by. 3. Now, if there's a smile

Verse 2:
Now if I appear to be carefree,
It's only to camouflage my sadness;
In order to shield my pride I try
To cover this hurt with a show of gladness.
But don't let my show convince you
That I've been happy since you
Decided to go,
I need you so,
I'm hurt and I want you to know,
But for others I put on a show.

Now there's some sad things known to man,
But ain't too much sadder than
The tears of a clown, when there's no one around.

Verse 3: (ad lib.)
Now if there's a smile on my face,
Don't let my glad expression
Give you a wrong impression.
Don't let this smile I wear
Make you think that I don't care. . .*(fade)*

*Cue notes are counter-melody - start here for intro.

TEEN ANGEL

By JEAN SURREY
and RED SURREY

Freely

G C G C
1. That fate - ful night the car was stalled up - on the rail - road track. I
was it you were look - ing for that took your life that night. They
sweet six - teen and now you're gone; they've tak - en you a - way. I'll

G C Moderately slow D7 G
pulled you out and we were safe, but you went run - ning back.
said they found my high school ring clutched in your fin - gers tight.
nev - er kiss your lips a - gain; they bur - ied you to - day.

Chorus:

D7 G
Teen An - gel, can you hear me? Teen An - gel, can you see me? Are you some - where

C D7 1.2. G D7 G *freely* D.S.
up a - bove, and am I still your own true love?
2. What
3. Just

3. G *freely* Em C D7 G
own true love. Teen An - gel, teen an - gel, *rit.* an - swer me, please.

From the Metro-Goldwyn-Mayer Musical Production "GOING HOLLYWOOD"

TEMPTATION

Words by ARTHUR FREED
Music by NACIO HERB BROWN

Moderately
C Db C Db C Db C C
To Coda
You came, I was a - lone. I should have known you were temp - ta - tion. ta - tion.
You smiled, lur - ing me on. My heart was gone, you were temp -
you were born to be kissed. I can't re - sist
Bbm D7 Db7 C7 B7 Bb7 A7 G7(#5) G7
D.C. al Coda
It would be thrill - ing if you were will - ing. If it can nev - er be, pit - y me. For
Coda
Db Bbm C7 F Bbm F Bb F Gb
you are temp - ta - tion and I am yours. Here is my heart, take it and say we'll nev - er
F Db C Db C Db C Fm6 Cm6
part. I'm just a slave, on - ly a slave to you, temp - ta - tion.

TENNESSEE WALTZ

Words and Music by
REDD STEWART and PEE WEE KING

Moderately slow
C C7 F C
I was waltz-ing with my dar-lin' to the Ten-nes-see waltz, when an old friend I
G7 C C7
hap-pened to see. I in-tro-duced him to my loved one, and while they were
F C G7 C E7 F
waltz-ing my friend stole my sweet-heart from me. I re-mem-ber the night and the Ten-nes-see
C G7 C
waltz. Now I know just how much I have lost. Yes, I lost my lit-tle dar-lin' the
C7 F C G7 1. C 2. C
night they were play-ing the beau-ti-ful Ten-nes-see waltz. I was waltz.

THAT LUCKY OLD SUN

(Just Rolls Around Heaven All Day)

Words by HAVEN GILLESPIE
Music by BEASLEY SMITH

Moderately
C Cmaj7 Am Fm/A♭ C/G F6
Up in the morn-in', out on the job, work like the dev-il for my
Fuss with my wom-an, toil for my kids, sweat 'til I'm wrin-kled and
Show me that riv-er, take me a-cross and wash all my trou-bles a-
C/E G7/D C F6 C/E Am Fm6/A♭ C/G G7
pay. But that luck-y old sun has noth-in' to do but roll a-round heav-en all
gray, while that luck-y old sun has noth-in' to do but roll a-round heav-en all
way, like that luck-y old sun give me noth-in' to do but roll a-round heav-en all
1. C 2. C F/C C To Next Strain 3. C F6 C Fine Am Em/G F6 C/E Am G7
day. day. Good day. Lawd a-bove, can't you know I'm pin-in', tears all in my
C Am Em/G F6 C/E C Cmaj7 Am Am7 D7 Dm7/G G7 D.C. al Fine
eyes. Send down that cloud with a sil-ver lin-in', lift me to Par-a-dise.

THANKS FOR THE MEMORY

Words and Music by
LEO ROBIN and
RALPH RAINGER

Moderately
Thanks for the mem - o - ry of can - dle light and wine, cas - tles on the Rhine, the
Thanks for the mem - o - ry of sen - ti - men-tal verse, noth - ing in my purse, and
Par - the - non and mo - ments on the Hud - son Riv - er Line. How love - ly it was!
chuck - les when the preach - er said, "For bet - ter or for worse." How love - ly it was!
Thanks for the mem - o - ry of rain - y af - ter - noons, swing - y Har-lem tunes, and
Thanks for the mem - o - ry of lin - ge - rie with lace, Pils - ner by the case, and
mo - tor trips and burn - ing lips and burn - ing toast and prunes. How love - ly it was!
how I jumped the day you trumped my one and on - ly ace. How love - ly it was!
Man - y's the time that we feast - ed and man - y's the time that we fast - ed. Oh
We said good bye with a high - ball; then I got as "high" as a stee - ple. But
well, it was swell while it last - ed. We did have fun and no harm done. And
we were in - tel - li - gent peo - ple. No tears, no fuss, hur - ray for us. So
thanks for the mem - o - ry of sun - burns at the shore, nights in Sing - a - pore. You
thanks for the mem - o - ry and strict - ly en - tre - nous. Dar - ling, how are you? And
might have been a head - ache but you nev - er were a bore. So thank you so much.
how are all the lit - tle dreams that
nev - er did come true? Awf - 'ly glad I met you; chee-ri - o and too-dle - oo, and thank you so much!

THAT GIRL

Words and Music by
STEVIE WONDER

Moderate rock
Verse:
G♯m9 G♯m6/9 Emaj7/G♯
1. 3. That girl thinks that she's so fine___ that soon she'll have my mind.___
2. That girl thinks that she's so bad,___ she'll change my tears to joy from sad.___
C♯m9 Emaj7 D♯m7 G♯m9 G♯m6/9 Emaj7/G♯
That girl thinks that she's so smart,_ that soon she'll have my heart._
She says she keeps the up - per hand___ 'cause she can please her man.___
C♯m9 Emaj7 D♯m7 F♯ C♯m7 A♯m7(♭5) D♯m7(♯9)
She thinks in no time flat that she'll be free and clear_ to start___
She does-n't use her love to make him weak, she us - es love to keep_ him strong;___
G♯m7 Em9/A Dmaj9 Gmaj7 C/F♯
with her e - mo - tion - al res - cued love,__ that you'll leave___ torn a - part.________
and in - side me there's no_____ room for doubt_ that it won't___ be too long________
1. E/F♯ 2.3. E/F♯
Chorus:
C♯m7 A♯m7/G♯
___ be - fore I tell her that I love her; that I want_ her; that my
C♯m7 F♯maj7 F♯m7 C♯m7 A♯m7/G♯
mind, soul,__ and bod - y need her. Tell her that I'd love to; that I want_ to; that I
1. To Next Strain 2. Repeat ad lib. and fade
C♯m7 F♯maj7 F♯m7 C♯m7 F♯maj7 F♯m7
need to do___ all that I have_ to, to win her love._ need to do;__ all that I have to, to win her love. I
Bridge:
C♯m9 A♯m7(♭5) D♯7 C♯m7(♭5) G/B C♯m7(♭5) G/B
I've been hurt-ing for a long time,_ and you've been play-ing for a long time._ You
G♯m7 C♯m7(♭5) G/B C♯m7(♭5)
know_ it's true.____________ I've been hold-ing for a long time,__ and you've been run-ning for a
G/B G♯m7 A♯m7(♭5) A13 D.C.
long time.__ It's time to do______________ what we have to do._____________

From the Paramount Picture "STAR SPANGLED RHYTHM"

THAT OLD BLACK MAGIC

Words by JOHNNY MERCER
Music by HAROLD ARLEN

Moderately bright
E♭ E♭6 E♭maj7 E♭6 E♭ E♭6
That old black_ mag - ic has me in its_ spell,_ that old black_ mag - ic that you
Fm7 B♭7 Fm7 B♭7 Fm B♭7 Fm7
weave so_ well._ Those i - cy_ fin - gers up and down my_ spine;_ the same old_ witch-
B♭7(♯5) Gm7 C9 Fm7 B♭9 E♭ E♭6 E♭maj7 E♭6
- craft when your eyes meet_ mine;_ the same old_ tin - gle that I feel in - side._ And
E♭ E♭6 D♭ D♭7 A♭ A♭m
then that_ el - e - va - tor starts its_ ride,_ and down and_ down_ I go,
E♭ C7(♯5) Fm7 D♭7 3 E♭6 Cm
'round and_ 'round_ I go like a_ leaf_ that's caught in the tide._ I should stay a - way_
Cm7 3 A♭9(♭5) G9 G7(♭5) C7 Fm 3
_ but what can I do?_ I hear your name_ and I'm a flame,_ a flame with such_ a burn-ing de-
D♭7 3 A♭m6 3 B♭9 Fm7 B♭7 E♭ E♭6
sire_ that on-ly your kiss_ can put out the fire._ For you're the_ lov - er I have
E♭maj7 E♭6 B♭m7 B♭m7(♯5) E♭7 E♭7sus E♭7 A♭
wait - ed_ for,_ the mate that_ fate_ had me cre - at - ed_ for._ And ev - 'ry_ time_
D♭7 A♭ A♭m E♭maj7 C7(♯5)
_ your lips meet mine,_ dar - ling, down and_ down_ I go, 'round and_ 'round_ I go
Fm7 3 D♭7 3 Fm7 B♭7sus E♭
in a_ spin,_ lov-ing the spin I'm_ in_ un-der that old black_ mag - ic called love!_

From the Walter Wanger Production "VOGUES OF 1938"

THAT OLD FEELING

Words and Music by
LEW BROWN and
SAMMY FAIN

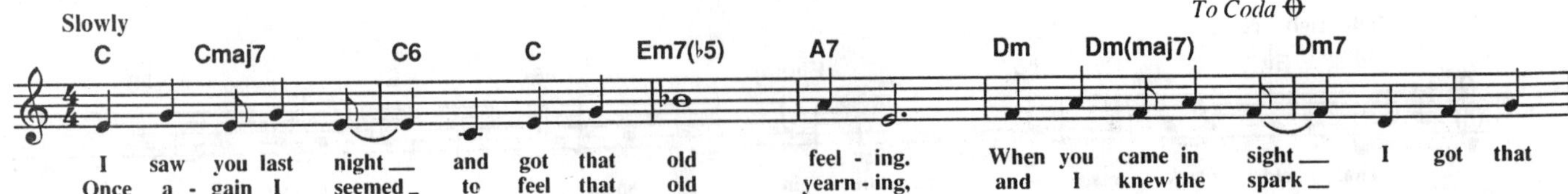
Slowly
To Coda
C Cmaj7 C6 C Em7(♭5) A7 Dm Dm(maj7) Dm7
I saw you last night — and got that old feel - ing. When you came in sight — I got that
Once a - gain I seemed — to feel that old yearn - ing, and I knew the spark —

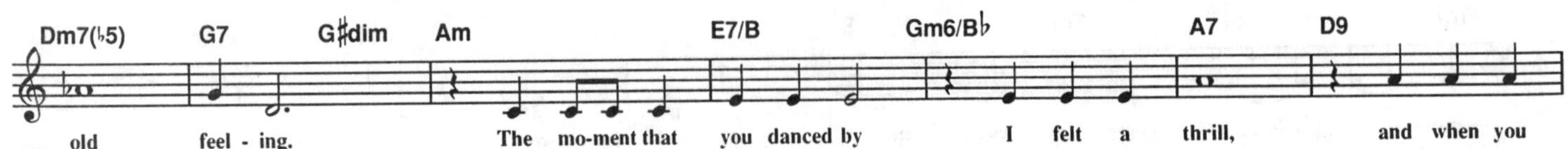
Dm7(♭5) G7 G♯dim Am E7/B Gm6/B♭ A7 D9
old feel - ing. The mo-ment that you danced by I felt a thrill, and when you

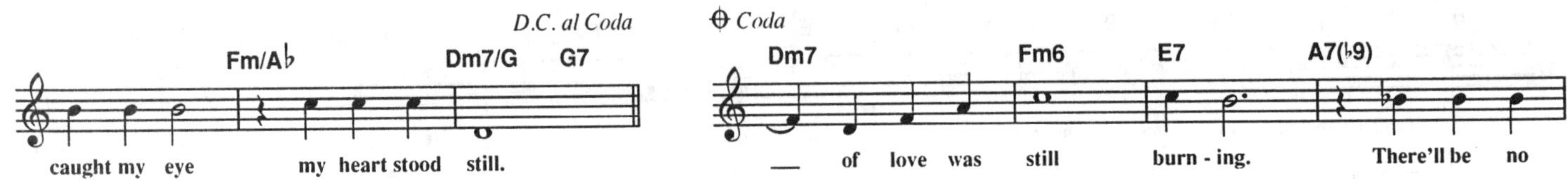
D.C. al Coda
Coda
Fm/A♭ Dm7/G G7 Dm7 Fm6 E7 A7(♭9)
caught my eye my heart stood still. — of love was still burn - ing. There'll be no

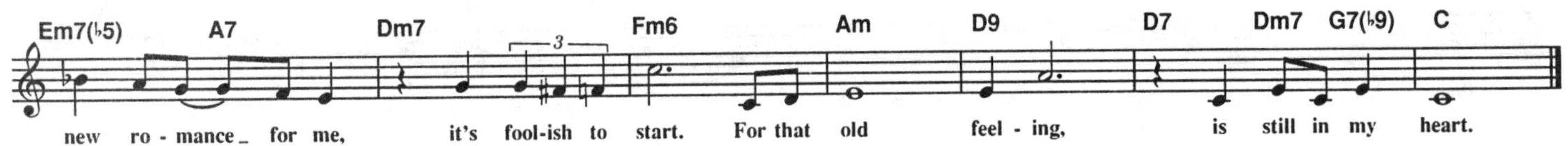
Em7(♭5) A7 Dm7 Fm6 Am D9 D7 Dm7 G7(♭9) C
new ro - mance — for me, it's fool-ish to start. For that old feel - ing, is still in my heart.

THAT'S ALL

Words and Music by ALAN BRANDT and BOB HAYMES

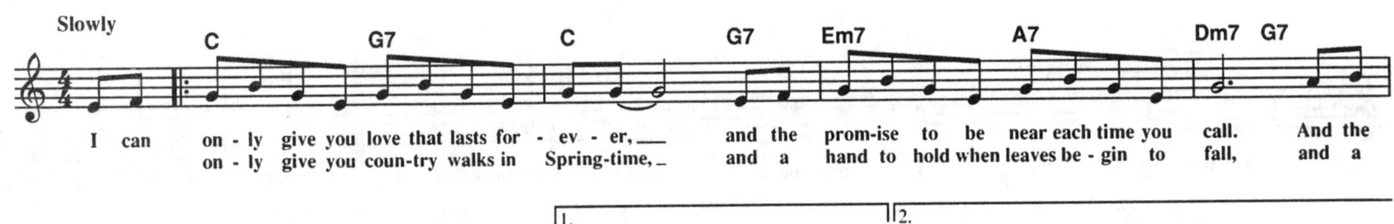
Slowly
C G7 C G7 Em7 A7 Dm7 G7
I can on - ly give you love that lasts for - ev - er, — and the prom-ise to be near each time you call. And the
on - ly give you coun-try walks in Spring-time, — and a hand to hold when leaves be - gin to fall, and a

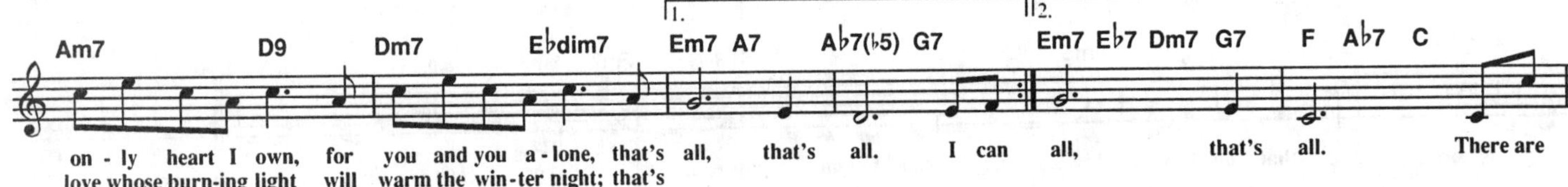
Am7 D9 Dm7 E♭dim7 Em7 A7 A♭7(♭5) G7 Em7 E♭7 Dm7 G7 F A♭7 C
on - ly heart I own, for you and you a - lone, that's all, that's all. I can all, that's all. There are
love whose burn-ing light will warm the win-ter night; that's

Gm7 C9 Fmaj7 F6 Gm7 C9 Fmaj7 F6 Am7 D9
those, I am sure, who have told you they would give you the world for a toy. All I have are these arms to en -

Gmaj7 G6 Am7 D9 Dm7 G7 C G7 C G7
fold you, and a love time can nev - er de - stroy. If you're won-d'ring what I'm ask - ing in re - turn, dear, — you'll be

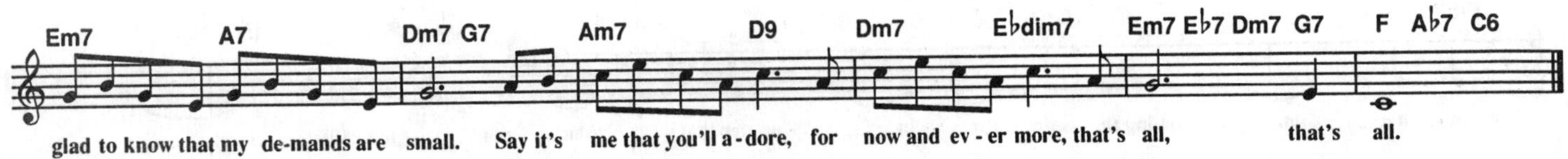
Em7 A7 Dm7 G7 Am7 D9 Dm7 E♭dim7 Em7 E♭7 Dm7 G7 F A♭7 C6
glad to know that my de-mands are small. Say it's me that you'll a - dore, for now and ev - er more, that's all, that's all.

THAT'S AMORE

(That's Love)

Words by JACK BROOKS
Music by HARRY WARREN

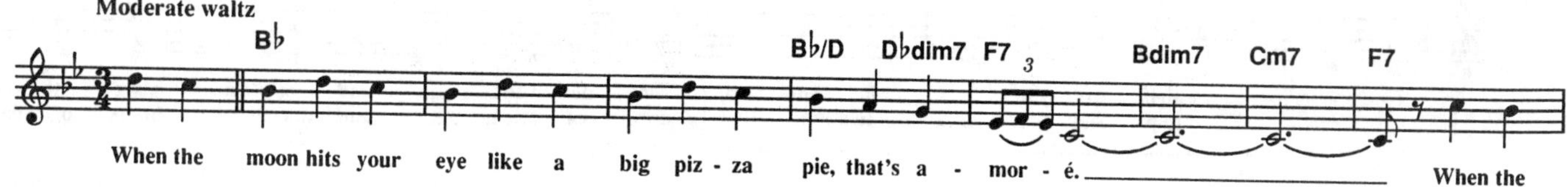
Moderate waltz
B♭
B♭/D
D♭dim7
F7
3
Bdim7
Cm7
F7
When the moon hits your eye like a big piz - za pie, that's a - mor - é. When the

B♭
world seems to shine like you've had too much wine, that's a - mor - é. Bells will

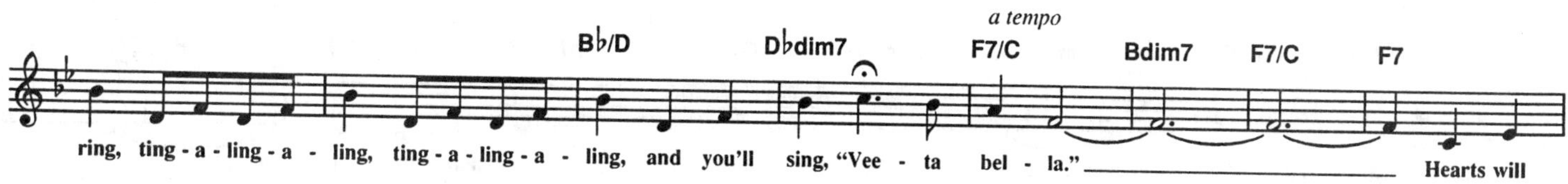
B♭/D
D♭dim7
a tempo
F7/C
Bdim7
F7/C
F7
ring, ting - a - ling - a - ling, ting - a - ling - a - ling, and you'll sing, "Vee - ta bel - la." Hearts will

Cm7/G
F7/A
B♭
3
play tip - py - tip - py - tay, tip - py - tip - py - tay like a gay tar - an - tel - la. (Luck - y

3
B♭6
B♭maj7
B♭/D
D♭dim7
F7/C
3
Bdim7
fel - la.) When the stars make you drool just like pas - ta fa - zool, that's a - mor - é.

Cm7
F7
D7/A
D7(♭5)/A♭
G7
When you dance down the street with a cloud at your feet, you're in love.

Cm
C♯dim
B♭
B♭maj7
B♭6
B♭/F
D♭dim7
When you walk in a dream but you know you're not dream-ing, Sig - nor - e, Scuz - za

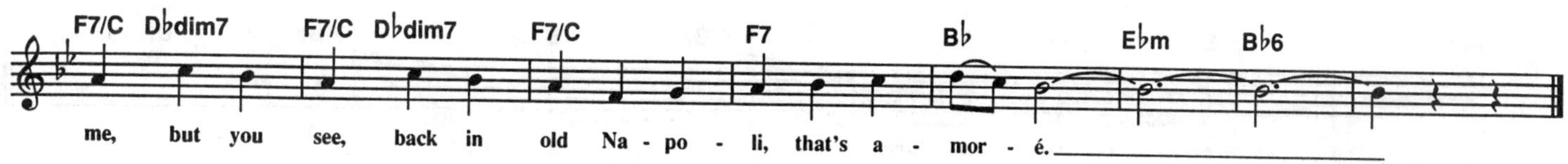
F7/C
D♭dim7
F7/C
D♭dim7
F7/C
F7
B♭
E♭m
B♭6
me, but you see, back in old Na - po - li, that's a - mor - é.

THAT'S MY DESIRE
Copyright © 1931 (Renewed) by MILLS MUSIC, INC., c/o EMI MUSIC PUBLISHING
All Rights Reserved
Words by CARROLL LOVEDAY
Music by HELMY KRESA
Slowly
To spend one night with you in our old ren - dez - vous, and re - mi - nisce with you, that's my de - sire.
gyp - sies play, down in that dim ca - fe, and dance till break of day,
To meet where
sire. We'll sip a lit - tle glass of wine, I'll gaze in - to your eyes di - vine. I'll feel the touch of your lips press - ing on mine. To hear you whis - per low just when it's time to go, "Che - rie," I love you so; that's my de - sire.
THEME FROM "CHEERS"
(Where Everybody Knows Your Name)
Copyright © 1982 by ADDAX MUSIC CO., INC.
All Rights Reserved
Words and Music by
GARY PORTNOY and JUDY HART ANGELO
Moderately
Verse:
Mak-ing your way in the world to-day takes ev-'ry-thing you've got.
Tak-ing a break from all your wor-ries sure would help a lot.
Would-n't you like to get a-way?
Chorus:
Some-times you wan-na go where ev-'ry-bod - y knows your name, and they're al - ways glad you came.
You wan-na be where you can see our trou-bles are all the same.
You wan-na be where ev-'ry-bod-y knows your name.
You wan-na go where peo - ple know peo-ple are all the same.
You wan-na go where ev-'ry-bod-y knows your name.

From the Columbia Motion Picture "CLOSE ENCOUNTERS OF THE THIRD KIND"

THEME FROM CLOSE ENCOUNTERS™ OF THE THIRD KIND

Music by JOHN WILLIAMS

Slowly
N.C.
Gmaj7
Em7
Cmaj7
Bm7
Dmaj7/F♯
Fmaj7
Dm7
Repeat and fade
From the Columbia Picture "ICE CASTLES"
THEME FROM ICE CASTLES
(Through the Eyes of Love)
Copyright © 1978 by GOLD HORIZON MUSIC CORP. and GOLDEN TORCH MUSIC CORP.
All Rights Reserved
Lyrics by CAROLE BAYER SAGER
Music by MARVIN HAMLISCH
Slowly
1. Please don't let this feel-ing end. It's ev - 'ry-thing I am, ev-'ry-thing I want to be. I can see what's mine now, find-ing out what's true
(2.) now I can take the time. I can see my life as it comes up shin - ing now. Reach-ing out to touch you, I can feel so much
(3.) Please, don't let this feel-ing end. It might not come a - gain, and I want to re - mem - ber how it feels to touch you, how I feel so much
since I found you, look - ing
1. through the eyes of love.
2. 2. And through the eyes of love.
To Next Strain
3. And through the eyes of love.
Fine
Bridge:
now I do be-lieve that e-ven in the storm we'll find some light. Know-ing you're be - side me, I'm all right.
D.C. al Fine

THIS TIME THE DREAM'S ON ME

Words by JOHNNY MERCER
Music by HAROLD ARLEN

Slowly
D13 G Em Am7 G♯dim Am7 D7(♭9) D7 D13 G G♯dim
Some-where, some - day we'll be close to-geth-er, wait and see, oh, by the way,
hand and you'll look at me a - dor - ing - ly, but as things stand,
Am7 D11 D7(♭9) Gm G♯dim D7 D13 G F6 G6 G+ F♯7(♭9) A/B B7 B7(♯5) B7
1. 2.
this time the dream's on me. You'll take my me. It would be fun to be cer-tain that I'm the
Bm7/E E7 Ddim C♯m7(♭5) Cm6 G/B A7(♯5) A7 D7 G♯dim D7 D13 G Em
one, to know that I at least sup - ply the shoul-der you cry up - on. To see you through
Am7 G♯dim Am7 D7(♭9) D7 B7(♯5) B7 E7(♭9) A7 A7(♯5) Am7/D D7(♭9) G Am7(♭5) G
till you're ev-'ry-thing you want to be, it can't be true, but this time the dream's on me.

THESE THINGS I OFFER YOU

(For a Lifetime)

Words and Music by
MORTY NEVINS, BENNIE BENJAMIN
and GEORGE DAVID WEISS

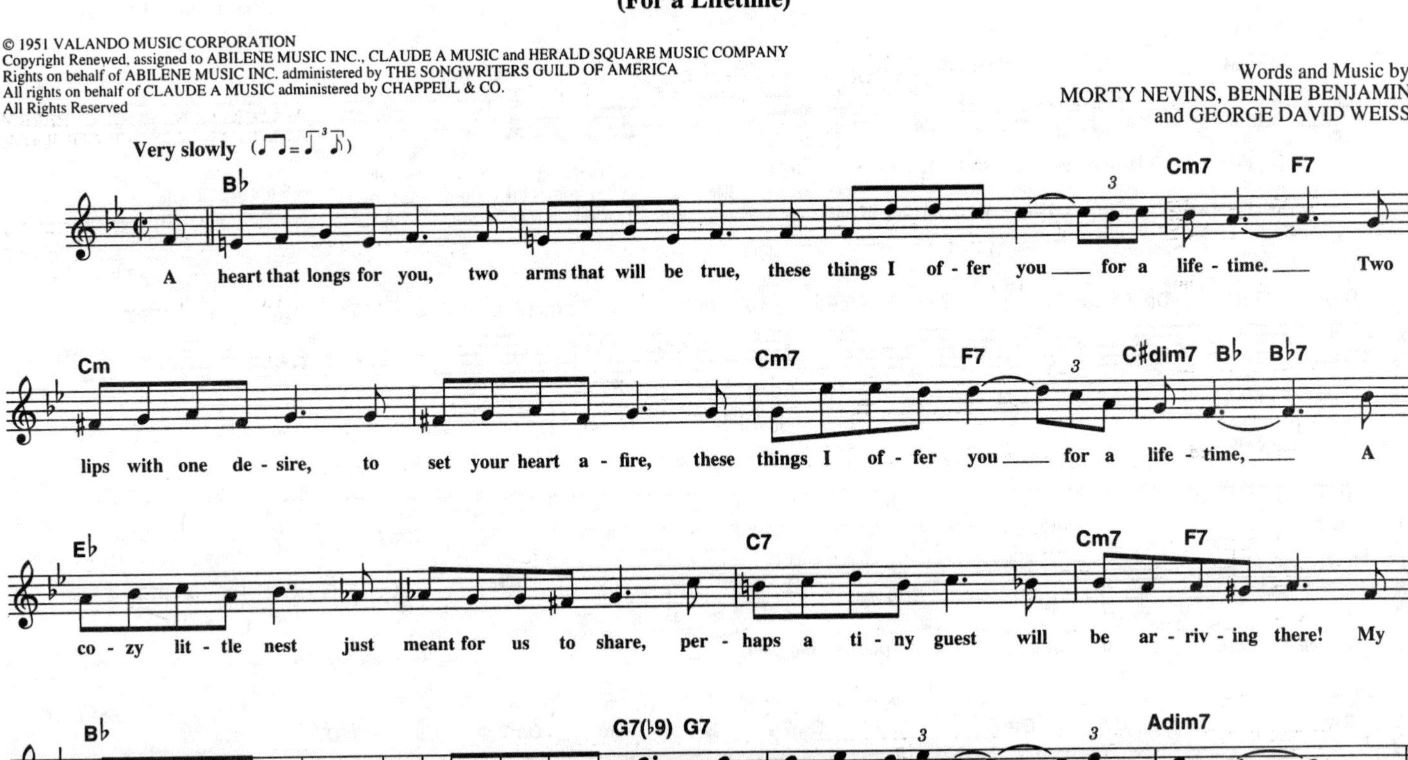
Very slowly
B♭ Cm7 F7
A heart that longs for you, two arms that will be true, these things I of - fer you for a life - time. Two
Cm Cm7 F7 C♯dim7 B♭ B♭7
lips with one de - sire, to set your heart a - fire, these things I of - fer you for a life - time, A
E♭ C7 Cm7 F7
co - zy lit - tle nest just meant for us to share, per - haps a ti - ny guest will be ar - riv - ing there! My
B♭ G7(♭9) G7 Adim7
life, my love, my all, are at your beck and call, these things I of - fer you for a life - time.

From the United Artists Motion Picture "NEW YORK, NEW YORK"

THEME FROM NEW YORK, NEW YORK

Words by FRED EBB
Music by JOHN KANDER

Moderate swing
(Keyboard:)
F Gm7 Gm7/C F
Start spread-in' the news; I'm leav-ing to-day. I wan-na be a part_ of it, New York, New York. These vag-a-bond
shoes are long-ing to stray, and step a-round the heart_ of it,
blues are melt-ing a-way. I'll make a brand new start_ of it.
Gm7 C7 Gm7/C C7 F Gm7 Gm7/C
To Coda
1. 2.
Fmaj7 F7 B♭maj7 B♭m F6 Am7
New York, New York. I wan-na wake up in the cit-y that does-n't sleep to find I'm king of the hill,_
D7 Gm7 C7
_ top of the heap. My lit-tle town
D.S. al Coda
Coda
Cm7 F7 B♭ B♭m6
in old New York. If I can make it_ there,_
F D7(♯5) D7 C7/E D7/F♯ Gm7 Am B♭maj7 Gm7/C F
_ I'd make it an-y-where._ It's up to you New York, New York._
From the Paramount Television Series "STAR TREK"
THEME FROM "STAR TREK"
Copyright © 1966 and 1970 by BRUIN MUSIC COMPANY
All Rights Reserved
Words by GENE RODDENBERRY
Music by ALEXANDER COURAGE
Brightly
C A♭13 C E♭7(♯11 ♯5)
Be-yond_ the rim of the star-light_ my love_ is wan-d'ring in star flight._ I
D6 D♭9(♭5) E♭6 G7(♯5)
know he'll find in star clus-tered reach-es_ love, strange love a star-wom-an teach-es._
C A♭13 C F9(♭5) E9
I know_ his jour-ney ends nev-er; his star trek_ will go on for-ev-er._ But
F B♭9 C A7(♭9 ♯5) Dm7 G7 C D♭(4)/C D♭(4)/C C6/9
1. 2.
tell him while he wan-ders his star-ry sea re-mem-ber,_ re-mem-ber me._

THEME FROM SHAFT

Lyrics and Music by
ISAAC HAYES

Moderate funk

Fmaj9 Em7 Fmaj9

Em7 Fmaj9

1. Em7 2. Em7

G

Fmaj9 Em Fmaj9 Em

(spoken:) Who's the black private dick that's a sex machine to all the chicks? Shaft!

Fmaj9 Em Fmaj9 Em

Who is the man that would risk his life for his broth-er man? *Shaft!* *Can you dig it?*

Fmaj9 Em Fmaj9

Who's the cat that won't cop-out when there's dan-ger all a-bout? *Shaft!* *Right on!* *They say this cat Shaft is a bad mother. (Shut your mouth!)*

Em Fmaj9 Em

But I'm talkin' about Shaft. He's a com-pli-cat-ed man, but no one un-der-stands him but his wom-an. *John* *Shaft!*

G Fmaj7

N.C. Fmaj7 N.C. Em7 Fmaj7

THEME FROM "TERMS OF ENDEARMENT"

By MICHAEL GORE
Moderately, flowing
To Coda
espressivo
D.C. al Coda
Coda
dim.
rit.
THERE GOES MY EVERYTHING
Copyright © 1965 by ACUFF-ROSE MUSIC, INC. & HUSKY MUSIC
All Rights Reserved
Words and Music by
DALLAS FRAZIER
Moderately slow
Verse:
1. I hear foot-steps slow - ly walk - ing, as they gent - ly walk a - cross a lone-ly floor. And a
mem-'ry turns back the pag - es, I can see the hap-py years we had be - fore. Now the
voice is soft - ly say - ing: "Dar-ling, this will be good - bye for - ev - er - more."
love that kept this old heart beat - ing has been shat - tered by the clos - ing of the door.
Chorus:
There goes my rea - son for liv - ing, there goes the one of my dreams. There goes my
on - ly pos - ses - sion, there goes my ev - 'ry - thing. 2. As my thing.

From the 20th Century-Fox Motion Picture "ZORBA THE GREEK"

THEME FROM "ZORBA THE GREEK"

MIKIS THEODORAKIS

Slowly
A little faster
Moderately
poco accel.
Brightly
accel. poco a poco
sfz

THEN YOU CAN TELL ME GOODBYE

Words and Music by
JOHN D. LOUDERMILK

Slowly

F Dm B♭ C7 F Dm B♭ C7 F Dm B♭ C7
Kiss me each morn-ing for a mil - lion years. Hold me each eve-ning by your side. Tell me you love me for a mil - lion years.

F B♭ F B♭ F B♭ C7 F Dm B♭ C7
Then if it don't work out, then if it don't work out, then you can tell me good - bye. Sweet-en my cof-fee with a morn-ing kiss.

F Dm B♭ C7 F Dm B♭ C7 F B♭ F B♭
Sof-ten my dreams _ with your sigh. Af-ter you've loved me for a mil - lion years, then if it don't work out, then if it don't work out,

F B♭ F F7 B♭ F Dm G7 Gm7 C7
then you can tell me good - bye. If you must go, I won't grieve if you just ___ wait a life-time be-fore you leave.

F Dm B♭ C7 F Dm B♭ C7 F Dm B♭ C7
If you must go, I won't say "no" just so we can say ___ that we tried. Tell me you love me for a mil - lion years,

F B♭ F B♭ 1. F B♭ F 2. F B♭ F
then if it don't work out, then if it don't work out, then you can tell me good - bye. then you can tell me good - bye.

THERE IS A TAVERN IN THE TOWN

TRADITIONAL

Brightly

C G7
There is a tav - ern in the town, in the town. And there my dear love sits him down, sits him
dieu, a - dieu kind friends a - dieu, adieu a - dieu. I can no long - er stay with you, stay with

C C+ F G7 1. To Next Strain C G7 C Gdim7 2. Fine C
down, _ and _ drinks his wine 'mid laugh - ter ___ free, and nev - er, nev - er thinks of me. ______ Fare-thee ___
you. _ I'll _ hang my harp on a weep - ing wil - low tree, and may the world go well with thee. ___

D.S. 𝄋 al Fine
G7 C G7 C F C G7
well, for I must leave thee, do not let the part-ing grieve thee, and re - mem-ber that the best of friends must part, must part. A -

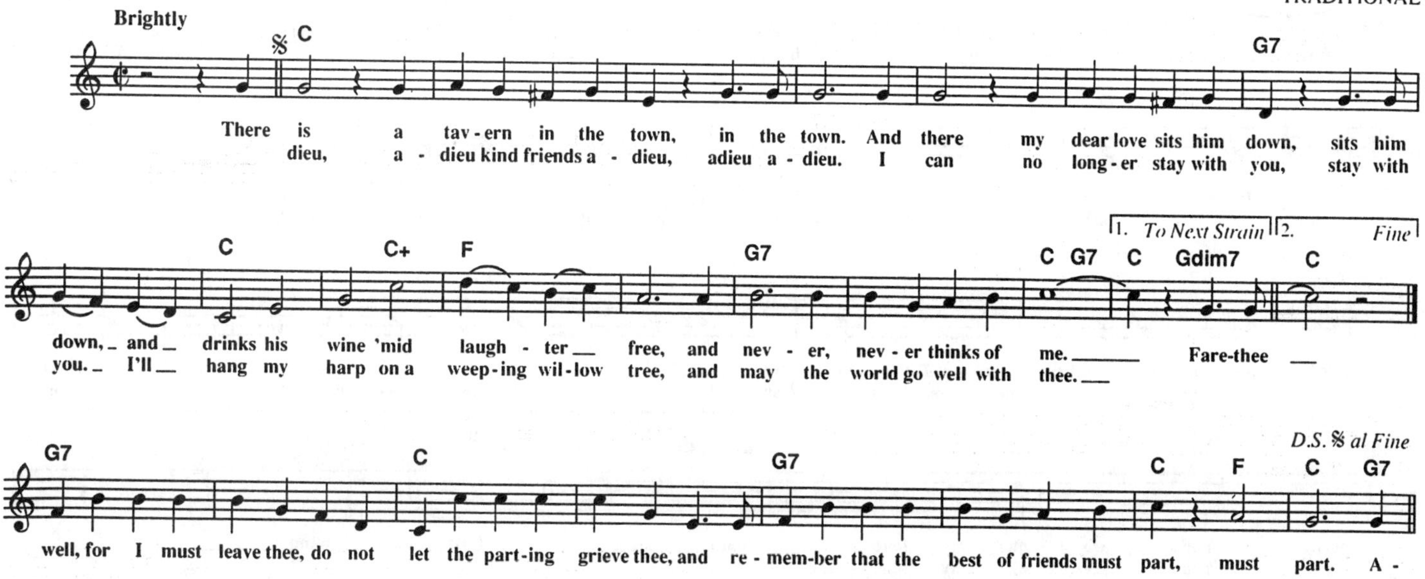

THERE GOES MY HEART

Words and Music by
BENNY DAVIS and ABNER SILVER

Moderately

B♭maj7 G+ Cm Cm7 F7

There goes my heart, there goes the one I love. There goes the {girl / boy} I was-n't

B♭ Dm7(♭5) G7 Cm G7 Cm Gm7 C7

wor-thy of. There goes my hap-pi-ness. It could-n't be! There goes some-bod-y else

Cm7/F F7 B♭maj7 G+ Cm

in place of me. Good-bye ro-mance, it could-n't last some-how. I had my

Cm7 F7 B♭ Dm7(♭5) G7 Dm7 G7 Cm

chance but it's all o-ver now. I nev-er thought that {she / he} could pass me by!

E♭m6 B♭/F Cm7 F7 1. B♭ D♭dim7 F7/C F7 2. B♭ E♭6 B♭

There goes my heart and here am I. There goes my I.

THERE'S A TEAR IN MY BEER

Words and Music by
HANK WILLIAMS

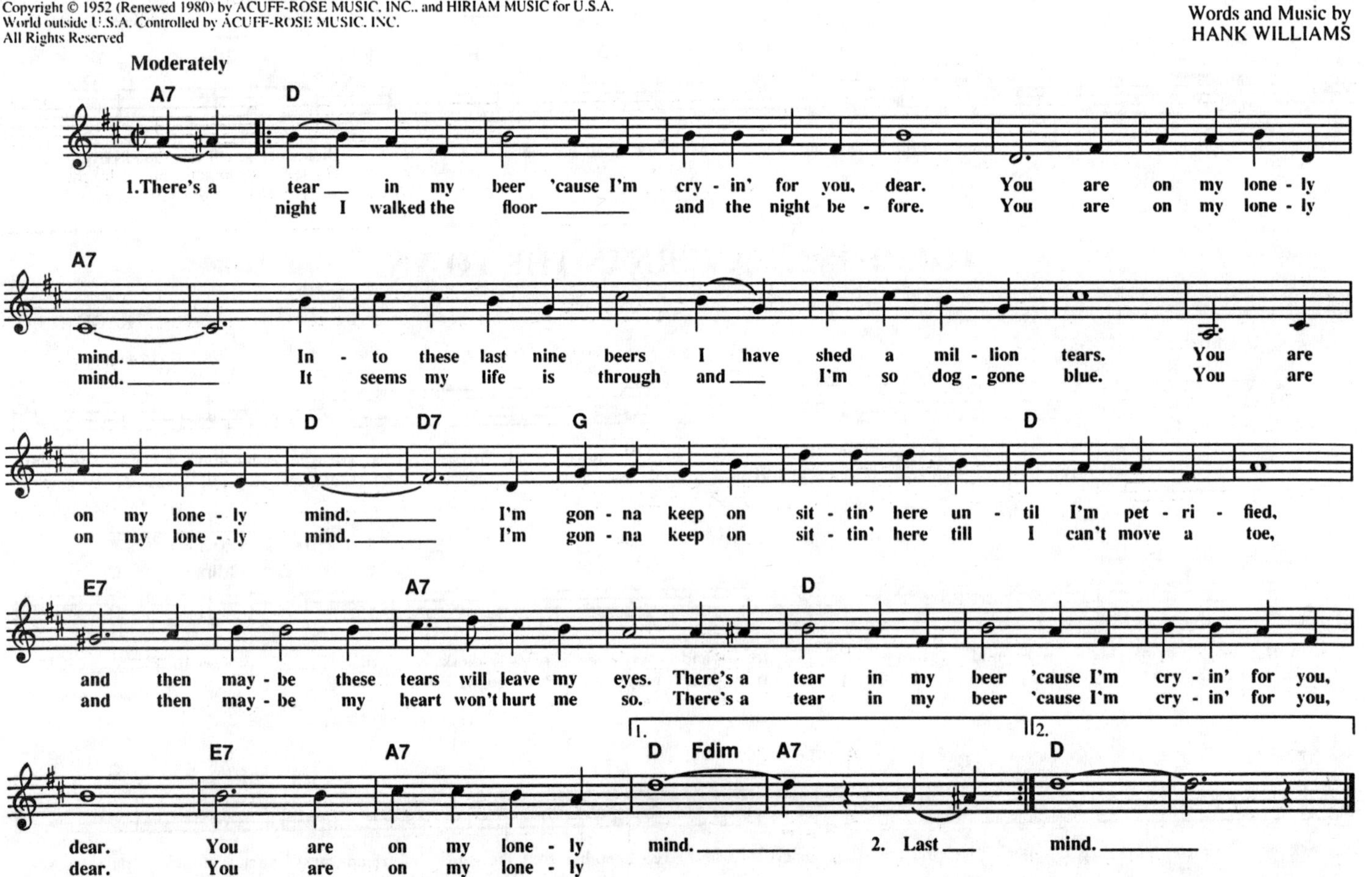
Moderately
A7 D
1.There's a tear in my beer 'cause I'm cry-in' for you, dear. You are on my lone-ly
night I walked the floor and the night be-fore. You are on my lone-ly
A7
mind. In-to these last nine beers I have shed a mil-lion tears. You are
mind. It seems my life is through and I'm so dog-gone blue. You are
D D7 G D
on my lone-ly mind. I'm gon-na keep on sit-tin' here un-til I'm pet-ri-fied,
on my lone-ly mind. I'm gon-na keep on sit-tin' here till I can't move a toe,
E7 A7 D
and then may-be these tears will leave my eyes. There's a tear in my beer 'cause I'm cry-in' for you,
and then may-be my heart won't hurt me so. There's a tear in my beer 'cause I'm cry-in' for you,
E7 A7 1. D Fdim A7 2. D
dear. You are on my lone-ly mind. 2. Last mind.
dear. You are on my lone-ly

THERE IS NO CHRISTMAS LIKE A HOME CHRISTMAS

Words by CARL SIGMAN
Music by MICKEY J. ADDY

Moderately
C Gm7/C C7 F C G7 Fmaj7 Em7 Dm7 Cmaj7 D7 Dm7 Fm6/G
There is no Christ-mas like a home Christ-mas with your dad and moth-er, sis and broth - er there.
G7 C Gm7/C C7 F C Am G7 Fmaj7 Em7 Dm7 Cmaj7 G7 C F/C C7
With their hearts hum - ming at your home - com-ing, and that mer-ry yule-tide spir - it in the air. Christ -
F F+ F6 F F+ F6 F G7 C Am E+ Am7 D9 Dm7/G C♯dim/G Dm7/G G7
mas bells, Christ - mas bells ring - ing loud and strong. Fol - low them, fol - low them, you've been a - way too long. There is no
C Gm7/C C7 F A♭7/G♭ C/G G7 Fmaj7 Em7 Dm7 G9 C Cmaj7 C7 F/C Fm/C C
Christ - mas like a home Christ - mas, for that's the time of year all roads lead home.

THIRTY-TWO FEET AND EIGHT LITTLE TAILS

(Dasher, Dancer, Prancer, Vixen, Comet, Cupid, Donner, Blitzen)

By JOHN REDMOND, JAMES CAVANAUGH and FRANK WELDON

Moderately bright

C G7 C F
Dash - er, Danc - er, Pranc - er, Vix - en. Com - et, Cu - pid, Don - ner, Blit - zen. O - ver the moon so bright;
Ol' Saint Nick he works so quick - ly leav - in' toys for girls and boys. Then o - ver the roof so high;

C F♯dim G7 C G7
1. 2.
thir-ty-two feet and eight lit-tle tails of white, hur - ry, hur - ry, hur - ry through the night. fast - er through the
thir-ty-two feet and eight lit-tle tails they fly, fast - er, fast - er,

C Dm7 Cdim C F C G7 C D7 G7
sky. Ohhh! Look at 'em go. San - ta laugh-in', "Ho, ho, ho, ho, ho, ho, ho, ho, ho."

C G7 C F C
Dash-er, Danc-er, Pranc-er, Vix-en, Com-et, Cu-pid, Don-ner, Blit-zen; o-ver the gar-den wall." Thir-ty-two feet and eight lit-tle tails an' all.

F♯dim G7 A7 G6 Cm A7 G7 C
See 'em can - ter, hear ol' San - ta call, "Mer - ry, Mer - ry Christ-mas to you all."

THERE'LL BE A HOT TIME IN THE OLD TOWN TONIGHT

HAYDEN/METZ

Brightly
G
When you hear them-a bells go ding ling ling, all join 'round, and sweet-ly you must sing. And when the
D7
1. G Am7
2. G G6
verse am through, in the cho-rus all join in: there'll be a hot time in the old town to - night.
night.

THIS MOMENT IN TIME

Words and Music by
ALAN BERNSTEIN and
RITCHIE ADAMS

Moderately slow
Verse:
B♭7(♭9)
E♭ E♭6 E♭maj7 E♭ D7sus G7 Cm7 E♭+
1. This mo-ment in time, this right time of day. Oh, I love be-ing with you and
(2.) time, this time - less em-brace, and like a kid in a store, I'll
(3.) time, this right time of day. Oh, I love be-ing with you and
(4.5.etc.) la. (ad lib. lyric)
Cm7 Cm6 B♭m7
1.4.5.etc.
E♭7 A♭maj7 Fm7 Gm7 Cm7
watch-ing my life at play.
al - ways want more to taste.
watch-ing my life at play.
My love in your eyes is light-ing my dreams, and the

Repeat ad lib. and fade
F9 F6/9 F7 Fm7 B♭7 B♭7(♭9)
2.3.
E♭7 A♭maj7
feel-ings you choose have touch-es of blues and greens. This mo - ment in (2.3.) And no mat - ter what comes, I know the
1. To Next Strain
D7 Gm Gm7 C7(♭9) Fm7 Gm7 Fm7 Emaj7(♯9) E♭ Fm7 /B♭
sun is gon - na shine; be - cause of you and me there'll be this mo - ment in time.
2.
D.S. 𝄋
Bridge:
E♭ Fm7 F♯dim7 E♭/G B♭7 Cm7 Fm7 G7sus G7
time. La la la la More than a rip - ple, less than a splash, the heir to a long line of

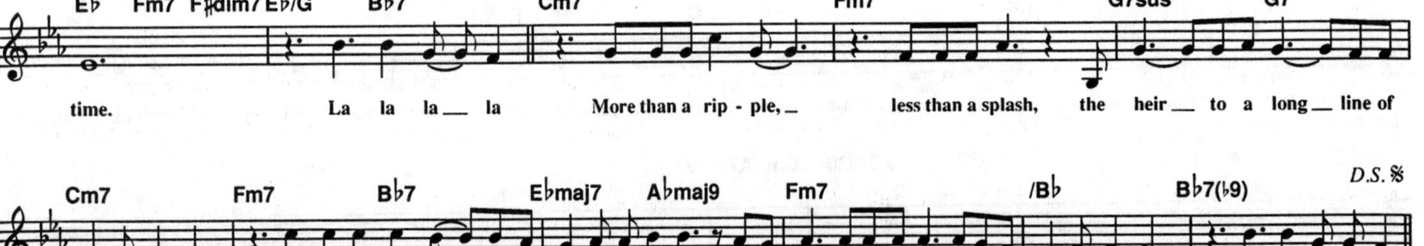
D.S. 𝄋
Cm7 Fm7 B♭7 E♭maj7 A♭maj9 Fm7 /B♭ B♭7(♭9)
glo - ry. Give me the morn-ing, and I'll give you a song; it's so good be-ing part of the sto - ry. 3. This mo-ment in

THEY DIDN'T BELIEVE ME

Words by HERBERT REYNOLDS
Music by JEROME KERN

Moderately

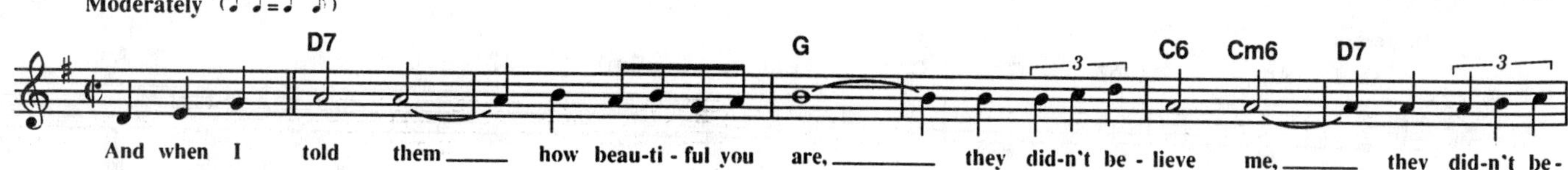
D7
G
C6
Cm6
D7
And when I told them how beau-ti-ful you are, they did-n't be-lieve me, they did-n't be-

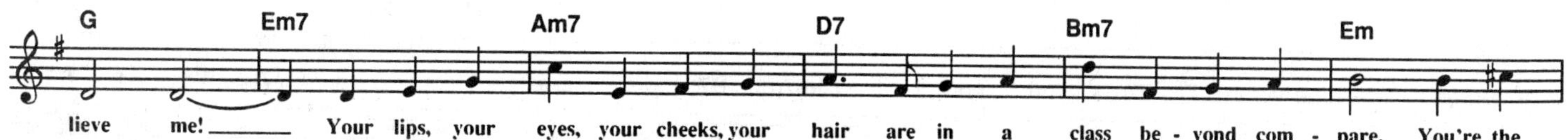
G
Em7
Am7
D7
Bm7
Em
lieve me! Your lips, your eyes, your cheeks, your hair are in a class be-yond com-pare. You're the

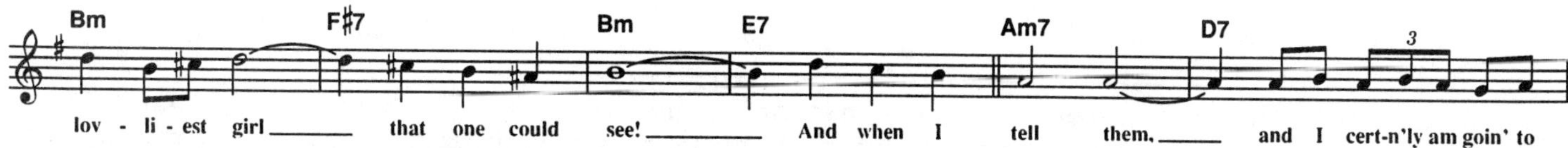
Bm
F#7
Bm
E7
Am7
D7
lov-li-est girl that one could see! And when I tell them, and I cert-n'ly am goin' to

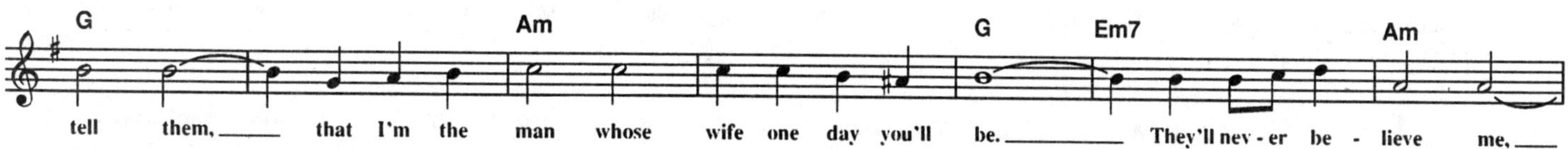
G
Am
G
Em7
Am
tell them, that I'm the man whose wife one day you'll be. They'll nev-er be-lieve me,

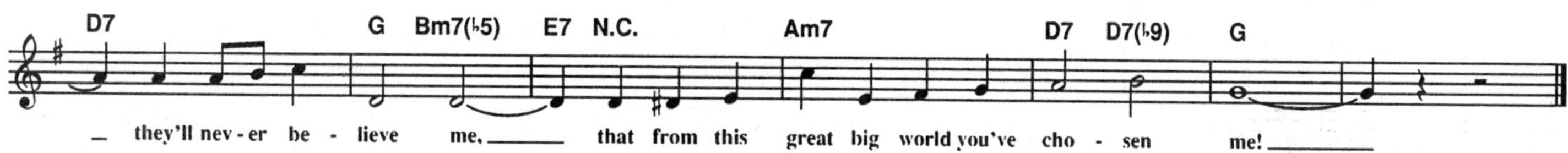
D7
G
Bm7(♭5)
E7
N.C.
Am7
D7
D7(♭9)
G
they'll nev-er be-lieve me, that from this great big world you've cho-sen me!

THIS OLD MAN

TRADITIONAL

Moderately

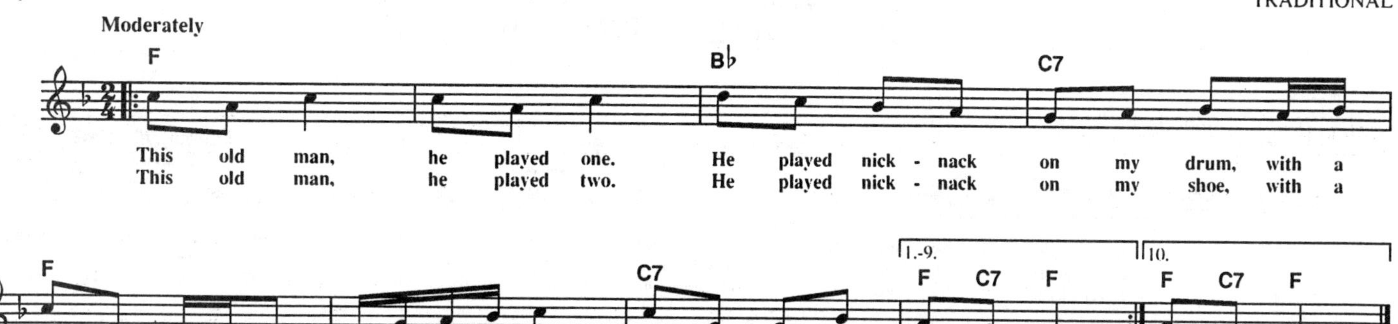
F
B♭
C7
This old man, he played one. He played nick-nack on my drum, with a
This old man, he played two. He played nick-nack on my shoe, with a
F
C7
1.-9.
F C7 F
10.
F C7 F
nick-nack, pad-dy whack, give a dog a bone. This old man came roll-ing home. roll-ing home.
nick-nack, pad-dy whack, give a dog a bone. This old man came roll-ing home.

Verse 3:
This old man, he played three.
He played nicknack on my knee,
With a nicknack, paddy whack,
Give a dog a bone.
This old man came rolling home.

Verse 4:
This old man, he played four.
He played nicknack on my door,
With a nicknack, paddy whack,
Give a dog a bone.
This old man came rolling home.

Verse 5:
This old man, he played five.
He played nicknack on the hive,
With a nicknack, paddy whack,
Give a dog a bone.
This old man came rolling home.

Verse 6:
This old man, he played six.
He played nicknack on my sticks,
With a nicknack, paddy whack,
Give a dog a bone.
This old man came rolling home.

Verse 7:
This old man, he played seven.
He played nicknack up in heaven,
With a nicknack, paddy whack,
Give a dog a bone.
This old man came rolling home.

Verse 8:
This old man, he played eight.
He played nicknack on my gate,
With a nicknack, paddy whack,
Give a dog a bone.
This old man came rolling home.

Verse 9:
This old man, he played nine.
He played nicknack on the line,
With a nicknack, paddy whack,
Give a dog a bone.
This old man came rolling home.

Verse 10:
This old man, he played ten.
He played nicknack once again,
With a nicknack, paddy whack,
Give a dog a bone.
This old man cam rolling home.

TIME AFTER TIME

Words by SAMMY CAHN
Music by JULE STYNE

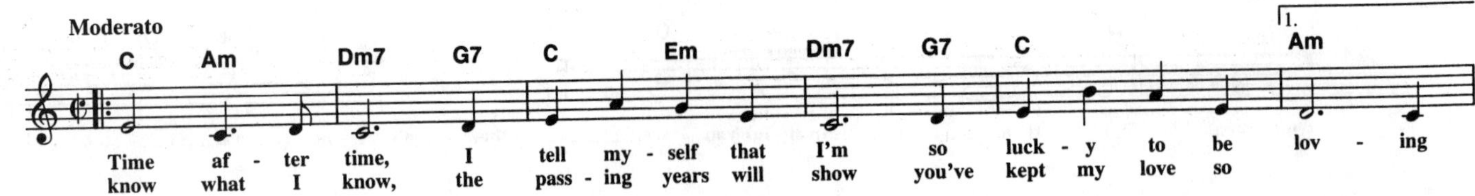
Moderato
C Am Dm7 G7 C Em Dm7 G7 C Am
1.
Time af - ter time, I tell my - self that I'm so luck - y to be lov - ing
know what I know, the pass - ing years will show you've kept my love so

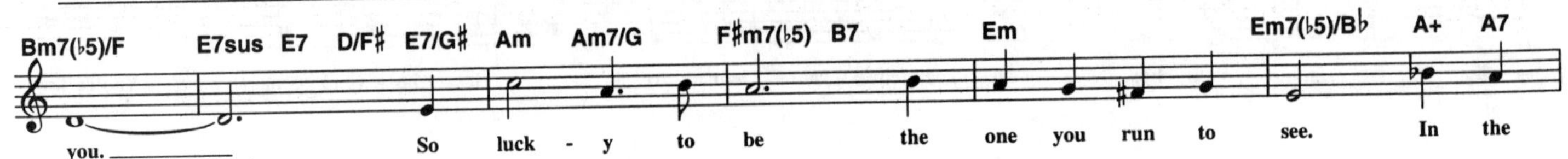
Bm7(♭5)/F E7sus E7 D/F♯ E7/G♯ Am Am7/G F♯m7(♭5) B7 Em Em7(♭5)/B♭ A+ A7
you. So luck - y to be the one you run to see. In the

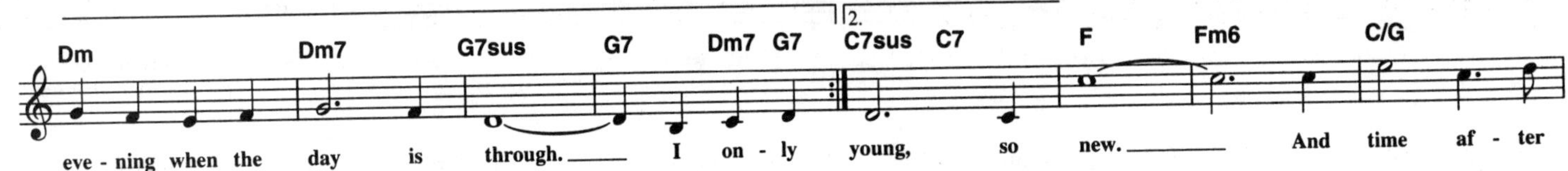
Dm Dm7 G7sus G7 Dm7 G7 C7sus C7 F Fm6 C/G
2.
eve - ning when the day is through. I on - ly young, so new. And time af - ter

F♯m7/(♭5) Fm6 Em7 Am D7 D7sus D7/A C/G Am Dm7 G7 C Em Dm7 G13 C
time, you'll hear me say that I'm so luck - y to be lov - ing you.

Theme Melody from the 20th Century-Fox CinemaScope Production "THREE COINS IN THE FOUNTAIN"

THREE COINS IN THE FOUNTAIN

Words by SAMMY CAHN
Music by JULE STYNE

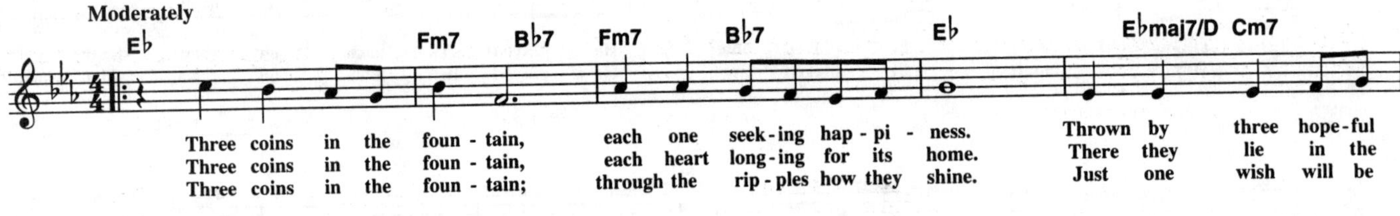
Moderately
E♭ Fm7 B♭7 Fm7 B♭7 E♭ E♭maj7/D Cm7
Three coins in the foun - tain, each one seek - ing hap - pi - ness. Thrown by three hope - ful
Three coins in the foun - tain, each heart long - ing for its home. There they lie in the
Three coins in the foun - tain; through the rip - ples how they shine. Just one wish will be

To Coda
1.
2.
F7 A♭m6 B♭7 E♭ E♭ A♭ E♭
lov - ers; which one will the foun - tain bless? Rome. Which one will the foun - tain bless?
foun - tain some - where in the heart of
grant - ed; one heart will wear a val - en -

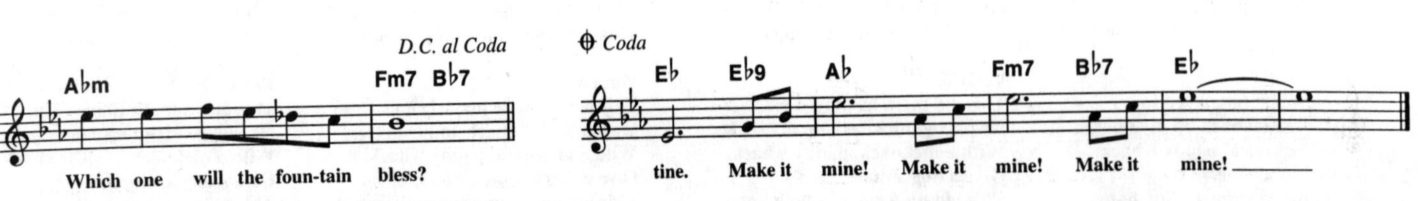
D.C. al Coda
Coda
A♭m Fm7 B♭7 E♭ E♭9 A♭ Fm7 B♭7 E♭
Which one will the foun - tain bless? tine. Make it mine! Make it mine! Make it mine!

THOSE GOOD OLD DREAMS

Words by JOHN BETTIS
Music by RICHARD CARPENTER

Moderately
Gb Gb6 Gbmaj7 Gb6 Gb Gb6 Abm7
As a child I was known for make-be-liev - in'; all a-lone, I cre-at - ed fan-ta-sies.
of a long for-got-ten fire; you're a touch of a slow - ly grow-in' wind;
Db Abm7 Abm7/Db Db Cbm/Db Db7 Gb
As I grew peo-ple called it self-de-ceiv - in'; but my heart helped me hold the mem-o - ries.
you're a taste of the ev - er chang-ing sea - sons tell-in' me there are some things that don't end.
Gb6 Gbmaj7 Gb6 Gb Gb6 Gbmaj7 Gb6
As I walk through the world I find a-round me some-thing new
We have left all the dark - ness far be-hind us; all those hopes
Gb Gb6 Gb7 Cb Db/Cb Bbm7 Eb7 Abm7 Db Gbmaj7
yet fa-mil - iar's in the air. I feel it ev - 'ry-where. Like a child's eyes on a Christ-mas night,
that we held a-long the way have made it to this day. Like an old love song gone for much too long,
Gdim Abm7 Cb/Db Db Eb Ebmaj7 Eb6 Eb
I'm look-in' at you now, find-in' an - swers to my prayers. It's a new
you hear it once a-gain, and it car - ries you a - way.
Fm7 Ab/Bb Bb7 Eb Ebmaj7 Eb7
day for those good old dreams; one by one it seems they're com - in' true. Here's a morn -
Fm7 Ab/Bb Eb Fm7/Eb Eb
in' that my heart had seen; here's a morn - in' that just had to come through. Same old
Fm7 Ab/Bb Bb7 Eb Eb/D Db6
stage but what a change of scene. No more dark hor-i - zons, on - ly blue. It's a new
C7 Fm7 Ab/Bb Gb Abm7/Gb Gb Abm7/Gb
1. D.S. 𝄋
day for those good old dreams. All my life I dreamed of lov - ing you. You're a spark
2.
Eb Bbm7/Eb Eb Abmaj7 Ab/Bb Eb Ebsus Eb
I dreamed of you. It's a new day for those good old dreams, and it's all be-cause of

THREE O'CLOCK IN THE MORNING

Words by DOROTHY TERRISS
Music by JULIAN ROBLEDO

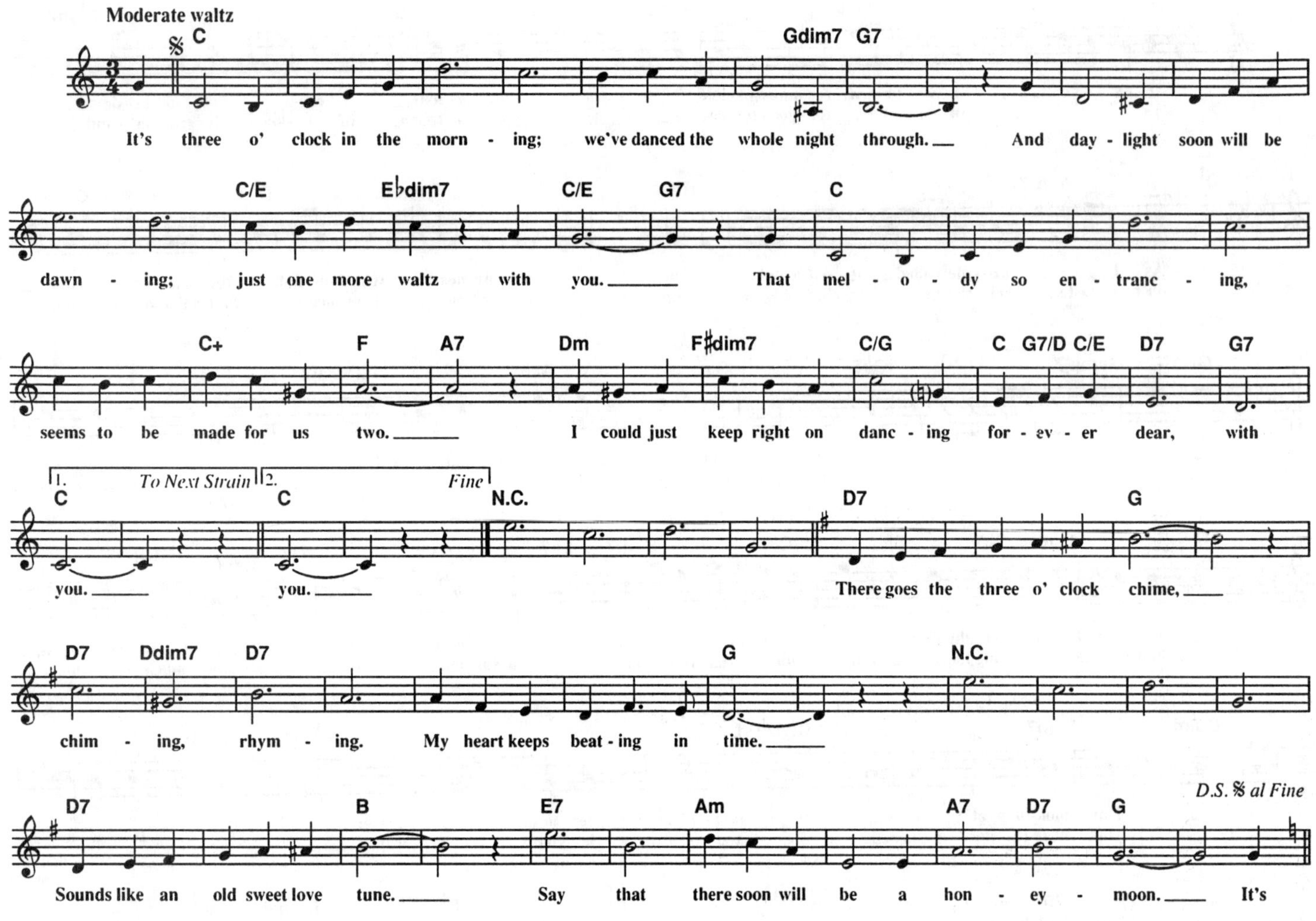

Moderate waltz

C Gdim7 G7

It's three o' clock in the morn - ing; we've danced the whole night through. And day - light soon will be

C/E E♭dim7 C/E G7 C

dawn - ing; just one more waltz with you. That mel - o - dy so en - tranc - ing,

C+ F A7 Dm F♯dim7 C/G C G7/D C/E D7 G7

seems to be made for us two. I could just keep right on danc - ing for - ev - er dear, with

1. *To Next Strain* 2. *Fine*

C C N.C. D7 G

you. you. There goes the three o' clock chime,

D7 Ddim7 D7 G N.C.

chim - ing, rhym - ing. My heart keeps beat - ing in time.

D.S. 𝄋 al Fine

D7 B E7 Am A7 D7 G

Sounds like an old sweet love tune. Say that there soon will be a hon - ey - moon. It's

TIGER RAG
(Hold That Tiger!)

Words by HARRY DeCOSTA
Music by ORIGINAL DIXIELAND JAZZ BAND

Bright two-beat

G D7

Where's that Ti - ger? Where's that Ti - ger? Where's that Ti - ger? Where's that Ti - ger? Hold that

G D7 G

Ti - ger! Hold that Ti - ger! Hold that Ti - ger! Choke him, poke him, kick him and soak him! Where's that

G7 C C♯dim7

Ti - ger? Where's that Ti - ger? Where, oh where can he be? Low or

G/D E7 A7 D7 D7(♯5) 1. G 2. G

high - brow, they all cry now, "Please play that Ti-ger Rag for me." me."

TIME IN A BOTTLE

Words and Music by
JIM CROCE

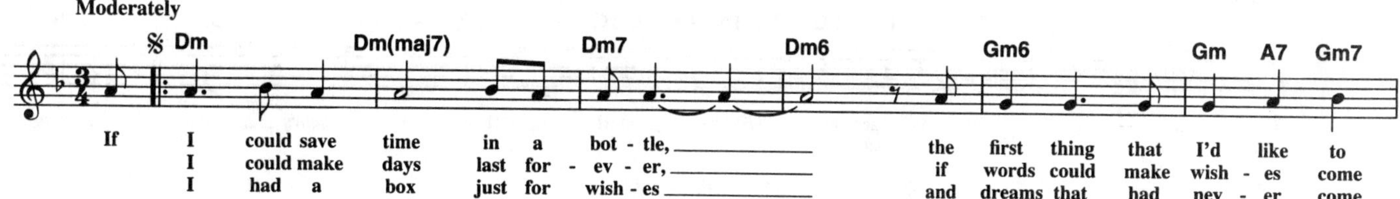
Moderately
Dm Dm(maj7) Dm7 Dm6 Gm6 Gm A7 Gm7
If I could save time in a bot - tle, the first thing that I'd like to
I could make days last for - ev - er, if words could make wish - es come
I had a box just for wish - es and dreams that had nev - er come

A7 Dm6 A7 Dm A7 Dm Dm7 B♭ Gm7 Dm Gm
do is to save ev - 'ry - day 'til e - ter - ni - ty pass - es a - way just to spend them with
true; I'd save ev - 'ry - day like a treas - ure and then a - gain I would spend them with
true the box would be emp - ty ex - cept for the mem - 'ry of how they were an - swered by

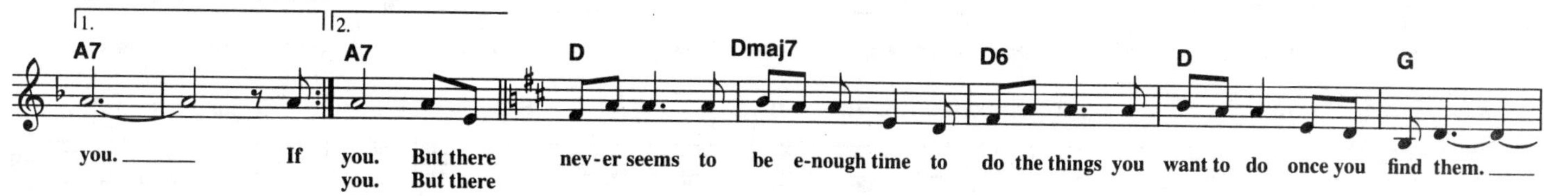
1. 2.
A7 A7 D Dmaj7 D6 D G
you. If you. But there nev - er seems to be e - nough time to do the things you want to do once you find them.
you. But there

Gmaj7 Em7 A7 D Dmaj7 D6 D G
I've looked a - round e - nough to know that you're the one I want to go thru time with.

Last time To Coda D.S. (with repeat) al Coda
Coda
Gmaj7 Em7 A7 A7 Dm (Repeat 3x)
If

THREE TO GET READY

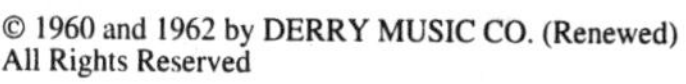

By DAVE BRUBECK

Light and playful
C C7 F G7 C F Dm7 G F F7 Em7 A7

Dm7 G7 C C7 F G7(♭9) 1. C 2. C Cm C7 Cm

THROUGH THE YEARS

Words by EDWARD HEYMAN
Music by VINCENT YOUMANS

Slowly

C F/C C7/B♭ F/A C/G F6 Dm7(♭5) C2/G G9 G7 C C7 F/A C/E
Through the years, I'll take my place, be - side you, smil - ing through the years. Through your

F6 G/F C/E Dm7 G C/E Am7 G/D Am7 D9 G C B♭6 F/A
tears, I'll keep my place be - side you; smil - ing through your tears. I'll be near, no mat-ter when or

C7/G Fmaj7 F7 B♭maj7 Bm7(♭5) F/C Dm7(♭5) C/G Gm7(♭5) Am7
where. Re - mem - ber, what is mine, I'll al - ways share. Through the night, I'll be a star to

Fm(♯7) Fm6 C/G Fmaj9 Em7(♭5) A7(♭9) A7 Dm7 /C Bm7(♭5)
guide you, shin - ing bright, though clouds may come and hide you. Through the years till love

F/A F Dm7(♭5) C/G D7/G C+/G D7/G C/G F/G C/G G7sus C
is gone and time first dis - ap - pears. I'll come to you, smil-ing through the years.

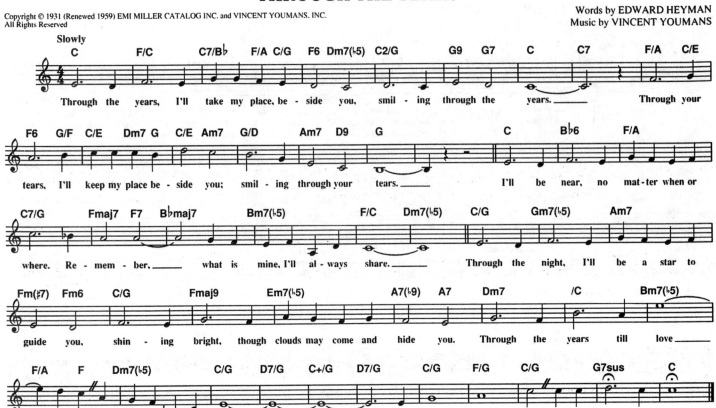

From the United Artists Motion Picture "THUNDERBALL"

THUNDERBALL

Words by DON BLACK
Music by JOHN BARRY

Moderately
Gm Cm7 Gm Gm7 Gm6 Gm A♭ D7 Gm Gm7 Gm6 Gm
He al - ways runs while oth - ers walk. He acts while oth - er men just talk. He
He knows the mean-ing of suc - cess. His needs are more, so he gives less. They
Cm D7 Bm Bm(♯5) Bm6 Bm(♯5) Cm 1. A7(♭5) D7 D7(♯9) D7(♭9)
looks at this world and wants it all, so he strikes like Thun - der - ball.
call him the win - ner who takes all, and he strikes like
2. D7 Gm Gm7 Gm6 Gm Cm Fm7 G A♭maj7 Fm7 Dm7(♭5) D7
Thun - der - ball. An - y wom-an he wants he'll get. He will break an - y heart with-out re -
Gm Am7(♭5) D7 Gm Cm7 Gm Gm7 Gm6 Gm A♭ D7 Gm Gm7
gret. His days of ask - ing are all gone. His fight goes on and on and on,
Gm6 Gm Cm D7 Bm Bm(♯5) Bm6 Bm(♯5) Cm D7 Gm
but he thinks the fight is worth it all, so he strikes like Thun - der - ball.

TICO TICO

(Tico Tico No Fuba)

Music by ZEQUINHA ABREU
English Lyrics by ERVIN DRAKE

Bright samba

Am E7 E7 Am
Oh Ti - co - Ti - co tick! _ Oh Ti - co - Ti - co tock! _ This Ti - co - Ti - co he's the cuck-oo in my clock. And when he

Dm Am Am7 B7 E Am
says: "Cuck - oo!" _ he means it's time to woo; _ it's "Ti - co - time" for all the lov-ers in the block. I've got a heav-y date _ a tete - a -

E7 Am Dm Am
tete at eight, _ so speak, oh Ti - co, tell me is it get-ting late? If I'm on time: "Cuck - oo!" _ but if I'm late, "Woo - woo!" _ The one my

E7 Am C G7
heart has gone to may not want to wait! For just a bir-die, and a bir-die who goes no - where. He know of ev-'ry Lov-ers' Lane and how to

C A+ Dm G7 C G7
go there. For in af - fairs of the heart, _ my Ti-co's ter - ri - bly smart, _He tells me: "Gent-ly sen - ti - ment-'ly at the start!" Oh-oh, I

C G7 C Dm F♯dim7
hear my lit - tle Ti - co - Ti - co call - ing, be-cause the time is right and shades of night are fall - ing. I love that not-so-cuck-oo cuck-oo in the

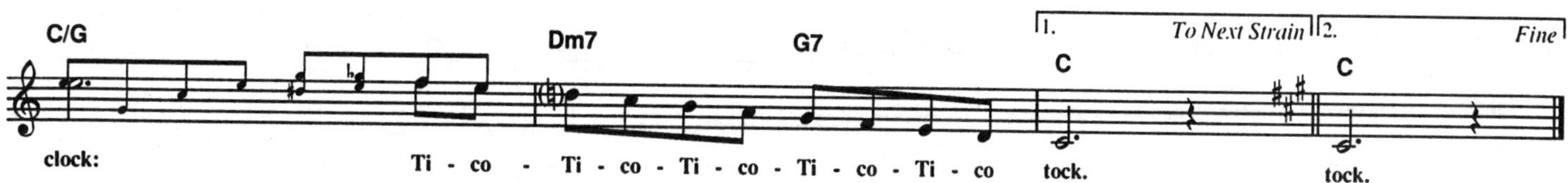
C/G Dm7 G7
1. To Next Strain C
2. Fine C
clock: Ti - co - Ti - co - Ti - co - Ti - co - Ti - co tock. tock.

Interlude:

A Amaj7 A6 A A6 A E7

A Amaj7 A6

F♯7 Bm D B7/D♯ A/E E7 A
D.S. 𝄋 al Fine

TIE A YELLOW RIBBON ROUND THE OLE OAK TREE

Words and Music by
IRWIN LEVINE and L. RUSSELL BROWN

Moderately bright swing

F Am Gm C7

Verse:

F Am Cm D7

1. I'm com-in' home I've done my time, now I've got to know what is and is-n't mine.
2. Bus driv-er, please look for me, 'cause I could-n't bear to see what I might see.

Gm B♭m Dm

If you re-ceived my let-ter tell-in' you I'd soon be free,
I'm real-ly still in pris-on and my love she holds the key. A

G7 B♭m6 C7 B♭m6 C7

Then you'll know just what to do if you still want me, if you still want me.
sim-ple yel-low rib-bon's what I need to set me free, I wrote and told her please:

Chorus:

F Am Cm

Tie a yel-low rib-bon 'round the ole oak tree. It's been three long years, do ya

D7 Gm B♭m F A7/C♯ Dm

still want me? If I don't see a rib-bon 'round the ole oak tree I'll

F/C F+/C♯ Dm D7 Gm B♭m

stay on the bus, for-get a-bout us, put the blame on me, if I don't see a yel-low rib-bon

Gm7 C7 1. F Dm Gm C7

'round the ole oak tree.

2. F *Rubato* Gm B♭m F D7

tree. Now the whole damn bus is cheer-ing and I can't be-lieve I see a

a tempo Gm B♭m Gm7 C7 F

hun-dred yel-low rib-bons 'round the ole oak tree.

TIJUANA TAXI

Music by ERVAN F. COLEMAN

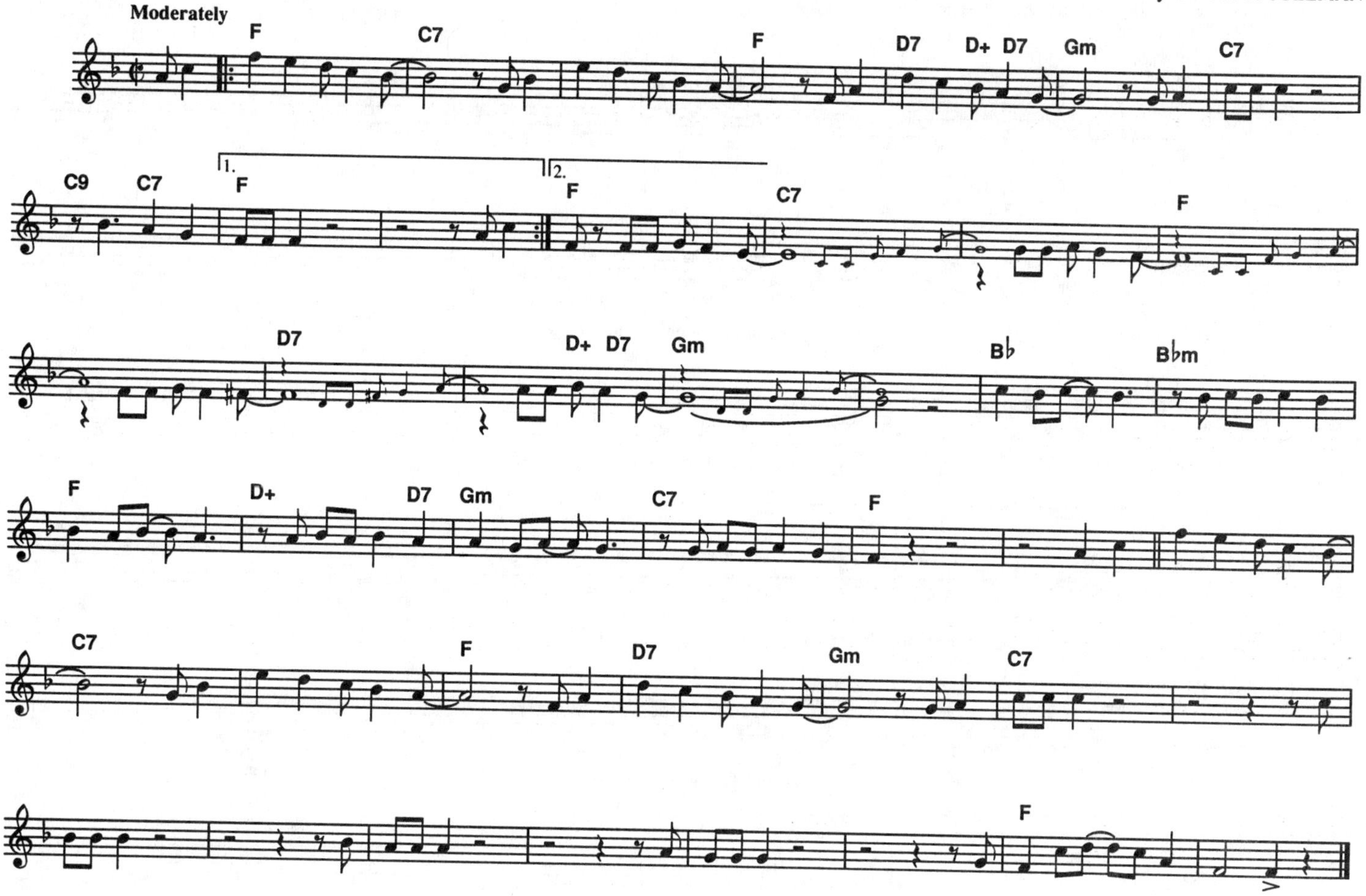

Moderately

From the Paramount Picture "ROMEO AND JULIET"

A TIME FOR US

(Love Theme from "ROMEO AND JULIET")

Words by LARRY KUSIK and EDDIE SNYDER
Music by NINO ROTA

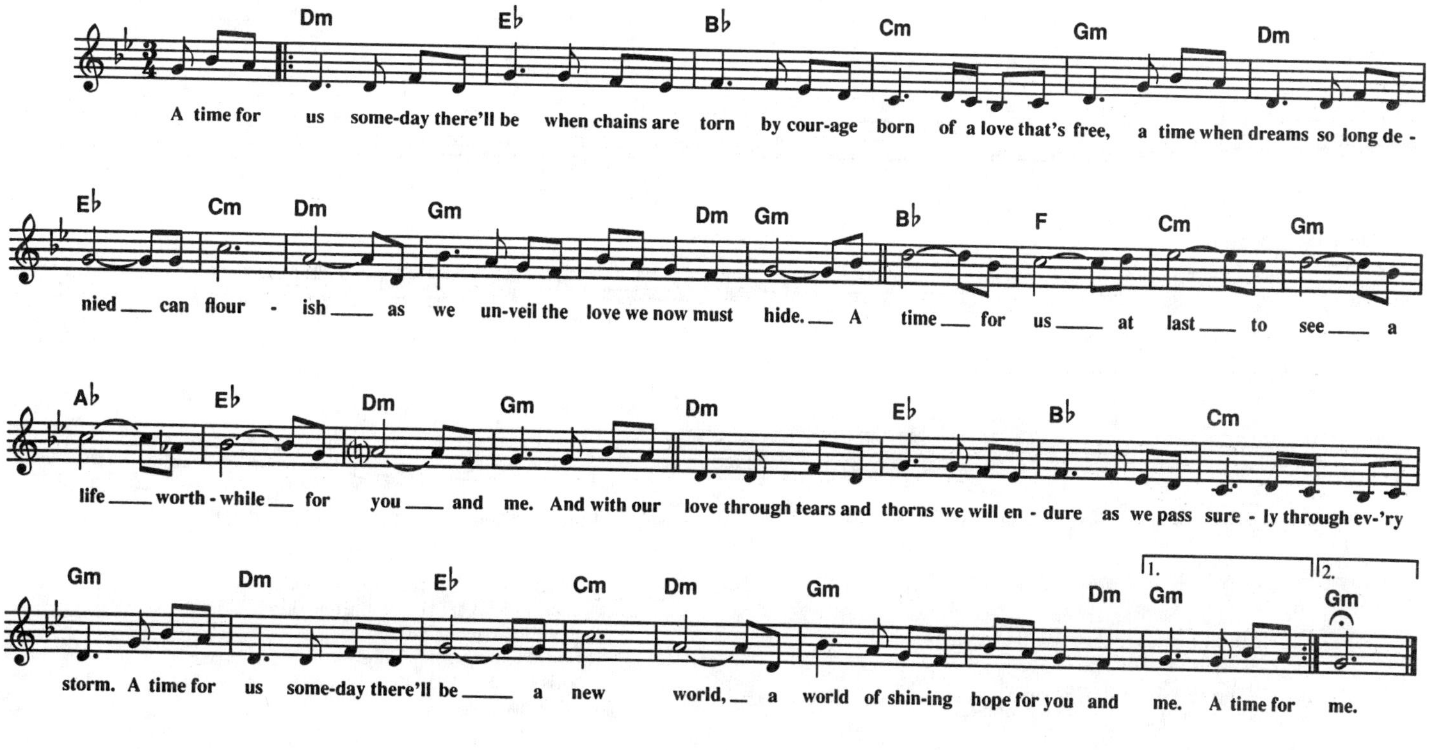

Slowly and very expressively

A time for us some-day there'll be when chains are torn by cour-age born of a love that's free, a time when dreams so long de-nied ___ can flour - ish ___ as we un-veil the love we now must hide. ___ A time ___ for us ___ at last ___ to see ___ a life ___ worth - while ___ for you ___ and me. And with our love through tears and thorns we will en - dure as we pass sure - ly through ev-'ry storm. A time for us some-day there'll be ___ a new world, ___ a world of shin-ing hope for you and me. A time for me.

From the Vestron Motion Picture "DIRTY DANCING"

(I'VE HAD) THE TIME OF MY LIFE

Words and Music by
FRANKE PREVITE, DONALD MARKOWITZ
and JOHN DeNICOLA

Moderately
(Bass:)
1. I've been
Verse:
wait-ing for so long, now I've fi-n'lly found some-one to stand by me.
We saw the writ-ing on the wall as we felt this mag-i-cal fan-ta-sy.
Now with pas-sion in our eyes there's no way we could dis-guise it se-cret-ly.
Omit these measures 2nd time
So we take each oth-er's hand, 'cause we seem to un-der-stand the ur-gen-cy.
Just re-mem-ber: you're the one thing I can't get e-nough of, so I'll tell you some-thing, this could be love. Be-cause
Chorus:
I've had the time of my life; no, I nev-er felt this way be-fore. Yes, I swear it's the truth, and I owe it all to you.
I've had the time of my life, and I've searched through ev-'ry o-pen door till I've found the truth,
D.S.
2. With my
2.4.5.etc.
Repeat ad lib. and fade
owe it all to you. Be-cause owe it all to you.
(Instr. solo ad lib. . .
D Pedal
. . . end solo)
I've had the time of my life, and I nev-er felt this way be-fore. Yes, I swear it's the truth, and I owe it all to you.
D.S.S.
E D/E F♯7sus B7sus C♯m D G A B D/F♯ E/G♯ D/A B7sus

Verse 2:
With my body and soul
I want you more than you'll ever know.
So we'll just let it go,
Don't be afraid to lose control.
Yes, I know what's on your mind
When you say, "Stay with me tonight."
Just remember: you're the one thing
I can't get enough of,
So I'll tell you something,
This could be love. Because . . .
(To Chorus:)

TIRED OF BEING ALONE

Lyrics and Music by AL GREEN

Moderately
Chorus:
C
Cmaj7
C7
Am
A7
I'm so tired __ of be-in' a-lone. I'm so tired _ of no love. _ Won't you help _ me, girl, _ just as soon _ as you can? _
1. Peo-

Verse:
D
Dmaj7
D7
Bm
B7
G
A
G
- ple say _ that I've _ found a way to make _ you say _ that you love ______ me. ____
Hey, ba-by, you did-n't go for that.

A
G
A
Dm7/G
1.
2.
It's a nat-'ral fact
that I wan-na come back.
Show me where it's
at, ____ ba - by. I'm so tired _
will. ____

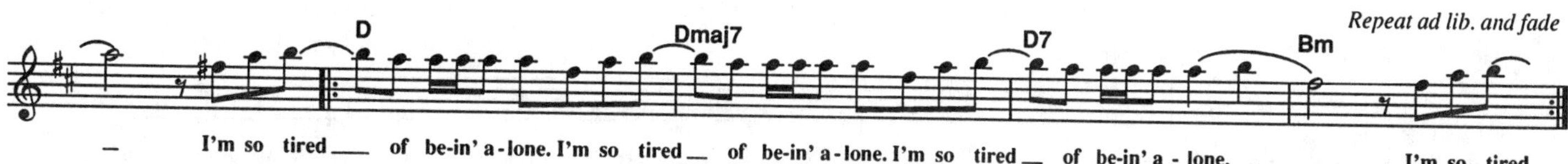
D
Dmaj7
D7
Bm
Repeat ad lib. and fade
_ I'm so tired ___ of be-in' a-lone. I'm so tired _ of be-in' a-lone. I'm so tired _ of be-in' a - lone. ______
I'm so tired _

Verse 2:
I guess you know that I love you so,
Even though you don't want me no more.
I've cried tears, honey, through the years.
I'll tell it like it is, honey, love me if you will.

TO A WILD ROSE

EDWARD MacDOWELL

Moderately
G
D7
G
A7
D9
Bm
D9
G
D7
Em
A7
G
Bm
D9
G
D7
C
Cdim
G
Cmaj7
Gdim
Gmaj7
Gdim
D7
Am6
G
D7
G
A7
D9
Bm
D9
G
D7
C
Cdim
G
Gdim
C
Cdim
G
Cdim
G
Em6
D7
G

TO EACH HIS OWN
Copyright © 1946 (Renewed 1973) by PARAMOUNT MUSIC CORPORATION
All Rights Reserved
Words and Music by
JAY LIVINGSON and RAY EVANS
Moderately
A rose must re - main with the sun and the rain or its love - ly prom - ise won't come true. To each his own, to each his own and my own is you. What
good is a song if the words just don't be - long and a dream must be a dream for two. No good a - lone, to each his own
for me there's you. If a flame is to grow there must be a glow, to o - pen each door there's a key. I need you, I know. I can't let you go. Your touch means too much to me. Two lips must in - sist on two more to be kissed or they'll nev - er know what love can do. To each his own, I've found my own one and on - ly you.
TO ME
Copyright © 1983 by COLLINS COURT MUSIC, INC. and LODGE HALL MUSIC, INC.
All Rights Reserved
Words and Music by
MACK DAVID and MIKE REID
Slowly and expressively
Verse:
To me, you are the hand that I reach for when I've lost my way. To me, you are the first star of eve - ning, the sun that warms my day.
me, you are the truth I be-lieve in; I be-lieve in you. To me, you are the love I have looked for my whole life through.
Chorus:
Just as sure as I'm sure there's a heav - en, this was meant to be. No road is too long as long as you be - long to me. To to me.

From the M-G-M Motion Picture "ADVANCE TO THE REAR"

TODAY

Words and Music by
RANDY SPARKS

Slowly Chorus:
F Dm Gm7 C7 F Dm Gm7 C7 F
To - day while the blos-soms still cling to the vine, I'll taste your straw - ber-ries, I'll drink your sweet wine. A mil-lion to -
F7 Bb Bbm F Dm Gm7 C9
mor-rows shall all pass a - way, ere I for - get all the joy that is mine,
1.2. To Next Strain
F Dm Gm C7
to - day.
1. 2. I
3. Fine Verse:
F Dm Gm7 Gm7/C F
day.
F Dm Gm C7 F Dm
(1.) I'll be a dan - dy and I'll be a rov - er. You'll know who I am by the
(2.) can't be con - tent - ed with yes - ter-day's glo - ry. I can't live on prom - is - es
Gm7 C7 F Dm Gm C7 Bb C7 F C7 D.S.
song that I sing. I'll feast at your ta - ble; I'll sleep in your clo - ver. Who cares what to - mor-row shall bring.
win - ter to spring. To - day is my mo-ment and now is my sto - ry. I'll laugh, and I'll cry, and I'll sing.
To-

TOMORROW

Words by MARTIN CHARNIN
Music by CHARLES STROUSE

Slowly

F Fmaj7 Bbmaj7 Am7 Dm Bbmaj7 C
The sun-'ll come out to - mor-row, bet your bot-tom dol-lar that to - mor-row there'll be sun! Just

F Fmaj7 Bbmaj7 Am7 Dm Bbmaj7 Csus C
think-in' a - bout to - mor-row clears a-way the cob-webs and the sor-row till there's none. When I'm stuck with a

Fm Db Eb Ab Abmaj7 C7sus C7
day that's gray and lone - ly, I just stick out my chin and grin and say: Oh! The

F Fmaj7 Bbmaj7 Am7 Dm Gbmaj7 C7sus C7
sun-'ll come out to - mor - row, { so you / oh! I } got to hang on till to - mor-row come what may! To -

F Fmaj7 F7 Bb F C7sus C7
mor-row, to - mor-row I love ya to - mor-row, you're { al - ways / on - ly } a day a - way!

1. F Fmaj7 Bbmaj7 C7sus
The

2. F C7sus
way! To -

F Fmaj7 F7 Bb F C7sus C7 F Fmaj7 Bbmaj7 C7sus F
mor-row, to - mor-row, I love ya to - mor-row, you're al - ways a day a - way!

TONIGHT, I CELEBRATE MY LOVE

Copyright © 1983 SCREEN GEMS-EMI MUSIC INC., ALMO MUSIC CORP. and PRINCE STREET MUSIC
All Rights Administered by SCREEN GEMS-EMI MUSIC INC. and ALMO MUSIC CORP.
All Rights Reserved
By MICHAEL MASSER
and GERRY GOFFIN
Slowly
(Keyboard:)
1. To - night I cel - e - brate my love for you; it seems the nat - u - ral thing to do. To - night no one's gon - na find us; we'll leave the world be - hind us,
night I cel - e - brate my love for you; and hope that deep in - side you feel it too. To - night our spir - its will be climb - ing to a sky lit up with dia - monds,
night I cel - e - brate my love for you, and soon this old world will seem brand new. To - night we will both dis - cov - er how friends turn in - to lov - ers,
when I make love to you.
2. To - love to you to - night. To -
To Next Strain
3. love to you.
Chorus:
To - night I cel - e - brate my love for you, and the mid-night sun is gon-na come shin - in' through. To - night there'll be no dis-tance be - tween us. What I want most to do is to get close to you to - night.
D.S.
3. To - night; I cel - e - brate my love for you, to - night.
TOOT, TOOT, TOOTSIE!
(Good-bye)
Copyright © 1922 (Renewed 1950) EMI FEIST CATALOG INC.
All Rights Reserved
Words and Music by
GUS KAHN, ERNIE ERDMAN,
DAN RUSSO and TED FIORITO
Brightly
To Coda
Toot, Toot, Toot - sie, good - bye! Toot, Toot, Toot - sie, don't cry.
Kiss me, Toot - sie, and then, Do it o - ver a -
D.C. al Coda
The choo choo train that takes me, a - way from you, no words can tell how sad it makes me.
Coda
gain. Watch for the mail, I'll nev - er fail. If you don't get a let - ter then you'll know I'm in jail, Toot, toot, Toot-sie, don't cry, Toot, Toot, Toot-sie, good - bye.

TOO MARVELOUS FOR WORDS

Words by JOHNNY MERCER
Music by RICHARD A. WHITING

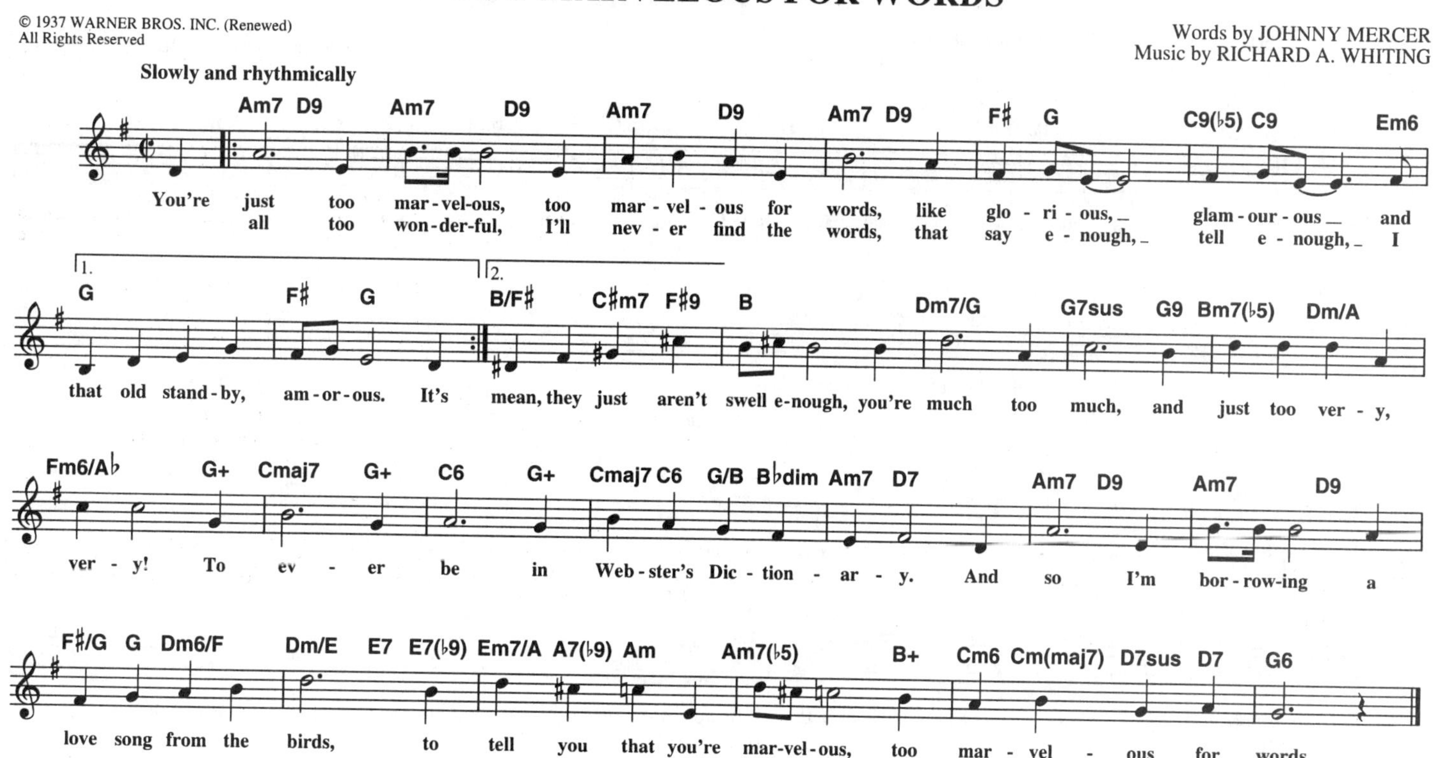
Slowly and rhythmically
Am7 D9 Am7 D9 Am7 D9 Am7 D9 F♯ G C9(♭5) C9 Em6
You're just too mar-vel-ous, too mar-vel-ous for words, like glo-ri-ous, glam-our-ous and
all too won-der-ful, I'll nev-er find the words, that say e-nough, tell e-nough, I
1. 2.
G F♯ G B/F♯ C♯m7 F♯9 B Dm7/G G7sus G9 Bm7(♭5) Dm/A
that old stand-by, am-or-ous. It's mean, they just aren't swell e-nough, you're much too much, and just too ver-y,
Fm6/A♭ G+ Cmaj7 G+ C6 G+ Cmaj7 C6 G/B B♭dim Am7 D7 Am7 D9 Am7 D9
ver-y! To ev-er be in Web-ster's Dic-tion-ar-y. And so I'm bor-row-ing a
F♯/G G Dm6/F Dm/E E7 E7(♭9) Em7/A A7(♭9) Am Am7(♭5) B+ Cm6 Cm(maj7) D7sus D7 G6
love song from the birds, to tell you that you're mar-vel-ous, too mar-vel-ous for words.

TOO-RA-LOO-RA-LOO-RAL
(That's an Irish Lullaby)

Words and Music by J.R. SHANNON

Moderately, with expression

O-ver in Kil-ar-ney, man-y years a-go, me Mith-er sang a song to me in tones so sweet and low. Just a sim-ple lit-tle dit-ty, in her good old I-rish way, and I'd give the world if she could sing that song to me this day.

Oft, in dreams, I wan-der to that cot a-gain. I feel her arms a-hug-gin' me as when she held me then. And I hear her voice a hum-min' to me as in days of yore, when she used to rock me fast a-sleep out-side the cab-in door.

Refrain:

Too-ra-loo-ra-loo-ral, too-ra-loo-ra-li. Too-ra-loo-ra-loo-ral; hush now, don't you cry! Too-ra-loo-ra-loo-ral, too-ra-loo-ra-li, Too-ra-loo-ra-

1. loo-ral; that's an I-rish lul-la-by.

2. loo-ral; That's an I-rish lul-la-by.

TOO LATE TO TURN BACK NOW

Words and Music by EDDIE CORNELIUS

Moderately slow, with a beat
Verse:
Gmaj7 Am7 Gmaj7 Am7 Gmaj7 Am7
1. My ma-ma told __ me, she said, "Son, please be - ware. __ There's this thing called love, ____ and it's, ah,
Gmaj7 Am7 Gmaj7 Am7 Gmaj7 Am7
ev-'ry - where." _ And she told me, "It can break your heart, ____ and put you in __ mis - er - y." ____
Gmaj7 Am7 Gmaj7 Am7
Since I met this lit-tle wom - an, __ I feel it's hap-pened to me, __ and I'm tell - in' you _
Chorus:
Gmaj7
it's too late _ to
Am7 Gmaj7 Am7 Gmaj7 Am7
turn back now. _ I be-lieve, I be-lieve, I be-lieve I'm fall-ing in __ love. It's too late _ to turn back now. _
Gmaj7 Am7 Am7
1. 2.
I be-lieve, I be-lieve, I be-lieve I'm fall-ing in __ love. fall-ing in __ love.
Bridge:
Em A
I would-n't mind __ it if I
Em A Em A Am7
knew she real - ly loved me, too, ____ but I'd hate to think that I'm in love __ a - lone, _ and noth-ing __ that I can do, __
Repeat ad lib. and fade
D7 Gmaj7 Am7 Gmaj7 Am7
_ oh. It's too late _ to turn back now. _ I be-lieve, I be-lieve, I be-lieve I'm fall-ing in __ love.

Verse 2:
I find myself phoning her at least ten times a day.
It's so unusual for me to carry on this way.
I tell you, I can't sleep at night, a-wanting to hold her tight.
I tried so hard to convince myself that this feeling just can't be right,
And I'm telling you
(To Chorus:)

From the Opera "CARMEN"

TOREADOR SONG

GEORGES BIZET

Moderately
F Gm7 C F Dm7 G C Gm Dm
To - re - a-dor on __ your _guard! To - re - a-dor! To - re - a-dor! Our in-spir - a - tion ev-'ry-one can see.
Am E7sus E7 A Gm Gm7 F C7 F
Love - ly dark eyed _ la - dy ____ and _ love a - waits _ thee. To - re - a - dor! Love _ waits for thee, for thee!

From the Motion Picture "TOP GUN"

TOP GUN ANTHEM

By HAROLD FALTERMEYER

To Next Strain

D.C.

Repeat and fade

From "BABES IN TOYLAND"

TOYLAND

Lyric by GLEN MACDONOUGH
Music by VICTOR HERBERT

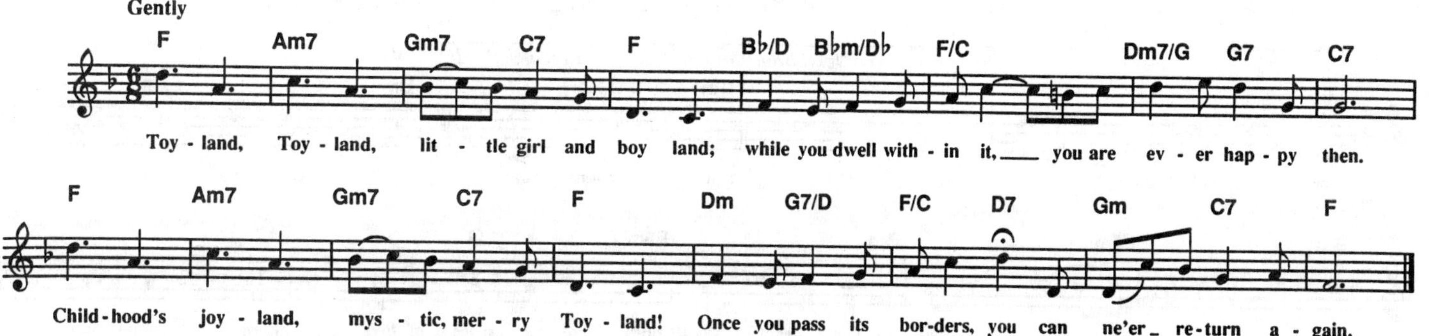
Gently
Toy - land, Toy - land, lit - tle girl and boy land; while you dwell with - in it, you are ev - er hap - py then.
Child - hood's joy - land, mys - tic, mer - ry Toy - land! Once you pass its bor-ders, you can ne'er re-turn a - gain.

TOP OF THE WORLD
Copyright © 1972 ALMO MUSIC CORP. and HAMMER AND NAILS MUSIC
All Rights Reserved
Lyric by JOHN BETTIS
Music by RICHARD CARPENTER
Moderately bright
Verse:
Such a feel - in's com - in' o - ver me. There is won-der in most ev - 'ry - thing I see, not a cloud in the sky got the sun in my eyes, and I won't be sur - prised if it's a dream.
Ev - 'ry - thing I want the world to be, is now com-ing true es - pe - cial-ly for me. And the rea - son is clear it's be - cause you are here, you're the nearest thing to heav - en that I've seen.
Chorus:
I'm on the top of the world look-in' down on cre - a - tion and the on - ly ex - pla-na - tion I can find, is the love that I've found, ev - er since you've been a - round, your love's put me at the top of the world.
TRACES
Copyright © 1969 LOW-SAL, INC.
All Rights Reserved
Words and Music by
BUDDY BUIE, JAMES COBB
and EMORY GORDY
Moderately slow
1. Fad - ed pho - to - graphs cov-ered now with lines and creas - es; tick - ets torn in half, mem - o - ries in bits and piec - es.
2. Rib - bons from her hair, sou - ve - nirs of days to - geth - er; the rings she used to wear, pag - es from an old love let - ter.
3. Inst. solo ad lib.
(eyes.) 4.5.etc. Inst. solo ad lib.
3rd. time end solo
Trac - es of love long a - go that did - n't work out right; trac - es of love.
Trac - es of love long a - go that did - n't work out right; trac - es of
Trac - es of hope in the night that she'll come back and dry these trac - es of
love with me to - night.
To Next Strain
3.4. etc.
tears 'round my
Repeat and fade
Bridge:
I close my eyes and say a prayer that in her heart she'll find a trace of love still there some - where.
D.S. 𝄋

TRYIN' TO GET THE FEELING AGAIN

Words and Music by
DAVID POMERANZ

Moderately slow

Cm(9) Gm7 A♭ Cm/D D7(♭9) Gm7 C7(♭9) Fm7

Doc - tor, my wom - an is com - in' back home _ late to - day. __ Could you may - be give me some-thing? 'Cause the
Where did it run _ to, I thought I did all __ that I could __ just to keep the love-light burn - in'. But what-

Cm(9) Gm7 A♭ D7(♯9) G(9) F♯dim Gm7 Fm7 B♭11

feel - ing is gone _ and I must get it back _ right a - way, __ be - fore she sees __ that I've been
ev - er I've done, _ I guess I just have-n't done _ it too good, __ 'cause all that's left __ is yearn-in'. I've been

E♭ Gm7/D Cm7 B♭11 E♭ Gm7/D Cm7 B♭11

up, down, try'n to get _ the feel - ing a - gain, __ all a - round, try'n' to get _ the feel - ing a - gain, _

A♭maj7 D7(♭9) Gm7 C7(♭9) Fm7 B♭11

_ the one that made _ me shiv-er, made my knees start to quiv-er ev-'ry time she walked in. ___ And I've looked

E♭ Gm7/D Cm7 B♭11 E♭ Gm7/D Cm7 D7(♭9)

high, low, ev - 'ry - where _ I pos - si - bly can, __ but there's no try'n' to get _ the feel - ing a - gain. _

Gm7 C7(♭9) Fm7 B♭11

_ It seemed to dis - ap - pear as fast as it came. ___

TURKEY IN THE STRAW

TRADITIONAL

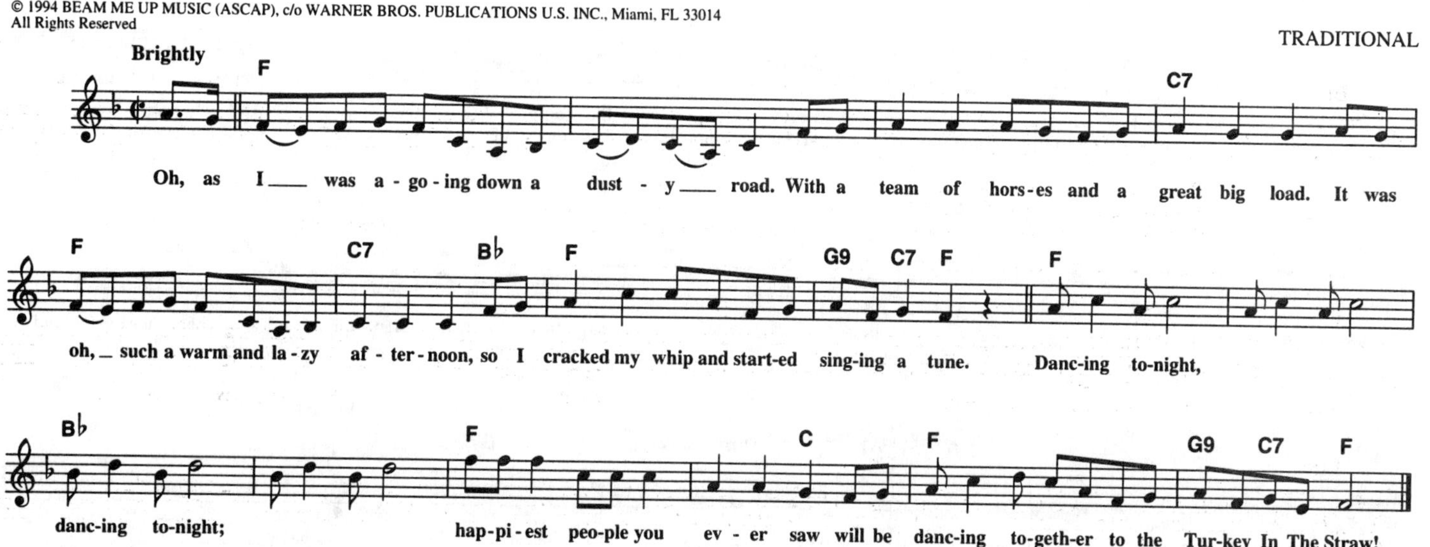
Brightly
F C7
Oh, as I ___ was a - go - ing down a dust - y ___ road. With a team of hors - es and a great big load. It was
F C7 B♭ F G9 C7 F F
oh, _ such a warm and la - zy af - ter - noon, so I cracked my whip and start-ed sing-ing a tune. Danc-ing to-night,
B♭ F C F G9 C7 F
danc-ing to-night; hap-pi-est peo-ple you ev - er saw will be danc-ing to-geth-er to the Tur-key In The Straw!

TUPELO HONEY

Words and Music by
VAN MORRISON

Slowly

Bb Dm/A E Bb Dm/A Eb F6 F7
1. You can take all the tea in Chi-na, put it in a big brown bag for me.

Bb Dm/A Eb Bb Dm/A Eb Bb
Sail right round all the sev-en o-ceans, drop it straight in-to the deep-blue sea.

Bb Dm/A Eb Bb Dm/A Eb F6 F7
She's as sweet as Tu-pe-lo hon-ey, she's an an-gel of the first de-gree.

Bb Dm/A Eb Bb Dm/A Eb Bb Eb/Bb
She's as sweet, she's as sweet as Tu-pe-lo hon-ey, just like hon-ey, ba-by, from the bee.

Bb Dm/A Eb Bb Dm/A Eb F6
2.3. You can't stop us on the road to free-dom, you can't keep us, 'cause our eyes can see.

Bb Dm/A Eb Bb Eb/Bb Bb Dm/A Eb Bb
Men with in-sight, men in gran-ite, Knights in (Knight) ar-mour bent on (in-tent on) chiv-al-ry.

TRY A LITTLE TENDERNESS

Words and Music by
HARRY WOODS, JIMMY CAMPBELL
and REG CONNELLY

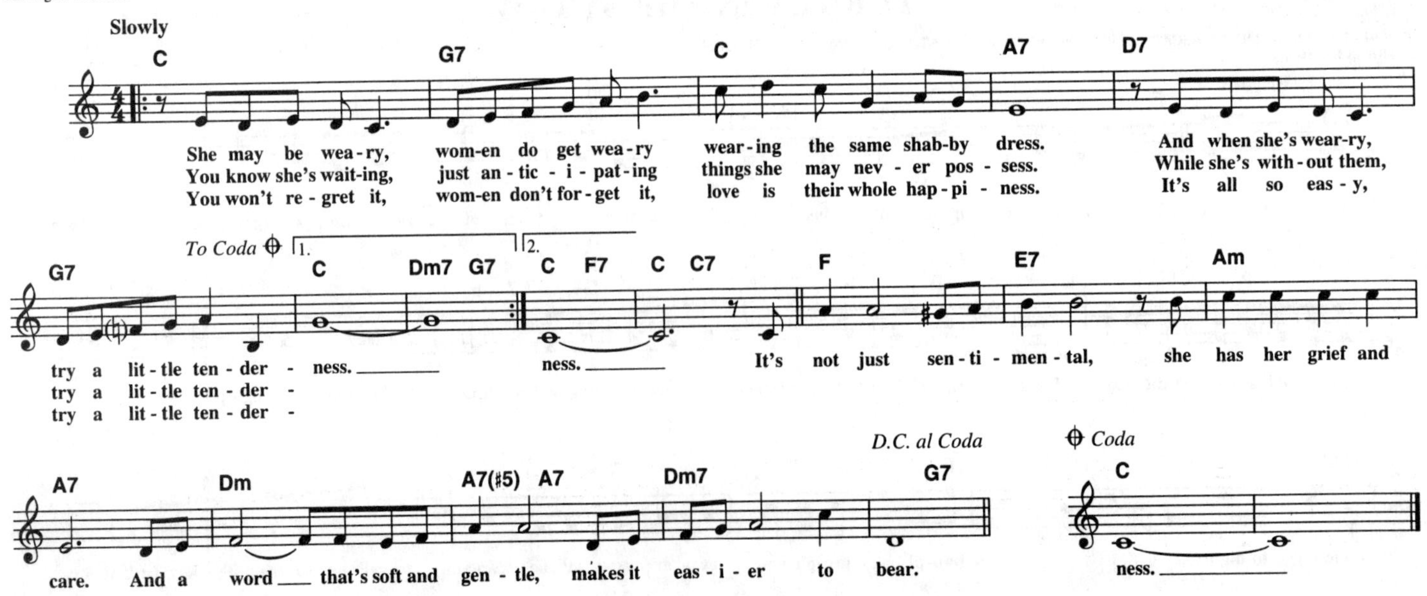
Slowly
C G7 C A7 D7
She may be wea-ry, wom-en do get wea-ry wear-ing the same shab-by dress. And when she's wear-ry,
You know she's wait-ing, just an-tic-i-pat-ing things she may nev-er pos-sess. While she's with-out them,
You won't re-gret it, wom-en don't for-get it, love is their whole hap-pi-ness. It's all so eas-y,
To Coda
G7 1. C Dm7 G7 2. C F7 C C7 F E7 Am
try a lit-tle ten-der-ness. ness. It's not just sen-ti-men-tal, she has her grief and
try a lit-tle ten-der-
try a lit-tle ten-der-
D.C. al Coda
A7 Dm A7(#5) A7 Dm7 G7
care. And a word that's soft and gen-tle, makes it eas-i-er to bear.
Coda
C
ness.

TRAVELIN' MAN

Words and Music by
JERRY FULLER

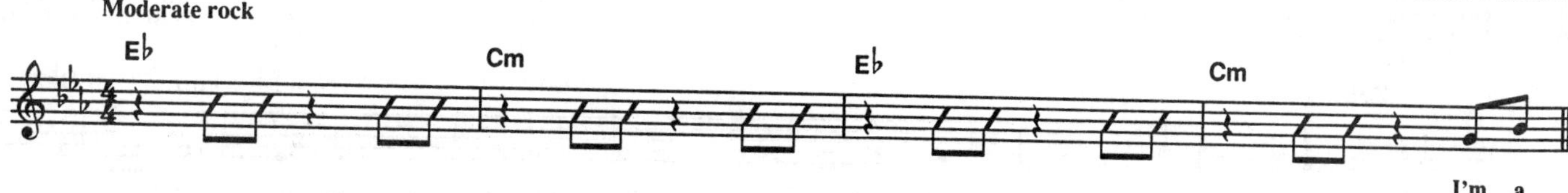
Moderate rock
E♭
Cm
E♭
Cm
I'm a

E♭
Cm
E♭
Cm
E♭
E♭7
trav-el-in' man, and I've made a lot o' stops all o-ver the world. And in ev-er-y port I

A♭
E♭
B♭7
E♭
B♭7
E♭
own the heart of at least one love-ly girl. I've a pret-ty se-ño-ri-ta

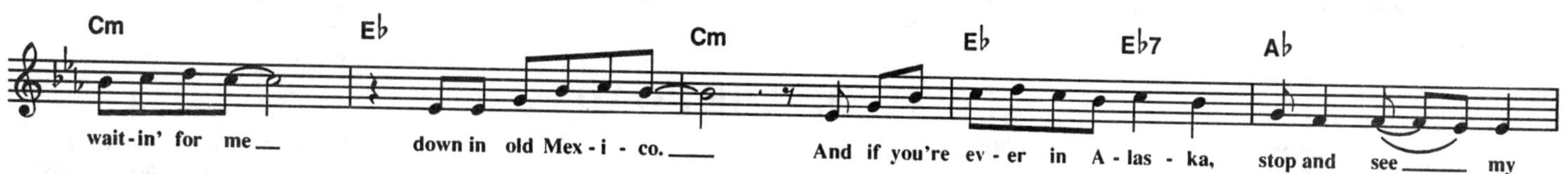
Cm
E♭
Cm
E♭
E♭7
A♭
wait-in' for me down in old Mex-i-co. And if you're ev-er in A-las-ka, stop and see my

E♭
B♭7
E♭
B♭m7/F
E♭/G
A♭
Gm
A♭
cute lit-tle Es-ki-mo. Oh, my sweet frau-lein down in Ber-lin town makes my heart start to

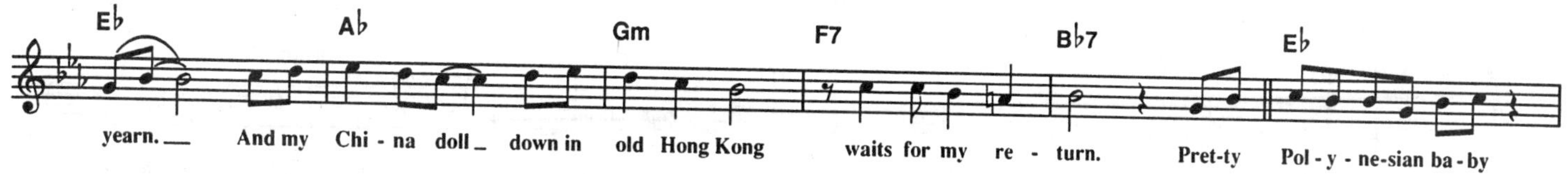
E♭
A♭
Gm
F7
B♭7
E♭
yearn. And my Chi-na doll down in old Hong Kong waits for my re-turn. Pret-ty Pol-y-ne-sian ba-by

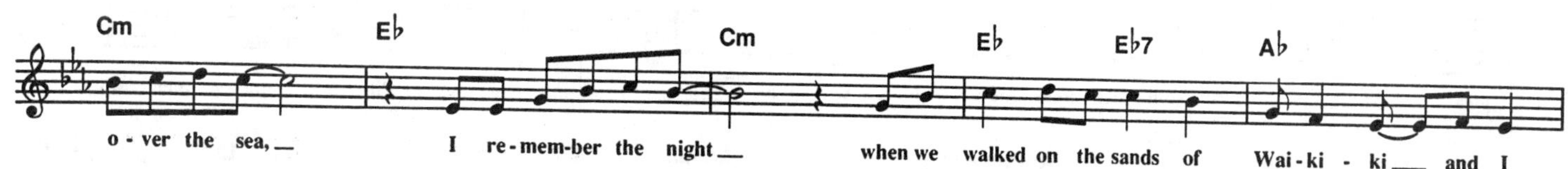
Cm
E♭
Cm
E♭
E♭7
A♭
o-ver the sea, I re-mem-ber the night when we walked on the sands of Wai-ki-ki and I

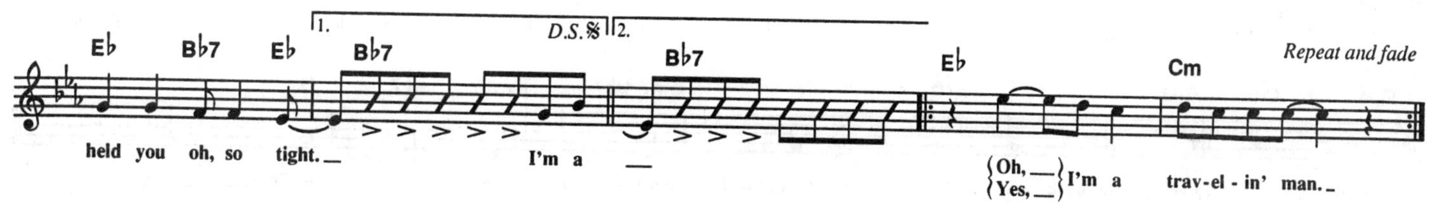
E♭
B♭7
E♭
1.
B♭7
D.S.
2.
B♭7
E♭
Cm
Repeat and fade
held you oh, so tight. I'm a
{Oh, Yes,} I'm a trav-el-in' man.

From the M-G-M Musical Production "MEET ME IN ST. LOUIS"

THE TROLLEY SONG

Lyrics by HUGH MARTIN
Music by RALPH BLANE

Brightly
"Clang, clang, clang," went the trol - ley. "Ding, ding ding," went the bell.
"Chug, chug, chug," went the mo - tor. "Bump, bump, bump," went the brake.
"Zing zing, zing," went my heart - strings, for the mo - ment I saw him I fell.
"Thump, thump, thump," went my heart - strings, when he smiled I could feel the car shake.
Fine
He tipped his hat, and took a seat. He said he hoped he had - n't stepped up - on my feet.
D.C. al Fine
He asked my name, I held my breath. I could-n't speak be-cause he scared me half to death.
TWO FOR THE ROAD
Copyright © 1967 by NORTHRIDGE MUSIC COMPANY and WB MUSIC CORP.
NORTHRIDGE MUSIC COMPANY c/o ALL NATIONS MUSIC
All Rights Reserved
Words by LESLIE BRICUSSE
Music by HENRY MANCINI
Slowly
If you're feel - ing fan - cy free, come wan - der through the world with me, and an - y place we
chance to be will be our ren - dez - vous. Two for the road, we'll trav - el down the
years col - lect - ing pre-cious mem - o - ries, se - lect - ing sou - ve - nirs, and liv - ing life the way we
please. In sum - mer - time the sun will shine; in win - ter we'll drink sum - mer wine.
And ev - 'ry day that you are mine will be a - love - ly day as long as love still wears a
smile, I know that we'll be two for the road, and that's a long, long while.

From the Paramount Picture "TRUE GRIT"

TRUE GRIT

Words by DON BLACK
Music by ELMER BERNSTEIN

Moderately
One day, lit-tle girl, the sad-ness will leave your face __ as soon as you've won your fight to get jus-tice done. Some days, lit-tle
girl, you'll won-der what life's a - bout, _ but oth-ers have known few bat-tles are won a - lone.
So, you'll look a - round to find ____ some - one who's kind, some-one who is fear-less like you. ______ The pain of it ___
__ will ease a bit when you find a man with true grit.
One day you will rise and you won't be-lieve your eyes. __You'll wake up and see
a world that is fine and free. __Though sum-mer seems far ______ a - way, you will find the sun ______ one day. _____

From the Paramount Picture "THANKS FOR THE MEMORY"

TWO SLEEPY PEOPLE

Words by FRANK LOESSER
Music by HOAGY CARMICHAEL

Moderately slow

Here we are, out of cig - a - rettes, _ hold - ing hands and yawn - ing, look how late it gets. __
Here we are, in the co - zy chair, _ pick - ing on a wish - bone from the Frig - i - daire. _

Two sleep - y peo - ple, by dawn's ear - ly light, and too much in love to say "Good - night."
Two sleep - y peo - ple with noth - ing to say, and too much in love to break a - way.

Bridge:

Do you re - mem - ber the nights we used to lin - ger in the hall? _ Fa - ther did - n't like you at all.

Do you re - mem - ber the rea - son why we mar - ried in the fall; to rent this lit - tle nest, _ and get a bit of rest? Well,

here we are just a - bout the same; _ fog - gy lit - tle fel - la, drow - sy lit - tle dame. _

Two sleep - y peo - ple, by dawn's ear - ly light, and too much in love to say "Good - night."

12th STREET RAG

By EUDAY L. BOWMAN

Brightly
Eb
Bb7
Eb
1
Bb7
F9
Bb7 N.C.
2
Eb7
Ab7
B7
Eb
Cm7
F9
Bb7
Eb
Eb
Bb7
Eb
1
Bb7
F7
Bb7
2
G7
Cdim7
Eb
F9
Bb7
Eb
Bb7
Eb
Bb7
Eb
1
Bb7
F9
Bb7
2
Eb7
Ab
B7
Eb
Cm7
F9
Bb7
Eb

TZENA, TZENA, TZENA

Hebrew Lyric by YEHIEL HAGGIZ
English lyric by GORDON JENKINS
Music (First Two Parts) by
ISSACHAR MIRON (MICHROVSKY)
(Third Part) by
JULIUS GROSSMAN

Bright Hora

C7 C C6
(Keyboard:)
Tze - na, Tze - na, Tze - na, Tze - na,
Tze - na, Tze - na, Tze - na, Tze - na,

F6 Fmaj7 G9 G7 Cmaj7 C G7/C C
can't you hear the mu - sic play - ing in the cit - y square? Tze - na, Tze - na,
ha - ba - not ur' - e - na cha - ya - lim ba - mo - sha - va. Al na al na

C6 F6 Fmaj7 G9 G7 Cmaj7 C G7/C
Tze - na, Tze - na, come where all our friends will find us with the danc - ers there.
al na al na al na tit - cha - be - na mi - ben cha - yil ish ta - va.

C C6 F6 Fmaj7 G9 G7 Cmaj7
Tze - na, Tze - na, join the cel - e - bra - tion. There'll be peo - ple there from ev - 'ry
Tze - na, Tze - na, ha - ba - not ur' - e - na cha - ya - lim ba - mo - sha - va.

C G7/C C C6 F6 Fmaj7 Dm6 G7
na - tion. Dawn will find us laugh - ing in the sun - light danc - ing in the cit - y
Al na al na al na tit cha - be - na mi - ben chi - yil ish tza -

C B♭ B C C+ F6 Fmaj7 G9
square. Tze - na, Tze - na, (clap) come and dance the Ho - ra. One, two,
va. Tze - na, Tze - na, (clap) Tze - na, Tze - na, Tze - na, Tze - na,

G7 Cmaj7 C G7/C C C+ F6 Fmaj7
three, four, all the boys will en - vy me for Tze - na, Tze - na. (Clap!) When the band is play - ing,
Tze - na, Tze - na, Tze - na, Tze - na, Tze - na, Tze - na, (Clap!) Tze - na, Tze - na, Tze - na,

Dm6 G7 Cmaj7 C C+ C C+ C
my heart's say - ing, Tze - na, Tze - na, Tze - na! Tze - na! Tze - na! Ho!
Tze - na, Tze - na, Tze - na, Tze - na, Tze - na! Tze - na! Tze - na! Ho!

UNITED WE STAND

By TONY HILLER
and PETER SIMONS

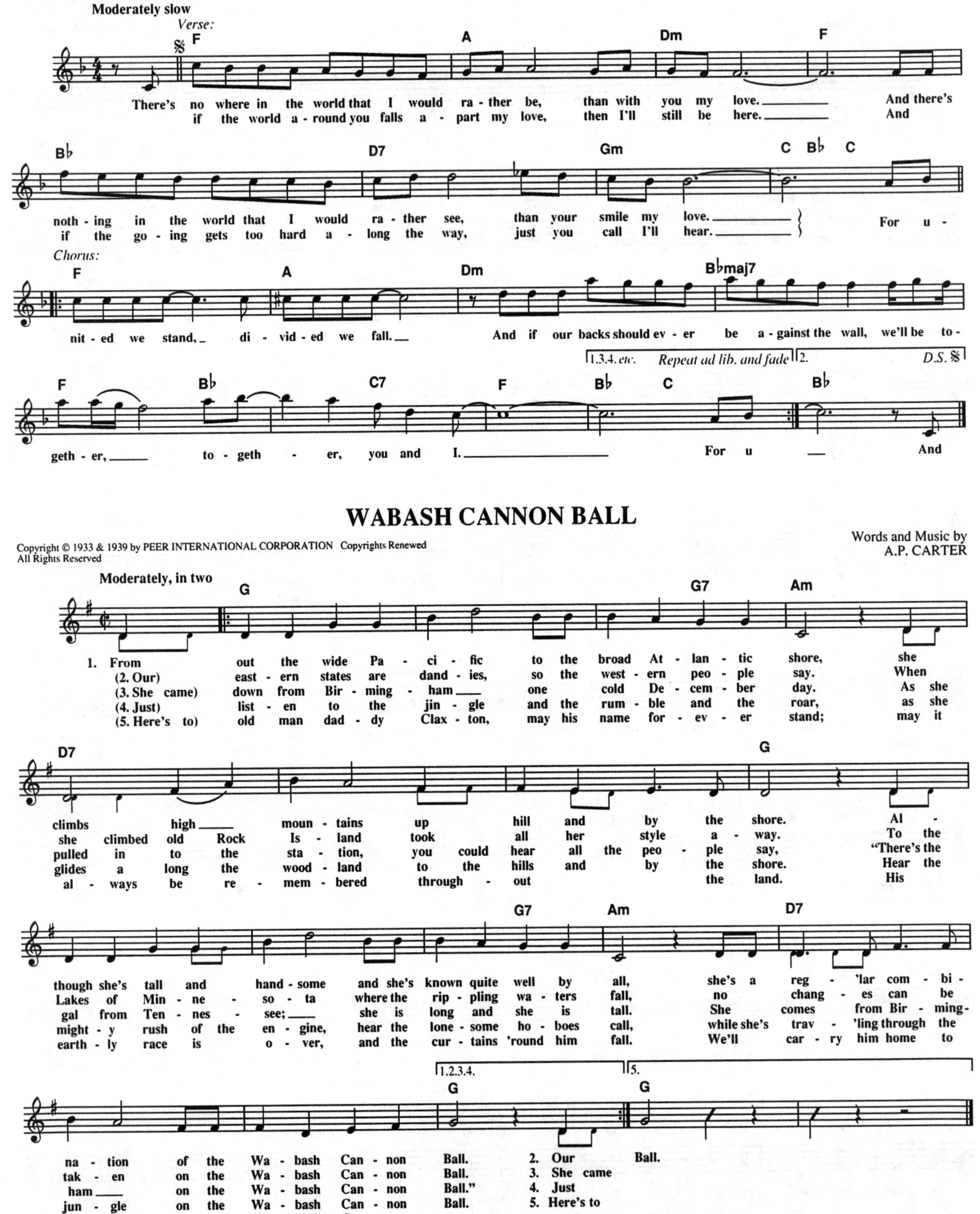
Moderately slow
Verse:
F A Dm F
There's no where in the world that I would ra - ther be, than with you my love. And there's
if the world a - round you falls a - part my love, then I'll still be here. And
B♭ D7 Gm C B♭ C
noth - ing in the world that I would ra - ther see, than your smile my love. For u -
if the go - ing gets too hard a - long the way, just you call I'll hear.
Chorus:
F A Dm B♭maj7
nit - ed we stand, di - vid - ed we fall. And if our backs should ev - er be a - gainst the wall, we'll be to -
1.3.4. etc. Repeat ad lib. and fade 2. D.S.
F B♭ C7 F B♭ C B♭
geth - er, to - geth - er, you and I. For u - And

WABASH CANNON BALL

Words and Music by
A.P. CARTER

Moderately, in two
G G7 Am
1. From out the wide Pa - ci - fic to the broad At - lan - tic shore, she
(2. Our) east - ern states are dand - ies, so the west - ern peo - ple say. When
(3. She came) down from Bir - ming - ham one cold De - cem - ber day. As she
(4. Just) list - en to the jin - gle and the rum - ble and the roar, as she
(5. Here's to) old man dad - dy Clax - ton, may his name for - ev - er stand; may it
D7 G
climbs high moun - tains up hill and by the shore. Al -
she climbed old Rock Is - land took all her style a - way. To the
pulled in to the sta - tion, you could hear all the peo - ple say, "There's the
glides a long the wood - land to the hills and by the shore. Hear the
al - ways be re - mem - bered through - out the land. His
G7 Am D7
though she's tall and hand - some and she's known quite well by all, she's a reg - 'lar com - bi -
Lakes of Min - ne - so - ta where the rip - pling wa - ters fall, no chang - es can be
gal from Ten - nes - see; she is long and she is tall. She comes from Bir - ming -
might - y rush of the en - gine, hear the lone - some ho - boes call, while she's trav - 'ling through the
earth - ly race is o - ver, and the cur - tains 'round him fall. We'll car - ry him home to
1.2.3.4. 5.
G G
na - tion of the Wa - bash Can - non Ball. 2. Our Ball.
tak - en on the Wa - bash Can - non Ball. 3. She came
ham on the Wa - bash Can - non Ball." 4. Just
jun - gle on the Wa - bash Can - non Ball. 5. Here's to
vic - t'ry on the Wa - bash Can - non

UNTIL YOU COME BACK TO ME

(That's What I'm Gonna Do)

Words and Music by STEVIE WONDER, MORRIS BROADNAX AND CLARENCE PAUL

Moderate shuffle
Verse:
Amaj7 C/D Gmaj7 Amaj7
1. Though you don't call an - y more, I sit and wait in vain. I guess I'll rap on you door,
C/D Gmaj7 Em7
tap on your win - dow - pane. I want to tell you, ba - by, the
A7 F♯m7(♭5) B7(♭9)
chang-es I've been go - ing through miss - ing you. Lis-ten you.
Chorus:
Em7
'Til you come back to me,
Asus Dmaj7
that's what I'm gon - na do.
To Coda
1. Dm7/G G13 D.S.
2. Why did you
2. To Next Strain
3.4. (4th time To Coda)
Bridge:
Dm7 G7 Cmaj7
Liv - ing for you my dear is like liv - ing in a world of con - stant fear. Hear my plea;
Em7 E7 A7 D.S.
I've got to make you see that our love is dy - ing. 3. Al-though your
Coda
Dm7/G G13 Amaj7 C/D Gmaj7
Repeat ad lib. and fade
I'm gon - na rap on your door, tap on your win - dow - pane. I'm gon - na

Verse 2:
Why did you have to decide
You had to set me free?
I'm going to swallow my pride,
And beg you to please see me.
I'm going to walk by myself
Just to prove that my love is true;
All for you baby.
(To Chorus:)

Verse 3:
Although your phone you ignore,
Somehow I must, somehow I must,
How I must explain.
I'm going to rap on your door,
Tap on your windowpane.
I'm gonna camp on your steps
Until I get through to you
I've got to change your view, baby.
(To Chorus:)

UP ON THE HOUSETOP

Words and Music by
BENJAMIN RUSSELL HANBY

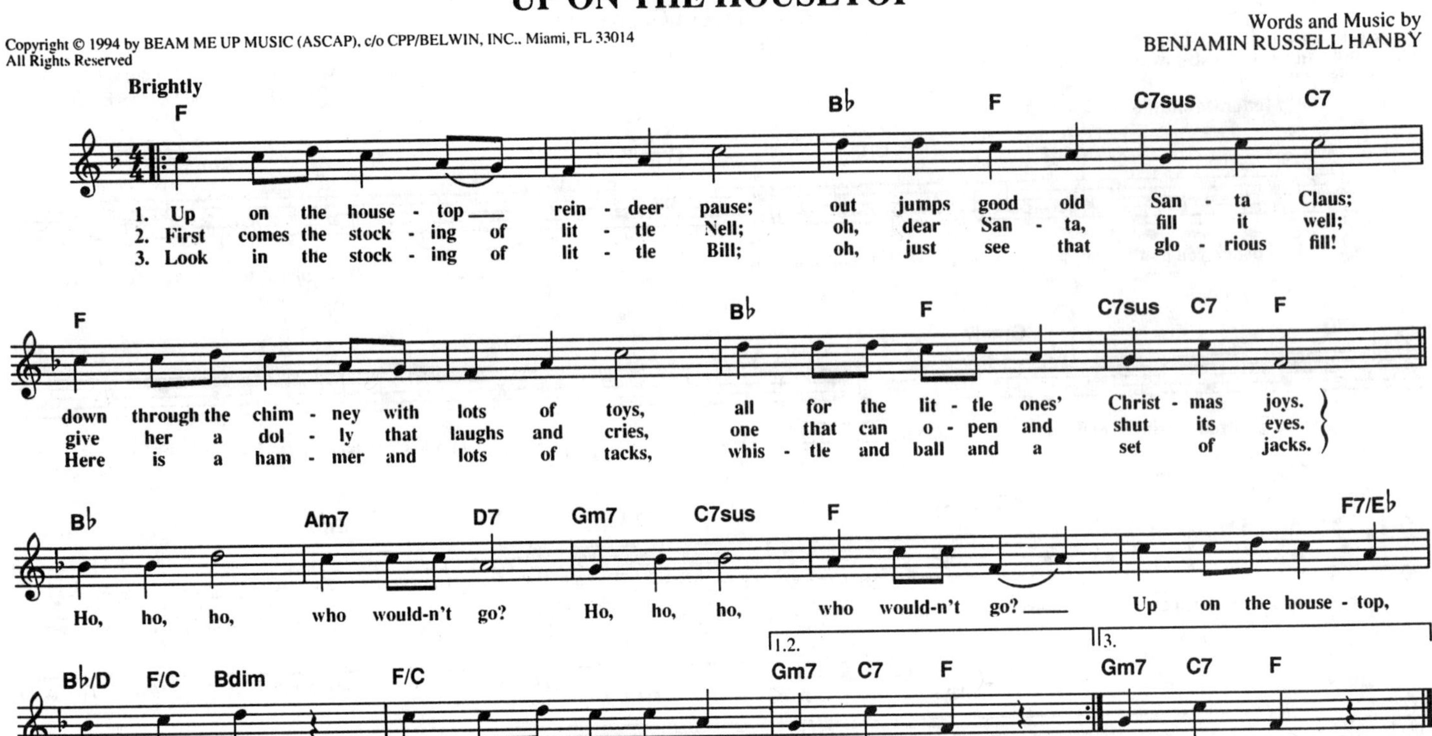
Brightly
F Bb F C7sus C7
1. Up on the house - top rein - deer pause; out jumps good old San - ta Claus;
2. First comes the stock - ing of lit - tle Nell; oh, dear San - ta, fill it well;
3. Look in the stock - ing of lit - tle Bill; oh, just see that glo - rious fill!
F Bb F C7sus C7 F
down through the chim - ney with lots of toys, all for the lit - tle ones' Christ - mas joys.
give her a dol - ly that laughs and cries, one that can o - pen and shut its eyes.
Here is a ham - mer and lots of tacks, whis - tle and ball and a set of jacks.
Bb Am7 D7 Gm7 C7sus F F7/Eb
Ho, ho, ho, who would-n't go? Ho, ho, ho, who would-n't go? Up on the house - top,
Bb/D F/C Bdim F/C 1.2. Gm7 C7 F 3. Gm7 C7 F
click, click, click, down through the chim - ney with good Saint Nick. good Saint Nick.

WALTZ OF THE FLOWERS

(From "The Nutcracker Suite")

Music by
PETER ILYICH TCHAIKOVSKY

Moderately

D C♯dim/D D C♯dim/D D A/C♯

C7 Em/B Em/G Em Em/B B♭7(♯5)

A7 N.C. D C♯dim/D D C♯dim/D D

D7 F♯m/C♯ C♯7/B F♯m/A C♯7/G♯ F♯m A/E

D7 F♯m/C♯ C♯7 F♯mN.C. D Em7/A A7

G/B A7 D Em7/A A7

1. Gm/B♭ B+ C A7/C♯ 2. D6/F♯ F7(♭5) A7/E A7 D

Paramount Pictures Presents a Lorimar-Martin Elfand Production-
a Taylor Hackford Film "AN OFFICER AND A GENTLEMAN"

UP WHERE WE BELONG

Words by WILL JENNINGS
Music by BUFFY SAINTE-MARIE and JACK NITZSCHE

Soulfully
(Keyboard:)
Verse:
1. Who knows what to - mor-row brings; in a world, few hearts sur - vive? All I know is the way I feel; when it's real, I keep it a - live.
2. Some hang on to "used-to - be" live their lives look - ing be - hind. All we have is here and now; all our life, out there to find.
The road is long. There are moun - tains in our way, but we climb a step ev-'ry day.
Chorus:
Love lift us up where we be - long, where the ea - gles cry on a moun - tain high.
Love lift us up where we be - long, far from the world we know; up where the clear winds blow.
1.
D.S. 𝄋
2.
clear winds blow. Time goes by, no time to cry, life's you and I, a - live, to - day.
Love lift us up where we be - long, where the ea - gles cry, on a moun - tain high.
Repeat ad lib. and fade
Love lift us up where we be - long far from the world we know; where the clear winds blow.

UPTIGHT
(Everything's Alright)

Words and Music by
STEVIE WONDER, SYLVIA MOY
and HENRY COSBY

Moderately bright

D C/D G D G/D

Ba - by, ev - 'ry - thing is all right, up - tight, out ___ of sight. _ 1. I'm a

Verse:

D C/D D C/D

poor man's son _ from a - cross the rail-road tracks. _ The on - ly shirt I own is hang - in' on ___ my back, but I'm ___
pearl of a girl, _ I guess that's what you might say. _ I guess her folks ___ brought her up that way; the right

D C/D D

___ the en - vy of ev - 'ry sin - gle guy ___ since I'm ___ the ap - ple of my ___
side of the tracks, she was born and raised _ in a great big old house full of

C/D D C/D D C/D

_ girl's eye. ___ When we go out step-ping on the town ___ for a while _ my mon-ey's low and my suit's _
but - lers and maids. She says give her the things that ___ money can buy _ but I'll nev - er, nev - er nev - er make my

D C/D D

_ out of style. But it's all right if my clothes _ are - n't new; _ out ___ of sight be - cause my
ba - by cry, _ and it's all right; what I ___ can't do, ___ out ___ of sight be - cause my

Chorus:

C/D D C/D G/D D

heart is true. ___ She says ba - by, ev - 'ry - thing is all right, up - tight, ___ out _
heart is true. ___ She says ba - by, ev - 'ry - thing is all right, up - tight, ___ clean

C/D G/D D C/D G/D D

_ of sight. Ba - by, ev - 'ry - thing is all right, up - tight, clean _
out of sight. Ba - by, ev - 'ry - thing is all right, up - tight, clean _

1.
C/D G/D D C/D D C/D *D.S.* 𝄋

_ out of sight. _ 2. I'm a
_ out of sight. _

2.
C/D G/D D C/D G/D D C/D G/D *Repeat and fade*

_ Ba - by, ev - 'ry-thing is all right, up - tight, way ___ out of sight.

From the Broadway Musical Production "GOOD NEWS"

THE VARSITY DRAG

Words and Music by
B.G. DE SYLVA, LEW BROWN
and RAY HENDERSON

Moderately
C /B C7/B♭ F/A Fm C/E To Coda
Here is the Drag, see how it goes; Down on the heels, up on the toes. That's the way to
Hot-ter than hot, new-er than new! Mean-er than mean, blu-er than blue. Gets as much ap-
down on the heels, up on the toes. Stay af-ter school, learn how it goes. Ev-'ry-bod-y
E♭dim7 G7 C B7 E Am E Am E G7 C
do the Var-si-ty Drag. flag! You can pass man-y a class, wheth-er you're dumb or wise. If you all
plause as wav-ing the
Fm C F C G7 D.C. al Coda
an-swer the call, when your pro-fess-or cries: "Ev-'ry-bod-y,
Coda Cdim G7 G+ C
do the Var-si-ty Drag."
THE VOWS GO UNBROKEN
(Always True to You)
Copyright © 1988 GARY BURR MUSIC/ZENA MUSIC
All Rights Reserved
Words and Music by
GARY BURR and ERIC KAZ
Slowly Verse:
D G D G A D G Bm/A
1. From the mo-ment I met you, you made my life com-plete. This wave of pure e-
night when we kissed, you still took my breath a-way. It goes with-out
I have been tempt-ed, oh, I have nev-er strayed. I'd die be-fore I'd
G D G G/A A G/A A G/A A G/A A To Next Strain G/A A
mo-tion has swept me off my feet. 2. And to-way. The made. The
say-ing, but I'll say it an-y-
dam-age this un-ion we have
Chorus:
D A G/A D G A D D7/F♯ G A G/A D D/F♯ G
vows go un-bro-ken and you still know I do. Love, keep and hon-or,
D/A Em7/A D D.S. D Bm7 E7/G♯ A D/F♯ Bm7 E/G♯
al-ways true to you. 3. Though you. I knew from the first, for bet-ter or worse, I'd stand by you all my life.
G/A A G/A A D G A G/A D D/F♯ G D/A Em7/A D
And the you. Love, keep and hon-or, al-ways true to you.

VOLARE
(Nel Blu, Dipinto Di Blu)

English Lyric by MITCHELL PARISH
Original Italian Text by
D. MODUGNO - F. MIGLIACCI
Music by DOMENICO MODUGNO

Freely
Verse:
B♭ Bdim7 Cm Cm7 F7 Cm7
Some-times the world is a val - ley of heart-aches and tears, and in the hus - tle and

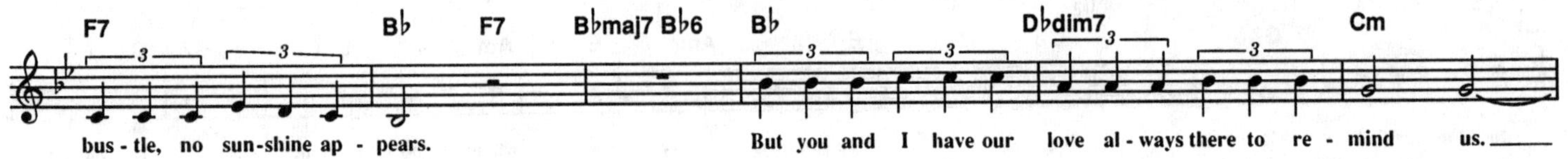
F7 B♭ F7 B♭maj7 B♭6 B♭ D♭dim7 Cm
bus - tle, no sun-shine ap - pears. But you and I have our love al - ways there to re - mind us.

C7 Gm7 C7 Cm7/F F G7(♭9)
There is a way we can leave all the sha - dows be - hind us. Vo -

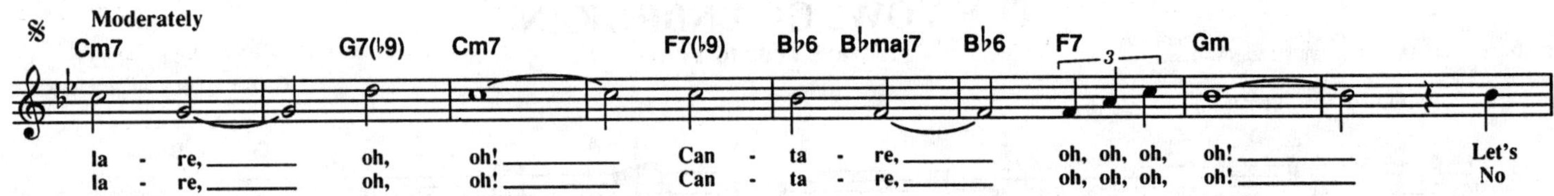
Moderately
Cm7 G7(♭9) Cm7 F7(♭9) B♭6 B♭maj7 B♭6 F7 Gm
la - re, oh, oh! Can - ta - re, oh, oh, oh, oh! Let's
la - re, oh, oh! Can - ta - re, oh, oh, oh, oh! No

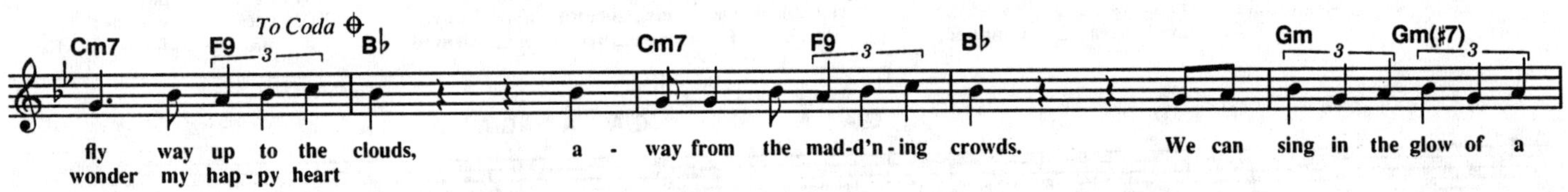
Cm7 F9 To Coda B♭ Cm7 F9 B♭ Gm Gm(♯7)
fly way up to the clouds, a - way from the mad-d'n - ing crowds. We can sing in the glow of a
wonder my hap - py heart

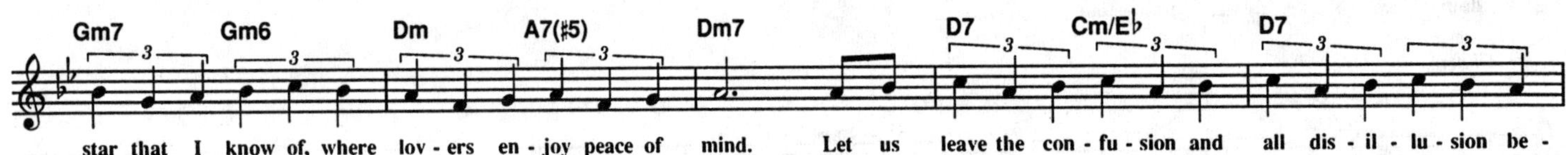
Gm7 Gm6 Dm A7(♯5) Dm7 D7 Cm/E♭ D7
star that I know of, where lov - ers en - joy peace of mind. Let us leave the con - fu - sion and all dis - il - lu - sion be -

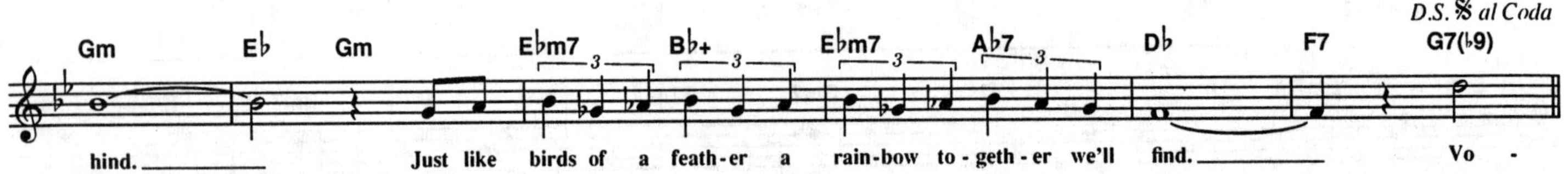
D.S. al Coda
Gm E♭ Gm E♭m7 B♭+ E♭m7 A♭7 D♭ F7 G7(♭9)
hind. Just like birds of a feath - er a rain - bow to - geth - er we'll find. Vo -

Coda
B♭ Cm7 F9 B♭ Cm7 F9 B♭
sings. Your love has giv - en me wings. Your love has giv - en me wings.

THE VOLGA BOATMEN

Copyright © 1994 by BEAM ME UP MUSIC (ASCAP), c/o CPP/BELWIN, INC., Miami, FL 33014
All Rights Reserved
RUSSIAN FOLK SONG
Slowly
WAS THAT THE HUMAN THING TO DO
© 1931 WARNER BROS. INC.
Copyright Renewed and assigned to WARNER BROS. INC. and WAROCK MUSIC CORP.
Canadian rights controlled by WARNER BROS. INC.
All Rights Reserved
Words by JOE YOUNG
Music by SAMMY FAIN
Moderately
Nev - er thought that an - y - one in their right mind could ev - er treat an - oth - er hu - man so un - kind;
Al - ways thought that yours was such a heart of gold, but af - ter I was sold on all the tales you told,
did - n't you sneak a - way and leave a note be - hind,
did - n't you let your kiss - es turn from hot to cold,
Was that the hu - man thing to do?
do? Now I'm not try - ing to patch things up, what's been done must be,
Now I just wan - na be un - der - stood, I'm no false a - larm,
Lord! I would - n't e - ven treat a pup, the way you treat - ed me,
If I could - n't do a hu - man good, I would - n't do 'em harm.
how could an - y - bod - y be so darn un - fair, you let me hang a - round un - til I learned to care,
How you let me fall and how you let me be! And when I begged you for a lit - tle sym - pa - thy,
did - n't you e - ven laugh and leave me cry - ing there!
did - n't you e - ven try to hi - de hi - de me?
Was that the hu - man thing to do?
D.S.
Do?

WADE IN THE WATER

TRADITIONAL FOLK SONG

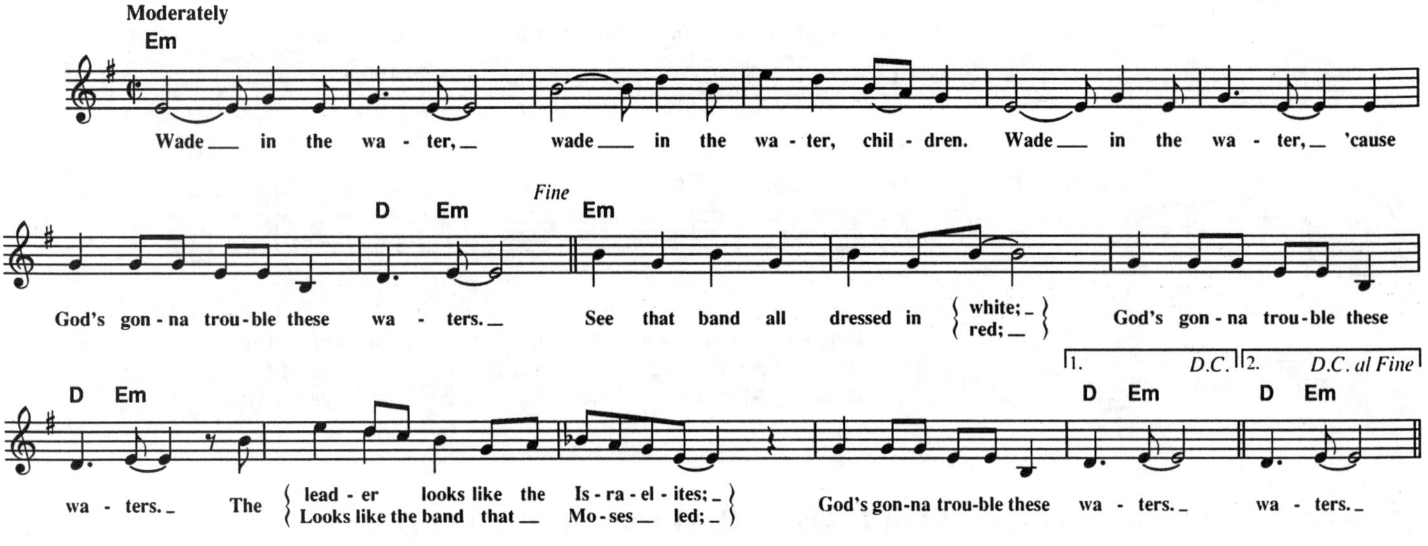

Moderately

Wade in the wa - ter, wade in the wa - ter, chil - dren. Wade in the wa - ter, 'cause God's gon - na trou - ble these wa - ters. *Fine*

See that band all dressed in { white; / red; } God's gon - na trou - ble these wa - ters. The { lead - er looks like the Is - ra - el - ites; / Looks like the band that Mo - ses led; } God's gon - na trou - ble these wa - ters. *1. D.C.* *2. D.C. al Fine* wa - ters.

WALKIN' AFTER MIDNIGHT

Words by DON HECHT
Music by ALAN BLOCK

Moderately

I go out walk - in' af - ter mid - night in the moon - light just like we used to do. I'm al - ways walk - in' af - ter mid - night search - in' for you.

I walk for miles a - long the high - way that's just my way of be - ing close to you. I go out walk - in' af - ter mid - night search - in' for you.

I stop to see a weep - in' wil - low cry - in' on his pil - low, may - be he's cry - in' for me. And as the sky turns gloom - y, night winds whis - per to me I'm lone - ly as lone - ly as can be.

I'll go out walk - in' af - ter mid - night in the star - light and pray that you may be some - where just walk - in' af - ter mid - night search - in' for me.

WAIT TILL THE SUN SHINES, NELLIE

Music by
HARRY VON TILZER

Moderately

Bb D7 Eb Bb F7 F7/A Bb Bbdim7 Bb F7/C Bb7/D
Wait till the sun shines, Nel - lie, and the gray skies turn to blue.

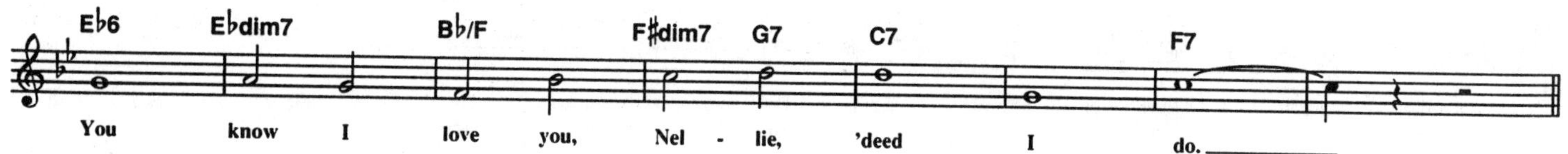
Eb6 Ebdim7 Bb/F F#dim7 G7 C7 F7
You know I love you, Nel - lie, 'deed I do.

Bb D7 Eb Bb F7 A7(b5)/Eb D
We'll face the years to - geth - er, sweet - hearts you and I. So won't you

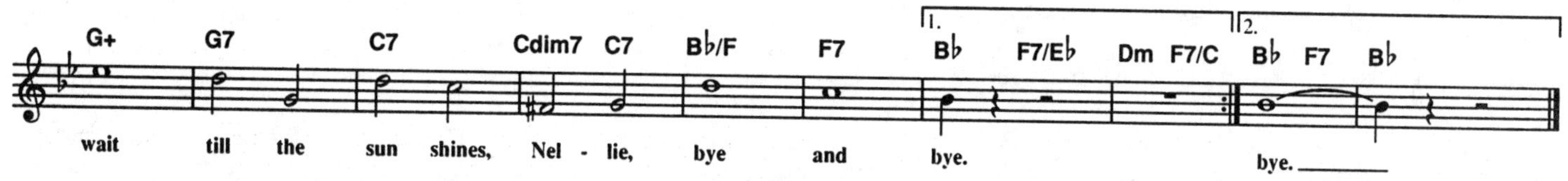
G+ G7 C7 Cdim7 C7 Bb/F F7 1. Bb F7/Eb Dm F7/C 2. Bb F7 Bb
wait till the sun shines, Nel - lie, bye and bye. bye.

WALK RIGHT IN

Words and Music by
GUS CANNON and H. WOODS

Moderately

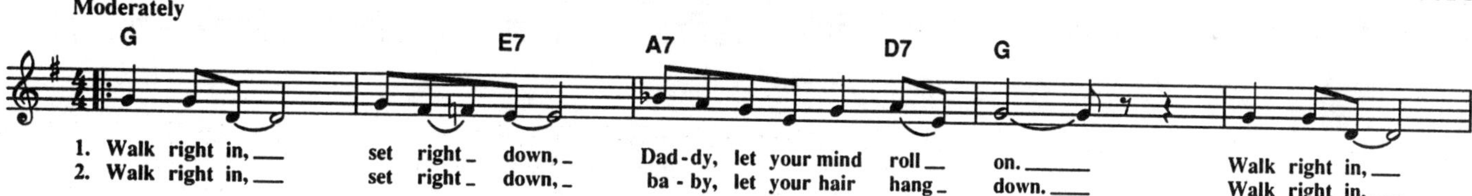
G E7 A7 D7 G
1. Walk right in, set right down, Dad-dy, let your mind roll on. Walk right in,
2. Walk right in, set right down, ba - by, let your hair hang down. Walk right in,

E7 A7 D7 G
set right down, Dad - dy, let your mind roll on. Ev - 'ry - bod - y's talk - in' 'bout a
set right down, ba - by, let you hair hang down. Ev - 'ry - bod - y's talk - in' 'bout a

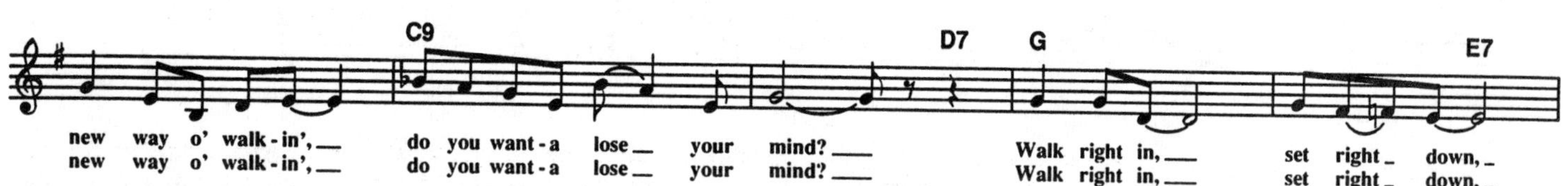
C9 D7 G E7
new way o' walk - in', do you want - a lose your mind? Walk right in, set right down,
new way o' walk - in', do you want - a lose your mind? Walk right in, set right down,

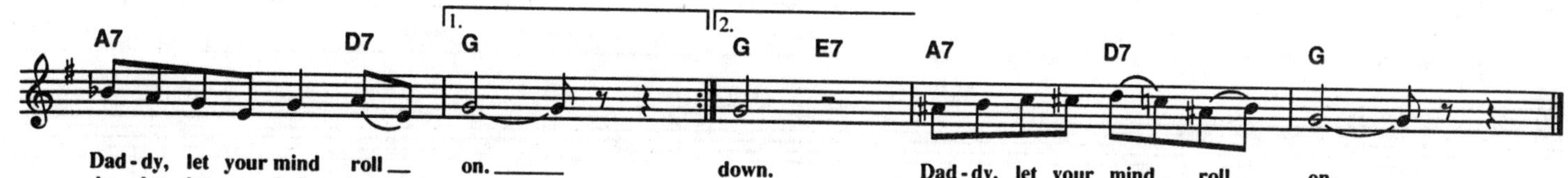
A7 D7 1. G 2. G E7 A7 D7 G
Dad - dy, let your mind roll on. down. Dad - dy, let your mind roll on.
ba - by, let your hair hang

WAITING FOR THE ROBERT E. LEE

Lyric by L. WOLFE GILBERT
Music by LEWIS F. MUIR

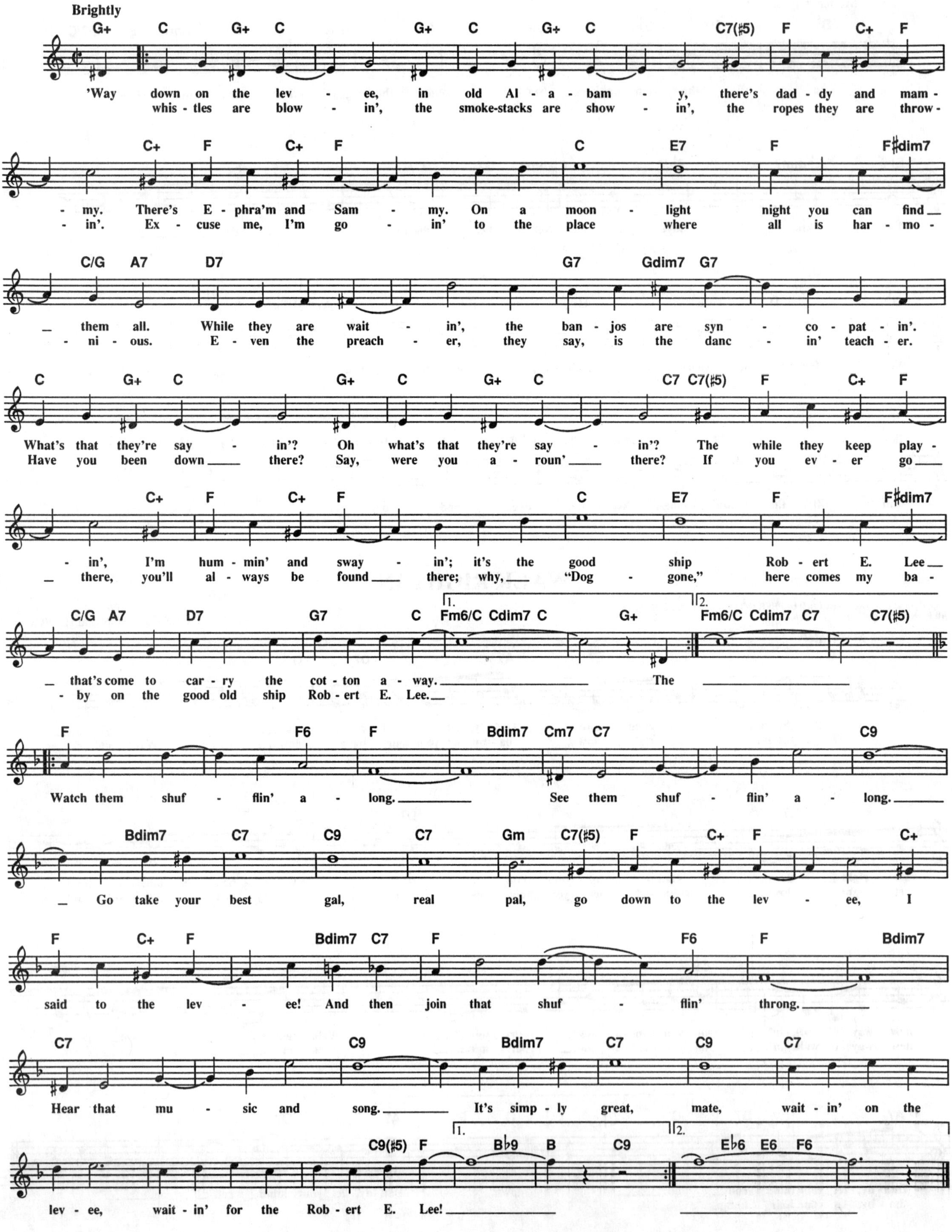

Brightly

'Way down on the lev - ee, in old Al - a - bam - y, there's dad - dy and mam -
whis - tles are blow - in', the smoke-stacks are show - in', the ropes they are throw -

- my. There's E - phra'm and Sam - my. On a moon - light night you can find _
- in'. Ex - cuse me, I'm go - in' to the place where all is har - mo -

_ them all. While they are wait - in', the ban - jos are syn - co - pat - in'.
- ni - ous. E - ven the preach - er, they say, is the danc - in' teach - er.

What's that they're say - in'? Oh what's that they're say - in'? The while they keep play -
Have you been down _ there? Say, were you a - roun' _ there? If you ev - er go _

- in', I'm hum - min' and sway - in'; it's the good ship Rob - ert E. Lee _
_ there, you'll al - ways be found _ there; why, _ "Dog - gone," here comes my ba -

_ that's come to car - ry the cot - ton a - way. _ The _
- by on the good old ship Rob - ert E. Lee. _

Watch them shuf - flin' a - long. _ See them shuf - flin' a - long. _

_ Go take your best gal, real pal, go down to the lev - ee, I

said to the lev - ee! And then join that shuf - flin' throng. _

Hear that mu - sic and song. _ It's simp - ly great, mate, wait - in' on the

lev - ee, wait - in' for the Rob - ert E. Lee! _

WASHINGTON POST MARCH

By JOHN PHILIP SOUSA

March
N.C.
D
Am D7 G D7 G
mf
Am D7 G Gm D A7 D A7 D A7
1. D 2. D D7 G D7
G D7 G E♭ G
D7 1. G 2. G C G7 C G7 C
G7 C F A7 Dm A7 Dm C
Cdim G7 C G
C G7 C G7 C
G7 C F A7 Dm
A7 Dm C Cdim G7 C G7 C

WALKING IN MEMPHIS

Words and Music by
MARC COHN

Moderate Rock ♩ = 132
Verse:
Put on my blue suede shoes and I boarded the plane.
Touched down in the land of the Del - ta Blues in the mid-dle of the pour - ing rain.
W. C. Han - dy, won't you (dou - ble u)
look down o - ver me?
Yeah, I got a first class tick - et, but I'm as blue as a boy can be.
Chorus:
Then I'm walk-ing in Mem - phis,
I was walk-ing with my feet ten feet off of Beale.
Walk-ing in Mem - phis,
but do I real - ly feel the way I feel?
Verse:
Saw the ghost of El - vis on Un - ion Av - e - nue.
Fol-lowed him up to the gates of Grace - land,
then I watched him walk right through.
Now, se - cu - ri - ty, they did not see him.
They just hov - ered 'round his tomb.
But there's a pret - ty lit - tle thing wait - ing for the King,
down in the Jun - gle Room.
Chorus:
When I was walk-ing in Mem - phis,
I was walk-ing with my feet ten feet off of Beale.
Walk-ing in Mem - phis,
but do I real - ly feel the way I feel?
They've got
Bridge:
cat-fish on the ta - ble.
They've got gos - pel in the air.

*Chord symbols in parentheses indicate implied harmony.

Rubato - vocal ad lib.
And Rev - er - end Green be glad to see you when you have-n't got a prayer. But
a tempo
boy you got a prayer in Mem - phis...
Verse:
Now, Mu - ri - el plays pi - a - no ev - 'ry Fri - day at the Hol - ly - wood.
And they brought me down to see her, and they asked me if I would do a lit - tle num - ber.
And I sang with all my might. She said, "Tell me, are you a Christ - ian, child?" And I said,
"Ma'am, I am to - night."
Chorus:
Walk-ing in Mem - phis, I was walk-ing with my feet ten feet off of Beale. Walk-ing in Mem - phis, but do I real - ly feel the way I feel?
Walk - ing in Mem - feel the way I feel?
Put on my blue suede shoes and I board-ed the plane. Touched down in the land of the Del - ta Blues in the mid-dle of the pour - ing rain.
Touched down in the land of the Del - ta Blues in the mid-dle of the pour - ing
rit.
Tempo I
rain.

WASTED DAYS AND WASTED NIGHTS

Words and Music by
WAYNE M. DUNCAN
FREDDY FENDER

Moderately
N.C.
Wast-ed days and wast-ed nights
you
I have left for you be - hind,
when I know that you're not true?
for you don't be-long to
And why should I call your
me; your heart be - longs to some-one else.
name when you're the
Why should I keep lov - ing
blame for mak-ing me blue?
Don't you re - mem-ber the day that you went a-way and left me?
I was so lone-ly, prayed for you on - ly, my love.
Why should I keep lov-ing you when I know that you're not true?
And why should I call your name when you're the blame for mak-ing me blue?

WHY SHOULDN'T I?

Words and Music by
COLE PORTER

Slowly, with tender expression
Why should-n't I take a chance when ro-mance pass-es by, why should-n't I know of love?
Why wait a - round, when each age has a sage who has found that up - on this earth, love is
all that is real-ly worth think-ing of.
It must be fun, lots of fun, to be sure when day is
done, that the hour is com - ing when you'll be kissed and then you'll be kissed a - gain, all de - bu - tantes say it's
good, and ev-'ry star out in far Hol-ly - wood seems to give it a try, so why should-n't I?

From the Original Motion Picture Soundtrack "YENTL"

THE WAY HE MAKES ME FEEL

Lyrics by ALAN and MARILYN BERGMAN
Music by MICHEL LEGRAND

Slowly, with expression

Dm Dm/C♯ Dm/C Bm7(♭5) B♭maj7 Gm7 E♭maj7
There's no chill, and yet I shiv-er. There's no flame and yet I burn. I'm not sure what I'm a-fraid of and yet I'm
(feel.) *(2nd time instrumental.)*

A7sus A7 Dm Dm/C♯ F/C Bm7(♭5) Am/E Bm7/E Amaj7
trem-b'ling. There's no storm yet I hear thun-der, and I'm breath-less; why, I won-der? Weak one mo-ment, then the next I'm fine.

D6/A Bdim7/A Asus Amaj7
(end instr.) I feel as if I'm fall-ing ev-'ry time I close my eyes, and flow-ing through my bod-y is a
Oh, why is it that ev-'ry time I close my eyes he's there, the wa-ter shin-ing on his skin, the

Dmaj7 G♯m7(♭5) C♯7sus C♯7 F♯m9 F9(♯5) F♯m/E F7(♯5)/E
riv-er of sur-prise. Feel-ings are a-wak-en-ing I hard-ly re-cog-nize as mine!
sun-light in his hair? And all the while I'm think-ing things that I can nev-er share with him.

Dm Dm/C♯ Dm7/C Bm7(♭5) B♭maj7 G9
What are all these new sen-sa-tions? What's the se-cret they re-veal? I'm not sure I un-der-stand, but I
I'm a bun-dle of con-fu-sion, yet it has a strange ap-peal. Did it all be-gin with him and the

1. B♭maj7 A7sus *D.C.* 2. B♭maj7 A7sus Dm Dm7/C B♭maj7 F/A A7 Dm
like the way I way he makes me feel? I like the way he makes me feel.

WE GATHER TOGETHER TO ASK THE LORD'S BLESSING

(Prayer of Thanksgiving)

TRADITIONAL

With expression
D G/D D Em7 /F♯ A7 D A/C♯
We gath-er to-geth-er to ask the Lord's bless-ing. He chas-tens and
side us, to guide us, our God with us join-ing, or-dain-ing, main-
all do ex-tol Thee, Thou lead-er tri-um-phant, and pray that Thou
Bm7 E7 A Bm/D E7 A A7 D/A D/F♯ Em7 A7
has-tens His will to make known. The wick-ed op-press-ing now cease from dis-
tain-ing His king-dom di-vine. So from the be-gin-ning the fight we were
still our de-fend-er wilt be. Let Thy con-gre-ga-tion es-cape tri-bu-
D D7 G/B G A/C♯ A D Em7 A7 1.2. D 3. D
tress-ing. Sing prais-es to His name: He for-gets not His own. Be-free!
win-ing. Thou Lord, wast at our side; all glo-ry be thine. We
la-tion. Thy name be ev-er praised! O Lord, make us

From the 20th Century-Fox Warner Bros. film "THE TOWERING INFERNO"

WE MAY NEVER LOVE LIKE THIS AGAIN

Words and Music by
AL KASHA and JOEL HIRSCHHORN

Moderately slow

C Dsus D G A7 Dsus D G
We may nev - er love like this a - gain; don't stop the flow, we can't let go.

C Dsus D G A A/C♯ Dsus D
We may nev - er love like this a - gain, and touch the sky though we may try.

G Em G G7/B C
So while we're here let's give our all; re - lease the dreams in - side us and set them free.

Am F D D/C G/B G7
Oh, while we're here let's leave a mark; there's a can - dle in the dark, it's here to guide us.

C Dsus D G Am7 Dsus D G
We may nev - er love like this a - gain, but through the days, be - yond the haze I see you

C G/B Am7 G D D/C G/B
reach - ing out to hold me. I don't know just where or when, still I'm sure we'll love a -

G F/G G F/G G
gain. We may nev - er love like this a - gain; we'll love a - gain. We may nev - er love like this a - gain; we'll love a - gain.

WHEN I GROW TOO OLD TO DREAM

Lyric by OSCAR HAMMERSTEIN II
Music by SIGMUND ROMBERG

Slowly
F Gm7 C7 F F7 B♭ C7
When I grow too old to dream, I'll have you to re - mem - ber. When I grow too
F Dm F/C C7 F Am Gm F
old to dream, your love will live in my heart. So kiss me, my sweet, and so
A7 Dm F7 B♭ C7 F Dm D♭7 F/C C7 F
let us part. And when I grow too old to dream, that kiss will live in my heart.

From the Tri-Star Pictures Feature Film, "Hook"

WE DON'T WANNA GROW UP

Lyrics by LESLIE BRICUSSE
Music by JOHN WILLIAMS

Moderately
C Dm7 G7 C F C F F♯ G C Dm7 C/E F
We wan-na be like Pe-ter Pan, we don't wan-na grow up! Wan-na stay kids as long as we can,
F♯ G F F♯ G C F C F F♯ G C Dm7
that's our plan! Pret-ty neat plan!! Then when it's time to be a man, we're not gon-na show up! Gon-na stay kids like
C/E F Dm7 G7 C F D♯dim7 Em
we be-gan, just like Pe-ter Pan! Be-in' a man means you got-ta show up for work each day in a shirt an' a tie!
F F♯7 G7 Gdim7 G7 Gdim7 G7 Gdim7 G7 C
Be-in' grown up means you got-ta call up your friends and say, "Can't stay! Got-ta fly!" Yuck! We got an e-ven
F C F F♯ G C Dm7 C/E F Dm7 G7
neat-er plan, sit down and lis-ten up. We all ought-a be like Pe-ter Pan, we don't wan-na grow
C Dm C♯dim7 Dm C Cdim7 C Dm7 G7 C
up! We nev-er, nev-er, nev-er, nev-er, nev-er, nev-er, nev-er, nev-er, nev-er, nev-er wan-na grow up! Yuck!

WHEN IRISH EYES ARE SMILING

Words by CHAUNCEY OLCOTT & GEO. GRAFF JR.
Music by ERNEST R. BALL

Moderately, with expression
D D/F♯ G D
When I-rish eyes are smil-ing, sure it's like a morn in Spring. In the
G D B7 E7 A7 D
lilt of I-rish laugh-ter, you can hear the an-gels sing. When I-rish
D/F♯ G D G G♯dim
hearts are hap-py, all the world seems bright and gay. And when I-rish eyes are
D/A B7 E7 A7 1. D A7 2. D
smil-ing, sure they steal your heart a-way. When way.

WE HAD IT ALL

Words and Music by
TROY SEALS and
DONNIE FRITTS

Moderately
Verses 1 & 2:
C G/B Am C/G F
1. I can hear the wind a - blow - ing in my mind, just the way it
mem - ber how I used to touch your hair, while reach-ing for the
G7 F C G/B Am
used to sound through the Geor - gia pines, and you were there to an - swer when I called.
feel - ing that was al - ways there. You were the best thing in my life I can re - call.
C/G F G7 1. C C/G 2. C
You and me, Lord knows, we had it all. 2. Re - all.
You and me, we had it
Chorus:
C C/B♭ F/A C C/B♭
I know that we can nev - er live those times a - gain, so I let my dreams take me
F/A C C/B♭ F/A C C/E
back to where we've been; then I'll stay there with you just as long as I can.
F C F C F C
Oh, it was so good, oh, it was so good, oh, it was so good,
G7 C A7
when I was your man.
Verse 3:
D A/C♯ Bm
3. And I'll nev - er stop be - liev - ing in your smile,
D/A G A G D
e - ven though you did - n't stay, it was all worth while. You were the best thing in my
A/C♯ Bm D/A G A D
life I can re - call, you and me, we had it all.

WE THREE KINGS OF ORIENT ARE

Words and Music by
JOHN HENRY HOPKINS

Moderately
1. We three kings of O - ri - ent are, bear - ing gifts we tra - verse a - far, field and foun - tain, moor and moun - tain, fol - low - ing yon - der star.
2. Born a King on Beth - le - hem's plain, gold I bring to crown Him a - gain, King for - ev - er, ceas - ing nev - er, o - ver us all to reign.
3. Frank - in - cense to of - fer have I, in - cense owns a De - i - ty nigh. Pray'r and prais - ing all men rais - ing, wor - ship Him, God most high.
4. Myrrh is mine, its bit - ter per - fume, breathes of life of gath - er - ing gloom; sor - row - ing, sigh - ing, bleed - ing, dy - ing, sealed in the stone - cold tomb.
5. Glo - rious now be - hold Him a - rise, King and God and Sac - ri - fice. Al - le - lu - ia, al - le - lu - ia, Earth to heav'n re - plies.
O, star of won - der, star of night, star with roy - al beau - ty bright; west - ward lead - ing still pro - ceed - ing, guide us to Thy per - fect light. light.
1.2.3.4. D.C.
5.

WE WISH YOU A MERRY CHRISTMAS

TRADITIONAL

Brightly, with spirit
1. We wish you a Mer - ry Christ - mas; we wish you a Mer - ry Christ - mas; we wish you a Mer - ry Christ - mas and a Hap - py New Year.
bring us a fig - gy pud - ding; oh, bring us a fig - gy pud - ding; oh, bring us a fig - gy pud - ding and a cup of good cheer.
won't go un - til we've got some; we won't go un - til we've got some; we won't go un - til we've got some, so bring some out here.
Good tid - ings to you wher - ev - er you are; good tid - ings for Christ - mas and a Hap - py New Year.
2. Oh,
3. We
Year. We wish you a Mer - ry Christ - mas; we wish you a Mer - ry Christ - mas; we wish you a Mer - ry Christ - mas and a Hap - py New Year.

WEDDING MARCH
(from "A Midsummer Night's Dream")

FELIX MENDELSSOHN

Brightly

Am6 B7 Em Dm C G7 C Am6 B7 Em Dm C G7
C G7 C G7 C Dm D7 G7
Am6 B7 Em Dm C G7 C Am6 B7 Em Gdim Dm C G7 C

WE'VE ONLY JUST BEGUN

Lyric by PAUL WILLIAMS
Music by ROGER NICHOLS

Slowly

Eb Abmaj7 Gm7 Cm7 Fm9

1. We've on - ly just be - gun ___ to live. ___ White lace and prom - is - es;
2. Be - fore the ris - ing sun ___ we fly. ___ So man - y roads to choose,
3.4. And when the eve - ning comes ___ we smile. ___ so much of life a - head.

To Coda 1. 2.3.

Cm9 Fm9 Bb7sus Bb7 Bb7sus

a kiss for luck _ and we're on our way. ___
we start out walk - ing and learn to run. ___
We'll find a place _ where there's room to grow. ___
And yes, we've just be -

Ebmaj7 Abmaj7 Ebmaj7 Abmaj7 Bb C Fmaj7 C Fmaj7

gun. ___ Shar - ing hor - i - zons that are new to us,

C Fmaj7 Cmaj7 Fmaj7 E Amaj7 E Amaj7

watch-ing the signs a - long the way. Talk - ing it o - ver just the two of us,

1. D.C. 2. D.C. al Coda

E Amaj7 Bb7sus Bb9sus Bb9sus

work-ing to - geth - er day to day. to - geth - er. ___ geth - er, ___ to - geth - er. ___

Coda

Bb7sus Ebmaj7 Abmaj7 Ebmaj9 Abmaj7 G

And yes, we've just be - gun. ___

WEEKEND IN NEW ENGLAND

Words and Music by
RANDY EDELMAN

Moderately
Verse:
1. Last night I said good-bye; now it seems years. I'm back in the cit-y where_ noth-ing is__ clear__ but thoughts of me hold-ing_ you, bring-ing us__ near.__
2. Time in New Eng-land__ took me a-way to long rock-y beach-es and__ you by the__ bay.__ We start-ed a sto-ry__ whose end must now_ wait.__
And tell me,
Chorus:
when will our eyes meet? When_ can I touch you? When_ will this strong yearn-ing end?__ And when will I hold you__ a-gain?__
gain? I
Bridge:
feel the change com-in',__ I feel the wind blow. I feel brave and dar-ing, I feel my blood_ flow.__
With you, I could bring out all the love that I have. With you, there's_ a heav-en,__ so earth ain't so__ bad.__
And tell me,__ when will our eyes meet? When_ can I touch you? When_ will this strong yearn-ing end?__ And when will I hold you__ a-gain,__ a-gain?__
a tempo

From the M-G-M Picture "THE WIZARD OF OZ"

WE'RE OFF TO SEE THE WIZARD
(The Wonderful Wizard of Oz)

Lyrics by E.Y. HARBURG
Music by HAROLD ARLEN

Moderate march

C G7 C G7 C Dm7 F G7
Fol-low the yel-low brick road. Fol-low the yel-low brick road. Fol - low, fol - low, fol - low, fol - low,

Am7 D7 Dm7 G7 Dm7 G7 C Dm7 G7 C Dm7
fol-low the yel-low brick road. Fol-low the rain-bow o-ver the stream; fol-low the fel-low who fol-lows a dream. Fol - low, fol - low,

Chorus:

F G7 Am7 D7 Dm7 G7 C G7 C Dm7 G7 C F F/A
fol - low, fol - low, fol-low the yel-low brick road. We're off to see the Wiz-ard, the won-der-ful Wiz-ard of Oz. We hear he is a

Em/G Dm/F Am7 D7 G7 Dm7 D♯dim7 C/E Am7 Dm7 G7 C F /A
whiz of a Wiz if ev-er a Wiz there was. If ev-er, oh, ev-er a Wiz there was, the Wiz-ard of Oz is one be-coz, be - coz, be-coz, be -

Em/G F Em7 D7 G7 D7(♭5) Am7 D7 G7 C G7
coz, be-coz, be - coz, be - coz of the won-der-ful things he does. *(Whistle)* We're off to see the

C Dm7 G7 C F C G7 1. C G7 2. C
Wiz-ard, the won-der-ful Wiz-ard of Oz. We're

WHEN YOUR LOVER HAS GONE

Words and Music by
E. A. SWAN

Moderato
Gmaj7 G7 G6 Gm Gm(maj7) Gm7 Gm6 C A9 A7(♭9)
When you're a - lone, who cares for star - lit skies, when you're a -
What lone - ly hours, the eve - ning shad - ows bring, what lone - ly
A7 Cm(maj7) Cm7 Cm6 G/B B7 Em Cm6
lone, the mag - ic moon - light dies; at break of dawn,
hours, with mem - 'ries lin - ger - ing; like fad - ed flow'rs,
1.
A7 A6 A7 G/D A9/D D+ G A♭m6 D7/A D7(♯5)
there is no sun - rise, when your lov - er has gone.
2.
G/D D7/C Cdim B6 E7 E7(♯5) E7 Am E♭7 D7(♯5) G G9 A9 E♭9 G9
life can't mean an - y - thing, when your lov - er has gone.

From the United Artists Motion Picture "THE HAPPY ENDING"

WHAT ARE YOU DOING THE REST OF YOUR LIFE?

Lyrics by ALAN and MARILYN BERGMAN
Music by MICHEL LEGRAND
Slowly
What are you do - ing the rest of your life, north and south and east and west of your life? I have on - ly one re - quest of your life: that you spend it all with me!
time of your days, all the nick - els and the dimes of your days. Let the rea-sons and the rhymes of your days
deep in your eyes, in the world of love you keep in your eyes, I'll a - wa-ken what's a - sleep in your eyes.
To Coda
All the sea-sons and the all be-gin and end with me.
I want to see your face in ev-'ry kind of light, in fields of dawn and for-ests of the night. And when you stand be-fore the can-dles on a cake, oh, let me be the one to hear the si - lent wish you make! Those to - mor-rows wait-ing
D.S. al Coda
Coda
It may take a kiss or two! Through all of my life, sum-mer, win-ter, spring and fall of my life, all I ev - er will re - call of my life is all of my life with you!
WHAT'S NEW
Copyright © 1939 (Renewed 1966) MARKE MUSIC PUBLISHING CO., INC., LIMERICK MUSIC CORPORATION, REGANESQUE MUSIC CO., TIMO-CO MUSIC and WARNER BROS. MUSIC
All Rights Administered by THE SONGWRITERS GUILD OF AMERICA, New York, N.Y. excluding WARNER BROS. MUSIC Used by permission
All Rights Reserved
Words by JOHNNY BURKE
Music by BOB HAGGART
Slowly
What's new? How is the world treat - ing you? You have-n't changed a bit; love - ly as ev - er, I must ad - mit. What's new?
How did that ro - mance come through? We have-n't met since then. Gee! But it's nice to see you a - gain.
What's new? Prob-a-bly I'm bor-ing you, but see-ing you is grand, and you were sweet to of - fer your hand. I un - der - stand, a - dieu!
Par-don my ask-ing what's new. Of course you could-n't know, I have-n't changed, I still love you so.

WHAT IS THIS THING CALLED LOVE?

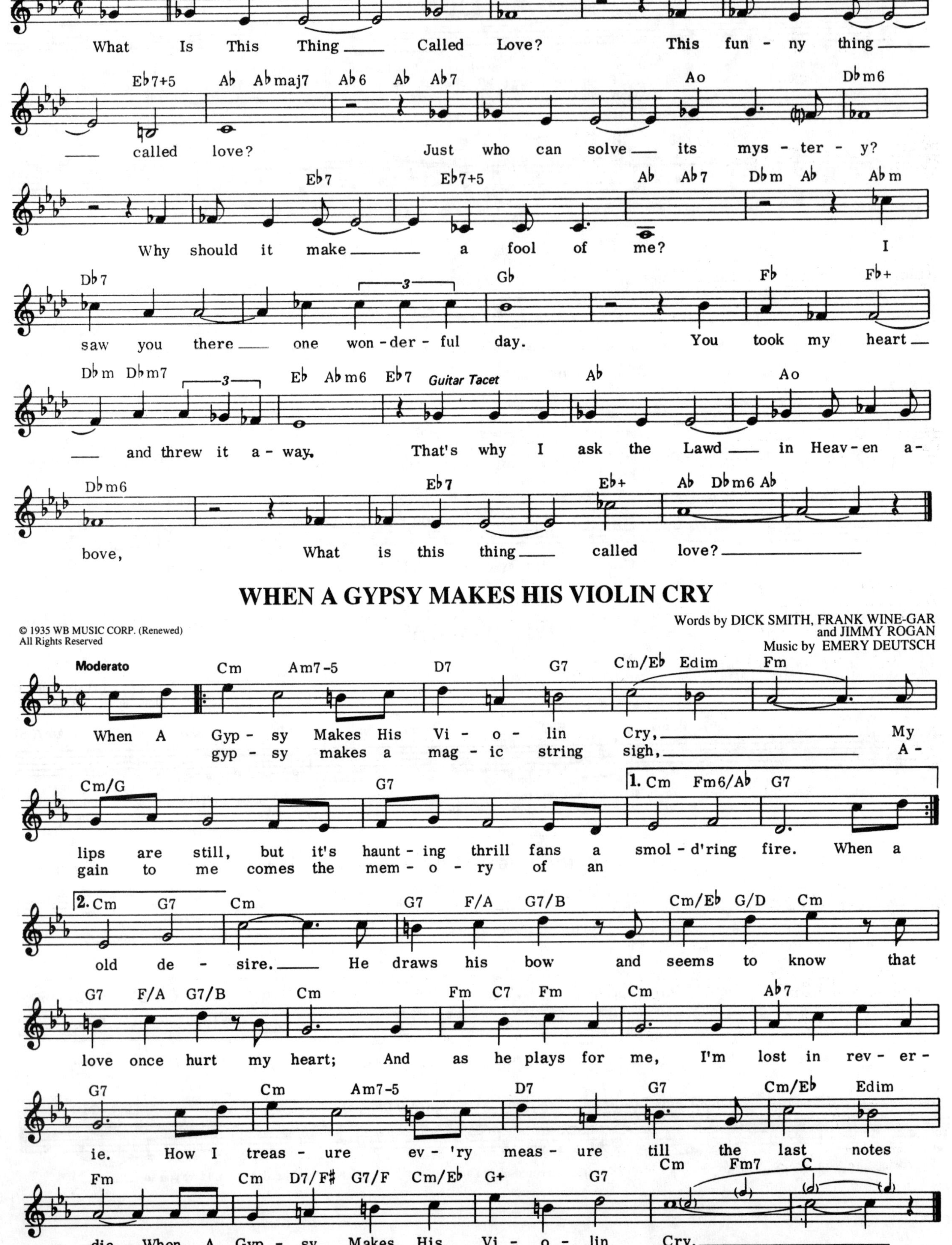
© 1929 WARNER BROS. INC. (Renewed)
All Rights Reserved
Words and Music by
COLE PORTER
Slow (in the manner of a "Blues")
What Is This Thing Called Love? This fun - ny thing called love?
Just who can solve its mys - ter - y?
Why should it make a fool of me?
I saw you there one won - der - ful day. You took my heart
and threw it a - way.
Guitar Tacet
That's why I ask the Lawd in Heav - en a - bove,
What is this thing called love?
WHEN A GYPSY MAKES HIS VIOLIN CRY
© 1935 WB MUSIC CORP. (Renewed)
All Rights Reserved
Words by DICK SMITH, FRANK WINE-GAR
and JIMMY ROGAN
Music by EMERY DEUTSCH
Moderato
When A Gyp - sy Makes His Vi - o - lin Cry, My lips are still, but it's haunt - ing thrill fans a smol - d'ring fire. When a
gyp - sy makes a mag - ic string sigh, A - gain to me comes the mem - o - ry of an
old de - sire. He draws his bow and seems to know that love once hurt my heart;
And as he plays for me, I'm lost in rev - er - ie.
How I treas - ure ev - 'ry meas - ure till the last notes die, When A Gyp - sy Makes His Vi - o - lin Cry.

WHATEVER LOLA WANTS
(Lola Gets)

Words and Music by
RICHARD ADLER and JERRY ROSS

Bolero
Dm9 Dm A+ Dm7 E7 Em7(♭5) B♭ A7
What-ev-er Lo - la wants, Lo - la gets, and lit-tle man, lit-tle Lo - la wants you.
Dm9 Dm A+ Dm7 E7 Gm B♭ Gm A7
Make up your mind to have no re - grets. Re - cline your-self, re - sign your-self, you're
Dm E♭ D E♭
through. { I / She'll } al - ways get what { I / she'll } aim for, and your heart and soul

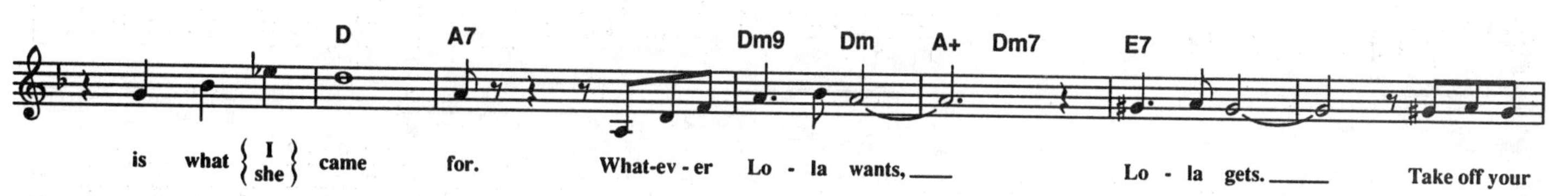
D A7 Dm9 Dm A+ Dm7 E7
is what { I / she } came for. What-ev - er Lo - la wants, Lo - la gets. Take off your

Em7(♭5) B♭ A7 Dm B♭
coat, don't you know you can't win? You're no ex - cep - tion to the rule; { I'm / she's } ir - re -
Dm A♭ A7 1. Dm A7 2. Dm D♭ Dm Dm6/9
sist - i - ble, you fool, give in! What-ev - er in!

WHEN IT'S SPRINGTIME IN THE ROCKIES

Words by MARY HALE WOOLSEY
Music by ROBERT SAUER

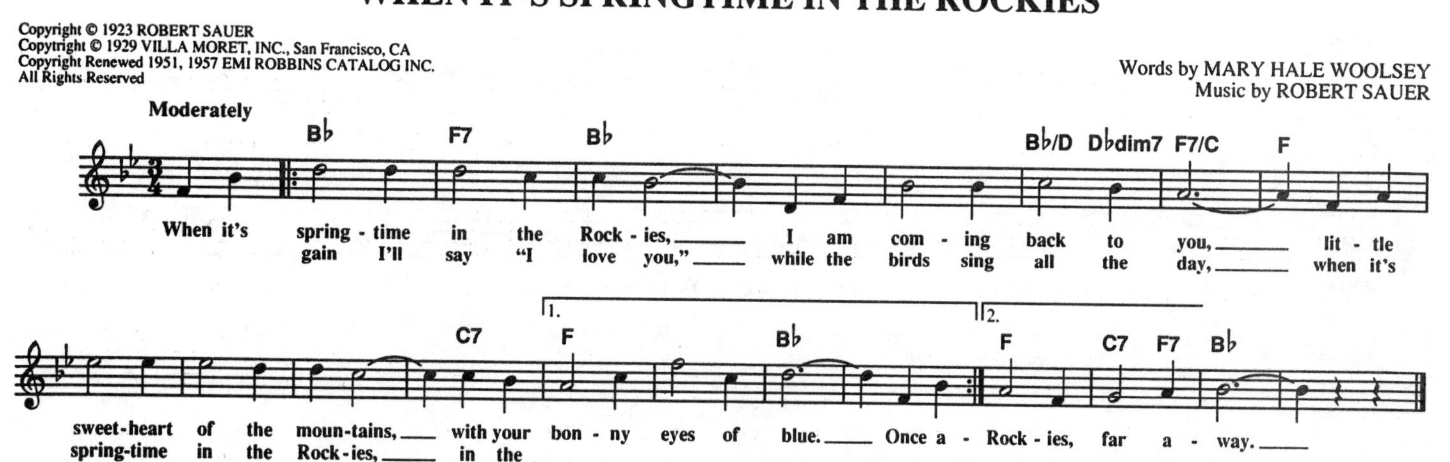
Moderately
B♭ F7 B♭ B♭/D D♭dim7 F7/C F
When it's spring - time in the Rock - ies, I am com - ing back to you, lit - tle
gain I'll say "I love you," while the birds sing all the day, when it's
C7 1. F B♭ 2. F C7 F7 B♭
sweet-heart of the moun-tains, with your bon - ny eyes of blue. Once a - Rock - ies, far a - way.
spring-time in the Rock-ies, in the

WHERE AM I GOING?

From the Musical "SWEET CHARITY"

Music by
CY COLEMAN
Lyrics by
DOROTHY FIELDS

Moderate 4, very rhythmically
Where am I go - ing and what will I find? What's in this grab - bag that I call my mind?
What am I do - ing a - lone on the shelf? Ain't it a shame, but no one's to blame but my -
self. Which way is clear when you've lost your way
year af - ter year? Do I keep fall - ing in love for just the kick of it?
Stag - ger - ing through the thin and thick of it, Hat - ing each old and ti - red trick of it.
Know what I am, I'm good and sick of it! Where am I go - ing? Why do I care?
Run to the Bronx, or Wash - ing - ton Square, No mat - ter where I run I meet my - self there,
look - ing in - side me. What do I see? An - ger and hope and doubt,
What am I all a - bout? And where am I go - ing? You tell me!

WHAT'S LOVE GOT TO DO WITH IT

Words and Music by TERRY BRITTEN
and GRAHAM LYLE

Moderate rock

Gm7 F/G 1. 2.

1. You

Verse:

Gm7 F/G Gm7

must un - der-stand, though the touch of your hand makes my pulse re - act; that it's on - ly the thrill of
may seem to you that I'm act - ing con - fused when you're close to me. If I tend to look dazed, I

F/G E♭maj7 F E♭maj7 F

boy meet - ing girl op - po - sites at - tract. It's phys - i - cal, only log - i - cal,
read it some-place; I've got cause to be. There's a name for it, there's a phrase that fits.

E♭maj7 F B♭ *Chorus:* N.C. Gm F E♭maj9 F

you must try to ig - nore that it means more than that.
But what - ev - er the rea - son, you do it for me.
Oh, what's love got to do, got to do with it?

N.C. Gm F E♭maj9 F N.C. Gm F E♭maj9 F

What's love but a sec - ond hand e - mo - tion? What's love got to do, got to do with it?

Gm F 1. E♭maj9 F 2. E♭maj9 F N.C. Am G F G

Who needs a heart, when a heart can be bro - ken? 2. It heart can be bro - ken?

N.C. Am G F G N.C. Am G F G N.C. Am G Fmaj7 *Bridge:* B♭/C

I've been tak - ing on a

C B♭/C C F C A♭ B♭/C

new di - rec - tion. But I have to say I been think - ing a - bout my own pro - tec - tion. It

Gm7sus C *Chorus:* Am G Fmaj9 G Am

scares me to feel this way. Oh, what's love got to do, got to do with it? What's love but a
bro - ken? What's love but a

Fmaj9 G Am G Fmaj9 G Am G Fmaj9

Repeat ad lib. and fade

sec - ond hand e - mo - tion?
sweet old fash - ioned no - tion?
What's love got to do, got to do with it? Who needs a heart when a heart can be

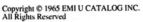

From the United Artists Motion Picture "WHAT'S NEW PUSSYCAT?"

WHAT'S NEW PUSSYCAT?

Words by HAL DAVID
Music by BURT BACHARACH

Moderately
Chorus:

C F6 G6 C F6 G6
What's new Pus-sy-cat? Whoa! What's new Pus-sy-cat? Whoa,

C D D7
oh, oh.

Verse:
G B♭
1. Pus - sy - cat, Pus - sy - cat, I've got flow - ers and lots of
2. Pus - sy - cat, Pus - sy - cat, you're so thrill - ing and I'm so
3. Pus - sy - cat, Pus - sy - cat, you're de - li - cious and if my

A♭
hours to spend with you. So go and pow - der your cute lit - tle pus - sy - cat nose.
will - ing to care for you. So go and make up your big lit - tle pus - sy - cat eyes.
wish - es can all come true, I'll soon be kiss - ing your sweet lit - tle pus - sy - cat lips.

G Cmaj7 Bm7 Am7 D6 Bm7 Em7 | 1.2. Am7 D7
Pus - sy - cat, Pus - sy - cat, I love you, yes I do. You and your pus - sy - cat nose.
Pus - sy - cat, Pus - sy - cat, I love you, yes I do. You and your pus - sy - cat eyes.
Pus - sy - cat, Pus - sy - cat, I love you, yes I do.

G D.C. | 3. Am7 D7 G Am7 D7 G
You and your pus - sy - cat lips. You and your pus - sy - cat nose.
You and your pus - sy - cat eyes.

WHEN JOHNNY COMES MARCHING HOME

Words and Music by
LOUIS LAMBERT

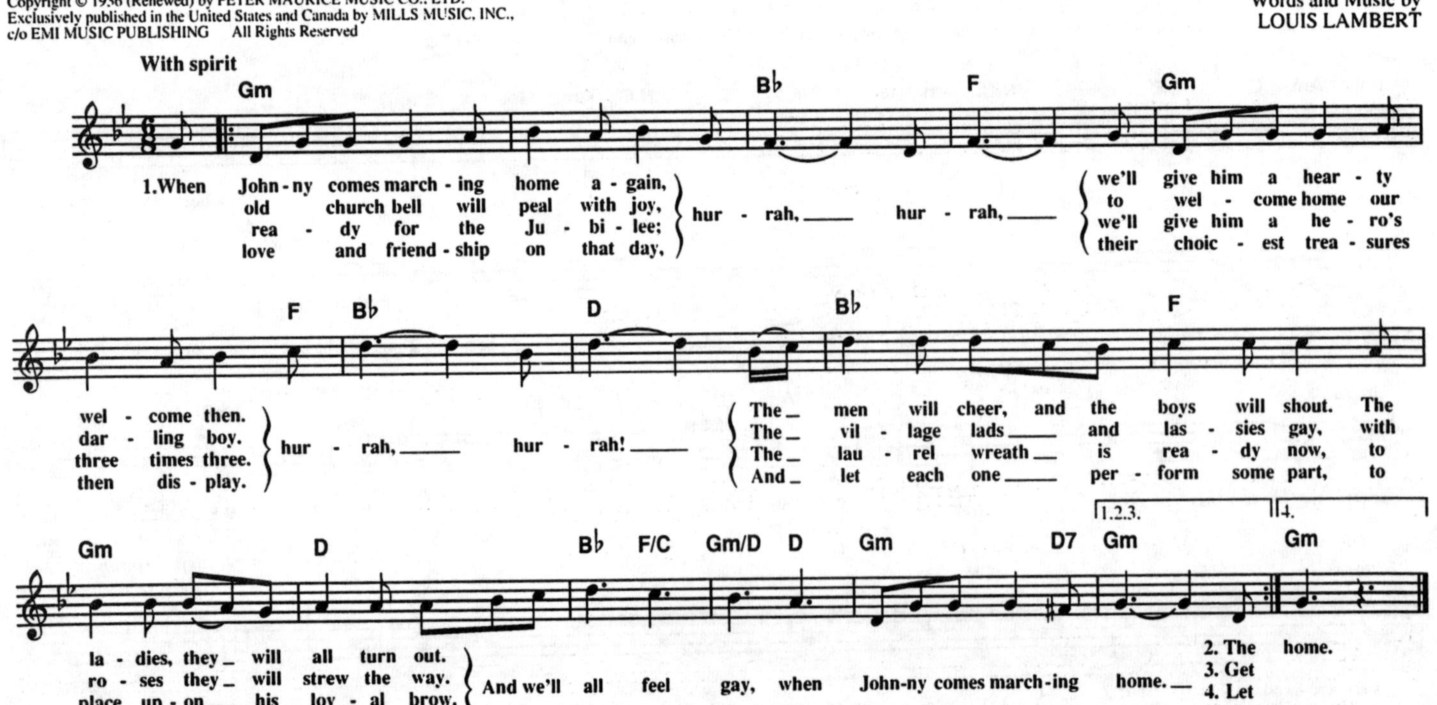
With spirit
Gm B♭ F Gm
1.When John-ny comes march-ing home a-gain, hur-rah, hur-rah, we'll give him a hear-ty
old church bell will peal with joy, to wel-come home our
rea-dy for the Ju-bi-lee; we'll give him a he-ro's
love and friend-ship on that day, their choic-est trea-sures
F B♭ D B♭ F
wel-come then. hur-rah, hur-rah! The men will cheer, and the boys will shout. The
dar-ling boy. The vil-lage lads and las-sies gay, with
three times three. The lau-rel wreath is rea-dy now, to
then dis-play. And let each one per-form some part, to
Gm D B♭ F/C Gm/D D Gm D7 Gm Gm
la-dies, they will all turn out. And we'll all feel gay, when John-ny comes march-ing home. 2. The home.
ro-ses they will strew the way. 3. Get
place up-on his loy-al brow. 4. Let
fill with joy the war-rior's heart.
1.2.3.
4.

WHEN MY BLUE MOON TURNS TO GOLD AGAIN

Words and Music by
WILEY WALKER and
GENE SULLIVAN

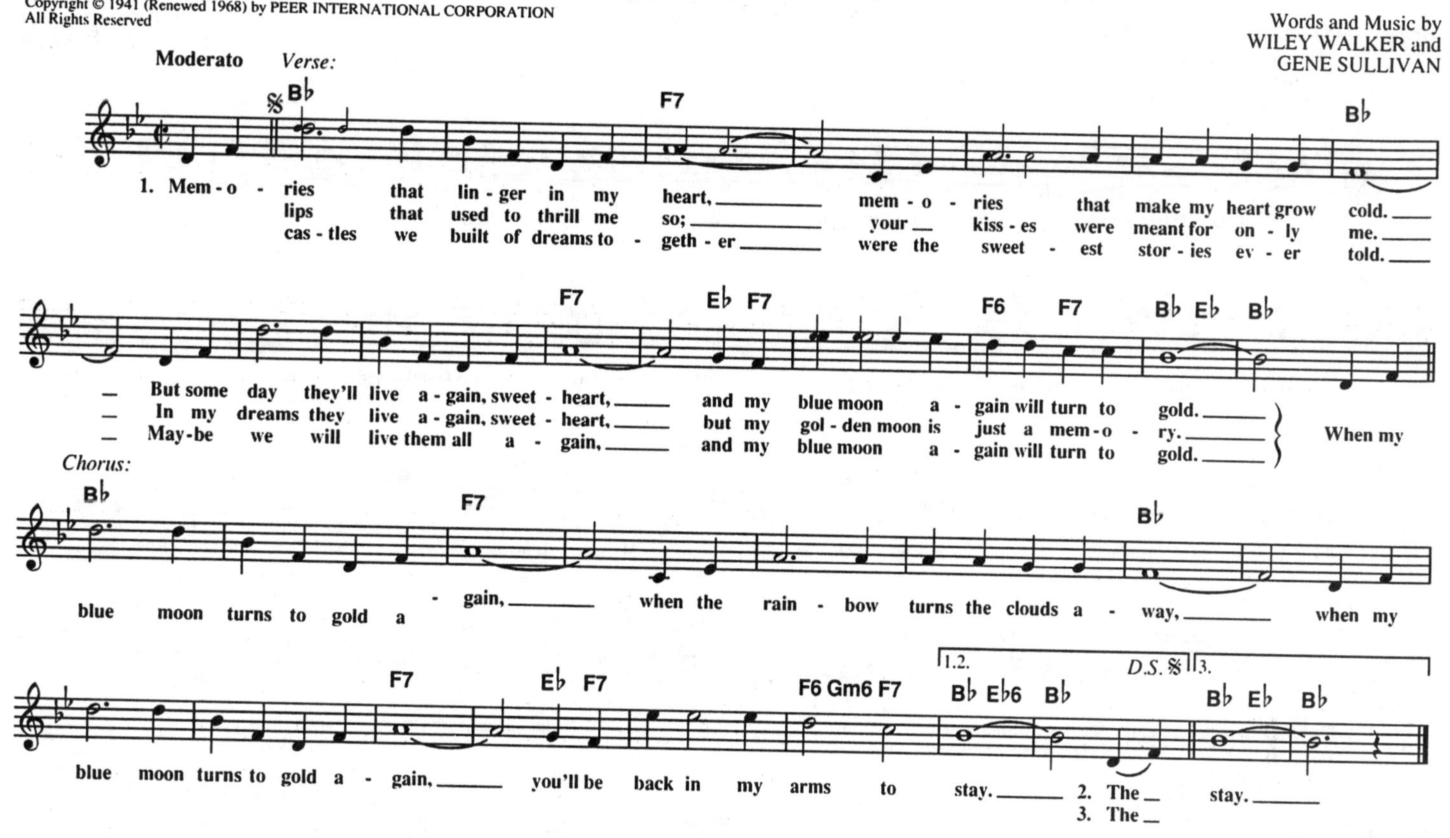
Moderato Verse:
B♭ F7 B♭
1. Mem-o-ries that lin-ger in my heart, mem-o-ries that make my heart grow cold.
lips that used to thrill me so; your kiss-es were meant for on-ly me.
cas-tles we built of dreams to-geth-er were the sweet-est stor-ies ev-er told.
F7 E♭ F7 F6 F7 B♭ E♭ B♭
But some day they'll live a-gain, sweet-heart, and my blue moon a-gain will turn to gold.
In my dreams they live a-gain, sweet-heart, but my gol-den moon is just a mem-o-ry.
May-be we will live them all a-gain, and my blue moon a-gain will turn to gold.
When my
Chorus:
B♭ F7 B♭
blue moon turns to gold a-gain, when the rain-bow turns the clouds a-way, when my
F7 E♭ F7 F6 Gm6 F7 B♭ E♭6 B♭ B♭ E♭ B♭
blue moon turns to gold a-gain, you'll be back in my arms to stay.
1.2. D.S. 3.
2. The 3. The stay.

WHEN MY SUGAR WALKS DOWN THE STREET

(All the Little Birdies Go Tweet, Tweet, Tweet)

By GENE AUSTIN, JIMMY McHUGH
and IRVING MILLS

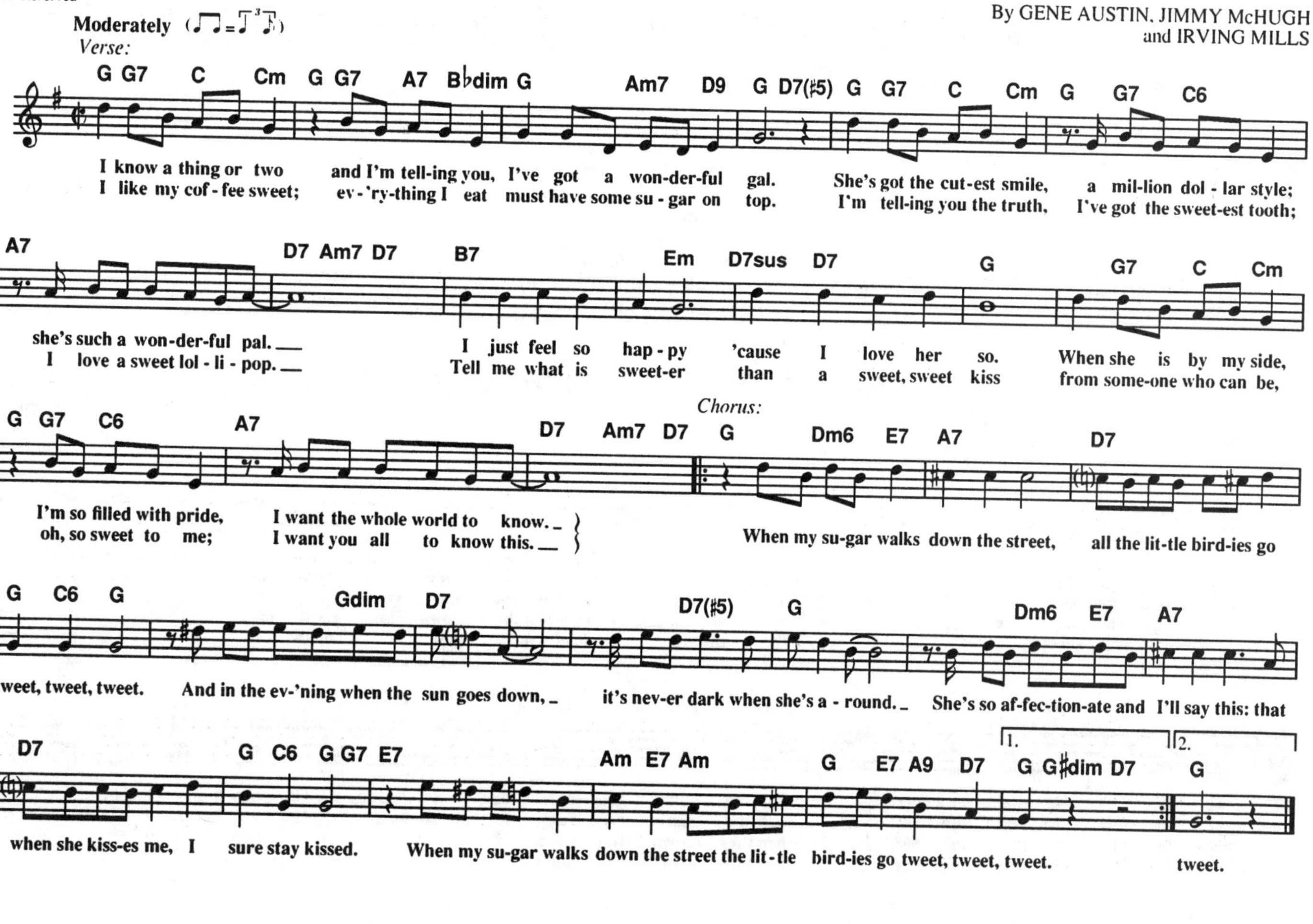

Moderately

Verse:

G G7 C Cm G G7 A7 B♭dim G Am7 D9 G D7(♯5) G G7 C Cm G G7 C6

I know a thing or two and I'm tell-ing you, I've got a won-der-ful gal. She's got the cut-est smile, a mil-lion dol-lar style;
I like my cof-fee sweet; ev-'ry-thing I eat must have some su-gar on top. I'm tell-ing you the truth, I've got the sweet-est tooth;

A7 D7 Am7 D7 B7 Em D7sus D7 G G7 C Cm

she's such a won-der-ful pal. I just feel so hap-py 'cause I love her so. When she is by my side,
I love a sweet lol-li-pop. Tell me what is sweet-er than a sweet, sweet kiss from some-one who can be,

G G7 C6 A7 D7 Am7 D7

I'm so filled with pride, I want the whole world to know.
oh, so sweet to me; I want you all to know this.

Chorus:

G Dm6 E7 A7 D7

When my su-gar walks down the street, all the lit-tle bird-ies go

G C6 G Gdim D7 D7(♯5) G Dm6 E7 A7

tweet, tweet, tweet. And in the ev-'ning when the sun goes down, it's nev-er dark when she's a-round. She's so af-fec-tion-ate and I'll say this: that

D7 G C6 G G7 E7 Am E7 Am G E7 A9 D7 G G♯dim D7 G

when she kiss-es me, I sure stay kissed. When my su-gar walks down the street the lit-tle bird-ies go tweet, tweet, tweet. tweet.

WHEN SOMETHING IS WRONG WITH MY BABY

Words and Music by
ISAAC HAYES and
DAVID PORTER

Moderately slow

Verse:

Db Bbm Gb Ab

1. *He:* When some-thing is wrong with my ba - by, some-thing is wrong with me.

Db Bbm Gb Ab G Gb

And if I know that she's wor - ried, I know I'd feel the same mis-er-y.

Fm Bb7 Fm Gb7

She: We've been through so much to-geth - er. We stand as one, that's what makes it bet - ter.

Db/Ab Ebm7 Db/Ab Gb | 1. Db Gb/Ab Ab

Both: When some-thing is wrong with my ba - by some-thing is wrong with me.

2. Db N.C. Db/Ab Ebm N.C. *(Play 3 times)*

me. When some-thing is wrong with my ba - by,

Db/Ab Gb Db N.C. Db/Ab Ebm N.C. *Repeat and fade*

some-thing is wrong with me.

Verse 2:

He: Just what she means to me now,
Oh, you just wouldn't understand.
People can say that she's no good,
But ah, she's my woman and I know I'm her man.

She: And if he's got a problem,
Oh, I know I got to help him solve'em.

Both: When something is wrong with my baby,
Something is wrong with me.

WHEN THE SAINTS GO MARCHING IN

By DAVE BARTHOLOMEW
and ANTOINE DOMINO

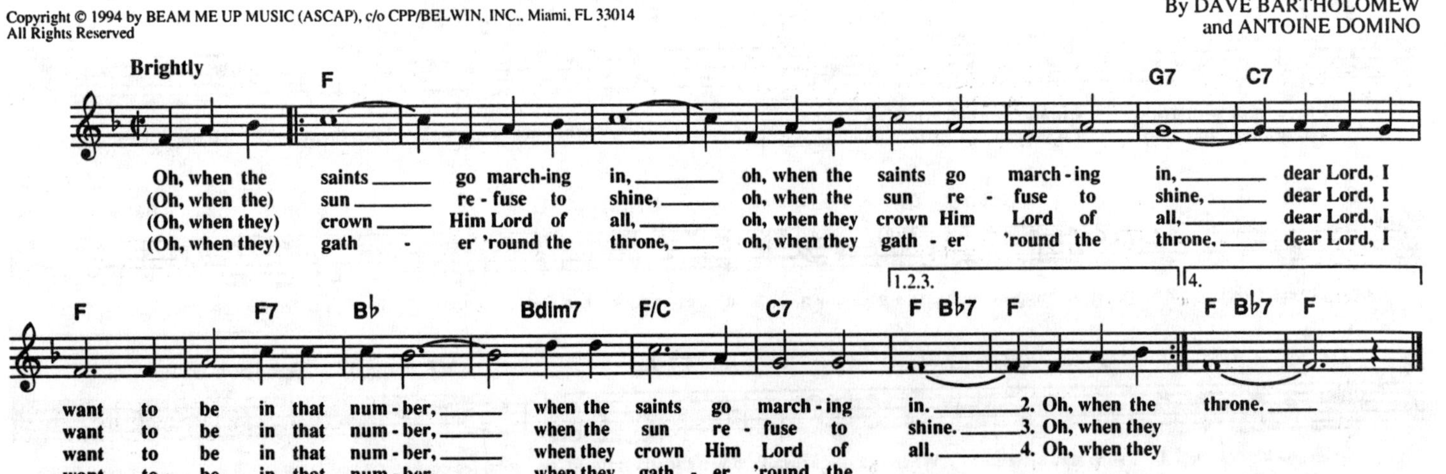
Brightly
F G7 C7
Oh, when the saints go march-ing in, oh, when the saints go march-ing in, dear Lord, I
(Oh, when the) sun re - fuse to shine, oh, when the sun re - fuse to shine, dear Lord, I
(Oh, when they) crown Him Lord of all, oh, when they crown Him Lord of all, dear Lord, I
(Oh, when they) gath - er 'round the throne, oh, when they gath - er 'round the throne, dear Lord, I
F F7 Bb Bdim7 F/C C7 1.2.3. F Bb7 F 4. F Bb7 F
want to be in that num - ber, when the saints go march - ing in. 2. Oh, when the throne.
want to be in that num - ber, when the sun re - fuse to shine. 3. Oh, when they
want to be in that num - ber, when they crown Him Lord of all. 4. Oh, when they
want to be in that num - ber, when they gath - er 'round the

WHEN THE RED, RED ROBIN COMES BOB, BOB, BOBBIN' ALONG

By HARRY WOODS

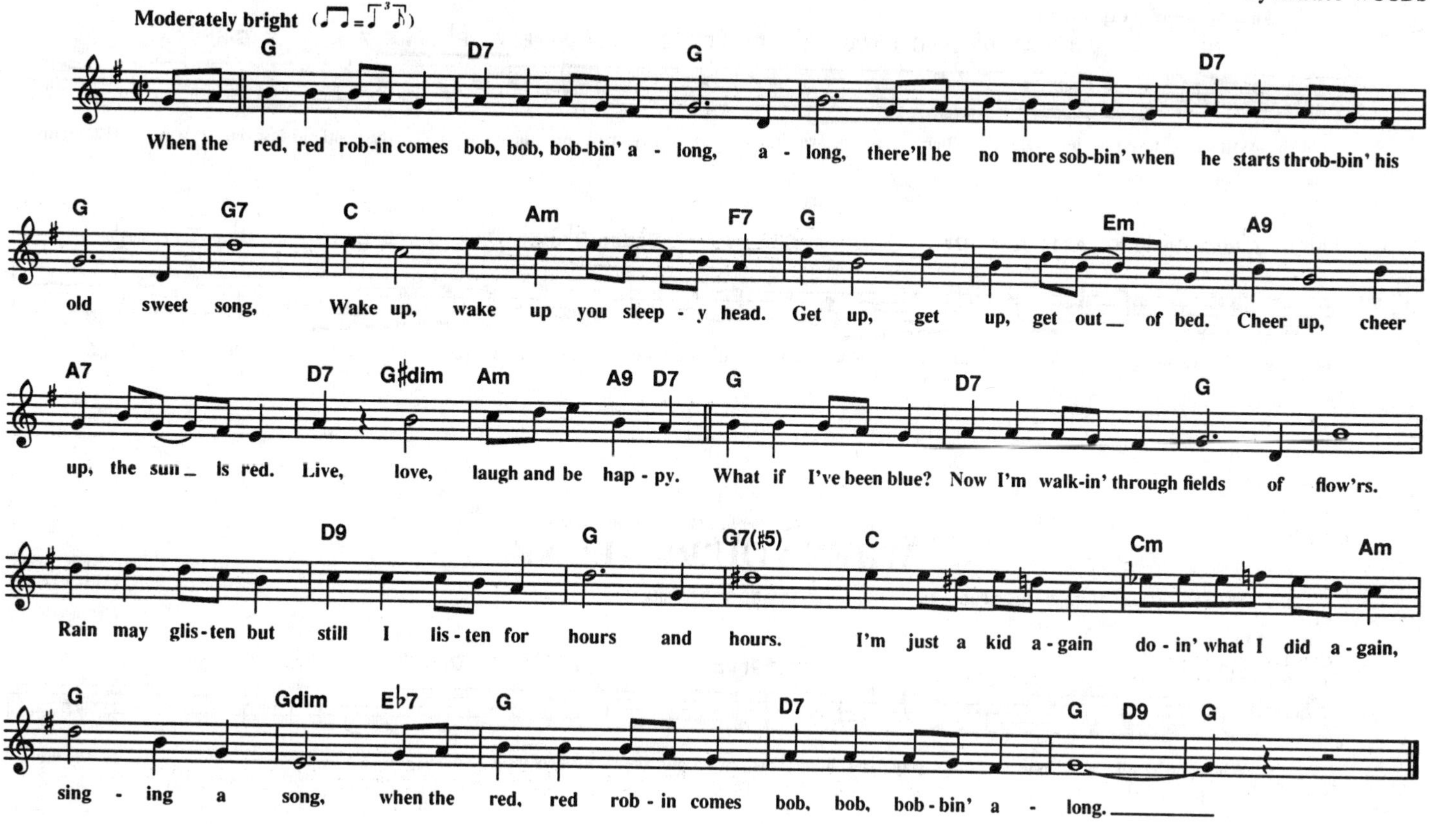

Moderately bright

When the red, red rob-in comes bob, bob, bob-bin' a - long, a - long, there'll be no more sob-bin' when he starts throb-bin' his old sweet song, Wake up, wake up you sleep - y head. Get up, get up, get out of bed. Cheer up, cheer up, the sun is red. Live, love, laugh and be hap - py. What if I've been blue? Now I'm walk-in' through fields of flow'rs. Rain may glis-ten but still I lis - ten for hours and hours. I'm just a kid a - gain do - in' what I did a - gain, sing - ing a song, when the red, red rob - in comes bob, bob, bob - bin' a - long.

WHEN WILL I BE LOVED

Words and Music by
PHIL EVERLY

Moderately bright rock shuffle

I've been cheat - ed, been mis - treat - ed. When will I be - loved?

I've been pushed down; I've been pushed 'round.
I've been made blue; I've been lied to.
I've been cheat - ed; been mis - treat - ed.

When will I be loved?

To Coda

When I find a new man that I want for mine, he al - ways breaks my heart in two; it hap-pens ev - ery time.

1st time D.S.
2nd time D.S. al Coda

Coda

When will I be loved? Tell me when will I be loved?

freely

WILL YOU LOVE ME IN DECEMBER
(As You Do In May?)

Words by JAMES J. WALKER
Music by ERNEST R. BALL

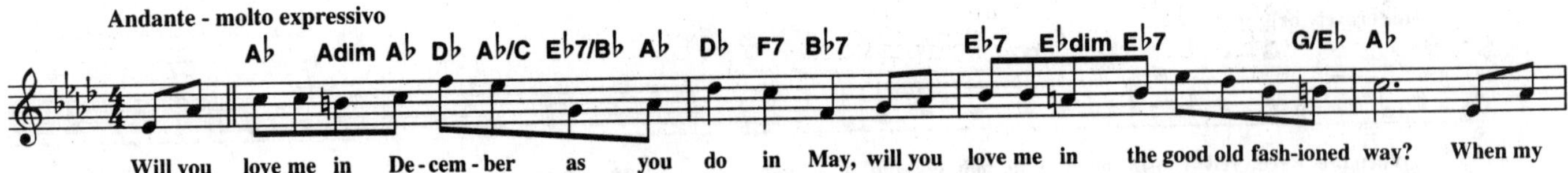
Andante - molto expressivo
Ab Adim Ab Db Ab/C Eb7/Bb Ab Db F7 Bb7 Eb7 Ebdim Eb7 G/Eb Ab
Will you love me in De-cem-ber as you do in May, will you love me in the good old fash-ioned way? When my

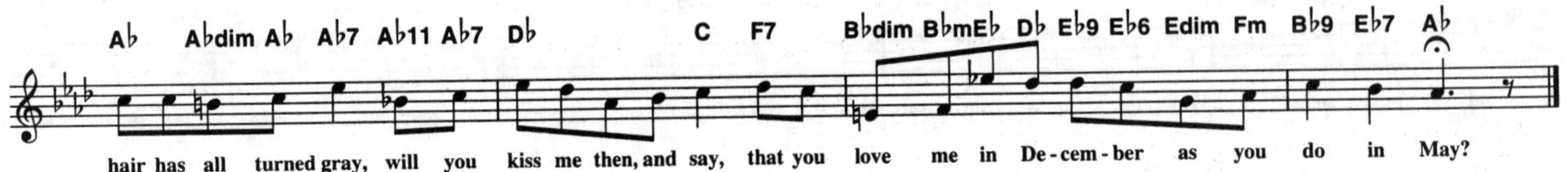
Ab Abdim Ab Ab7 Ab11 Ab7 Db C F7 Bbdim BbmEb Db Eb9 Eb6 Edim Fm Bb9 Eb7 Ab
hair has all turned gray, will you kiss me then, and say, that you love me in De-cem-ber as you do in May?

From the TriStar Pictures Feature Film "HOOK"

WHEN YOU'RE ALONE

Lyrics by LESLIE BRICUSSE
Music by JOHN WILLIAMS

Moderately
E(2) F#m/E E(2) D(2) E(2)
When you're all a - lone far a-way from home, there's a gift the an-gels send when you're a - lone. Ev-'ry day must

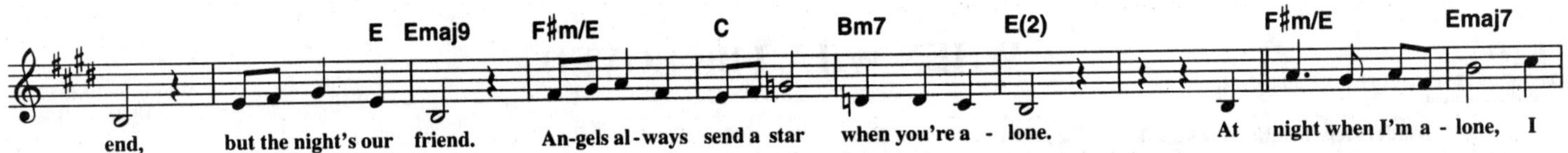
E Emaj9 F#m/E C Bm7 E(2) F#m/E Emaj7
end, but the night's our friend. An-gels al-ways send a star when you're a - lone. At night when I'm a - lone, I

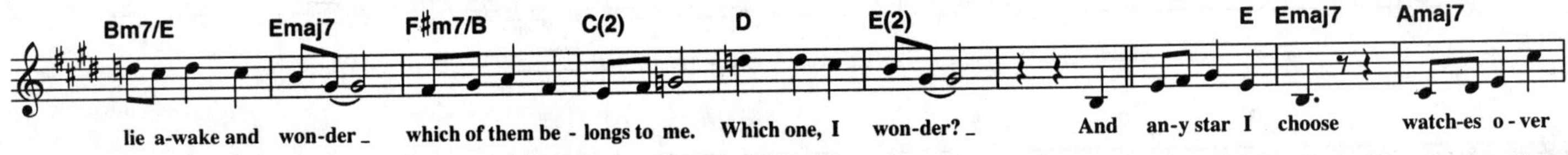
Bm7/E Emaj7 F#m7/B C(2) D E(2) E Emaj7 Amaj7
lie a-wake and won-der which of them be - longs to me. Which one, I won-der? And an-y star I choose watch-es o - ver

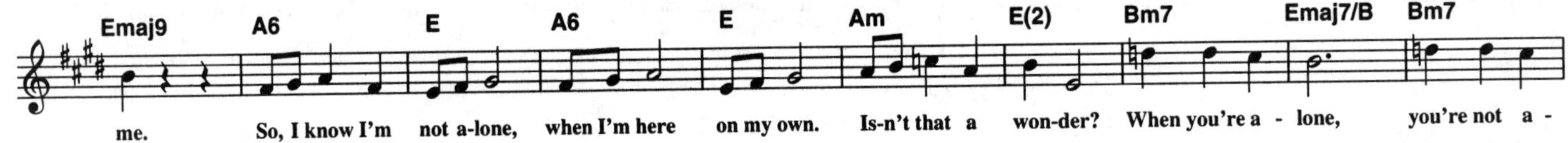
Emaj9 A6 E A6 E Am E(2) Bm7 Emaj7/B Bm7
me. So, I know I'm not a-lone, when I'm here on my own. Is-n't that a won-der? When you're a - lone, you're not a -

Emaj7/B C E(2) E(2) E Emaj7 Amaj7 Emaj9 A6 E
lone, not real-ly a - lone. The stars are all my friends till the night-time ends. So, I know I'm not a-lone

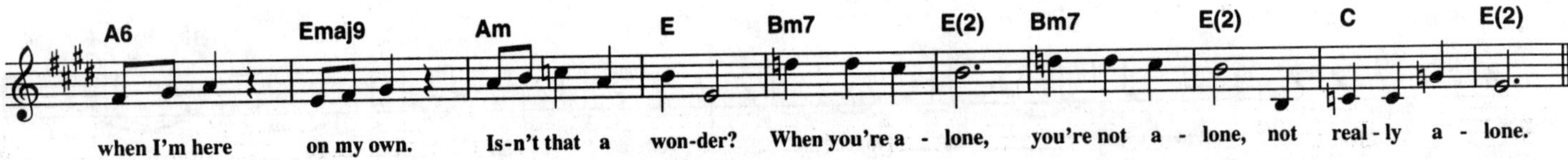
A6 Emaj9 Am E Bm7 E(2) Bm7 E(2) C E(2)
when I'm here on my own. Is-n't that a won-der? When you're a - lone, you're not a - lone, not real-ly a - lone.

WITH THIS RING (I Thee Wed)

© 1943 WB MUSIC CORP. (Renewed)
All Rights Reserved
Words by REMUS HARRIS
Music by JOHN SACCO
Moderato (with expression)
With this ring I come to you, to pledge my heart for-ev-er true. I give my heart for you to share, through sun-shine and laugh-ter, through heartache and care. With this ring I make this vow, I'll love you al-ways just as now; And my joy will be so deep, it can't be sung, It can't be said, when With This Ring I Thee Wed.
2nd time
To Coda
Through life's green pas-tures we'll walk to-geth-er and love will fol-low ev'ry-where. We'll find a hid-den treas-ure of hap-pi-ness in our hearts, so come with me, my dar-ling; let us say a prayer.
(Alternate:) So come be-fore the al-tar; let us kneel in prayer.
D.S. al Coda
Coda
said, when With This Ring I Thee Wed.
WITH A SONG IN MY HEART
© 1929 WARNER BROS. INC. (Renewed)
All Rights Reserved
Words by LORENZ HART
Music by RICHARD RODGERS
Moderately slow
With A Song In My Heart. I be-hold your a-dor-a-ble face, Just a song at the start, But it soon is a hymn to your grace. When the mu-sic swells
At the sound of your voice Heav-en o-pens its por-tals to me. Can I help but re-joice, That a song such as ours came to be? But I al-ways knew
To Coda
I'm touch-ing your hand; It tells that you're stand-ing near, and
D.C. al Coda
Coda
I would live life through, With A Song In My Heart for you.

WHERE DO I GO?

Words by JAMES RADO and GEROME RAGNI
Music by GALT MacDERMOT

Moderately

Dm G7 Dm C Dm G7 C Gm7 C7

Where do I go? __ Fol-low the riv - er. Where do I go? __ Fol-low the gulls. Where is the some-thing,
Where do I go? __ Fol-low the chil-dren. Where do I go? __ Fol-low their smiles. Is there an an - swer

Gm C7 Gm7 C7 F C F E♭ F E♭

where is the some-one that tells me why I live and die? ______ Fol-low the wind song, fol-low the thun-der.
in their sweet fac - es that tells me why I live and die? ______

F F♯m7(♭5) B7 Em G F G F G F D7 G7

Fol-low the ne - on in young lov - ers' eyes. Down to the gut - ter, _ up to the glit-ter, in-to the cit - y where the truth lies. _

Dm G7 Dm C Dm G7 C Gm7 C7 Gm C7

Where do I go? _ Fol-low my heart-beat. Where do I go? _ Fol-low my hand. Where will they lead me, and will I ev - er

Gm7 C F C F C F C F C F6

dis-cov - er why I live and die? ______ I live and die, ______ I live and die.

WHILE SHEPHERDS WATCHED THEIR FLOCKS BY NIGHT

Words by NAHUM TATE and NICHOLAS BRODY
Music by GEORGE FREDERICK HANDEL

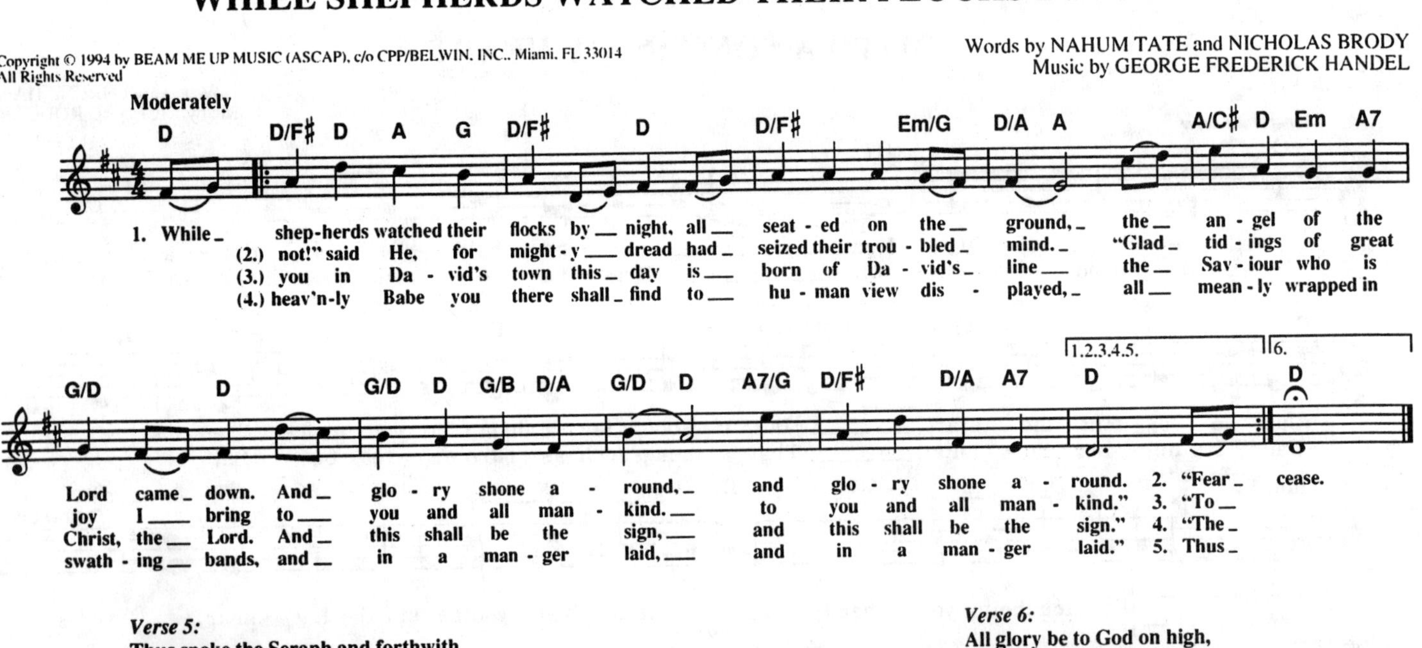
Moderately
D D/F♯ D A G D/F♯ D D/F♯ Em/G D/A A A/C♯ D Em A7
1. While _ shep-herds watched their flocks by __ night, all __ seat - ed on the __ ground, _ the __ an - gel of the
(2.) not!" said He, for might - y __ dread had _ seized their trou - bled _ mind. _ "Glad _ tid - ings of great
(3.) you in Da - vid's town this _ day is __ born of Da - vid's _ line __ the __ Sav - iour who is
(4.) heav'n-ly Babe you there shall _ find to __ hu - man view dis - played, _ all __ mean - ly wrapped in
G/D D G/D D G/B D/A G/D D A7/G D/F♯ D/A A7 D D
1.2.3.4.5.
6.
Lord came _ down. And _ glo - ry shone a - round, _ and glo - ry shone a - round. 2. "Fear _ cease.
joy I __ bring to __ you and all man - kind. __ to you and all man - kind." 3. "To _
Christ, the __ Lord. And _ this shall be the sign, __ and this shall be the sign." 4. "The _
swath - ing __ bands, and _ in a man - ger laid, __ and in a man - ger laid." 5. Thus _

Verse 5:
Thus spoke the Seraph and forthwith
Appeared a shining throng
Of angels praising God, who thus
Addressed their joyful song,
Addressed their joyful song.

Verse 6:
All glory be to God on high,
And to the earth be peace,
Good will hence forth from heav'n to men,
Begin and never cease,
Begin and never cease.

WOULD YOU LIKE TO TAKE A WALK
(Sump'n Good'll Come from That)

Words by MORT DIXON and BILLY ROSE
Music by HARRY WARREN

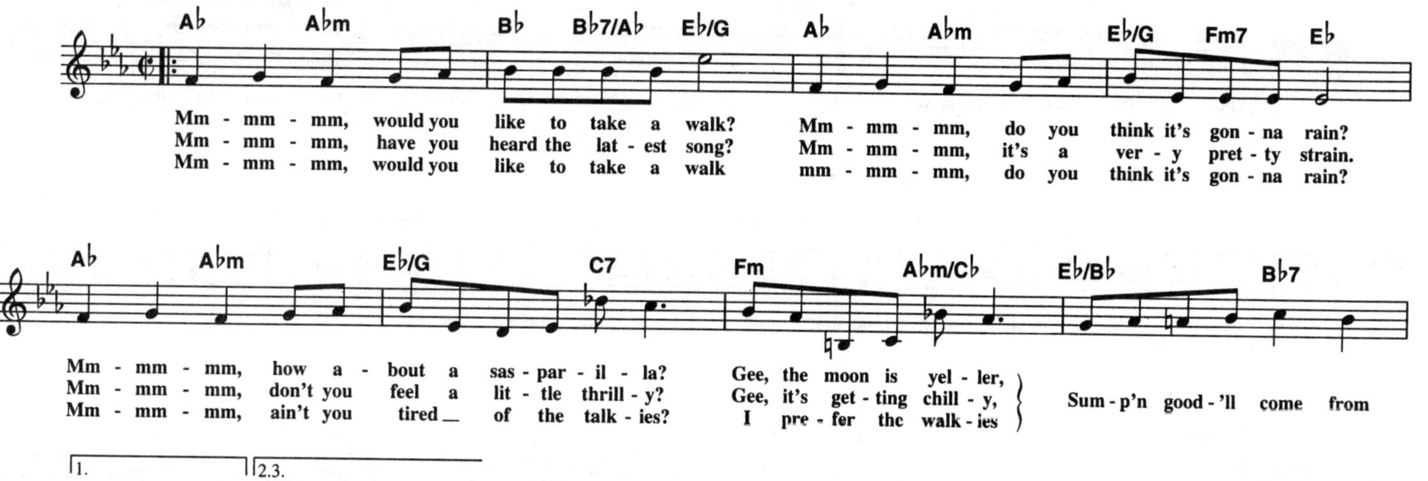
Moderato
Ab Abm Bb Bb7/Ab Eb/G Ab Abm Eb/G Fm7 Eb
Mm - mm - mm, would you like to take a walk? Mm - mm - mm, do you think it's gon - na rain?
Mm - mm - mm, have you heard the lat - est song? Mm - mm - mm, it's a ver - y pret - ty strain.
Mm - mm - mm, would you like to take a walk mm - mm - mm, do you think it's gon - na rain?
Ab Abm Eb/G C7 Fm Abm/Cb Eb/Bb Bb7
Mm - mm - mm, how a - bout a sas - par - il - la? Gee, the moon is yel - ler,
Mm - mm - mm, don't you feel a lit - tle thrill - y? Gee, it's get - ting chill - y,
Mm - mm - mm, ain't you tired of the talk - ies? I pre - fer the walk - ies
Sum - p'n good - 'll come from

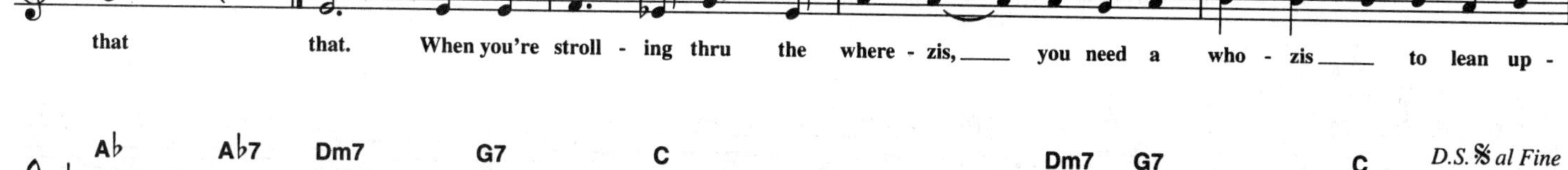
1. 2.3.
Eb Eb Fine Bbm7 Eb7 Ab Eb7
that that. When you're stroll - ing thru the where - zis, you need a who - zis to lean up -

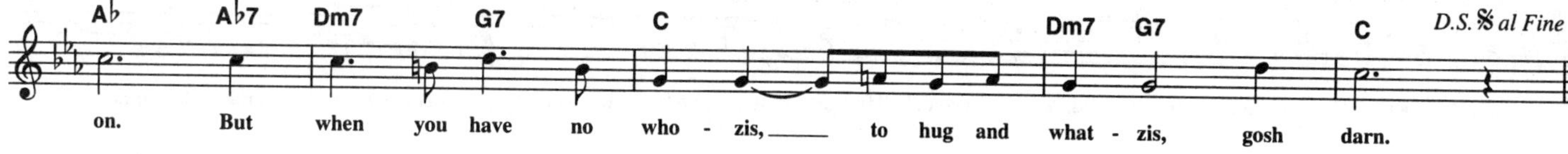
Ab Ab7 Dm7 G7 C Dm7 G7 C D.S. al Fine
on. But when you have no who - zis, to hug and what - zis, gosh darn.

THE WHIFFENPOOF SONG
(Baa! Baa! Baa!)

Words by MEADE MINNIGERODE and GEORGE S. POMEROY
Revision by RUDY VALLEE
Special Lyrics by MOSS HART
Music by TOD B. GALLOWAY

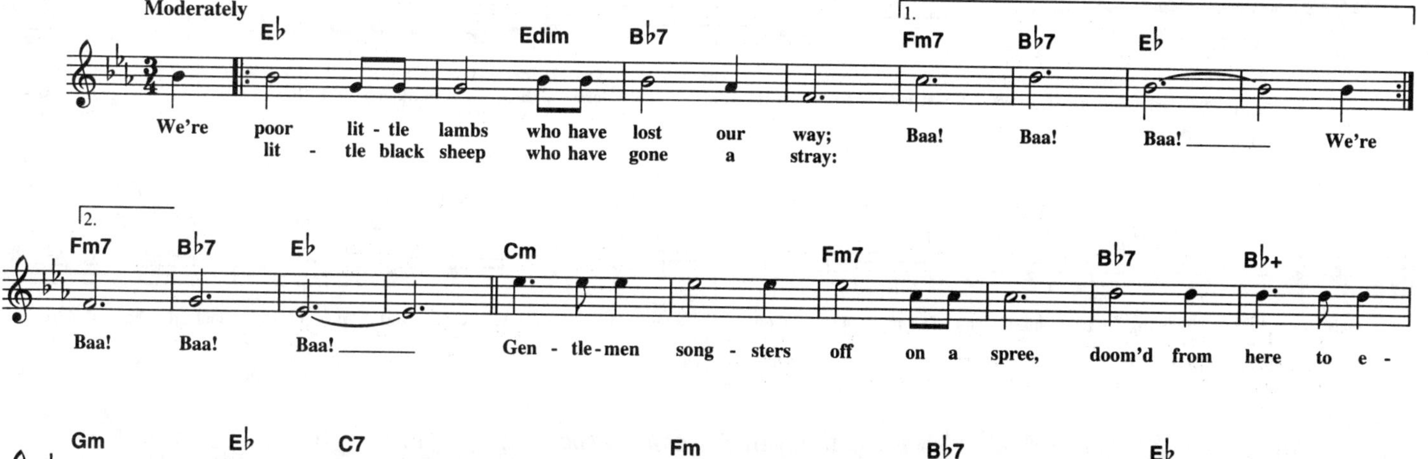
Moderately
Eb Edim Bb7 1. Fm7 Bb7 Eb
We're poor lit - tle lambs who have lost our way; Baa! Baa! Baa! We're
lit - tle black sheep who have gone a stray:
2. Fm7 Bb7 Eb Cm Fm7 Bb7 Bb+
Baa! Baa! Baa! Gen - tle - men song - sters off on a spree, doom'd from here to e -
Gm Eb C7 Fm Bb7 Eb
ter - ni - ty, Lord have mer - cy on such as we. Baa! Baa! Baa!

WHILE STROLLING THROUGH THE PARK ONE DAY

TRADITIONAL

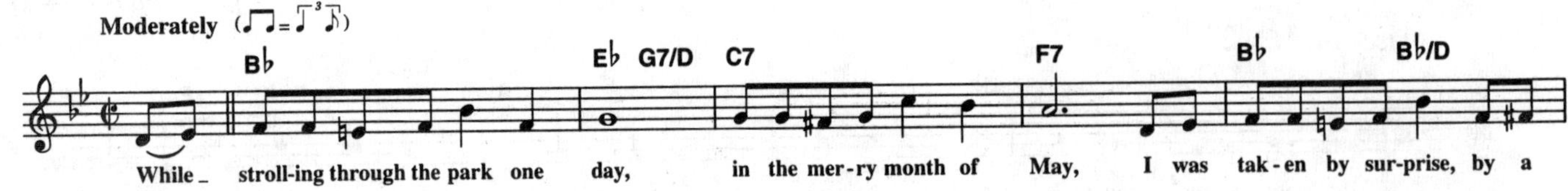
Moderately
B♭ E♭ G7/D C7 F7 B♭ B♭/D
While_ stroll-ing through the park one day, in the mer-ry month of May, I was tak-en by sur-prise, by a

C7 F7 B♭ D7 Gm D7 Gm D7
pair of ro-guish eyes. In a mo-ment, my poor heart was stole a - way.__ A smile was all she gave to me.

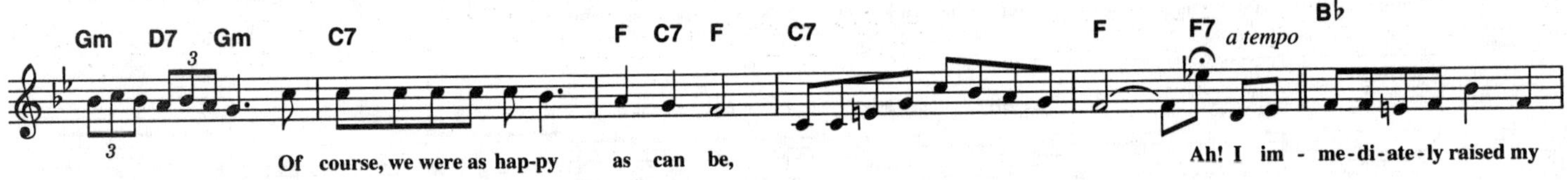
Gm D7 Gm C7 F C7 F C7 F F7 a tempo B♭
Of course, we were as hap-py as can be, Ah! I im - me-di-ate-ly raised my

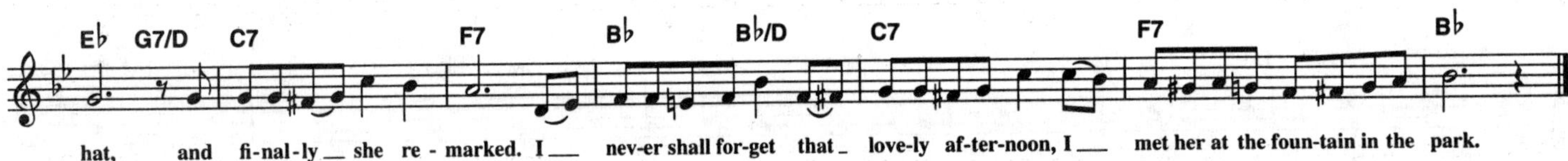
E♭ G7/D C7 F7 B♭ B♭/D C7 F7 B♭
hat, and fi-nal-ly__ she re - marked. I__ nev-er shall for-get that_ love-ly af-ter-noon, I__ met her at the foun-tain in the park.

WHEN DAY IS DONE

Madonna, du bist shoner als der Sonnenschein!

English version by B.G. DeSYLVA
Music and original text by DR. ROBERT KATCHER

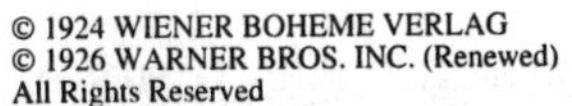

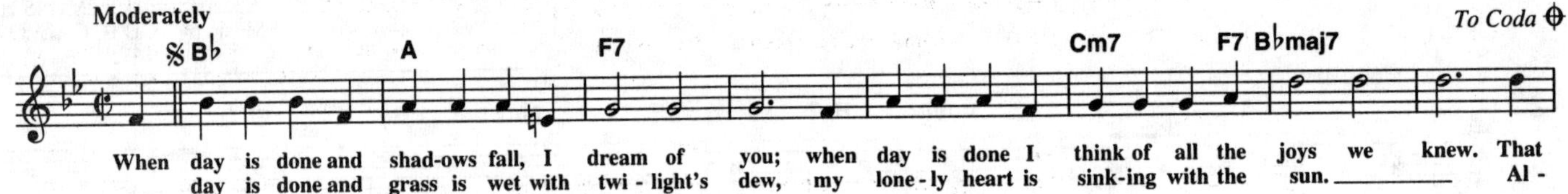
Moderately
To Coda
B♭ A F7 Cm7 F7 B♭maj7
When day is done and shad-ows fall, I dream of you; when day is done I think of all the joys we knew. That
day is done and grass is wet with twi - light's dew, my lone-ly heart is sink-ing with the sun.__ Al -

D.S. al Coda
B♭ Dm7 G7 C7(♯5) C7 Cm7 F7 C♯dim B♭/D Bdim Cm7 F7
yearn-ing re - turn-ing to hold you in my arms, won't go love, I know love, with - out you night has lost its charms! When

Coda
B♭9 Fm Fm7 B♭+ E♭maj7 D7(♭5) D7 G7/D F♯7/C Cm7 F7 B♭ G♭ E A B♭
though I miss your ten-der kiss the whole day through, I miss you most of all when day is done!__

From the United Artists Motion Picture "THE THOMAS CROWN AFFAIR"

THE WINDMILLS OF YOUR MIND

Lyric by MARILYN and ALAN BERGMAN
Music by MICHEL LEGRAND

Moderately slow
Em
B7
Round like a cir - cle in a spi - ral, like a wheel with - in a wheel, nev - er end - ing or be -
mind. Like a tun - nel that you fol - low to a tun - nel of its own, down a hol - low to a
Em
E7
Am7
gin - ning on an ev - er spin - ning reel; like a snow - ball down a moun - tain or a car - ni - val bal - loon, like a car - ou - sel that's
cav - ern where the sun has nev - er shone; like a door that keeps re - volv - ing in a half for - got - ten dream, or the rip - ples from a
D7
Gmaj7
Cmaj7
F♯m7(♭5)
turn - ing run - ning rings a - round the moon.
peb - ble some - one toss - es in a stream.
Like a clock whose hands are sweep - ing past the min - utes of its face, and the world is like an
B7
A♯dim7
B7
Em
ap - ple whirl - ing si - lent - ly in space, like the cir - cles that you find in the wind - mills of your mind! Keys that jin - gle in your
Am7
D7
Gmaj7
pock - et, words that jan - gle in your head. Why did sum - mer go so quick - ly? Was it some - thing that you said? Lov - ers walk a - long a
G7
Cmaj7
F♯7
Bm
shore and leave their foot - prints in the sand. Is the sound of dis - tant drum - ming just the fin - gers of your hand? Pic - tures hang - ing in a
E7
Am
D7
Gmaj7
hall - way and the frag - ment of a song; half re - mem - bered names and fac - es, but to whom do they be - long? When you knew that it was
(Girl) When you knew that it was
Cmaj7
F♯m7(♭5)
B7
Em
o - ver you were sud - den - ly a - ware that the au - tumn leaves were turn - ing to the col - or of her hair! Like a cir - cle in a
o - ver in the au - tumn of good - byes, for a mo - ment you could not re - call the col - or of his eyes!
B7
spi - ral, like a wheel with - in a wheel, nev - er end - ing or be - gin - ning on an ev - er spin - ning
A♯dim7
Em/B
B7
Em
reel; as the im - ag - es un - wind, like the cir - cles that you find in the wind - mills of your mind.

WHILE YOU SEE A CHANCE

Lyrics by WILL JENNINGS
Music by STEVE WINWOOD

Moderate rock

D A/C# Bm7 Em A D A/C# Bm7

Stand up in a clear blue morn-ing, un-til you see what can be; a-lone in a cold day dawn-ing,

Em A 𝄋 D A/D G/D A/D G/D D A/D G/D D

are you still free; can you be?

A/C# G/B G Em7/A D G/B G D/A A F#m F#m(♭5) D9

G Gmaj7 Em9 D/A Gmaj7 D/A G

When some cold to-mor-row finds you; when some sad old dream re-minds you how the end-less road un-winds
When there's no one left to leave you; e-ven you don't quite be-lieve you; that's when noth-ing can de-ceive
And that old, grey wind is blow-ing; and there's noth-ing left worth know-ing; and it's time you should be go-

E/G# D/A F#/A# Bm D/C Bm G/B A7 *To Coda* 𝄌 D

you; / you; / -ing; while you see a chance, take it; find ro-mance, fake it; be-cause it's all on you.

1. *To Next Strain* 2. *D.C. al Coda* B♭ E♭/B♭ F/B♭ B♭ F/B♭ E♭/B♭

Don't you know by now, no one gives you an-y-thing;

B♭ F/B♭ E♭/B♭ F/B♭ C/G D/A A7sus *D.S.* 𝄋

and don't you won-der how you keep on mov-ing one more day, your way?

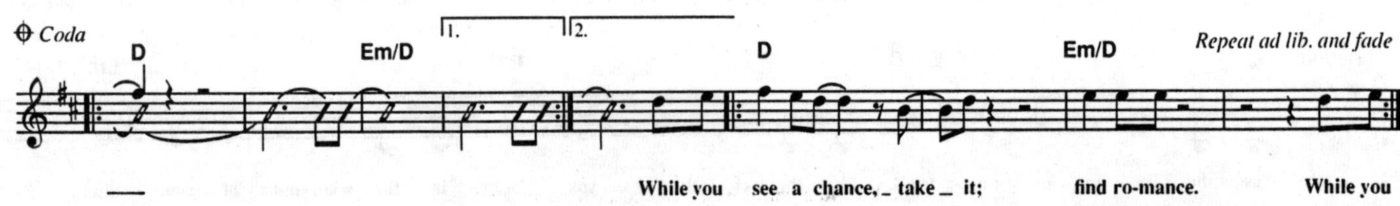
𝄌 Coda
D
Em/D
1.
2.
D
Em/D
Repeat ad lib. and fade
While you see a chance, take it; find ro-mance. While you

WHISPERING
Copyright © 1920 (Renewed 1948) EMI MILLER CATALOG INC.
All Rights Reserved
Words and Music by
JOHN SCHONBERGER, RICHARD COBURN
and VINCENT ROSE
Moderately
Whis - per - ing while you cud - dle near me, whis - per - ing so no one can hear me; each lit - tle whis - per seems to cheer me. I know it's true. There's no one dear, but you. You're
whis - per - ing why you'll nev - er leave me, whis - per - ing why you'll nev - er grieve me; whis - per and say that you be - lieve me.
Whis - per - ing that I love you.
WHO'LL STOP THE RAIN
Copyright © 1969 by JONDORA MUSIC
All Rights Reserved
J.C. FOGERTY
Moderately
Verse:
1. Long as I remem - ber, the rain been com - in' down. Clouds of mys - t'ry pour - in', con - fus - ion on the ground. Good men through the ag - es, try - in' to find the sun, and I won - der, still I won - der, who'll stop the rain?
Repeat and fade

Verse 2:
I went down Virginia, seekin' shelter from the storm.
Caught up in the fable, I watched the tower grow.
Five year plans and new deals wrapped in golden chains,
And I wonder, still I wonder, who'll stop the rain?

Verse 3:
Heard the singers playin'; how we cheered for more.
The crowd had rushed together, tryin' to keep warm.
Still the rain kept pourin', fallin' on my ears.
And I wonder, still I wonder, who'll stop the rain?

WHO'S SORRY NOW
Copyright © 1923, 1975 (Renewed 1951) MILLS MUSIC, INC.
All Rights Reserved
Words by
BERT KALMAR and HARRY RUBY
Music by TED SNYDER
Moderately
B♭ D7 G+ G7 D7 G7 C7
Who's sor - ry now? Who's sor - ry now? Whose heart is ach - ing for break - ing each vow?
F7 B♭ Bdim7 F/C C7 F7 Cm7 Cm7(♭5) F7 Cm7 F7
Who's sad and blue? Who's cry - ing too? Just like I cried o - ver you.
B♭ D7 G+ G7 G+ G7 Cm G7
Right to the end, just like a friend, I tried to warn you some - how.
Cm Cm7(♭5) B♭ G7 C7 Cm7(♭5) F7 B♭ E♭ E♭m B♭
You had your way, now you must pay. I'm glad that you're sor - ry now.
WICHITA LINEMAN
Copyright © 1968 CANOPY MUSIC (ASCAP)
All Rights Reserved
Words and Music by
JIMMY WEBB
Moderately
B♭maj9 Am7 Dm7 Fsus/C
1. I am a line - man for the coun - ty, and I drive the main road,
ca - tion, but it don't look like rain. And
Dm7 Am7 G D
search - in' in the sun for an - oth - er o - ver - load. I hear you sing - in' in the
if it snows, that stretch down south will nev - er stand the strain. And I need you more than
C6/9 G/B Gm/B♭ D/A
wires; I can hear you through the whine.
want you, and I want you for all time.
And the Wi - chi - ta line - man
G/A B♭maj7 C2 B♭maj7
1.
is still on the line.
2.
Gm7/C B♭maj7 C2 D
2. You know I need a small va -

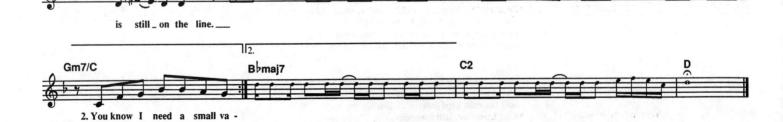

WHY DON'T YOU LOVE ME

Words and Music by
HANK WILLIAMS

Moderately
F C7
Well, why don't you love me like you used to do? How come you treat me like a worn out shoe? My
why don't you be just like you used to be? How come you find so man-y faults with me?
F Bb F C7 F Bb
hair's still curl-y and my eyes are still blue.
Some-body's changed so let me give you a clue.
Why don't you love me like you used to do? Ain't had no lov-in' like a hug-gin' and a
C7 F C7
kiss-in' in a long, long while. We don't get near-er or fur-ther or clos-er than a coun-try mile.
F C7
Why don't you spark me like you used to do and say sweet noth-ings like you used to coo? I'm the
Why don't you say the things you used to say? What makes you treat me like a piece of clay? My
F Bb F 1. C7 F 2. C7 F
same old trou-ble that you've al-ways been thru.
hair's still curl-y and my eyes are still blue.
So why don't you love me like you used to do? Well, used to do?
WILL IT GO 'ROUND IN CIRCLES
Copyright © 1972 by IRVING MUSIC, INC. and WEP MUSIC CORP.
All Rights Reserved
Words and Music by
BILLY PRESTON and
BRUCE FISHER
Moderate rock
Verse:
Ab Db Ab Db Ab Cb Db Ab Cb Db
1.3. I've got a song I ain't got no mel-o-dy how'm I gon-na sing it to my friends.
2. I've got a sto-ry ain't got no mor-al, let the bad guy win every once in a while.
Ab Cb Db Ab F Gb G
I've got a song I ain't got no mel-o-dy how'm I gon-na sing it to my friends.
I've got a sto-ry ain't got no mor-al, let the bad guy win every once in a while.
Will it go 'round in
Chorus:
Ab7 Db Ab7 Db Ab7 Db Ab7 Db Ab7 Db
cir-cles? Will it fly high like a bird up in the sky? Will it go 'round in cir-cles?
Ab7 Db 1.2. Ab7 Db Ab Db D.S. 3. Ab F Gb G
Will it fly high like a bird up in the sky?
Repeat ad lib. and fade
Will it go 'round in

Dedicated to George Gershwin

WILLOW WEEP FOR ME

Words and Music by
ANN RONELL

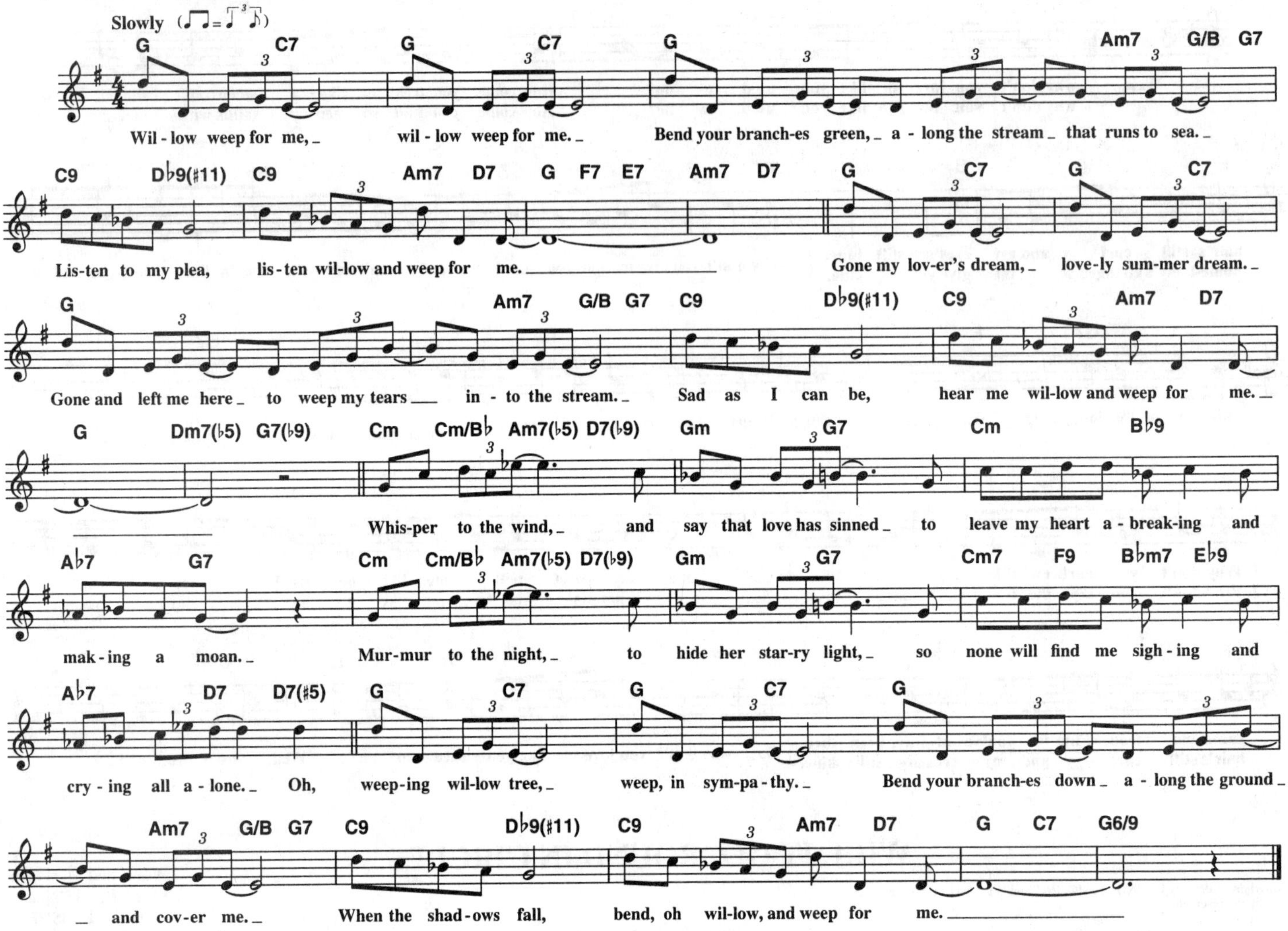

Slowly

Wil - low weep for me, _ wil - low weep for me. _ Bend your branch-es green, _ a - long the stream _ that runs to sea. _
Lis-ten to my plea, lis-ten wil-low and weep for me. ___ Gone my lov-er's dream, _ love-ly sum-mer dream. _
Gone and left me here _ to weep my tears ___ in - to the stream. _ Sad as I can be, hear me wil-low and weep for me. _
Whis-per to the wind, _ and say that love has sinned _ to leave my heart a - break-ing and
mak - ing a moan. _ Mur-mur to the night, _ to hide her star-ry light, _ so none will find me sigh - ing and
cry - ing all a - lone. _ Oh, weep-ing wil-low tree, _ weep, in sym-pa - thy. _ Bend your branch-es down _ a - long the ground _
_ and cov-er me. _ When the shad - ows fall, bend, oh wil-low, and weep for me. ___

WHO CARES?

(So Long As You Care for Me)

Words by IRA GERSWIN
Music by GEORGE GERSHWIN

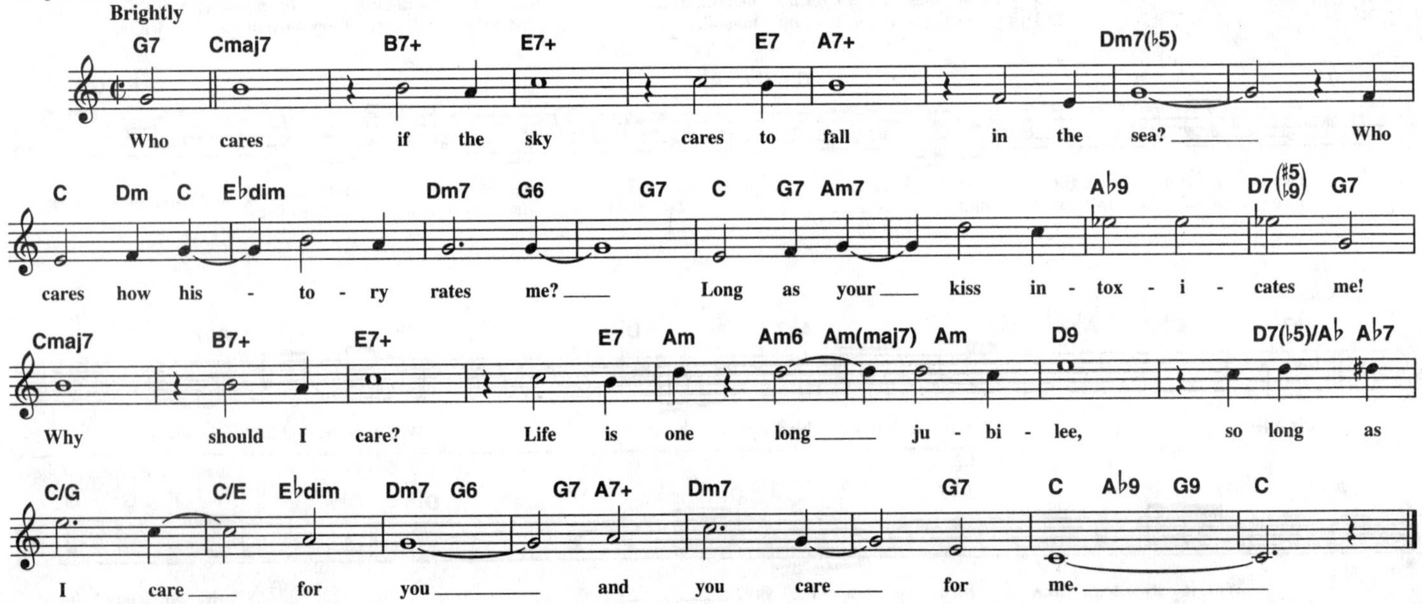

Brightly

Who cares if the sky cares to fall in the sea? ___ Who
cares how his - to - ry rates me? ___ Long as your ___ kiss in - tox - i - cates me!
Why should I care? Life is one long ___ ju - bi - lee, so long as
I care ___ for you ___ and you care ___ for me. ___

WINCHESTER CATHEDRAL
Copyright © 1966 by METEOR MUSIC PUBLISHING CO. LTD. London
Sole Selling Agent: SOUTHERN MUSIC PUBLISHING CO., INC. All Rights Reserved
Words and Music by
GEOFF STEPHENS
Moderately
Win-ches-ter Cath-e - dral _
you're bring-ing me down. ___ You stood and you watched as _ my ba-by left town. _ You could have done some-
- thing _ but you did-n't try. ___ You did-n't do noth - ing: _ you let her walk by.
Now ev-'ry-one knows _ just how much _ I need-ed that girl. _ She would-n't have gone _ far a - way _ if on-ly you'd
start-ed ring-ing your bell. _ Win-ches-ter Cath-e - dral _ you're bring-ing me down. ___ You stood and you watched as _
my ba-by left town. town.
WINDY
Copyright © 1967 IRVING MUSIC, INC. (BMI)
All Rights Reserved
Words and Music by
RUTHANN FRIEDMAN
Moderately bright rock
1. Who's peek-in' out from un - der a stair-way call - ing a name that's light - er than air? Who's bend - in' down to give _
2.3.etc. Who's trip-pin' down the streets _ of the cit - y smil - in' at ev - 'ry - bod - y she sees? Who's reach-ing out to cap -
_ me a rain - bow? - ture a mo - ment? Ev - 'ry - one knows it's Wind - y. - y. And Wind - y has
To Next Strain
Repeat and fade
- y storm - y ___ eyes ___ that flash _ at the sound of ___ lies. ___ And Wind - y has
wings to ___ fly ___ a - bove the clouds, _ a - bove the clouds, _ a - bove the clouds, _ a - bove the clouds. _
D.C.

WITCHCRAFT

Lyric by CAROLYN LEIGH
Music by CY COLEMAN

Moderate swing

F6/9 A♭dim7 Gm7 C11 Fmaj7
Those fin-gers in my hair, that sly come-hith-er stare that strips my con-science bare, it's witch-craft.

B♭ B♭m Dm7(♭5)/A♭ G7(♯5) Cmaj7 C7
And I've got no de-fense for it; the heat is too in-tense for it. What good would com-mon sense for it do? 'Cause it's

Fmaj7 C11 Fmaj7 Bm7(♭5) E7
witch-craft, wick-ed witch-craft. And al-though I know it's strict-ly ta-boo,

Am Am(♯5) Am6 Am(♯5) Am Gm Gm(♯5) Gm7 C7 (F♯7)
when you a-rouse the need in me, my heart says, "Yes, in-deed," in me. "Pro-ceed with what you're lead-ing me to!"

F6/9 A♭dim7 Gm7 C11 F6/9 (G♭7) F6/9
It's such an an-cient pitch, but one I would-n't switch, 'cause there's no nic-er witch than you.

WITH PEN IN HAND

Words and Music by
BOBBY GOLDSBORO

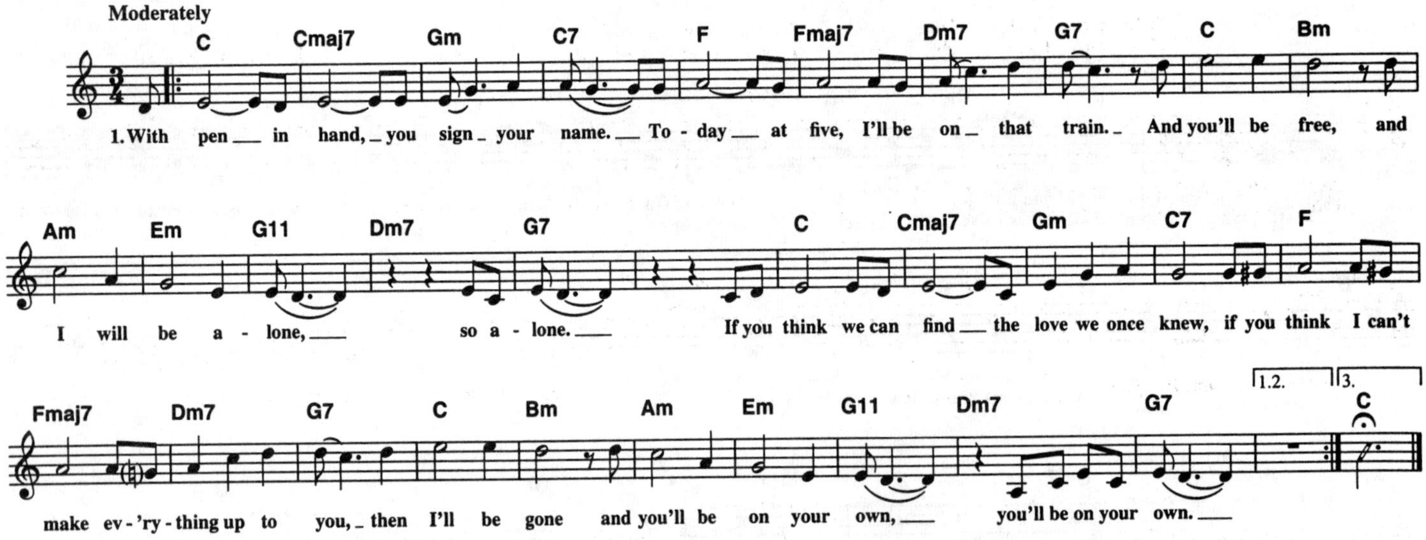

Moderately

C Cmaj7 Gm C7 F Fmaj7 Dm7 G7 C Bm
1. With pen in hand, you sign your name. To-day at five, I'll be on that train. And you'll be free, and

Am Em G11 Dm7 G7 C Cmaj7 Gm C7 F
I will be a-lone, so a-lone. If you think we can find the love we once knew, if you think I can't

Fmaj7 Dm7 G7 C Bm Am Em G11 Dm7 G7 C
make ev-'ry-thing up to you, then I'll be gone and you'll be on your own, you'll be on your own.

Verse 2:
Can you take good care of Johnny?
Can you take him to school everyday?
Can you teach him how to catch a fish and keep all those bullies away?
Hear what I say?
Can you teach him how to whistle a tune?
Can you tell him about the man in the moon?
If you can do those things, then maybe he won't miss me,
Maybe he won't miss me.

Verse 3:
And tonight as you lay in that big lonely bed,
And you look at the pillow where I laid my head,
With your heart on fire, will you have no desire to kiss me,
And to hold me?
And if you can forget the good times we had,
If you think that the good times don't outweigh the bad,
Then sign your name and I'll be on my way,
I'll be on my way.

WINTERGREEN FOR PRESIDENT

Words by IRA GERSHWIN
Music by GEORGE GERSHWIN

Tempo di marcia
Gm Gm6 Gm Gm6 Gm
Win - ter - green for pres - i - dent!
Fine
Gm F6 E7 E♭7
He's the man the peo - ple choose;
A♭ E♭7(♭5) A♭ E♭7(♭5) A♭m G♭6 F7 E7
loves the I - rish and the Jews,
A E7 A E+ A
ta ta ta ta ta ta
Am6 Esus E7
ta!
Am Am6 Am D Am Am6 Am D
Win - ter - green for Pres - i - dent!
A B7 E7
Ta ta ta ta ta ta!
A C♯ F♯m B7 F♯m B
Ta ta ta ta. Win - ter - green for
F♯m D A F♯ C♯ F♯6 F♯ D7
Pres - i - dent! Ta ta ta ta ta ta!
D.C. al Fine

Inspired by the Paramount Picture "WIVES AND LOVERS"

WIVES AND LOVERS
(Hey, Little Girl)

Lyric by HAL DAVID
Music by BURT BACHARACH

Moderate jazz waltz
B♭9sus B♭13 C9sus
Hey, lit-tle girl, comb your hair, fix your make-up; soon he will o-pen the door. Don't think be-cause there's a
Day af-ter day, there are girls at the of - fice, and men will al-ways be men. Don't send him off with your
C13 Cm7 F7(♭9) Am7(♭5) D7 E♭maj7
ring on you fin-ger you need-n't try an - y - more.
hair still in curl-ers; you may not see him a - gain.
For wives should al-ways be lov-ers too. Run to his arms the mo-ment
D7sus D7 D♭maj7 C7sus C7 C7sus C7 Fm7
1. 2.
he comes home to you. I'm warn - ing you. He's al - most here.
Hey, lit-tle girl, bet-ter wear some-thing pret-ty,

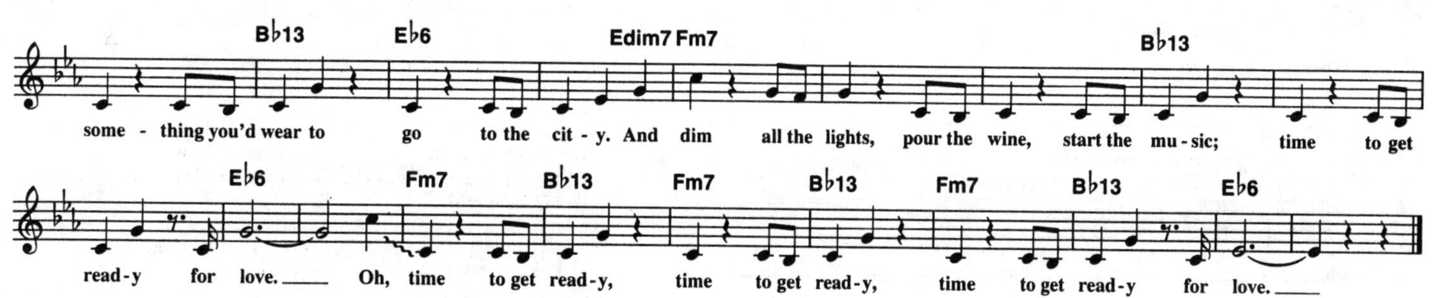
B♭13 E♭6 Edim7 Fm7 B♭13
some - thing you'd wear to go to the cit - y. And dim all the lights, pour the wine, start the mu - sic; time to get
E♭6 Fm7 B♭13 Fm7 B♭13 Fm7 B♭13 E♭6
read - y for love. Oh, time to get read - y, time to get read - y, time to get read - y for love.

From the Musical Play "GREAT DAY"

WITHOUT A SONG

Lyrics by WILLIAM ROSE and EDWARD ELISCU
Music by VINCENT YOUMANS

Slowly
Fmaj7
B♭maj7/F
Fmaj7
B♭
With-out a song the day would nev-er end. With-out a song the road would nev-er bend. When things go
corn would nev-er see a plow. That field of corn would be de-sert-ed now. A dark-y's
know what makes the rain to fall. I'll nev-er know what makes the grass so tall. I on-ly
To Coda
F/C
C7
F
Dm
Gm7
C7
C7(♯5)
F
Gm7 C7
wrong a man ain't got a friend, with-out a song. That field of song.
born, but he's no good no-how, with-out a
know there ain't no love at all, with-out a
F
F7
B♭/D
F7/C B♭
F7/E♭
B♭/D F7/C
B♭ C/B♭
F/A
Am
E7/G♯ Am7/G
I got my trou-bles and woe, but sure as I know the Jor-dan will roll, I'll get a-long as
D.S. al Coda
Coda
D7/F♯
C/G
G7
C
F/C
C9
F
G7
B♭m
F
long as a song is strong in my soul. I'll nev-er
song.
WOMAN, WOMAN
Copyright © 1967, 1972 & 1973 by ENSIGN MUSIC CORPORATION
All Rights Reserved
Words and Music by
JIM GLASER and
JIMMY PAYNE
Moderately slow
Verse:
B♭
Dm
E♭
F
B♭
Gm
Cm
F
1. Some-thing's wrong be-tween us that your laugh-ter can-not hide. And you're a-fraid to let your eyes meet
(2.) seen the way men look at you when they think I don't see. And it hurts to have them think that you're that
(3.) wom-an wears a cer-tain look when she is on the move. And the man can al-ways tell what's on her
B♭
Dm
E♭
E♭m
mine. And late-ly when I love you, I know you're not sat-is-fied.
kind. And it's know-ing that you're look-ing back that's real-ly kill-ing me.
mind. I hate to have to say it, but their looks are o-ver you.
Chorus:
B♭
Dm
E♭
Dm
E♭
Dm
Wom-an, woh, wom-an, have you got cheat-ing on your
1.2.
D.C.
3.4. etc.
Repeat ad lib. and fade
Cm
F9
B♭
E♭
B♭
E♭
Cm
F9
mind, on your mind? 2. I've mind? Oh.
3. A

WOMAN TO WOMAN
Copyright © 1974 EAST/MEMPHIS MUSIC CORP. Copyright Assigned to IRVING MUSIC, INC., 1982
All Rights Reserved
Lyrics and Music by
JAMES BANKS, EDDIE MARION
and HENDERSON THIGPEN
Moderately
Verse:
1.3. Woman to woman, if you've ever been in love, then you know how I feel.
2. Woman to woman, I've just got to make you see, woman to woman, that you can't take him from me.
And woman to woman, now if you were in my shoes, wouldn't you have done the same thing too?
Woman to woman, now I just can't step aside and let you take what is rightfully mine.
To Coda
Chorus:
Woman to woman, right or wrong, I ain't gonna let you break up my happy home. I hope you understand, I love that man and he's mine.
D.C. al Coda
Coda
same thing too?
Repeat ad lib. and fade
Woman to woman, now I just can't step aside and let you take what is rightfully mine.
YANKEE DOODLE
Copyright © 1994 by BEAM ME UP MUSIC (ASCAP), c/o CPP/BELWIN, INC., Miami, FL 33014
All Rights Reserved
TRADITIONAL
March tempo
Verse:
1. Yankee Doodle went to town a-riding on a pony, stuck a feather in his hat and called it macaroni.
Chorus:
Yankee Doodle, keep it up, Yankee Doodle Dandy. Mind the music and the step, and with the girls be handy. 2. And handy.
Verse 2:
Father and I went to camp
Along with Captain Gooding.
There we saw the men and boys
As thick as hasty pudding. (To Chorus:)
Verse 3:
There was Captain Washington
Upon a slapping stallion,
Giving orders to his men,
I guess there was a million. (To Chorus:)
Verse 4:
There we saw a thousand men
As rich as Squire David.
What they wasted every day,
I wish it could be saved. (To Chorus:)
Verse 5:
There I saw a pumpkin shell
As big as mother's basin.
Everytime they touched it off,
They scampered like the nation. (To Chorus:)

WORDS GET IN THE WAY

Words and Music by
GLORIA ESTEFAN

Rock ballad

Verse:

F6/9 Fmaj9 Dm9 Dm7

1. I re - al - ize you're see - ing some-one new. I don't be - lieve she knows you like I do; your

B♭maj7 B♭m7 C7sus 1. C7 2.3. C7

tem-pera-men-tal mood-y side, the one you al - ways try to hide from me. 2. But I But the

Chorus:

F6/9 Fmaj7 G/F G Dm7 C

words get in the way. There's so much I want to say, but it's locked deep in - side, and if you

B♭ C7sus C F6/9 Fmaj7

look in my eyes we might fall in love a - gain. I won't e - ven start to cry. and be -

G/F G B♭maj9 C7sus F6/9

fore we say good - bye. I tried to say I love you, but the words got in the way.

1. Fmaj7 *D.S.* 𝄋 2. Fmaj7 B♭maj9 C7sus F6/9

3. Your I'm try'n' to say I love you, but the words get in the way.

Verse 2:
But I know when you have something on your mind.
You've been trying to tell me for the longest time.
And before you break my heart in two,
There's something I've been trying to say to you.
(To Chorus:)

Verse 3:
Your heart has always been an open door.
But baby, I don't even know you any more.
And despite the fact it's hurting me,
I know the time has come to set you free.
(To Chorus:)

THE YANKEE DOODLE BOY

G.M. COHAN

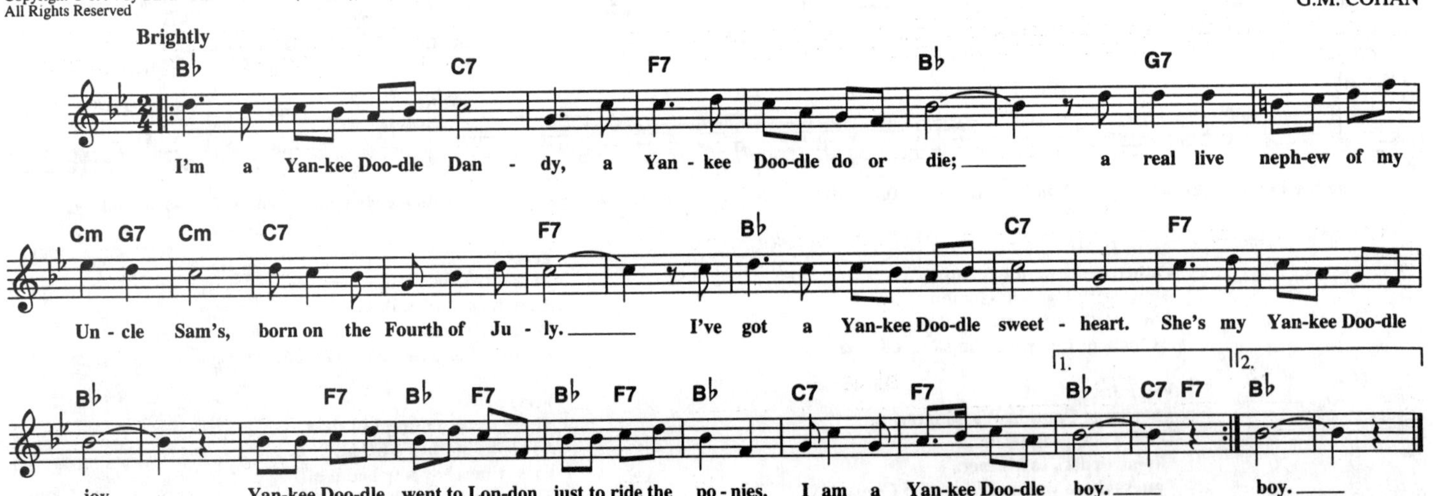
Brightly
B♭ C7 F7 B♭ G7
I'm a Yan-kee Doo-dle Dan - dy, a Yan - kee Doo-dle do or die; a real live neph-ew of my
Cm G7 Cm C7 F7 B♭ C7 F7
Un - cle Sam's, born on the Fourth of Ju - ly. I've got a Yan-kee Doo-dle sweet - heart. She's my Yan-kee Doo-dle
B♭ F7 B♭ F7 B♭ F7 B♭ C7 F7 1. B♭ C7 F7 2. B♭
joy. Yan-kee Doo-dle went to Lon-don just to ride the po - nies. I am a Yan-kee Doo-dle boy. boy.

WOULDN'T IT BE NICE?

Words by BRIAN WILSON and TONY ASHER
Music by BRIAN WILSON

Moderate rock shuffle

G9 C F6 Dm G9
Would-n't it be nice if we were old - er? Then we would-n't have to wait so long. And would-n't it be
nice if we could wake up in the morn-ing when the day is new, and af - ter that to

C F6 Dm G9 Am7 Gm7/C
nice to live to-geth - er in the kind of world where we'd be - long? Though it's gon-na make it that much bet - ter
spend the day to-geth - er; hold each oth-er close the whole night through? The hap - py times to-geth-er we'd be spend-ing,

Am Em Dm7 1. G9 2. G9 Dm7/G C
when we can say good-night and stay to-geth - er. Would-n't it be Oh, would-n't it be nice?
I wish that ev-'ry kiss was nev - er end - ing.

A D C♯m F♯m A
Well, may-be if we think and wish and hope and pray, it might come true. Ba - by, then there

D C♯m F♯m7 C♯m7 F♯m7
would-n't be a sin-gle thing we could-n't do. We could be mar - ried, and then we'd be hap -

C♯m7 G9 Dm7/G C F6 Dm7 G9
- py. Oh, would-n't it be nice? Oh, would-n't it be
Repeat and fade

From the Metro-Goldwyn-Mayer Musical Production "BROADWAY MELODY OF 1936"

YOU ARE MY LUCKY STAR

Words by ARTHUR FREED
Music by NACIO HERB BROWN

Brightly
F C7 F
To Coda
You are my luck - y star. I saw you from a - far. Two love - ly
You're all my luck - y charms, I'm luck - y in your arms
G7 C7 F B♭ B7 C7
D.C. al Coda
eyes at me, they were gleam - ing, beam - ing. I was star - struck.
Coda
F7
You've o - pened
F9 F7(♭9) B♭6 B♭m6 F C7 F
heav - en's por - tal here on earth for this poor mor - tal. You are my luck - y star.

THE YELLOW ROSE OF TEXAS

TRADITIONAL

Vigorous march tempo
G D7 Am7 D7
There's a yel-low rose in Tex-as I'm go-ing there to see. No oth-er fel-ler knows her, no oth-er one but me. She
G D7 G C G/D D7 G
cried so when I left her; I know it broke her heart. And if we ev-er meet a-gain, we nev-er more will part. She's the
G D7 Am7 D7
sweet-est rose of col-or a fel-ler ev-er knew. Her eyes are bright as dia-monds; they spar-kle like the dew. You may
1. 2.
G D7 G C G/D D7 G G
talk a-bout your dear-est maids and sing of Ro-sy Lee, but the Yel-low Rose of Tex-as beats the belles of Ten-nes-see. There's a see.

From the 20th Century-Fox Musical "THREE LITTLE GIRLS IN BLUE"

YOU MAKE ME FEEL SO YOUNG

Words by MACK GORDON
Music by JOSEF MYROW

Medium tempo (with a lilt)

B♭ Bdim Cm7 F7 F7/E♭ B♭/D Bdim Fm7/C F7 B♭/D B♭7 B♭7(♯5)

You make me feel so young, you make me feel so spring has sprung, and ev-'ry time I
The mo-ment that you speak, I wan-na go play hide and seek, I wan-na go and

E♭maj7 Cm7 1. Dm7 Gm7 C7 F7 2. Dm7 Gm7 C7 F7 B♭7/F Edim

see you grin, I'm such a hap-py in-di-vid-u-al. a toy bal-loon. You and
bounce the moon, just like

B♭7/F F♯dim B♭7/F Edim Fm7 B♭7 F♯dim Gm7 B♭dim E♭ Cm

I are just like a cou-ple of tots, run-ning a-cross a mead-ow, pick-

G7/D Cm/E♭ C7/E F7 Cm7/G F7 C♭ B♭ Bdim Cm7 F7 F7/E♭ B♭/D Bdim

-ing up lots of for-get-me-nots. You make me feel so young. You make me feel there are

Fm7/C F7/E♭ B♭/D B♭9(♯5) E♭maj7 E♭m6 B♭/D Bm7(♭5) Bdim Cm7 F7/E♭

songs to be sung, bells to be rung, and a won-der-ful fling to be flung. And e-ven when I'm old and

B♭/D Bm7(♭5) Bdim Cm7 F7/E♭ D7(♯5) D7 G7(♭9) Cm G7/D Cm/E♭ C7/E F7 B♭

gray, I'm gon-na feel the way I do to-day, 'cause you make me feel so young.

YESTERDAY ONCE MORE
Copyright © 1973 ALMO MUSIC CORP. and HAMMER & NAILS MUSIC
All Rights Reserved
Words and Music by
RICHARD CARPENTER and JOHN BETTIS
Moderately
Verse:
1. When I was young, I'd lis-ten to the ra - di - o, wait-in' for my fav-'rite songs. When they played, I'd sing a - long; it made me smile.
back on how it was in years gone by and the good times that I had makes to - day seem rath-er sad; so much has changed.
Those were such hap-py times and not so long a - go how I won-dered where they'd gone.
It was songs of love that I would sing to them and I'd mem-or - ize each word.
But they're back a - gain, just like a long lost friend; all the songs I love so well.
Those old mel-o - dies still sound so good to me, as they melt the years a - way.
Ev-'ry
Chorus:
sha-la-la-la, ev-'ry wo - wo still shines. Ev-'ry shing-a-ling-a-ling that they're start-in' to sing so fine.
When they get to the part where he's break-ing her heart, it can real-ly make me cry just like be - fore.
All my best mem-o - ries come back clear-ly to me; some can e - ven make me cry just like be - fore.
It's yes-ter-day once more. (Shoo-bie do lang lang.) 2. Look-in' Ev - 'ry
D.S. 𝄋
Repeat and fade
YESTERDAY'S GONE
© 1964 ROGERS MUSIC LTD., London, England
Rights for the U.S. and Canada Controlled by EMI UNART CATALOG INC.
All Rights Reserved
Words and Music by
D. STUART and W. KIDD
Moderately
I loved you all the sum-mer through. I thought I found my dream in you. For me you were the one, but that was yes-ter - day, and yes-ter-day's gone. We
walked to - geth-er hand in hand, 'cross miles and miles of gold-en sand. But now it's o - ver and done, 'cause that was yes-ter - day, and yes-ter-day's gone.
Wait till sum-mer comes a - gain, I'll hope that you re-mem-ber when our love had just be - gun, I loved you yes-ter - day, and yes-ter-day's gone.
To Next Strain
Fine
We had such hap-pi-ness to - geth - er. I can't be - lieve it's gone for - ev - er.
D.S. 𝄋 al Fine

YA YA

Words and Music by
CLARENCE L. LEWIS and MORRIS LEVY

Moderately

𝄋 F

Oh, well, I'm sit - tin' on my la __ la, wait - in' for my ya __ ya, ah, hm.

1. Ah, hm.

2. hm.

C It may sound fun - ny, Bb I don't be - lieve { he's / she's } ev - er com - in' F home. __ Ah, hm.

F Ba - by, hur - ry, don't make me wor - ry, ah, hm. Ah, hm. Bb Yeah, ba - by, hur - ry, don't make me wor - ry, ah,

F hm. Ah, hm. C You know that I love you, Bb7 oh, how I love you ah, F hm. Ah, hm.

D.S. 𝄋 and fade-out

YOU AND I
(Stevie Wonder)

Words and Music by
STEVIE WONDER

Slowly

Fmaj7 Bb/F Bbm/F Fmaj7 Bb/F Bbm/F E7sus A+

Here we are on earth to - geth - er it's you and I. God __ has made __ us fall in __ love, it's true. __
I am glad at least in my life I found some - one that may not be here for - ev - er to see me through. __

Dmaj7 F#m7(b5) B7(#9/#5) Em7(b5) Bb6 Csus C Fmaj7 Bb/F

I've real - ly found __ some - one like you. Will it stay,
But I found strength __ in __ you. I on - ly pray

Bbm/F Fmaj7 Bb/F Bbm/F E7sus A+ Dmaj7

the love you feel for me? Will it say that you will be by my side to __ see me through, __ un -
that I have shown you a bright - er day. Be - cause that's all that I am liv - ing __ for, you see. __ Don't

F#m7(b5) B7(#9/#5) Em7(b5) Bb6 Csus C Gm7 Bbm F

til my life is through? Well __ in my mind __ we can con - quer the world.
wor - ry what hap - pens to me. 'Cause __ in my mind __ you will stay here al - ways.

D7 G7 C7
1. F Bb/F Bbm/F F Bb/F Bbm/F
2. Fmaj7
In love, you and I, you and I, you and I.
In love, you and I, you and I, you and
I. ____

from the Motion Picture "HELLO FRISCO HELLO"

YOU'LL NEVER KNOW

Words by MACK GORDON
Music by HARRY WARREN

Moderato

F | F/A Db7/Ab | Gm | Gm(maj7) Gm7 | Gm | Gm7 C7/Bb
You'll nev-er know just how much I miss you, you'll nev-er know just how much I

F/A Fmaj7 | F6 | F | | Abdim | Gm | D7(b9/#5) | Gm
care.
1. And if I tried, I still could-n't hide my love for you.
2. You said good-bye, no stars in the sky re-fuse to shine.

C11 C7 | Gm | C11 C7/Bb | Am7 | F/A Db7/Ab | Gm | G7 C7 | F
You ought to know, for have-n't I told you so, a mil-lion or more times?
Take it from me, it's no fun to be a-lone with moon-light and mem-'ries.
You went a-way and my heart

F/A | Db7/Ab | Gm | Gm(maj7) Gm7 | Gm | Gm7 | C7/Bb | D7/A | Am7 Ddim
went with you, I speak your name in my ev-'ry prayer.

D7 | Ddim D7 | Gm | D | Gm7(b5) | Bbm6 | F/C | A7/E | Cm/Eb | D7
If there is some oth-er way to prove that I love you, I swear I don't know how.

Gm | G7 | C7 | 1. F | Abdim | Gm7 | C7(#5) | 2. F | Abm6 | Db7/Ab | F6/9
You'll nev-er know if you don't know now. now.

YOU TELL ME YOUR DREAM
(I'll Tell You Mine)

Words and Music by
GUS KAHN and CHAS. N. DANIELS

Ab Abdim7 Ab F7 Bb7 Eb7 Ebdim7 Eb7 Eb
You tell me your dream, I'll tell you mine. My dreams are sweet,
Ab/C E7/B Eb7/Bb Eb7 Ab Abdim7 Ab F7 Bb7
dear, with love di-vine. Why keep me wait-ing, why let me
Db Ddim7 Ab/Eb F7 Bb7 Bbm7 Eb7 1. Ab Abdim7 Eb7 2. Ab
pine? You tell me your dream, I'll tell you mine. mine.

YOU AND ME AGAINST THE WORLD

Words and Music by
PAUL WILLIAMS and KEN ASCHER

Moderately slow

Ab7 Dbmaj7 Gbmaj7 Dbmaj9 Cm7 F7
You and me a-gainst the world; some-times it feels like you and me a-gainst the world. When all the oth-ers turn their

Bbm7 Gdim C7 Fm
back and walk a-way you can count on me to stay. Re-mem - ber when the
cir - cus came to town
Life can be a circus;

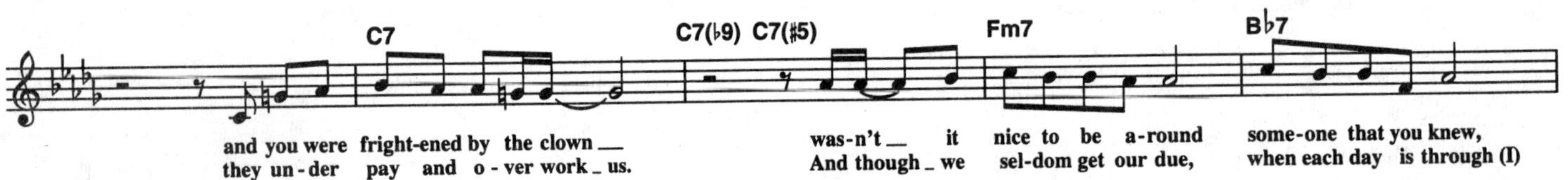
C7 C7(b9) C7(#5) Fm7 Bb7
and you were fright-ened by the clown wasn't it nice to be a-round some-one that you knew,
they un-der pay and o - ver work us. And though we sel-dom get our due, when each day is through (I)

Ebm7 Ab13 Dbmaj7 Gbmaj7
some-one who was big and strong and look-in' out for you and me
bring my tired bod - y home and look a-round for me and you
a-gainst the world. Some-times it feels like you and

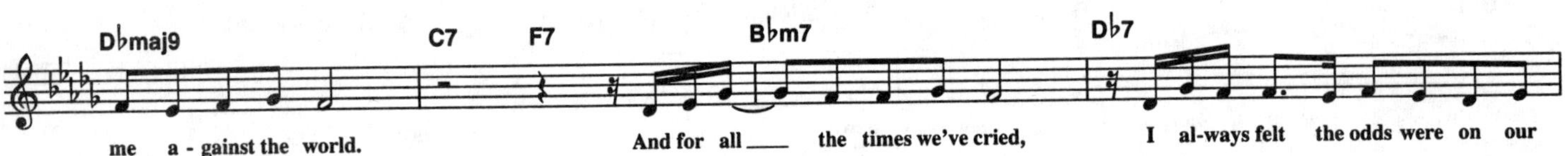
Dbmaj9 C7 F7 Bbm7 Db7
me a - gainst the world. And for all the times we've cried, I al-ways felt the odds were on our

Gdim Cm7 Fm Db7 Gb6
side. And when one of us is gone and one is left a - lone to car-ry on,

Gbm6 Fm7 Ebm7 Fm7(b5)
well, then re - mem-ber-ing will have to do; our mem - o - ries a - lone will get us through.

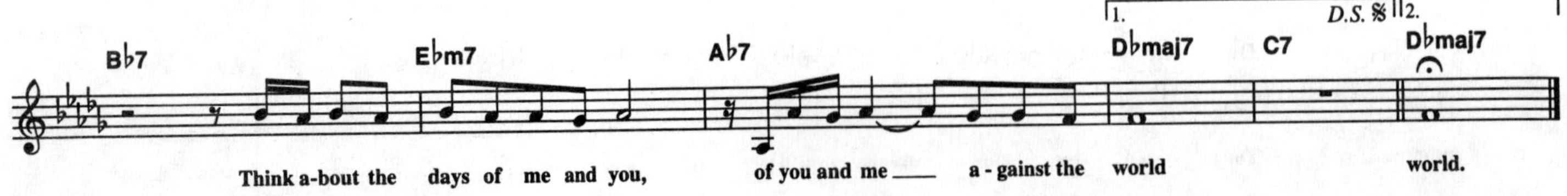
1. D.S. 2.
Bb7 Ebm7 Ab7 Dbmaj7 C7 Dbmaj7
Think a-bout the days of me and you, of you and me a - gainst the world world.

YOU ARE MY SUNSHINE

Words and Music by
JIMMIE DAVIS and
CHARLES MITCHELL

Moderato

Verse:
F Fdim F F7 B♭ F
1. The oth - er night dear as I lay sleep - ing I dreamed I held you in my arms.
love you and make you hap - py if you will on - ly say the same.
once dear you real - ly loved me and no one else could come be - tween.

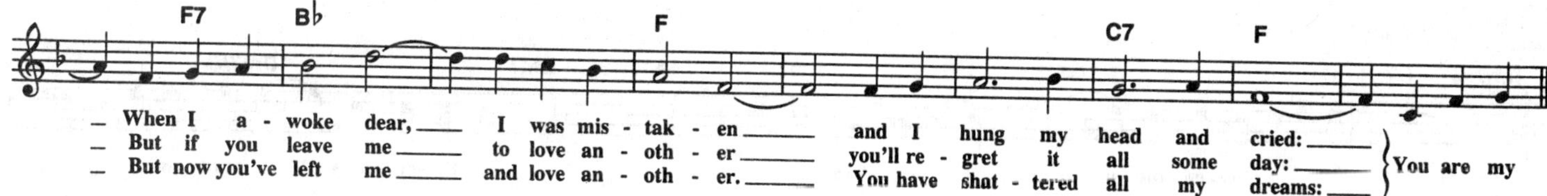
F7 B♭ F C7 F
When I a - woke dear, I was mis - tak - en and I hung my head and cried:
But if you leave me to love an - oth - er you'll re - gret it all some day:
But now you've left me and love an - oth - er. You have shat - tered all my dreams:
You are my

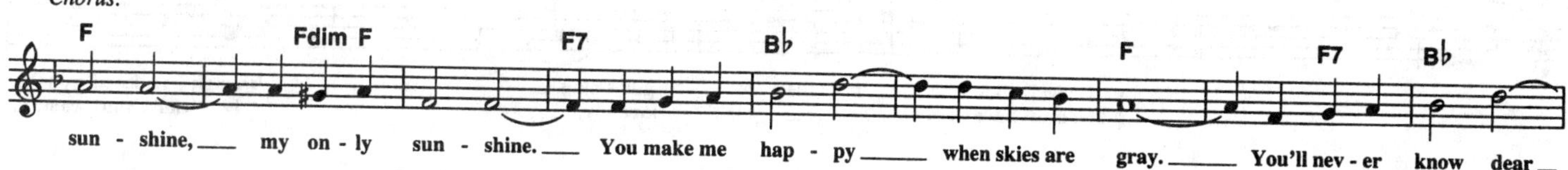
Chorus:
F Fdim F F7 B♭ F F7 B♭
sun - shine, my on - ly sun - shine. You make me hap - py when skies are gray. You'll nev - er know dear

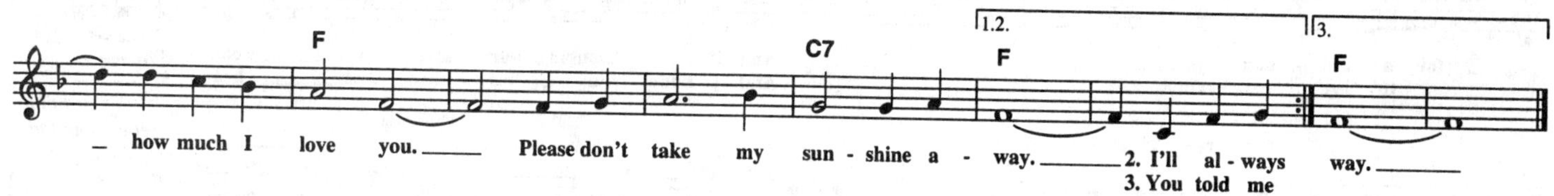
F C7 1.2. F 3. F
how much I love you. Please don't take my sun - shine a - way. 2. I'll al - ways way.
3. You told me

YOU ARE SO BEAUTIFUL

Words and Music by
BILLY PRESTON and BRUCE FISHER

Slowly
F Fmaj7 F7 B♭ B♭m F B♭ F B♭/C C7 F Fmaj7 F7
You are so beau-ti - ful to me. You are so
(Instr. 2nd time)
B♭ B♭m F Cm7 F9 B♭ A
beau-ti - ful to me. Can't you see (2nd-sing) you're ev-'ry-thing that I hope for and what's more,
Dm G9 B♭m6 F/C Fmaj7/C F7/C B♭ B♭m F B♭/F F
Repeat & fade
you're ev - 'ry - thing I need. You are so beau - ti - ful, ba - by; to me.

YOU ARE THE SUNSHINE OF MY LIFE

Words and Music by
STEVIE WONDER

Moderately, with feeling

Cmaj9 F7(♯5)

C G/F Em7 A13(♭9) Dm7 Dm7/G C

You are the sun - shine of my life, that's why I'll al - ways {be / stay} a - round.

Dm7/G G7 C G7/F Em7 A13(♭9) Dm7 Dm7/G

You are the ap - ple of my eye. For-ev - er you'll stay in my heart.

C Dm7 Dm7/G C F6 F/G Cmaj7 Fmaj9 F/G Cmaj7

{I feel like this is the be - gin - ning, 'though I've loved you
{You must have known that I was lone - ly, be - cause you came

F6 F/G Bm7(♭5) E7 A D E Am9

for a mil - lion years. And if I thought our love was end - ing,
to my res - cue. And I know that this must be heav - en;

D7 G7

3rd time
Repeat and fade

I'd find my - self, drown - ing in my own tears. Whoa, whoa.
how could so much love be in - side of you? Whoa.

From the United Artists Motion Picture "YOU ONLY LIVE TWICE"

YOU ONLY LIVE TWICE

Lyric by LESLIE BRICUSSE
Music by JOHN BARRY

Moderately
F Cm B♭m F B♭m7 C7 B♭m7 C C7(♭9/♭5) C9
You on - ly live twice or so it seems. One life for your - self and one for your dreams.
F Cm B♭m F B♭m7 C7 B♭m F
You drift through the years and life seems tame, till one dream ap - pears and love is its name.
B♭m7 C E♭m C B♭m7 C B♭m7 C7
And love is a stran - ger who'll beck - on you on. Don't think of the dan - ger or the stran - ger is gone.
F Cm B♭m F B♭m7 C7 B♭m F
This dream is for you, So pay the price. Make one dream come true; you on - ly live twice.

YOU WILL BE MY MUSIC

Words and Music by
JOE RAPOSO

Freely
When all the songs are out of tune and all the rhymes ring so un - true,
when I don't find the words to say, the thoughts I long to bring to you. When
I hear lone - ly sing - ers who are just as lost as me, mak - ing noise
not mel - o - dy.
Moderately slow, with a beat
You will be my mu - sic, you will be my song.
You will be my mu - sic, I can't wait an - y long - er if I'm wrong.
To Coda
I'll nev - er find the song to tell me all the things I need to say, and I'm a - fraid as time goes by that
some - day soon you'll go a - way. And I'll be lost and try - ing for songs I'll nev - er sing, want - ing you is ev - 'ry - thing.
D.S. al Coda
CODA
wrong. I can't wait an - y long - er for my song.

YOU BELONG TO MY HEART

Spanish Lyrics and Music by AGUSTIN LARA
English Lyrics by RAY GILBERT

Moderately
You be-long to my heart now and for-ev-er. And our love had its start not long a-go.
So-la-men-te u-na vez a-mé en la vi-da, so-la-men-te u-na vez y na-da-más.
We were gath-er-ing stars while a mil-lion gui-tars played our love song; when I said, "I love you," ev-'ry beat of my heart said it too.
U-na nez na-da más en mi huer-to bri-lló la es-pe-ran-za, la es-pe-ran-za que a-lum-bra el ca-mi-no de mi so-le-dad.
'Twas a mo-ment like this, do you re-mem-ber? And your eyes threw a kiss when they met mine.
U-na vez na-da más se en-tre-ga el al-ma, con la dul-ce y to-tal re-nun-cia-ción.
Now we own all the stars and a mil-lion gui-tars are still play-ing. Dar-ling, you are the song and you'll al-ways be-long to my heart. You be-long to my al-ways be-long to my heart.
Y cuan-do é-se mi-la-gro rea-li-za el pro-di-gio de a-mar-se, hay cam-pa-nas de fies-ta que can-tan en el co-ra-zón. So-la-men-te u-na can-tan en el co-ra-zón.
YOUNG LOVE
Words and Music by CAROLE JOYNER and RIC CARTEY
Copyright © 1956 (Renewed) by LOWERY MUSIC COL., INC. All Rights Reserved.
Moderately
Verse:
They say for ev-'ry boy and girl there's just one love in this old world, and I know I've found mine.
Just one kiss from your sweet lips will tell me that your love is real, and I can feel that it's true.
The heav-en-ly touch of your em-brace tells me no one can take your place ev-er in my heart.
We will vow to one an-oth-er, there will nev-er be an-oth-er love for you or for me.
Chorus:
Young love, first love, filled with true de-vo-tion. Young love, our love we share with deep e-mo-tion. Young
1. D.S.
2.3. etc. Repeat ad lib. and fade

YOU CAN DEPEND ON ME
Copyright © 1932 (Renewed 1959) by PEER INTERNATIONAL CORPORATION
All Rights Reserved
Words and Music by
CHARLES CARPENTER
LOUIS DUNLAP and EARL HINES
Moderato
Verse:
Dear one, you were all I had, and that's why I feel so bad, to think that you will be so far a - way.
Love's a game where stakes are high, so be - fore we say, "Good-bye", I've on - ly this, my fare-well words, to
say:
Chorus:
Though you say we're through, I'll al - ways love you, and you can de - pend on me.
Though some - one you've met has made you for - get, you know you can count on me. I
wish you suc - cess, loads of hap - pi - ness, but I must con - fess, I'll be lone - ly. If you need a
friend, I'm yours to the end, and you can de - pend on me. Though me.
YOU DON'T HAVE TO SAY YOU LOVE ME
Copyright © 1965, 1966 BY ACCORDO EDIZIONI MUSICALI, Milan, Italy
Rights controlled by EMI MILLER CATALOG INC.
All Rights Reserved
English Lyrics by VICKI WICKHAM and SIMON NAPIER-BELL
Original Italian Lyrics by V. PALLAVICINI
Music by P. DONAGGIO
Moderately slow
1. When I said I need - ed you. you said you would al - ways stay. It was - n't me who changed, but you and
now you're gone and I'm left here on my own; that I have to fol - low you and
mem - o - ry, life seems dead and quite un - real. All that's left is lone - li - ness; there's
now you've gone a - way. 2. Dont' you see that beg you to come home?
noth - ing left to feel.
Chorus:
You don't have to say you love me just be close at hand. You don't have to stay for-ev - er, I will un-der-stand. Be - lieve me be-lieve me, I can't help but love you, but be-
lieve me, I'll nev - er let you down. 3. Left a-lone with just a
D.S.
lieve me, be - lieve me, be - lieve me.

YOU'RE AN OLD SMOOTHIE

Words by B.G. DeSYLVA
Music by RICHARD A. WHITING and NACIO HERB BROWN

Moderato
G7 C7 F Cm6/Eb D7 G7 F C7/G F/A
You're An Old Smooth - ie, I'm an old soft - ie; I'm just like
You're an old mean - ie, I'm a big boob - ie, I just go
Sil - ly old smooth - ie, Craft - y old soft - ie, I'll stick like
Gm7 F Gm E7-5 (C7) last time 1.A7+5 A7 D7-9 D7 2.3. F Fine A
put - ty in the hands of a girl like you. you. Poor me, you
nut - ty, in the hands of a girl like
put - ty to the hand of a girl like
E7 A E7 C
played me for a sap; Poor you, you thought you'd laid a trap! Well, dear, I
G7 C C+ D.C. al Fine
think it's time you knew, You've done just what I want - ed you to.
YOU'RE GONNA HEAR FROM ME
© 1965 WARNER BROS. INC.
All Rights Reserved
Words by DORY PREVIN
Music by ANDRE PREVIN
Slowly, but rythmically
G7-9 C Dm7 G7 Gm7/C C9 C7-9
Move o - ver, sun, and give me some sky, I've got me some wings, I'm eag - er to
room, you peo - ple up there, On top of the world, I'll meet you, I
F Ab/Bb Bb9 C/G A7-9 Am7 D7-9
try; I may be un - known, But wait till I've flown,
swear; I'm stak - in' my claim, re - mem - ber my name,
You're Gon - na Hear From Me!
1.Dm7/G G7 G7-9 2.G7sus4 G7 Gm7/C C7-9 Fmaj7 F6 Fm C/G
Make me some For - tune smiled On the road be -
B6/G C6/C Bbm7 Am7 D7 G7sus4 Gdim Dm7/G G7+5
fore me, I'm for - tune's child, Lis - ten world, you can't ig - nore me!
Eb/Bb Fm7 Bb7 Bbm7 Eb9 Eb7-9
I've got a song that longs to be played. Raise up my flag, be - gin my pa -
Ab C/G A7-9 D7 G7sus4 G7
rade, Then watch the world o - ver, start com - in' up clo - ver, That's how it's gon - na be,
Cmaj7 Em7 A7 D9 G7sus4 G7 C Ab/C C
you'll see! You're Gon - na Hear From Me!

YOU GOT IT

Words and Music by
ROY ORBISON, JEFF LYNNE
and TOM PETTY

Moderate rock
Verse:
1. Ev-'ry time I look in - to your lov - ing eyes, I see a love that mon-ey just can't buy. One look from you, I drift a - way. I pray that you are here to stay.
Chorus:
An - y - thing you want, you got it. An - y - thing you need, you got it. An - y - thing at all, you got it, ba - by.
To Coda
1.
D.C.
2.
An-y-thing you want, (you got it.) An-y-thing you need, (you got it.) An-y-thing at all.
3.
Bridge:
I'm glad to give my love to you. I know you feel the way I do.
D.S. al Coda
Coda
An - y - thing at all, (you got it.) Ba - by, you got it.

Verse 2:
Every time I hold you
I begin to understand.
Everything about you
Tells me I'm your man.
I live my life
To be with you.
No one can do
The things you do.
(To Chorus:)

YOU GOT IT ALL

Words and Music by
RUPERT HOLMES

Moderately slow

Verse:

Db Gb/Db Db Gbm/Db Db Gb/Db Db Gbm(#7)/Db

I, I was a game _ he would play; _ he brought the clouds _ to my day. _

F7sus/C F7 Ab/Bb Bbm Db2/Ab Gb2 Gb Db/F Ebm7 D G/D

_ Then like a ray _ of light you came my way _ one night. Just one look and I knew you would make ev - 'ry-thing clear, _
2. No, don't let him wor - ry you so. _

To Coda ⊕ *(Key of Eb)*

D Gm(#7)/D F#7sus/C# F#7 A/B Bm D2/A G2 G D/F# Em7 G/A G

_ make all the clouds _ dis-ap - pear. _ Put all your fears _ to rest. Who do I love _ the best? Don't you know? Don't you
_ Once I met you, _ I let go. _ Oh, you can sure - ly see, you're so much more _ to me. Just one look and I

Chorus:

F#m7 Bm7 Em7 A Em7 Gmaj7 A Em7 A Asus/G F#m7 Bm7 Em7

know? You got it all o - ver him. You got me o - ver him hon - ey, it's true. _ There's just you; you must have been heav-

A C#m7(b5) F#7sus F#7 Bm7 E9 Em9 D/F#

- en sent. Hear-ing me call, _ you went out on a limb. _ And you're all _ that he's not; _ just look _

D.S. 𝄋 *al Coda*

Gmaj7 D/F# Em7 G/A D G/D D Gm/D

_ what I got. _ 'Cause you got it all _ o - ver him.

⊕ *Coda*

Eb Ab/Eb Eb Abm(#7)/Eb G7sus/D G7 Bb/C

knew you would make ev - 'ry-thing clear, _ make all the clouds _ dis - ap - pear. _ You're bet - ter than all _

Cm Eb2/G Ab2 Ab Eb/G Fm7 Ab/Bb Ab Gm7 Cm7 Fm7

_ the rest. Who do I love? _ Don't you know? Don't you know? You got it all o -

Bb Fm7 Abmaj7 Bb Fm7 Bb Bbsus/Ab Gm7 Cm7 Fm7

- ver him. You got me o - ver him hon - ey, it's true. _ There's just you; you must have been heav-

Bb Dm7(b5) G7sus G7 Cm F9 Fm9 Eb/G

- en sent. Hear-ing me call, _ you went out on a limb. _ And you're all _ that he's not; _ just look _

Repeat and fade

Abmaj7 Eb/G Fm7 Ab/Bb Ab Gm7 Cm7 Fm7

_ what I got. _ 'Cause you've got it all, _ all o - ver him. _ You've got it all o -

YOU'RE MY EVERYTHING
© 1931 WARNER BROS. INC. (Renewed)
All Rights Reserved
Words by MORT DIXON and JOE YOUNG
Music by HARRY WARREN
Slowly, with much espression
You're My Ev - 'ry - thing __ un - der - neath the sun, __ You're My Ev - 'ry - thing
__ rolled up in - to one. __ You're my on - ly dream, my on - ly real re -
al - i - ty, __ You're my i - dea of a per - fect per - son - al - i - ty. __
__ You're My Ev - 'ry - thing, __ Ev - 'ry - thing I need, __ You're the song I sing __
__ And the book I read. __ You're a - way be - yond be - lief, And just to make it brief, __
__ You're my win - ter, sum - mer, spring, my ev - 'ry - thing. __
YOUNG AT HEART
© 1954 CHERIO CORPORATION
Copyright Renewed 1982 and Assigned to CAROLYN LEIGH and CHERIO CORPORATION
All Rights Reserved
Words by CAROLYN LEIGH
Music by JOHNNY RICHARDS
Slowly
Fair - y tales __ can come true, __ it can hap - pen to you, __ if you're Young At Heart. __
know __ that it's worth __ ev - 'ry treas - ure on earth, __ to be Young At Heart. __
__ For it's hard, __ you will find, __ to be nar - row of mind __ if you're Young At Heart. __
__ For, as rich __ as you are, __ it's much bet - ter by far __ to be Young At Heart. __
__ You can go __ to ex - tremes __ with im - pos - si - ble schemes, __ You can
__ And if you __ should sur - vive __ to a hun - dred and five __ look at
laugh __ when your dreams __ fall a - part at the seams, And life gets more ex - cit - ing with each pass - ing day, __ And
all __ you'll de - rive __ out of
To Coda
love is ei - ther in your heart or on the way. __ Don't you
D.S. al Coda
Coda
be - ing a - live, And
here is the best part, __ you have a head start, __ if you are a - mong the ver - y Young At Heart. __

From the Columbia Pictures Release "YOU LIGHT UP MY LIFE"

YOU LIGHT UP MY LIFE

Words and Music by
JOE BROOKS

Moderately slow

Bbm Eb Ab Fm Gm7 C7 Fm Eb/F F7

So man - y nights I'd sit by my win - dow wait - ing for some-one to sing me his song.
Roll - in' at sea, a - drift on the wa - ters, could it be fi - n'lly I'm turn - ing for home.

Bbm Eb Ab Eb/G Fm G Bb7 Fm7/Bb Bb7

So man - y dreams I kept deep in - side me, a - lone in the dark, but now you've come a - long.
Fi - n'lly a chance to say, "Hey! I love you." Nev - er a - gain to be all a - lone. And

𝄋 Eb Ebmaj7 Eb7 C7 Fm Fm7 Bb7 *To Coda* 𝄌

you light up my life. You give me hope, to car - ry on. You light up my days and fill my

1. Eb Bb/D Cm Fm Bb7 — 2. Eb Bb/D Cm Fm Bb *D.S. 𝄋 al Coda* — 𝄌 *Coda* G Cm

nights with song. nights with song. nights with song.

F Eb/Bb G Cm F7 Eb/Bb Fm/Bb Bb Ab Eb Bb Ab Eb

It can't be wrong when it feels so right, 'cause you, you light up my life.

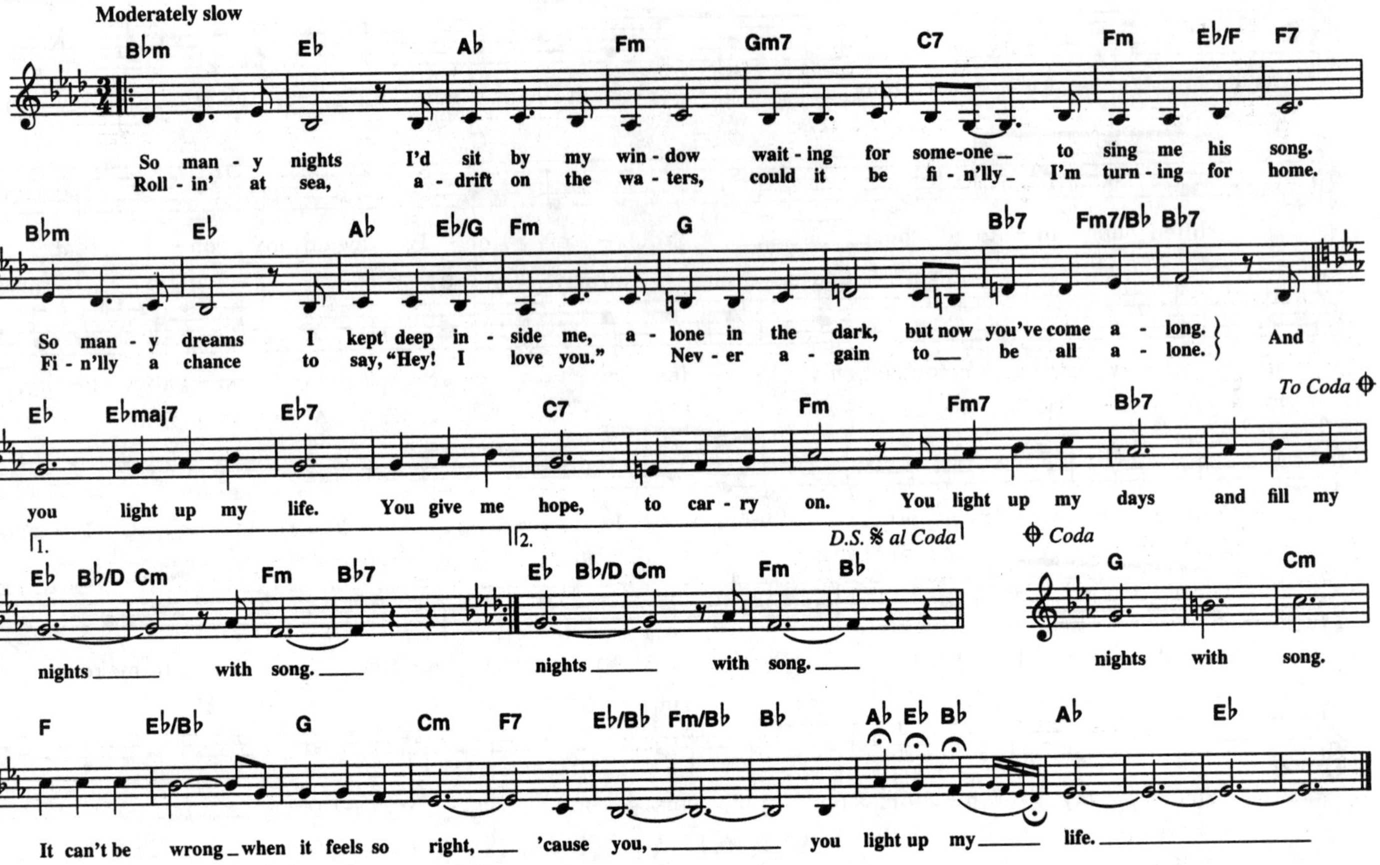

YOU MADE ME LOVE YOU
(I Didn't Want to Do It)

Words by JOE McCARTHY
Music by JAMES V. MONACO

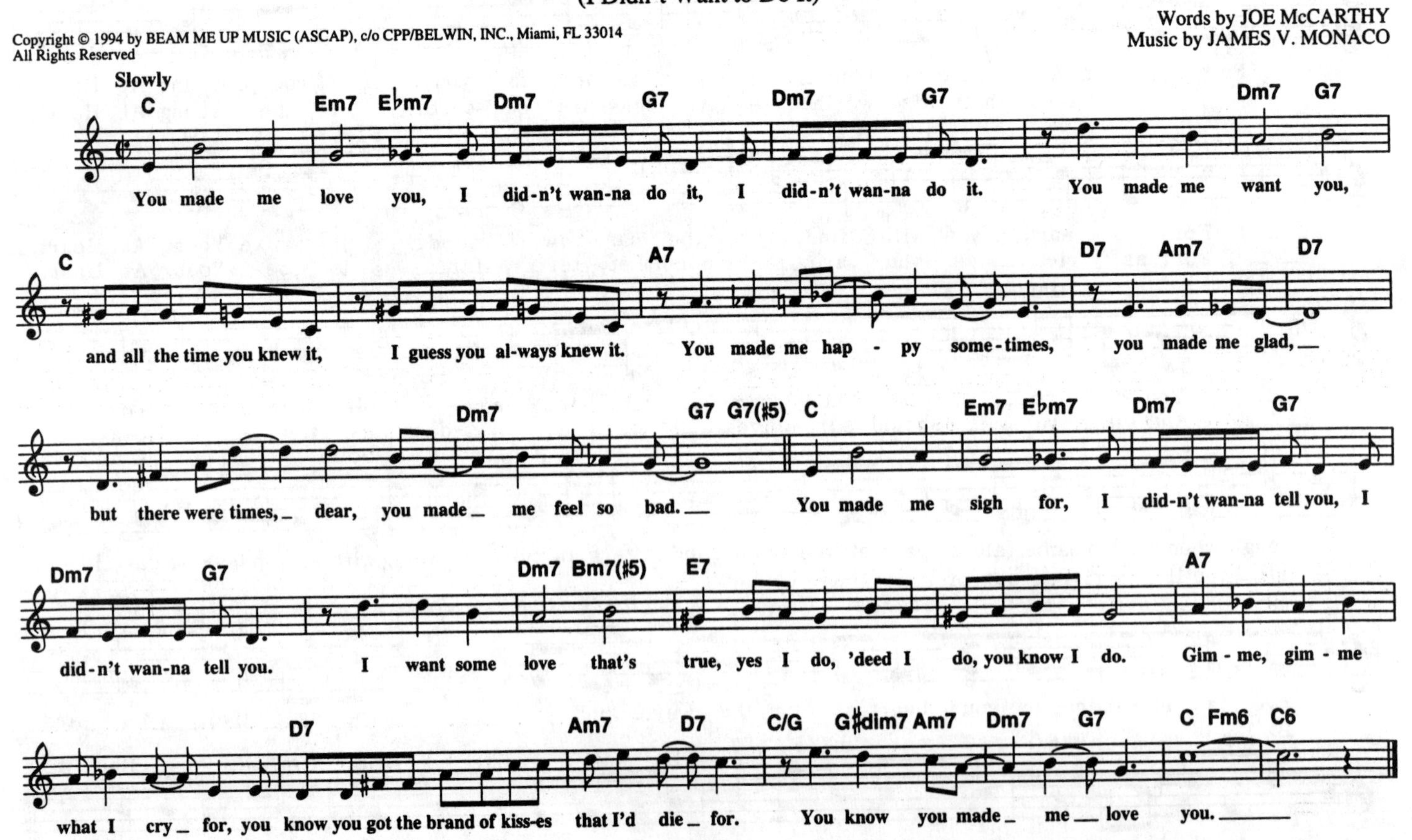
Slowly
C Em7 Ebm7 Dm7 G7 Dm7 G7 Dm7 G7
You made me love you, I did-n't wan-na do it, I did-n't wan-na do it. You made me want you,
C A7 D7 Am7 D7
and all the time you knew it, I guess you al-ways knew it. You made me hap - py some-times, you made me glad,
Dm7 G7 G7(#5) C Em7 Ebm7 Dm7 G7
but there were times, dear, you made me feel so bad. You made me sigh for, I did-n't wan-na tell you, I
Dm7 G7 Dm7 Bm7(#5) E7 A7
did-n't wan-na tell you. I want some love that's true, yes I do, 'deed I do, you know I do. Gim - me, gim - me
D7 Am7 D7 C/G G#dim7 Am7 Dm7 G7 C Fm6 C6
what I cry for, you know you got the brand of kiss-es that I'd die for. You know you made me love you.

From the Metro-Goldwyn-Mayer Musical Production "ZIEGFIELD GIRL"

YOU STEPPED OUT OF A DREAM

Words by GUS KAHN
Music by NACIO HERB BROWN

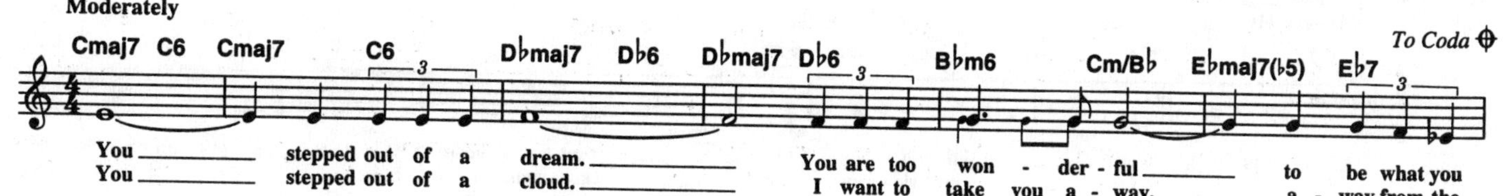
Moderately
Cmaj7 C6 Cmaj7 C6 D♭maj7 D♭6 D♭maj7 D♭6 B♭m6 Cm/B♭ E♭maj7(♭5) E♭7
To Coda
You stepped out of a dream. You are too won - der - ful to be what you
You stepped out of a cloud. I want to take you a - way, a - way from the

A♭ A♭maj7 A♭6 A♭ Gm7 C7 Fmaj7 Am7
seem! Could there be eyes like yours? Could there be lips like yours? Could there be smiles like yours,

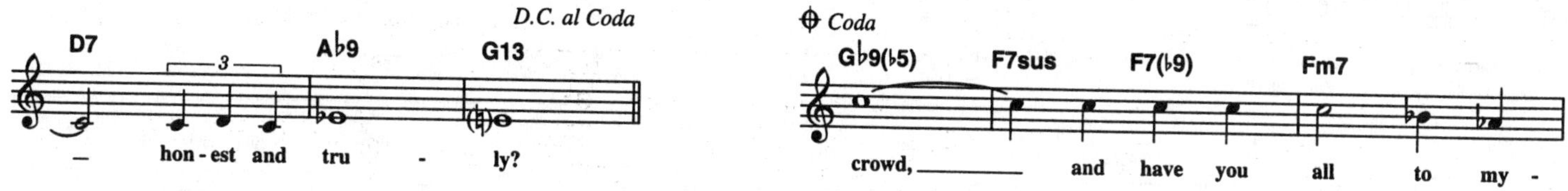
D7 A♭9 G13
D.C. al Coda
– hon - est and tru - ly?
Coda
G♭9(♭5) F7sus F7(♭9) Fm7
crowd, and have you all to my -

Cmaj7 Dm7 G7 G7(♯5) Cmaj7 C6 C
self, a - lone and a - part out of a dream, safe in my heart.

YOU WERE MEANT FOR ME

Words by ARTHUR FREED
Music by NACIO HERB BROWN

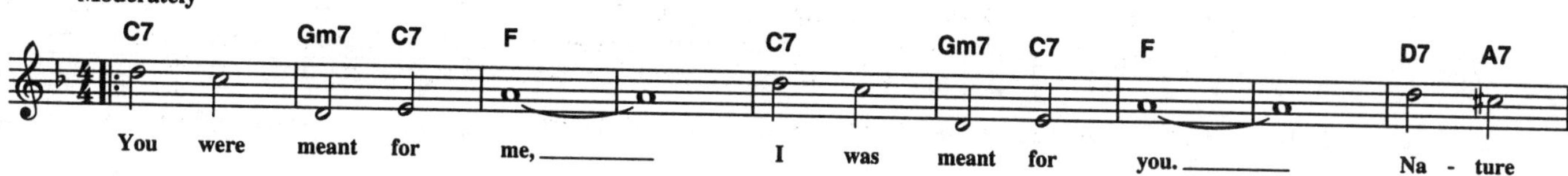
Moderately
C7 Gm7 C7 F C7 Gm7 C7 F D7 A7
You were meant for me, I was meant for you. Na - ture

D7 G7 Cdim C7 Ddim C7 D♭7
pat - terned you and when she was done you were all the sweet things rolled up in one. You're like a

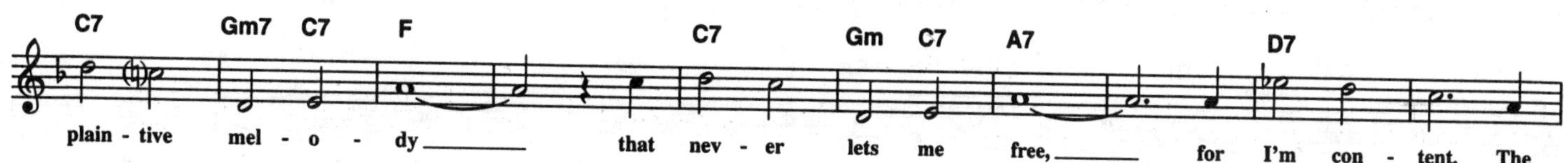
C7 Gm7 C7 F C7 Gm C7 A7 D7
plain - tive mel - o - dy that nev - er lets me free, for I'm con - tent. The

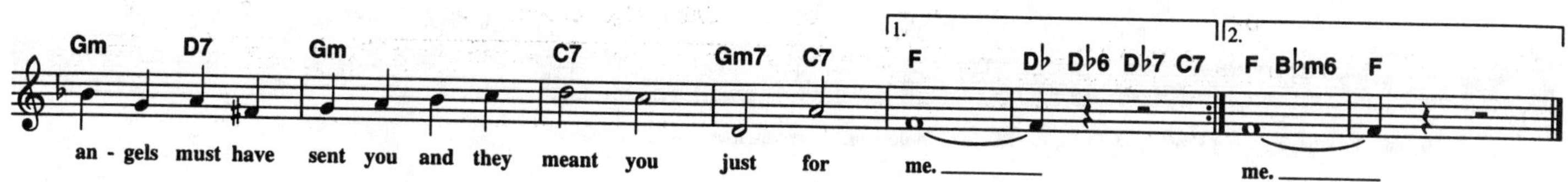
Gm D7 Gm C7 Gm7 C7 F D♭ D♭6 D♭7 C7 F B♭m6 F
1. 2.
an - gels must have sent you and they meant you just for me. me.

YOU WIN AGAIN

Words and Music by
HANK WILLIAMS

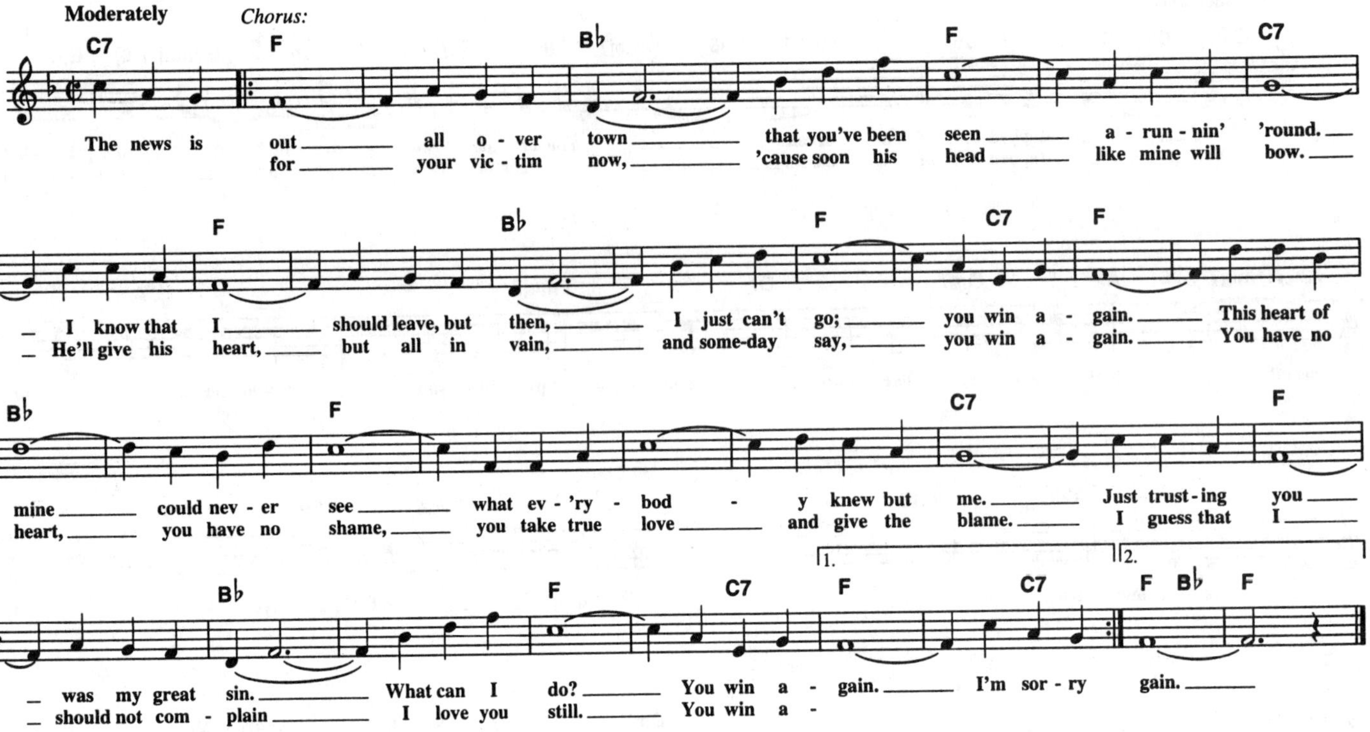

Moderately *Chorus:*

C7 F Bb F C7

The news is out ___ all o - ver town ___ that you've been seen ___ a - run - nin' 'round. ___
for ___ your vic - tim now, ___ 'cause soon his head ___ like mine will bow. ___

F Bb F C7 F

_ I know that I ___ should leave, but then, ___ I just can't go; ___ you win a - gain. ___ This heart of
_ He'll give his heart, ___ but all in vain, ___ and some-day say, ___ you win a - gain. ___ You have no

Bb F C7 F

mine ___ could nev - er see ___ what ev - 'ry - bod - y knew but me. ___ Just trust - ing you ___
heart, ___ you have no shame, ___ you take true love ___ and give the blame. ___ I guess that I ___

Bb F C7 F C7 | 1. | 2. F Bb F

_ was my great sin. ___ What can I do? ___ You win a - gain. ___ I'm sor - ry gain. ___
_ should not com - plain ___ I love you still. ___ You win a -

YOUNG WORLD

Words and Music by
JERRY FULLER

Bb7 Eb Eb7 Ab

It's a young world, when you're in love, you're in a young world. So, take my hand and let me

Eb Bb7 Eb Bb Ab Bb6 Eb Eb7

show you just how true _ young love can be. It's a young world, and if you'll tell me you're my

Ab Eb Bb7 Eb Ab Eb

one girl, you'll make my whole life worth liv - in', just by giv - in' your love to me. ___

Bb7 Eb Bb7 Eb Bb7 Eb G7 Cm

All of the world is a trea - sure, when you have some-one to care. Prom-ise me your love for - ev - er and

F7 Bb7 Eb Eb7 Ab

we'll have the whole world to share. ___ And it's a young world, when you're in love, you're in a young world.

Eb Bb7 | 1. Eb Bb Ab Bb6 | 2. Eb Ab Eb

If you be - lieve _ what I've told you, let me hold you, say you love me. It's a me. ___

YOUR CHEATIN' HEART

Words and Music by
HANK WILLIAMS

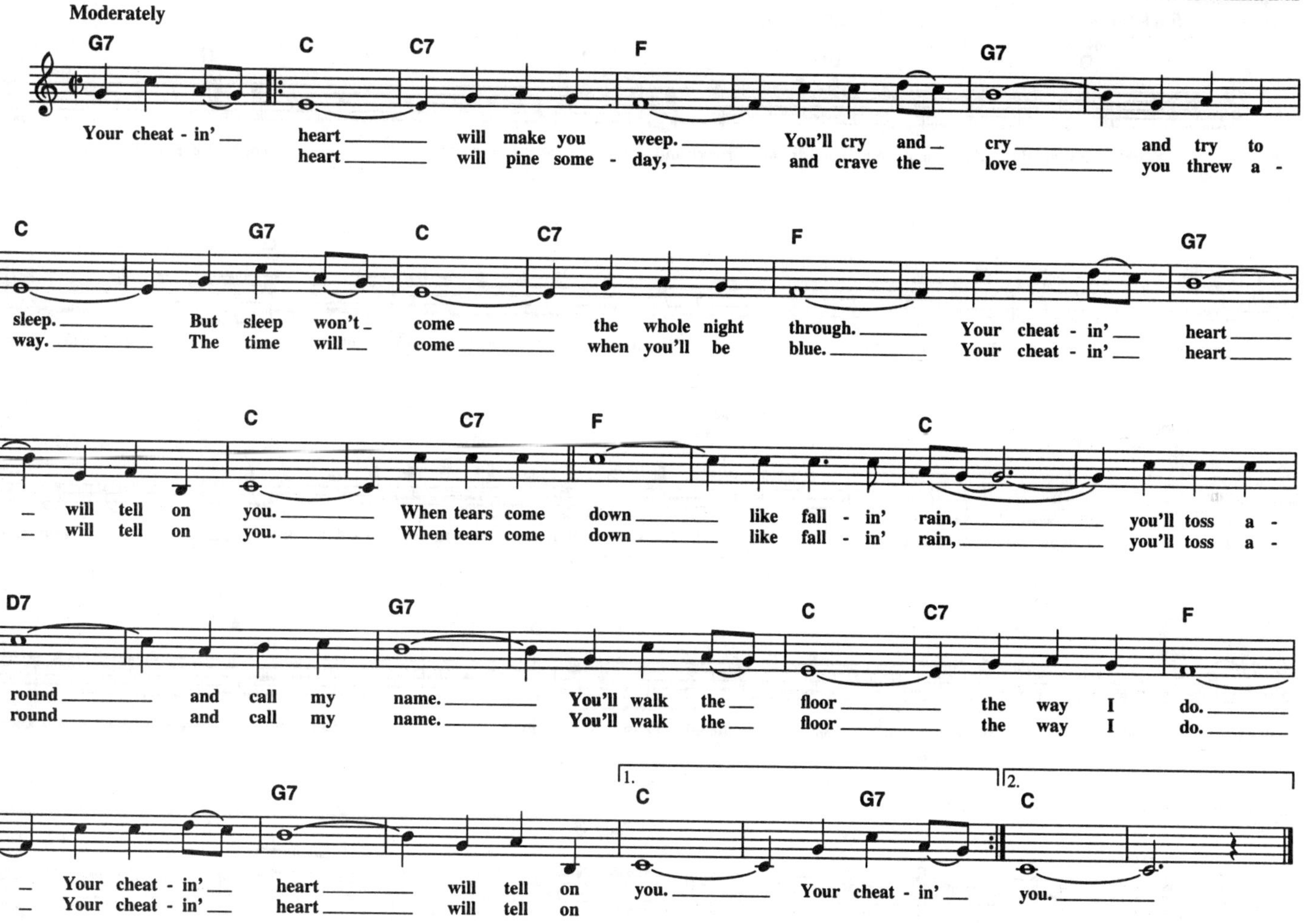

Moderately

G7 C C7 F G7

Your cheat - in' heart will make you weep. You'll cry and cry and try to sleep. But sleep won't come the whole night through. Your cheat - in' heart will tell on you. When tears come down like fall - in' rain, you'll toss a - round and call my name. You'll walk the floor the way I do. Your cheat - in' heart will tell on you. Your cheat - in' you.

heart will pine some - day, and crave the love you threw a - way. The time will come when you'll be blue. Your cheat - in' heart will tell on you. When tears come down like fall - in' rain, you'll toss a - round and call my name. You'll walk the floor the way I do. Your cheat - in' heart will tell on

YOU'RE A GRAND OLD FLAG

G.M. COHEN

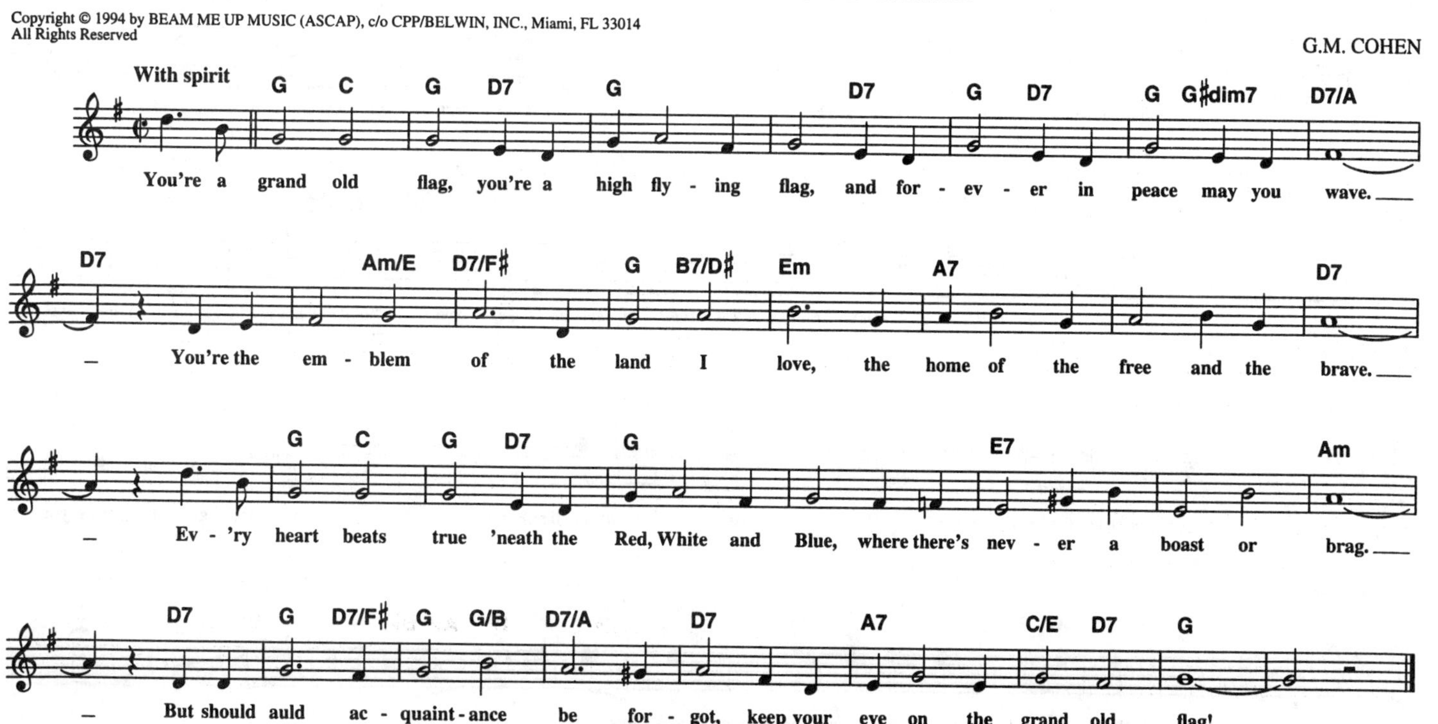
With spirit
You're a grand old flag, you're a high fly - ing flag, and for - ev - er in peace may you wave.
You're the em - blem of the land I love, the home of the free and the brave.
Ev - 'ry heart beats true 'neath the Red, White and Blue, where there's nev - er a boast or brag.
But should auld ac - quaint - ance be for - got, keep your eye on the grand old flag!

YOUR MAMA DON'T DANCE

Words and Music by
JIM MESSINA and
KENNY LOGGINS

Rock shuffle
Chorus:
D G D G
Your ma-ma don't dance and your dad-dy don't rock and roll. Your ma-ma don't dance and your
D A G
dad-dy don't rock and roll. When eve - nin' rolls a-round and it's time to hit the town, where do you
Verse:
D D G D
go? You've got to rock it! The old folks say that you got-ta end your day by ten, mm-mm.
(2nd time ad lib. solo)
G D A
But if you're out on a date don't you bring her home late, 'cause it's a sin. You know there's no ex-cuse, you know
To Coda
G D 1. 2. F♯
you're gon-na lose; you nev-er win; I'll say it a-gain. And it's all be-cause your Yeah, we
Bridge:
G F♯ G F♯ G F♯ G F♯
pull in-to a drive-in and I find a place to park. We hop in-to the back seat, where I know it's nice and dark. We're
G F♯ G F♯ G F♯ G N.C.
just a-bout to move, think-in' mmm yeah, this is a breeze. Then there's a light in my eye, and a guy says, "Out-ta the car, long hair, but ooo-wee,
D.S. al Coda
A
you're com-in' with me to the lo-cal po-lice." And it's all be-cause your
Coda
A G D
Your ma-ma don't dance and your dad-dy don't rock and roll.

From the Broadway Musical "ANYTHING GOES"

YOU'RE THE TOP

Words and Music by
COLE PORTER

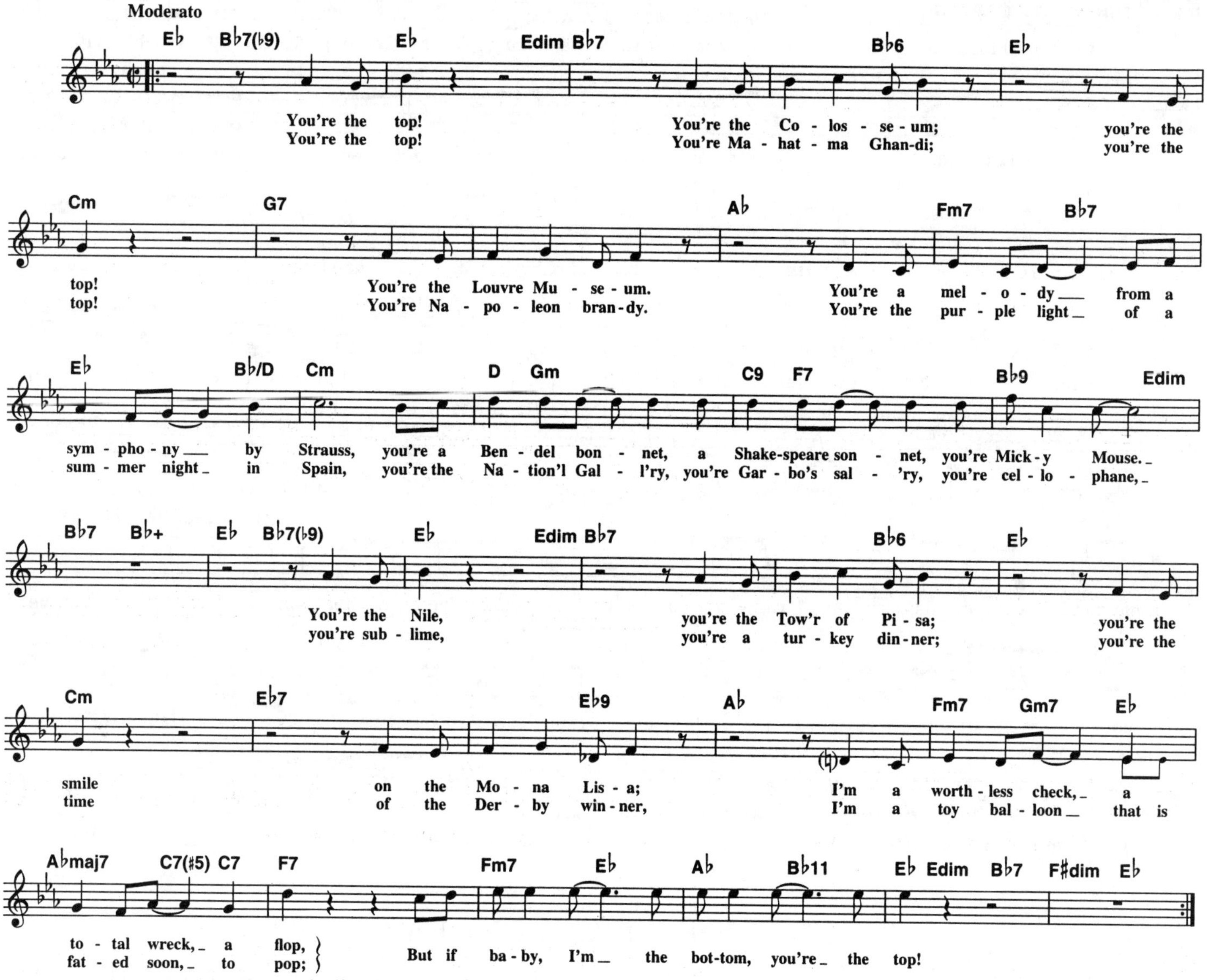

Moderato

E♭ B♭7(♭9) E♭ Edim B♭7 B♭6 E♭
You're the top! You're the Co - los - se - um; you're the
You're the top! You're Ma - hat - ma Ghan-di; you're the

Cm G7 A♭ Fm7 B♭7
top! You're the Louvre Mu - se - um. You're a mel - o - dy___ from a
top! You're Na - po - leon bran - dy. You're the pur - ple light_ of a

E♭ B♭/D Cm D Gm C9 F7 B♭9 Edim
sym - pho - ny___ by Strauss, you're a Ben - del bon - net, a Shake-speare son - net, you're Mick - y Mouse._
sum - mer night_ in Spain, you're the Na - tion'l Gal - l'ry, you're Gar - bo's sal - 'ry, you're cel - lo - phane,_

B♭7 B♭+ E♭ B♭7(♭9) E♭ Edim B♭7 B♭6 E♭
You're the Nile, you're the Tow'r of Pi - sa; you're the
you're sub - lime, you're a tur - key din - ner; you're the

Cm E♭7 E♭9 A♭ Fm7 Gm7 E♭
smile on the Mo - na Lis - a; I'm a worth - less check,_ a
time of the Der - by win - ner, I'm a toy bal - loon___ that is

A♭maj7 C7(♯5) C7 F7 Fm7 E♭ A♭ B♭11 E♭ Edim B♭7 F♯dim E♭
to - tal wreck,_ a flop, }
fat - ed soon,_ to pop; }
But if ba - by, I'm_ the bot - tom, you're_ the top!

ZUM GALI GALI

JEWISH FOLK SONG

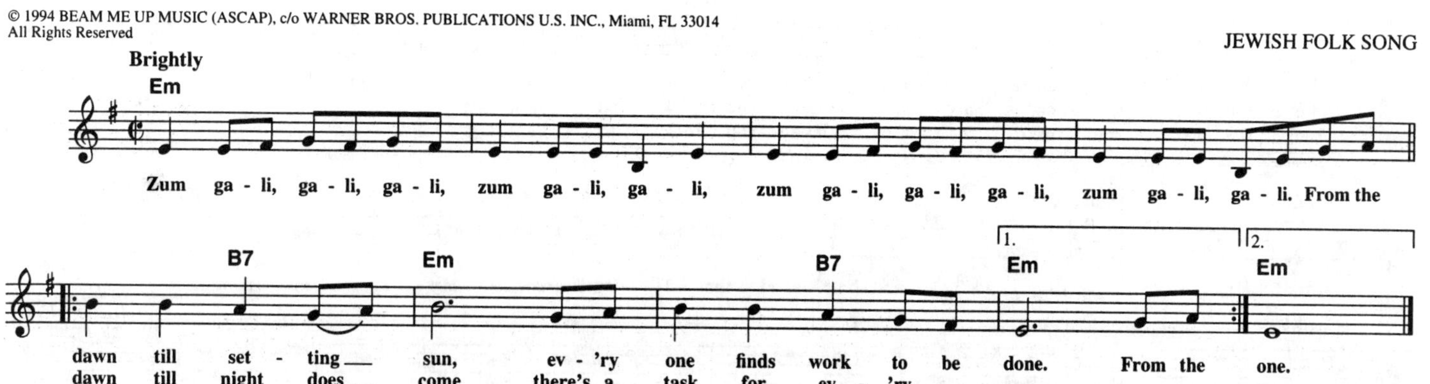
Brightly
Em
Zum ga - li, ga - li, ga - li, zum ga - li, ga - li, zum ga - li, ga - li, ga - li, zum ga - li, ga - li. From the
B7 Em B7 1. Em 2. Em
dawn till set - ting___ sun, ev - 'ry one finds work to be done. From the one.
dawn till night does___ come there's a task for ev - 'ry___

YOU'RE GETTING TO BE A HABIT WITH ME

Words by AL DUBIN
Music by HARRY WARREN

Moderato

F7 Bb6 C7 Bb6 C7 Fmaj7 F6
Ev - 'ry kiss, ev-'ry hug seems to act just like a drug; You're Get-ting To Be A Hab-bit With Me.

Fmaj7 F7 Bb6 C7 Bb6 C7
Let me stay in your arms, I'm ad - dict - ed to your charms; You're

Fmaj7 F6 A7+5 A7 D7-9 D7 Gm C7
Get-ting To Be A Hab - it With Me. I used to think your love was

F F/A Abdim Gm7 C11 C+ F6 F#dim Gm C7
some-thing that I could take or leave a - lone, But now I could- n't do with-

F Dm Dm7 G6 G9 C7/6 C7+5 C7 F7 Bb6 C7
out my sup - ply, I need you for my own. Oh, I can't break a - way, I must

Bb6 C7 Fmaj7 F6 E7/B E7-5/Bb A7 D7
have you ev - 'ry day; As reg - u - lar - ly as cof - fee or tea. You've

Gm E7 A7 D7 Adim Gm G7 C7
got me in your clutch-es, and I can't get free; You're Get-ting To Be A Hab - it With

F A7/E Am7 D7 Adim Gm C7 F
Me, (can't break it!) You're Get - ting To Be A Hab - it With Me.

YOU TOOK ADVANTAGE OF ME

Words by LORENZ HART
Music by RICHARD RODGERS

Allegretto
Eb E dim Bb7 Eb Ebdim Fm7 Bb7 F-9
I'm a sent - i - ment - al sap, that's all. What's the use of try - ing not to fall? I
I'm just like an ap - ple on a bough. And you're gon - na shake me down some-how, So
Here am I with all my bridg - es burned, Just a babe in arms where you're con-cerned, So
Eb Eb7 Ab Abm6 Eb Eb+ Bb7
have no will, You've made your kill 'Cause you took ad - vant- age of
what's the use, you've cooked my goose 'Cause you took ad - vant- age of
lock the doors and call me yours 'Cause you took ad - vant- age of
1. Eb B7 Bb7
me!
2.3. Eb
me!
Fine
Gm Cm D7 G7 C7 F7 Bb7
I'm so hot and both - ered that I don't know My el - bow from my
Eb Cm D7 G7 C7 F7 Bb7
ear; I suf - fer some-thing aw - ful each time you go And much worse when you're near.
D.C. al Fine
Bb Eb Bb7

From "ANNIE"

YOU'RE NEVER FULLY DRESSED WITHOUT A SMILE

Lyric by MARTIN CHARNIN
Music by CHARLES STROUSE

Moderately
Hey, ho - bo man, hey, Dap - per Dan, you both got your style. But broth - er, you're nev - er ful - ly
Your clothes may be "Beau Brum - el - ly;" they stand out a mile. But broth - er,
dressed with - out a smile! smile! Who cares what they're wear - ing on Main Street or Sa - ville
Row? It's what you wear from ear to ear and not from head to toe that mat - ters. So Sen - a - tor,
so jan - i - tor, so long for a - while. Re - mem - ber you're nev - er ful - ly dressed, though you may wear the
best, you're nev - er ful - ly dressed with - out a smile.
YOU'RE NOBODY TILL SOMEBODY LOVES YOU
Words and Music by RUSS MORGAN, LARRY STOCK and JAMES CAVANAUGH
Copyright © 1944 (Renewed) by SOUTHERN MUSIC PUBLISHING CO. INC.
All Rights Reserved
Moderately
You're no - bod - y till some - bod - y loves you. You're no - bod - y till some - bod - y cares.
You may be king, you may pos - sess the world and its gold, but gold won't bring you
hap - pi - ness when you're grow - ing old. The world still is the same, you'll nev - er change it,
as sure as the stars shine a - bove. You're no - bod - y till some - bod - y loves
you, so, find your - self some - bod - y to love. You're love.

YOU GO TO MY HEAD
© 1938 WARNER BROS. INC. (Renewed)
All Rights Reserved
Words by HAVEN GILLESPIE
Music by J. FRED COOTS
Tenderly
You Go To My Head — and you lin-ger like a haunt-ing re-frain, — And I find you spin-ning 'round in my brain, — Like the bub-bles in a glass of cham-pagne. —
like a sip of spar-kling Bur-gun-dy brew, — And I find the ver-y men-tion of you, — Like the kick-er in a ju-lep or two. —
with a smile that makes my tem-p'ra-ture rise, — Like a sum-mer with a thou-sand Ju-lys, — You in-tox-i-cate my
To Coda
You
The thrill of the thought — that you might give a thought — to my plea casts a spell o-ver me. — Still I say to my-self, "Get a hold of your-self, can't you see that it nev-er can be." You
D.S. (To Verse 3) al Coda
Coda
soul with your eyes. — Tho' I'm cer-tain that this heart of mine — Has-n't a ghost of a chance in this cra-zy ro-mance, — You go to my head. — You Go To My Head. —
YOU MUST HAVE BEEN A BEAUTIFUL BABY
© 1938 WARNER BROS. INC. (Renewed)
All Rights Reserved
Words by JOHNNY MERCER
Music by HARRY WARREN
Moderato
You Must Have Been A Beau-ti-ful Ba-by, — You must have been a won-der-ful child; — When you were on-ly start-in' to go to kin-der-gar-ten, I bet you drove the lit-tle boys — wild,
when it came to win-ning blue rib-bons, — You must have shown the oth-er kids how; — I can see the judg-es' eyes as they hand-ed you the prize, — I
And bet you made the cut-est bow, Oh! You Must Have Been A Beau-ti-ful Ba-by, — 'Cause ba-by look at you now. —

YOU'VE CHANGED

Words by BILL CAREY
Music by CARL FISCHER

Moderately
B♭7(♯5) E♭maj7 D7 Gm7(♭5)/D♭ C7 F7 1. B9 B♭9
You've changed. That spar-kle in your eyes is gone. Your smile is just a care-less yawn. You're break-ing my heart; _ you've changed. _
changed. Your kiss-es now are so bla - sé. You're bored with me in ev - 'ry way. I
E♭6 Cm7 Fm7 B♭7 B♭7(♯5) 2. B9 B♭9 E♭maj9 E♭7 E♭6 B♭m7 E♭7 E♭7(♯5) A♭maj7 A♭m7
You've can't un-der-stand; _ you've changed. _ You've for - got-ten the words, _ "I love _ you," _
E♭maj7 E♭7(♯5) A♭maj7 A♭m7 E♭/G G♭9 Fm7/B♭ B♭7 B♭7(♯5)
each mem-o - ry _ that we've shared. _ You ig - nore ev-'ry star _ a - bove _ you. _ I can't re - a - lize you ev - er cared. _ You've
E♭maj7 D7 Gm7(♭5)/D♭ C7 F7 B9 B♭9 E♭6 A♭m7 E♭6
changed. You're not the an-gel I once knew. No need to tell me that we're through. It's all o-ver now; _ you've changed. _

YOU OUGHTA BE IN PICTURES

Words by EDWARD HEYMAN
Music by DANA SUESSE

Moderato

C Cmaj7 C D♯dim7 Dm7 G7
You ough - ta be in pic - tures, _ you're won - der - ful to see,
Your voice would thrill a na - tion, _ your face would be a - dored,

Dm7 G7 C Cmaj7 C6 1. Dm G9 G9(♯5) 2. B7
you ough-ta be in pic - tures, _ oh what a hit! _ you would be! _ your re - ward; _
you'd make a great sen - sa - tion _ with wealth and fame _

Em G+ Em G+ Em G A9 G Em
and if you should kiss the way _ you kiss, when we are all a - lone, _ you'd make ev - 'ry

G D7 Am7 D13 G9 C Cmaj7 C D♯dim7
girl and man _ a fan wor-ship - ing at your throne. _ You ough-ta shine as bright-ly _

Dm7 G7 Dm7 G7 F Dm/G G7 C
As Ju - pi - ter and Mars: You ough-ta be in pic - tures, _ my star of stars!

YOU'RE SIXTEEN

Words and Music by
RICHARD M. SHERMAN and
ROBERT B. SHERMAN

An easy four feel
Ooh, you come on like a dream, peach-es and cream, lips like straw-ber-ry wine. You're six-teen,
rib-bons and curls, ooh, what a girl, eyes that spar-kle and shine.
you're beau-ti-ful, and you're mine. and you're mine. You're all
You're my ba-by, you're my pet. We fell in love on the night we met. You touched my hand, my
heart went 'pop', and ooh, when we kissed we could not stop. You walked out of my dreams, in-to my arms,
now you're my an-gel di-vine. You're six-teen, you're beau-ti-ful, and you're mine. Ooh
you're beau-ti-ful, you're six-teen and you're mine.
ZING A LITTLE ZONG
Copyright © 1952 by BURVAN MUSIC CORPORATION (Renewed)
Sole Selling Agent: FAMOUS MUSIC CORPORATION All Rights Reserved
Words by LEO ROBIN
Music by HARRY WARREN
Moderately
Zing, zing, zing a lit-tle zong with me. I know we're not be-side the Zui-der Zee,
Zing zome zen-ti-men-tal mel-o-dy a-bout a chap-el or an ap-ple tree,
Zing, zing, zing, it's get-ting late, my pet, we've got a most im-por-tant date to set.
but when you're zit-tin' by the zide of me, I want to zing a lit-tle zong. long. It ain't the
a-bout a cou-ple liv-in' hap-pi-ly and I'll be glad to zing a
I'm sure that we could make a great du-et and we could zing a lit-tle
To Coda
zea-son that has me kind-a zill-y. You real-ly are a dol-ly, a dol-ly and a dil-ly. You've got a rea-son to cud-dle sort-a
D.S. al Coda
close to me and we could do a ver-y clev-er bit of close har-mo-ny.
Coda
love zong all night long.